Organometallic Compounds

VOLUME ONE

The Main Group Elements

ORGANOMETALLIC COMPOUNDS

by

G. E. COATES M.A., D.Sc.
Professor of Chemistry in the University of Durham

M. L. H. GREEN Ph.D., M.A.
Fellow and Tutor in Inorganic Chemistry, Balliol College, Oxford

K. WADE B.Sc., Ph.D.
Lecturer in Chemistry in the University of Durham

VOLUME ONE

The Main Group Elements

by

G. E. COATES *and* K. WADE

METHUEN & CO LTD

11 NEW FETTER LANE · LONDON E C 4

First published 1956
Second edition published 1960
Third edition published in two volumes 1967
Third edition, Volume I © 1967 *G. E. Coates*
Printed in Great Britain by
Butler & Tanner Ltd, Frome and London

Distribution in the U.S.A.
by Barnes & Noble, Inc.

Preface to the Third Edition, Volume One

In all three editions of this book organometallic compounds have been regarded as substances containing metal–carbon bonds. Thus metal alkoxides and the variety of co-ordination compounds, often so useful for analytical purposes, containing metals bound to organic systems commonly *via* oxygen, nitrogen, or sulphur, are all excluded. In the first edition boron was included as if it were a metal but silicon, phosphorus and arsenic were excluded. This perhaps arbitrary distinction has been retained in the later editions, and in the meantime these gaps have to a considerable extent been filled by other books.

As mentioned in the preface to the first edition, organometallic compounds are often of great value for synthetic purposes and they have frequently provided problems of interest in connexion with valency theory. Many of the extensive recent developments of the chemistry of organo-alkali compounds are primarily concerned with synthetic methods for organic chemistry, but only a fraction of this aspect has been included in the present edition. In much of Volume One of this edition, the emphasis has tended towards preparative and co-ordination chemistry. Features of structural and valency interest are also mentioned.

Though attempts have been made to include major developments to early 1966, and some later material has been added in proof, the choice of what constitutes a major development must to some extent be influenced by the interests and prejudices of the authors, both of whom regard themselves as inorganic chemists. References are far from comprehensive, and the treatment has been particularly selective in respect of the Grignard reagents and of elements whose organic chemistry has become especially extensive, for example some alkali metals, boron, aluminium and tin.

Since the second edition was written, there have been some notable additions to the review literature of organometallic chemistry, *Advances* (edited by Stone and West), *Annual Surveys* by Seyferth and King, and *Organometallic Chemistry Reviews* being particularly helpful.

The authors are grateful to Dr Frank Glockling and Dr George Kohnstam for their helpful comments, and to Dr Jean Coates and Miss Helen Coates for help with the index.

G. E. C.
K. W.

Contents

CHAPTER ONE

The alkali metals

Though the term organometallic has often been applied to almost any substances containing carbon and metal atoms, and these have included alkoxides, various chelate complexes and even soaps, restriction of the term to compounds containing a metal-carbon bond has become quite general.

The organic derivatives of the alkali metals, and many of these are very useful chemical reagents, include some of the best examples of *ionic* metal–carbon bonds; others clearly have a covalent constitution.

All the organic derivatives of the alkali metals are highly reactive, and on any view of their constitution some part of the molecule must be in a relatively unusual state of combination, and that part would be the source of the high reactivity. If they are regarded as salts, $M^+R_3C^-$, then the seat of high energy and reactivity is the *carbanion*; if they are regarded as essentially covalent, R_3C—M, then the seat of reactivity is the alkali metal, since these elements normally enter into chemical combination by ionization rather than by covalent bonding.

The small size and high polarizing power of the lithium ion results in lithium compounds in general, e.g. the halides, having more covalent character than those of the other alkali metals. This effect is even more apparent in the organolithium compounds, many of which have properties characteristic of covalent compounds and impossible to associate with a simple salt-like constitution. n-Butyl-lithium (n-C_4H_9Li), for example, is a colourless rather viscous liquid readily soluble in paraffin solvents. n-Butylsodium (n-C_4H_9Na), on the other hand, is a white powder which decomposes when heated (and does not melt), insoluble in paraffin solvents and reacting with all others investigated; it is commonly regarded as a salt, Na^+n-$C_4H_9^-$. Organolithium compounds are more stable and less reactive than corresponding derivatives of the other alkali metals, and this may in part be due to the lower polarity (more covalent nature) of lithium–carbon bonds compared to bonds between carbon and the other alkali metals. Not only have organolithium compounds a predominantly co-valent constitution, but they are associated and the co-ordination number of the lithium atom is greater than one. This aspect is discussed in more detail later in the chapter, but it is worth referring now to some of the funda-mental properties of the alkali metal atoms which bear on the difference between organic derivatives of lithium and those of the other alkali metals.

Table 1

Atom	Li	Na	K	Rb	Cs
Ionic radius,[a] Å	0·60	0·95	1·33	1·48	1·69
Ionization energy, eV	5·39	5·14	4·34	4·18	3·89
sp Promotion energy, eV	1·84	2·10	1·60	1·56	1·38

[a] Pauling radii.

The formation of salts is favoured by *high* ionic radius and *low* ionization energy, and there is a monotonic change in both these properties from lithium to caesium (see Table 1). The association of many organolithium compounds implies *p*-orbital participation, and the latter would be favoured by low $s \rightarrow p$ promotion energy. This quantity is least for caesium, increases steadily to sodium, and then falls. The low promotion energy of lithium, taken in comparison with the relatively high ionization energy and low ionic radius, is an important factor bearing on the considerable difference between the organoderivatives of lithium and those of the heavier alkali metals. Low promotion energies of potassium, rubidium and caesium would be outweighed by their very low ionization energies and large ionic radii. The organic derivatives of the heavier alkali metals have been relatively little studied, but they appear to resemble those of sodium.

The most reactive organoalkali metal compounds are the alkyl derivatives of sodium and the heavier alkali metals, and their high reactivity is to be ascribed to the presence of a carbon atom bearing nearly a full unit of negative charge, e.g. butylsodium, $n\text{-}C_3H_7C^-H_2[Na^+]$.

If the negative charge on the organic radical can be *dispersed over several carbon atoms* by means of conjugation, then the chemical reactivity should diminish. This effect is apparent in a very large number of organoalkali compounds, and is usually accompanied by the appearance of vivid colours. For example, benzylsodium (bright red) is less reactive than phenylsodium (colourless), and indeed results when the latter reacts with toluene.

$$C_6H_5^-Na^+ + C_6H_5CH_3 = C_6H_5CH_2^-Na^+ + C_6H_6$$

Whereas the negative charge on a phenyl anion would be mainly confined to one doubly occupied orbital of the σ-framework, the negative

doubly occupied sp^2 orbital

charge on a *benzyl* ion is distributed mainly over four carbon atoms, though to some extent over all seven, as indicated in the following formulae:

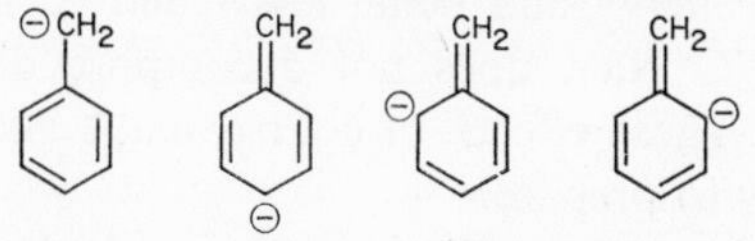

A particularly important example of his effect is to be found in the alkali metal derivatives of cyclopentadiene. This non-aromatic hydrocarbon reacts directly with alkali metals to form a symmetrical anion to which the extra electron imparts aromatic character (there being six π-electrons in the anion).

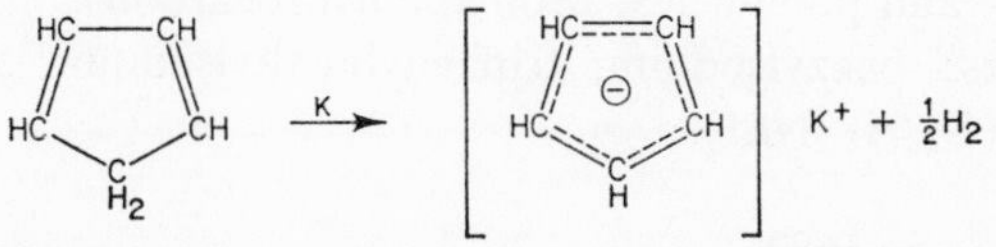

A large class of charge-delocalized organoalkali compounds consists of the *addition* compounds between alkali metals and bi- or poly-nuclear aromatic hydrocarbons. Naphthalene, for example, reacts with sodium in strongly donor ethers, like tetrahydrofuran or 1,2-dimethoxyethane, the reaction consisting of an electron transfer from the sodium to the lowest vacant π molecular orbital of the aromatic compound. Though these brightly coloured compounds are salts, and would exist mainly as ion-pairs (or higher aggregates) in these not very polar solvents, the alkali metal atoms should not be regarded as being associated with any particular carbon atoms as the negative charge is spread over the whole of the extended π orbital involved.

$$C_{10}H_8 + Na \rightarrow C_{10}H_8^- Na^+$$

On the basis of the above considerations the organoalkali compounds may conveniently be classified in three groups:

(1) Lithium compounds, characteristically covalent in constitution and associated. Examples: $n\text{-}C_4H_9Li$, C_6H_5Li.
(2) Derivatives of the other alkali metals in which there is little or no means whereby the negative charge on the organic radical can be dispersed over several carbon atoms. These essentially *ionic* compounds are distinguished by intense reactivity due to the localization of nearly a full negative charge on one carbon atom.
Examples: $CH_3CH_2^- Na^+$, and phenylsodium (see above).

The *acetylides* comprise an important subgroup. Though the charge is virtually localized,

$$R \cdot C \vdots C^- Na^+$$

the greatly increased electronegativity of carbon in the *sp* valency state (compared with *sp³*) results in the carbanion derived therefrom having lower energy and being less reactive. Thus phenylethynyl-sodium, $PhC{:}C^-Na^+$, does not decompose diethyl ether (unlike ethylsodium). These effects, of course, make alkali metal acetylides relatively easy to prepare.

(3) Derivatives of any of the alkali metals in which suitable conjugation results in the *dispersal* of the negative charge on the organic radical over several carbon atoms. This class is distinguished by diminished reactivity, bright colours, higher stability and relative ease of preparation; it includes as a special class the *addition* (as opposed to substitution) compounds obtained from the alkali metals – including lithium – and polynuclear aromatic hydrocarbons.

Examples: benzylsodium, triphenylmethylsodium, sodium naphthalene ($C_{10}H_8^-Na^+$).

Organolithium compounds

The singular combination of high reactivity, relatively easy preparation, and solubility in inert solvents characteristic of organolithium compounds has made them of ever-increasing value in chemical synthesis. Though mainly used for the same kinds of synthesis as the more familiar Grignard reagents, they offer substantial advantages in many instances. Numerous reactions can be carried out with their use, which fail with Grignard reagents, and the 'working up' of reaction products is often cleaner and more convenient.

Preparative methods

All the useful methods for preparing organolithium compounds start from metallic lithium. The most convenient source of lithium is in the form of dispersions in mineral oil, now commercially available, and both lithium wire and tape, protected by petroleum jelly, are sold. When small amounts of lithium reagents are required occasionally, it is generally more convenient (or economical) to start from the metal in the form of lumps which, however, have to be cleaned from adherent oxide, carbonate, or nitride, and reduced in particle size before use. A commonly used method is to beat a weighed piece of lithium into sheet; the sheet is then scraped clean under hexane or a similar solvent, which also dissolves the protective grease. The clean sheet metal is then cut with a pair of scissors as quickly as possible into chips which are allowed to fall at once into the solvent to be used for the subsequent reaction. An atmosphere of oxygen-free dry nitrogen must, of course, be provided, and the lithium used without delay.

A more satisfactory method is to stir the molten metal in an inert oil. The apparatus shown in Figure 1 is convenient for this purpose. Weighed lumps of lithium, which need not be cleaned from adherent corrosion products, are allowed to float on the paraffin oil (b.p. 200–230°) in the lightly creased flask. The direction of the crease should cause a *downward* deflection of the oil when it is stirred. The stirrer is best made from two short lengths of gauge 20 tantalum wire, tantalum being one of the small number of metals not rapidly attacked by molten lithium. Since nitrogen attacks hot lithium appreciably, an argon atmosphere should be provided (or a petroleum vapour). The oil and the lithium are heated, conveniently by a small ring gas burner, until the metal is all melted, the gas burner is then turned off and the stirrer at once started. In a few seconds the lithium is reduced to more or less fine shot which quickly solidifies. When the contents of the vessel have cooled to about 40–50° the dirt and corrosion products from the metal, which will have sunk to the bottom, are drained off together with most of the oil (which can, of course, be used again after cleaning). The lithium shot, which floats on all solvents, is then washed twice or more with an appropriate solvent, and finally is washed through the wide-bore tap (at *least* 8–9 mm. bore) into the reaction vessel against a counter current of dry nitrogen.

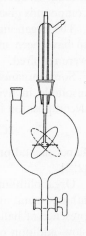

Fig. 1. Apparatus for preparation of lithium 'shot'

Quantities greater than about 10 grams of lithium are more conveniently converted into shot with the use of a 'vibromixer' instead of a rotating stirrer. Fine lithium dispersion is now commercially available, the dispersion in wax (in rod form) being particularly convenient since the appropriate weight can be measured out by length.

When the *isolation of an organolithium compound* is desired, the preparation is more difficult than in cases when the product is intended for more or less immediate use for synthetic purposes, and the method of choice is the reaction between lithium and an organomercury compound:

$$2Li + R_2Hg = 2RLi + Hg$$

An excess of lithium is desirable, to drive the reaction to completion and thus to avoid the presence of any soluble material except the desired product. An inert solvent is necessary, and may be light petroleum or benzene; ether is sometimes used but the product must then be worked up without delay. The reaction mixture is shaken, preferably in the presence of broken glass to help to keep the metal surface clean [1]. Onset of reaction is apparent when the amalgamated lithium sinks to the bottom of the reaction vessel. Solid products, e.g. C_2H_5Li, C_6H_5Li, are crystallized from the

[1] G. Wittig, F. J. Meyer and G. Lange, *Annalen*, 1951, **571**, 167.

reaction mixture after filtration from insoluble matter, while liquid products, e.g. n-C_3H_7Li, must be obtained by evaporation of the solvent *in vacuo* and cannot readily be purified. The reaction is reversible since stirring RLi with a large excess of mercury produces R_2Hg, except when lithium is bound to a tertiary carbon atom, though some aryl-lithium compounds give low yields of Ar_2Hg [1a].

The organomercury route to organolithium compounds seems mainly to have been used when halogen-free ether solutions of phenyl-lithium were required.

Some organolithium compounds, for example methyl-lithium [2], are insoluble in hydrocarbon solvents and are best obtained by a double decomposition in hexane:*

$$2C_2H_5Li + (CH_3)_2Hg = 2CH_3Li \downarrow + (C_2H_5)_2Hg$$

Experimental procedures have been described in detail by several authors [2, 3].

Organolithium compounds can also be prepared by reaction between lithium metal and alkyl halides, but one of the difficulties is to avoid the presence of halide in the product. Ethyl-lithium may be obtained by the slow addition of ethyl bromide to a well-stirred mixture of lithium and pentene [4] (mixed isomers) or pentane [5]. Good yields result only when the ethyl bromide is added steadily and slowly (at least 3–4 hours). The first product is a precipitate consisting of lithium bromide and ethyl-lithium, the latter being only moderately soluble [5] (7·6 g. in a litre of n-pentane at 20°). Since ethyl-lithium is about ten times as soluble in benzene as in pentane at room temperature, it is separated from lithium bromide by solution in benzene, removal of pentene or pentane by distillation followed by crystallization of the ethyl-lithium from benzene.

Methyl-lithium has been prepared from ethyl-lithium by reaction with methyl iodide in benzene solution at 5–10°; a fine white precipitate appears in a few seconds, but this contains about 5 mole % of iodide [6]. The exchange between n-butyl-lithium and aryl iodides in a benzene–hexane mixture is a still more satisfactory method for the preparation of *lithium aryls*, which are precipitated from the reaction mixture. Phenyl-lithium

[1a] G. Beinert and J. Parrod, *Compt. rend.*, 1966, **263C**, 492.

[2] W. Schlenk and J. Holtz, *Ber.*, 1917, **50**, 262.

[3] H. I. Schlesinger and H. C. Brown, *J. Amer. Chem. Soc.*, 1940, **62**, 3431; T. V. Talalaeva and K. A. Kocheskov, *Zhur. obshchei Khim.*, 1953, **23**, 392; idem, *Izvest. Akad. Nauk S.S.S.R.*, 1953, 126; *Chem. Abs.*, 1954, **48**, 3245.

[4] T. V. Talalaeva and K. A. Kocheskov, *J. Gen. Chem. U.S.S.R.*, English translation, 1953, **23**, 399.

[5] D. Bryce-Smith and E. E. Turner, *J. Chem. Soc.*, 1953, 861.

[6] T. L. Brown and M. T. Rogers, *J. Amer. Chem. Soc.*, 1957, **79**, 1859.

* This reaction, and that between MeI and EtLi, are now stated to yield a 1 : 1 MeLi : EtLi complex; see [100] and E. Weiss, *Chem. Ber.*, 1964, **97**, 3241.

prepared in this way may be purified (99·8%) by solution in ether followed by crystallization at low temperature [6a].

Generally, however, organolithium compounds are not isolated but used immediately for synthetic purposes, like the familiar Grignard reagents, and are prepared by a similar method (compare ethyl-lithium mentioned above):

$$2Li + RX = RLi + LiX$$

The reaction is carried out in light petroleum, cyclohexane, benzene or an ether, in an atmosphere of dry nitrogen. In the aliphatic series chlorides are generally preferred to bromides, and with the important exception of methyl iodide [7], iodides cannot be used since they react too quickly with the organolithium compound:

$$RLi + R'I = RR' + LiI$$

The less reactive *aryl* bromides and iodides often give good yields of lithium derivatives, and in some important instances the corresponding Grignard reagent cannot be obtained directly, or at best in poor yield. Thus p-bromdimethylaniline [7] gives $Me_2NC_6H_4Li$ in about 95% yield, but does not react satisfactorily with magnesium, except in tetrahydrofuran solution [8].

It is not always easy to choose between using an organolithium compound and the corresponding Grignard reagent. In many instances only the lithium compounds are sufficiently reactive for the synthesis under consideration. Sometimes the Grignard reagent is more accessible than its lithium analogue. But of considerable practical advantage is the clean separation of volatile reaction products by distillation in syntheses where hydrolysis is not permissible, in contrast to the rather messy residue, tenaciously retaining ether, which results when the separation of product by distillation without previous hydrolysis is attempted after a Grignard synthesis.

Lithium metal, as supplied commercially, contains small amounts of sodium, and the sodium content has a considerable effect on the yields of organolithium reagents obtained from halides [9]. For example, lithium containing less than 0·005% sodium does not react with p-bromdimethylaniline in ether, and lithium containing 2% sodium gives over 80% yields of tert-butyl-lithium in pentane. For the preparation of n-butyl-lithium and phenyl-lithium the optimum sodium content appears to be about 0·02%.

[6a] M. Schlosser and V. Ladenberger, *J. Organometal. Chem.*, 1967, **8**, 193.

[7] H. Gilman, E. A. Zöllner and W. M. Selby, *J. Amer. Chem. Soc.*, 1933, **55**, 1252; T. D. Perrine and H. Rapoport, *Anal. Chem.*, 1948, **20**, 635; H. Gilman, W. Langham and F. W. Moore, *J. Amer. Chem. Soc.*, 1940, **62**, 2327.

[8] T. C. Owen, *J. Chem. Soc.*, 1961, 465.

[9] C. W. Kamienski and D. L. Esmay, *J. Org. Chem.*, 1960, **25**, 1807.

The use of a lithium dispersion containing about 2% sodium has allowed the direct preparation of vinyl-lithium (60–65% yields) from vinyl chloride in tetrahydrofuran at 0 to −10°. An argon rather than a nitrogen atmosphere is advised for this rather delicate preparation [10]. Vinyl-lithium has generally been prepared by transmetalation reactions (described below) developed largely by D. Seyferth, for example:

$$(CH_2:CH)_4Sn + 4PhLi = 4CH_2:CHLi + Ph_4Sn \downarrow$$

The use of organolithium reagents derived from substituted vinyl halides was largely developed by the late E. A. Braude [11]. Alkyl substituted vinyl bromides (but not vinyl bromide itself), for example isobutenyl bromide $Me_2C:CHBr$, readily form lithium derivatives in ether and these have found numerous synthetic applications. isoButenyl-lithium reacts with dimethylformamide, by way of example, to give a good yield of aldehyde:

$$Me_2C{=}CHLi + Me_2NCHO = Me_2NLi + Me_2C{=}CH{-}CHO$$

The retention of configuration of unsymmetrical vinyl-lithium compounds is a feature of special value, thus carboxylation of the lithium derivative of *trans*-2-brom-2-butene affords a good yield of angelic and only a little (5–6%) tiglic acid.

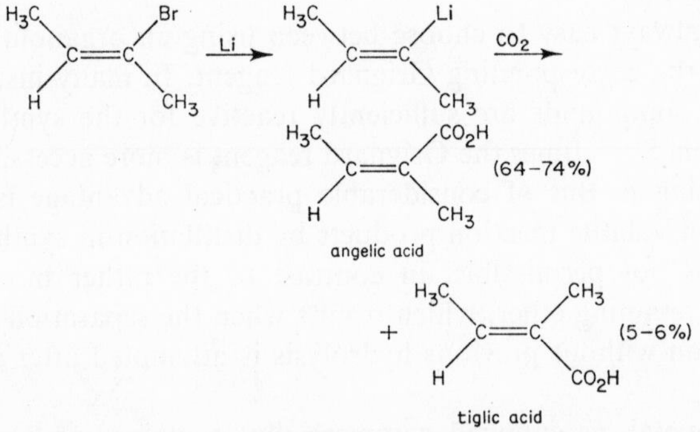

angelic acid

tiglic acid

Some organolithium compounds have been difficult to prepare from halides because they react so quickly with halides. For example, benzyl-lithium cannot be prepared from benzyl chloride and lithium; bibenzyl is formed instead. In such cases the fission of ethers by means of lithium metal may be used. This is an extension of the reaction between ethers and the heavier alkali metals (see p. 52) described by Schorigin in 1927 and Ziegler in 1929.

[10] R. West and W. H. Glaze, *J. Org. Chem.*, 1961, **26**, 2096.
[11] E. A. Braude and E. A. Evans, *J. Chem. Soc.*, 1955, 3324, 3331, 3334; 1956, 3333; A. S. Dreiding and R. J. Pratt, *J. Amer. Chem. Soc.*, 1954, **76**, 1902; D. Y. Curtin and J. W. Crump, ibid., 1958, **80**, 1922; E. A. Braude, Ch. 4 of Vol. III of *Progress in Organic Chemistry*, ed. J. W. Cook, 1955.

Dibenzylether and benzylmethylether react with lithium suspended in tetrahydrofuran, preferably at −5 to −15°:

$$PhCH_2OMe + 2Li = PhCH_2Li + MeOLi$$

The benzyl ether should be added slowly to the stirred lithium suspension, or bibenzyl is formed, and a final benzyl-lithium concentration of about 0·2M is optimum [12] (see also p. 13). 1-Phenylethyl-lithium (PhMeCHLi), similarly prepared, is decomposed by tetrahydrofuran rather faster than methyl-lithium, whereas benzyl-lithium reacts more slowly than methyl-lithium [13].

Though benzyl chloride gives bibenzyl on reaction with lithium, diphenylmethyl chloride gives good yields (∼80%) of lithium derivative when stirred with the metal 18 hours at room temperature. This is because the coupling product is itself split by lithium [14].

$$Ph_2CHCl + 2Li = Ph_2CHLi + LiCl$$
$$Ph_2CHCl + Ph_2CHLi = Ph_2CH \cdot CHPh_2 + LiCl$$
$$Ph_2CH \cdot CHPh_2 + 2Li = 2Ph_2CHLi$$

Solvents

The choice of a suitable *solvent* both for the preparation and use of organo-lithium compounds is important. Both methyl- and phenyl-lithium are usually prepared in diethyl ether. n-Butyl-lithium, very much used as an intermediate for the preparation of other lithium compounds, may be prepared either in diethyl ether or in pentane. Ethers are attacked by most organolithium compounds, but there are wide differences in the reaction rates [15]. The most stable of the common organolithium compounds, towards diethyl ether, is methyl-lithium; a 0·54M solution was 0·14M after one year. Phenyl-lithium is less stable, a 0·4M solution in ether dropped to 0·2M after refluxing for twelve days and to 0·09M after thirty days. Phenyl-lithium is much more stable in ether–hydrocarbon mixtures containing about 70 volume % hydrocarbon than in ether alone, and may be kept at least a year in such mixed solvents [15a]. The concentration of n-butyl-lithium in diethyl ether drops to half its original value in about a week at 25°; it is often advantageous to store it in a refrigerator. Secondary and

[12] H. Gilman and H. A. McNinch, *J. Org. Chem.*, 1961, **26**, 3723; H. Gilman and G. L. Schwebke, ibid., 1962, **27**, 4259.

[13] H. Gilman and H. A. McNinch, ibid., p. 1889.

[14] C. Tamborski, G. J. Moore and E. J. Sokolski, *Chem. and Ind.*, 1962, 696.

[15] A. H. Haubein, *Iowa State College J. Science*, 1943, **18**, 48; see also A. Rembaum, Shiao-Ping Siao and N. Indictor, *J. Polymer Sci.*, 1962, **56**, S17; H. Gilman, A. H. Haubein and H. Harzfeld, *J. Org. Chem.*, 1954, **19**, 1034; H. Gilman and G. L. Schwebke, *J. Organometal. Chem.*, 1965, **4**, 483.

[15a] D. L. Esmay and C. W. Kamiensky, Fr.P. 1,346,692; *Chem. Abs.*, 1964, **60**, 14537.

tertiary lithium alkyls are even less stable in ether and the order of increasing stability to boiling diethyl ether is t-butyl < sec.-butyl ≈ isopropyl ≈ cyclohexyl < isobutyl < n-propyl < ethyl < n-butyl < n-pentyl < 1-naphthyl < phenyl < p-dimethylaminophenyl < p-biphenyl < methyl. The reaction consists mainly of nucleophilic attack on the α-carbon atom followed by olefin elimination [15b]:

$$Bu^nLi + Et_2O \rightarrow CH_3CHLiOC_2H_5 + C_4H_{10}$$
$$\downarrow$$
$$C_2H_4 + LiOC_2H_5$$

Tetrahydrofuran is more rapidly attacked by a given lithium alkyl than is diethyl ether, because the more basic (donor) solvent increases the carbanion (nucleophilic) character of the carbon atom bound to the lithium.

n-Butyl-lithium is much more stable in paraffin hydrocarbons than in ether and concentrated solutions of this very useful reagent (e.g. for the preparation of other organolithium compounds by the exchange reactions discussed below) in specially purified hexane and heptane are now commercially available; they last well if properly protected against air and moisture. Since lithium n-butoxide, though sparingly soluble in hydrocarbons, is freely soluble in hydrocarbon solutions of n-butyl-lithium [16], it should be noted that the absence of a precipitate in stored butyl-lithium solutions is no proof that oxygen has been excluded.

The importance of excluding air and moisture is worth special emphasis. Not only does access of these destroy the organolithium reagent, but more significantly in many instances the lithium alkoxides thus formed catalyse the decomposition of lithium alkyls. This is important not only in connexion with the storage of n-butyl-lithium, but also with the use of secondary and tertiary lithium alkyls. For example, solutions of t-butyl-lithium may be boiled in hexane without appreciable loss due to thermal decomposition of the reagent, but they decompose relatively quickly in the presence of the butoxide.

The concentration of solutions of n-butyl-lithium (or of equally or more reactive compounds) may be determined by the double titration method of Gilman [17]. In the absence of any reaction between the lithium alkyl and ether (or air or moisture), the product of hydrolysis, lithium hydroxide, would represent the quantity of organolithium compound present, and this can easily be found by titration of a hydrolysed aliquot. However, complete decomposition of the reagent by attack on ether or accidental access of air or moisture would leave unchanged the total alkali produced on

[15b] R. L. Burwell, *Chem. Rev.*, 1954, **54**, 615.
[16] C. W. Kamienski and D. H. Lewis, *J. Org. Chem.*, 1965, **30**, 3498.
[17] H. Gilman and J. W. Morton, *Organic Reactions*, Vol. VIII, Ch. 6, Wiley, 1954; see also ref. [128].

hydrolysis, but advantage can be taken of the rapid reaction between n-butyl-lithium and benzyl chloride *in ether* whereby benzyl-lithium is formed (a transient yellow colour is seen),

$$Bu^nLi + C_6H_5CH_2Cl = Bu^nCl + C_6H_5CH_2Li$$

followed at once by reaction with excess benzyl chloride

$$C_6H_5CH_2Li + C_6H_5CH_2Cl = LiCl + (C_6H_5CH_2)_2$$

Butyl-lithium also reacts with benzyl chloride by direct elimination of lithium chloride:

$$Bu^nLi + C_6H_5CH_2Cl = LiCl + C_6H_5(CH_2)_4CH_3*$$

Since these reactions produce no alkali, the titration of an aliquot (usually 1 or 2 c.c.) added to pure dry benzyl chloride (about 1 c.c.) in ether (about 10 c.c.), before hydrolysis, gives the amount of alkali due to lithium ethoxide – or any source of alkali other than butyl-lithium. On account of the rapid reaction of butyl-lithium with air it is best to run the butyl-lithium aliquot into the benzyl chloride with the end of the pipette (or syringe) dipping under the surface of the benzyl chloride solution. The difference between two titrations, one giving total alkali after hydrolysis, the other after the benzyl chloride treatment, gives the butyl-lithium concentration. This analysis is *not* applicable to methyl-lithium, phenyl-lithium or phenylethynyl-lithium, which do not undergo a rapid exchange reaction with benzylchloride. The double titration method gives misleading results in hydrocarbon solvents unless the benzyl chloride is diluted with exceptionally pure ether [19].

Of the two other commonly used organolithium compounds, methyl-lithium is sufficiently unreactive to ether for a simple acid–alkali titration to suffice for its analysis, unless the solution has been kept for a matter of a month or more. Phenyl-lithium is usually analysed in the same way, and the result will be sufficiently accurate for most preparative purposes if the solution is used within two days. Alternatively an aliquot can be added to a small excess of benzophenone in ether; after hydrolysis excess benzophenone may be removed by vacuum distillation and the triphenylcarbinol recovered as quantitatively as possible and weighed [20].

Another widely applicable method is based on reaction with excess of iodine, the excess then being titrated with sodium thiosulphate. Error due to coupling of RI with RLi is minimized by slow addition of the organolithium reagent to the iodine in ether. The error due to biphenyl formation

[18] D. F. Hoeg and D. I. Lusk, *J. Amer. Chem. Soc.*, 1964, **86**, 928.

[19] C. W. Kamienski and D. L. Esmay, *J. Org. Chem.*, 1960, **25**, 115; P. F. Collins, C. W. Kamienski, D. L. Esmay and R. B. Ellestad, *Anal. Chem.*, 1961, **33**, 468.

[20] G. Wittig, R. Ludwig and R. Polster, *Chem. Ber.*, 1955, **88**, 294.

* The presence of tetrahydrofuran, even in small amount, complicates the reaction still more, as stilbene is formed as well [18].

in the analysis of phenyl-lithium solutions is 2–3%, and the method is claimed to be more accurate than that based on acid titration [21]. In all these methods great care has to be taken in respect of solvent purity and avoiding contamination by air or moisture at least until all the organolithium reagent has been destroyed, otherwise meaningful results are not obtained and it would be better to guess. A useful method has been devised for the analysis of MeLi (and Me_2Mg or MeMgX) solutions, involving methylation of $PhMe_2SiCl$ and gas chromatographic determination of the $PhSiMe_3$ formed [22].

One of the notes [23] on the Gilman double titration method includes a useful description of the preparation of heptane solutions of n-butyl-lithium from butyl chloride and lithium dispersion. In another evaluation [24] of the double titration method, allyl bromide and ethylene dibromide are preferred to benzyl chloride. Two recently developed methods appear to have considerable advantage over the double titration described above. In one of these [24a] a weighed amount of benzoic acid in a mixture of dimethylsulphoxide, 1,2-dimethoxythane and ether or hydrocarbon is titrated with the organolithium solution. The indicator is triphenylmethane, which develops a red colour when all the benzoic acid is used up:

$$RLi + PhCO_2H \rightarrow PhCO_2Li + RH$$
$$RLi + Ph_3CH \rightarrow RH + Ph_3CLi \text{ (red)}$$

The described procedure also copes satisfactorily with the problem of water adsorbed on the surface of the reaction vessel.

The second new method [24b] consists of the titration of the organolithium reagent with acetone, the progress of the titration being followed by means of the dielectric constant of the solution. The dielectric constant rises as acetone is added, due to the formation of polar RLi–ROLi complexes, drops to a sharp minimum at the equivalence point, and rises again as the solution contains more and more excess acetone. The last two methods are particularly valuable for the analysis of *solutions of organolithium compounds in hydrocarbons*.

So far, methods for the preparation of organolithium compounds *directly* from lithium metal and organic halides (or very occasionally organomercury compounds) have been discussed. Many organolithium compounds are better obtained, and in many instances have only been obtained, by *exchange reactions* in which a relatively easily prepared

[21] A. F. Clifford and R. R. Olsen, *Anal. Chem.*, 1960, **32**, 544.
[22] H. O. House and W. L. Respess, *J. Organometal. Chem.*, 1965, **4**, 95.
[23] K. C. Eberly, *J. Org. Chem.*, 1961, **26**, 1309.
[24] H. Gilman and F. K. Cartledge, *J. Organometal. Chem.*, 1964, **2**, 447.
[24a] R. L. Eppley and J. A. Dixon, *ibid.*, 1967, **8**, 176.
[24b] S. C. Watson and J. F. Eastham, *Anal. Chem.*, 1967, **39**, 171; see also idem, *J. Organometal. Chem.*, 1967, **9**, 165.

derivative, generally butyl-, methyl- or phenyl-lithium, is converted into another.

The three main types of exchange reaction which have been used in the preparation of organolithium compounds are:

(a) *Metal–metal exchange*, e.g.

$$PhLi + Ph_3SnCH_2CH:CH_2 \rightarrow CH_2:CHCH_2Li + Ph_4Sn \downarrow$$

(b) *Metal–halogen exchange*, e.g.

$$Bu^nLi + p\text{-}BrC_6H_4NMe_2 \rightarrow Bu^nBr + p\text{-}LiC_6H_4NMe_2$$

(c) *Metal–hydrogen exchange*, e.g.

$$PhLi + PhC:CH \rightarrow C_6H_6 + PhC:CLi$$

Transmetalation

Metal–metal exchange, also known as the *transmetalation reaction* [25], now provides the most convenient route to vinyl, allyl, methallyl, and isopropenyl-lithium, geometric configuration being retained in the latter [26]. Both phenyl- and butyl-lithium exchange rapidly with tetravinyltin and with tetravinyl-lead, either in ether or in pentane, the reaction being complete within half an hour at room temperature. For most purposes, when for example vinyl-lithium is required in solution for a subsequent vinylation reaction, reaction between phenyl-lithium and tetravinyltin (now commercially available) in diethyl ether is convenient:

$$4PhLi + (CH_2:CH)_4Sn \rightarrow 4CH_2:CHLi + Ph_4Sn \downarrow$$

The tetraphenyltin (solubility about 1 gram per litre at room temperature) is precipitated nearly quantitatively. Exchange between n-butyl-lithium and tetravinyltin in pentane does not go to completion, but vinyl-lithium is precipitated as a white highly pyrophoric solid. Tetrahydrofuran is not a satisfactory solvent for the preparation of vinyl-lithium from tetravinyltin; however, it is of interest that vinyl-lithium is decomposed by tetrahydrofuran much less rapidly than most lithium alkyls or aryls. Solutions of vinyl-lithium in diethyl ether or in tetrahydrofuran do not decompose significantly in a week at room temperature.

Vinyl-lithium has also been prepared from tetravinyl-tin or -lead and metallic lithium in diethyl ether. The reaction is catalysed by a trace of benzophenone [27].

$$(CH_2:CH)_4Pb + 4Li = 4CH_2:CHLi + Pb \downarrow$$

[25] D. Seyferth and M. A. Weiner, *Chem. and Ind.*, 1959, 402; *J. Amer. Chem. Soc.*, 1961, **83**, 3583.

[26] D. Seyferth and L. G. Vaughan, ibid., 1964, **86**, 883.

[27] E. C. Juenge and D. Seyferth, *J. Org. Chem.*, 1961, **26**, 563.

Allyl- and methallyl-lithium have been obtained by transmetalation reactions [28] e.g.

$$(CH_2:CH\cdot CH_2)_4Sn + 4PhLi \xrightarrow{Et_2O} 4CH_2:CH\cdot CH_2Li + Ph_4Sn \downarrow$$

$$(CH_2:CH\cdot CH_2)_4Sn + Bu^nLi \xrightarrow{C_5H_{12}} (CH_2:CH\cdot CH_2)_3Bu^nSn + CH_2:CH\cdot CH_2Li \downarrow$$

A detailed recipe [29] has been given for the preparation of allyltriphenyl-tin, its conversion into allyl-lithium, and subsequent reaction of the latter with a ketone. A similar tin–lithium exchange reaction has been recommended as providing a convenient route to *benzyl-lithium* [30]:

$$(PhCH_2)_3SnCl + 4MeLi \rightarrow 3PhCH_2Li + Me_4Sn + LiCl$$

However, if the presence of tetramethylethylenediamine (TMED) is no disadvantage, benzyl-lithium is even more easily obtained from toluene and the n-butyl-lithium TMED complex (see p. 19).

Metal–halogen exchange

n-Butyl-lithium is the most used source of lithium for the preparation of organolithium compounds by *metal–halogen exchange*. In these reactions lithium becomes preferentially attached to the more electronegative organic radical (see Table 2), or the radical which would form the more stable carbanion. Butyl- is preferred to phenyl-lithium because the relatively low electronegativity of the butyl radical tends to drive reaction to completion, particularly with aryl halides.

Table 2 *Lithium–halogen exchange equilibria* [31]
$$RLi + PhI \rightleftharpoons RI + PhLi^a$$

R	$\log K$	R	$\log K$
vinyl	−2·4	isobutyl	4·6
cyclopropyl	1·0	neopentyl	5·5
ethyl	3·5	cyclobutyl	6·1
n-propyl	3·9	cyclopentyl	6·9

[a] in ether, or 40% ether 60% pentane, at −70°

[28] D. Seyferth and M. A. Weiner, *J. Org. Chem.*, 1961, **26**, 4797; C. S. Johnson, M. A. Weiner, J. S. Waugh and D. Seyferth, *J. Amer. Chem. Soc.*, 1961, **83**, 1306.

[29] D. Seyferth and M. A. Weiner, *Organic Syntheses*, 1961, **41**, 30.

[30] D. Seyferth, R. Suzuki, C. J. Murphy and C. R. Sabet, *J. Organometal. Chem.*, 1964, **2**, 431.

[31] D. E. Applequist and D. F. O'Brien, *J. Amer. Chem. Soc.*, 1963, **85**, 743; see also H. J. S. Winkler and H. Winkler, ibid., 1966, **88**, 964, 969.

As an example of the use of the metal–halogen exchange reaction for preparative purposes, which has been reviewed [32], *para*-dibrombenzene gives a good yield (about 90%) of *para*-bromphenyl-lithium in ether, though it does not react directly with lithium metal,

$$p\text{-}C_6H_4Br_2 + Bu^nLi = p\text{-}BrC_6H_4Li + Bu^nBr$$

Similarly, 3-brompyridine does not react satisfactorily with metallic lithium but affords 3-pyridyl-lithium with n-butyl-lithium in ether at $-35°$.

At higher temperatures addition across the azomethine bond also occurs.

The reaction also allows the preparation of organolithium compounds containing acidic hydrogen, e.g. as $-OH$, $-SH$, $-NH_2$ or $-CO_2H$ groups, though larger proportions of butyl-lithium are, of course, necessary:

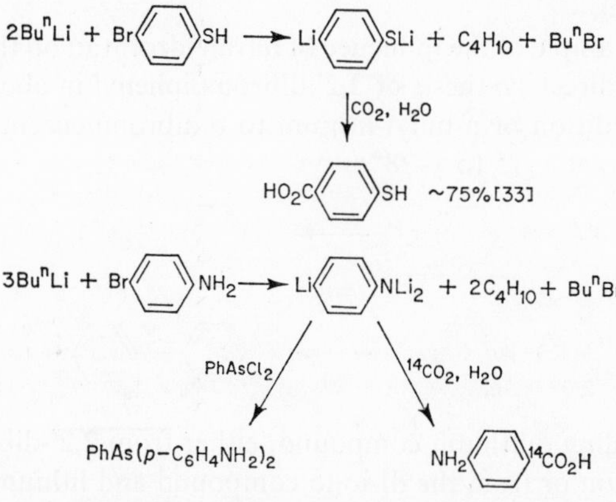

The solvent can influence these reactions to a considerable extent, the rate of halogen-metal exchange being greater in ether than in light petroleum. For example, the bromphenylarsine (1.1, $R = Me$) after five hours' boiling with butyl-lithium in light petroleum followed by addition of chlorodiethylphosphine yielded 49% crude phosphine–arsine (1.2) together with an appreciable amount of $PhAsMe_2$, whereas the arsine (1.1, $R = Et$) after only one hour's boiling with butyl-lithium in ether and similar subsequent treatment gave 63% crude product and no $PhAsEt_2$ as byproduct [34].

[32] H. Gilman and R. G. Jones, *Organic Reactions*, Vol. VI, Ch. 7, Wiley, 1951.
[33] H. Gilman and G. C. Gainer, *J. Amer. Chem. Soc.*, 1947, **69**, 1946.
[34] E. R. H. Jones and F. G. Mann, *J. Chem. Soc.*, 1955, 4472.

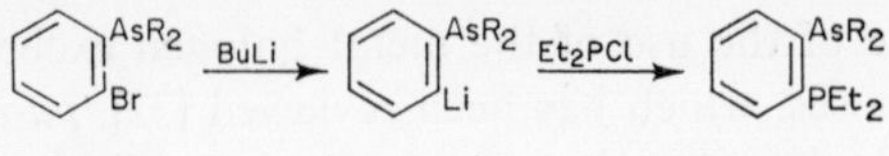

1.1   1.2

The use of tetrahydrofuran promotes these reactions, but it has an even more strongly accelerating effect on coupling reactions, in which lithium halide is eliminated, and is itself very rapidly attacked by the more reactive organolithium compounds [35]. The maximum temperatures at which reactions of methyl-, phenyl- and n-butyl-lithium should be conducted in tetrahydrofuran are $0°$, 0 to $-30°$, and $-35°$. The stability of butyl-lithium *in the presence* of tetrahydrofuran (mixed solvent) decreases rapidly as the temperature is raised from -10 to $+25°$. Even methyl chloride couples readily with methyl-lithium in this solvent

$$CH_3Cl + CH_3Li = LiCl + C_2H_6$$

and methyl-lithium cannot be prepared in good yield unless care is taken to avoid excess of methyl chloride at any time; the coupling reaction is so rapid that methyl-lithium cannot be prepared from methyl iodide in tetrahydrofuran.

A striking example of the influence of tetrahydrofuran on the course of a reaction is the direct synthesis of 2,2′-dibrombiphenyl in about 70% yield by the slow addition of n-butyl-lithium to *o*-dibrombenzene (2 mols.) in tetrahydrofuran at -75 to $-78°$:

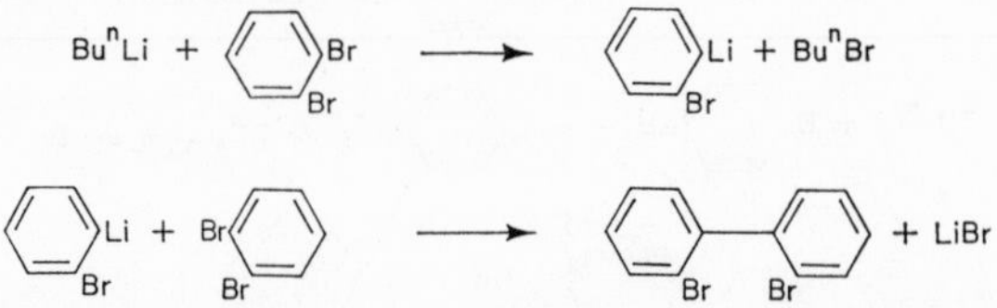

The corresponding dilithium compound, either from 2,2′-dibrombiphenyl and butyl-lithium or from the di-iodo compound and lithium, has proved a useful intermediate for the preparation of a variety of heterocyclic organometallic compounds, for example of arsenic (1.3) [36], silicon (1.4) [37], and phosphorus (1.5) [38], boron (1.6) [39] and of macrocyclic aromatic compounds [40].

[35] H. Gilman and B. J. Gaj, *J. Org. Chem.*, 1957, **22**, 1165; H. Gilman and S. Gray, ibid., 1958, **23**, 1476; H. Gilman and G. L. Schwebke, *J. Organometal. Chem.*, 1965, **4**, 483.

[36] F. G. Mann, Ch. 6 of Vol. IV of *Progress in Organic Chemistry*, ed. J. W. Cook, 1958; H. Heaney, D. M. Heinekey, F. G. Mann and I. T. Millar, *J. Chem. Soc.*, 1958, 3838.

[37] H. Gilman and R. D. Gorsich, *J. Amer. Chem. Soc.*, 1955, **77**, 6380.

[38] G. Wittig and G. Geissler, *Annalen*, 1953, **580**, 44.

[39] G. Wittig and W. Herwig, *Chem. Ber.*, 1955, **88**, 962.

[40] G. Wittig and G. Lehmann, ibid., 1957, **90**, 875; G. Wittig and G. Klar, *Annalen*, 1967 **704**, 91.

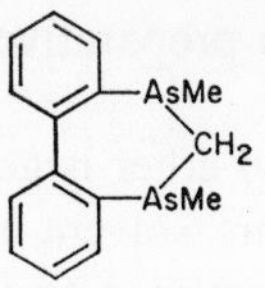

1.3 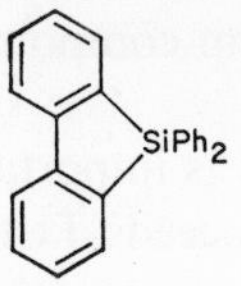　　　　　　　1.4 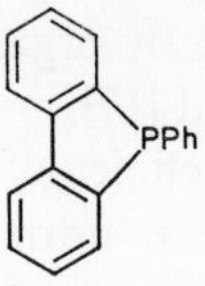　　　　　　　1.5

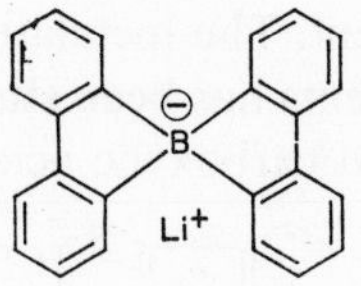

1.6

Metal–hydrogen exchange (*metalation*)

The third type of exchange reaction, *metal–hydrogen exchange*, also known simply as *metalation*, is exemplified by the formation of 2-furyl-lithium from phenyl-lithium and furan:

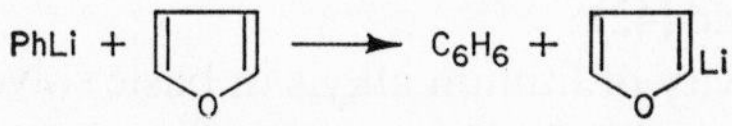

Both phenyl-lithium and, more often, n-butyl-lithium are extensively used in this reaction, which has been of particular value for the preparation of lithium derivatives of anisole, resorcinol ethers, benz- and dibenz-furans and thiophens. Lithiated crosslinked polystyrene, from the bromopoly-styrene and butyl-lithium, has also been used for metalation; its reactivity is comparable to that of phenyl-lithium [41]. The course of the reaction is less predictable than with the halogen–metal exchange, since the question of *orientation* has to be considered. The lithium commonly enters in the *ortho* position to the functional group, but sometimes the aliphatic side chain is metalated (giving a benzyl type of derivative) in preference to the nucleus.

These homogeneous metalation reactions are thought to involve attack by the nucleophilic (hydrocarbon) part of the organolithium reagent on a *hydrogen* atom of the molecule being metalated. That anisole and benzo-trifluoride, for example, are both metalated mainly in the *ortho* position is due to the $-I$ inductive effect of the $-OMe$ and $-CF_3$ groups making the *ortho* hydrogen more acidic, not to any mesomeric effect. Similarly an aliphatic hydrocarbon radical deactivates the *ortho* hydrogen atoms, and, for example, isopropylbenzene, though not metalated by butyl-lithium, is metalated by sodium and potassium alkyls in the *meta* and *para* positions (e.g. as shown by the work of Bryce-Smith [129], discussed below in con-nexion with organosodium compounds).

[41] D. Braun and E. Seelig, *Chem. Ber.*, 1964, **97**, 3098.

Metalation by organolithium compounds as a preparative method has been reviewed [17].

Again the choice of solvent is important. Ethyl ether is generally used, and metalation normally proceeds faster in this solvent than in light petroleum. The reaction appears to go very rapidly in tetrahydrofuran, even at low temperatures, and indeed, low temperatures are essential to avoid reaction with the solvent. The metalation of dibenzfuran (1.7) with butyl-lithium in various solvents has been studied, the product being converted into the easily isolated carboxylic acid (1.8).

1.7   1.8

In diethyl ether, di-n-butyl ether and light petroleum yields of (1.8) were 56%, 76% and 1%, but addition of a diethyl ether solution of butyl-lithium to a tetrahydrofuran solution of (1.7) at −55° to −60°, followed by slow warming to 0°, stirring for an hour, and then carbonation at −50° gave (1.8) in 86% yield [42].

The greater reactivity of lithium alkyls in basic solvents may reasonably be attributed to an increased anionic character of the carbon atom bound to the metal. Most tertiary amines are more basic than ethers, and complex more strongly to lithium alkyls, particularly when steric hindrance is minimized. Consequently lithium alkyls have very strong carbanion character in the presence of suitable tertiary amines and behave similarly to sodium alkyls in metalation reactions. Moreover the CH bonds adjacent to nitrogen in tertiary amines are less susceptible to nucleophilic attack than those adjacent to oxygen in ethers. Triethylenediamine forms crystalline sparingly soluble complexes with a range of organolithium compounds, the complexes generally having the composition

$$(RLi)_2N(C_2H_4)_3N(LiR)_2$$

Such complexes, which can be handled in hydrocarbons, metalate toluene at room temperature (carbonation then giving phenylacetic acid) and the butyl-lithium complex even metalates benzene when boiled with it (carbonation then giving benzoic acid in high yield) [43].

An enhancement of the reactivity of alkyl groups bound to magnesium due to increased carbanion character in more basic solvents has also been observed for organomagnesium compounds (see p. 97) and the effect is likely to be general.

The most remarkable and reactive of the lithium alkyl complexes are those formed by tetramethylethylenediamine [44].

[42] H. Gilman and R. D. Gorsich, *J. Org. Chem.*, 1957, **22**, 687.
[43] C. G. Screttas and J. F. Eastham, *J. Amer. Chem. Soc.*, 1965, **87**, 3276.
[44] A. W. Langer, *Trans. New York Acad. Sci.*, 1965, 741.

The n-butyl-lithium chelate complex is monomeric, and very soluble in

$$H_2C\text{---}NMe_2$$
$$\searrow Li\text{---}Bu^n$$
$$H_2C\text{---}NMe_2 \nearrow$$

paraffin solvents. The metal–carbon bond is so strongly polarized that the complex may be regarded as the best source of highly reactive soluble carbanions currently available. In contrast to the slow hydrogenolysis of Bu^nLi in benzene (100 atm., ca. 60 hours), the tetramethylethylenediamine (TMED) complex is hydrogenolysed rapidly at 25° under atmospheric pressure:

$$TMED\text{--}LiBu^n + H_2 \longrightarrow LiH + C_4H_{10} + TMED$$

The n-butyl-lithium TMED complex metalates benzene completely within one hour at 50° and evidently at a useful rate even at 25°. From the homogeneous reactions of BuLi–TMED with benzene, toluene, and p-xylene at 25° the crystalline TMED complexes of phenyl-, benzyl- and p-xylyl-lithium may be isolated in high yield, the only loss arising from the fairly high solubility of the products. Potassium t-butoxide also exerts a strong activating effect, and in its presence butyl-lithium metalates benzene at room temperature [44a].

The TMED complex of butyl-lithium is a much more active catalyst for the polymerization of ethylene than is butyl-lithium itself. This could be connected both with the polarity of the carbon–lithium bond and the coordinative unsaturation of the metal in these monomeric complexes. Whereas the polymerization of ethylene at 10,000 to 15,000 p.s.i. by butyl-lithium gives waxy products of molecular weight up to about 17,000 the TMED complex gives products of molecular weight about 26,000 at 40° and only 2500 p.s.i.

The complex slowly metalates itself on one of the methyl groups:

$$TMED\text{--}LiBu^n \xrightarrow[\text{room temp.}]{40 \text{ days}} \left[\begin{array}{c} H_2C\text{---}NMe_2 \\ H_2C \quad\quad Li \leftarrow \\ MeN\text{---}CH_2 \end{array} \right]_n$$

The product of this self-metalation appears to polymerize ethylene (e.g. 22–44° and 2500–5000 p.s.i.) giving a tough plastic, molecular weight in the 140,000 range and density about 0·97. This polythene is, of course, highly linear.

[44a] M. Schlosser, J. Organometal. Chem., 1967, 8, 9; see also B.P. 1,029,445 to Phillips Petroleum, 1964.

The reaction of BuLi–TMED with ethylene in benzene as solvent results in metalation of the benzene, followed by a telomerization process:

$$Bu^nLi\text{–}TMED + C_6H_6 \longrightarrow C_6H_5Li\text{–}TMED + C_4H_{10}$$

$$C_6H_5Li\text{–}TMED + nC_2H_4 \xrightarrow[\text{150–1000 p.s.i.}]{60\text{–}130°} C_6H_5(C_2H_4)_nLi\text{–}TMED$$

$$C_6H_5(C_2H_4)_nLi\text{–}TMED + C_6H_6 \longrightarrow C_6H_5Li\text{–}TMED + C_6H_5(C_2H_4)_nH$$

The range of suitable hydrocarbons is limited since at the same time the acidity must be great enough to result in metalation of the hydrocarbon by the BuLi–TMED (the first of the processes shown above) and also the reactivity of the resulting organolithium compound must be great enough for the second of the above reactions to take place. Suitable hydrocarbons ('telogens' in this context) include benzene, toluene, and propylene. In these reactions, n may range between 1 and 100 and, of course, benzene gives products containing an *even* and toluene an *odd* number of methylene groups in the side chain. Over 500 grams of telomer may be obtained per gram of butyl-lithium [45]. The use of propylene as telogen results in a complex mixture of products since addition to the double bond takes place as well as metalation on the methyl group.

Hydrocarbon groups which are activated, for example by proximity to olefinic or acetylenic bonds, and thereby develop 'acidic' character, are very readily metalated by reaction with phenyl- or butyl-lithium forming benzene or butane and the corresponding organolithium compound. The examples of cyclopentadiene and acetylenes RC:CH fall into this class and have been mentioned earlier (see also p. 13). Another example is 2-picoline, which is readily metalated in the side chain and the resulting lithium compound has found many synthetic uses [46].

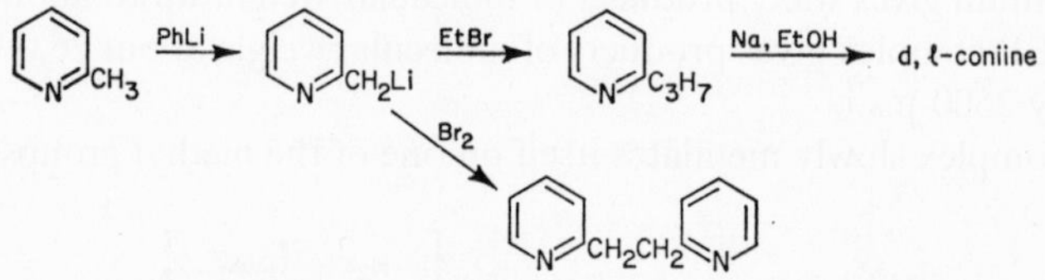

An unusual example of metalation is the reaction between methyl-lithium and triphenylphosphine oxide. Radical exchange takes place, and the P-methyl group is sufficiently acidic to indergo metalation.

$$Ph_3PO + MeLi \longrightarrow MePh_2PO + PhLi \quad \text{(fast)}$$
$$MePh_2PO + RLi \longrightarrow Ph_2P(O)CH_2Li + RH \quad \text{(slow)}$$

[45] G. G. Eberhardt and W. A. Butte, *J. Org. Chem.*, 1964, **29**, 2928; G. G. Eberhardt and W. R. Davis, *J. Polymer Sci* [A], 1965, **3**, 3753; G. G. Eberhardt, *Organometal. Chem. Rev.*, 1966, **1**, 491.

[46] P. G. Campbell and P. C. Teague, *J. Amer. Chem. Soc.*, 1954, **76**, 1371.

The resulting organolithium compound may then react, for example, with triphenyltin chloride [47].

$$Ph_2P(O)CH_2Li + Ph_3SnCl \rightarrow Ph_2P(O)CH_2SnPh_3$$

The metalation of a partly reduced aromatic system sometimes results in dehydrogenation with elimination of lithium hydride and the formation of a fully aromatic ring [48]. This reaction has been used for the synthesis of an iso-indole [49].

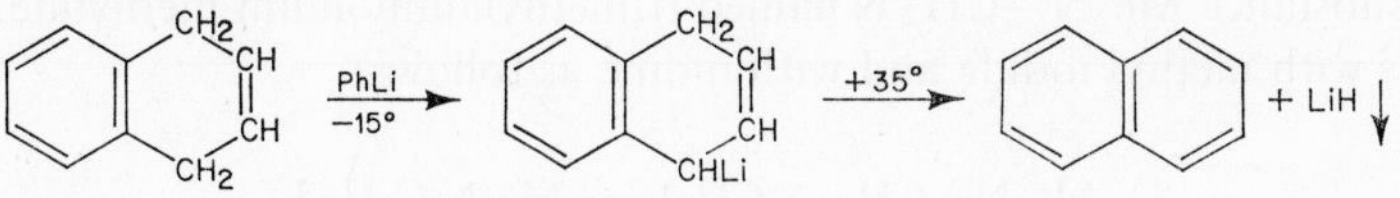

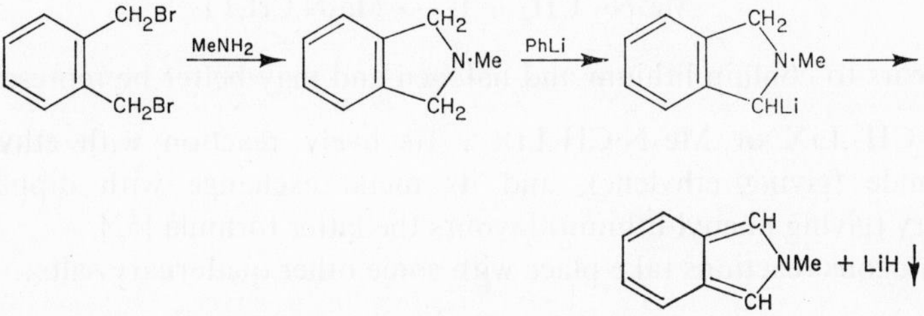

The synthesis of dilithium pentalenide by the same type of reaction provides another example of the use of this method as a route to not easily accessible aromatic systems:

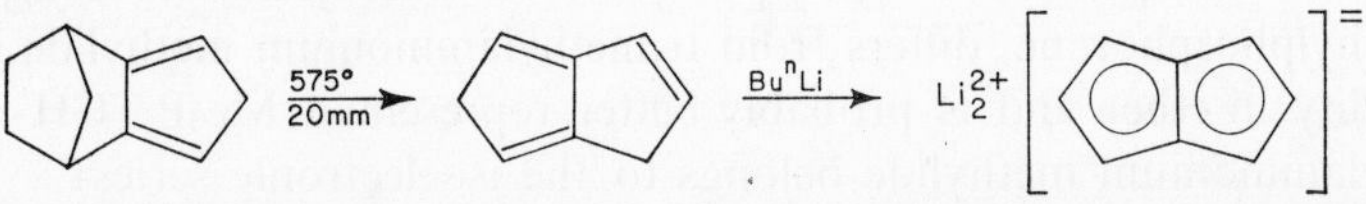

The colourless crystalline dilithium salt is formed when rather more than two mols. of butyl-lithium in heptane are added to a tetrahydrofuran solution of dihydropentalene [50]. Both this anion and the cyclo-octatetraene dianion mentioned later in this chapter, $C_8H_8^{2-}$, are aromatic according to the Hückel rule, $(4n + 2)\pi$ electrons, $n = 2$.

Wittig reaction and -ylides
Metalation of 'onium' halides commonly results in elimination of lithium halide, and has led to the preparation by G. Wittig of a series of

[47] D. Seyferth, D. E. Welch and J. K. Heeren, ibid., 1963, **85**, 642; 1964, **86**, 1100; see also J. J. Richard and C. V. Banks, *J. Org. Chem.*, 1963, **28**, 123.
[48] H. Gilman and C. W. Bradley, *J. Amer. Chem. Soc.*, 1938, **60**, 2333.
[49] G. Wittig, H. Tenhaeff, W. Schoch and G. Koenig, *Annalen*, 1951, **572**, 1.
[50] T. J. Katz and M. Rosenberger, *J. Amer. Chem. Soc.*, 1962, **84**, 865; T. J. Katz, M. Rosenberger and R. K. O'Hara, ibid., 1964, **86**, 249.

compounds known as -ylides [51]. Addition of phenyl-lithium to an ether suspension of tetramethylammonium chloride gives an insoluble precipitate, characterized by reaction with benzophenone:

$$Me_4N^+Cl^- \xrightarrow{PhLi} LiCH_2 \cdot \overset{+}{N}Me_3Cl^- \longrightarrow Me_3\overset{+}{N}{-}\overset{-}{C}H_2 + LiCl$$

$$Me_3\overset{+}{N}{-}\overset{-}{C}H_2 \xrightarrow[HCl]{Ph_2CO} Ph_2C(OH) \cdot CH_2\overset{+}{N}Me_3Cl^-$$

The substance $Me_3\overset{+}{N}{-}\overset{-}{C}H_2$ is named trimethylammonium methylide, and reacts with methyl iodide and with iodine as follows:

$$Me_3\overset{+}{N}{-}\overset{-}{C}H_2 + CH_3I \longrightarrow Me_3\overset{+}{N} \cdot C_2H_5 \ I^-$$

$$Me_3\overset{+}{N}{-}\overset{-}{C}H_2 + I_2 \longrightarrow Me_3\overset{+}{N} \cdot CH_2I \ I^-$$

It appears to contain lithium and halogen and may better be represented $Me_3\overset{+}{N} \cdot \overset{-}{C}H_2,LiX$ or $Me_3\overset{+}{N} \cdot CH_2LiX^-$. Its lively reaction with ethylene dibromide (giving ethylene), and its metal exchange with diphenylmercury (giving phenyl-lithium) favours the latter formula [52].

Analogous reactions take place with some other quaternary salts:

$$Me_3\overset{+}{N} \cdot NH_2I^- + PhLi \longrightarrow C_6H_6 + LiI + Me_3\overset{+}{N}{-}\overset{-}{NH}$$

$$Me_4\overset{+}{P}I^- + PhLi \longrightarrow C_6H_6 + LiI + Me_3\overset{+}{P}{-}\overset{-}{C}H_2$$

The latter compound, trimethylphosphonium methylide or methylenetrimethylphosphorane, differs from trimethylammonium methylide in its solubility in ether and is probably better represented $Me_3P{=}CH_2$. Trimethylammonium methylide belongs to the isoelectronic series:

$$Me_3\overset{+}{N}{-}\overset{-}{B}H_3 \quad Me_3\overset{+}{N}{-}\overset{-}{C}H_2 \quad Me_3\overset{+}{N}{-}\overset{-}{N}H \quad Me_3\overset{+}{N}{-}\overset{-}{O}$$

The metalation of alkyltriphenylphosphonium salts is of particular importance since the resulting methylene derivative undergoes a most useful reaction with carbonyl compounds; this is known as the *Wittig reaction* and the intermediates such as $Ph_3P{=}CH_2$ are called Wittig reagents. They convert $R_2C{=}O$ into $R_2C{=}CH_2$ (or $R_2C{=}CR'_2$) generally under very mild conditions [53]. Monomeric Me_3PCH_2 has been isolated [53a].

[51] G. Wittig and M. H. Wetterling, *Annalen*, 1947, **557**, 193; G. Wittig and M. Rieber, ibid., 1949, **562**, 177.

[52] H. Daniel and J. Paetsch, *Chem. Ber.*, 1965, **98**, 1915.

[53] G. Wittig, *Experientia*, 1956, **12**, 41; *Angew. Chem.*, 1956, **68**, 505; U. Schöllkopf, ibid., 1959, **71**, 260; S. Trippet, *Advances in Organic Chemistry*, Vol. 1, Ch. 3, ed. R. A. Raphael, E. C. Taylor and H. Wynberg, Interscience, New York, 1960; S. Trippett, *Quart. Rev.*, 1963, **17**, 406.

[53a] H. Schmidbaur and W. Tronich, *Angew. Chem., Internat. Edn.*, 1967, **6**, 448.

$$Ph_3P \xrightarrow{\text{MeBr}} Ph_3\overset{+}{P}CH_3Br^- \xrightarrow{\text{PhLi}} \begin{array}{c} Ph_3P{=}CH_2 \\ + \\ O{=}CR_2 \end{array} \rightarrow \begin{array}{c} \overset{+}{Ph_3P}{-}CH_2 \\ | \\ {}^-O{-}CR_2 \end{array} \rightarrow \begin{array}{c} Ph_3P \quad CH_2 \\ || + || \\ O \quad CR_2 \end{array}$$

The reaction between ylides and aldehydes is first order in each reactant, and the rate increases with solvent polarity [54]. In one rather special case an intermediate has been isolated [54a].

$$Ph_3P{=}C{=}PPh_3 + (CF_3)_2CO \xrightarrow{40°} \begin{array}{c} Ph_3P{-}C{=}PPh_3 \\ | \quad | \\ O{-}C(CF_3)_2 \end{array}$$

$$\xrightarrow{110°}$$

$$Ph_3PO + Ph_3P{=}C{=}C(CF_3)_2$$

Benzyne

The metalation of aromatic halides (as distinct from metal–halogen exchange) has also led to some very useful synthetic reagents. Fluorine bound to an aromatic nucleus does not easily undergo metal-halogen exchange or react with metallic lithium, though aryl-lithium compounds have been obtained from aryl fluorides and lithium in tetrahydrofuran [55], and hexafluorobenzene reacts smoothly with methyl-lithium

$$C_6F_6 + MeLi \rightarrow C_6F_5CH_3 + LiF$$

However, the reaction between phenyl-lithium and fluorobenzene gives 2-lithiobiphenyl, since biphenyl-2-carboxylic acid results after carbonation [56].

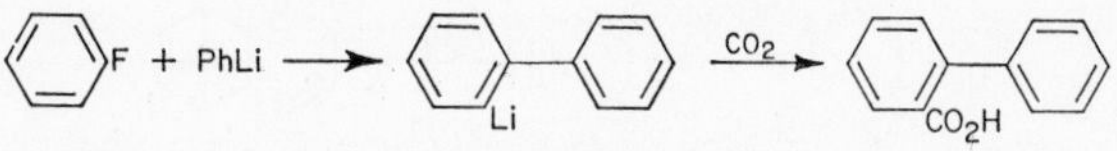

Wittig [57] suggested that the reaction must proceed by metalation followed by elimination of lithium fluoride and formation of an intermediate C_6H_4,

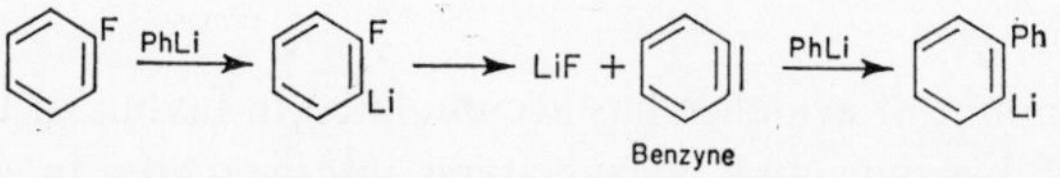

Benzyne

since 2-lithiobiphenyl is *not* obtained from biphenyl and phenyl-lithium.

[54] A. J. Speziale and D. E. Bissing, *J. Amer. Chem. Soc.*, 1963, **85**, 3878; M. E. Jones and S. Trippett, *J. Chem. Soc.*, (C), 1966, 1090.

[54a] G. H. Birum and C. N. Matthews, *Chem. Comm.*, 1967, 137.

[55] H. Gilman and T. S. Soddy, *J. Org. Chem.*, 1957, **22**, 1121.

[56] G. Wittig, G. Pieper and G. Fuhrmann, *Ber.*, 1940, **73**, 1193.

[57] G. Wittig, *Naturwiss.*, 1942, **30**, 696.

The suggestion of a symmetrical intermediate was later confirmed by the use of isotopic tracers [58]:

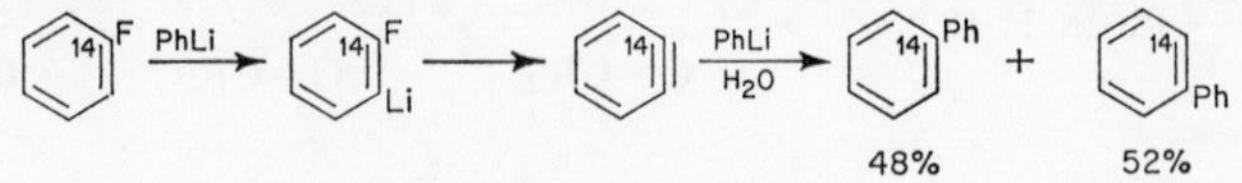

48%　　52%

Metalation of 1-fluoronaphthalene, followed by carbonation, yields isomeric products consistent with the transient formation of naphthalyne [59]:

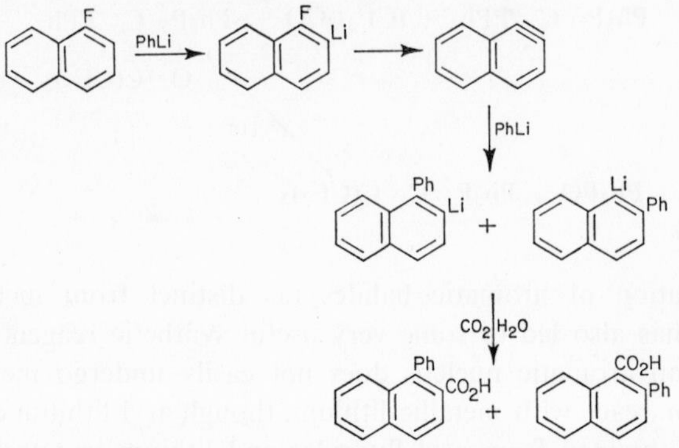

Benzyne can also be formed from ortho dihalides and lithium (or magnesium), advantageously as amalgam; its very high reactivity permits some unusual syntheses of the Diels–Alder type [60].

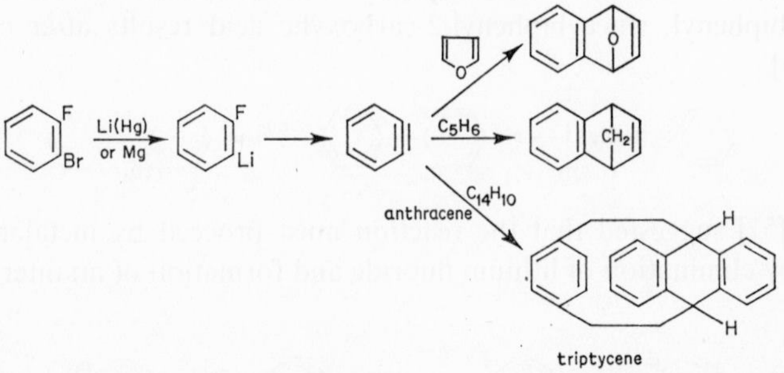

triptycene

A large amount of evidence has accumulated in favour of the transient formation of benzyne and benzyne-type intermediates in a variety of reactions which generally involve the action of a strongly nucleophilic reagent on an aromatic halide. Nucleophilic reagents such as alkali metal amides in liquid ammonia, or lithium piperidide have frequently been used

[58] E. Jenny and J. D. Roberts, *Helv. Chem. Acta*, 1955, **38**, 1248.

[59] R. Huisgen and H. Rist, *Annalen*, 1955, **594**, 137.

[60] G. Wittig and L. Pohmer, *Angew. Chem.*, 1955, **67**, 348; *Chem. Ber.*, 1956, **89**, 1334.

as well as organolithium compounds. There are good reviews of benzyne chemistry and its synthetic applications [61].

The metalation of *gem*-dihalides may lead to yet another special class of reactive intermediate, namely the *carbenes*. Like the benzynes, carbenes are also formed by the action of various other strong bases, as well as organo-lithium compounds, on suitable halides (see also trichloromethylmercury compounds, p. 170). Both carbenes and benzynes exist only as transient reaction intermediates, the presence of either being deduced from products of addition to suitable reagents or from their decomposition products. Thus carbenes typically add to olefins forming cyclopropanes, and may themselves rearrange to form cyclopropanes.

As an example, reaction between n-amyl-lithium and methylene chloride in ether or pentane gives a mixture of 1-hexene and n-propylcyclopropane [62]:

$$\text{n-}C_5H_{11}Li + CH_2Cl_2 \longrightarrow \text{n-}C_5H_{12} + LiCHCl_2$$

$$\text{n-}C_5H_{11}\overset{..}{C}H + LiCl \longleftarrow \text{n-}C_5H_{11}CHLiCl \overset{\text{n-}C_5H_{11}Li}{\longleftarrow} \overset{..}{C}HCl + LiCl$$

$$\text{n-}C_4H_9CH{:}CH_2 + \text{n-}C_3H_7{\cdot}\overset{CH_2}{\underset{CH_2}{\overset{|}{C}H}}$$

Both $CHCl_2Li$ and the even less stable CCl_3Li (decomp. from $-60°$) have been prepared from Bu^nLi and CH_2Cl_2 or $CHCl_3$ in a $4:1:1$ THF/Et_2O/petrol mixture at $-110°$. With $HgCl_2$ these lithium reagents yield $(CHCl_2)_2Hg$ and $(CCl_3)_2Hg$. The rate of decomposition of these compounds is sensitive to the solvent composition, thus $CHCl_2Li$ is stable at $-78°$ in THF/Et_2O mixtures containing between 20 and 100% THF but as the THF concentration is reduced below 20% so the decomposition rate rapidly increases. The decomposition process depends on the electrophilic character of the metal atom as well as on the nucleophilic character of the carbon, and the electrophilic character of lithium would be reduced by strong solvation by very basic ethers such as tetrahydrofuran. If decomposition by a β-elimination is possible, as in the case of tri-chlorovinyl-lithium, then the rate of decomposition in tetrahydrofuran is faster than in diethyl ether.

Several observations suggest that reactions between $CHCl_2Li$ or CCl_3Li and olefins involve electrophilic attack by lithium on the double bond, and are not typical carbene reactions. The thermal decomposition of compounds of the type $RR'C{:}CXLi$ (X = Cl or Br), which are commonly

[61] R. Huisgen, Ch. 2 of *Organometallic Chemistry*, ed. H. Zeiss, Reinhold, 1960; H. Heaney, *Chem. Rev.*, 1962, **62**, 81; G. Wittig, *Angew. Chem., Internat. Edn.*, 1962, **1**, 415.

[62] G. L. Gloss, *J. Amer. Chem. Soc.*, 1962, **84**, 809; see also G. L. Gloss and L. E. Closs, ibid., 1959, **81**, 4996; 1960, **82**, 5723; 1961, **83**, 599, 1003, 2015; 1963, **85**, 99.

called *carbenoids*, is the basis of synthetic routes to a variety of acetylenic and allenic systems. Thus $Ph_2C:CClLi$ decomposes in diethyl ether giving diphenylacetylene almost quantitatively, and $alkyl_2C:CXLi$ decomposes by dimerization and trimerization giving allenes, $alkyl_2 C:C:C alkyl_2$, and cyclopropanes [63].

Addition to olefins

Organolithium compounds find several applications in reactions involving *addition across double bonds*, and some of the benzyne reactions mentioned earlier are, of course, rather unusual examples of addition of RLi across a triple bond (though the electronic situation in these compounds is not altogether clear). The continued addition of RLi across ethylene, resulting in telomerization and polymerization of the latter, has already been described in connexion with the exceptional properties of the butyl-lithium tetramethylethylenediamine complex.

Butyl-lithium adds to diphenylacetylene in diethyl ether, though not in pentane, and *trans*-butylstilbene may be isolated after hydrolysis [64]. Its addition to 1,1-diphenylethylene is faster in ether than in hydrocarbons, and is accompanied by the development of a red colour due to a benzyl-type structure, which can reasonably be written as an ion-pair (in donor solvents):

$$Ph_2C:CH_2 + Bu^nLi \longrightarrow Bu^nCH_2CPh_2^-Li^+$$

The kinetics of this reaction have been studied [65]; the initial reaction rate is proportional to

$$[BuLi]^{0.17} [Ph_2C:CH_2],$$

the exponent 0·17 having been considered to result from monomeric butyl-lithium being the reactive species although any equilibrium

$$(BuLi)_6 \rightleftharpoons 6BuLi$$

would be very much in favour of the hexamer. However, doubts have been expressed about this view on several occasions,* since there is little or no physical evidence for the occurrence of monomeric lithium alkyls (except in donor solvents), even in mass spectra, and dimers or *complexed* hexamers

[63] G. Köbrich, K. Flory and W. Drischel, *Angew. Chem.*, 1964, **76**, 536; G. Köbrich and H. Heinemann, *Angew. Chem., Internat. Edn.*, 1965, **4**, 49. G. Köbrich, K. Flory, H. R. Merkle and H. Trapp, ibid., p. 706; G. Köbrich, Lecture to Organometallic Symposium, Madison, 1965; see also D. F. Hoeg, D. I. Lusk and A, L. Crumbliss, *J. Amer. Chem. Soc.*, 1965, **87**, 4147; G. Köbrich, *Angew, Chem., Internat. Edn.*, 1967, **6**, 41.

[64] J. E. Mulvaney, Z. G. Gardlund and S. L. Gardlung, *J. Amer. Chem. Soc.*, 1963, **85**, 3897.

[65] A. G. Evans and D. B. George, *J. Chem. Soc.*, 1961, 4653; 1962, 141.

* Dr T. L. Brown, Lectures at XIXth International Congress of Pure and Applied Chemistry, London, 1963, and Organometallic Symposium, Madison, 1965.

are more likely to be the reactive species in this type of process. The existence of a monomer-hexamer equilibrium is widely regarded as unlikely [66].

The addition of isopropyl-lithium to ethylene appears to have been discovered by chance, as a consequence of the formation of ethylene by attack of the lithium alkyl on diethyl ether. Whereas carbonation at $-50°$ of Pr^iLi prepared at that temperature results in the normal products, Pr^i_2CO and Pr^iCO_2H, an exothermic reaction set in when Pr^iLi in ether was allowed to reach room temperature and subsequent carbonation yielded $(Pr^iCH_2CH_2)_2CO$ and $Pr^iCH_2CH_2CO_2H$. The same products are formed when ethylene is bubbled into a solution of Pr^iLi in diethyl ether at $-60°$ and subsequently carbonated. Tertiary butyl-lithium similarly adds ethylene. Only *one* mole of ethylene adds since the product is a primary lithium alkyl, and these do not readily add ethylene [67] (unless activated by co-ordination to a ditertiary amine, see pp. 19–20).

Lithium alkyls, in paraffin hydrocarbon solution, add to various aromatic hydrocarbons and then eliminate lithium hydride leaving an alkylated arene. The order of reactivity is parallel to the presumed carbanion character of the alkyl, namely $Bu^t \gg Bu^s > Bu^n >$ aryl $>$ vinyl. The addition of Bu^tLi to naphthalene has been extensively studied, and an intermediate $C_{10}H_8Bu_tLi$ has been isolated. Both 1- and 2-tert-butyl-naphthalene are formed [68]:

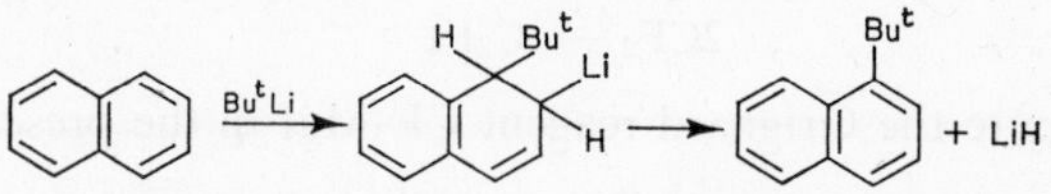

The addition of lithium alkyls (or metallic lithium) to *conjugated diolefins* can result in stereoregular polymerization, the best-known examples being the conversion of isoprene into a synthetic 1,4-*cis* polymer similar to natural *Hevea* rubber by lithium, butyl- or ethyl-lithium in pentane, and into a

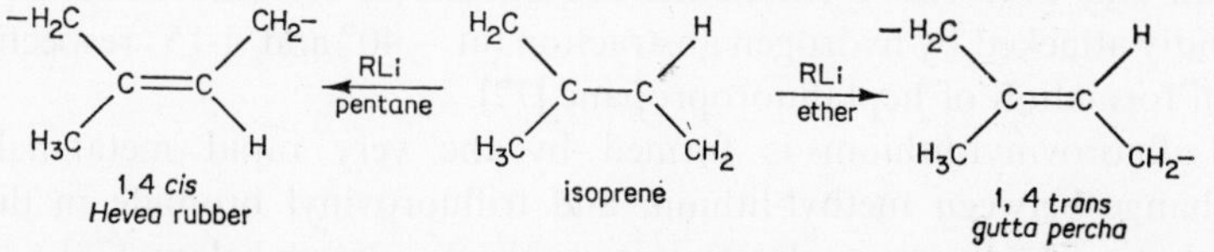

largely 1,4-*trans* polymer, similar to gutta percha, by similar reagents in

[66] T. L. Brown, *J. Organomental Chem.*, 1966, **5**, 191; *Advances in Organometallic Chemistry*, 1965, **3**, 365; see also R. Waack, P. West and M. A. Doran, *Chem. and Ind.*, 1966, 1035.

[67] P. D. Bartlett, S. Friedman and M. Stiles, *J. Amer. Chem. Soc.*, 1953, **75**, 1771.

[68] J. A. Dixon and D. H. Fishman, ibid., 1963, **85**, 1356; J. A. Dixon, D. H. Fishman and R. S. Dudinak, *Tetrahedron Letters*, 1964, 613; J. A. Dixon, Lecture to Organometallic Symposium, Madison, 1965.

diethyl ether. Such conjugated dienes are very much more readily polymerized than are simple olefins. The subject of stereoregular polymerization, including the use of lithium and lithium alkyls for this purpose, has been excellently reviewed [69].

The addition of lithium alkyls to carbonyl, azomethine, and other such functional groups does not properly come within the scope of this book. The reaction between RLi and *carbon monoxide* at $-70°$, leading to the ketones R_2CO in about 30–55% yield, should however be noted [70].

Fluoro derivatives

The preparation of *perfluoro*-alkyl or -aryl-lithium derivatives has presented special problems, in part due to the ease with which lithium fluoride is eliminated,

$$C_3F_7Li \longrightarrow C_3F_6 + LiF$$

Heptafluoro-n-propyl and -isopropyl-lithium [71] have been prepared by metal–halogen exchange reactions between C_3F_7I and lithium alkyls in ether at $-78°$. The reagent should be used at once. Attempts to prepare trifluoromethyl-lithium by similar reactions have not been successful; evidently lithium fluoride is eliminated very readily and in fact tetrafluoroethylene has been isolated among reaction products, though it may be noted that no cyclopropane derivative was detected when attempts were

$$CF_3Li \longrightarrow CF_2 + LiF$$
$$2CF_2 \longrightarrow C_2F_4$$

made to prepare the Grignard reagent CF_3MgI in the presence of cyclohexene.

The remarkable effect of a small proportion (about 2%) of sodium in enhancing the reactivity of metallic lithium towards halides has already been mentioned, and it has been applied to the direct preparation of n-C_3F_7Li from n-C_3F_7I and lithium in diethyl ether at $-40°$. Tetrahydrofuran and di-(2-ethoxyethyl)ether are unsuitable solvents since they are rapidly attacked by hydrogen abstraction (at $-40°$ and $+15°$ respectively) with formation of heptafluoropropane [72].

Trifluorovinyl-lithium is formed by the very rapid metal–halogen exchange between methyl-lithium and trifluorovinyl bromide in diethyl ether at $-78°$. In ether solution it is usable at $-25°$ or below. [73]

$$CF_2:CFBr + MeLi \longrightarrow CF_2:CFLi + MeBr$$

[69] C. E. H. Bawn and A. Ledwith, *Quart. Rev.*, 1962, **16**, 361.
[70] S. Tsutsumi and M. Ryang, *Trans. New York Acad. Sci.*, 1965, **27**, 724.
[71] O. R. Pierce, E. T. McBee and G. F. Judd, *J. Amer. Chem. Soc.*, 1954, **76**, 474;
R. D. Chambers, W. K. R. Musgrave and J. Savory, *J. Chem. Soc.*, 1962, 1993.
[72] J. A. Beel, H. C. Clark and D. Whyman, ibid., p. 4423.
[73] P. Tarrant, P. Johncock and J. Savory, *J. Org. Chem.*, 1963, **28**, 839.

Trifluorovinyl-lithium has also been obtained from trifluorovinyl-triphenyltin (itself made by means of CF_2:CFMgBr) and phenyl-lithium by the transmetalation reaction [74]. It is of interest that reaction between phenyl-lithium and a trifluorovinylsilane takes a different course:

$$Et_3SiCF:CF_2 + PhLi \longrightarrow Et_3SiCFLi \cdot CF_2Ph \longrightarrow Et_3SiCF:CFPh + LiF$$

Pentafluorophenyl-lithium may be prepared from C_6F_5Br by exchange with butyl-lithium in ether at $-78°$, by reaction with lithium amalgam in ether at $0°$, and from C_6F_6 and butyl-lithium in hexane. It is much more stable in solution than heptafluoropropyl-lithium, and more stable than trifluorovinyl-lithium,

$$stable \quad C_6F_5Li > CF_2:CFLi > C_3F_7Li \quad unstable$$

its half-life being rather more than one day in ether at $-10°$.

However, loss of fluoride ion can occur, since reaction between C_6F_5Br and lithium amalgam in furan is vigorous and gives a product which must have involved a benzyne intermediate.

The epoxide resulting from tetrafluorobenzyne addition to furan was identified by conversion to a tetrafluoro-1-naphthol [75]. Pentafluoro-phenyl-lithium may also be prepared from pentafluorobenzene and alkyl-lithium at low temperature and may be converted to pentafluorobenzoic acid in high yield by carbonation [76]. Penta*chloro*phenyl-lithium, whose half-life is about seven hours at $20°$ in ether–hexane, may be obtained in good yield from n-butyl-lithium in hexane and hexachlorobenzene in diethyl ether (0 to $-10°$) or in tetrahydrofuran ($-78°$) [77].

Miscellaneous organolithium compounds

Derivatives of acetylene might also be considered a special class of organolithium compound. Lithium acetylide, Li_2C_2, is precipitated as a white powder when acetylene is led into ether to which phenyl-lithium is added with stirring [78]. If the ether is decanted, and tetrahydrofuran

[74] D. Seyferth, T. Wada and G. Raab, *Tetrahedron Letters*, 1960, 20; D. Seyferth, D. E. Welch and G. Raab, *J. Amer. Chem. Soc.*, 1962, **84**, 4266.
[75] P. L. Coe, R. Stephens and J. C. Tatlow, *J. Chem. Soc.*, 1962, 3227.
[76] R. J. Harper, E. J. Soloski and C. Tamborski, *J. Org. Chem.*, 1964, **29**, 2385; C. Tamborski, E. J. Soloski and S. M. Dec, *J. Organometal. Chem.*, 1965, **4**, 446.
[77] M. D. Rausch, F. E. Tibbetts and H. B. Gordon, ibid., 1966, **5**, 493.
[78] H. H. Inhoffen, H. Pommer and E. G. Meth, *Annalen*, 1949, **565**, 50.

added, the acetylide dissolves and will then react with, for example, benzophenone giving $Ph_2C(OH)\cdot C(OH)Ph_2$ in good yield [79]. A solid ethylenediamine complex, $LiHC_2en$, soluble in tetrahydrofuran, dioxan, and dimethylsulphoxide, has become commercially available [80].

Reaction between lithium alkyls and monosubstituted acetylenes, $RC:CH$, naturally yields $RC:CLi$, but further reaction can take place when a methyl or methylene group is adjacent to the triple bond. This is presumably similar to the nucleophilic attack of lithium alkyls on CH bonds alpha to oxygen in ethers, the acetylenic group having an electron-attracting effect similar to but probably rather less than that of ether-oxygen. When methylacetylene is added to an excess of n-butyl-lithium in hexane, and the solution is boiled several hours, metalation of all the hydrogen atoms takes place:

$$CH_3C:CH \rightarrow CH_3C:CLi \rightarrow CLi_3C:CLi$$

$$\overset{Me_3SiCl}{\swarrow} \qquad \overset{D_2O}{\downarrow}$$

$$(Me_3Si)_2CH\cdot C:CSiMe_3 \qquad CD_3C:CD$$
$$+ (Me_3Si)_2C:C:C(SiMe_3)_2$$

The lithiated product C_3Li_4 is soluble in hydrocarbon in the presence of butyl-lithium and the solutions are red-brown. Removal of solvent or excess butyl-lithium gives a red solid which does not redissolve in hydrocarbons. The isomerization from an acetylenic to an allenic structure is believed to occur during the reaction with Me_3SiCl, and it may be difficult to obtain $(Me_3Si)_3C\cdot C:CSiMe_3$ due to steric crowding. When $(Me_3Si)_2CH\cdot C:CSiMe_3$ reacts with butyl-lithium it is metalated, but reaction with Me_3SiCl then gives the *allene* in high yield [81].

Hydroboration of acetylenes by dicyclohexylborane, followed by exchange with butyl-lithium, provides a route to *gem-dilithium* compounds [81a].

$$RC:CH + 2(C_6H_{11})_2BH \rightarrow RCH_2CH[B(C_6H_{11})_2]_2$$

$$\overset{}{\downarrow} {\scriptstyle Bu^nLi}$$

$$RCH_2CH(CO_2H)_2 \overset{CO_2}{\longleftarrow} RCH_2CHLi_2$$

Detection of organolithium compounds

The *estimation* of organolithium compounds has already been mentioned. The use of these reagents in halogen–metal, and more particularly

[79] G. E. Coates and J. Graham, unpublished observations.

[80] *Chemical and Engineering News*, 1962, Sept. 3, p. 48; O. F. Beumel and R. F. Harris, *J. Org. Chem.*, 1963, **28**, 2775.

[81] R. West, P. A. Carney and I. C. Mineo, *J. Amer. Chem. Soc.*, 1965, **87**, 3788; see also J. E. Mulvaney, T. L. Folk and D. J. Newton, *J. Org. Chem.*, 1967, **32**, 1674.

[81a] G. Cainelli, G. DalBello and G. Zubiani, *Tetrahedron Letters*, 1965, 3429; idem, ibid., 1966, 4315.

hydrogen–metal, exchange reactions which are sometimes rather slow is complicated by the reaction with the solvent. A *qualitative* test for the reagent is therefore necessary, and three useful colour tests have been developed by Gilman [82].

Colour test I detects any organometallic compound that is sufficiently reactive to add to an aryl ketone, and a positive reaction is given by organo-lithium compounds, Grignard reagents and, for example, organozinc compounds. About 1 c.c. of the solution to be tested is withdrawn by a syringe (or a safety-pipette flushed with nitrogen), and added to about a c.c. of 1% solution of Michler's ketone in benzene. The reaction product is then hydrolysed by the addition of a little water, followed by addition of a 0·2% solution of iodine in glacial acetic acid. The development of a blue to green colour indicates the presence of a reactive organo-metallic compound, since a di- or -tri-phenylmethane dye is produced. Phenyl-lithium for example, gives malachite green:

$$(p\text{-}Me_2N\cdot C_6H_4)_2CO + PhLi \longrightarrow (p\text{-}Me_2N\cdot C_6H_4)_2PhCOLi$$
$$\downarrow H_2O$$
$$[(p\text{-}Me_2N\cdot C_6H_4)_2PhC]^+I^- \xleftarrow[\text{HOAc}]{I_2} (p\text{-}Me_2N\cdot C_6H_4)_2PhCOH$$

Malachite green iodide

This test is much used to show when a reaction is completed, but it is necessary to remember that in the event of the main reaction product being a reducing agent a correspondingly large amount of iodine must be added or the dye will be reduced and no colour will develop.

Colour test II detects only those organometallic compounds which are sufficiently reactive to undergo a rapid halogen–metal exchange reaction with *p*-bromdimethylaniline. Its great value in organolithium chemistry is that it gives a positive reaction for alkyl-lithium compounds (in particular butyl-lithium), but *not* for methyl-lithium, nor for aryl-lithium compounds. It is therefore of particular value in halogen–metal or hydrogen–metal exchange reactions for showing when all the butyl-lithium is consumed. About 1 c.c. of the solution to be tested is added to an equal volume of a 15% solution of *p*-bromdimethylaniline in dry benzene. One c.c. of a 15% solution of benzophenone in dry benzene is then added, followed by hydrolysis with water and finally acidification with concentrated hydrochloric acid. A red colour in the aqueous layer indicates that *p*-dimethyl-aminophenyl-lithium has been formed, and that a reactive organolithium

[82] H. Gilman and F. Schulze, *J. Amer. Chem Soc.*, 1925, **47**, 2002; H. Gilman and J. Swiss, ibid., 1940, **62**, 1847; H. Gilman and H. L. Yablunky, ibid., 1941, **63**, 839; for a discussion and improvements of these tests see J. M. Gaidis, *J. Organometal. Chem.*, 1967, **8**, 385.

compound was present in the test solution. The course of the reaction with butyl-lithium is as follows:

$$Bu^nLi + p\text{-}Br\cdot C_6H_4NMe_2 \rightarrow p\text{-}LiC_6H_4NMe_2 + Bu^nBr$$

$$p\text{-}LiC_6H_4NMe_2 + Ph_2CO \xrightarrow[HCl]{H_2O} [Ph_2C{=}\!\!\!\bigcirc\!\!\!{=}NMe_2]^+Cl^-$$

bright red

A positive reaction is obtained with butyl-lithium when the concentration is above 0·02 to 0·03 molar, but it should be noted that solutions of butyl-lithium in tetrahydrofuran cease to give a positive colour test II when their concentration is less than 0·2 molar, though colour test I is positive at low concentrations in this solvent [35].

Colour test III distinguishes *aryl*-lithium compounds or *aryl* Grignard reagents from alkyl compounds. One c.c. of test solution is added to about an equal volume of a 1% solution of triphenylbismuth dichloride in dry benzene. If aryl-lithium or -magnesium compounds are present a deep purple colour appears. The mechanism of this test is not clear but may be connected with the formation of penta-arylbismuth since, for example, pentaphenylbismuth has a purple colour.

Properties and constitution

The organolithium compounds are with few exceptions soluble not only in ether but also in benzene and in paraffin hydrocarbons. Highly sensitive to moisture and to oxygen (the pure compounds of high lithium content inflame in air), they must be handled *in vacuo* or in an inert atmosphere, conveniently nitrogen.

Methyl-lithium, precipitated from benzene or light petroleum by either of the reactions,

$$2EtLi + Me_2Hg \rightarrow Et_2Hg + 2MeLi$$
$$EtLi + MeI \rightarrow EtI + MeLi$$

is an apparently involatile microcrystalline white powder [83], but these methods tend to give products contaminated with ethyl groups. Crystallographic examination [84] of the isotropic crystals of methyl-lithium reveals cubic symmetry with 8 molecules in the unit cell. Though the solid has an electron-deficient polymeric constitution, which is discussed below (p. 35), its solutions in ether are most unlikely to contain carbanions since methyl-lithium is relatively stable in ether and its solutions are less reactive than those of its higher homologues (e.g. butyl-lithium) whose constitutions are probably essentially covalent.

Evaporation at −70° of the ether solution obtained by reaction of methyl chloride with lithium metal, and removal of precipitated lithium

[83] T. L. Brown and M. T. Rogers, *J. Amer. Chem. Soc.*, 1957, **79**, 1859.
[84] E. Weiss and E. A. C. Lucken, *J. Organometal. Chem.*, 1964, **2**, 197.

chloride, gives an ether complex MeLiOEt$_2$ (containing about 2% Cl). Addition of pentane before solid methyl-lithium separates raises its chloride content. The solid isolated from the reaction between methyl bromide and lithium has the composition MeLi, LiBr, 2Et$_2$O [85].

Ethyl-lithium, m.p. 95°, crystallizes from benzene in which it has a fairly high temperature coefficient of solubility (solubility about 1 molar at room temperature). It has a layered lattice with 16 monomer units in the unit cell and tetramer units can be identified in the structure (Figure 3). Each tetramer consists of two closely associated dimers which together form two interpenetrating tetrahedra, one of lithium and the other of methylene-carbon atoms. Each tetramer is bound to neighbouring tetramer units, forming the sheet-like structure, and crystalline ethyl-lithium is easily cleaved like mica. The structure is described in more detail below. It can be sublimed with some difficulty at about 90° but has enough vapour pressure at 80° to give appreciable infrared absorption in a 12-cm. cell [88].

n-Propyl-lithium and *n-butyl-lithium* are both liquids at room temperature. The latter may be distilled very slowly at 80–90° in a good vacuum, but distillation is generally accompanied by some decomposition. Both normal and secondary butyl-lithium become very viscous when cooled to −76° but do not freeze [87]; this reference includes useful preparative detail.

Solid *phenyl-lithium* has been obtained by the exchanges

$$EtLi + PhBr \longrightarrow EtBr + PhLi$$

and $$Bu^nLi + PhI \longrightarrow Bu^nI + PhLi$$

in benzene [88], or benzene–hexane [6a].

Thermal decomposition [89] of ethyl-lithium gives mainly lithium hydride and ethylene: $CH_3CH_2Li \longrightarrow CH_2{:}CH_2 + LiH$

Small amounts of butane and butene are also formed, but practically no ethane. n-Butyl-lithium decomposes slowly at about 100° and is rapidly and completely decomposed at 150°, mainly to butene ($\sim$92%), butane ($\sim$8%), and lithium hydride which is permeated with resinous matter. The course of the reaction is:

$$CH_3CH_2CH_2CH_2Li \longrightarrow CH_3CH_2CH{:}CH_2 + LiH$$
$$CH_3CH_2CH{:}CH_2 + n\text{-}C_4H_9Li \longrightarrow CH_3CHLiCH{:}CH_2 + C_4H_{10}$$
$$CH_3CHLiCH{:}CH_2 \longrightarrow CH_2{:}CH{\cdot}CH{:}CH_2 + LiH$$
$$CH_2{:}CH{\cdot}CH{:}CH_2 \longrightarrow \text{resinous polymer}$$

[85] T. V. Talalaeva, A. N. Rodianov and K. A. Kocheshkov, *Doklady Akad. Nauk S.S.S.R.*, 1961, **140**, 847; *Chem. Abs.*, 1962, **56**, 5989.

[86] H. Dietrich, *Acta Cryst.*, 1963, **16**, 681.

[87] D. H. Lewis, W. S. Leonhardt and C. W. Kamienski, *Chimia*, 1964, **18**, 134.

[88] R. West and W. Glaze, *J. Amer. Chem. Soc.*, 1961, **83**, 3580; A. N. Rodionov, D. N. Shigorin, T. V. Talalaeva and K. A. Kocheshkov, *Doklady Akad. Nauk S.S.S.R.*, 1962, **143**, 137 (Eng. trans. p. 175).

[89] K. Ziegler and H. G. Gellert, *Annalen*, 1950, **567**, 179.

The reaction products become more nearly butene and lithium hydride alone when the decomposition is carried out at a lower temperature (about 80°) in vacuum, allowing butene to be removed as it is formed. In boiling n-octane (126°) the gaseous products are about 95% butene and about 5% butane. The apparent activation energy for the thermal decomposition of n-butyl-lithium in decane solution over the temperature range 130–150°, is 31 kcal. mole^{-1} and is first order to 1–2 half-lives [90]. The thermal decomposition of n-butyl-lithium in isopropylbenzene solution at 135° does not involve alkyl radicals as intermediates, since no 2,3-dimethyl-2,3-diphenylbutane, $(PhMe_2C)_2$, is formed; the organic reaction products consist of butane and, mainly, butene [91]. The reaction in decane is believed to proceed by a concerted four-centre elimination of lithium hydride [90]. The thermal decomposition of *sec. butyl-lithium* [92] at about 80° gives lithium hydride and mixtures of 1-butene, *cis*-2-butene and *trans*-2-butene.

Though *t-butyl-lithium* has been prepared in solution for synthetic use by numerous workers, the preparation of the crystalline alkyl (from t-butyl chloride in pentane and lithium containing 2% sodium) has only recently been described [93]. t-Butyl-lithium is colourless, crystalline, and pyrophoric, readily soluble in hydrocarbons, and may be sublimed at 70° and 0·1 mm.; it is thus the most volatile of the lithium alkyls, possibly on account of relatively weak interaction between neighbouring (probably tetramer) units in the crystal. It does not melt, but slowly decomposes above 140°, and when its solution in heptane is boiled it turns brown and evolves isobutene (94%) together with a little isobutane (6%):

$$(CH_3)_3CLi \rightarrow LiH + Me_2C{:}CH_2$$

The molecular weights of several alkyl- and aryl-lithium compounds have been measured in solution [1, 83, 93, 94, 95, 96], the results being summarized in Table 3.

Trimethylsilylmethyl-lithium, Me_3SiCH_2Li, m.p. 112° (without decomposition) has been prepared from the chloride and finely divided lithium. It may be purified by sublimation at 100°/10^{-5} mm. [97], and like t-butyl-lithium it is tetrameric in solution in hydrocarbon solvents [98].

[90] R. A. Finnegan and H. W. Kutta, *J. Org. Chem.*, 1965, **30**, 4138.
[91] D. Bryce-Smith, *J. Chem. Soc.*, 1955, 1712.
[92] W. H. Glaze, J. Lin and E. G. Felton, *J. Org. Chem.*, 1965, **30**, 1258.
[93] M. Weiner, G. Vogel and R. West, *Inorg. Chem.*, 1962, **1**, 654.
[94] F. Hein and H. Schramm, *Z. physik. Chem.*, 1930, **A151**, 234.
[95] T. L. Brown, D. W. Dickerhoof and D. A. Bafus, *J. Amer. Chem. Soc.*, 1962, **84**, 1371.
[96] D. Margerison and J. P. Newport, *Trans. Faraday Soc.*, 1963, **59**, 2058.
[97] J. W. Connolly and G. Urry, *Inorg. Chem.*, 1963, **2**, 645.
[98] G. E. Hartwell and T. L. Brown, ibid., 1964, **3**, 1656; R. H. Baney and R. J. Krager, ibid., p. 1657.

Table 3

Compound	Degree of association	Solvent
CH_3Li	4	Ether or tetrahydrofuran [99]
C_2H_5Li	$6^{a,\ b}$	Freezing benzene [100]
n-C_4H_9Li	6	Benzene or cyclohexane [96]
n-C_4H_9Li	4	Ether or tetrahydrofuran [99]
t-C_4H_9Li	4	Boiling benzene or hexane [93]
$CH_2{:}CHLi$	3^c	Tetrahydrofuran [100a]
C_6H_5Li	2	Ether or tetrahydrofuran [99]
$C_6H_5CH_2Li$	1	Ether or tetrahydrofuran [99]

^{a} Tetrameric in crystal ^{b} Hexameric in vapour ^{c} Inferred from kinetic data.

The chemical constitution of the lithium alkyls and the nature of their association had been one of the outstanding problems in organometallic chemistry for many years. A reasonably clear picture has only recently begun to emerge, mainly due to the spectroscopic work of T. L. Brown and R. West [88, 93, 95], and to the crystal structure analyses of methyl-[84] and ethyl- [86] lithium. It is now evident that the lithium alkyls are electron-deficient oligomers somewhat analogous to the beryllium, magnesium, and aluminium alkyls. The subject has been discussed in an excellent review [100b].

The crystal structure of methyl-lithium [84], which is insufficiently soluble to allow its molecular weight to be determined in hydrocarbon solvents, reveals *tetramer* units $(CH_3Li)_4$ (see Figure 2), resembling the structure earlier proposed for t-butyl-lithium and shown in Figure 4. The Li–Li distances in the Li_4 tetrahedra are 2·56 Å, the Li–C distances being 2·28 Å. The carbon atoms are six-co-ordinate (approximately octahedral co-ordination), and each can be regarded as bound to three hydrogen atoms in a normal way and to three lithium atoms by a two-electron four-centre bond. The eight electrons holding the Li_4C_4 tetramer unit together are distributed between one molecular orbital (the lowest in energy) derived from the lithium and carbon $2s$ atomic orbitals, and three molecular orbitals of equal energy derived from the lithium and carbon $2p$ atomic orbitals.

The methyl groups of each tetramer unit are quite close (Li–C, 2·52 Å) to lithium atoms of an *adjacent* tetramer. This results in strong three-dimensional association which is responsible for the low volatility and solubility of methyl-lithium. Inclusion of this interaction increases the

[99] P. West and R. Waack, *J. Amer. Chem. Soc.*, 1967, **89**, 4395.

[100] T. L. Brown, R. L. Gerteis, D. A. Bafus and J. A. Ladd, ibid., 1964, **86**, 2135; see also F. A. Settle, M. Haggerty and J. F. Eastham, ibid., p. 2076.

[100a] R. Waack and P. E. Stevenson, ibid., 1965, **87**, 1183; R. Waack and P. West, *J. Organometal. Chem.*, 1966, **5**, 188.

[100b] T. L. Brown, *Advances in Organomentallic Chemistry*, 1965, **3**, 365.

effective co-ordination of both carbon and lithium from six to seven, and it will be seen below that a somewhat similar situation obtains in ethyl-lithium. The effect of the replacement of all the hydrogen atoms in methyl-lithium by methyl groups, giving t-butyl-lithium, is necessarily to diminish

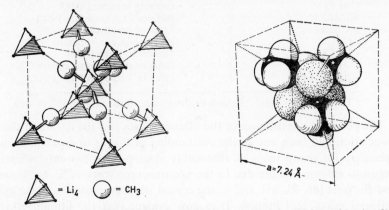

Fig. 2. Unit cell of methyl-lithium. The (CH₃Li)₄ tetramer (after Weiss and Lucken [84])

very greatly the interaction between tetramers: it has already been mentioned that t-butyl-lithium is the most volatile lithium alkyl.

The structure of ethyl-lithium is more complicated in detail, the lower

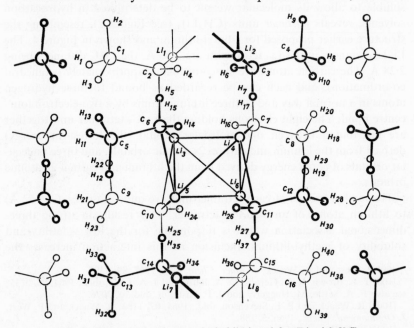

Fig. 3. The crystal structure of ethyl-lithium (after Dietrich [86])

symmetry of the ethyl group resulting essentially in linear (instead of three-dimensional) association of tetramer units – which are themselves not quite symmetrical.

The atomic arrangement in crystalline ethyl-lithium is given in Figure 3. The nearly regular Li_4 tetrahedron is shown in the diagram, and full lines are also drawn to the two methylene carbon atoms which are near neighbours (2·19 and 2·25 Å) of each lithium atom. For example C_7 and C_{11} are the near neighbours of Li_6, but this lithium atom has two slightly more distant methylene groups, C_{10} at 2·47 and C_{15} at 2·53 Å. It appears that the interactions exemplified by Li_6–C_{15} hold neighbouring tetramer units together. However, the positions of the methylene hydrogen atoms, which were clearly defined in the structure analysis, are all in directions away from the Li_4 tetrahedron, so it is probable that a given methylene carbon is principally bound to *six* other atoms. For example C_{10}, obviously bound to C_9, H_{24} and H_{25}, is clearly also bound to Li_3 (2·19 Å) and Li_5 (2·25 Å) so its co-ordination number must be at least five. If these were the only important interactions, ethyl-lithium could be regarded as a dimer exemplified by the following fragment of the structure,

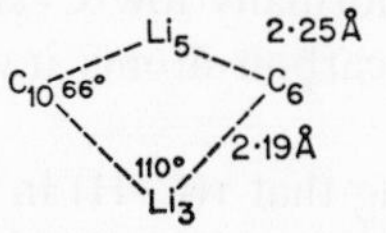

in which a small metal–carbon–metal angle may be noted, as in the electron-deficient structures Me_2Be and Me_6Al_2.

However, C_{10} must also be bound to Li_6 (2·47 Å) causing association to tetramers and in an individual tetramer, ignoring neighbouring tetramers, the co-ordination number of the carbon would be six. But there is interaction between neighbouring tetramers as described earlier, and involving some sort of interaction between C_{10} and Li_7 in spite of the positions of H_{24} and H_{25}, and between the three other pairs C_6–Li_1, C_7–Li_2 and C_{11}–Li_8. If these interactions are included, then the co-ordination number of the methylene carbon atoms becomes seven. Clearly these seven neighbours are not equally strongly bound, and in summary one may describe the binding of C_{10} to Li_3 and Li_5 as strong, giving the *dimer*, to Li_6 as weaker, giving the *tetramer*, and to Li_7 as still weaker, giving the *polymer*.

Similarly the co-ordination number of the lithium could also be regarded as seven, thus Li_5 has three other lithium atoms at distances considerably shorter than that between lithium atoms in the metal (3·04 Å) and even shorter than in the Li_2 molecule (2·67 Å), viz. Li_3 at 2·42, Li_6 at 2·60 and Li_4 at 2·63 Å. It is strongly bound to C_{10} and C_6 bringing the co-ordination number up to five, less strongly to C_{11} (2·47 Å) and still less to C_{14} (2·53 Å) which occupies the seventh co-ordination position.

Though the structure may reasonably be regarded as a polymer derived from weakly associated tetramers, each of which consists of two strongly associated dimers, the process of vaporization, which does not take place very readily, involves some reorganization since the main species present are tetramer and hexamer.

The infrared spectra of organolithium compounds have not been easy to interpret, and it should be emphasized that experimental difficulties have been considerable. Many of the conclusions based on early data require revision as several bands attributed to Li–C vibrations have been shown to be due to Li–O and C–O vibrations arising from the presence of alkoxide impurities.

Carbon–hydrogen stretching vibrations are at unusually low frequencies in many of these compounds [88], e.g. 2840 and 2780 cm^{-1} in CH_3Li (mull) changed to 2150 and 2027 cm^{-1} in CD_3Li (mull) and unaffected by substitution of ^6Li for ^7Li. Similarly C–H stretching bands at 2940, 2840 and 2760 cm^{-1} have been observed in the spectrum of ethyllithium (^6Li and ^7Li) both in solution and as vapour; the 2940 cm^{-1} band is considered to be due to a terminal methyl group, the other two being due to the CH_2 group. Abnormally low C–H stretching frequencies are apparently associated with carbon atoms involved in the formation of electron-deficient polymers.

It is particularly interesting that $\nu(C–H)$ in the spectrum of tert-butyllithium are also abnormally low [93], 2805 and 2725 cm^{-1} for both $(Bu^t\ ^6Li)_4$ and $(Bu^t\ ^7Li)_4$ in benzene solution.

In all the compounds studied, absorption bands above 600 cm^{-1} are unaffected by substitution of ^6Li for ^7Li, and are not due to vibrational modes involving the metal atom to a significant extent. Bands due to vibrations of the lithium–carbon framework are, for example, at 560 and 398 cm^{-1} (Et ^6Li), at 538 and 382 cm^{-1} (Et ^7Li) [88], and at 496 and 429 cm^{-1} (Bu^t ^6Li) and 480 and 420 cm^{-1} (Bu^t ^7Li) [93], all these measured for benzene solutions. A particularly important observation is that the strongly polarized Raman line at 563 cm^{-1} (Bu^t ^6Li) and 521 cm^{-1} (Bu^t ^7Li), which can be identified as a totally symmetric vibration of the carbon–lithium framework, does not appear in the infrared spectrum; this result favours the structure (of T_d symmetry) shown in Figure 4 over possible alternative structures of lower symmetry involving two-coordinate lithium. The interpenetrating tetrahedra shown in Figure 4 resemble the tetramer units in the crystal structure of methyl-lithium (Figure 2).

The mass spectrum of ethyl-lithium vapour [101] indicates that the hexamer and the tetramer are the predominant species. Though currents due to the ions $(Li_nR_{n-1})^+$, n = 1, 2, 3, 4, 5 and 6 are observed, the appearance potentials of $Li_6Et_5^+$ and $Li_4Et_3^+$ are 3–4 volts lower than those of

[101] J. Berkowitz, D. A. Bafus and T. L. Brown, *J. Phys. Chem.*, 1961, **65**, 1380.

any of the other ions. The hexamer $(EtLi)_6$ is evidently the predominant species in benzene solution, and it is significant that infrared absorptions of ethyl-lithium in solution obey Beer's law which makes the presence of more than one species in solution rather improbable. The chemical shift values in the proton magnetic resonance spectrum of ethyl-lithium do not change significantly with concentration in the range 0·4–1·2M. The ^{7}Li resonance signal of ethyl-lithium in benzene consists of a single line (half intensity width about 2 c.p.s.), which is a little surprising since ^{7}Li (spin 3/2) has a considerable quadrupole moment. This suggests that the lithium atoms are in an averaged field of high symmetry, probably due to an exchange or inversion process. Low-temperature ^{7}Li spectra or MeLi and EtLi and mixtures of the two in diethyl ether can be interpreted in terms of an exchange process

$$(RLi)_4 \rightleftharpoons 2(RLi)_2$$

There is evidence that alkoxy groups can be incorporated in the tetramer in place of alkyl, e.g. Et_3Li_4OEt [101a]. In hydrocarbons one or two lithium ethoxide units become attached to a molecule of ethyl-lithium *hexamer* [101b].

The structure suggested [95] for the ethyl-lithium tetramer and hexamer (and the t-butyl-lithium tetramer) in solution and as vapour are shown in Figures 4 and 5 respectively. In these structures the lithium atoms are regarded as bound to carbon by four-centre bonds, the lithium making use

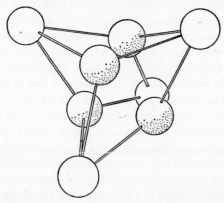

Fig. 4. Model for proposed structure of the t-butyl-lithium tetramer (after T. L. Brown [95]). Stippled spheres represent lithium atoms; methyl groups are not included

of 2s and 2p orbitals. The lithium atoms are considered to have a configuration rather like the chair form of cyclohexane, and inversion to the

[101a] L. M. Seitz and T. L. Brown, *J. Amer. Chem. Soc.*, 1966, **88**, 2174.
[101b] T. L. Brown, J. A. Ladd and G. N. Newman, *J. Organometal. Chem.*, 1965, **3**, 1.

other chair form is thought to proceed through a higher energy inter-mediate in which the lithium atoms are in a regular plane hexagon, but in which each metal atom is bound to another by a single carbon bridge.

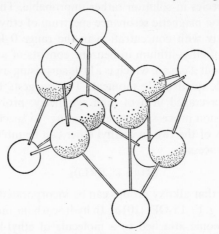

Fig. 5. Model for proposed structure of ethyl-lithium hexamer. Stippled spheres repre-sent lithium atoms; blank spheres represent the methylene carbon atoms. The two hydrogens and the methyl group on each carbon are not shown (after T. L. Brown [95])

The co-ordination number of the metal would decrease as the hexamer passes through the transition state.

It is suggested [95] that interaction between $(EtLi)_6$, in which the lithium atom would have one entirely vacant atomic orbital, and weak donor molecules might not break down the hexameric structure. This would account for the fact that ethyl-lithium solutions in benzene dissolve lithium ethoxide (which is not itself soluble in benzene) without signifi-cantly altering that part of the infrared spectrum due to the ethyl-lithium; the main effect is the addition of bands due to the ethoxide [see 101*b*].

Ethyl- and tertiary butyl-lithium form complexes with each other. The solubility of ethyl-lithium in benzene is greatly increased on addition of tertiary butyl-lithium, and evaporation of the benzene leaves a colourless solid which is readily soluble in pentane (unlike ethyl-lithium) and is much more volatile than ethyl-lithium as it may be sublimed, like $(Bu^tLi)_4$, at 70°/0·1 mm. Products with Et: Bu^t ratios of 1·1 : 1 (m.p. 68–72°) and 1·7 : 1 (m.p. 56–59°) have been obtained. As might be expected the proton and ^7Li magnetic resonance spectra are more complex than those of $(EtLi)_6$ and $(Bu^t Li)_4$, and indicate, for the 1 : 1 complex, at least two butyl and three different lithium environments [102].

By taking advantage of the relations between the viscosity of polymer solutions and the molecular weight of the polymer, it has been possible to

[102] M. A. Weiner and R. West, *J. Amer. Chem. Soc.*, 1963, **85**, 485.

study the molecular weights of long-chain lithium alkyls obtained by polymerizing styrene or isoprene with a lithium alkyl. By this technique these lithium-ended polymers have been shown to be monomeric in donor solvents, and *dimeric* in hydrocarbons. Decomposition of the lithium chain-end by addition of the right amount of, say, methanol, causes virtually no change in viscosity in the donor solvents and a considerable decrease in viscosity in the hydrocarbon solvents. The same technique has allowed the cross-association between polymer $(RLi)_2$ and ethyl-lithium to be studied (hexane solution), the product being an Li_4 unit [103]:

$$(RLi)_2 + (EtLi)_6 \rightleftharpoons 2(RLi \cdot 3EtLi)$$

The co-ordination chemistry of lithium alkyls has been developed considerably in recent years. Ethyl-lithium in benzene adds ether and triethylamine: at low base concentrations the hexamer units appear to survive, but at high concentrations co-ordinated dimer is formed [100]. However, MeLi and Bu^nLi are tetrameric both in ether and THF (Table 3).

A series of crystalline complexes, sparingly soluble in ethers and hydrocarbons, has been prepared from triethylenediamine and a range of organolithium compounds [43]. Most of these complexes have the composition $(RLi)_2N(C_2H_4)_3N(LiR)_2$, though benzyl- and 9-fluorenyllithium give 1 : 1 complexes. The high reactivity of these complexes in metalation reactions has been mentioned earlier (pp. 18–20), together with the reactions of tetramethylethylenediamine complexes.

The heats of combustion of ethyl- and n-butyl-lithium have been measured (11·549 and 11·273 kcal. g^{-1} respectively) [104], also the heat of hydrolysis of the latter [105]. The dipole moments of several organolithium compounds have been measured in benzene solution by conventional methods and are all about 1·4–1·5 D [106] and it has been argued [95] that an average moment of this magnitude might be expected for hexamers such as depicted in Figure 5.

Few vapour pressure data on lithium alkyls are available, but n-butyllithium is reported to have a vapour pressure of about $4·5.10^{-4}$ mm. at $60°$ and about 2.10^{-3} mm. at $70°$, corresponding to a rather large heat of

[103] M. Morton, L. J. Fetters and R. A. Pett, Lecture to Organometallic Symposium, Madison, 1965.
[104] Y. A. Lebedev, E. A. Miroshnichenko and A. M. Chaikin, *Doklady Akad. Nauk S.S.S.R.*, 1962, **145**, 1288.
[105] P. A. Fowell and C. T. Mortimer, *J. Chem. Soc.*, 1961, 3793.
[106] M. T. Rogers and T. L. Brown, *J. Phys. Chem.*, 1957, **61**, 366.

vaporization ($\sim$33 kcal. mole^{-1}) [107]. The vapour pressure of ethyl-lithium has recently been measured by an effusion method and over the range 25–60°, $\log_{10} P$ (mm.) $= 16 \cdot 28 - 6090/T$; the heat of sublimation is $27 \cdot 9 \pm 0 \cdot 2$ kcal. mole^{-1} [108].

Some data on the ultraviolet spectra of organolithium compounds in tetrahydrofuran solution have been discussed on the basis of a carbanion–Li$^+$ ion-pair or ion-aggregate constitution [109].

Organoderivatives of sodium and the heavier alkali metals [110]
These compounds are intensely reactive, due to the presence of a carbanion, and combine with nearly all substances except nitrogen, the noble gases, and the paraffin hydrocarbons. Their easy thermal decomposition, lack of volatility, and insolubility in the latter solvents add to the difficulty of manipulation. Rarely isolated, they are usually prepared for immediate use, sometimes only as transient reaction intermediates.

Preparative methods
The usual method [2] when the organocompound must be isolated (free from by-product such as alkali halide) is the exchange between an alkali metal and the appropriate mercury compound R_2Hg:

$$R_2Hg + Na \text{ (excess)} = 2RNa \downarrow + Na(Hg) \text{ amalgam}$$

The reaction is carried out in light petroleum, in an atmosphere of pure nitrogen. The crust of reaction product is broken by shaking the amalgam (frozen by cooling), and the resulting powder decanted on to a sintered filter and washed with light petroleum. Butyl- and amyl-potassium [111], the preparation of which is described in some detail, react to a considerable extent (mainly metalation) even with paraffin hydrocarbons within a few hours at 10°.

A new preparative method, based on double decomposition between alkyl-lithium and soluble sodium or potassium alkoxides, has recently been devised [111a].

Phenyl derivatives are best obtained by stirring the alkali metal with a *benzene* solution of di-n-butylmercury [112]:

$$Bu^n_2Hg + 2M = 2Bu^nM \downarrow + Hg$$
$$Bu^nM + C_6H_6 = C_4H_{10} + PhM \downarrow$$

[107] E. Warhurst, *Faraday Society Discussions*, 1947, **2**, 239.
[108] A. M. Chaikin, *Zh. Fiz. Khim.*, 1962, **36**, 130.
[109] R. Waack and M. A. Doran, *J. Amer. Chem. Soc.*, 1963, **85**, 1651; see also [100].
[110] M. Schlosser, *Angew. Chem., Internat. Edn.*, 1964, **3**, 287 and 362.
[111] R. A. Finnegan, *Trans. New York Acad. Sci.*, 1965, 730.
[111a] L. Lochmann, J. Pospišil and D. Lim, *Tetrahedron Letters*, 1966, 257.
[112] H. Gilman, A. L. Jacoby and H. Ludemann, *J. Amer. Chem. Soc.*, 1938, **60**, 2336; D. Bryce-Smith and E. E. Turner, *J. Chem. Soc.*, 1953, 861.

The continued action of an alkylpotassium on benzene gives some *meta* and *para* dimetalated phenylenes, since a mixture of *iso* and *tere*phthalic acids is obtained after carbonation. These reactions do not always proceed in a simple way since some disproportionation can occur [113]:

$$2C_5H_{11}Na \longrightarrow C_5H_{12} + C_5H_{10}Na_2$$

Thus addition of carbon dioxide to the mixture obtained by shaking sodium with a pentane solution of di-n-amylmercury gives a large amount of n-butylmalonic acid $[n-C_4H_9CH(CO_2H)_2]$ in addition to the normal product, caproic acid.

Reaction between organic halides and sodium (or potassium) normally leads to coupling products, the usual products of a Wurtz–Fittig reaction.

$$RX + 2Na \longrightarrow RNa + NaX$$

The organosodium compound is so reactive that it rapidly combines with more halide:

$$RNa + RX \longrightarrow R_2 + NaX$$

or, in the presence of another halide $R'X$,

$$RNa + R'X \longrightarrow RR' + NaX$$
$$RNa + R'X \longrightarrow R'Na + RX$$
$$R'Na + R'X \longrightarrow R'_2 + NaX$$

so a variety of products can be formed. These reactions have been extensively investigated by A. A. Morton [114].

Recent developments in the technique of preparing fine *dispersions* of sodium, particle size in the range 0·5–20 microns, have made the direct preparation of suspensions of phenylsodium relatively easy [115]. If chlorobenzene is added slowly to a well-stirred sodium dispersion in a hydrocarbon solvent at room temperature, reaction generally starts within about five minutes (a little amyl alcohol helps to start the reaction if it does not begin on its own within twenty minutes). When the reaction has started, *and not before*, the reaction vessel is cooled, and chlorobenzene (diluted with hydrocarbon solvent) slowly added at such a rate as to maintain a reaction temperature about 30–35°. The success of this method depends on the large surface area of the sodium and avoiding an appreciable concentration of chlorobenzene in the reaction mixture (otherwise much biphenyl would result). Phenylsodium has several attractions relative to phenyl-lithium or phenylmagnesium bromide, particularly from an

[113] A. A. Morton and I. Hechenbleikner, *J. Amer. Chem. Soc.*, 1936, **58**, 1024.
[114] A. A. Morton and F. Fallwell, ibid., 1937, **59**, 2387.
[115] I. Fatt and M. Tashima, *Alkali Metal Dispersions*, van Nostrand, New York, 1961; *Sodium Dispersions*, by U.S. Industrial Chemicals Co., New York, 1957.

industrial point of view, since both chlorobenzene and sodium are cheap (relative to bromobenzene and lithium), and the use of large amounts of ether is a source of danger. Although phenylmagnesium chloride can be prepared from chlorobenzene, an expensive solvent (tetrahydrofuran, alone or mixed with ether) is required. Unreacted sodium and unused phenyl sodium may be rendered comparatively safe by the addition of several volumes of kerosene; a mixture of kerosene with a little isopropanol is also useful for this purpose if care is taken with respect to hydrogen evolution. Methods for the continuous preparation of phenylsodium have been developed [116].

Suspensions of vinylpotassium, mixed with potassium chloride, have been obtained by the slow addition of a solution of vinyl chloride in tetrahydrofuran to a well-stirred suspension of 90% potassium–sodium alloy in the same solvent at 0°. Vinylpotassium reacts with tetrahydrofuran so should be used at once [117].

Properties and reactions

All the alkyls and (simple) phenyls of sodium [2], potassium [118, 119], rubidium and caesium [119] which have been prepared are colourless, nonvolatile solids insoluble in light petroleum or benzene and they decompose without melting when heated. They immediately take fire in the air and decompose ether much more rapidly than the lithium compounds. These properties are consistent with their formulation as salts, e.g. $CH_3CH_2^-$ Na^+. They dissolve in diethylzinc, with the formation of a complex salt, and the solution has about the conductance [120] to be expected for a solvent of low dielectric constant in which a salt would very largely be associated to ion-pairs:

$$C_2H_5Na + (C_2H_5)_2Zn \rightarrow Na^+[Zn(C_2H_5)_3]^-$$

Crystalline compounds of this type have been obtained on evaporation of excess diethylzinc, and they also result from the action of diethylzinc on the alkali metal [121], e.g.

$$2Rb + 3(C_2H_5)_2Zn \rightarrow 2Rb[Zn(C_2H_5)_3] \ (m.p.\ 70\text{--}75°) + Zn$$

[116] H. Ruschig, R. Fugman and W. Meixner, *Newer Methods of Preparative Organic Chemistry*, Vol. 2, 1963, ed. W. Foerst.

[117] R. G. Anderson, M. B. Silverman and D. M. Ritter, *J. Org. Chem.*, 1958, **23**, 750.

[118] H. Gilman and R. H. Kirby, *J. Amer. Chem. Soc.*, 1933, **55**, 1265; 1936, **48**, 2074.

[119] H. Gilman and R. V. Young, *J. Org. Chem.*, 1936, **1**, 315.

[120] F. Hein and H. Schramm, *Z. physik. Chem.*, 1930, **151**, 234; G. Jander and L. Fischer, *Z. Elektrochemie*, 1958, **62**, 965, 971.

[121] A. von Grosse, *Ber.*, 1926, **59**, 2646.

The reaction product separates into a lower viscous layer consisting of a solution of diethylzinc in the salt and an upper mobile layer consisting of a dilute solution of the salt in diethylzinc. This curious separation into two phases, also observed in many Grignard preparations (even in the reaction between magnesium and ethylene bromide in ether) and reactions involving aluminium chloride, is no doubt due to the formation of phases of widely differing polarity and dielectric constant. Triethylaluminium is another ionizing solvent for these compounds [122], forming salts like $K^+[AlEt_4]^-$.

The existence of the complex salt $Na^+[Ph_2LiOEt_2]^-$, which does not contain a carbanion and is relatively stable to ether, in contrast to phenylsodium, has already been noted [20]. It is remarkable that much less than one molar proportion of phenyl-lithium greatly reduces the rate of attack of phenylsodium on ether [123]. Several *alkyl* complex anions of lithium, e.g. $Na[Me_2Li]$ and $Na[Bu^n_2Li]$, have also been investigated and recommended as powerful metalating agents. The aryl complex range has also been extended to include $Na[(p\text{-}CH_3C_6H_4)_2Li]$, $Na[(p\text{-}Me_2NC_6H_4)_2Li]$, $K[Ph_2Li]$ and $Cs[Ph_2Li]$ [124].

The organoderivatives of the heavier alkali metals are even less stable thermally [125] than those of lithium. Methylsodium and methylpotassium decompose fairly rapidly at about 200°, mainly according to the equation:

$$8CH_3Na = 6CH_4 + Na_2C_2 + 6Na$$

but the reaction is a little more complex since methane, ethane and ethylene are obtained on hydrolysis in addition to acetylene and hydrogen. There is some evidence for the formation of compounds like CH_2K_2 and CHK_3 in the thermal decomposition of methylpotassium. The higher alkyls are much less stable to heat (this is parallel to the behaviour of the alkyls of the Group II elements) and ethylsodium, for example, decomposes slowly at room temperature, particularly in the presence of sodium amalgam, and rapidly at 100°. The fast decomposition at 90–100° proceeds mainly according to:

$$C_2H_5Na \longrightarrow C_2H_4 + NaH$$

but some ethane is also formed. At lower temperatures the proportion of ethane increases and it becomes the main product at room temperature.

[122] F. Hein, E. Petschner, K. Wagler and F. A. Seglitz, *Z. anorg. Chem.*, 1924, **141**, 171; see also Ch. 3, pp. 313–315.

[123] G. Wittig, Ger. P. 955,596 (1957); *Chem. Abs.*, 1959, **53**, 13108.

[124] G. Wittig and F. Bickelhaupt, *Chem. Ber.*, 1958, **91**, 865; G. Wittig and E. Benz, ibid., p. 873.

[125] W. H. Carothers and D. D. Coffmann, *J. Amer. Chem. Soc.*, 1929, **51**, 588; 1930, **52**, 1254; A. A. Morton and E. J. Lanpher, *J. Org. Chem.*, 1956, **21**, 93.

This suggests a disproportionation reaction in which one ethylsodium ion-pair metalates another:

$$2C_2H_5Na \rightarrow C_2H_4Na_2 + C_2H_6$$
$$2C_2H_4Na_2 \rightarrow C_2H_2Na_4 + C_2H_6$$
$$C_2H_2Na_4 \rightarrow Na_2C_2 + 2NaH$$

Hydrogen, ethane and acetylene are formed on hydrolysis of the residue.

Pyrolysis of neopentylsodium apparently results in β-elimination of methylsodium which then causes polymerization of the isobutene also formed, but reaction between neopentyl chloride and sodium under Wurtz conditions gives products derived from a carbene intermediate [126].

$$Bu^tCH_2Na + Bu^tCH_2Cl \rightarrow Bu^t\overset{-}{C}H\overset{+}{N}a + Bu^tCH_3$$

$$(CH_3)_2C\underset{CH_2}{\overset{CH_2}{\diagup\!\diagdown}}| \quad + (CH_3)_2C{:}CHCH_3 + C_2H_5\overset{..}{C}{:}CH_2 \leftarrow CH_3-\underset{CH_3}{\overset{CH_3}{\underset{|}{\overset{|}{C}}}}-\overset{..}{C}H$$

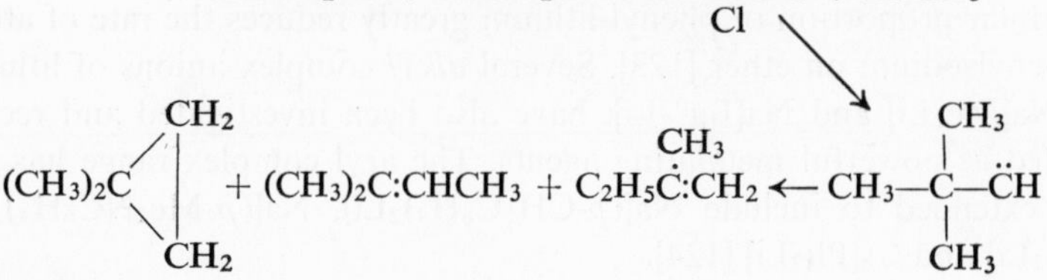

Metalation

The *metalation* reaction

$$RNa + R'H \rightarrow RH + R'Na$$

results in the formation of the sodium compound of lowest energy, and in which there is maximum delocalization of negative charge. Thus a sodium alkyl reacts with benzene

$$\text{n-}C_4H_9{}^-Na^+ + C_6H_6 \rightarrow \text{n-}C_4H_{10} + C_6H_5{}^-Na^+$$

a phenyl ion being more polarizable than an alkyl ion. Bryce-Smith [127] has described experiments which support an interpretation of the reaction as a 'protophilic' displacement process in which the driving force is the high energy and electric field of the alkyl carbanion

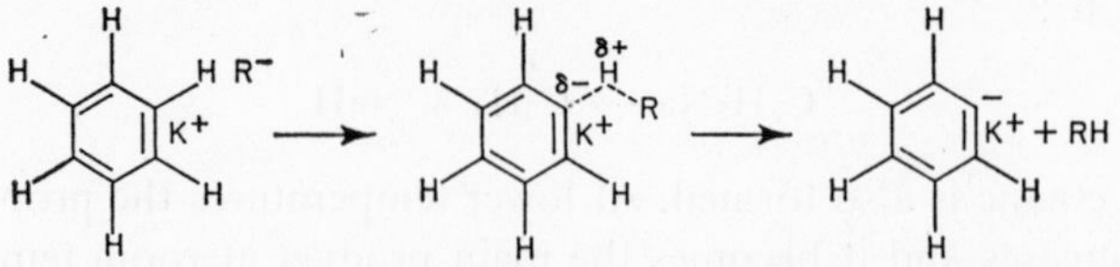

Similarly phenylsodium reacts with toluene, giving benzylsodium since extensive delocalization of charge over at least four carbon atoms is pos-

[126] L. Friedman and J. G. Berger, *J. Amer. Chem. Soc.*, 1961, **83**, 500; P. S. Skell and A. P. Kropcho, ibid., p. 754; R. A. Finnegan, *Chem. and Ind.*, 1962, 895.

[127] D. Bryce-Smith, *J. Chem. Soc.*, 1954, 1079; D. Bryce-Smith, V. Gold and D. P. N. Satchell, ibid., p. 2743.

sible in the latter compound (see p. 3). The most convenient approach to benzylsodium is the preparation of phenylsodium in toluene as described above, after which two hours' reflux affords nearly quantitative yield of benzylsodium. In like manner benzylsodium reacts with di- or tri-phenyl-methane, giving products in which the negative charge is even more delocalized. Since these compounds may reasonably be regarded as salts, Na^+R^-, the exchange reactions could be considered as examples of the displacement of weaker acids (e.g. C_2H_6) by stronger (e.g. C_6H_6). In this way an order of hydrocarbon 'acidities' may be drawn up and linked with those of the more familiar weak acids:

$$C_2H_6 < C_6H_6 < CH_3Ph < CH_2Ph_2 < \text{fluorene} < \text{phenylacetylene}$$
$$(< \text{alcohols} < \text{phenol})$$

Gaseous hydrogen displaces benzene from the alkali metal phenyls [112]:

$$C_6H_5^-K^+ + H_2 \longrightarrow K^+H^- + C_6H_6$$

The relative rates of this reaction illustrate the order of reactivities of the alkali metal aryls, since the reaction rate increases in the order

$$Li < Na < K < Rb < Cs$$

The greater reactivity of sodium, compared with lithium, compounds is sometimes of synthetic value, though this advantage is now doubtful since

the reactivity of lithium compounds can be so much enhanced by complex formation with amines or alkoxides. Thus dibenzfuran is rapidly dimetal-ated by ethylsodium while reaction with butyl-lithium gives the *mono*-lithium derivative. This type of reaction has been of value for the preparation of carboxylic acids by carbonation of the sodium derivative.

The possibility of further metalation should always be borne in mind when organosodium compounds containing carbanions are used. For example [115], by varying the experimental conditions it is possible to obtain phenylacetic acid or as much as 70% phenylmalonic acid by carbonation of benzylsodium. The latter arises through metalation of the phenylacetate ion by unreacted benzylsodium:

$$PhCH_2Na \xrightarrow{CO_2} PhCH_2CO_2^- \xrightarrow{PhCH_2Na} PhCHNaCO_2^- \xrightarrow{CO_2} PhCH(CO_2H)_2$$

Metalation by insoluble organo-sodium and -potassium compounds must be a heterogeneous reaction, though Bryce-Smith [127] points out many similarities between homogeneous (RLi) and heterogeneous metala-tions. A recent study [128] of the metalation of ethylbenzene by n-amyl-

[128] R. A. Benkeser, A. E. Trevillyan and J. Hooz, *J. Amer. Chem. Soc.*, 1962, **84**, 4971.

sodium and by n-amylpotassium (prepared in different ways) showed that *meta* and *para* metalation takes place to a greater extent than *ortho*, though the main product is the α-metalated product, $M^+[CHMePh]^-$, with benzyl anion stabilization as discussed earlier. *Meta* and *para* metalated products are formed first and are then converted to the benzylic carbanion in the presence of free ethylbenzene. Carbanions, as in amylsodium, must be about the most powerful of all nucleophilic reagents. The metalation of isopropylbenzene by ethylsodium or by an ethyl-lithium–potassium complex follows a similar pattern, the proportion of isomers being *meta > para >> ortho* [129], since the isopropyl group acts as a deactivating substituent decreasing the acidity of the *ortho* hydrogens. Ethylsodium does not metalate isopropylbenzene appreciably in the α-position, though the ethyl-lithium–potassium complex does so.

Metalation by organosodium compounds has been critically reviewed [130], see also ref. [129].

So far only those sodium salts of hydrocarbons have been considered, which can reasonably be formulated as containing a carbanion. Numerous sodium salts of β-diketones, keto-esters and similar compounds have long been among the most familiar of organic reagents. The sodium derivative of malonic ester is a well-known example. Since the charge is spread over

many atoms, and much of it resides on the oxygen atoms, discussion of this type of organoalkali metal compound would be out of place in this book. However, attention should be drawn to the sodium derivative of dimethylsulphoxide, in which the negative charge is shared mainly between oxygen and carbon.

This reagent [131], which undergoes a variety of analytically and synthetically useful reactions, is prepared by warming sodium hydride with an excess of *dry* dimethylsulphoxide to 75°; it also be obtained from the sulphoxide and the alkali metal [132]. The resulting solution is very

[129] D. Bryce-Smith, *J. Chem. Soc.*, 1963, 5983.
[130] R. A. Benkeser, D. J. Foster and D. M. Sauve, *Chem. Rev.*, 1957, **57**, 867.
[131] E. J. Corey and M. Chaykovsky, *J. Amer. Chem. Soc.*, 1962, **84**, 866.
[132] A. Ledwith and N. McFarlane, *Proc. Chem. Soc.*, 1964, 108.

strongly basic and reacts immediately at room temperature with di- or tri-phenylmethane:

$$MeSOCH_2^- + Ph_3CH \rightleftharpoons Me_2SO + Ph_3C^- \quad K \approx 20 \ (25°)$$

Consequently very weak acids, though they must be stronger than triphenylmethane, may be titrated in dimethylsulphoxide solution using triphenylmethane as indicator. The end point, located to one drop of 1 M. $MeSOCH_2^-$ solution, is shown by the bright red colour of the Ph_3C^- ion [133]. Acids quantitatively titrated in this way (as monobasic acids) include n-butanol, phenol, nitromethane, acetone, diethyl malonate, ethylene glycol, diphenylamine, cyclopentadiene and phenylacetylene. Aniline, hydrazine, n-butylacetylene, methyl cyanide and dimethylsulphone are weaker acids than triphenylmethane.

The reagent, for which Price and Whiting proposed the name 'dimsylsodium', has been used to prepare Wittig reagents [131],

$$\overset{+}{Ph_3P}-CH_2CH_3Br^- \xrightarrow{MeSOCH_2^-} Ph_3P{=}CHCH_3 \xrightarrow{Ph_2CO} Ph_2C{:}CHCH_3 \ (97·5\%)$$

and itself reacts directly with benzophenone giving $Ph_2C:CH_2$, Ph_2CH_2, 1,1-diphenylcyclopropane, $Ph_2CH·CHO$ and $Ph_2C:CH·SMe$ [134]. Diphenylethylene is formed by a modified Wittig olefin synthesis:

$$Ph_2CO + MeSOCH_2^- \rightarrow Ph_2\overset{\overset{\displaystyle O^-}{\diagup}}{C}·CH_2SOMe \rightarrow Ph_2C{:}CH_2 + MeSO_2^-$$

Coloured aromatic organoalkali compounds with delocalized negative charge

This group is characterized by vivid colours, enhanced stability, and solubility in ether. These properties arise from the delocalization of the negative charge in the hydrocarbon anion; in the latter at least there is no source of high electric field, and the alkali metal cation has its energy reduced by solvation in ether, both factors favouring ether solubility. The high relative stability of this group, typical members of which are benzylsodium and related compounds such as $PhCMe_2K$ and Ph_3CNa, is reflected in the variety of methods available for their preparation. It must, of course, always be remembered that although the stability of these compounds is high relative to substances like butyl-lithium and ethylpotassium, it is essential in their manipulation to exclude air and moisture rigorously.

The above-mentioned compounds are derived from hydrocarbons by *substitution* of a hydrogen by an alkali metal followed by ionization:

$$RH \rightarrow R^-M^+$$

[133] G. G. Price and M. C. Whiting, *Chem. and Ind.*, 1963, 775.

[134] M. Chaykovsky and E. J. Corey, *J. Org. Chem.*, 1963, **28**, 254; C. Walling and L. Bollyky, ibid., p. 256; E. J. Corey and M. Chaykovsky, *J. Amer. Chem. Soc.*, 1965 **87**, 1345, 1353.

There is, however, another class of aromatic alkali metal compound again with delocalized negative charge but which are addition compounds; their formation is not accompanied by loss of hydrogen. Examples are sodium-naphthalene and disodium tetraphenylethylene, $Na^+C_{10}H_8^-$ and $Na_2^{++}Ph_4C_2^{--}$, the former being quite a different compound from 1- or 2-naphthylsodium $C_{10}H_7Na$.

SUBSTITUTION COMPOUNDS

Preparative methods
The methods applicable to the preparation of the colourless alkali metal aryls and alkyls are also of some use for this group. Reaction between powdered sodium and dibenzylmercury in benzene solution, complete after shaking for two days at room temperature, gives benzylsodium, which may be purified by solution in ether and precipitation in the form of red crystals by addition of light petroleum.

$$2Na + (PhCH_2)_2Hg = 2PhCH_2^-Na^+ + Hg$$

This method is severely limited by the instability and difficulty of preparation of many of the required mercury compounds.

It is sometimes convenient to combine the above type of reaction with a metalation. For example, the action of sodium on a benzene solution of triphenylmethane and di-n-butylmercury gives triphenylmethylsodium in a two-stage process:

$$2Na + Bu^n_2Hg = 2Bu^nNa + Hg$$
$$Bu^nNa + Ph_3CH = C_4H_{10} + Ph_3C^-Na^+$$

This method has not been applied very much since other preparations are more convenient. Special methods applicable only to this group of compounds are as follows:

1. Substitution of *hydrogen* by alkali metal.
Generally, hydrocarbons containing the benzhydryl group, $Ph_2CH—$, also triphenylmethane, afford alkali metal derivatives in this way [135]. The reaction goes more easily when the alkali metal is dissolved in liquid ammonia, and better still when it has been converted to amide:

$$Ph_3CH + NH_2^- = Ph_3C^- + NH_3$$

The lithium derivatives of triphenylmethane and diphenylmethane can be prepared in about 95–98% and about 50–60% yields from the hydrocarbons and lithiumbiphenyl in tetrahydrofuran.

[135] C. B. Wooster and N. W. Mitchell, ibid., 1930, **52**, 688; C. B. Wooster and J. F. Ryan, ibid., 1932, **54**, 2419; see also P. Tomboulian, *J. Org. Chem.*, 1959, **24**, 229.

$$Ph_3CH + (Ph_2)^-Li^+ \longrightarrow Ph_3C^-Li^+$$

Benzyl-lithium is formed in about 1% yield by this reagent. The reaction between lithium-biphenyl and triphenylmethane is catalysed by lithium metal and by lithium piperidide. It is suggested that a lone-pair attached to the nitrogen interacts with the methyl-hydrogen facilitating proton transfer from the triphenylmethane

$$Ph_3CH + C_5H_{10}N^- \rightleftharpoons Ph_3C^- + C_5H_{10}NH$$
$$C_5H_{10}NH + Ph_2^- \rightleftharpoons C_5H_{10}N^- + (C_{12}H_{11})^{\cdot}$$

The reaction is also catalysed by reduction products of biphenyl, such as 1-phenylcyclohexene [136]. As a preparative method for triphenylmethyl-sodium solutions the reaction between CH_3SOCH_2Na and Ph_3CH, already mentioned, should not be overlooked.

A rather special case arises when the removal of a proton leads to the creation of a new aromatic system. Cyclopentadiene, which is not aromatic, gives cyclopentadienylsodium (which is) by reaction with sodium metal in tetrahydrofuran, or 1,2-dimethoxyethane [137], or, at lower cost for large-scale preparations, with a sodium dispersion in ether–hydrocarbon mixtures [138].

$$3C_5H_6 + 2Na = 2C_5H_5^-Na^+ + C_5H_8$$

Cyclopentadiene forms the aromatic anion also by reaction with bases such as NH_2^-, Me_3CO^-, and even concentrated aqueous potassium hydroxide.

2. Substitution of *halogen* by alkali metal.

The more reactive organoalkali compounds cannot easily be prepared in this way since the Wurtz–Fittig reaction predominates (but see *phenylsodium*, p. 43). However, less reactive compounds may be prepared, particularly by the use of alkali metal *amalgams*. For example, triphenylmethyl chloride in ether gives triphenylmethylsodium when shaken with sodium amalgam [138a].

$$Ph_3CCl + Na(Hg) \longrightarrow Ph_3C^-Na^+ + NaCl$$

The reaction may also be carried out in liquid ammonia, but is often limited by the low solubility of the organic halides in that solvent. Metallic sodium does not react with triphenylmethyl chloride in organic solvents, though potassium reacts at elevated temperature and the heavier alkali metals at room temperature (ether solution).

[136] J. J. Eisch and W. C. Kaska, ibid., 1962, **27**, 3745.

[137] G. Wilkinson, F. A. Cotton and J. M. Birmingham, *J. Inorg. Nuclear Chem.*, 1956, **2**, 95; R. B. King and F. G. A. Stone, *Inorg. Syntheses*, 1963, **7**, 99.

[138] U.S.P. 2,777,887; *Chem. Abs.*, 1957, **51**, 10569.

[138a] W. B. Renfrow and C. R. Hauser, *Org. Syntheses*, Coll. Vol. 2, p. 607.

3. Cleavage of ethers.

Ethers react with alkali metals,

$$ROR' + 2M = RM + R'OM$$

if the organometallic product RM is sufficiently stable, e.g. if R is a benzyl-type radical such as $PhMe_2C—$, $Ph_2CH—$ or $Ph_3C—$. The very reactive sodium–potassium alloy, liquid at room temperature, is particularly useful for this purpose; the organo*potassium* compound is produced. 2-Phenyl-2-propylpotassium, $PhMe_2C^-K^+$, which has been used for many investigations on the reactions of this type of compound, is conveniently prepared [139] from methyl 2-phenyl-2-propyl ether:

$$PhMe_2COMe + 2K = PhMe_2C^-K^+ + MeOK$$

A greatly improved method has been devised for the preparation of the ether, from α-methylstyrene and methanol. This renders 2-phenyl-2-propylpotassium a relatively accessible compound, and it has been recommended for various purposes including the purification of nitrogen from traces of oxygen. Disappearance of the bright red colour of the organopotassium compound makes it obvious when the reagent is exhausted [140]. The preparation of benzyl-lithium by fission of benzyl methyl ether has already been mentioned (p. 9).

These reactions must involve electron transfer from the alkali metal. The related reaction, between a hydrocarbon anion and an ether, is homogeneous and generally faster than corresponding reactions of the metals themselves. For example, diphenyl ether reacts with lithium-biphenyl in tetrahydrofuran at 0°.

$$Ph_2^- + Ph_2O \rightarrow Ph_2 + PhO^- + Ph^- \xrightarrow{CO_2, H_2O} PhOH + PhCO_2H$$

Anisole at 66° gives phenol and, probably, methane [141].

4. Cleavage of C–C bonds.

Substituted ethanes are split by alkali metals when at least two aryl groups are attached to each carbon atom, for example,

$$Ph_2CH·CHPh_2 + 2K(Na) \rightarrow 2Ph_2CH^-K^+$$

Liquid sodium–potassium alloy is also useful in this method, but triphenylmethylsodium is formed even with the use of sodium amalgam:

$$Ph_3C·CPh_3 + 2Na(Hg) \rightarrow 2Ph_3C^-Na^+$$

This is a simple electron transfer reaction involving the free radical:

$$Ph_3C· + Na \rightarrow Ph_3C^-Na^+$$

[139] K. Ziegler, F. Crössman, H. Kleiner and O. Shäfer, *Annalen*, 1929, **473**, 1.
[140] K. Ziegler and H. Dislich, *Chem. Ber.*, 1957, **90**, 1107.
[141] J. J. Eisch, *J. Org. Chem.*, 1963, **28**, 707.

A solution of triphenylmethyl/hexaphenylethane prepared, for example, from the triphenylmethyl chloride and finely divided silver, gives the sodium salt when shaken with sodium amalgam [142] and the colour changes from orange-yellow to red. The metal alone, in this instance, promotes a rearrangement:

$$2Ph_3C^· \longrightarrow Ph_2CHC_6H_4CPh_3$$

Bibenzyl does not react with alkali metals, at least in solution, but the non-aromatic compound hexa-tert-butylethynylethane is cleaved by sodium–potassium alloy in ether [143]:

$$(Me_3C·C\vdots C)_3C·C(C\vdots C·CMe_3)_3 + 2K(Na) \longrightarrow 2(Me_3C·C\vdots C)_3C^-K^+$$

The tri- and tetra-phenyl ethanes are cleaved by lithium-biphenyl in tetra-hydrofuran [141], e.g.

$$Ph_2CH·CHPh_2 + (Ph_2)Li_2 \longrightarrow Ph_2CHLi \xrightarrow{CO_2} Ph_2CH·CO_2H$$

$$Ph_3C·CH_2Ph + (Ph_2)Li_2 \longrightarrow Ph_3CLi + PhCH_2Li \xrightarrow{CO_2}$$
$$Ph_3C·CO_2H\ (93\%) + PhCH_2CO_2H\ (detected)$$

Properties and reactions
The vivid colours and ether solubility (sometimes only slight) have already been mentioned. The more reactive members of this group of compounds, like benzylsodium, react with ethers at an appreciable rate at room temperature,

$$PhCH_2Na + Et_2O = PhMe + EtONa + C_2H_4$$

But the stabler compounds, like triphenylmethylsodium, with more extensive charge delocalization may be kept unchanged in ether solution. The conductance of these solutions is low, but this is due to extensive ion-pair formation (to be expected in a solvent of low dielectric constant, 4·3 at 20°) rather than lack of ionization. Conductances in liquid ammonia (dielectric constant 22 at −33°) are of the same order as those of un-doubted 1 : 1 electrolytes. The lithium, sodium and potassium salts of the $PhOCPh_2$ anion have very closely similar spectra, indicating that the lithium compound is ionized like the others [144]. In general there is no reason to believe the lithium compounds differ in any marked way from those of the other alkali metals. They may thus be regarded as salts, e.g. $PhCH_2^-Li^+$, or $Ph_3C^-Li^+$, *unlike* EtLi. Although less reactive than the alkali metal derivatives with localized negative charge, they still commonly inflame in air and must be handled with rigorous exclusion of moisture and oxygen.

[142] W. Schlenk and E. Marcus, *Ber.*, 1914, **47**, 1664.
[143] P. L. Salzberg and C. S. Marvel, *J. Amer. Chem. Soc.*, 1928, **50**, 1737.
[144] G. Wittig and E. Stahnecker, *Annalen*, 1957, **605**, 69.

The reactions of triphenylmethylsodium have been investigated in fair detail. Similarities to Grignard reactions are the general rule, but exceptions are frequent. Hydrolysis gives the parent hydrocarbon

$$Ph_3C^-Na^+ + H_2O = Ph_3CH + NaOH$$

Slow oxidation gives peroxides, both organic and inorganic, by electron transfer and radical reactions, e.g.

$$Ph_3C^-Na^+ + O_2 \longrightarrow Ph_3C^{\cdot} + Na^+O_2^-$$
$$Ph_3C^-Na^+ + Na^+O_2^- \longrightarrow Ph_3C^{\cdot} + Na_2O_2$$
$$2Ph_3C^{\cdot} \longrightarrow Ph_6C_2$$
$$Ph_3C^{\cdot} + O_2 \longrightarrow Ph_3C{\cdot}OO^{\cdot}$$
$$Ph_3C{\cdot}OO^{\cdot} + Ph_3C^{\cdot} \longrightarrow Ph_3C{\cdot}OO{\cdot}CPh_3$$

Aldehydes and ketones react like hydroxy compounds regenerating the hydrocarbon if enolization can occur (e.g. acetone), otherwise a Grignard type of addition takes place:

$$PhCHO + Ph_3C^-Na^+ \longrightarrow PhCH(ONa)CPh_3$$

In certain cases an ion-radical transfer equilibrium may be realized, sometimes with striking colour changes [145]:

$$\underset{\text{red}}{Ph_3C^-Na^+} + \underset{\text{colourless}}{Ph_2CO} \rightleftharpoons \underset{\text{yellow}}{Ph_3C^{\cdot}} + \underset{\text{blue}}{Ph_2CO^{-\cdot}Na^+}$$

In this particular instance the equilibrium lies to the right in ether at room temperature and a green colour results.

Like the Grignard reagents, triphenylmethylsodium combines with nitric oxide, but its reaction with nitrous oxide [146] is one of the small number of instances where this somewhat inert gas undergoes a reaction at room temperature:

$$Ph_3C^-Na^+ + N_2O \longrightarrow Ph_3C{\cdot}N_2O^-Na^+ \xrightarrow{\text{EtOH}} Ph_3COH + N_2 + EtONa$$

Additions to olefins have been thoroughly studied by Ziegler [147] mainly with the use of 2-phenyl-2-propylpotassium, which adds more rapidly than $[Ph_2C{\cdot}CH_3]^-K^+$ or $Ph_3C^-K^+$. A C:C bond does not add $PhMe_2C^-K^+$ unless it is conjugated to an aromatic system, and a metal–hydrogen exchange reaction sometimes occurs instead of addition to the double bond. Some examples are given in Table 4.

ADDITION COMPOUNDS

These are of two kinds, namely those that could be regarded as alkali metal salts of a hydrocarbon acid and those that cannot. For example, 1,1-diphenylethylene and other compounds in which only one carbon of

[145] W. Schlenk and R. Ochs, *Ber.*, 1916, **49**, 608.
[146] W. Schlenk and E. Bergmann, *Annalen*, 1928, **464**, 1.
[147] K. Ziegler and K. Bähr, *Ber.*, 1928, **61**, 253.

Table 4 *Reactions between 2-phenyl-2-propylpotassium and unsaturated hydrocarbons*

Hydrocarbon	Type of reaction	Product $R = PhMe_2C\cdot$
$CH_2:CH_2$	None	—
$PhCH:CH_2$	Addition	$Ph\bar{C}H\cdot CH_2R\}K^+$
$Ph_2C:CH_2$	,,	$Ph_2\bar{C}\cdot CH_2R\}K^+$
$Ph_2C:CHPh$	None	—
$Ph_2C:CHCH_3$	Exchange	$Ph_2C:CH\cdot\bar{C}H_2\}K^+$

the olefin link is bound to aryl groups, *add* alkali metal by a one-electron transfer reaction and this is followed by dimerization:

$$Ph_2C:CH_2 + Na \longrightarrow Ph_2\bar{C}\cdot\dot{C}H_2\}Na^+$$

$$2Ph_2\bar{C}\cdot\dot{C}H_2\}Na^+ \longrightarrow Ph_2\bar{C}\cdot CH_2CH_2\cdot\bar{C}Ph_2\}Na_2^{++}$$

The product, of benzyl type, is the disodium derivative of 1,4-tetra-phenylbutane and could thus be regarded as a substitution compound. However, it is convenient to classify it as a product of the *dimerizing addition* of alkali metal to an olefin [148].

The other kind of addition compound, exemplified by sodium-naphthalene, cannot be regarded as a substitution product, as it is formed simply by the addition of one or more electrons to the lowest vacant molecular orbitals of an aromatic hydrocarbon.

The disodium salt resulting from the dimerizing addition of sodium to 1,1-diphenylethylene reacts normally with water, methyl iodide, benzophenone, and carbon dioxide:

$$Ph_2\bar{C}\cdot CH_2CH_2\cdot\bar{C}Ph_2\}Na_2^{++}$$

$$\nearrow^{H_2O} Ph_2CH\cdot CH_2CH_2\cdot CHPh_2$$

$$\xrightarrow{MeI} Ph_2CMeCH_2CH_2CMePh_2$$

$$\searrow^{PhCHO} \begin{array}{c} Ph_2C\cdot CH_2CH_2\cdot CPh_2 \\ | \qquad\qquad | \\ PhCHOH \quad PhCHOH \end{array}$$

$$\downarrow^{CO_2} \begin{array}{c} Ph_2CCH_2CH_2CPh_2 \\ | \qquad\qquad | \\ \dot{C}O_2H \quad \dot{C}O_2H \end{array}$$

Dissociation into radical anions

$$Ph_2\bar{C}\cdot CH_2CH_2\cdot\bar{C}Ph_2 \longrightarrow 2Ph_2\bar{C}\cdot\dot{C}H_2$$

is slow at 30°, and has been studied by following the rate of exchange with isotopically labelled diphenylethylene in tetrahydrofuran [149]. The dissociation involves the fission of a carbon–carbon bond, though the heat

[148] K. N. Campbell and B. K. Campbell, *Chem. Rev.*, 1942, **31**, 77.

[149] G. Spach, H. Monteiro, M. Levy and M. Szwarc, *Trans. Faraday Soc.*, 1962, **58**, 1809.

of dissociation is less than 27 kcal. mole^{-1}. Processes involving only electron exchange, for example

$$naphthalene^- + naphthalene \quad [150]$$
$$benzophenone^- + benzophenone \quad [151]$$

are very fast. The incorporation of isotopically labelled $Ph_2C{:}CH_2$ into the disodium salt involves the slow dissociation into ion-radicals as the rate-determining step, followed by a rapid exchange:

$$Ph_2\overset{-}{C}{\cdot}\overset{\cdot}{C}H_2 + Ph_2C{:}^{14}CH_2 \rightleftharpoons Ph_2C{:}CH_2 + Ph_2\overset{-}{C}{\cdot}^{14}\overset{\cdot}{C}H_2$$

The system is complicated by further equilibria, such as

$$Ph_2\overset{-}{C}{\cdot}CH_2CH_2{\cdot}\overset{-}{C}Ph_2 + Ph_2C{:}CH_2 \rightleftharpoons Ph_2\overset{-}{C}{\cdot}CH_2CH_2\overset{\cdot}{C}Ph_2 + Ph_2\overset{-}{C}{\cdot}\overset{\cdot}{C}H_2$$

Anionic polymerization

The addition of an electron to a *styrene* molecule can result in polymerization. For example, if styrene is added to a dilute solution of sodium-naphthalene in tetrahydrofuran, the green colour changes to red. The sodium-naphthalene has acted as an *anionic polymerization initiator* [152], by an electron transfer process:

$$C_{10}H_8{}^- + PhCH{:}CH_2 \rightarrow C_{10}H_8 + Ph\overset{-}{C}H{\cdot}\overset{\cdot}{C}H_2$$

The styrene anion then propagates polymerization, one end of the chain growing as a radical, the other (about 30 times faster at 25°) as a carbanion. Since radical ends can come together, propagation in due course continues by an anionic mechanism only,

$$\sim CH_2{\cdot}\overset{-}{C}HPh + CH_2{:}CHPh \rightarrow \sim CH_2{\cdot}CHPh{\cdot}CH_2{\cdot}\overset{-}{C}HPh$$

both ends of the polymer chain being anionic and there being no termination mechanism. In accordance with this picture, in which a 'living polymer' is produced even when all the available monomer is consumed, addition of further monomer, which may be styrene or another monomer such as isoprene, results in further polymerization. Naturally, such 'living polymers' are mortally affected by traces of impurities such as water which remove the negative charge on the polymer ends, and work on these systems requires very careful attention to experimental detail.

This kind of polymerization is reversible and an increase in the ratio of sodium to monomer can result in a decrease in degree of polymerization. Thus addition of a solution of styrene in 1,2-diethoxyethane to an excess of sodium dispersion containing a little *o*-terphenyl (as electron transfer agent) in the same solvent at −40 to −50°, followed by carbonation, gives 35–50% yields of diphenyladipic acids:

[150] R. L. Ward and S. I. Weissman, *J. Amer. Chem. Soc.*, 1957, **79**, 2086.
[151] F. C. Adam and S. I. Weissman, ibid., 1958, **80**, 1518.
[152] M. Szwarc, M. Levy and R. Milkovich, ibid., 1956, **78**, 2656; C. Geacintov, J. Smid and M. Szwarc, ibid., 1962, **84**, 2508.

$$PhCH{:}CH_2 \xrightarrow{e^-} Ph\overline{C}H{\cdot}\dot{C}H_2 \rightarrow Ph\overline{C}H{\cdot}CH_2CH_2{\cdot}\overline{C}HPh$$
$$\downarrow CO_2$$
$$PhCH{\cdot}CH_2CH_2{\cdot}CHPh$$
$$\overset{|}{C}O_2H \qquad \overset{|}{C}O_2H$$

The main competing reaction is polymerization. α-Methylstyrene does not polymerize so easily and may be converted largely to dimer at room temperature and thence to 2,5-dimethyl-2,5-diphenyladipic acid or to 2,5-diphenylhexane by carbonation or hydrolysis [153].

There is evidence to suggest that the dianion of the tetramer of α-methylstyrene may grow by addition of monomer, but does not depolymerize, and a solution of the tetramer salt can be prepared by allowing 0·3–0·4M solution of α-methylstyrene in tetrahydrofuran to react with a small excess of sodium (as a mirror). This tetramer is built up by head-to-head and tail-to-tail addition [154]:

$$\overline{C}MePh{\cdot}CH_2CH_2{\cdot}CMePh{\cdot}CMePh{\cdot}CH_2CH_2{\cdot}MePh\overline{C}$$

All these compounds contain ion-pairs, in the sense that an alkali metal cation is nearly always close to the carbanions. Conductance measurements [155] on the sodium-naphthalene-styrene system in tetrahydrofuran indicate that the ion-pairs have dissociation constants of about 10^{-7}.

The polymerization of a variety of monomers, other than aryl-ethylenes, may be initiated by hydrocarbon anions, but the process may involve bonding to the hydrocarbon as a first step instead of an electron transfer. Ethylene oxide polymer grows from sodium-naphthalene in the 1,2- and 1,4-positions [156]:

---

[153] C. E. Frank, J. R. Leebrick, L. F. Moormeier, J. A. Scheben and O. Homberg, *J. Org. Chem.*, 1961, **26**, 307.

[154] A. Vrancken, J. Smid and M. Szwarc, *Trans. Faraday Soc.*, 1962, **58**, 2036, see also C. L. Lee, J. Smid and M. Szwarc, *J. Amer. Chem. Soc.*, 1963, **85**, 912.

[155] D. J. Worsfold and S. Bywater, *J. Chem. Soc.*, 1960, 5234.

[156] M. Morton, A. Rembaum and E. E. Bostick, *J. Polymer Sci.*, 1958, **32**, 530; D. H. Richards and M. Szwarc, *Trans. Faraday Soc.*, 1959, **55**, 1644.

Anions derived from hydrocarbons of relatively low electron affinity, such as biphenyl, generally polymerize methyl methacrylate by electron transfer and the hydrocarbon is not then incorporated in the polymer. Anions derived from hydrocarbons of higher electron affinity, such as anthracene, polymerize methyl methacrylate by a bonding mechanism as illustrated above for ethylene oxide, and are then incorporated in the polymer [157].

Two more examples of dimerizing addition are of particular interest. In all compounds so far considered, the carbanions formed are stabilized by charge delocalization of the type associated with a *benzyl* type of structure, for example as in $Ph_2\bar{C}\cdot CH_2CH_2\cdot \bar{C}Ph_2$. But there is good evidence that under suitable experimental conditions dimerizing addition of sodium to butadiene may be realized, the conditions being similar to those required for the promotion of dimerizing addition to styrene at the expense of the competing polymerization reaction, namely the slow addition of the olefin to an excess of very fine sodium dispersion in a solvent such as 1,2-diethoxyethane at low temperature and containing an electron transfer agent (the blue sodium–*p*-terphenyl complex):

$$CH_2{:}CH\cdot CH{:}CH_2 + Na \rightarrow Na^+\bar{C}H_2\cdot CH{:}CH\cdot \dot{C}H_2$$

$$2Na^+\bar{C}H_2\cdot CH{:}CH\cdot \dot{C}H_2 \rightarrow Na^+\bar{C}H_2\cdot CH{:}CH\cdot CH_2CH_2\cdot CH{:}CH\cdot \bar{C}H_2Na^+$$

It should be noted that the negative charges are spread over the three carbon atoms at each end of the chain, and this element of charge delocalization is a feature in common with the benzyl-type anions considered earlier. Carbonation yields a mixture of unsaturated di-carboxylic acids, which are reduced to di-acids in the proportions shown [158]:

$$(Na^+\overset{\ominus}{\overline{CH_2{-}CH{-}CH{-}CH_2}})_2$$

$$+ \, CO_2, \, H^+, \, H_2/Pt \nearrow (CH_2CH_2CH_2CH_2CO_2H)_2 \; 3\cdot 5 \; parts$$
$$\rightarrow HO_2C\cdot(CH_2)_5\cdot CHEt\cdot CO_2H \; 5 \; parts$$
$$\searrow (CH_2CHEt\cdot CO_2H)_2 \; 1 \; part$$

Another example of dimerizing addition, which has led to the synthesis of many novel heterocyclic systems, is the formation of a tetraphenyl-butadiene dianion from lithium and diphenylacetylene.

$$PhC{:}CPh + Li \rightarrow LiPh\bar{C}{:}\dot{C}Ph \rightarrow LiCPh{:}CPh\cdot CPh{:}CPhLi$$

Hydrolysis yields 1,2,3,4-tetraphenylbutadiene and, particularly when excess metal is used, 1,2,3-triphenylnaphthalene [159]. Examples of

[157] A. V. Tobolsky and D. B. Hartley, *J. Amer. Chem. Soc.*, 1962, **84**, 1391.
[158] C. E. Frank and W. E. Foster, *J. Org. Chem.*, 1961, **26**, 303.
[159] L. I. Smith and H. H. Hoehn, *J. Amer. Chem. Soc.*, 1941, **63**, 1184.

heterocyclic syntheses include [160]

pentaphenylborole

pentaphenylarsole

pentaphenylphosphole

octaphenyl-1, 1'-spirobistannole

Hydrocarbon anions

These are derived from aromatic hydrocarbons by the transfer of an electron from an alkali metal to the lowest unoccupied molecular orbital and have already been mentioned as electron transfer agents, e.g. in the initiation of anionic polymerization reaction: they are now considered in greater detail.*

Aromatic hydrocarbons containing two or more aromatic rings, joined (biphenyl, terphenyls), conjugated (1,4-diphenylbutadiene), or fused (naphthalene, anthracene), react with alkali metal without loss of hydrogen. These addition compounds are all strongly coloured, and their formation is greatly influenced by the reaction medium.

Early work [146, 161] was carried out mainly using diethyl ether as solvent; in this anthracene, α,ω-diphenylpolyenes and polyarylethylenes add sodium, but the often rather low solubility of the products and the relative inaccessibility of some of the starting materials restricted their application. Similar reactions were also observed with some aromatic cyanides and ketones, the latter forming ketyls, that derived from benzophenone being blue in colour, very sensitive to oxygen and water and finding application in the purification of ether.

$$Ph_2CO + Na \rightarrow Ph_2\overset{.}{C}-O^-Na^+$$
sodium-diphenyl-ketyl

The discovery by N. D. Scott, J. F. Walker and V. L. Hansley [162] (1936) that these addition reactions take place very much more easily in

[160] F. C. Leavitt, T. A. Manuel and F. Johnson, ibid., 1959, **81**, 3163; F. C. Leavitt, T. A. Manuel, F. Johnson, L. U. Matternas and D. S. Lehman, ibid., 1960, **82**, 5099; E. H. Braye, W. Hübel and I. Caplier, ibid., 1961, **83**, 4406.

[161] C. B. Wooster, *Chem. Rev.*, 1932, **11**, 1; F. Runge, *Organometallverbindungen*, Stuttgart, 1944.

[162] N. D. Scott, J. F. Walker and V. L. Hansley, *J. Amer. Chem. Soc.*, 1936, **58**, 2442; H. E. Bent and N. B. Keevil, ibid., 1938, **60**, 193.

* For a recent review see E. de Boer in Vol. 2 of *Advances in Organometallic Chemistry*, Academic Press, 1964.

ethers with a high oxygen-to-carbon ratio has greatly widened the scope of their application. Naphthalene adds sodium in dimethyl ether and methyl ethyl ether, which are inconvenient on account of their low boiling points, and particularly easily in 1,2-dimethoxyethane (b.p. 84°). The efficacy of the last solvent has been ascribed to its strong donor character, the energy of the alkali metal ion being reduced by solvation [163]:

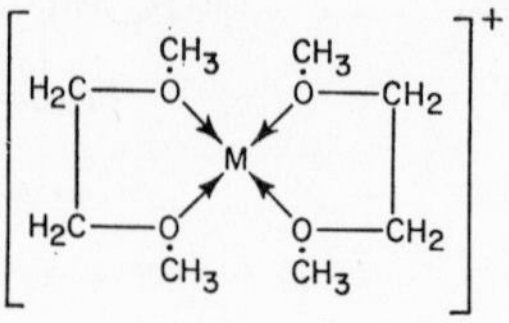

Tetrahydrofuran is also a good solvent for alkali metal addition reactions, since it is a stronger donor than diethyl ether (less steric hindrance), but appears to be not so good as 1,2-dimethoxyethane. The latter has the disadvantage of higher cost, but the advantage of not forming peroxides so readily, and of giving solutions of sodium-naphthalene or sodium-biphenyl of higher concentration than can be attained in tetrahydrofuran.

Lithium adds to aromatic hydrocarbons rather more readily than sodium, and very slowly dissolves in solutions of biphenyl or of naphthalene in diethyl ether; it dissolves easily in solutions of naphthalene in diethyl ether if the temperature is reduced [164]. The formation of sodium complexes in tetrahydrofuran or in dimethoxyethane is experimentally much more convenient.

Solutions of sodium-naphthalene in dimethoxyethane are dark green in colour and are electrically conducting [162], and it should be observed that both the glycol ether and tetrahydrofuran have considerably greater dielectric constants (7·2 and 7·4 at 25°) than diethyl ether [165]. There is no doubt that the solutions of alkali metal addition compounds with aromatic hydrocarbons consist of solvated alkali metal cations, and hydrocarbon anions, for example sodium-naphthalene $Na^+C_{10}H_8^-$. Solutions of sodium-naphthalene, sodium-biphenyl, and other related compounds in tetrahydrofuran and in 1,2-dimethoxyethane are paramagnetic, as would be expected for anions with an odd number of electrons. It is likely that the hydrocarbon anions are solvated as well as the alkali metal cations. The electrical conductance of solutions of these compounds shows the formation of ion-pairs (ion-triplets in the case of di-negative anions), and the ions are separated by at least one layer of solvent molecules. Ion solva-

[163] A. Jeanes and R. Adams, *J. Amer. Chem. Soc.*, 1937, **59**, 2608; A. C. Aten, J. Dieleman and G. J. Hoijtink, *Faraday Society Discussions*, 1960, No. **29**, 182.
[164] H. L. Hsieh, *J. Organometal. Chem.*, 1967, **7**, 1.
[165] J. Smid and M. Szwarc, *J. Amer. Chem. Soc.*, 1965, **87**, 5548.

tion is stronger at low temperatures (increase of dielectric constant of the solvent).

The approximate energy levels of the π molecular orbitals in benzene, naphthalene and anthracene are represented in Figure 6, which shows the six π-electrons of benzene, the ten of naphthalene and the fourteen of anthracene accommodated in the bonding three, five, and seven orbitals respectively. The reaction between an alkali metal and naphthalene consists in the transfer of an electron from the sodium metal into the lowest vacant orbital of a naphthalene molecule, and the transfer of the resulting sodium ion into solution where its energy drops due to solvation. The lowest unoccupied orbital of benzene is at too high an energy for this electron transfer to take place at all readily. In naphthalene the lowest unoccupied orbital is lower but the formation of $C_{10}H_8^-$ still has to be compensated by the relatively high solvation energy of the alkali metal in ethers of strong donor character. In anthracene the lowest unoccupied orbital lies at a lower energy than in naphthalene, and the formation of the anion $C_{14}H_{10}^-$ occurs in diethyl ether as well as in tetrahydrofuran.

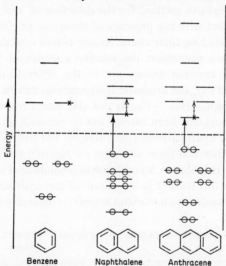

Fig. 6. Approximate relative energy levels of π-molecular orbitals in benzene, naphthalene and anthracene, ignoring configuration interaction

The singly occupied orbital in $C_{10}H_8^-$ and $C_{14}H_{10}^-$ is the cause of the observed paramagnetism of the compounds. The electron spin resonance spectra of a number of hydrocarbon anions have been studied; they are generally rather complex (the spectrum of anthracene$^-$ has 19 lines), but give useful information about the distribution of the unpaired electron among the various possible positions in the anions. When the orbital occupied by the electron in a hydrocarbon anion is non-degenerate, as is the case with naphthalene and anthracene, a *second* electron (formation of anion^{2-}) would enter the same orbital. The two electrons must then form a closed pair and both the paramagnetism and the electron spin resonance spectra disappear. Naphthalene does not readily add a second electron, except in liquid ammonia (and in tetrahydrofuran in which the purple $Li_2C_{10}H_8$ is formed [166]), but anthracene does, and solutions of the double-charged anion anthracene^{2-} have been shown to be diamagnetic and to show no spin resonance spectrum [167].

Figure 6 illustrates a further point. The longest wavelength light absorptions of naphthalene and anthracene are in the ultraviolet (vertical continuous arrows), but the longest wavelength absorption of the *anions* (the shorter vertical dotted arrows) lie at much longer wavelengths and are in fact to be found in the visible region at 7550 Å and 7250 Å respectively [168].

A low concentration of anions derived from benzene, toluene, and the three xylenes can be obtained by reaction between potassium and the hydrocarbon in 1,2-dimethoxyethane at $-80°$. The solutions are paramagnetic, absorb light at about 6750 Å, and their electron spin resonance spectra (a very sensitive method for the detection of 'odd-electron' molecules) are consistent with the presence of these anions. On warming from $-80°$ the solutions lose their characteristic colour and decompose [169].

From the above discussion the relative energies of the anthracene, naphthalene and benzene anions are in the order $C_{14}H_{10}^- < C_{10}H_8^- < C_6H_6^-$. Conversely, the aromatic hydrocarbons can be put in an order of electron affinity, $C_{14}H_{10} > C_{10}H_8 > C_6H_6$, and a considerable amount of quantitative work has been carried out to establish an electrochemical series of aromatic hydrocarbons (see Table 5). The hydrocarbon of lowest electron affinity that will form an anion on reaction with sodium in 1,2-dimethoxyethane is biphenyl. So addition of a solution of sodium-biphenyl ($Na^+C_{12}H_{10}^-$) in this solvent to a solution of any hydrocarbon of greater electron affinity results in an electron transfer, frequently accompanied by a colour change:

$$\text{biphenyl}^- + \text{pyrene} \longrightarrow \text{biphenyl} + \text{pyrene}^-$$
$$\quad\text{green}\qquad\qquad\qquad\qquad\qquad\qquad\text{brown}$$

These electron exchange reactions have been studied quantitatively by potentiometric titration of a series of hydrocarbons using sodium-biphenyl in tetrahydrofuran, and in dimethoxyethane, and platinum electrodes

[166] J. Smid, ibid., p. 655.

[167] T. L. Chu and S. C. Yu, ibid., 1954, **76**, 3367; T. R. Tuttle, R. L. Ward and S. I. Weissman, *J. Chem. Phys.*, 1956, **25**, 189; E. de Boer, ibid., p. 190.

[168] N. S. Hush and J. R. Rowlands, ibid., p. 1076. See also H. V. Carter, B. J. McClelland and E. Warhurst, *Trans. Faraday Soc.*, 1960, **56**, 455; S. N. Khanna, M. Levy and M. Szwarc, ibid., 1962, **58**, 747; A. Streitwieser and J. I. Bauman, *J. Amer. Chem. Soc.*, 1963, **85**, 2633.

[169] T. R. Tuttle and S. I. Weissman, *J. Amer. Chem. Soc.*, 1958, **80**, 5342.

[170]. A typical titration is represented in Figure 7 which illustrates not only the electron transfer from biphenyl⁻ to anthracene but also the formation of anthracene⁻ ⁻.

Table 5 *Reduction potentials of aromatic hydrocarbons,
E_1, and of their univalent anions, E_2, against sodium-
biphenyl, in 1,2-dimethoxyethane*

Hydrocarbon	E_1	E_2 volts
Biphenyl	0	—
Naphthalene	0·09	—
Phenanthrene	0·17	~0·05
Chrysene	0·38	—
Pyrene	0·60	—
1,2-Benzanthracene	0·76	0·24
Anthracene	0·78	0·20
Fluoranthene	0·94	0·43
Perylene	1·09	0·46
Tetracene	1·28	0·66

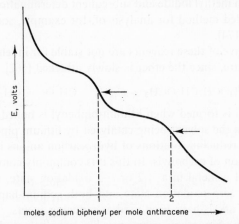

Fig. 7. Potentiometric titration of anthracene with sodium biphenyl

The formation of hydrocarbon anions can also be followed by polaro-graphic reduction in dimethylformamide containing tetrabutylammonium iodide (0·15M) as supporting electrolyte [171].

The strong colours of hydrocarbon anions have been mentioned earlier. Colours of some of these are: biphenyl, blue-green; *o*-terphenyl, brown; *p*-terphenyl, blue; phenanthrene, olive-green; anthracene, blue; tripheny-lene, lavender; naphthacene, blue-green.

Solutions of sodium-naphthalene and similar compounds are very

[170] G. J. Hoijtink, E. de Boer, P. H. van der Meij and W. P. Weijland, *Rec. Trav. chim.*, 1956, **75**, 487.
[171] S. Wawzonek and D. Wearring, *J. Amer. Chem. Soc.*, 1959, **81**, 2067; A. Streitwieser, *Molecular Orbital Theory*, Wiley, New York, 1961.

strong reducing agents, behaving in many ways as solutions of electrons. Halogen present in any organic halide is converted to halide ion:

$$C_{12}H_{10}^- + RX \longrightarrow C_{12}H_{10} + R^{\cdot} + X^-$$

The free radicals produced react with molecules of solvent, hydrocarbon, hydrocarbon anion, or they dimerize, but the halide ion remains as such and may quantitatively be extracted from the reaction mixture by water. Even fluorine is removed from the chemically unreactive fluorocarbons in this way, and it has been shown that the reaction rates of chloro- and fluoro-benzene with sodium-anthracene are about equal [172]. Decomposition with sodium-biphenyl is the basis of one of the most convenient methods for the determination of halogen in organic compounds, particularly those containing much fluorine [173]. The analysis is carried out at room temperature, a solution of sodium-biphenyl in 1,2-dimethoxy ethane being added to the organic compound dissolved in di-isopropyl-ether until the green colour persists.

Reaction with methyl iodide and subsequent determination of iodide ion is a recommended method for analysis of, for example, sodium-naphthalene solutions [174].

The more active of these reagents are not stable for indefinite periods at room temperature, since the ether is slowly attacked [162]:

$$C_{10}H_8^- + CH_3OCH_2CH_2OCH_3 = C_{10}H_8 + CH_3O^- + \dot{C}H_2{\cdot}CH_2{\cdot}OCH_3$$

Some n-butanol is formed when lithium-biphenyl is boiled in tetrahydrofuran, attack on the solvent being catalysed by lithium piperidide [141].

The strongly reducing solutions of hydrocarbon anions have been used in the preparation of carbonyls. In this it is commonly convenient to start from the salt of a metal in a $+2$ or $+3$ oxidation state, which must be reduced to the zero oxidation state and both sodium-naphthalene [175] and aluminium alkyls have been used as reducing agents.

The reduction of inorganic substances has been little studied. Cobalt(II) chloride, which is soluble in tetrahydrofuran (light blue solution), is reduced by sodium-naphthalene in stages, the first product being very deep green (due to Na_2CoCl_3 or a tetrahydrofuran complex of this); the final product is a dark brown solution of colloidal cobalt, the presence of metallic cobalt being demonstrated by the ferromagnetism of the solution [176].

[172] D. J. Morantz and E. Warhurst, *Trans. Faraday Soc.*, 1955, **51**, 1375. See also H. V. Carter, B. J. McClelland and E. Warhurst, ibid., 1960, **56**, 343; A. Mathias and E. Warhurst, ibid., p. 348.

[173] P. Johncock, W. K. R. Musgrave and A. Wiper, *Analyst*, 1959, **84**, 245; L. M. Liggett, *Anal. Chem.*, 1954, **26**, 748; A. Sezerat, *Ann. Pharm. France*, 1955, **13**, 745.

[174] C. Stretch and G. Allen, *Proc. Chem. Soc.*, 1959, 399.

[175] H. Shapiro and H. E. Podall, *J. Inorg. Nuclear Chem.*, 1962, **24**, 925.

[176] T. L. Chu and J. V. Friel, *J. Amer. Chem. Soc.*, 1955, **77**, 5838.

Reduction of the ruthenium complex, $RuCl_2(PP)_2$, in which PP is $Me_2PC_2H_4PMe_2$, with sodium-naphthalene gives a product which in several reactions in solution behaves as an arene complex of Ru(O), $Ru(C_{10}H_8)(PP)_2$, though the infrared spectrum indicates the presence of an Ru–H bond and the proton magnetic resonance spectrum suggests that one aromatic proton is missing from the naphthalene. The compound loses naphthalene when heated, forming $Ru(PP)_2$ [177].

Sodium-naphthalene reacts with water or alcohols or practically any source of acidic hydrogen to give 1,4-dihydronaphthalene [162]. Likewise anthracene is reduced to 9,10-dihydro-anthracene [178]. With carbon dioxide, sodium-naphthalene affords 1,4-dihydronaphthalenedicarboxylic acid and the 1,2-isomer (and each of these has *cis* and *trans* isomers), but carbonation at low temperature is necessary to obtain good yields [179]. In all these reactions half of the naphthalene originally present is converted back to naphthalene. The formation of dihydro derivatives or dicarboxylic acids is not good evidence for the existence of disodium adducts in the reaction mixture.

The reactions involve a series of electron transfers [180].

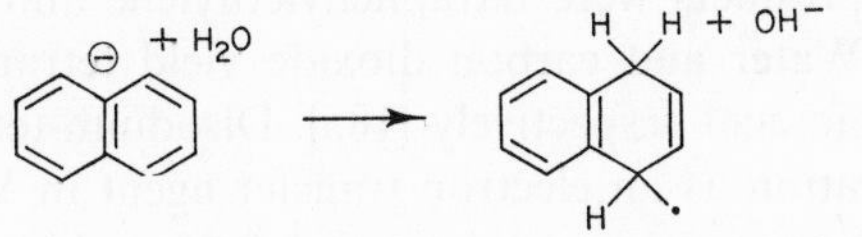

The organic product, which is a free radical, then reacts with another naphthalene anion to give a stabilized benzyl-type anion:

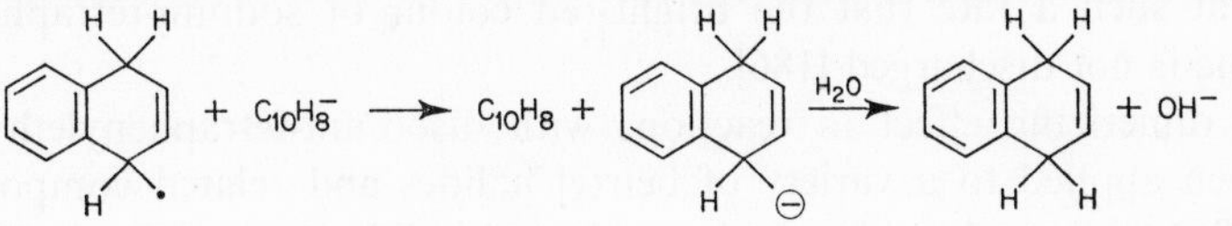

Similarly with the carbonation reaction:

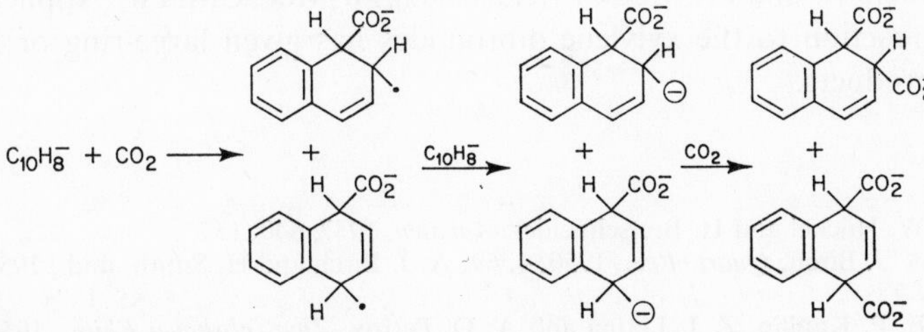

[177] J. Chatt and J. M. Davidson, *J. Chem. Soc.*, 1965, 843.
[178] W. Schlenk, *Ber.*, 1914, **47**, 473.
[179] J. F. Walker and N. D. Scott, *J. Amer. Chem. Soc.*, 1938, **60**, 951; T. M. Lyssy, *J. Org. Chem.*, 1962, **27**, 5.
[180] D. E. Paul, D. Lipkin and S. I. Weissman, *J. Amer. Chem. Soc.*, 1956, **78**, 116.

It should be noted that naphthalene takes up two electrons from sodium in liquid ammonia, giving a deep *red* solution [181]; for reviews relating to this see [182]. Hydrocarbons which take only one electron from sodium may in some cases take two from lithium; this is mainly due to the greater solvation energy of the lithium ion. Biphenyl, for example, forms a dianion, $Li_2(C_{12}H_{10})$.

There have been few studies on the *organic* products of reactions with organic halides. Reaction rates with various halides have been measured in dioxan solution [172] and are in the order sodium-tetraphenylethylene (1), -anthracene (27), -naphthalene (3.10⁶). In some instances alkyl halide or sulphate adds to the hydrocarbon. 1-Methyl-1,4′-dihydrobiphenyl and 1,4′-dimethyl-1,4′-dihydrobiphenyl have been obtained from lithium-biphenyl and methyl sulphate [183].

Reactions with polyhalo compounds have been applied to the etching of the surface of polytetrafluorethylene; an active surface is produced which is then able to form strong bonds to an epoxy resin [184].

The reactions of disodium-tetraphenylethylene have attracted some attention, partly due to early experiments with halides in which the reported reaction products were tetraphenylethylene and the dimer R_2 of the halide RX. Water and carbon dioxide yield tetraphenylethane and tetraphenylsuccinic acid respectively [185]. Disodium-tetraphenylethylene has found application as an electron transfer agent in Wurtz reductions, in which it may be present in catalytic (e.g. 0·05 mol.) quantities. The reactions proceed satisfactorily at $-80°$, and the reagent is self-indicating; the organic halide is added to a stirred suspension of sodium in tetrahydrofuran at such a rate that the bright-red colour of sodium-tetraphenylethylene is not discharged [186].

The dimerizing effect in reactions with disodium-tetraphenylethylene has been applied to a variety of benzyl halides and related compounds [187]. Benzyl fluoride, chloride, bromide and iodide yielded 68, 82, 78 and 74% bibenzyl, and Ph_2MeCCl yielded 66% $Ph_2MeC·CMePh_2$. Application of the reaction to the xylylene dibromides has given large-ring or polymeric products.

[181] W. Hückel and H. Bretschneider, *Annalen*, 1937, **540**, 157.
[182] A. J. Birch, *Quart. Rev.*, 1950, **4**, 69; A. J. Birch and H. Smith, ibid., 1958, **12**, 17.
[183] E. P. Kaplan, Z. I. Letina and A. D. Petrov, *Zhur. obshchei Khim.*, 1956, **26**, 1243.
[184] G. Rapoport, U.S.P. 2,809,130; *Chem. Abs.*, 1958, **52**, 2460.
[185] A. G. Brook, H. L. Cohen and G. F. Wright, *J. Org. Chem.*, 1953, **18**, 447.
[186] E. Müller, *Angew. Chem.*, 1957, **69**, 98.
[187] E. Müller and G. Röscheisen, *Chem. Ber.*, 1957, **90**, 543.

A study of the reaction of disodium-tetraphenylethylene with aromatic monohalides [188] has cast some doubts on many of the earlier results [189], in which dimerized products were so often reported (e.g. biphenyl from bromobenzene, benzil from benzoyl chloride). Biphenyl is formed only in trace amounts when bromo- (or fluoro-) benzene is added to disodium-tetraphenylethylene. Besides much tar, benzene is the main product and the yield of biphenyl is much increased when benzene is present in the reaction mixture as co-solvent. These observations, together with the isolation of 4-phenylpyridine when pyridine is used as co-solvent, indicate that the main reaction intermediate is the free phenyl radical, whose further reaction will normally be hydrogen abstraction or coupling with the solvent.

The relatively high yield of dimerized coupling products from *benzyl* halides is quite understandable, since benzyl radicals are considerably less reactive than phenyl radicals and generally survive long enough to dimerize rather than to react by hydrogen abstraction. However, it is possible that benzyl (and benzyl-type) anions are formed as intermediates since these too are *relatively* unreactive:

$$Ph_4C_2{}^{2-} + PhCH_2X \rightarrow Ph_4C_2 + PhCH_2{}^- + X^-$$
$$PhCH_2{}^- + PhCH_2X \rightarrow PhCH_2CH_2Ph + X^-$$

Both the kinetic experiments of Warhurst [172] and the absence of any electron spin resonance spectrum in dioxan solutions of disodium-tetra-

[188] Idem, ibid., 1958, **91**, 1106.
[189] W. Schlenk and E. Bergmann, *Annalen*, 1928, **463**, 15.

phenylethylene to which an excess of tetraphenylethylene has been added [190] show that the equilibrium

$$2(Ph_4C_2)^-Na^+ \rightleftharpoons Ph_4C_2 + (Ph_4C_2^{2-})Na_2^{++}$$

lies far to the right. A similar result has been obtained for diethyl ether solutions, and the equilibrium constant, K, for the above reaction is estimated to exceed 10^5. However, *blue* solutions containing the anion $Ph_4C_2^-$ may be obtained in tetrahydrofuran [191] and, particularly, 1,2-dimethoxy-ethane [192], both these solvents having higher dielectric constants than those of dioxan or diethyl ether. In 1,2-dimethoxyethane K is less than $1 \cdot 8$ at $22°$, and the solution shows an electron spin resonance spectrum. Garst and Cole [192] argue that the dianion is destabilized by coulombic repulsion between the negative charges, but that the effect is minimized by the formation of ion-pairs with alkali metal ions. Consequently solvents of low dielectric constant, in which ionic dissociation is least, should favour the dianion relative to the mono-anion. The observed formation of mono-anions in the more polar solvents shows that the ion-aggregation effects just mentioned are more important in deciding the value of K than the anionic solvation energy. It is of interest that blue solutions containing the mono-anions in tetrahydrofuran are more readily obtained with lithium than with sodium as counter-ions. In tetrahydrofuran, solutions of $Ph_4C_2Na_2$ contain contact ion-pairs $Ph_4C_2^{2-}(2Na^+)$ which dissociate to $(Ph_4C_2^{2-}Na^+)$ and solvated Na^+. The monosodium derivative, $Ph_4C_2^{-\cdot}Na^+$, forms solvent-separated ion-pairs [193].

The non-aromatic non-planar hydrocarbon cyclo-octatetraene adds two electrons in tetrahydrofuran, forming a *planar aromatic* dianion. The equilibrium

$$2C_8H_8^- \rightleftharpoons C_8H_8 + C_8H_8^{2-}$$

lies far to the right, and the concentration of paramagnetic species, though big enough to be detected, is still very small ($<10^{-3}$M in a $0 \cdot 6$M solution of $K_2C_8H_8$) since the proton magnetic resonance spectrum would otherwise be obliterated [194]. The dianion obeys the Hückel $(4n + 2)$ π-electron rule, for the case $n = 2$. The planar and aromatic character of the colourless salt $K_2C_8H_8$ (THF) has also been deduced from its ultraviolet and infrared spectrum [195].

[190] D. W. Ovenall and D. H. Whiffen, Chemical Society Special Publication No. 12, 1958, p. 140; see also M. J. S. Dewar, N. S. Hush and P. Gray, ibid., pp. 164–7.

[191] A. G. Evans, J. C. Evans, E. D. Owen, B. J. Tabner and J. E. Bennett, *Proc. Chem. Soc.*, 1962, 226; A. G. Evans and B. J. Tabner, *J. Chem. Soc.*, 1963, 5560.

[192] J. F. Garst and R. S. Cole, *J. Amer. Chem. Soc.*, 1962, **84**, 4352; J. F. Garst, E. R. Zabolotny and R. S. Cole, ibid., 1964, **86**, 2257.

[193] R. C. Roberts and M. Szwarc, ibid., 1965, **87**, 5542.

[194] T. J. Katz, ibid., 1960, **62**, 3784, 3785.

[195] H. P. Fritz and H. Keller, *Z. Naturforsch.*, 1961, **16b**, 231.

Alkali metals add to many aromatic compounds other than hydrocarbons, particularly in media such as tetrahydrofuran and 1,2-dimethoxyethane. Azobenzene [196] yields PhN_2PhM_2, where M = Li, Na or K, and the addition compounds react with benzyl chloride forming 1,2-dibenzyl-1,2-diphenylhydrazine; the sodium-stilbene compound, on the other hand, reverts to stilbene and yields bibenzyl [197] (like $Ph_4C_2^{2-}$). The azobenzene dianion reacts with dichlorodiphenylsilane to form a rather novel heterocyclic system [198]:

$$PhN_2Ph^{2-} + Ph_2SiCl_2 \longrightarrow \underset{\substack{Ph \quad Ph \\ N-N \\ Ph_2Si \qquad SiPh_2 \\ N-N \\ Ph \quad Ph}}{}$$

The reduction of several heterocyclic compounds by alkali metals (or by $Mg + MgI_2$ mixtures) gives products arising from the intermediate formation of aromatic anions. Thus reduction of phenanthridine by lithium in tetrahydrofuran results first in the development of a deep red colour due to the ion-radical which deposits a yellow precipitate of dimer after a few minutes. In due course this dissolves to give an olive-green solution of the dianion [199].

red   yellow   olive-green

Hydrolysis of the yellow precipitate gives the tetrahydrobiphenanthridyl, and hydrolysis of the olive-green solution yields, mainly, 5,6-dihydrophenanthridine.

2,2′-Bipyridyl in ether adds alkali metals, giving, for example, the deep red lithium salt, Li^+bipy^-, and in tetrahydrofuran further addition takes place with formation of a deep green solution of the $bipy^=$ (dianion). These reagents have been used in the preparation of an extensive series of complexes of metals in low oxidation states (for a comprehensive review, see [200]). Whereas the complexes of transition metals such as Ti bipy$_3$, V bipy$_3$ and Cr bipy$_3$, are reasonably regarded as derivatives of the metals in their zero oxidation level (the Ti and Cr compounds are diamagnetic),

[196] J. W. B. Reesor and G. F. Wright, *J. Org. Chem.*, 1957, **22**, 375.
[197] J. W. B. Reesor, J. G. Smith and G. F. Wright, ibid., 1954, **19**, 940.
[198] M. V. George, D. Wittenberg and H. Gilman, *J. Amer. Chem. Soc.*, 1959, **81**, 361.
[199] J. J. Eisch and R. M. Thompson, *J. Org. Chem.*, 1962, **27**, 4171.
[200] S. Herzog and R. Taube, *Z. Chemie*, 1962, **2**, 208, 225.

the neutral bipyridyl compounds of non-transition metals must be considered co-ordination complexes of the bipyridyl anion, e.g. [(bipy⁻)₂Be⁺⁺]
[200, 201] particularly since they are paramagnetic and very intensely
coloured. Both types of complex owe their existence to the ability of the
bipyridyl to accept an electron, shared with the metal in the transition
metal complexes, and localized on the bipyridyl π-orbital system in the
others. The presence of two unpaired electrons in [bipy₂Be] and related
compounds such as [bipy₂Zn] has been demonstrated by electron paramagnetic resonance measurements [202].

Addition of electrons to many heterocyclic systems, ethers, amines,
phosphines etc., can also result in fission of one of the bonds to the hetero-
atom. The fission of ethers has been mentioned several times; it is often a
tiresome nuisance experimentally, but similar reactions with tertiary
phosphines and arsines have provided useful synthetic methods [203]:

$$Ph_3P \xrightarrow{Li} Ph_2P^-Li^+ + Ph^{\cdot} \quad or \quad Ph^-$$

$$Ph_2P^-Li^+ \xrightarrow{H_2O} Ph_2PH \quad (about \ 70\% \ from \ Ph_3P)$$

The phenyl ion or radical at once attacks the tetrahydrofuran used as
solvent. Triarylphosphinoxides and related compounds react with alkali
metals in a more complex way [204].

The electron affinities of organic molecules are discussed in a general
review [205].

[201] G. E. Coates and S. I. E. Green, *J. Chem. Soc.*, 1962, 3340.
[202] I. M. Brown and S. I. Weissman, *J. Amer. Chem. Soc.*, 1963, **85**, 2528.
[203] D. Wittenberg and H. Gilman, *J. Org. Chem.*, 1958, **23**, 1063.
[204] F. Hein and H. Hecker, *Z. Naturforsch.*, 1956, **11b**, 677; A. K. Hoffman and
A. G. Tesch, *J. Amer. Chem. Soc.*, 1959, **81**, 5519.
[205] G. Brieglieb, *Angew. Chem., Internat. Edn.*, 1964, **3**, 617.

CHAPTER TWO

Group II

The organic compounds of the Group II metals, including in the Group both the A and B Subgroup elements, show a most striking gradation of properties, general chemical reactivity in particular, running parallel to the electronegativity of the elements.

Ba Sr Ca Mg Be Zn Cd Hg

←— electropositive   electronegative —→

←— more reactive : less reactive —→
organic derivatives

The organic derivatives of the most electropositive elements, calcium, strontium and barium, have been very little studied, possibly on account of the relative inaccessibility of some of the metals themselves and the absence of any significant advantages over the more readily prepared Grignard and organolithium reagents. However, those compounds that have been examined appear rather similar to those of lithium and sodium; for example, they add to ethylenic double bonds and undergo metalation reactions in much the same way, but are generally somewhat less reactive.

Magnesium and beryllium form organic derivatives which are essentially covalent in structure and highly reactive; they resemble organolithium compounds in many respects.

The special place occupied by the Grignard reagents is due both to their reactivity and the comparative ease of their preparation from metallic magnesium, which itself is exceptional among the more electropositive metals in being readily available and requiring little or no cleaning from corrosion products before use.

Grignard reagents have the advantage over organic derivatives of the alkali metals in their stability in ether solution. Metals which are much more electronegative than magnesium, e.g. mercury, thallium or tin, form organic compounds of comparatively low reactivity which undergo fewer useful chemical reactions. Metals which are a little more electronegative than magnesium, e.g. aluminium, beryllium or zinc, form relatively reactive organic compounds, though less reactive than the Grignard reagents, but the metals themselves are not sufficiently active to form organic derivatives under convenient laboratory conditions. Organic compounds of aluminium have attained a position of considerable importance, but their preparation is generally much better suited to industrial than laboratory processes (in contrast to the Grignard reagents).

The great tendency of elements of Groups II and III (particularly the lighter elements) to make use of three or more usually four orbitals for bonding purposes results in the appearance of compounds with 'electron-deficient' structures.

These are compounds in which an atom makes use of more orbitals than the number of available valence electrons, leading to a situation in which the total number of bonding electrons is less than twice the number of covalent bonds. The best-known example of an electron-deficient molecule is diborane B_2H_6, in which there are twelve electrons available for bond-

ing and eight bonds, four of which – shown by dotted lines – are regarded as 'half-bonds'. The most typical reaction of electron-deficient molecules is co-ordination with donor molecules forming compounds of normal structure, this is illustrated by the reactions of typical electron-deficient molecules, diborane and dimethylberyllium, with trimethylamine:

$$B_2H_6 + 2NMe_3 \longrightarrow 2H_3B{\leftarrow}NMe_3$$
$$(Me_2Be)_n + nNMe_3 \longrightarrow nMe_2Be{\leftarrow}NMe_3$$

Both these co-ordination compounds are held together by ordinary electron-pair covalent and co-ordinate bonds.

The organic derivatives of zinc, cadmium and mercury are covalent compounds of normal structure. These elements do not have sufficient tendency to increase their covalency above the group valency of two, to give rise to many compounds with electron-deficient structures. The decrease of reactivity with increasing electronegativity in the sequence zinc, cadmium, mercury is illustrated by the behaviour of the lower alkyls towards water: the dialkyls of zinc are hydrolysed with explosive violence, those of cadmium slowly and those of mercury not at all.

During the past few years a much clearer picture has emerged about the complex-forming tendencies of the alkyls and aryls of the zinc, cadmium and mercury sub-group. The acceptor characters of these are considerably less than those of beryllium and magnesium alkyls and aryls. However, dialkyl derivatives of zinc form a variety of complexes with tertiary amines, and ethers (particularly chelating ethers), and their complexes with some heterocyclic bases such as bipyridyl have bright colours attributed to electron-transfer transitions. The acceptor character of cadmium alkyls is considerably less, but various R_2Cd complexes are now known. Though the RHg^+ cation forms a range of complexes, the dialkyls and diaryls, R_2Hg, have pronounced acceptor character only when the organic group is strongly electron-withdrawing, e.g. CCl_3 or C_6F_5.

Amino-, oxy- and thio-derivatives of the Group II alkyls and aryls sometimes contain metal or other atoms in relatively unusual co-ordination states. For example, several amino-complexes contain three-co-ordinate metal, $(MeBeNMe_2)_3$, $(EtMgNPr^i_2)_2$ and $(MeZnNPh_2)_2$. Oxy-complexes are commonly tetrameric, e.g. $(MeBeOBu^t)_4$, $(MeZnOMe)_4$ and $(MeCdOEt)_4$, and the cubane structure of the zinc compound, containing four-coordinate zinc and oxygen, has been elucidated by X-ray diffraction.

The organic compounds of beryllium, calcium, strontium and barium have been reviewed [1] (literature to early 1961), as have the co-ordination complexes of the alkyls of Be, Zn, Cd and Hg[1a].

CALCIUM, STRONTIUM AND BARIUM

The organic chemistry of these elements is not well developed. Reaction between dimethylmercury and the metals does not produce the dimethylmetals [2] but diphenylbarium has been prepared in poor yield from metallic barium and diphenylcadmium [3]. The metals also partially displace zinc from diethylzinc when heated with it in benzene solution. Addition of ether and filtration from solid matter gives a solution of unknown constitution, but possibly containing complexes $(Et_2M)_m(Et_2Zn)_n$ (M = Ca, Sr or Ba) [4]. Much of what is known of the organic chemistry of calcium, strontium and barium derives from experiments carried out with these solutions. An ethyl-strontium–zinc complex, soluble in benzene, has been prepared in crystalline form, but was not analysed [5]. Various metalation reactions [3, 5] have been investigated, using these complexes whose reactivities are generally comparable with those of alkali metal alkyls, though the orientation in metalations of aromatic compounds appears to be unusual in some instances. The same complexes add to 1,1-diphenylethylene [3, 5] and 1,1-diphenylvaleric acid may be isolated after carbonation,

$$Ph_2C{:}CH_2 \xrightarrow{\text{`Et}_2\text{Sr'}} \underset{\underset{SrEt}{|}}{Ph_2C{\cdot}CH_2Et} \xrightarrow{CO_2} \underset{\underset{CO_2H}{|}}{Ph_2C{\cdot}C_3H_7}$$

Some complex ethyls, $M(AlEt_4)_2$, M = Ca, Sr, Ba, are described later (p. 315).

The preparation of the dimethyls of calcium, strontium and barium, has

[1] G. A. Balueva and S. T. Ioffe, *Russian Chemical Reviews*, 1962, **31**, 439 (English trans.).

[1a] K. H. Thiele and P. Zdunneck, *Organometal. Chem. Rev.*, 1966, **1**, 331.

[2] F. Schulze, *Iowa State Coll. J. Sci.*, 1933, **8**, 225.

[3] H. Gilman, A. H. Haubein, G. O'Donnell and L. A. Woods, *J. Amer. Chem. Soc.*, 1945, **67**, 922.

[4] H. Gilman and L. A. Woods, ibid., p. 520.

[5] H. Gilman, R. N. Meals, G. O'Donnell and L. A. Woods, ibid., 1943, **65**, 268.

been described in a 'Communication' [6]. The metals react with methyl iodide in anhydrous pyridine with precipitation of solids said to be pyridine complexes containing both methyl and iodine attached to metal. Refluxing, followed by prolonged extraction of these solids with fresh pyridine, yields nearly colourless residues containing only a little iodine, and claimed to be the dimethyl derivatives of the metals of at least 95% purity. The compounds, said to be stable to 400° in vacuum, are rapidly hydrolysed and become incandescent when exposed to oxygen or carbon dioxide. In a recent examination of the reactions involving calcium the product has been shown to consist of calcium hydride apparently solvated by pyridine and 4,4'-bipyridyl [7].

The *biscyclopentadienyls* of calcium, strontium and barium have been prepared and studied by several groups [8, 9]. They result from reaction between cyclopentadiene (and in some instances dicyclopentadiene) and the metal, metal carbide or hydride. The strontium and barium compounds were obtained only in low yield, and were purified by vacuum sublimation. An ionic constitution is indicated by their spectra in the 15–35 μ region [10].

Solutions of organocalcium iodides may be prepared from calcium and various organic halides in ether solution [11], though the reactions have been described as slow, erratic and difficult to initiate. The reactivity of organocalcium halides is of interest since a position in this respect intermediate between Grignard reagents and alkali metal derivatives might be expected. In fact a recent investigation [12] demonstrates this quite clearly and resolves a number of apparent anomalies evident in earlier work. Commercial calcium metal commonly contains appreciable amounts of sodium or magnesium. Sodium, in contrast to its effect on the preparation of organolithium compounds, has an adverse effect, but magnesium has a beneficial effect and the use of a little preformed Grignard reagent has about the same result. The formation of organocalcium halides is also promoted by the addition of mercury; equiatomic proportions of the two metals lead to the formation of appreciable amounts of organomercury compounds, but superficial amalgamation (under argon) with 2 atoms % mercury gives a satisfactory form of activated calcium. Ease of reaction increases in the order RCl < RBr < RI and low reaction temperatures are normally recommended to avoid Wurtz-type coupling. Phenyl-

[6] D. A. Payne and R. T. Sanderson, *J. Amer. Chem. Soc.*, 1958, **80**, 5324.

[7] D. Bryce-Smith and P. Morris, personal communication.

[8] K. Ziegler, H. Froitzheim-Kühlhorn and K. Hafner, *Chem. Ber.*, 1956, **89**, 434.

[9] E. O. Fischer and G. Stölzle, ibid., 1961, **94**, 2187.

[10] H. P. Fritz and R. Schneider, ibid., 1960, **93**, 1171.

[11] H. Gilman and F. Schulze, *Bull. Soc. chim. France*, 1927, **41**, 1333; H. Gilman, R. H. Kirby, M. Lichtenwalter and R. V. Young, *Rec. Trav. chim.*, 1936, **55**, 79; C. Glacet, *Bull. Soc. chim. France*, 1938, **5**, 895; R. N. Meals, *J. Org. Chem.*, 1944, **9**, 211.

[12] D. Bryce-Smith and A. C. Skinner, *J. Chem. Soc.*, 1963, 577.

calcium iodide may be obtained in 90% yield in tetrahydrofuran at −30°, and reacts practically quantitatively with carbon dioxide (giving benzoic acid) and, in contrast to earlier reports, with benzoyl chloride giving triphenylmethanol.

Resemblance to organolithium compounds is shown by the rapid attack on pyridine (Grignard reagents scarcely react), phenylcalcium iodide giving 2-phenyl- and either 2,5- or 2,6-diphenylpyridine according to reaction conditions. Similarly, n-butylcalcium iodide resembles n-butyl-lithium in forming dibutylketone as well as valeric acid on reaction with carbon dioxide. Like phenyl-lithium, but unlike phenylsodium, phenyl-calcium iodide does not metalate toluene, though it does metalate anisole in the *ortho* position. It undergoes halogen–metal exchange, for example with 1–naphthyl bromide.

The reaction between methylcalcium iodide and tetrahydrofuran is complicated, giving methane, ethane and ethylene in molar ratio about 9 : 1 : 90, together with tarry matter and some isopropanol. Phenyl-calcium iodide reacts with tetrahydrofuran mainly by metalation, since benzene is a major product.

The constitutions of the organocalcium halides are at least as obscure as those of the Grignard reagents. Experiments on decomposition rates in tetrahydrofuran indicate the presence of at least two species differing in reactivity. The rate of ether-cleavage is also much affected by the halide present; methylcalcium bromide reacts with tetrahydrofuran more slowly than the iodide, and n-butylcalcium chloride, once made – only 22% yields were obtained by two experimental methods – is remarkably stable to tetrahydrofuran even at the boiling point.

The formation of hydrocarbon anions and related compounds by re-actions with alkali earth metals has been studied very much less than cor-responding reactions of alkali metals. 1,1-Diphenylethylene adds calcium, strontium or barium in liquid ammonia solution, with colour change from blue to red, and subsequent treatment with ammonium chloride and water gives a mixture of 1,1,4,4-tetraphenylbutane and 1,1-diphenylethane [3, 13]. Addition of triphenylmethane to a solution of barium in liquid ammonia gives a red solution, which could contain the hydrocarbon anion, or, more likely, the triphenylmethyl anion

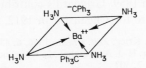

Similarly the red complex $Ph_3CCaCl(THF)_2$, from calcium amalgam and Ph_3CCl in THF, probably contains PhC_3 anions. It is monomeric

[13] H. Gilman and J. C. Bailie, *J. Amer. Chem. Soc.*, 1943, **65**, 267.

in benzene, and would be in the form of ion-pairs [13a]. The magnesium compound $Ph_3CMgBr(OEt_2)_2$ is colourless

The orange-yellow silylbarium compound [14], $(Ph_3Si)_2Ba$, is formed from hexaphenyldisilane and barium in liquid ammonia; the analogous calcium and strontium compounds are very readily ammonolysed.

Attempts to prepare hydrocarbon anion complexes of naphthalene, anthracene, stilbene and tri- and tetra-phenylethylene, with alkali earth metals as counter-ions, have not been successful, and this is attributed to the relatively high ionization potential of the metal. Presumably the additions in liquid ammonia, mentioned earlier, are possible because of the high solvating power of that solvent. However, alkali earth analogues of the alkali metal ketyls have been examined and the relative reactivities of the benzophenone complexes towards n-propyl bromide in dioxan found to be:

$$2Ph_2CO + M \rightarrow Ph_2\overset{.}{C}-\overset{-}{O} \ M^{2+} \ \overset{-}{O}-\overset{.}{C}Ph_2 \xrightarrow{Pr^nBr} Ph_2\overset{.}{C}-\overset{-}{O} \ M^{2+} \ Br^- + Ph_2CO$$
$$Mg^{2+} \ 0\cdot15 \ < \ Ca^{2+} \ 4\cdot9 \ < \ Sr^{2+} \ 26 \ < \ Ba^{2+} \ 112.$$

etc.

The reactivities of the alkali metal ketyls similarly decrease with size of the counter-ion [15].

MAGNESIUM

The organic derivatives of magnesium fall into two groups, the Grignard reagents RMgX and the dialkyls and diaryls R_2Mg. The former are without doubt the most important of all organometallic compounds encountered in the chemical laboratory, not only because many other types are prepared by their use in some stage of the synthesis, but mainly on account of their great value as reagents for general laboratory synthetic purposes. Although so familiar, they present structural and constitutional problems which are far from solved.

The Grignard reagents

These are named after Victor Grignard (1871–1935), who developed their chemistry in 1900 and the following years. Some dialkyls of magnesium had been prepared, with some difficulty, by Wanklyn [16] in 1866 and possibly by Cahours [17] in 1859. Grignard's contribution, for which he was awarded the Nobel Prize for Chemistry in 1912, was the discovery that

[13a] R. Masthoff and G. Krieg, *Zeit. Chem.*, 1966, **6**, 433.

[14] E. Wiberg, O. Stecher, H. J. Andraschek, L. Kreuzbichler and E. Staude, *Angew. Chem., Internat. Edn.*, 1963, **2**, 507.

[15] H. V. Carter, B. J. McClelland and E. Warhurst, *Trans. Faraday Soc.*, 1960, **56**, 455.

[16] J. A. Wanklyn, *Annalen*, 1866, **140**, 353.

[17] A. Cahours, ibid., 1859, **114**, 240.

organomagnesium halides could be prepared, and used for a wide variety of useful reactions, from an organic halide and metallic magnesium using a suitable solvent, normally diethyl ether.

Preparation
Grignard reagents are normally prepared by the slow addition of a solution of the halide to a stirred suspension of magnesium turnings. Since the reagents are very sensitive to air and moisture it is desirable that air should be excluded and that both reactants and apparatus should be dry. Reaction cannot start until the reagents have penetrated the thin oxide film (or imperfections in it) which coats all magnesium which has been exposed to the air. The formation of a Grignard reagent is generally a strongly exothermic process, and though slow to begin with commonly accelerates very markedly when an appreciable amount of reagent has been formed. Care is therefore necessary to avoid adding too much halide before it has been established that the reaction is well started. Halide is then added at such a rate as to maintain steady boiling of the ether. It is desirable to complete the preparation of the reagent in one operation, and the maintenance of steady boiling has the advantage that the atmosphere of ether vapour keeps air away from the reagent. If boiling is allowed to cease before the reagent is used, then an atmosphere of dry oxygen-free nitrogen should be provided and there is much to be said in favour of making provision for an inert atmosphere at all stages of work with reactive organometallic compounds. The use of an argon or helium atmosphere is said to result in better yields, less coupling product and less coloured solutions [18].

The induction period at the beginning of the preparation of a Grignard reagent is in part due to the presence of moisture, and in fact it increases rapidly with water content [19]. Addition of a small crystal of iodine without stirring until reaction is well started, or the use of some magnesium which has previously been heated in the presence of iodine[20] are favoured methods for starting reaction. These methods owe their efficacy to the attack of iodine on the magnesium giving ether-soluble magnesium iodide and exposing an active metal surface. Magnesium bromide and iodide also form ether-insoluble hydrates which have a very advantageous effect in further drying the reagents [21]. A similar effect may be achieved by the use of a little ethylene dibromide, which attacks magnesium rapidly forming ethylene and magnesium bromide. This method is particularly to be recommended when there is any reason to suspect the dryness of the ether,

[18] F. H. Owens, R. P. Fellman and F. E. Zimmerman, *J. Org. Chem.*, 1960, **25**, 1808.
[19] M. Meyer and C. Shimodaira, *Compt. rend.*, 1956, **243**, 846.
[20] F. G. Holliman and F. G. Mann, *J. Chem. Soc.*, 1942, 739.
[21] M. Meyer and C. Shimodaira, *Compt. rend.*, 1957, **244**, 1378.

and is generally to be preferred to the 'entrainment method' whereby a particularly reactive halide such as methyl iodide or ethyl bromide is added to the magnesium along with the less reactive halide from which a Grignard reagent is desired. The disadvantage of the entrainment method is the simultaneous formation of two Grignard reagents and, later, necessarily, of two sets of products, but ethylene dibromide may itself be used in an entrainment method [22]. Magnesium turnings can be activated by stirring them for a day or more (dry) in a nitrogen atmosphere. The metal becomes grey and is finely divided [22a].

Apart from methyl iodide, which gives good yields of methylmagnesium iodide, chlorides and particularly bromides are preferred for the preparation of Grignard reagents. In order to reduce the extent of coupling reaction,

$$RMgX + RX \longrightarrow MgX_2 + R_2$$

the least reactive halides should be used consistent with an adequate reaction rate. Methyl sulphate gives good yields of the Grignard reagent $MeMg(SO_4Me)$ when the reaction is carried out in tetrahydrofuran [23]. Generally bromides or chlorides may be used in the aliphatic series, but aromatic chlorides are generally insufficiently reactive. However, chlorobenzene affords phenylmagnesium chloride in dibutyl ether [24], owing to the higher temperatures permissible, or in tetrahydrofuran [25].

Di-Grignard reagents, XMgRMgX, have considerable synthetic value, but are often not very easy to prepare. Methylenemagnesium bromide and iodide have been described; hydrolysis of the solution obtained from methylene iodide and magnesium in ether gave a 32% yield of methane, and some ethylene was formed in the preparation of the Grignard reagent. These reagents are quite abnormal since they appear to react neither with benzaldehyde nor with benzoyl chloride [26]. As mentioned earlier, ethylene dibromide gives ethylene and magnesium bromide, and propylene dibromide undergoes a complex reaction leading to propylene, cyclopropane and other products. The most useful aliphatic di-Grignard reagents have been $BrMg(CH_2)_4MgBr$ and $BrMg(CH_2)_5MgBr$, both of which have found use in the synthesis of heterocyclic compounds [27], for example [28]

[22] D. E. Pearson, D. Cowan and J. D. Becker, *J. Org. Chem.*, 1959, **24**, 504.
[22a] A. Mendel, *J. Organometal. Chem.*, 1966, **6**, 97.
[23] H. Normant and P. Perrin, *Bull. Soc. chim. France*, 1957, 801.
[24] T. Hukada and T. Kusama, *Nippon Kagaku Zasshi*, 1955, **76**, 28; *Chem. Abs.*, 1957, **51**, 17793.
[25] H. E. Ramsden, A. E. Balint, W. R. Whitford, J. J. Walburn and R. Cserr, *J. Org. Chem.*, 1957, **22**, 1202.
[26] D. A. Fidler, J. R. Jones, S. L. Clark and H. Stange, *J. Amer. Chem. Soc.*, 1955, **77**, 6634.
[27] I. T. Millar and H. Heaney, *Quart. Rev.*, 1957, **11**, 109.
[28] G. Grüttner and E. Krause, *Ber.*, 1916, **49**, 442.

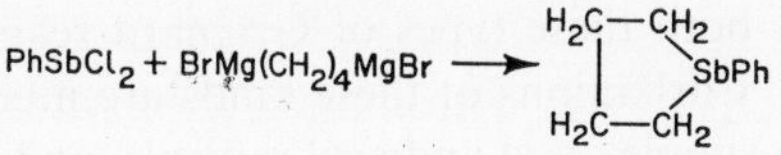

$$\text{PhSbCl}_2 + \text{BrMg(CH}_2)_4\text{MgBr} \longrightarrow \begin{array}{c} \text{H}_2\text{C}-\text{CH}_2 \\ | \quad\quad \rangle\text{SbPh} \\ \text{H}_2\text{C}-\text{CH}_2 \end{array}$$

Di-Grignard reagents derived from aromatic dihalides have proved particularly difficult to prepare. *Meta* and *para* dihalides do not give good yields of di-Grignard reagents in ether, but do so in tetrahydrofuran [29]. *Para*-dibrombenzene gives *para*-dilithiobenzene by reaction with butyllithium in various solvents. *Ortho* dihalides such as *o*-bromo-iodobenzene have afforded di-Grignard reagents which have found application in the synthesis of *o*-phenylene tertiary diphosphines [30]. A peculiar complication with *ortho* dihalides is the side reaction resulting in the elimination of magnesium halide and the formation of the very reactive 'benzyne' intermediate which immediately undergoes addition reactions, either with itself or with, for example, furan:

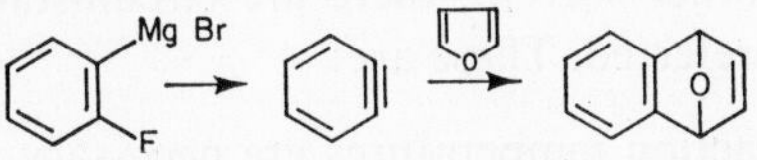

Highly electronegative halogens are especially readily eliminated in this way [31], though bromopentafluorobenzene (see below) gives good yields of Grignard reagent.

Several *indirect* methods for the preparation of organolithium compounds are described in Chapter 1, particularly the metal–halogen and the metal–hydrogen exchange reactions. Analogous methods are much less frequently applied to the preparation of Grignard reagents.

An organolithium compound can, if desired, be converted to the corresponding Grignard reagent simply by adding an appropriate amount of magnesium bromide.

$$\text{RLi} + \text{MgBr}_2 \longrightarrow \text{RMgBr} + \text{LiBr}$$

The metal–hydrogen exchange reaction is very useful for the preparation of Grignard reagents derived from relatively acidic hydrocarbons. Such hydrocarbons usually derive their acidic character from the enhanced electronegativity of acetylenic carbon,

$$\text{PhC:CH} + \text{C}_2\text{H}_5\text{MgBr} \longrightarrow \text{PhC:CMgBr} + \text{C}_2\text{H}_6$$

or from the formation of an aromatic from a non-aromatic system,

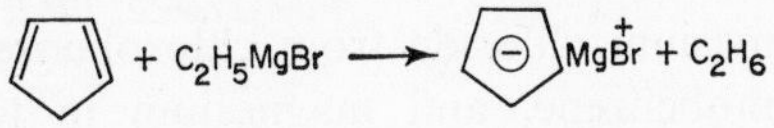

[29] D. R. Nielsen and W. E. McEwen, *J. Amer. Chem. Soc.*, 1957, **79**, 3081.

[30] F. A. Hart and F. G. Mann, *J. Chem. Soc.*, 1957, 3939; H. Heaney, F. G. Mann and I. T. Millar, ibid., 1956, 4692.

[31] G. Wittig and L. Pohmer, *Chem. Ber.*, 1956, **89**, 1334.

It is probable that both these types of Grignard reagent have essentially ionic constitutions. Carbanions of these kinds are much less reactive than those derived from simple alkyl and aryl radicals, and do not attack ether. Acetylene itself affords a di-Grignard reagent,

$$C_2H_2 + 2C_2H_5MgBr \rightarrow BrMgC:CMgBr + 2C_2H_6$$

which forms a heavy rather viscous oil only slightly soluble in ether. It may be kept in solution by the use of tetrahydrofuran as reaction medium, and the mono-Grignard reagent has been prepared by the slow addition of ethylmagnesium bromide (in tetrahydrofuran) to tetrahydrofuran which is kept saturated with acetylene [32],

$$C_2H_2 \text{ (excess)} + C_2H_5MgBr \xrightarrow{\text{THF}} HC:CMgBr + C_2H_6$$

Although Grignard reagents are prepared and used in diethyl ether far more than in any other solvent, there are circumstances in which other solvents are to be preferred. These are:

(a) when high reaction temperatures are necessary,
(b) when the reaction product has a volatility comparable with that of ether,
(c) when the use of ethers of more strongly donor character than diethyl ether is necessary to promote the formation of Grignard reagents from relatively unreactive halides.

The first case is the simplest; the Grignard reagent may then be prepared in ether in the usual way, the reactant of choice added followed by a higher boiling solvent such as benzene, xylene or di-n-butyl ether. The reaction mixture may then be heated well above the boiling point of diethyl ether, when much ether (but not all of it) will distil away.

The second case requires the absence of diethyl ether. The preparation of trimethylarsine (b.p. 52°),

$$AsCl_3 + 3MeMgI \rightarrow Me_3As + 3MgClI$$

is an example in which a troublesome separation of the product from diethyl ether can be avoided by the use of di-n-butyl ether (b.p. 142°).

The third case is the most important, since many Grignard reagents which cannot be prepared (or only with difficulty) in diethyl ether can readily be prepared in the more basic ether *tetrahydrofuran*. The formation of phenylmagnesium chloride from chlorobenzene, which is much cheaper than bromobenzene, and magnesium in tetrahydrofuran has already been mentioned, and it is of interest that in this instance a diethyl ether–tetrahydrofuran mixture is also satisfactory and the THF : Mg ratio

[32] E. R. H. Jones, L. Skatterböl and M. C. Whiting, *J. Chem. Soc.*, 1956, 4765; *Org. Syntheses*, 1959, **39**, 56.

need be only a little greater than unity. Grignard reagents have been prepared in good yield in hydrocarbon–tetrahydrofuran mixtures in which there is only one mole of tetrahydrofuran per atom magnesium, [33]. *p*-Bromdimethylaniline, which does not give good yields of Grignard reagent in ether, reacts satisfactorily in tetrahydrofuran. Care should be taken to avoid a large excess of halide in the preparation of Grignard reagents in tetrahydrofuran. For example, if methyl bromide is bubbled into magnesium suspended in tetrahydrofuran until the metal disappears then the products are ethane and magnesium bromide [34]

$$CH_3MgBr + CH_3Br \rightarrow C_2H_6 + MgBr_2$$

It should also be noted that *radical exchange* may take place [35],

$$RMgX + R'X \rightleftharpoons R'MgX + RX$$

the rates of such reactions being greater in the more polar solvents (1,2-dimethoxyethane > THF > diglyme > diethyl ether), and also being greatest for iodides (I > Br > Cl). As in the case of exchanges between organolithium compounds and organic halides, the metal tends to become bound to the more electronegative organic radical. Thus α-naphthyl iodide exchanges with n-amylmagnesium bromide in 1,2-dimethoxyethane, but the equilibrium between methyl iodide and phenylmagnesium bromide in the same solvent is wholly in favour of the latter reagents, i.e. no methyl Grignard is formed.

One of the best known and most valuable applications of tetrahydrofuran has been in the preparation of *vinyl* and *substituted vinyl* Grignard reagents, developed to a large extent by H. Normant [36]. The chelating diether, 1,2-dimethoxyethane, also promotes the formation of Grignard reagents but has been used much less than tetrahydrofuran. It has the disadvantage, however, of causing the ready precipitation of sparingly soluble 1,2-dimethoxyethane complexes of magnesium halides.

Organomagnesium halides may also be prepared in hydrocarbon solvents, though careful attention to experimental detail is necessary to obtain good yields [37]. Solvents, such as isopropylbenzene, tetrahydronaphthalene, decahydronaphthalene or domestic paraffin-lamp oil, must be dry and free from peroxides, and the magnesium should be in the form of bright ca. 150-mesh powder. Though phenylmagnesium chloride prepared from chlorobenzene and magnesium in hydrocarbons would seem

[33] T. Leigh, *Chem. and Ind.*, 1965, 426.
[34] N. M. Bikales and E. I. Becker, *Canad. J. Chem.*, 1963, **41**, 1329.
[35] L. I. Zakharkin, O. Y. Okhlobystin and K. A. Bilevitch, *J. Organometal. Chem.*, 1964, **2**, 309.
[36] H. Normant, *Compt. rend.*, 1954, **239**, 1510; idem in *Advances in Organic Chemistry*, Vol. II, Ch. 1, ed. R. A. Raphael, E. C. Taylor and H. Wynberg, Interscience 1960, New York; D. Seyferth and F. G. A. Stone, *J. Amer. Chem. Soc.*, 1957, **79**, 515.
[37] D. Bryce-Smith and G. F. Cox, *J. Chem. Soc.*, 1958, 1050; 1961, 1175.

to be a cheaper phenylating agent than the more conventional Grignard reagents (from chlorobenzene in more costly ether solvents or, worse still, costly bromobenzene also in costly solvents) the reagent as prepared in hydrocarbons has not been extensively developed, most likely on account of the experimental difficulty in obtaining high and reproducible yields. The hydrocarbon-soluble material commonly has an empirical formula close to R_3Mg_2X, and similar solutions have been obtained by removal of ether from ethereal Grignard reagents. Unsolvated phenyl-magnesium chloride $(Ph_3Mg_2Cl)_x$ has been crystallized from tetrahydronaphthalene but no structural data have yet been reported. The presence of significant amounts of R_2Mg and MgX_2 in solutions of butyl- and phenylmagnesium halides in hydrocarbons is excluded since the MgX_2 is virtually insoluble in these solvents. A study of the reactions between magnesium and n-$C_5H_{11}X$ ($X = Cl$, Br, I) in benzene has shown that the ratio $C_5H_{11} : X$ in the resulting solution is ca. 5 (I), ca. 15 (Br) and ca. 120 (Cl). Thus the product from n-amyl chloride is almost entirely di-n-amylmagnesium, which differs from the lower dialkyls in being soluble in benzene, in which it is described as dimeric [37a].

Another investigation of the formation of Grignard reagents in hydrocarbon solvents [38] suggests that aliphatic are better than aromatic hydrocarbons, and it is recommended that the boiling point of the solvent should not differ widely from that of the organic halide. Chlorobenzene is said to be inert to magnesium in boiling benzene, but gives a good yield of Grignard reagent in boiling toluene*. Only primary alkyl halides, a few aromatic halides and no polyhalides yield Grignard reagents in hydrocarbon media. A shallow cut is necessary to obtain satisfactorily reactive magnesium chips.

Grignard reagents are formed in good yield in benzene solution when one mole of triethylamine is present for every gram atom of magnesium [38a].

Grignard reagents have been prepared, though with some difficulty, from perfluoroalkyl halides. Attempts at the preparation of trifluoromethyl Grignard reagents have only recently been even moderately successful. Magnesium, activated with mercury, reacts with CF_3Br in ether at $-20°$ and up to 20% yields of CF_3CMe_2OH have been isolated after addition of acetone. The corresponding iodide (from CF_3I) gives even lower yields (e.g. 14% at $-65°$), as CF_3MgI evidently decomposes very easily giving C_2F_4 and fluorocarbon polymers. Curiously, attempts to trap any CF_2 formed, by carrying out reactions in the presence of cyclohexene,

[37a] W. H. Glaze and C. M. Selman, *J. Organometal Chem.*, 1966, **5**, 477.

[38] F. J. Buescher, A. H. Frye, G. J. Goepfert and V. G. Soukup, Paper presented to the Cincinnati Symposium on Organometallic Chemistry, June 1963.

[38a] E. C. Ashby and R. Reed, *J. Org. Chem.*, 1966, **31**, 971.

* And in boiling chlorobenzene when the metal has been activated by a little aluminium chloride (see ref. 47).

resulted in the addition of CF_3—I across the double bond [39]. Hepta-fluoro-n-propyl iodide gives a Grignard reagent in up to 65% yield [40]:

$$C_3F_7I + Mg \rightarrow C_3F_7MgI$$

but the preparation requires great care. Reaction, using the best quality magnesium, is started at $0°$ to $-20°$, the temperature then being reduced to $-50°$ and the rest of the perfluoropropyl iodide being added very slowly. The main difficulty is the tendency of these compounds to lose a fluoride ion and form an olefin,

$$C_3F_7MgI \rightarrow C_3F_6 + MgIF$$

The Grignard reagent derived from heptafluoro-isopropyl iodide [41] is formed by metal–halogen exchange at $-78°$:

$$(CF_3)_2CFI + PhMgBr \rightarrow (CF_3)_2CFMgBr + PhI$$

The reagent decomposes readily to C_3F_6, but derivatives such as $C_3F_7CHEtOH$ and $C_3F_7SiMe_3$ have been prepared by reaction at low temperature.

Trifluorovinylmagnesium bromide is formed from $CF_2{:}CFBr$ and activated magnesium in tetrahydrofuran at $-25°$. The reagent has, for example, been used for the preparation of $Me_2Sn(CF{:}CF_2)_2$ [42].

Though pentafluorophenyl-lithium eliminates lithium fluoride with transient formation of tetrafluorobenzyne [43], pentafluorophenylmagnesium bromide is formed without difficulty and in good yield in diethyl ether [44]:

$$C_6F_5Br + Mg \rightarrow C_6F_5MgBr$$

It is of interest that chloropentafluorobenzene gives a Grignard reagent in diethyl ether [45], if the magnesium is activated by ethylene dibromide, but reaction between magnesium and C_6F_5Cl in tetrahydrofuran gives a good yield of polymeric fluoro-aromatic material, evidently by attack of C_6F_5MgCl on C_6F_5Cl.

Compounds analogous to Grignard reagents, but with magnesium

[39] E. T. McBee, R. D. Battershell and H. P. Braendlin, ibid., 1963, 28, 1131.
[40] R. N. Haszeldine, J. Chem. Soc., 1953, 1748.
[41] R. D. Chambers, W. K. R. Musgrave and J. Savory, ibid., 1962, 1993.
[42] I. L. Knunyants, R. N. Sterlin, R. D. Yatsenko and L. N. Pinkina, Izvest. Akad. Nauk S.S.S.R., 1958, 1345; H. D. Kaesz, S. L. Stafford and F. G. A. Stone, J. Amer. Chem. Soc., 1959, 81, 6336.
[43] P. L. Coe, R. Stephens and J. C. Tatlow, J. Chem. Soc., 1962, 3227.
[44] E. Nield, R. Stephens and J. C. Tatlow, ibid., 1959, 166.
[45] G. M. Brooke, R. D. Chambers, J. Heyes and W. K. R. Musgrave, Proc. Chem. Soc., 1963, 94; J. Chem. Soc., 1964, 729; see also R. J. Harper, E. J. Sokolski and C. Tamborski, J. Org. Chem., 1964, 29, 2385.

D

bound to elements other than carbon, have long been known and are exemplified by the following:

$$2EtMgBr + PhPH_2 \longrightarrow PhP(MgBr)_2 + 2C_2H_6$$
$$EtMgBr + Ph_2AsH \longrightarrow Ph_2AsMgBr + C_2H_6$$

Recent additions to this class are the Grignard reagents derived from some of the higher boron hydrides [46]

$$B_{10}H_{14} + MeMgBr \longrightarrow B_{10}H_{13}MgBr + CH_4$$
$$B_{10}H_{13}MgBr + PhCH_2Cl \longrightarrow PhCH_2B_{10}H_{13}$$
$$B_{10}H_{13}MgBr + nBuF \longrightarrow nBuB_{10}H_{13}$$

The *hydrogenolysis* of Grignard reagents [47] in ether solution (350 atm.) gives the hydrocarbon and magnesium hydride:

$$2RMgX + 2H_2 \longrightarrow 2RH + MgX_2 + MgH_2$$

Of the reagents studied, isopropylmagnesium chloride reacts the most readily (50°) whereas aryl and benzyl Grignard reagents require temperatures in the range 125–150°. The hydrocarbon is not formed by addition of hydrogen after olefin elimination since the deuterium reaction gives a monodeuterated hydrocarbon:

$$2Pr^iMgCl + 2D_2 \longrightarrow 2Pr^iD + MgD_2 + MgCl_2$$

Hydrogenolysis has also been reported to give the diethyl ether complex of HMgCl [48]. An earlier claim [49] that tetrahydrofuran complexes of HMgX (X = Cl, Br or I) are formed from the ethyl Grignard reagent and diborane, has not been confirmed though $ClMgBH_4(THF)_2$ (dimeric in benzene) was isolated as a product of this reaction [50].

$$3EtMgCl + 2B_2H_6 \xrightarrow[25°]{THF} 3ClMgBH_4 + Et_3B$$

One Grignard reagent may in suitable cases be converted into another by a process of olefin exchange, catalysed by $TiCl_4$ or $Ti(OR)_4$,

$$n\text{-}C_3H_7MgBr + RCH:CH_2 \longrightarrow RCH_2CH_2MgBr + C_3H_6$$

Derivatives have been obtained in 20–60% yield by this reaction [51].

*Constitution**

Though usually, and for most purposes adequately, given the formula RMgX, the Grignard reagents evidently have rather complex constitu-

[46] B. Siegel, J. Mack, J. Lowe and J. Gallaghan, *J. Amer. Chem. Soc.*, 1958, **80**, 4523; J. Gallaghan and B. Siegel, ibid., 1959, **81**, 504.

[47] W. E. Becker and E. C. Ashby, *J. Org. Chem.*, 1964, **29**, 954.

[48] T. N. Dymova and N. G. Eleseeva, *Russ. J. Inorg. Chem.*, 1963, **8**, 820.

[49] E. Wiberg and P. Strebel, *Annalen*, 1957, **607**, 9.

[50] W. E. Becker and E. C. Ashby, *Inorg. Chem.*, 1965, **4**, 1816.

[51] H. L. Finkbeiner and G. D. Cooper, *J. Org. Chem.*, 1962, **27**, 3395.

* For recent reviews, see B. J. Wakefield, *Organometal. Chem. Rev.*, 1966, **1**, 131, and E. C. Ashby, *Quart. Rev.*, 1967, **21**, 259.

tions which have not yet altogether been clarified. Addition of dioxan to ether solutions of Grignard reagents results in the precipitation of dioxan complexes of magnesium halides, and subsequent evaporation of the solvents yields the dialkyls R_2Mg (themselves often complexed with dioxan). This led to a suggestion that equilibria of the type

$$2RMgX \rightleftharpoons R_2Mg + MgX_2$$
$$\text{or} \quad R_2Mg \cdot MgX_2 \rightleftharpoons R_2Mg + MgX_2$$

obtain in ethereal Grignard solutions. Though this reaction has been most useful as a preparative method for the dialkyls and diaryls of magnesium (for a recent description of technique see [52]), the various conclusions earlier drawn from it about the positions of such equilibria have been shown not to be valid since the rapidity of exchange processes and the various association reactions [53] complicate the situation.

For several years it appeared that species of the type RMgX did not exist in Grignard equilibria [54], the basis for this view mainly being lack of, or only slight, exchange between Mg^*Br_2 and Et_2Mg, the Mg^*Br_2 being labelled with ^{28}Mg. Since solutions obtained by mixing Et_2Mg and $MgBr_2$ appear to be identical with those obtained from magnesium and ethyl bromide, the Grignard reagent was regarded as better represented by R_2Mg, MgX_2, rather than by RMgX. It was noted, however, that experiments carried out with ^{25}Mg (from a different source than the ^{28}Mg) showed complete exchange, attributed to the effects of impurities in the metal. In the light of later experiments it seems that these isotopic exchange experiments are quite sensitive to impurities in ways that are not understood.

Solutions of Grignard reagents become viscous on concentration and ether is tenaciously retained; this indicates some sort of association and also that ether is chemically combined forming co-ordination complexes. Earlier measurements of the *molecular weights* of several Grignard reagents, e.g. ebullioscopically in ether, indicated degrees of association ranging from just over one to about four, and higher apparent degrees of association were observed when traces of oxygen had been allowed access [55].

Solutions of Grignard reagents in ether are electrically conducting and both anions and cations contain magnesium [53]. The extent of ionization is small and there would be extensive formation of ion-pairs or higher

[52] W. Strohmeier and F. Seifert, *Chem. Ber.*, 1961, **94**, 2356.

[53] W. V. Evans and R. Pearson, *J. Amer. Chem. Soc.*, 1942, **64**, 2865.

[54] R. E. Dessy, G. S. Handler, J. H. Wotiz and C. A. Hollingsworth, ibid., 1957, **79**, 3476; R. E. Dessy and G. S. Handler, ibid., 1958, **80**, 5824; R. E. Dessy, S. I. E. Green and R. M. Salinger, *Tetrahedron Letters*, 1964, 1369.

[55] A. Terentjew, *Z. anorg. Chem.*, 1926, **156**, 73; J. Meisenheimer and W. Schichenmaier, *Ber.*, 1928, **61**, 721; W. Slough and A. R. Ubbelohde, *J. Chem. Soc.*, 1955, 108; R. Stewart and A. R. Ubbelohde, ibid., 1949, 2649.

aggregates in a solvent of low dielectric constant such as ether; this makes transport experiments difficult to interpret. Evidence for the existence of ion aggregates has, in fact, been obtained since the amount of magnesium transported considerably exceeds the amount deposited on the cathode [56]. The electrolysis of Grignard reagents is consistent with the principal ion discharged at the cathode being essentially RMg^+, which would be solvated and may be associated as well. The organic products of electrolysis [57] are consistent with the formation of alkyl or aryl radicals at the electrode, since they consist mainly of substances expected to result from (a) abstraction of hydrogen from the solvent by the radical R, giving RH,

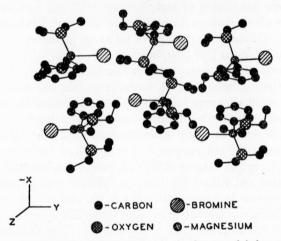

- ● –CARBON   ◈ –BROMINE
- ◉ –OXYGEN   ◍ –MAGNESIUM

Fig. 8. Packing of $C_6H_5MgBr \cdot 2C_4H_{10}O$ molecules in the crystal (ether carbon atoms included) (after Stucky and Rundle [58])

(b) disproportionation of R into olefin and RH, (c) coupling to R_2. For example, methylmagnesium halides give predominantly methane at low and ethane at high current densities, ethylmagnesium bromide gives mainly ethane and ethylene, while benzylmagnesium chloride gives bibenzyl as sole product since benzyl radicals are relatively stable and can persist until coupling takes place. Electrodes of zinc and lead are attacked by the liberated radicals with the formation of organometallic compounds.

The diether complex of phenylmagnesium bromide has been crystallized and its structure (Figure 8) determined by X-ray diffraction [58]. The crystals contain monomer units of $PhMgBr(OEt_2)_2$, in which each magnesium atom is bound tetrahedrally to a phenyl group, a bromine atom and two ether molecules. There is only Van der Waals interaction between

[56] R. E. Dessy and G. S. Handler, *J. Amer. Chem. Soc.*, 1958, **80**, 5824.
[57] W. V. Evans and others, ibid., 1934, **56**, 654; 1936, **58**, 720, 2284; 1939, **61**, 878; 1940, **62**, 534.
[58] G. D. Stucky and R. E. Rundle, ibid., 1963, **85**, 1002; idem, ibid., 1964, **86**, 4825.

separate molecules. The similar structure of the ethylmagnesium bromide bisdiethyl ether complex [59] is shown in Figure 9.

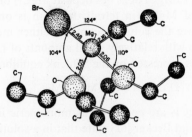

Fig. 9. The molecular configuration of EtMgBr·2Et$_2$O (after Guggenberger and Rundle [59])

It is not uncommon for substances to have different structures in the crystalline from the dissolved state. However, this structure analysis proves the existence of the monomer in the crystalline state, and both Slough and Ubbelohde [55], and Ashby and Becker [60] find several aryl-magnesium bromides have degrees of association between one and two in diethyl ether (this is further discussed below).

It is significant that the composition of the crystals obtained from phenyl-magnesium bromide solutions does not depend on the concentration of the solute provided that the ether : magnesium ratio exceeds 2 : 1. At the composition, PhMgBr(OEt$_2$)$_2$, the entire solution may be crystallized at 15–20°, and at lower ether contents amorphous polymer is formed. It is suggested that molecules in the liquid phase of overall composition PhMgBr + 2Et$_2$O would not have a structure such as

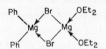

since this would have an ether : magnesium ratio of 1 : 1. The Mg–O bonds in the complex, PhMgBr(OEt$_2$)$_2$, are 2·01 and 2·06 Å, and are shorter than those in magnesium oxide, or hydroxide, or in the Mg6H$_2$O^{2+} cation.

Ethylmagnesium bromide and chloride have been shown to be mono-meric in tetrahydrofuran, and to remain so over a concentration range 0·1 to 0·3 molar [60]. The chloride appears to be monomeric (ebullio-scopically) in the same solvent at a 2 molar concentration, though the authors point out that molecular weight determinations at that concentra-tion may not be accurate. The possibility remains that ethylmagnesium

[59] L. J. Guggenberger and R. E. Rundle, ibid., p. 5344.
[60] E. C. Ashby and W. E. Becker, ibid., 1963, **85**, 118; E. C. Ashby and M. B. Smith, ibid., 1964, **86**, 4363.

chloride in tetrahydrofuran consists of a mixture of Et_2Mg and $MgCl_2$, both of course complexed with solvent, but this is most improbable since a 2 molar solution of EtMgCl does not deposit $MgCl_2$ on standing, though the solubility limit of $MgCl_2$ in tetrahydrofuran is only 0·5M at room temperature. Therefore the solution contains either monomeric EtMgCl or this in equilibrium with relatively small amounts of Et_2Mg and $MgCl_2$, i.e. the composition is expressed by the Schlenk equilibrium [61].

$$2EtMgCl \rightleftharpoons Et_2Mg + MgCl_2$$

Both Et_2Mg and $MgCl_2$ are described as monomeric in tetrahydrofuran [60], though Storfer and Becker [62] state that in a solution of Et_2Mg containing 0·316 gram-atoms of magnesium per litre of tetrahydrofuran the concentration of monomer is 0·173M and that of dimer 0·0715M (30°).

Addition of benzene to a solution of EtMgCl in tetrahydrofuran, followed by slow evaporation of solvent under reduced pressure, results in the deposition of a crystalline solid of composition $EtMg_2Cl_3,2THF$. The mother liquor eventually contains only Et_2Mg. These researches show that exchange of alkyl groups must take place, as had earlier been suggested by proton magnetic resonance data obtained for solutions of methylmagnesium iodide in diethyl ether [63]. Dimethylmagnesium also has been shown to exchange methyl groups very rapidly with dimethylzinc and with dimethylcadmium in tetrahydrofuran [64] the pre-exchange life of carbon–magnesium bonds being less than 0·04 seconds at the concentrations studied. The complex, $EtMg_2Cl_3,2THF$, dissolves again in tetrahydrofuran in which it is wholly dissociated into EtMgCl + $MgCl_2$.

As Grignard reagents are prepared and used in *diethyl ether* more than in any other solvent, particular interest is attached to the extent of their association in diethyl ether. Early measurements by Ashby and his colleagues [60] established that ethylmagnesium *bromide* and *iodide* are monomeric at low concentration (below at 0·1M) but that ethyl- and iso-propyl-magnesium *chlorides* are considerably more associated, at concentrations in the 0·1–1M range, than the bromide or iodide. Evidently chlorine acts as a better bridging group than bromine or iodine, in the sense that the halogen bridge is less readily opened by reaction with ether. Lower degrees of association in tetrahydrofuran, than at a similar concentration in diethyl ether, are to be expected since tetrahydrofuran is the stronger base and would compete more successfully with halide for co-ordination positions around the magnesium atoms. The degrees of association of a representative group of magnesium compounds measured at concentrations

[61] W. Schlenk and W. Schlenk, *Ber.*, 1929, **62**, 920.
[62] S. J. Storfer and E. I. Becker, *J. Org. Chem.*, 1962, **27**, 1868.
[63] C. R. McCoy and A. L. Allred, *J. Amer. Chem. Soc.*, 1962, **84**, 912.
[64] R. E. Dessy, F. Kaplan, G. R. Coe and R. M. Salinger, ibid., 1963, **85**, 1191.

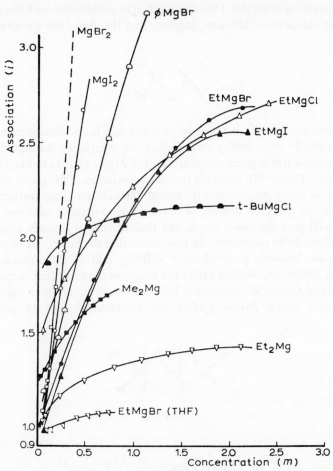

Fig. 10. Degree of association in diethyl ether (ebullioscopically) (after Ashby and Walker [64a])

up to 2·5M, are shown in Figure 10. The monomeric character of very dilute (10^{-3} to 10^{-2}M) solutions of diethylmagnesium, or magnesium bromide, or mixtures of these both in tetrahydrofuran and in diethyl ether has also been established [65]. From Figure 10 it can be seen that the degree of association both of magnesium bromide and of magnesium iodide in diethyl ether increases very rapidly with concentration. Tertiarybutyl-magnesium chloride tends toward a dimeric form over a considerable concentration range, and this could be connected with the relatively poor bridging character of the t-butyl group (e.g. Bu^t_2Be is monomeric unlike

[64a] E. C. Ashby and F. Walker, *J. Organometal. Chem.*, 1967, **7**, P.7.
[65] A. D. Vreugdenhil and C. Blomberg, *Rec. Trav. chim.*, 1963, **82**, 453, 461.

other beryllium dibutyls). This effect, taken in conjunction with the strong bridging character of chlorine, suggests that the dimer has the structure

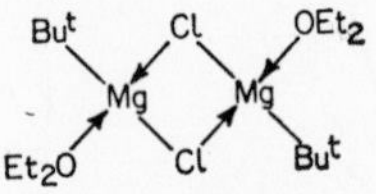

The mono-etherate of t-butylmagnesium chloride is also dimeric in benzene (cryoscopically [66]). Ashby and Walker, by comparing the high degrees of association (for a given concentration) of MgX_2 relative to Me_2Mg and Et_2Mg (see Figure 10), conclude that the association of Grignard reagents is likely to occur predominantly through the halogen. They further point out that the observed degrees of association sometimes continue to increase well past the dimer stage, and that trimers or linearly associated species have to be considered. In this connection the behaviour of phenylmagnesium bromide is particularly striking, and of the structures 2.1 and 2.2, Ashby and Walker prefer the latter on the basis that magnesium halides and Grignard compounds hold *one* molecule of ether tightly per magnesium atom. Ashby prefers the symmetrical type of structure

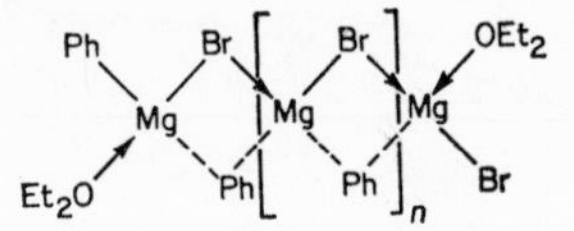

2.1

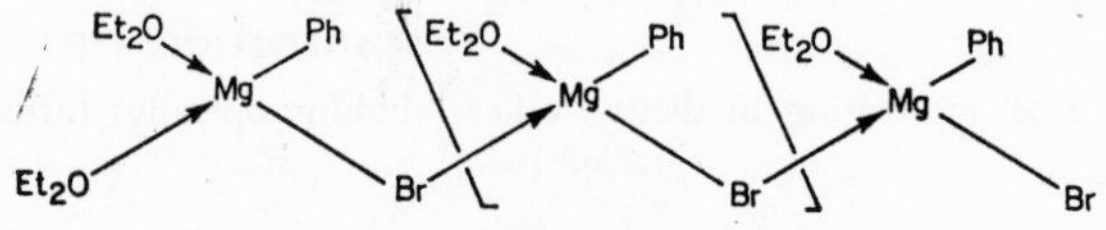

2.2

$(Et_2O)RMgX_2MgR(OEt_2)$ to the unsymmetrical $R_2MgX_2Mg(OEt_2)_2$ for the dimeric forms of Grignard reagents.

If triethylamine, a still stronger base, is added to ethylmagnesium bromide in diethyl ether, then a crystalline complex, $EtMgBr(NEt_3)_2$, can be isolated in high yield. This loses one mole of triethylamine under reduced pressure. The same complex can be obtained directly from magnesium, ethyl bromide, and triethylamine; it is monomeric in triethyla-

[66] G. E. Coates and J. A. Heslop, unpublished observation.

mine solution. The mono-amine complex is a dimer in benzene solution, $[Et(Et_3N)MgBr]_2$, and presumably contains a $MgBr_2Mg$ bridge [67].

In general, Grignard reagents could be regarded as mixtures involving the equilibria

together with small proportions of ionized species, and also of species more associated than dimeric. The nature of the equilibrium and the predominant species would vary with R, the halogen X, and the solvent, the more basic (strongly donor) solvents favouring monomeric species. The concentration and temperature of the solution also affect the equilibrium. All species should be assumed to contain magnesium atoms in at least a four-co-ordinate state in basic solvents.

The use of proton magnetic resonance spectra to demonstrate the rapid exchange of alkyl groups bound to magnesium and some other metals has already been mentioned. The actual τ value for dimethylmagnesium in diethyl ether [68] is 11·40, the rather high degree of diamagnetic shielding of the CH_3–Mg protons being consistent with a high degree of carbanion character for the methyl group due to the considerable polarity of the Mg–C bond. The τ values for methylberyllium protons are similar, and an even higher value (11·90) has been observed for methyl-lithium in diethyl ether [68].

A study of the proton magnetic resonance spectra of several Grignard reagents, with particular respect to temperature dependence, suggests that none of the species R_2Mg, $RMgX$, MgX_2 or complexes between these can have any prolonged separate existence in solution [69]. The exchange of pentafluorophenyl groups is slower, however, and ^{19}F resonances due to $(C_6F_5)_2Mg$ units and C_6F_5Mg units can be distinguished in an ethereal solution of C_6F_5MgBr. As the solution is heated from room temperature to 94°, the resonances due to *para* fluorine atoms coalesce to a single triplet [70].

The problem of isomerization of *allylic* Grignard reagents has also been studied by magnetic resonance methods [71]. The α and γ protons of

[67] E. C. Ashby, *J. Amer. Chem. Soc.*, 1965, **87**, 2509, and a personal communication.

[68] T. L. Brown, R. L. Gerteis, D. A. Bafus and J. A. Ladd, *J. Amer. Chem. Soc.*, 1964, **86**, 2135.

[69] G. M. Whitesides and J. D. Roberts, ibid., 1965, **87**, 4878.

[70] D. F. Evans and M. S. Khan, *Chem. Comm.*, 1966, 67.

[71] J. E. Nordlander and J. D. Roberts, *J. Amer. Chem. Soc.*, 1959, **81**, 1769; J. E. Nordlander, W. G. Young and J. D. Roberts, ibid., 1961, **83**, 494; G. M. Whitesides, J. E. Nordlander and J. D. Roberts, ibid., 1962, **84**, 2010; *Discuss. Faraday Soc.*, 1962, **34**, 185.

allylmagnesium bromide occupy magnetically equivalent positions, and the exchange.

$$BrMgCH_2—CH=CH_2 \rightleftharpoons CH_2=CH—CH_2MgBr$$

is rapid. The Grignard reagent $Me_2C:CH\cdot CH_2MgBr$ is mainly in this form, and conversion to $Me_2C(MgBr)\cdot CH:CH_2$ and back again is slow below $-40°$ but rapid at room temperature. The symmetrical structure is excluded.

It is of interest to note that the use of sublimed magnesium was necessary in this work, to avoid the broadening of resonances by the paramagnetic impurities commonly present.

Reactions

Discussion of the very numerous applications of Grignard reagents to organic synthesis is quite beyond the scope of this book, and the reader is referred to the compilation of Grignard reactions by Yoffe and Nesmeyanov [72], and the critical review by Kharasch and Reinmuth [73]. Carbon atoms bound to a rather electropositive metal such as magnesium have a pronounced nucleophilic character, and most reactions of Grignard reagents are intelligible on the basis of attack of the nucleophilic carbon atoms on the most positive part of the reactant, e.g.

It is worth noting that under the conditions normally used for the determination of active hydrogen by the Zerewitinoff method, methylmagnesium iodide reacts with only one of the two hydrogen atoms of water [74].

There have been many studies on the kinetics of Grignard reactions, and no really clear picture has yet emerged. Much attention has naturally been directed to reactions between Grignard reagents and organic compounds containing groups such as carbonyl and cyanide, but many of these reactions are complicated by the separation of solid matter when carried out in diethyl ether. Bikales and Becker [75] have pointed out the advan-

[72] S. T. Yoffe and A. N. Nesmeyanov, *Handbook of Magnesium-Organic Compounds*, 3 vols., Pergamon Press, London, 1957.

[73] M. S. Kharasch and O. Reinmuth, *Grignard Reactions of Non-Metallic Substances*, Constable & Co., London, 1954.

[74] D. L. Klass and W. N. Jensen, *J. Org. Chem.*, 1961, **26**, 2110.

[75] N. M. Bikales and E. I. Becker, *Canad. J. Chem.*, 1963, **41**, 1329.

tages of using tetrahydrofuran as a solvent for such kinetic studies, since the reaction mixture commonly remains homogeneous.

Here it is feasible to refer only to a few of the results of kinetic studies. The reactions between methylmagnesium halides and trimethylsilyl halides in diethyl ether are first order with respect to each reactant, until a second liquid phase separates [76]. The reaction rates and activation energies do not vary to any great extent for different combinations of halogen, nor when $ClCH_2 \cdot SiMe_2 \cdot Cl$ is substituted for Me_3SiCl. The reaction is considered to take place by the rearrangement of the co-ordination complex 2.3 via the cyclic transition state 2.4, co-ordinated ether

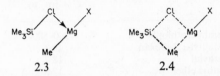

2.3   2.4

being omitted from the formulae. This somewhat resembles the rearrangement proposed by Swain [77] for the second-order (homogeneous) reaction between cyanides and Grignard reagents. A later study [78] of the reaction between benzonitrile and both diethylmagnesium and ethylmagnesium bromide in tetrahydrofuran revealed various complications. Only half of the ethyl groups react at all, and the rate constant of the reaction with Et_2Mg changes considerably when the reaction is one-third complete. Solutions of diethylmagnesium in tetrahydrofuran were shown to contain some $(Et_2Mg)_2$ in equilibrium with Et_2Mg monomer, and the observed kinetics were interpreted in terms of the formation of a complex 2.5, the

$$
\begin{array}{c}
Et \\
| \\
Mg \\
Et \diagup \quad \diagdown Et \\
| \qquad\qquad | \\
Ph \diagdown C^{+} \!\!=\!\! N \diagdown Mg^{-} \diagdown Et \\
\end{array}
$$

2.5

rate-determining step being the rearrangement of this by transfer of an ethyl group to the positive carbon atom. The second and slower stage is then the reaction between the rearranged 2.5 and a further molecule of benzonitrile.

The rates of reaction between diethylmagnesium and *para*-substituted benzonitriles [79] are much affected by the electronic character of the substituent, in the sense that electron-withdrawing groups such as Cl and CF_3 increase the rate, an effect attributed to faster rearrangements of intermediates of type 2.5 due to increased positive charge on the azomethine

[76] A. F. Reid and C. J. Wilkins, *J. Chem. Soc.*, 1955, 4029.
[77] C. G. Swain, *J. Amer. Chem. Soc.*, 1947, **69**, 2306.
[78] S. J. Storfer and E. I. Becker, *J. Org. Chem.*, 1962, **27**, 1868.
[79] J. D. Citron and E. I. Becker, *Canad. J. Chem.*, 1963, **41**, 1260.

carbon atom. It could also be claimed that electron-withdrawing groups would destabilize intermediates of the type 2.5 thus reducing its concentration at equilibrium. Presumably, however, the first effect predominates.

The effect of the solvent [80] on the second order rate constant, k, for the fast initial part of the reaction between ethylmagnesium bromide and benzonitrile is shown in Table 6. If, as is commonly believed, the first step

Table 6   *Effect of solvent on the EtMgBr + PhCN reaction*

Solvent	Initial rate constant, $k \times 10^4$, 30°
Tetrahydrothiophen	240–500
4-Methyl-1,3-dioxan	19·3
Methylal	18·7
Diethyl ether	17·8
Tetrahydrofuran	3·65
'Diglyme'	0·483

in this Grignard reaction is displacement of a solvent molecule by reactant, even though this may not be the main rate-controlling step, the greater energy needed to displace the more basic solvent could result in a lower equilibrium concentration of intermediates such as 2.5, and hence a lower reaction rate.

Grignard reactions with ketones are much faster than with nitriles and reproducible results have been achieved only recently, by the use of tetrahydrofuran as solvent giving homogeneous reaction mixtures, and by following the concentration of the ketone (benzophenone) spectrophotometrically [81]. The reactions between benzophenone and either dimethylmagnesium or methylmagnesium bromide are quite complicated. Initial reaction rates with dimethylmagnesium are about twice as great as with methylmagnesium bromide. The activation energy for the MeMgBr–Ph₂CO reaction is about 11 kcal. mole^{-1}, and the entropy of activation about −25 e.u. at 25°. Benzophenone reacts about 6000 times faster than benzonitrile with methylmagnesium bromide in tetrahydrofuran.

The reaction is first order in benzophenone and in magnesium (i.e. total gram-atoms Mg per litre), at least in the early stages of the reaction, but the specific rate falls by a factor of at least 85 when half of the (hydrolysable) methyl is consumed. The rate is also very considerably retarded by added magnesium bromide. If the extent of dimerization of methylmagnesium bromide in tetrahydrofuran is small, then the reaction would

[80] E. I. Becker, *Trans. New York Acad. Sci.*, 1963, **25**, 513; see also A. A. Scala and E. I. Becker, *J. Org. Chem.*, 1965, **30**, 3491.
[81] N. M. Bikales and E. I. Becker, *Canad. J. Chem.*, 1963, **41**, 1329.

be second order in magnesium if the rate-controlling step involves dimer, and first order if it involves monomer. The molecular weight measurements of Ashby on ethylmagnesium halides, and of Storfer and Becker on diethylmagnesium, suggest at least that very substantial proportions of monomer are present at the concentrations used in the kinetic experiments. The kinetic experiments of Bikales and Becker do not seem inconsistent with a rate-controlling step involving Ph_2CO and monomeric $MeMgBr$, at least in the initial stages of the reaction. These authors, however, prefer a scheme whereby an initial reaction

$$Ph_2CO + (MeMgBr)_2 \rightarrow Ph_2MeC \cdot O \cdot Mg_2Br_2Me$$

is followed by a slower step,

$$Ph_2MeC \cdot O \cdot Mg_2Br_2Me + Ph_2CO \rightarrow [Ph_2MeC \cdot O]_2Mg_2Br_2$$

The retarding effect of bromide remains to be explained. The effect of variation of the halide on the course of reaction with ketones has been discussed [82]. It is important to bear in mind, when considering possible mechanisms of Grignard reactions, that the species involved in the rate-determining step may not be the most abundant species in solution.

Considerable progress has been made in the elucidation of the mechanism of the reaction between benzophenone and methylmagnesium bromide in dilute ether solution [82a], and the mechanism which is now suggested is similar to that proposed by Swain several years ago [82b]. The first step is the reversible formation of a ketone–Grignard complex:

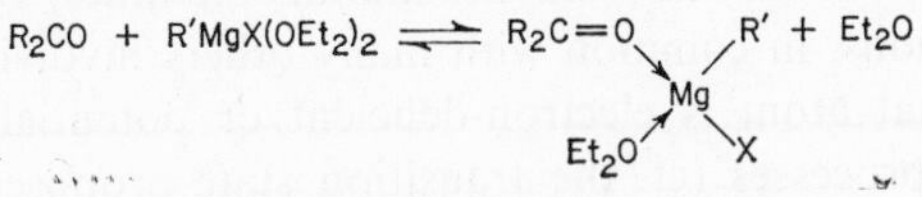

This is followed by the rate-determining irreversible step in which the complex reacts with another molecule of Grignard:

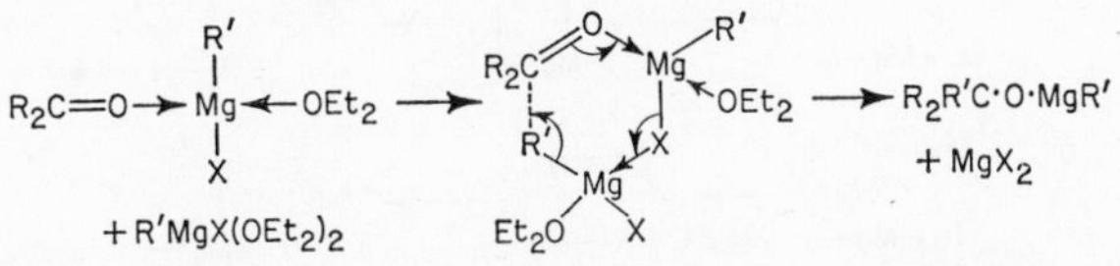

The final step in Swain's mechanism is reaction between the alkylmagnesium alkoxide and magnesium halide, regenerating Grignard reagent:

$$R_2R'C \cdot O \cdot MgR' + MgX_2 \rightleftharpoons R_2R'C \cdot O \cdot MgX + R'MgX$$

[82] J. Miller, G. Gregoriou and H. S. Mosher, *J. Amer. Chem. Soc.*, 1961, **83**, 3966; D. O. Cowan and H. S. Mosher, *J. Org. Chem.*, 1962, **27**, 1.

[82a] E. C. Ashby, R. B. Duke and H. M. Neumann, *J. Amer. Chem. Soc.*, 1967, **89**, 1964.

[82b] C. G. Swain and H. B. Boyles, ibid., 1951, **73**, 870.

To account for the drop in reaction rate observed after half of the available alkyl groups in the Grignard reagent have been consumed in reaction with a ketone, it is necessary to assume that the reaction between alkylmagnesium alkoxide and magnesium halide (regenerating Grignard reagent) is slow relative to the other stages of the overall reaction [82a], or that the alkylmagnesium alkoxide reacts slowly with more ketone [60].

Magnesium ti-butoxide bromide diethyl ether complex, which is dimeric

in benzene solution is the final product of the reaction between methylmagnesium bromide and acetone [82c]. This crystallizes readily from diethyl ether: the bridging butoxy oxygen and the *trans* bromine atoms have been confirmed by X-ray analysis [82d].

It has also been confirmed that methylmagnesium t-butoxide reacts with magnesium bromide in ether solution, giving the magnesium bromide t-butoxide, which as been described above, together with methylmagnesium bromide. Magnesium bromide t-butoxide is also formed when magnesium di-t-butoxide, which is insoluble in ether, dissolves in ethereal magnesium bromide [66].

On the basis of a long series of studies [83] on the reactions between Grignard reagents and both 1-alkynes and azomethines, Dessy concludes that these reactions, in common with many others involving compounds in which a metal atom is electron-deficient or potentially so, proceed by four-centre processes (cf. the transition state proposed by Reid and Wilkins [76]).

Many examples of reactions, mostly but not all involving organometallic compounds, considered to take place by four-centre processes

[82c] G. E. Coates and D. Ridley, *Chem. Comm.*, 1966, 560.
[82d] P. T. Moseley and H. M. M. Shearer, personal communication.
[83] R. E. Dessy, J. H. Wotiz and C. A. Hollingsworth, *J. Amer. Chem. Soc.*, 1955, **77**, 103; 1956, **78**, 1221; 1957, **79**, 358; *J. Org. Chem.*, 1955, **20**, 1545; 1956, **21**, 1063; R. E. Dessy and R. M. Salinger, *J. Amer. Chem. Soc.*, 1961, **83**, 3530; *J. Org. Chem.*, 1961, **26**, 3519.

have now accumulated [84]. Ashby, however, rejects the four-centre mechanism at least for reactions with ketones and analogous substances, partly since this mechanism does not account for the very marked rate reduction generally observed after about half the Grignard reagent is used up.

The order of the reaction between ethylmagnesium bromide and 1-hexyne depends on the solvent, being second order in diethyl ether and di-n-butyl ether, of order 2·5 in diethylene glycol dimethyl ether, and third order in tetrahydrofuran [85].

Reference has been made (for example, see Table 6) to the effect of the basicity of the solvent on the rates of Grignard reactions. In reactions between Grignard reagents and the types of reactants so far considered, which have mostly been substances of pronounced basic or electron-donor character, an increase in the basicity of the solvent *diminishes* the reaction rate because the more basic solvent molecules are less easily displaced from magnesium by the reactant. When the reaction may be regarded as involving a nucleophilic displacement, not of a solvent molecule but of some other species, then an increase in basicity of the solvent should *increase* reaction rate since it should increase the carbanion character (and hence the reactivity) of the carbon atom bound to the magnesium. This effect is exemplified by the fact that diethylthallium chloride may be converted to triethylthallium in good yield by means of ethylmagnesium bromide in tetrahydrofuran, but not in diethyl ether [86].

$$\begin{array}{c} \text{Br} \\ | \\ (\text{THF})_2\text{Mg}(\delta+) \\ | \\ \text{CH}_3\cdot\text{CH}_2(\delta-) \end{array} + \begin{array}{c} \text{Et} \\ | \\ \text{Tl}^+ \\ | \\ \text{Et} \end{array} \longrightarrow \text{Et}_3\text{Tl} + (\text{THF})_2\text{MgBr}^+ \xrightarrow{\text{Cl}^-} (\text{THF})_2\text{MgBrCl}$$

The effect of co-ordination on the reactivity of Grignard and similar reagents has been reviewed [86a].

Magnesium dialkyls and diaryls

These have been relatively little studied, in contrast to the attention which the Grignard reagents have received. They may be prepared by the action of R_2Hg on magnesium, the reaction being facilitated by the presence of ether [87]. Magnesium alkyls are also formed by a process somewhat

[84] R. E. Dessy and F. Paulik, *J. Amer. Chem. Soc.*, 1963, **85**, 1812; *J. Chem. Educ.*, 1963, 185.

[85] H. Hashimoto, T. Nakano and H. Okada, *J. Org. Chem.*, 1965, **30**, 1234.

[86] O. Y. Okhlobystin, K. A. Bilevitch and L. I. Zakharkin, *J. Organometal. Chem.*, 1964, **2**, 281.

[86a] O. Y. Okhlobystin, *Uspeckhi Khim.*, 1967, **36**, 34–47.

[87] W. Schlenk, *Ber.*, 1931, **64**, 734; see also D. O. Cowan and H. S. Mosher, *J. Org. Chem.*, 1962, **27**, 1.

similar to one of the new methods for the preparation of aluminium alkyls, namely by allowing olefins to react under pressure at about 100° with magnesium metal in the presence of hydrogen or magnesium hydride, or with magnesium hydride in the presence of ethers and some pre-formed alkyl [88]. Another method, more suitable for laboratory preparations, is the precipitation of the dioxan–magnesium halide complex from Grignard solutions [89]; the dialkyl R_2Mg is left in solution and may be isolated by evaporation of the solvent under reduced pressure. This method, however, does not always yield products which are entirely free from halogen, and if this is a significant consideration the $Mg–R_2Hg$ exchange procedure is to be preferred [82].

The magnesium dialkyls (up to and including butyls) and diaryls are insoluble in hydrocarbons, only one appears to be even slightly volatile, and they generally behave as if they had a polymeric constitution.

Dimethylmagnesium is a white solid which can be sublimed only with difficulty in a good vacuum [90] and very slowly sublimed in a stream of ether vapour (probably as an ether complex). It takes fire in the air and sometimes even in carbon dioxide. Trimethylamine is absorbed reversibly and chelating diamines form crystalline complexes, for example the tetramethylethylenediamine complex, m.p. 96–97°, which is monomeric in benzene solution, and which may readily be sublimed under reduced pressure. The tetramethyl-*o*-phenylenediamine complex, in contrast, loses

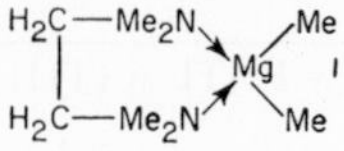

$$H_2C—Me_2N \diagdown \quad \diagup Me$$
$$\qquad\qquad\qquad Mg \quad |$$
$$H_2C—Me_2N \diagup \quad \diagdown Me$$

amine when heated under reduced pressure, leaving a residue of the polymeric dimethylmagnesium [91].

The polymeric structure of dimethylmagnesium has been confirmed by an elegant X-ray diffraction analysis of the material in crystalline powder form [92]. The unit cell and the structure are very similar to those of dimethylberyllium (discussed later in this chapter, p. 105), some comparative dimensions being given opposite:

[88] C. Randaccio, Ital.P. 548, 183; *Chem. Abs.*, 1959, **53**, 4134; H. E. Podall, U.S.P. 2,985,692; *Chem. Abs.*, 1961, **55**, 22133; S. M. Blitzer and T. H. Pearson, U.S.P. 2,959,625; *Chem Abs.*, 1961, **55**, 22134.

[89] A. C. Cope, *J. Amer. Chem. Soc.*, 1935, **57**, 2238; W. Strohmeier, *Ber.*, 1955, **88**, 1218; W. Strohmeier and F. Seifert, *Chem. Ber.*, 1961, **94**, 2356; J. H. Wotiz, C. A. Hollingsworth and R. E. Dessy, *J. Amer. Chem. Soc.*, 1956, **78**, 1221; C. A. Guthrie, E. Y. Spencer and G. F. Wright, *Canad. J. Chem.*, 1957, **35**, 873.

[90] H. Gilman and R. E. Brown, *Rec. Trav. chim.*, 1929, **48**, 1133; 1930, **49**, 724; idem, *J. Amer. Chem. Soc.*, 1930, **52**, 4480, 5045.

[91] G. E. Coates and J. A. Heslop, *J. Chem. Soc.*, A, 1966, 26.

[92] E. Weiss, *J. Organometal. Chem.*, 1964, **2**, 314.

Me$_2$Mg		Me$_2$Be	
Mg—Mg	$2.72_5 \pm 0.02$ Å	Be—Be	2.09 ± 0.01 Å
Mg—C	$2.24_4 \pm 0.03$	Be—C	1.93 ± 0.02
CH$_3$—CH$_3$^{a}	3.57 ± 0.06	CH$_3$—CH$_3$^{a}	3.15
CH$_3$—CH$_3$^{b}	$4.2, 4.4$	CH$_3$—CH$_3$^{b}	4.1
C—Mg—C	$105 \pm 2°$	C—Be—C	$114 \pm 1°$
Mg—C—Mg	$75 \pm 2°$	Be—C—Be	$66 \pm 1°$

^{a} within each four-membered ring
^{b} between neighbouring chains

The only significant difference between the structures of Me$_2$Mg and Me$_2$Be is the rather greater metal–metal distance in the former. However, in view of the different atomic radii of the two metals, there could well be stronger metal–metal interaction in dimethylmagnesium, which quite certainly is less readily depolymerized by heat or by reaction with donor substances than is dimethylberyllium.

Evidence for the formation of complexes Li$_2$MgMe$_4$ and Li$_3$MgMe$_5$ have been obtained from a study of the ^{1}H and ^{7}Li resonance spectra of mixtures of methyllithium and dimethylmagnesium in ether [93].

The solubility of dimethylmagnesium in diethyl ether is only about 0.8 moles per litre (20°) and it crystallizes *solvent-free* from ether [93a], though an etherate may crystallize at −78°. At about 250° dimethylmagnesium decomposes with evolution of methane and formation of spontaneously inflammable 'methylene-magnesium' [94]:

$$[(CH_3)_2Mg]_n \rightarrow [CH_2Mg]_n + nCH_4$$

Diethylmagnesium and higher homologues are also white solids, apparently involatile polymers like dimethylmagnesium, but easily soluble in ether and in some instances just perceptibly volatile in ether vapour [90]. The crystal structure [95] of diethyl- is very similar to that of dimethylmagnesium.

Although dimethylmagnesium is stable at least to 220°, the diethyl and higher homologues decompose readily between 175° and 200° with evolution of olefin leaving a residue of magnesium hydride [96], which is white, involatile, ether-insoluble, and it decomposes to metal and hydrogen at 280–300°. It had been claimed that a side reaction resulted in the formation of ethylenemagnesium, C$_2$H$_4$Mg, described as being sublimable. A butylene analogue, m.p. ca. 60°, was also described. The 'ethylene' compound has been re-examined [97] and shown to be ethylmagnesium

[93] L. M. Seitz and T. L. Brown, *J. Amer. Chem. Soc.*, 1966, **88**, 4140.
[93a] G. E. Coates and J. A. Heslop, unpublished observations.
[94] K. Ziegler, K. Nagel and M. Patheiger, *Z. anorg. Chem.*, 1955, **282**, 345.
[95] E. Weiss, *J. Organometal. Chem.*, 1965, **4**, 101.
[96] E. Wiberg and R. Bauer, *Z. Naturforsch.*, 1950, **5b**, 396, 397.
[97] W. H. Birnkraut, *Inorg. Chem.*, 1963, **2**, 1074; see also D. Bryce-Smith and B. J. Wakefield, *Proc. Chem. Soc.*, 1963, 376.

ethoxide (believed to be a cyclic trimer in diethyl ether solution [98]), the oxygen possibly arising from attack on ether used as solvent during the preparation of diethylmagnesium.

Diethylmagnesium reacts with diborane in ether solution, with formation of magnesium hydride if the diethyl is in excess,

$$3Et_2Mg + B_2H_6 \longrightarrow 3MgH_2 + Et_3B$$

and magnesium borohydride if diborane is in excess,

$$3Et_2Mg + 4B_2H_6 \longrightarrow 3Mg(BH_4)_2 + 2Et_3B$$

The magnesium borohydride is described as a white microcrystalline precipitate [50, 99].

Diethylmagnesium forms a crystalline monoether complex [87], $Et_2Mg \cdot OEt_2$, m.p. $\sim 0°$, which readily loses ether under reduced pressure. The separation of ether from the dialkyls becomes increasingly difficult proceeding from Me_2Me, which crystallizes without ether, through Et_2Mg to the branched-chain alkyls $Pr^i{}_2Mg$ and $Bu^t{}_2Mg$. The difficulty in the latter cases is the rather facile elimination of olefin, leaving hydride.

Dipropyl- and dibutyl-magnesium are insoluble in benzene and are likely to be electron-deficient polymers like the dimethyl and diethyl. Di-n-amylmagnesium [37a], in contrast, dissolves as a dimer in dilute solution in benzene, but its concentrated solutions are described as viscous, indicating a greater degree of association.

Diphenylmagnesium [100], also insoluble in benzene, results when excess magnesium is heated with diphenylmercury in a sealed tube. The reaction goes readily at room temperature when ether is used as a solvent [87], but a low melting ether co-ordination compound is formed, somewhat soluble in benzene [101]. An incomplete X-ray diffraction analysis of the diether complex $Ph_2Mg(OEt_2)_2$ indicates a monomeric structure in the crystalline state [58]. Addition of bipyridyl to an ether solution of diphenylmagnesium gives an orange-yellow precipitate of the co-ordination complex which decomposes within about ten minutes at room temperature [102]. In ether solution diphenylmagnesium reacts reversibly with phenyl-lithium [103] and on addition of xylene a crystalline compound, Li[Ph₃Mg], colourless leaflets dec. 212°, separates:

$$PhLi + Ph_2Mg \rightleftharpoons Li[Ph_3Mg]$$

[98] A. D. Vreugdenhil and C. Blomberg, *Rec. Trav. chim.*, 1965, **84**, 39.

[99] R. Bauer and E. Wiberg, *Z. Naturforsch.*, 1950, **5b**, 397; J. Plešek and S. Heřmánek, *Coll. Czech. Chem. Comm.*, 1966, **31**, 3845.

[100] W. Strohmeier, *Ber.*, 1955, **88**, 1218; H. Gilman and R. E. Brown, *Rec. Trav. chim.*, 1930, **49**, 202; G. Wittig and D. Wittenberg, *Annalen*, 1957, **606**, 15.

[101] S. Hilpert and G. Grüttner, *Ber.*, 1913, **46**, 1679.

[102] G. E. Coates and S. I. E. Green, *J. Chem. Soc.*, 1962, 3340.

[103] G. Wittig, F. J. Meyer and G. Lange, *Annalen*, 1951, **571**, 167.

Diphenylmagnesium alone decomposes about 280° to biphenyl and metallic magnesium [104]. In xylene and in the absence of ether, both diphenylmagnesium and phenylmagnesium bromide cause the *trimerization* of diphenylacetylene to hexaphenylbenzene and its *tetramerization* to *octaphenylcyclo-octatetraene* [105].

Biscyclopentadienylmagnesium, $(C_5H_5)_2Mg$, m.p. 176°, is obtained in good yield when cyclopentadiene is allowed to react with magnesium [106] at 500–600°. It sublimes readily from 100°, and is soluble not only in ethers but also in hydrocarbons. Its structure closely resembles that of ferrocene [107]. It is very reactive to air, moisture, carbon dioxide and carbon disulphide, and yields transition metal cyclopentadienyls on reaction with the corresponding halides [108]. The distribution of charge in the molecule has been in dispute as some authors believe it is a salt [109] and others [110], on the basis of the relatively low intensity of the infrared absorption due to the metal atom vibrating between the parallel rings, believe the charge separation to be much less than corresponds to the formulation $C_5H_5^-Mg^{++}C_5H_5^-$.

Infrared spectra. Absorptions due to magnesium–carbon stretching vibrations have been observed in the range 500–535 cm^{-1} for Me_2Mg, Et_2Mg and the methyl and ethyl Grignard reagents in diethyl ether and in tetrahydrofuran. The corresponding absorption is found between 365 and 383 cm^{-1} for phenylmagnesium compounds [111].

Aminomagnesium alklys [111a] are formed from secondary amines and magnesium dialkyls. For example di-isopropylmagnesium yields a diphenylamino derivative, $Pr^i(Ph_2N)Mg(OEt_2)_2$, which slowly loses ether when dissolved in toluene, and it then precipitates as a polymer in which polymerisation is likely to be propagated both by the nitrogen atoms and by the isopropyl groups. More sterically hindered amines yield dimers containing three-co-ordinate magnesium, examples being $(Pr^iMgNPr^i_2)_2$ and the product formed by addition of diethylmagnesium to benzylideneaniline:

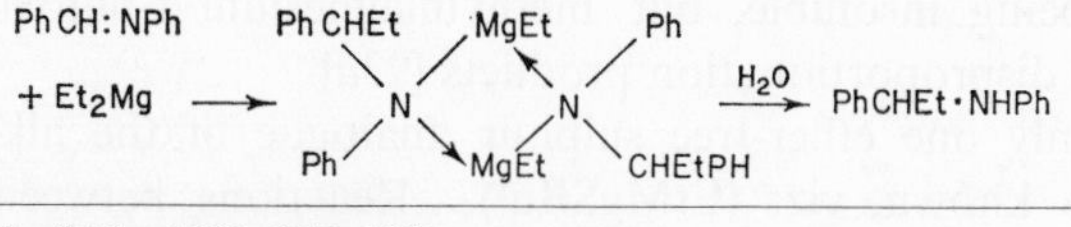

[104] H. Fleck, ibid., 1893, **276**, 138.
[105] H. P. Throndsen and H. Zeiss, *J. Organometal. Chem.*, 1964, **1**, 301.
[106] W. A. Barber, *Inorg. Syntheses*, 1960, **6**, 11.
[107] E. Weiss and E. O. Fischer, *Z. anorg. Chem.*, 1955, **278**, 219.
[108] E. O. Fischer and S. Schreiner, *Chem. Ber.*, 1959, **92**, 938.
[109] G. Wilkinson, F. A. Cotton and J. M. Birmingham, *J. Inorg. Nucl. Chem.*, 1956, **2**, 95; L. Friedman, A. P. Irsa and G. Wilkinson, *J. Amer. Chem. Soc.*, 1955, **77**, 3689; F. A. Cotton and L. T. Reynolds, ibid., 1958, **80**, 269.
[110] E. R. Lippincott, J. Xavier and D. Steele, ibid., 1961, **83**, 2262.
[111] R. M. Salinger and H. S. Mosher, ibid., 1964, **86**, 1782.
[111a] G. E. Coates and D. Ridley, *J. Chem. Soc.*, A, 1967, 56.

Trimethylethylenediamine forms dimeric amino-alkyls on reaction with R_2Mg ($R = Me$, Pr^i, Bu^i) [93a]:

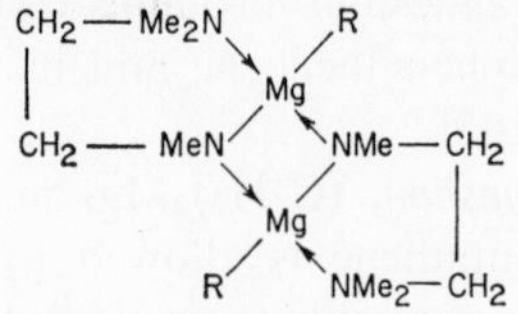

No dimeric alkylmagnesium alkoxides have yet been described. Several alkoxides have been obtained from magnesium and the appropriate alcohol and alkyl chloride in methylcyclohexane:

$$2Bu^nCl + 2Mg + Pr^iOH \rightarrow Bu^nMgOPr^i + MgCl_2 + C_4H_{10}$$

n-Butylmagnesium isopropoxide is an involatile liquid, which is trimeric in benzene [111b]. In a monomeric alkylmagnesium alkoxide each magnesium atom would have at least two vacant co-ordination sites and each oxygen atom has two lone-pairs, so polymer formation is possible. Several alkoxides, prepared from the dialkyl and the alcohol, in which there is chain-branching at the carbon α to oxygen, are tetramers, e.g. $(EtMgOPr^i)_4$, $(EtMgOBu^t)_4$ and $(Pr^iMgOPr^i)_4$, and these may have cubane-type structures similar to that of $(MeZnOMe)_4$ (see p. 135). Higher degrees of association are sometimes found, e.g. $EtMgOPr^n$, Pr^iMgOMe and Pr^iMgOEt are oligomeric in benzene solution [82c]. Ether can be separated from many of the alkylmagnesium alkoxides without great difficulty, indicating that ether and the *second* lone-pair on the alkoxy-oxygen atoms have similar donor character towards magnesium in these compounds. In these circumstances steric effects are significant: whereas $MeMgOBu^t$ is tetrameric in ether and thus unlikely to be complexed with it, $EtMgOCEt_3$ is dimeric and crystallizes as an ether complex which loses ether easily under reduced pressure. Several alkylmagnesium alkoxides are stable in hydrocarbon solution with respect to disproportionation, the alkoxides $Mg(OR)_2$ being insoluble, but methylmagnesium t-butoxide gradually precipitates disproportionation products [93a].

So far only one ether-free sulphur analogue of the alkylmagnesium alkoxides is known, viz. $(EtMgSBu^t)_4$. Reactions between magnesium dialkyls and thiols in ether or tetrahydrofuran yield dimers in which sulphur is co-ordinated to magnesium by only one lone-pair, e.g.

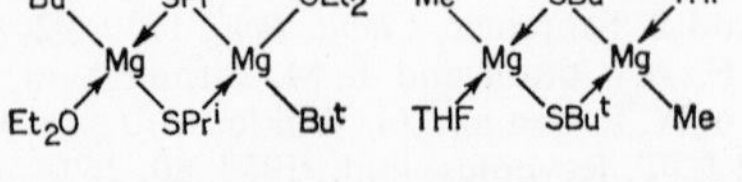

[111b] D. Bryce-Smith and B. J. Wakefield, *Proc. Chem. Soc.*, 1963, 376; D. Bryce-Smith and I. F. Graham, *Chem. Comm.*, 1966, 559; B. J. Wakefield, *Organometallic Chem. Rev.*, 1966, **1**, 131.

One would expect sulphur to be less basic than oxygen towards magnesium, and if ethers compete with the second lone-pair of oxygen in alkoxides for co-ordination positions about magnesium, they would certainly displace the second lone-pair of sulphur in the thio-complexes [93a].

BERYLLIUM

Since beryllium tends to make use of three or, more commonly, four atomic orbitals, many of its organic compounds are electron-deficient polymers or oligomers. Thus in crystalline dimethylberyllium each metal atom is nearly tetrahedrally surrounded by four carbon atoms, as discussed below. Diphenylberyllium may have a polymeric structure, with bridging phenyl groups as in the triphenylaluminium dimer. Though it is only very sparingly soluble in benzene, it is decidedly more soluble than is dimethylberyllium. Most of the dialkyls for which data are available are dimers, and would contain two bridging and two terminal alkyl groups in each molecule, the metal being three-co-ordinate. Di-t-butylberyllium is exceptional in being monomeric, and in containing two-co-ordinate beryllium.

Organoberyllium compounds have been prepared by three methods.

(1) The dialkyls are obtained by the action of the Grignard reagent on beryllium chloride [112].

$$Cl_2Be(OEt)_2)_2 + 2RMgX \longrightarrow R_2Be + MgX_2 + MgCl_2$$

The separation of the product from the reaction mixture presents some difficulties. The dimethyl may be obtained by a process of 'ether distillation' at atmospheric pressure, whereby ether continuously circulates carrying dimethylberyllium from the reaction mixture to a receiver which is kept well above room temperature, excess ether evaporating from the latter and returning to the reaction vessel via a condenser [113]. This method has been slightly modified for larger scale working [114]. The higher alkyls should be distilled from the reaction mixture at reduced pressure at as low a temperature as possible (generally 50–80°) to minimize thermal decomposition. The use of non-ethereal Grignard reagents [114a], or lithium alkyls in hydrocarbons, allows the preparation of ether-free beryllium alkyls directly from beryllium chloride.

(2) Dimethyl- [115], diphenyl- [116, 117] and di-p-tolyl-beryllium [117]

[112] H. Gilman and F. Schulze, *J. Chem. Soc.*, 1927, 2663.
[113] H. Gilman and R. E. Brown, *J. Amer. Chem. Soc.*, 1930, **52**, 4480.
[114] G. B. Wood and A. Brenner, *J. Electrochem. Soc.*, 1957, **104**, 29.
[114a] W. H. Glaze, C. M. Selman and C. H. Freeman, *Chem. Comm,*, 1966, 474.
[115] A. B. Burg and H. I. Schlesinger, *J. Amer. Chem. Soc.*, 1940, **62**, 3425.
[116] G. Wittig and D. Wittenberg, *Annalen*, 1957, **606**, 15.
[117] H. Gilman and F. Schulze, *J. Amer. Chem. Soc.*, 1927, **49**, 2904; F. Schulze, *Iowa State College J. Science*, 1933, **8**, 225.

have been prepared by the action of the corresponding organomercury compound on metallic beryllium:

$$Me_2Hg + Be \longrightarrow Me_2Be + Hg$$

(3) Some alkyl- and aryl-beryllium halides have been obtained in ether solution by heating the metal with the appropriate halide in ether (with a trace of mercury(II) chloride) to about 100° in a sealed tube [117]. Recently [118] the reaction has been carried out without a solvent or catalyst, and 65–70% Bu^nBeI has been obtained from beryllium and Bu^nI at 130° for 12 hours; it is said to be insoluble in the butyl iodide.

Dimethylberyllium, $(Me_2Be)_n$, is conveniently obtained on a small scale ($\sim$1 g.) by the second method ($Be + Me_2Hg$), the reactants being heated to about 100° for a day or two in an inert atmosphere. On a larger scale the Grignard method is more convenient. The fact that dimethyl sulphide does not co-ordinate to dimethylberyllium led to a suggestion [119] that the use of Grignard reagents prepared in that solvent would be a convenient method for obtaining ether-free beryllium alkyls. However, for most purposes ether can be separated adequately from dimethylberyllium by repeated sublimation of the latter at reduced pressure. Ether can be separated from the higher alkyls by the potassium fluoride method (see below), or by prolonged refluxing at 40–50° at ca. 10^{-2} mm.

Dimethylberyllium forms colourless needles when condensed slowly from the vapour; it has not been observed to melt but the vapour pressure [120] of the solid is given by the equations (there is no discontinuity):

$$100\text{–ca. } 150°: \log_{10} P \text{ (mm.)} = 12\cdot53\text{–}4770/T$$
$$\text{ca. } 150\text{–}180°: \log_{10} P \text{ (mm.)} = 13\cdot29\text{–}5100/T$$

Observed vapour pressures are 0·6 mm. at 100°, 5 mm. at 130° and 760 mm. (extrapolated) at 217°. The heat of sublimation is 23·5 kcal./mole of monomer. More recent measurements [121] give 220° as the extrapolated sublimation point and vapour pressure of 1 mm. at 115°, 5 mm. at 125°, 23 mm. at 150°.

X-ray analysis [122] reveals a long-chain polymer, the interchain distances excluding an ionic structure:

Be—C = 1·92Å   Be—C—Be = 66°

[118] L. I. Zakharkin, O. Y. Okhlobystin and B. N. Strunin, *Izvest Akad. Nauk S.S.S.R.*, 1961, 2254; *Chem. Abs.*, 1962, **57**, 13785.

[119] G. Bähr and K. H. Thiele, *Chem. Ber.*, 1957, **90**, 1578.

[120] G. E. Coates, F. Glockling and N. D. Huck, *J. Chem. Soc.*, 1952, 4496.

[121] J. Goubeau and K. Walter, *Z. anorg. Chem.*, 1963, **322**, 58.

[122] A. I. Snow and R. E. Rundle, *Acta Cryst.*, 1951, **4**, 348.

In the above formula dotted lines represent half-bonds [123]. Both beryllium and carbon atoms make use of four tetrahedral (sp^3) atomic orbitals and it is probable that three-centre molecular orbitals $Be(sp^3)$ + $C(sp^3)$ + $Be(sp^3)$ are formed from these. Each of these molecular orbitals would hold two electrons, giving a 'bent bond'; alternatively each Be–C bond may be regarded as a half-bond. The unusual Be–C–Be angle (66°) is small, but this would allow better overlap between the tetrahedral atomic orbitals (the Csp^3 orbital is directed towards a point equidistant between two beryllium atoms, and it may well have rather more than 25% s-character). The C–Be–C angle (114°) is only slightly different from the tetrahedral 109·5°. The Be–C distances (all equal, 1·92 Å) are greater than the calculated value 1·83 Å for a single bond, and support the half-bond formulation.

The vapour of dimethylberyllium does not consist of monomeric molecules only, but is a mixture of monomer, dimer and trimer, with appreciable amounts of higher polymers under near saturation conditions. Structures have been proposed for the first three:

$$CH_3-Be-CH_3 \qquad CH_3-Be\underset{CH_3}{\overset{CH_3}{\diamondsuit}}Be-CH_3$$

Monomer Dimer

$$CH_3-Be\overset{CH_3}{\diamondsuit}Be\overset{CH_3}{\diamondsuit}Be-CH_3$$

Trimer

Thermodynamic data have been calculated from the pressure and temperature dependence of the vapour density [120], and give, *inter alia* the heat and entropy of formation of dimer, trimer, and solid polymer from the monomer. The energy difference between two half-bonds and one whole bond is 9–12 kcal./mole, depending on the degree of polymerization.

The infrared and Raman spectra of solid dimethylberyllium have been studied [121], also the infrared spectrum of both saturated and unsaturated vapour [124]. The C–H stretching frequencies (solid) are rather low, 2912 and 2885 cm^{-1}, a similar effect having been mentioned in connexion with the lithium alkyls (p. 38). Perhaps the most remarkable feature of the spectra is the absence of any significant absorption in the 1400–1500 cm^{-1} region where most compounds absorb strongly on account of asymmetric methyl deformation (δ_{as} CH$_3$). On the other hand the solid has two very strong absorptions at 1243 and 1255 cm^{-1} (and a Raman band at

[123] See chapter by R. E. Rundle in *A Survey of Progress in Chemistry*, Vol. I, Academic Press, 1963.

[124] N. A. Bell and G. E. Coates, unpublished observations.

1255 cm^{-1}) in the region where δ_{sym} CH$_3$ would be expected. In the spectrum of related substances, Me$_6$Al$_2$ and Me$_4$Al$_2$Cl$_2$ [125], absorptions due to δ_{as} CH$_3$ are much weaker than those due to δ_{sym} CH$_3$, and in the infrared spectrum of trimethylgallium [126, 127] there is a very strong absorption due to δ_{sym} CH$_3$ and no significant absorption due to the asymmetric mode. The unsaturated vapour of dimethylberyllium, which consists mainly of monomer, has a fairly simple infrared spectrum in the range 650-2000 cm^{-1}: δ_{sym} CH$_3$ appears at 1262 cm^{-1}, methyl rocking modes at 1086, 1032 and 816 cm^{-1}. The spectrum of the saturated vapour is much more complex, since dimer and trimer molecules are present and monomer is not even the most abundant species (below 180°). There is absorption due to δ_{as} CH$_3$ at 1481 cm^{-1}, and two absorptions due to δ_{sym} CH$_3$, one at 1259-1264 cm^{-1} being similar to that of the predominantly monomeric unsaturated vapour (1262 cm^{-1}) and attributed to terminal Be–CH$_3$ groups, the other at 1211-1214 cm.$^{-1}$ attributed to bridging methyl groups. As the temperature of the saturated vapour is raised numerous strong absorptions appear in the 700–900 cm^{-1} region, and most of these are doubtless due to methyl rocking vibrations, particularly since Goubeau and Walter found a strong band due to methyl rocking at 835 cm^{-1} in the infrared spectrum of solid dimethylberyllium.

Thermal decomposition of dimethylberyllium sets in quite rapidly above 200°, with formation of methane and (above 217°) some hydrogen. Though beryllium carbide, Be$_2$C, is the ultimate product, together with a little carbon, a polymeric intermediate, (BeCH$_2$)$_n$, which is hydrolysed by water with formation of methane, can be obtained [121].

Dimethylberyllium is hydrolysed by liquid water with explosive violence, and for analytical purposes methanol, 2-methoxyethanol and trimethylamine have been used, followed by water and aqueous acid. It takes fire in the air giving very toxic beryllia fumes, and has been reported to inflame in carbon dioxide. Slow reaction with carbon dioxide, in ether solution, gives acetic acid (after acid hydrolysis). Dimethylberyllium undergoes several reactions similar to those of Grignard reagents, but it appears to be somewhat less reactive; for example, it gives Ph$_2$MeC·OH with benzophenone, PhMe$_2$C·OH with benzoyl chloride, and PhNH·CO·Me with phenyl isocyanate [117]. Oxidation in diethyl ether with molecular oxygen yields the insoluble dimethoxide containing varying amounts of peroxidic oxygen [128].

Diethylberyllium may be obtained from ethylmagnesium bromide and ethereal beryllium chloride [129], though the use of ethyl-lithium results in

[125] E. G. Hoffmann, Z. *Elektrochem.*, 1960, **64**, 616.
[126] G. E. Coates and R. N. Mukherjee, *J. Chem. Soc.*, 1964, 1295.
[127] G. E. Coates and A. J. Downs, ibid., p. 3353.
[128] R. Masthoff, Z. *anorg. chem.*, 1965, **336**, 252.
[129] J. Goubeau and B. Rodewald, ibid., 1949, **258**, 162; G. Scheibe, F. Baumgärtner and M. Genzer, *Angew. Chem.*, 1955, **67**, 512.

an easier separation of product. Prolonged pumping followed by vacuum distillation gives a product containing only 2% of ether and boiling at $63°/0.3$ mm. The vapour pressure of this material is given (approximately) by the equation: $\log_{10} P$ (mm.) $= 7.59-2200/T$ whence the extrapolated boiling point is $194°$ and the latent heat of vaporization 10.0 kcal./mole. The low vapour pressure indicates association, and oligomers with electron-deficient bonding are doubtless present. The degree of association of diethylberyllium in cyclohexane and in benzene gradually increases from just over two shortly after the solutions have been prepared to just over three after eight months [130]. This result is surprising in view of the dimeric character of many other beryllium alkyls, and it is conceivable that some oxidation took place during this lengthy experiment giving some tetrameric ethylberyllium ethoxide. Diethylberyllium is not polymeric like Me_2Be, Me_2Mg and Et_2Mg. since in the latter there is already considerable steric interference between methylene groups of one bridge and methyl groups of the adjacent bridge. Since the radius of beryllium is less than that of magnesium, such interaction prevents the formation of Et_2Be polymer [95]. From $85°$ a complicated thermal decomposition, rapid at $190-200°$, results in the formation of ethane, ethylene and butene in approx. ratio $2 : 1 : 1.5$, together with small amounts of 3-hexene, 1,3-hexadiene and benzene; the residue, which gives much hydrogen with ethane and ethylene on hydrolysis, is a viscous oil and must be a derivative of beryllium hydride of unknown constitution.

Diethylberyllium reacts explosively with water, and vigorously with hydrogen chloride and with alcohols. It reacts slowly with olefins, for example [131],

$$Et_2Be + MePr^nC{:}CH_2 \longrightarrow MeEtPr^nCCH_2BeEt$$

though there is no reason to believe the product is a single compound: alkyl exchange is likely to be rapid.

Di-isopropylberyllium [132], $[(Me_2CH)_2Be]_2$, has been prepared by the Grignard method as a colourless liquid from which ether can be separated only by prolonged reflux with continuous pumping; the ether-free di-isopropyl melts at $-9.5°$. It is soluble in benzene in which it is dimeric (tensimetrically). Its vapour pressure is 0.17 mm. at $20°$. From about $50°$, and rapidly at $200°$, it evolves propene giving the viscous involatile polymer, propylberyllium hydride (probably a mixture of normal and isopropyl):

$$\frac{x}{2}Pr^i_4Be_2 \longrightarrow \frac{1}{x}(PrBeH)_x + xC_3H_6$$

[130] W. Strohmeier, K. Humpfner, K. Miltenberger and F. Seifert, *Z. Elektrochemie*, 1959, **63**, 537.

[131] K. Ziegler, Brit. P. 763,824 (1956); *Chem. Abs.*, 1958, **52**, 1203.

[132] G. E. Coates and F. Glockling, *J. Chem. Soc.*, 1954, 22.

The optically active *di-(2-methylbutyl)beryllium*, which is also dimeric in benzene, racemizes faster than the corresponding aluminium and boron compounds (Be > Al > B) and its racemization is believed to be due to the reversible formation of the alkylberyllium hydride and the olefin [133].

Di-n-butyl- (114*a*, 117] and di-isobutyl-beryllium [133*a*] are both dimeric in benzene, the latter being easily separated from ether by reflux at 40–50° in vacuum.

Di-tert-butylberyllium [134], $(Me_3C)_2Be$, from tert-butylmagnesium chloride and beryllium chloride, decomposes even more readily than the di-isopropyl, with evolution of isobutene and can only be kept satisfactorily at a low temperature. It has been obtained free from ether [135] by treatment of the ether-containing product from the Grignard preparation with anhydrous beryllium chloride, which has a higher affinity for ether. The ether-free material is considerably more volatile than the ether complex; its density is about 0·65 g./c.c. and its freezing point −16°. Its vapour pressure, 35 mm. at 25°, is comparable with that of a branched-chain C_9 hydrocarbon. Its monomeric character is also apparent from its infrared and Raman spectrum, and from the spectra of $(C_4D_9)_2Be$ [136], so these and the silazane compound $[(Me_3Si)_2N]_2Be$ [137] are the only examples of beryllium forming a compound at room temperature in what is often regarded as its normal (i.e. *sp*) valency state:

$$Me_3C—Be—CMe_3$$

The structure of di-tert-butylberyllium has been determined by electron diffraction of the vapour [137*a*]. The angles CBeC and BeCC are 180° and 110·5° respectively, and the bond lengths are Be–C, 1·699 + 0·004 Å, and C–C, 1·550 ± 0·002 Å. The minimum energy conformation appears to be eclipsed, but the barrier to internal rotation is about 0·6 kcal. or less. Pyrolysis results in the formation of *two* moles of isobutene, the residue being mainly *beryllium hydride*:

$$(Me_3C)_2Be \longrightarrow BeH_2 + 2CH_2:CMe_2$$

Diphenylberyllium [138], Ph_2Be, m.p. 244–248° (decomp.), is prepared from diphenylmercury and beryllium by heating the mixture at 210–220° for 1–2 hours, and subsequent crystallization from benzene. It is more soluble in ether and in tetrahydrofuran than in benzene or xylene, and dis-

[133] L. Lardicci, L. Lucarini, P. Palagi and P. Pino, *J. Organometal. Chem.*, 1965, **4**, 341.

[133*a*] G. E. Coates and P. D. Roberts, unpublished observations.

[134] G. E. Coates and F. Glockling, *J. Chem. Soc.*, 1954, 2526.

[135] E. L. Head, C. E. Holley and S. W. Rabideau, *J. Amer. Chem. Soc.*, 1957, **79**, 3687.

[136] G. E. Coates, A. J. Downs and P. D. Roberts, *J. Chem. Soc.*, A, 1967, 1085.

[137] H. Bürger, C. Forker and J. Goubeau, *Monatsheft*, 1965, **96**, 597.

[137*a*] A. Haaland, personal communication.

[138] G. Wittig and D. Wittenberg, *Annalen*, 1957, **606**, 15; W. Strohmeier and K. Humpfner, *Z. Elektrochemie*, 1956, **60**, 111.

solves in the former solvents with heat evolution. A diether co-ordination complex $Ph_2Be(OEt_2)_2$, m.p. 28–32°, has been crystallized from the ether solution [139]. In accordance with the greater electronegativity of the phenyl group, diphenylberyllium co-ordinates with ether more strongly than does dimethylberyllium, and the ether complex has a dissociation pressure of 15–16 mm. at 0°. The complexes Ph_2BeNMe_3, Ph_2BeOEt_2 and $Ph_2Be(SMe_2)_2$ have negligible dissociation pressures at 0° [140].

Biscyclopentadienylberyllium, $(C_5H_5)_2Be$, has been prepared from cyclopentadienylsodium and beryllium chloride in diethyl ether (it reacts with tetrahydrofuran) [141]. It is separated from the reaction mixture, after removal of solvent, by sublimation in vacuum, and forms colourless air-sensitive crystals, m.p. 59–60°, extrapolated b.p. 233°. Its crystal structure [142] is similar to that of ferrocene. In benzene solution it is monomeric but has a dipole moment of $2·46 \pm 0·06$ D ($2·24 \pm 0·09$ in cyclohexane) suggesting a bent structure. The electron diffraction of the vapour, however, has revealed a sandwich structure rather similar to that of the crystalline material; the two C_5H_5 rings are planar, parallel and staggered (as opposed to eclipsed) and are $3·37 \pm 0·03$ Å apart. The most remarkable feature of the electron diffraction result is the conclusion that the metal atom may occupy two alternative positions on the fivefold rotation axis about 1·5 Å from the plane of one ring and about 2·0 Å from that of the other, thus the potential energy curve for the beryllium atom along this axis must have two minima. The need to assume a bent structure for the molecules in solution disappears, since the observed dipole moment may be explained even on the basis of a charge of only $+0·25e$ on the beryllium atom. The charge on the metal atom is considered to be rather larger than this, and the bonding is regarded as largely electrostatic. Since the metal atom is relatively small, the ring–ring distance is determined mainly by repulsion between electrons in the ring π orbitals, and the energetically most favourable position for the metal atom is, on a purely electrostatic basis, about 2 to 5 kcal. mole^{-1} below the energy of the symmetrical molecule. The apparently centrosymmetric structure of the crystalline phase is regarded as due to a random distribution of beryllium atoms between the two positions of minimum potential energy [143]. For a discussion of the infrared spectrum of $(C_5H_5)_2Be$, see [143a]. Aromatic solvents complex $(C_5H_5)_2Be$ strongly enough to induce paramagnetism [143b].

[139] G. Wittig and P. Hornberger, *Annalen*, 1952, **577**, 11.

[140] G. E. Coates and M. Tranah, *J. Chem. Soc.*, A, 1967, 236.

[141] E. O. Fischer and H. P. Hofmann, *Chem. Ber.*, 1959, **92**, 482; see also H. P. Fritz and S. Schneider, ibid., 1960, **93**, 1171.

[142] R. Schneider and E. O. Fischer, *Naturwiss.*, 1963, **50**, 349.

[143] A. Almenningen, O. Bastiansen and A. Haaland, *J. Chem. Phys.*, 1964, **40**, 3434.

[143a] H. P. Fritz and D. Sellmann, *J. Organometal. Chem.*, 1966, **5**, 501.

[143b] G. L. Morgan and G. B. McVicker, 153rd ACS Meeting, Miami, April 1967.

Co-ordination complexes

The most typical reaction of electron-deficient molecules is relief of the electron deficiency by co-ordination with donor molecules, and it is probable that reactions with oxygen, water, carbon dioxide and most reagents involve co-ordination as a first step. At present only those co-ordination complexes that may be isolated are considered, and these are conveniently classified in five groups, (a) complexes with monodentate ligands, (b) chelate complexes, (c) products of reaction with donor substances containing reactive hydrogen, (d) anionic, (e) spiro complexes.

(a) Complexes with monodentate ligands

Those of dimethylberyllium have been studied most, and only molecules with relatively strong donor properties combine with dimethylberyllium [144], since the heat of co-ordination must considerably exceed the heat of polymerization of dimethylberyllium (or the polymeric structure cannot be broken down). With trimethylamine a volatile compound $Me_2Be \cdot NMe_3$ is formed (m.p. 36°, v.p. 4 mm. at 36°); the vapour is monomeric. Tensimetric titration [145] of Me_2BeNMe_3 with trimethylamine at 0° indicates the formation of an unstable complex $Me_2Be(NMe_3)_2$ whose dissociation pressure is 22·7 mm. at 0°.

Whereas trimethylamine co-ordinates so strongly that it is able to break down the polymeric structure of dimethylberyllium without difficulty, this is not true of the somewhat weaker donor, trimethylphosphine. Complex equilibria result from the similarity between the affinities of dimethylberyllium molecules for trimethylphosphine and for each other; if a bulb containing a little dimethylberyllium and about four or five molar proportions of trimethylphosphine is slowly heated from 0° to 150° a remarkable series of phase changes may be seen. As the temperature increases the condensed phase alternately melts and freezes, perhaps five or six times, until only solid dimethylberyllium is left. The suggested explanation is the successive formation of compounds of increasing chain length, trimethylphosphine acting as a chain-ending group:

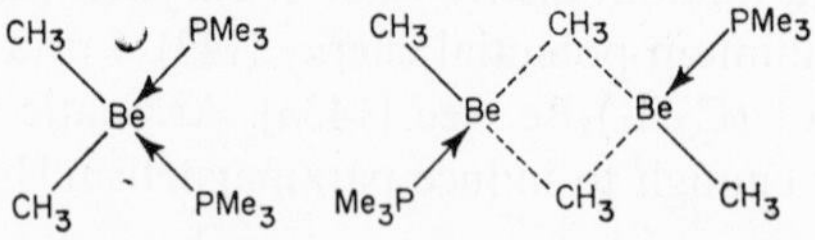

Dimethyl and diethyl ether also co-ordinate to dimethylberyllium and are good solvents for it, though the dissociation pressures of the complexes formed are in the 100–300 mm. range at room temperature. Neither trimethylarsine nor dimethylsulphide are sufficiently strong donors to break

[144] G. E. Coates and N. D. Huck, *J. Chem. Soc.*, 1952, 4501.
[145] N. A. Bell and G. E. Coates, *Canad. J. Chem.*, 1966, **44**, 744.

down the dimethylberyllium polymer, thus they form no co-ordination complexes with it. However, as mentioned earlier, di*phenyl*beryllium forms a bisdimethylsulphide complex.

Pyridine appears to act as a stronger donor than trimethylamine towards dimethylberyllium since it forms a colourless bis-complex, Me_2py_2Be, m.p. 91–92° to a yellow liquid. Similarly, though diethylberyllium forms a stable mono-trimethylamine complex, liquid at room temperature (also $Pr^i_2Be \cdot NMe_3$), and adds a second mole of amine only at low temperature [146], with pyridine it gives an orange-yellow complex Et_2py_2Be which is monomeric in benzene. With tetramethylhydrazine, diethylberyllium forms a complex $(Et_2Be)_2Me_4N_2$, m.p. 84–87° [147], in contrast to the fission of the O–O and S–S bond brought about by reaction of, for example, $Bu^tO \cdot OBu^t$ with Me_2Be giving $[MeBeOBu^t]_4$ and $EtS \cdot SEt$ with Et_2Be giving $[EtBeSEt]_4$.

The trimethylamine complex of di-t-butylberyllium, $Bu^t_2BeNMe_3$, m.p. 45–46°, is of some interest since it is iso-electronic with tri-t-butylborane, whose preparation has caused some difficulty. The relatively high melting point of the beryllium complex reflects its high degree of symmetry, since the trimethylamine and t-butyl groups are similar in size and shape [133a].

(b) Chelate complexes [148]

In contrast to the unstable complexes formed by dimethylberyllium and, for example, dimethyl ether, whose dissociation pressures are well over 100 mm. at room temperature, the chelating diether 1,2-dimethoxyethane forms a crystalline complex 2.6, m.p. 100–101°, which may be sublimed at 60–70°/ca. 0·2 mm.

2.6   2.7

Tetramethylethylenediamine similarly forms a complex, 2.7, m.p. 81–82°. Similar monomeric complexes are formed by various other beryllium alkyls. All are monomeric in benzene, but a model of the di-t-butyl compound shows that there is no room around the metal atom for both t-butyl groups and both nitrogen atoms. The proton magnetic resonance spectrum of this complex is consistent with a constitution in which only one nitrogen is co-ordinated at a time, but in which rapid exchange takes place between complexed and uncomplexed nitrogen. Due to this exchange, the spectrum is simple at room temperature but a distinction

[146] F. M. Peters, *J. Organometal. Chem.*, 1965, **3**, 334.
[147] N. R. Fetter, *Canad. J. Chem.*, 1964, **42**, 861.
[148] G. E. Coates and S. I. E. Green, *J. Chem. Soc.*, 1962, 3340.

between complexed and uncomplexed nitrogen is apparent below $-25°$ as the exchange becomes slow [133a, 148a]. In contrast the proton magnetic resonance spectrum of the tetramethylethylenediamine complex of di-t-butyl*magnesium* is temperature-independent [93a], since the metal atom is big enough to accommodate all four ligands.

Bipyridyl forms 1 : 1 complexes with beryllium alkyls and aryls, R_2bipyBe, distinguished by bright colours (e.g. R = Me, yellow; Et, red; Ph, yellow; p-$Me_2N \cdot C_6H_4$, orange), and greatly reduced reactivity to air and moisture. The absorption spectra of some of these complexes are shown in Figure 11, and it is evident that both λ_{max} and the extinction

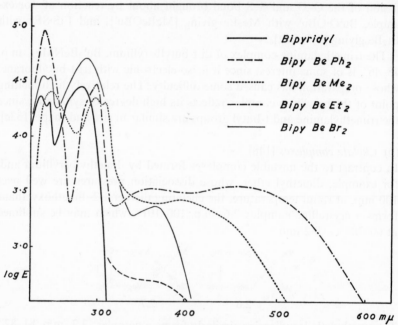

Fig. 11. Absorption spectra of organoberyllium bipyridyl complexes (after Coates and Green [148])

coefficients decrease as the electron-attracting character of the organic group increases. All the complexes have high intensity bands in the 220–300 mμ region, similar to those of free bipyridyl, but it is suggested that the absorptions at longer wavelengths causing visible colour are due to charge-transfer transitions in which light absorption causes the transfer of an electron from a Be–C bond to the lowest unoccupied π orbital of the bipyridyl. In the excited state the Be–C bond would become a half-bond.

These bipyridyl complexes are decomposed after some 10–15 minutes'

[148a] G. E. Coates, *Record Chem. Progress*, 1967, **28**, 3.

exposure to moist air, in contrast to the alkyls themselves which inflame at once.

(c) Products of reaction with donor substances containing reactive hydrogen

(i) *Aminoberyllium alkyls.* Primary and secondary amines form co-ordination complexes with beryllium alkyls, but the adducts readily eliminate alkane [149] unless the hydrogen bound to nitrogen is prevented by steric hindrance from access to the carbon atoms of the reactive alkyl groups. Thus the complex $Me_2Be \cdot NHMe_2$ melts at 44° with evolution of methane and formation of the trimer 2.8, which is a glass at room temperature and softens to a liquid in the range 51–54°. Diethyl- [150] and di-isopropyl- [134] beryllium react with dimethylamine below room temperature, forming $RBeNMe_2$ and finally $Be(NMe_2)_2$. In contrast, t-butyl-beryllium reacts incompletely with dimethylamine, even after many hours [151].

2.8 2.9

Compounds such as 2.8 are of interest since the metal atoms are only three-co-ordinate. Beryllium–nitrogen π bonding is unlikely on account of the disparity between the radial parts of the Be2p and N2p eigenfunctions, but the co-ordinative unsaturation becomes apparent in the formation of adducts with some bases. Thus 2.8 adds pyridine giving first, the dimer 2.9, and then monomeric $py_2Be(NMe_2)Me$. Bipyridyl complexes of the amino-alkyls, e.g. the brick-red $bipyBe(NPh_2)Et$, are likely to owe their colour to charge-transfer effects as mentioned above in connexion with bipyridyl complexes of beryllium alkyls. In the case of the amino-alkyls, the lone-pair on the amino-nitrogen could act as an electron source as well as the beryllium carbon bond.

The degree of association of the aminoberyllium alkyls, $RBeNR'_2$, appears to be determined mainly by steric factors. Cyclic trimers (like 2.8) would be preferred to dimers containing a four-membered Be_2N_2 ring (as in 2.9) on account of the valency angle distortion from 109° to an average of 90° in the dimers. However, as the size of R and R' is increased, steric interference between them becomes serious in trimers before it does in the corresponding dimer. Hence these compounds dissolve as trimers when R and particularly R' are small, and as dimers otherwise. Thus all

[149] G. E. Coates, F. Glockling and N. D. Huck, *J. Chem. Soc.*, 1952, 4512.
[150] N. R. Fetter and F. M. Peters, *Canad. J. Chem.*, 1965, **43**, 1884.
[151] G. E. Coates and A. H. Fishwick, *J. Chem. Soc.*, A. 1967, 1199.

the dimethylaminoberyllium alkyls so far described are trimers, viz. $(MeBeNMe_2)_3$, $(EtBeNMe_2)_3$, $(Pr^iBeNMe_2)_3$ and $(PhBeNMe_2)_3$, whereas the only trimeric diethylamino derivative is $(MeBeNEt_2)_3$. Dimers include $(MeBeNPr^n_2)_2$, $(EtBeNEt_2)_2$, $(MeBeNPh_2)_2$, $(EtBeNPh_2)_2$, $(PhBeNPh_2)_2$ and $[MeBeN(CH_2Ph)Ph]_2$ [151].

The reaction between dimethylberyllium and trimethylethylenediamine gives an adduct 2.10 which eliminates methane at about 18° forming 2.11, m.p. 116–118°

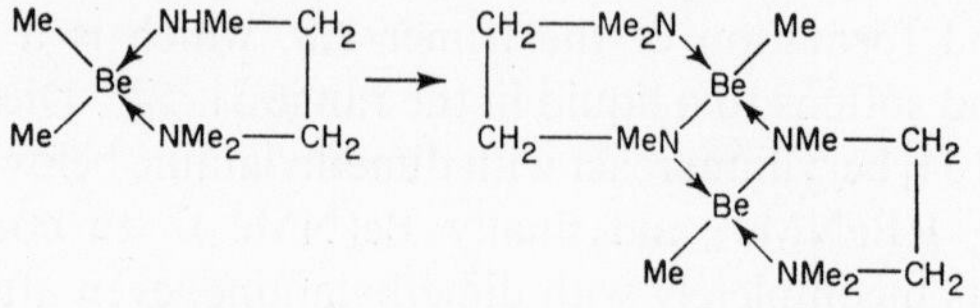

2.10   2.11

Ethylenediamines with two or more reactive hydrogen atoms give polymeric products, for example symmetrical dimethylethylenediamine forms the dimer 2.12, which may be sublimed in vacuum at about 90°, and polymerizes at a higher temperature with evolution of methane [148].

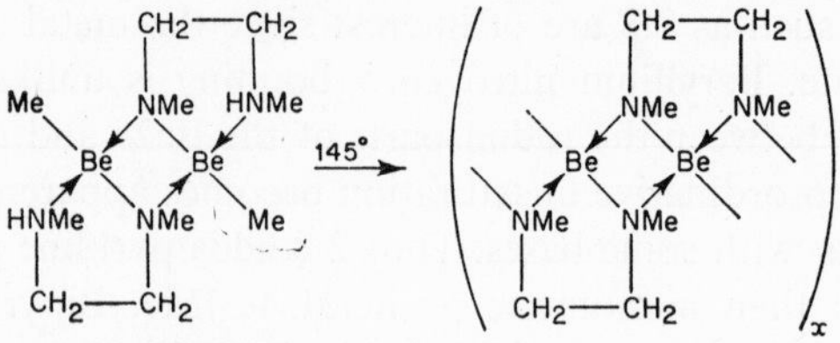

2.12

The trimethylamine complex, Me_2BeNMe_3, reacts with one mole of hydrogen cyanide giving an oligomer which becomes an insoluble polymer when the solvent is removed, $(\rightarrow MeBe(NMe_3)—C\equiv N \rightarrow)_x$. Polymeric material $(MeBeCN)_n$ and $[Be(CN)_2]_x$ is also formed when dimethylberyllium reacts with one or two moles of hydrogen cyanide [152].

(ii) *Alkylberyllium alkoxides* [148a, 152a]. No dialkylberyllium-alcohol adducts have been isolated, and alkane elimination generally takes place rapidly when an alcohol is added to a solution of R_2Be. In contrast, di-t-butylberyllium reacts slowly, doubtless for steric reasons. Most of the alkylberyllium alkoxides are tetrameric, and are likely to have structures similar to that of methylzinc methoxide (p. 135) in which case both metal and oxygen would be four-co-ordinate. Though methylberyllium t-butoxide

[152] G. E. Coates and R. N. Mukherjee, *J. Chem. Soc.*, 1963, 229.
[152a] G. E. Coates and A. H. Fishwick ibid., A, in the press.

crystallizes from ether in unsolvated form, it and several other alkoxides MeBeOR are dimeric in dilute solution in ether. These dimers are likely to contain three-co-ordinate bridging alkoxy oxygen (compare alkylmagnesium alkoxides, p. 102).

Alkylberyllium alkoxides derived from alcohols with relatively large steric requirements differ in two respects. They are commonly dimeric, e.g. $(Bu^tBeOBu^t)_2$ and $(MeBeOCPh_3)_2$, and they sometimes form ether complexes which are monomeric in benzene and thus contain three-co-ordinate beryllium,

The diphenylmethoxide is formed, not only from the dialkyl and the alcohol, but also by addition of methylberyllium hydride to benzophenone [162].

Several alkylberyllium alkoxides can be obtained by more than one route. Methylberyllium n-propoxide results from dimethylberyllium and n-propanol or ethylene oxide:

$$Me_2Be + Pr^nOH \rightarrow (MeBeOPr^n)_4 \leftarrow Me_2Be + \underset{O}{\overset{CH_2-CH_2}{\diagdown\diagup}}$$

Similarly, methylberyllium isopropoxide results from addition of CH_3-Be across the carbonyl group in acetaldehyde:

$$Me_2Be + Pr^iOH \rightarrow (MeBeOPr^i)_4 \leftarrow Me_2Be + CH_3CHO$$

The various routes to methylberyllium t-butoxide are quantitative:

$$Me_2Be + Bu^tOH$$
$$\downarrow$$
$$Me_2Be + Me_2CO \rightarrow (MeBeOBu^t)_4 \underset{Me_2Be}{\overset{Me_2CO}{\rightleftarrows}} [(Bu\ O)_2Be]_3$$
$$\uparrow$$
$$Me_2Be + Bu^tO \cdot OBu^t$$

(*iii*) *Alkylberyllium halides.* The chemistry of these has scarcely been developed. Reference has already been made to the formation of some alkylberyllium halides by direct reaction between the metal and alkyl halide, but nothing is known of their molecular complexity nor of the co-ordination about the metal. No doubt they are co-ordination oligomers or polymers.

t-Butylberyllium chloride diethyl ether complex was obtained as a by-product from the separation of ether from $Bu^t_2BeOEt_2$ by treatment with $BeCl_2$, but was not characterized [135]. This result has been con-

E

firmed [133a] and it is dimeric in benzene. As t-butyl undoubtedly has poorer bridging properties than chloride, this complex is formulated:

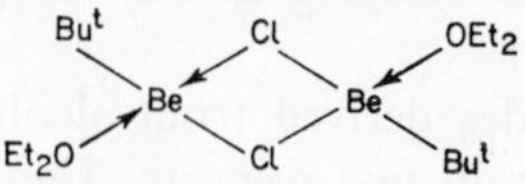

This is an extreme case. Replacement of t-butyl by more strongly bridging groups, such as methyl, and likewise substituting bromide or iodide for chloride could lead to different results.

(d) Anionic complexes

These may be formed by the addition of alkyl or aryl groups, or cyanide, fluoride, chloride or hydride ions to beryllium alkyls (or aryls).

Diphenylberyllium reacts exothermically with ethereal phenyl-lithium and a complex, LiBePh₃, may be crystallized on addition of xylene [153]. This may be a salt, Li[BePh₃], or it may be an electron-deficient polymer with a structure resembling that of LiAlEt₄ (p. 314). A dioxan addition compound, LiBePh₃(dioxan)₄, has also been described and this is more likely to be a salt. The complex NaBeEt₃ has been mentioned as a propene dimerization catalyst [154].

Diethylberyllium forms a series of complexes with fluorides and cyanides of unipositive cations, particularly those of large ionic radius [155]. The main factor which determines the complex-forming tendencies of alkali halides, and similar compounds, towards acceptors such as diethylberyllium and triethylaluminium is the lattice energy of the alkali halide [156]. The bigger the ions, the smaller is the lattice energy and the stronger the complex-forming tendency. The size of the anion is another, though subsidiary factor, in that smaller anions form more stable complexes than larger anions. In the case of the chloride anion, only tetraethylammonium chloride forms a complex with diethylberyllium (CsCl does not) [156a].

Potassium fluoride dissolves in a diethylberyllium–ether mixture, when stirred at room temperature. Most of the ether can then be removed by pumping at room temperature, and pumping at 60° causes the viscous reaction mixture to puff up and set solid; the product is KF.2Et₂Be, m.p. 83°. This is insoluble in saturated hydrocarbons such as heptane, and is partly soluble in benzene with decomposition:

$$\text{KF.2Et}_2\text{Be} \xrightleftharpoons[]{\text{C}_6\text{H}_6} \text{KF.Et}_2\text{Be} + \text{Et}_2\text{Be}$$

[153] G. Wittig and P. Hornberger, Annalen, 1952, 577, 11.
[154] K. Ziegler, Brit. P. 775, 384; Chem. Abs., 1958, 52, 12893.
[155] W. Strohmeier and F. Gernert, Chem. Ber., 1962, 95, 1420; G. Hans, Ger. P. 1,102,736; Chem. Abs., 1962, 57, 13800.
[156] K. Ziegler, R. Köster, H. Lehmkuhl and K. Reinert, Annalen, 1960, 629, 33.
[156a] W. Strohmeier, W. Haecker and G. Popp, Chem. Ber., 1967, 100, 405.

the 1 : 1 complex (m.p. 46–48°) being precipitated. The 1 : 2 complex KF.2Et₂Be decomposes when heated at 100–130° in vacuum, giving ether-free diethylberyllium. Beryllium has been deposited by the electrolysis of KF.2Et₂Be in the range 60–100° [156b]. Potassium cyanide dissolves in an Et₂Be–Et₂O mixture when stirred at ca. 65°; after ether has been removed at low pressure, addition of heptane yields crystalline KCN.4Et₂Be, m.p. 52–53°, which may also be decomposed in vacuum at 120–150° giving ether-free diethylberyllium.

Diphenylberyllium adds lithium hydride forming the complex [153] LiBePh₂H.OEt₂. Both dimethyl- and diethyl-beryllium add sodium hydride more readily than lithium hydride when the reagents are stirred together in boiling ether [157]. The sodium salt crystallizes with one mol. of ether, NaBeEt₂H.OEt₂, and has a dissociation pressure of 17 mm. at 20°. The ether is very readily lost at low pressure and the unsolvated salt then melts at 198°. The structure of the ether adduct is shown in Figure 12,

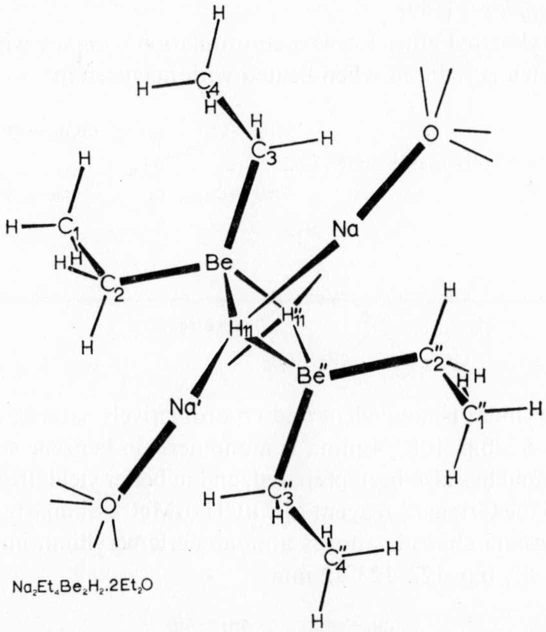

Na₂Et₄Be₂H₂.2Et₂O

Fig. 12. Structure of [NaOEt₂]₂.[Et₄Be₂H₂]. Ether ethyl groups are omitted (after Adamson and Shearer [158])

and it will be noted that the ether molecules are associated with the sodium ions rather than with the beryllium atoms. The ethyl groups of the co-

[156b] W. Strohmeier and F. Gernert, *Z. Naturforsch.*, 1965, **20b**, 829.
[157] G. E. Coates and G. F. Cox, *Chem. and Ind.*, 1962, 269.
[158] G. W. Adamson and H. M. M. Shearer, *Chem. Comm.*, 1965, 240.

ordinated ether molecules can occupy two alternative positions: this is indicated by the four (instead of two) thin lines from O in Figure 12. The positions of the hydridic hydrogen atoms were revealed by the crystallographic analysis. The structure 2.13 is therefore proposed for the ether-free salt, retaining the dimeric hydrogen bridged unit.

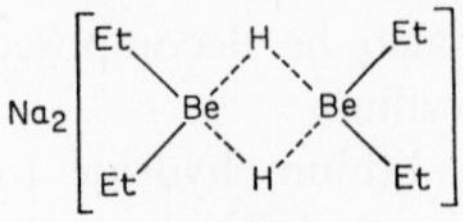

2.13

The lithium analogue, $[LiOEt_2]_2[Et_4Be_2H_2]$, m.p. 33–35°, is readily soluble in benzene in which it has an apparent molecular weight of 200–250 (cryoscopically, formula weight 298); its dissociation pressure is 17 mm. at 45°.

(e) Spiro-complexes [159]

4-Chlorobutylmethyl ether forms a co-ordination complex with beryllium chloride, which is reduced when heated with magnesium:

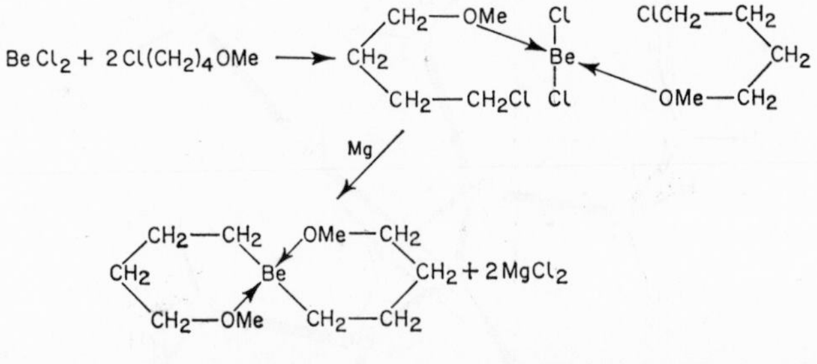

As the beryllium is 4-covalent and co-ordinatively saturated, this compound, m.p. 8°, b.p. 108°/4 mm., is monomeric in benzene solution. The same compound has also been prepared, and in better yield, from beryllium chloride and the Grignard reagent $MeO(CH_2)_4MgCl$. Similarly 3-ethylthiopropylmagnesium chloride affords a monomeric beryllium inner complex 2.14, m.p. 7–8°, b.p. 122–123°/2 mm.

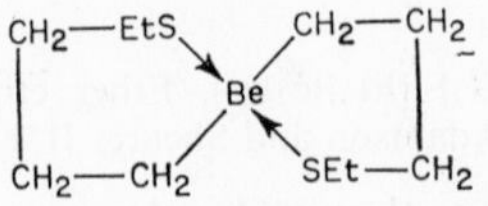

2.14

The existence of this complex is significant in view of the failure of dimethylsulphide to form a complex with dimethylberyllium. However, the

[159] G. Bähr and K. H. Thiele, *Chem. Ber.*, 1957, **90**, 1578.

formation of co-ordination complexes by dimethylberyllium only takes place if the heat of co-ordination is substantially greater than the heat of polymerization of dimethylberyllium itself. In the complex 2.16 there is no question of a similar equilibrium obtaining.

Organoberyllium hydrides and their complexes

The formation of beryllium hydride and of propylberyllium hydride by the pyrolysis of di-tert-butyl- and di-isopropyl-beryllium, respectively, has already been mentioned as have the anionic complexes $LiOEt_2.Et_2BeH$, $LiOEt_2.Ph_2BeH$ and $NaOEt_2.Et_2BeH$. Evidence for the formation of methylberyllium hydride by dissolving dimethylberyllium in a pentane solution of dimethylaluminium hydride was obtained some years ago [160], but the product was not studied and was difficult to obtain free from aluminium compounds.

$$Me_2Be + Me_2AlH \longrightarrow MeBeH + Me_3Al$$

Alkyl–hydrogen, but not alkyl–alkyl, exchange take place when triethyl-stannane is heated (75°) with dimethyl- or with diethyl-beryllium even in the presence of ether.

$$Me_2Be + Et_3SnH \longrightarrow MeBeH + Et_3MeSn$$

The hydride is conveniently separated as the trimethylamine complex, $(Me_3N \cdot BeMeH)_2$, m.p. 73°. The same products may also be prepared from the anionic hydride complexes [161]:

$$2NaMe_2BeH + BeCl_2 \longrightarrow 2NaCl + Me_2Be + 2MeBeH$$
$$Me_2Be + 2MeBeH + 3Me_3N \longrightarrow Me_2Be \cdot NMe_3 + (Me_3N \cdot BeMeH)_2$$

The organoberyllium hydrides (RBeH, R = Me, Et or Ph) can also be obtained by the reaction [162]

$$R_2Be + BeBr_2 + 2LiH \xrightarrow{Et_2O} 2LiBr + 2RBeH$$

If diethyl ether is evaporated from a solution of methylberyllium hydride until the Be : O ratio is 1 : 1, then the liquid product dissolves in benzene as a dimer analogous to the trimethylamine dimer, 2.15, which is readily obtained by displacement of ether by amine.

2.15

[160] G. D. Barbaras, C. Dillard, A. E. Finholt, T. Wartik, K. E. Wilzbach and H. I. Schlesinger, *J. Amer. Chem. Soc.*, 1951, **73**, 4585.

[161] N. A. Bell and G. E. Coates, *Proc. Chem. Soc.*, 1964, 59; *J. Chem. Soc.*, 1965, 692.

[162] Idem, ibid., A, 1966, 1069.

The hydride bridge in 2.14 (analogous to that shown in Figure 12) is evidently strong since it survives in the presence of an excess of trimethylamine, and since addition of tetramethylethylenediamine (TMED) to methylberyllium hydride in ether does not give the chelate MeBeH (TMED) complex but an insoluble product with a Be : N ratio of 1 : 1, shown spectroscopically to contain the BeH_2Be hydride bridge, and believed to be 2.16.

$$\left[\begin{array}{c} -CH_2Me_2N \quad \overset{H}{\underset{}{\nearrow}} \quad Me \\ \underset{Me}{\overset{}{Be}} \overset{}{\diamond} \overset{}{\diamond} \underset{H}{\overset{}{Be}} \underset{NMe_2CH_2-}{\overset{}{}} \end{array} \right]_n$$

2.16

Complexes such as 2.15 could have *cis* and *trans* isomers, and evidence for these has been obtained for 2.15 though not for other complexes. The proton magnetic resonance spectrum of this complex is shown in Figure

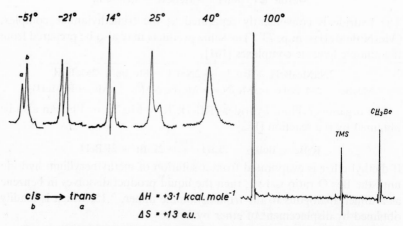

(Me₃N·BeMeH)₂ in C₇D₈

Effect of temperature on CH₃N resonance

Fig. 13. (Me₃N.BeMeH)₂ in C₇D₈. Effect of temperature on CH₃N resonance

13, and is interpreted in terms of the *cis-trans* interconversion being rapid at 100° (sharp resonance) and becoming sufficiently slow to result in splitting at room temperature and below. The *trans* form (low field N—CH₃ resonance) would have higher enthalpy and, in particular, higher entropy in solution than the *cis* form, since the latter would be highly polar and would cause considerably more ordering of solvent molecules in its vicinity [163].

[163] N. A. Bell, G. E. Coates and J. W. Emsley, *J. Chem. Soc.*, A, 1966, 1360.

The infrared absorptions due to stretching vibrations of the BeH_2Be bridge occur at 1065–1165 and 1294–1344 cm^{-1}, shifting to 835–870 and 920–1016 cm^{-1} on deuteration [161, 164]. The comparable absorptions due to the BH_2B bridge in diborane and some alkyldiboranes are in the region 1580–1606 and 1850–1972 cm^{-1}.

Alkylberyllium hydrides add rapidly to the carbonyl group, e.g. methyl-beryllium hydride and benzaldehyde give the tetramer $(MeBeOCH_2Ph)_4$ whereas benzophenone yields a monomeric complex $MeBeOCHPh_2OEt_2$. Benzalanil gives the dimeric amino derivative $[MeBeN(Ph)CH_2Ph]_2$, and pyridine first forms the hydride complex $(pyBeMeH)_2$ then reaction with more pyridine results in reduction of the heterocyclic ring and formation of $py_2RBeNC_5H_6$. The addition of methyl- and ethyl-beryllium hydride to olefins resembles additions of aluminium hydrides in that terminal olefins react very much faster than 1,2-substituted ethylenes. Addition of ethyl-beryllium hydride (in the presence of some ether) to pent-2-ene, followed by bromination yields mainly 1-brom-pentane along with less 2-brom-, and still less 3-brom-pentane, so addition is followed by migration of the beryllium to the end of the carbon chain [162].

ZINC

The simple organic compounds of zinc, first described in 1849 [165], have a notable place in the history of chemistry since studies on their vapour densities and chemical reactions led Frankland to make the first clear exposition of a theory of valency (1852) [166], in which he suggested that each element had a definite limiting combining capacity. Moreover, ethyl-zinc iodide and diethylzinc were among the earliest organometallic compounds to have been studied (Zeise's salt was described in 1827 and 'cacodyl' in 1842), and were certainly the first to achieve importance as chemical reagents.

Owing to their high chemical reactivity the organozinc compounds proved very useful for synthetic purposes until they were almost entirely superseded by the more conveniently prepared and still more reactive Grignard reagents (1900). Many of the reactions for which the latter are commonly used were first developed with the dialkyls of zinc, and it is very much to the credit of the chemists concerned that so many successful reactions were carried out with spontaneously inflammable zinc alkyls using carbon dioxide as a protective atmosphere and apparatus that would now seem primitive.

[164] Idem, ibid., A, 1966, 49.
[165] E. Frankland, ibid., 1848–9, 2, 263.
[166] Idem, *Phil. Trans.*, 1852, 142, 417.

Preparation

The di-*alkyls* of zinc may be prepared [167] by the thermal disproportionation of alkylzinc halides (this was Frankland's original method), the latter being obtained by direct reaction between alkyl iodides or mixtures of bromides and iodides and zinc containing a little copper, e.g.

$$Zn + EtI \rightarrow EtZnI$$
$$2EtZnI \rightarrow Et_2Zn + ZnI_2$$

These reactions are carried out in an inert atmosphere (N_2 or CO_2) without isolation of the alkylzinc halides, which usually appear as white crystalline substances. Improvements on the original method have mainly concerned the use of suitable zinc–copper alloys [167], or special methods for the preparation of zinc–copper couple (e.g. from zinc dust and dry copper(II) citrate [168]), and the use of high boiling ethers as solvents [169].

Small quantities of organozinc compounds can conveniently be obtained by heating the metal with the appropriate mercury alkyl, when a metal exchange occurs [170], though the methods using aluminium alkyls (mentioned below) are probably more convenient when these are available.

$$Zn + R_2Hg \rightarrow R_2Zn + Hg$$

The di-*aryls* of zinc are obtained by this reaction carried out in boiling xylene solution or from zinc chloride (or bromide) and an aryl-lithium reagent in ether [171].

Solutions of dialkyls, diaryls or of organozinc halides in ether may be obtained by addition of anhydrous zinc chloride in ether to a Grignard reagent:

$$ZnCl_2 + RMgX \rightarrow RZnCl + MgXCl$$

This reaction has been used as a device for obtaining alkylating or arylating agents which are less reactive than Grignard reagents [172].

Zinc alkyls have also been obtained by the alkylation of zinc chloride and fluoride by aluminium alkyls, mineral oil free from oxygen or sulphur compounds being used to moderate the reaction in the case of the chloride [173]. The reaction between trimethylaluminium and zinc chloride without a diluent is probably a convenient method for preparing dimethylzinc on

[167] C. R. Noller, *Organic Syntheses*, 1943, Collective Vol. II, 184.

[168] R. C. Krug and P. J. C. Tang, *J. Amer. Chem. Soc.*, 1954, **76**, 2262.

[169] L. F. Hatch, G. Sutherland and W. J. Ross, *J. Org. Chem.*, 1949, **14**, 1130.

[170] E. Frankland and D. F. Duppa, *J. Chem. Soc.*, 1864, **17**, 30; *Annalen*, 1864, **130**, 118; C. R. McCoy and A. L. Allred, *J. Amer. Chem. Soc.*, 1962, **84**, 912.

[171] W. Strohmeier, *Chem. Ber.*, 1955, **88**, 1218; D. Y. Curtin and J. L. Tveten, *J. Org. Chem.*, 1961, **26**, 1764.

[172] T. Weil, B. Prijs and H. Erlenmeyer, *Helv. Chim. Acta*, 1952, **35**, 1412.

[173] Brit. P. 768,765 to Kali-Chemie; Ger.P. 1,138,395 to Conoco.

the laboratory scale [174], though only one-third of the methyl introduced as trimethylaluminium is converted to dimethylzinc.

$$2Me_3Al + ZnCl_2 \rightarrow 2Me_2AlCl + Me_2Zn$$

The reaction between aluminium trialkyls and zinc acetate without diluent has also been recommended as a good route to zinc alkyls [174a].

Diphenylzinc reacts with phenylacetylene in ether solution:

$$Ph_2Zn + PhC:CH \rightarrow PhZnC:CPh + C_6H_6$$
$$PhZnC:CPh + PhC:CH \rightarrow (PhC:C)_2Zn + C_6H_6$$

Phenyl(phenylethynyl)zinc, m.p. 133°, slowly disproportionates in ether solution

$$2PhZnC:CPh \rightarrow (PhC:C)_2Zn \downarrow + Ph_2Zn$$

and it is interesting to note that a similar reaction takes place in liquid ammonia, with formation of the diammine $(PhC:C)_2Zn(NH_3)_2$ which crystallizes from solution, and diphenylzinc which remains dissolved without ammonolysis. If a solution of diphenylzinc in ammonia is evaporated, ammonolysis then occurs by reaction with gaseous ammonia:

$$Ph_2Zn + 2NH_3 \rightarrow Zn(NH_2)_2 + 2C_6H_6$$

The metalation of phenylacetylene by *diethyl*zinc, very slow in hydrocarbons or diethyl ether, takes place readily in more basic solvents such as THF and dimethylformamide. Solvent-free bisphenylethynylzinc decomposes at about 200° without melting. Both bisphenylethynyl-zinc and -cadmium are practically insoluble in non-polar organic solvents, though $(PhC:C)_2Zn$ dissolves readily in dimethylformamide, dimethylsulphoxide and in hexamethyltriamidophosphate [175]. Bisethynylzinc, from zinc amide and acetylene in liquid ammonia, forms a diammine $(HC:C)_2Zn(NH_3)_2$, and both this and $(PhC:C)_2Zn(NH_3)_2$ are non-electrolytes in liquid ammonia. Thus the ionic constitutions $[Zn(NH_3)_4][(RC:C)_4Zn]$ do not represent the diammines, at least in liquid ammonia solution [176].

Several new methods have been developed for the preparation of alkyzinc halides. Dimethylformamide has been recommended as a solvent for the preparation of alkylzinc halides from zinc dust and alkyl halides, though some iodide is necessary to start the reaction [177]. 1,2-Dimethoxyethane, diglyme and dimethylsulphoxide are other solvents in which the lower alkyl iodides react readily with zinc dust; in these solvents the lower alkyl bromides also react though some heating is necessary to

[174] A. P. Gray, A. B. Callear and F. H. C. Edgecombe, *Canad. J. Chem.*, 1963, **41**, 1502.   [174a] T. Mole, personal communication.
[175] O. Y. Okhlobystin and L. I. Zakharkin, *J. Organometal. Chem.*, 1965, **3**, 257.
[176] R. Nast, O. Künzel and R. Müller, *Chem. Ber.*, 1962, **95**, 2155.
[177] R. Joly and R. Bucourt, U.S.P. 3,040,079; *Chem. Abs.*, 1963, **58**, 10238; R. Bucourt and R. Joly, *Compt. rend.*, 1962, **254**, 1655.

initiate the reaction [178]. Allyl, propargyl and benzyl bromides in tetra-hydrofuran react with zinc giving RZnBr without any R_2 (in contrast to the reaction with magnesium). Saturated alkylzinc bromides are said to be insufficiently reactive to be useful as synthetic reagents [179].

Some arylzinc halide–ether complexes have been prepared by addition of a concentrated solution of diarylzinc in ether to just under one mol. zinc halide in the same solvent. Removal of much of the ether yields crystalline compounds, such as $PhZnBr \cdot OEt_2$, which have no definite melting points [180]. Ethylzinc iodide has been prepared from ethyl iodide and zinc dust, without the addition of copper which always yields a mixture of zinc iodide and ethylzinc iodide, and crystallized from excess ethyl iodide: it shrinks at 95° and decomposes at 98–99°. It has also been prepared by dissolving zinc iodide in excess diethylzinc and evaporating unreacted diethylzinc [181]. Ethylzinc chloride (m.p. 68°) and bromide (m.p. 81°) may be prepared similarly, and dissolve without decomposition in non-polar solvents; they are tetrameric in benzene and a structure has been proposed similar to that of methylzinc methoxide (see Figure 15, p. 135). Both these halides form co-ordination complexes, e.g. $EtZnClpy_2$ and $EtZnCl(TMED)$, $(TMED = tetramethylethylenediamine)$ [181a].

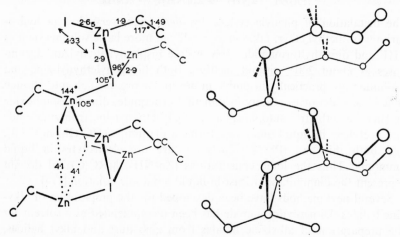

Fig. 14. Crystal structure of the ethylzinc iodide polymer (after Moseley and Shearer [181b])

[178] L. I. Zakharkin and O. Y. Okhlobystin, *Izvest. Akad. Nauk S.S.S.R.*, 1963, 193; *Chem. Abs.*, 1963, **58**, 12589.

[179] M. Gaudemar, *Compt. rend.*, 1958, **246**, 1229.

[180] N. I. Sheverdina, L. V. Abramova and K. A. Kocheshkov, *Doklady Akad. Nauk S.S.S.R.*, 1960, **134**, 853 (English p. 1111).

[181] G. Jander and L. Fischer, *Z. Elektrochemie*, 1958, **62**, 971.

[181a] J. Boersma and J. G. Noltes, *Tetrahedron Letters*, 1966, 1521.

[181b] P. T. Moseley and H. M. M. Shearer, *Chem. Comm.*, 1966, 876.

Ethylzinc iodide, in contrast, disproportionates when attempts are made to dissolve it in benzene, and zinc iodide is precipitated. In the crystalline state it is a co-ordination polymer (Figure 14), the zinc and iodine atoms forming a sheet-like layer lattice. When ethylzinc iodide dissolves in ethyl iodide, from which, as mentioned above, it can be crystallized, it must be at least partly depolymerized by the solvent acting as a Lewis base. Since it also dissolves in diethylzinc, the solvent in this instance must act as a Lewis acid.

Doubtless encouraged by the controversy concerning the nature of Grignard reagents in ether-type solvents, several workers have studied the constitution of alkylzinc halides in these solvents also. Ethylzinc iodide is monomeric both in diethyl ether and in tetrahydrofuran [181c], and the vibrational spectra support the formulation EtZnI rather than a mixture of Et_2Zn with ZnI_2 [181d]. Though equilibria in Grignard mixtures are established rapidly (except when C_6F_5 groups are involved), this is evidently not the case in the Et_2Zn–ZnI_2 system. If tetramethylethylene-diamine (TMED) is added to an equimolar Et_2Zn–ZnI_2 mixture in THF two hours after it has been prepared, then $ZnI_2(TMED)$, m.p. 201°, crystallizes, but if the TMED is added after the mixture has remained a week at 25°, then EtZnI(TMED), m.p. 103°, crystallizes [181c].

Some alkylzinc sulphates have been prepared from alkyl- or aryl-zinc halides and alkyl sulphates or sulphonates, e.g.

$$EtZnI + Et_2SO_4 \xrightarrow{85°} EtZnSO_4Et + EtI$$

Similar products are formed when metallic zinc reacts with alkyl sulphates in the presence of catalytic amounts of zinc alkyl:

$$Zn + Et_2SO_4 \xrightarrow{Et_2Zn} EtZnSO_4Et$$

Sulphates of the type $(RZn)_2SO_4$ have also been obtained, and the ethyl compound is soluble in tetrahydrofuran from which it may be recovered as a complex, $(EtZn)_2SO_4 \cdot THF$ [182].

$$2Zn + Et_2SO_4 \xrightarrow{EtI} (EtZn)_2SO_4$$

Heptafluoropropylzinc iodide has been prepared by the reaction between zinc dust and C_3F_7I in ether, tetrahydropyran, dioxan or 1,2-dimethoxyethane [183].

$$C_3F_7I + Zn \rightarrow C_3F_7ZnI + C_3F_6 + C_6F_{14} + C_3F_7H$$

[181c] M. H. Abraham and P. H. Rolfe, *J. Organometal. Chem.*, 1967, **7**, 35; see also R. E. Dessy and G. R. Coe, *J. Org. Chem.*, 1963, **28**, 3592.

[181d] D. F. Evans and I. Wharf, *J. Organometal. Chem.*, 1966, **5**, 108.

[182] H. E. Petree, U.S.P. 2,942,015–6–7 (to Ethyl Corporation).

[183] R. N. Haszeldine and E. G. Walaschewski, *J. Chem. Soc.*, 1953, 3607; W. T. Miller, E. Bergmann and A. N. Fainberg, *J. Amer. Chem. Soc.*, 1957, **79**, 4159.

Heptafluoropropylzinc iodide is much less reactive than the other alkyl or aryl zinc halides, as it is only slowly hydrolysed by water and does not react with oxygen. It has even been prepared in acetone solution. Trifluoropropynylzinc chloride has been postulated as an intermediate in a preparation of trifluoropropyne [184]:

$$CF_3CCl:CCl_2 + Zn + ZnCl_2 \xrightarrow{Me_2N\cdot CHO} CF_3C:CZnCl \text{ or}$$

$$(CF_3C:C)_2Zn$$
$$\downarrow H_2O$$
$$CF_3C:CH$$

Some remarkable halomethyl derivatives of zinc are formed when diazomethane reacts with zinc halides in ether solvents [185]. The product from zinc chloride is tetrameric (ebullioscopically), $[Zn(CH_2Cl)_2]_4$; it forms a quaternary salt $[(Me_3N\cdot CH_2)_2Zn]Cl_2$ with trimethylamine. The iodo compound $Zn(CH_2I)_2$ like its cadmium and mercury analogues, gives methyl iodide in about 80% yield when hydrolysed. The bischloromethyl compound reacts with iodine forming both CH_2ClI and CH_2I_2 in proportions which depend on the reaction conditions, and it exchanges halogen rapidly with zinc iodide:

$$(CH_2Cl)_2Zn \xrightarrow{ZnI_2} (CH_2I)_2Zn \xrightarrow{H_2O} CH_3I$$

The formation of CH_2I_2 from $(CH_2Cl)_2Zn$ and iodine is due to the halogen exchange being faster than Zn–C bond fission. Both the metal–carbon and the carbon–halogen bonds in these compounds are very reactive. Whereas dimethylzinc does not react with olefins, the halomethyl compounds add rapidly, giving cyclopropanes [186]:

$$X\cdot Zn\cdot CH_2X + \text{olefin} \rightarrow \text{cyclopropane} + ZnX_2$$

Since halomethyl derivatives of zinc (and other metals such as aluminium) may be obtained from diazomethane, the above reaction provides in effect a method for adding the methylene group from diazomethane across an olefin forming cyclopropanes. Iodomethylenezinc iodide was obtained in ether solution some time ago, by the reaction between methylene iodide and zinc–copper couple [187], and relatively recently it was found that, if this reaction is carried out in the presence of olefins, cyclopropanes are obtained, and often in good yield [188].

These reactions, exemplified by the formation of norcarane from cyclo-

[184] W. G. Finnegan and W. P. Norris, *J. Org. Chem.*, 1963, **28**, 1139.
[185] G. Wittig and K. Schwarzenbach, *Annalen*, 1961, **650**, 1.
[186] G. Wittig and F. Wingler, ibid., 1962, **656**, 18; H. Hoberg, ibid., p. 15.
[187] G. Emschwiller, *Compt. rend.*, 1929, **188**, 1555.
[188] H. E. Simmons and R. D. Smith, *J. Amer. Chem. Soc.*, 1958, **80**, 5323; 1959, **81**, 4256; W. Von E. Doehring and P. M. La Flamme, *Tetrahedron*, 1958, **2**, 75; see also *Org. Syntheses*, 1961, **41**, 72.

hexene, methylene iodide and zinc–copper couple in ether, were originally believed to involve carbenes as intermediates, but a thorough study of the reactions has provided good evidence that an intermediate (possibly $(ICH_2ZnI)_2$ or a species equivalent to this) reacts with the olefin in a kinetically bimolecular process. There is no kinetic evidence for the existence of free carbene in the reaction, which is now described as a *methylene transfer process* [189], the methylene carbon atom interacting with the olefin with zinc iodide elimination as a concerted reaction.

Ether is normally the best solvent for these reactions, in which (from CH_2I_2) ethylene (in the absence of added olefin this is the main product), methyl iodide and ethyl isopropyl ether are by-products. The formation of ethylene relative to a cyclopropane is favoured by increasing basicity of ether, the ratio of ethylene to cyclopropane being higher when tetrahydrofuran and still higher when 1,2-dimethoxyethane is used as solvent. The methyl iodide is formed by the ether acting as acid, giving $EtO\overline{CH}\cdot CH_3$ ions and methyl iodide, and thence some ethyl isopropyl ether.

Reaction between olefin, methylene iodide, and *diethylzinc* also leads to cyclopropanes, but is faster than the use of zinc–copper couple [189a].

Reaction between diazomethane and zinc benzoate results in insertion of methylene between zinc and oxygen. The product, whose infrared spectrum is consistent with the structure

acts as a poor 'carbene source' by itself, but as a good source in the presence of the iodides of lithium, magnesium or zinc, giving norcarane in high yield on reaction with cyclohexene [189b].

Organozinc compounds are formed as transient intermediates in the *Reformatsky reaction*, in which a zinc derivative of an α-bromo-ester reacts with an aldehyde or ketone:

$$BrCH_2CO_2Et \xrightarrow{Zn} [BrZnCH_2CO_2Et]$$
$$\text{not isolated}$$
$$\xrightarrow[(2) H_2O]{(1) R'_2CO} R'_2COH\cdot CH_2CO_2Et$$

The above intermediate has been prepared in high yield in methylal, and then allowed to react in the usual way with carbonyl compounds [189c].

[189] E. P. Blanchard and H. E. Simmons, *J. Amer. Chem. Soc.*, 1964, **86**, 1337; H. E. Simmons, E. P. Blanchard and R. D. Smith, ibid., p. 1347.
[189a] J. Furukawa, N. Kawabata and J. Nishimura, *Tetrahedron Letters*, 1966, 3353.
[189b] G. Wittig and M. Jautelat, *Annalen*, 1967, **702**, 24.
[189c] J. Curé and M. Gaudemar, *Compt. rend.*, 1966, **262C**, 213.

The Reformatsky intermediate [BrZnCH₂CONEt₂] from zinc and N,N-diethylbromacetamide, also prepared in methylal, has been isolated but scarcely anything is known about its constitution [189d]. It is almost certain to be a co-ordination oligomer or polymer.

Physical properties
The dialkyls are covalently bonded monomeric substances, the two bonds formed by the zinc (*sp*) being co-linear. The molecules are thus non-polar and the relatively high volatility of the dialkyls of zinc is in agreement with a molecular non-polar structure (Table 7), dimethylzinc being one of the most volatile organometallic compounds.

Table 7

		M.p.	B.p.
Dimethylzinc [190, 191]	CH_3—Zn—CH_3	−29·2°	44·0°
Diethylzinc [181]	C_2H_5—Zn—C_2H_5	−33·8 to −35·1	116·8
Di-n-propylzinc [190]	C_3H_7—Zn—C_3H_7	−81 to −84	139·4
Di-isopropylzinc [191a]	$(CH_3)_2CH$—Zn—$CH(CH_3)_2$	—	40°/12 mm.
Ethyl n-propylzinc [192]	C_2H_5—Zn—C_3H_7	—	27°/10 mm.
n-Propyl-n-butylzinc [191a]	C_3H_7—Zn—C_4H_9	—	38–43°/3 mm.
Di-n-butylzinc [191a]	C_4H_9—Zn—C_4H_9	—	61°/4 mm.
Di-t-butylzinc [193]	$(CH_3)_3C$—Zn—$C(CH_3)_3$	28·8	34–35°/9 mm.
Diphenylzinc [171]	C_6H_5—Zn—C_6H_5	107	280–285° (d)
Bis-pentafluoro-phenylzinc [194]	C_6F_5—Zn—C_6F_5	91–93	—

The infrared spectrum of dimethylzinc indicates that the methyl groups rotate freely [195]; the Zn–C stretching frequencies [196] are at 504 and 615 cm⁻¹. In crystalline dimethylzinc the carbon–zinc distance, 1·94 Å, is shorter than the sum of the single-bond covalent radii, 2·02 Å, and it is suggested that apparently vacant valence orbitals of the metal atom allow some multiple bond character by hyperconjugation [197, 123].

Diethylzinc has a very low specific conductivity (2.10⁻¹¹ ohm⁻¹ cm⁻¹

[189d] J. Curé and M. Gaudemar, *Compt. rend.*, 1967, **246C**, 97.
[190] C. H. Bamford, D. L. Levi and D. M. Newitt, *J. Chem. Soc.*, 1946, 468.
[191] L. H. Long and J. Cattanach, *J. Inorg. Nucl. Chem.*, 1961, **20**, 340.
[191a] M. H. Abraham and J. A. Hill, *J. Organometal. Chem.*, 1967, **7**, 23.
[192] E. Krause and W. Fromm, *Ber.*, 1926, **59**, 931.
[193] M. H. Abraham, *J. Chem. Soc.*, 1960, 4130; J. G. Noltes and J. Boersma, *J. Organometal. Chem.*, 1967, **9**, 1.
[194] J. G. Noltes and J. W. G. van den Hurk, *J. Organometal. Chem.*, 1964, **1**, 377.
[195] D. R. J. Boyd, H. W. Thompson and R. L. Williams, *Discuss. Faraday Soc.*, 1950, **9**, 154.
[196] H. S. Gutowsky, *J. Chem. Phys.*, 1949, **17**, 128.
[197] R. E. Rundle, D. H. Olson, G. D. Stucky and G. R. Engebretson, Internat. Union of Crystallography, Sixth Internat. Congress, Rome 1963, Abstracts of Communications, p. A 73.

at 20°), and the conductance of solutions in it of tetrabutylammonium iodide, ethylzinc iodide, ethyl-lithium (which reacts to form a complex) and aluminium bromide have been studied. Diethylzinc, though itself non-polar (dielectric constant 2·522 at 20°), appears to have a solvent character intermediate between those of ionizing and non-polar organic solvents [181].

Unsymmetrical compounds like ethyl n-propylzinc slowly disproportionate to the symmetrical dialkyls, even on standing at room temperature:

$$2EtZnPr^n \longrightarrow Et_2Zn + Pr^n_2Zn$$

This could be due to the occasional formation of an electron-deficient alkyl-bridged dimer whose dissociation would provide a means of alkyl exchange. The unsymmetrical alkyls have been prepared [191a, 192] by the action of a Grignard reagent on an alkylzinc halide and isolated by vacuum distillation at relatively low temperatures:

$$EtZnI + Pr^nMgBr \longrightarrow EtPr^nZn + MgBrI$$

Two cyclopentadienyl derivatives have been obtained by the reactions

$$2EtMgBr + C_5H_6 + ZnCl_2 \longrightarrow \underset{\text{m.p. } 69-70°}{C_5H_5ZnEt} + 2MgX_2 + C_2H_6$$

$$2PhMgBr + C_5H_6 + ZnCl_2 \longrightarrow \underset{\text{m.p. } 74-75°}{C_5H_5ZnC_6H_5} + 2MgX_2 + C_6H_6$$

These are volatile, air-sensitive, and give ferrocene immediately on reaction with iron(II) chloride [198]. The dipole moments of the ethyl and phenyl compounds in heptane, benzene and dioxan are 0·6, 0·6, 1·9 and 0·4, 1·0, 2·9 D respectively [199], the higher moments in dioxan being due to the formation of a proportion of co-ordination complex.

Chemical properties
Organozinc compounds are very sensitive to oxygen, the more volatile of them being spontaneously inflammable, and the others fume strongly. Unlike Grignard reagents they do not react with carbon dioxide (except slowly under pressure) and were commonly handled in that gas, but the more volatile compounds are now best manipulated in the usual type of 'vacuum apparatus'. Divinylzinc $(CH_2:CH)_2Zn$, b.p. $32°/22$ mm., from vinylmagnesium bromide and zinc chloride in tetrahydrofuran, is much less stable thermally than diethylzinc. The note [200] on this compound describes a good way of removing ethyl bromide from commercial vinyl bromide. The unstable diallyl may be isolated as the red bipyridyl complex, $bipyZn(C_3H_5)_2$, m.p. 94° [201], and free diallylzinc can be prepared from

[198] W. Strohmeier and H. Landsfelt, *Z. Naturforsch.*, 1960, **15b**, 332.
[199] W. Strohmeier and D. v. Hobe, *Z. Elektrochemie*, 1960, **64**, 945.
[200] B. Bartocha, H. D. Kaesz and F. G. A. Stone, *Z. Naturforsch.*, 1959, **14b**, 352.
[201] K. H. Thiele, W. Hanke and P. Zdunneck, *Z. anorg. Chem.*, 1965, **337**, 63.

triallylborane and dimethylzinc. It is a yellow crystalline solid, m.p. 84°, claimed to have an ionic constitution, and is monomeric in benzene solution [202].

If ampoules containing diethyl- or di-n-butyl-zinc are crushed under dry ether continuously saturated with oxygen at room temperature, soluble peroxides $RZnO \cdot OR$ (hydrolysed to $RH + RO_2H$) are first formed but after a few minutes there is a white precipitate of insoluble $Zn(O \cdot OR)_2$. If the absorption of oxygen is controlled so that the process takes several weeks, then insoluble solids are again formed but these consist for the most part of zinc alkoxides since they are hydrolysed mainly to the alcohol with formation of only a little peroxide. That the product of slow oxidation is formed by reactions of the type

$$RZnO \cdot OR + R_2Zn \rightarrow 2RZnOR$$
$$RZnOR + O_2 \rightarrow RO \cdot OZnOR$$
$$RO \cdot OZnOR + R_2Zn \rightarrow Zn(OR)_2 + RZnOR \quad \text{etc.}$$

is supported by the formation of $Zn(OEt)_2$ in 94% yield from $Et_2Zn + Zn(O \cdot OEt)_2$. Peroxides are initially formed by the reactions between oxygen and various other metal alkyls and the Grignard reagents, but reduction of the peroxide by unattacked alkyl is generally so fast that it is usually difficult to isolate any peroxidic product. The mechanism of these reactions is considered to involve initial co-ordination of oxygen to the metal atom which may be followed by, or synchronous with, migration of an alkyl group [193].

$$
\begin{array}{ccc}
R\text{—}Zn\text{—}R & \rightarrow & (R\text{—}Zn\ R)_x \\
\uparrow & & |\quad| \\
O\text{=}O & & O\text{—}O
\end{array}
$$

Nitric oxide is also believed to react with zinc and some other metal alkyls by initial co-ordination of the oxygen atom [203]:

$$Pr^n_2Zn \cdot O\dot{N} \rightarrow Pr^nZn \cdot O \cdot \dot{N}Pr^n \xrightarrow{NO} Pr^nZn \cdot O \cdot NPr^n \cdot NO$$

Hydrolysis yields the zinc complex of N-nitroso-N-propylhydroxylamine. The reactions between dimethyl- and diethyl-zinc and nitric oxide were investigated by Frankland [204] (1856–7), and nitrosohydroxylamines (or their derivatives) have been isolated from reactions between nitric oxide and Grignard reagents [205] and $Et_3Al \cdot OEt_2$ [206].

The chemical reactions of the organozinc compounds are generally similar to those of magnesium alkyls and Grignard reagents. The essential

[202] K. H. Thiele and P. Zdunneck, *J. Organometal. Chem.*, 1965, **4**, 10.
[203] M. H. Abraham, J. H. N. Garland, J. A. Hill and L. F. Larkworthy, *Chem. and Ind.*, 1962, 1615.
[204] E. Frankland, *Phil. Trans.*, 1857, **147**, 63; *Annalen*, 1856, **99**, 345, 369.
[205] J. Sand and F. Singer, ibid., 1903, **329**, 190.
[206] E. B. Baker and H. H. Sisler, *J. Amer. Chem. Soc.*, 1953, **75**, 5193.

difference lies in the considerably lower reactivity of the former, and this has proved useful in the preparation of tetra-alkyl methanes [207]. Whereas dialkylzinc reacts neither with primary nor secondary halides, nor with dimethyl sulphate (except at elevated temperature [182], *tertiary halides* afford hydrocarbons in much better yield than with Grignard reagents, since use of the latter results in much side reaction and olefin formation, e.g.

$$Me_3CCl + Et_2Zn \longrightarrow Me_3CEt$$

The relatively low rates of reaction with cyanides, isocyanates, esters and ketones allow these groups to remain unaffected in reactions involving some other and more active functional group such as ·COCl. Acid chlorides combine rapidly with organozinc compounds, a reaction which has been applied to the synthesis of ketones:

$$R·COCl + R'_2Zn \text{ (or } R'ZnCl) \longrightarrow R·CO·R'$$

Complications sometimes interfere: α-alkoxy acid chlorides react in two ways, often simultaneously:

(*a*) $RO·CH_2·COCl + R'ZnCl \longrightarrow RO·CH_2·CO·R' + ZnCl_2$
(*b*) $RO·CH_2·COCl \longrightarrow RO·CH_2Cl + CO$
$RO·CH_2Cl + R'ZnCl \longrightarrow RO·CH_2·R' + ZnCl_2$

The use of organozinc compounds for ketone synthesis [208] has been largely superseded by that of cadmium.

Reactions between organometallic compounds and ketones are often complex, and both Grignard reagents and organoaluminium compounds (p. 329) can give products due to *addition, reduction* and, when this is possible, *enolization*. Whereas dimethylzinc does not appear to react with benzophenone (other than by reversible formation of a co-ordination complex), diethylzinc reacts quantitatively to give the reduction product and ethylene [209].

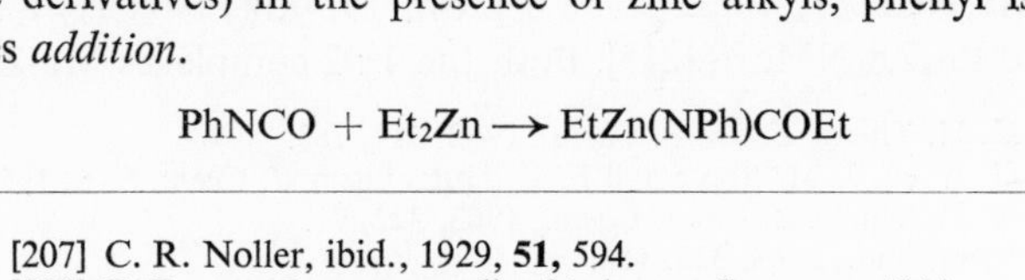

Whereas methyl and ethyl isocyanates are converted to their trimers (cyanuric derivatives) in the presence of zinc alkyls, phenyl isocyanate undergoes *addition*.

$$PhNCO + Et_2Zn \longrightarrow EtZn(NPh)COEt$$

[207] C. R. Noller, ibid., 1929, **51**, 594.
[208] F. Runge, *Organo-metallverbindungen*, Stuttgart, 1944.
[209] G. E. Coates and D. Ridley, *J. Chem. Soc.*, A, 1966, 1064.

The constitution of the product, which is tetrameric, is not known. Hydrolysis, of course, yields propionanilide and the tetramer can itself be obtained from the anilide:

$$PhNH·CO·Et + Et_2Zn \rightarrow \tfrac{1}{4}[EtZn(NPh)COEt]_4$$

Co-ordination complexes with ligands not containing acidic hydrogen

Zinc alkyls form relatively unstable complexes with simple ethers. The dimethyl ether complex, $Me_2Zn·OMe_2$, has a boiling point (47°) similar to that of dimethylzinc (44°), and is unchanged by a single distillation at atmospheric pressure. Partial separation of ether results from distillation through a fractionating column. *Cyclic ethers* form rather more stable complexes, and the tendency for dimethylzinc to combine with two mols. of ether increases with ring size from $(CH_2)_2O$ to $(CH_2)_5O$. The liquid bistetrahydrofuran complex, $Me_2Zn(THF)_2$, b.p. 83°, is evidently partly dissociated in the liquid state as it freezes over the range $-55°$ to $-67°$ and is extensively dissociated in dilute solution in benzene and in cyclohexane. In the vapour state it is almost completely dissociated into $Me_2Zn + 2THF$. The bistetrahydrofuran complex is conveniently prepared by boiling zinc turnings (containing 10% copper) with methyl iodide in tetrahydrofuran for eight hours. Unlike dimethylzinc it does not inflame in the air [210]. For a proton magnetic resonance study of R_2Zn-ether equilibria, see ref. [211].

Chelating diethers, as expected, form more stable complexes:

m.p. 5·5°   m.p. 66°   m.p. 23–24°

The formation of the thioxan complex is of interest since simple thioethers do not appear to form addition compounds with zinc alkyls. 1,2-Dimethoxyethane also forms the non-chelate complex $Me_2Zn(OMe·C_2H_4OMe)_2$, which, however, is almost wholly dissociated to the chelate complex and free diether in benzene solution [212].

Tertiary amine complexes include $Me_2Zn·NMe_3$ (b.p. 84°) [213], $Me_2Zn(Me_2NCH_2·)_2$ (m.p. 57–58°) [214], $Me_2Zn(Et_2NCH_2·)_2$ (m.p. 66°) [213], and $Ph_2Zn(NMe_3)_2$ [215]. Both the 1 : 2 complexes $Me_2Zn(NMe_3)_2$

[210] K. H. Thiele, *Z. anorg. Chem.*, 1962, **319**, 183.
[211] G. Allen, J. M. Bruce and F. G. Hutchinson, *J. Chem. Soc.*, 1965, 5476.
[212] K. H. Thiele, *Z. anorg. Chem.*, 1963, **322**, 71.
[213] Idem, ibid., 1963, **325**, 156.
[214] G. E. Coates and D. Ridley, *J. Chem. Soc.*, 1965, 1870.
[215] K. H. Thiele and J. Köhler, *Z. anorg. Chem.*, 1965, **337**, 260.

and $Me_2Zn(NEt_3)_2$ are considerably dissociated into $1:1$ complex and free amine in benzene solution [213].

Consistent with its character as an A-type acceptor (forming complexes more readily with oxygen and nitrogen than with heavier donors – sulphur, phosphorus – involving d-orbital participation), zinc forms relatively unstable complexes with sulphides, phosphines and arsines. However, if the metal is bound to relatively electron-attracting groups then its acceptor character is enhanced. This is nicely shown by the failure of dibutylzinc to complex with triphenylphosphine, whereas both diphenyl- and bispentafluorophenyl-zinc form bistriphenylphosphine complexes, e.g. $(C_6F_5)_2Zn(PPh_3)_2$, m.p. 166–167°. A series of complexes with chelating diphosphines and diarsines has also been prepared [194].

Perhaps the most interesting complexes formed by organozinc compounds are those containing heterocyclic bases. Many of these complexes have bright colours which are ascribed to charge-transfer transitions (see bipyridyl beryllium complexes, p. 112). In contrast to the dimethylzinc complexes [216], both of bipyridyl and 1,10-phenanthroline, which are relatively unreactive to moist air, the complexes of diphenylzinc and of the higher alkyls are very sensitive to air and moisture, particularly when in solution. The electron transferred to the heterocyclic π-orbital system during the absorption of light could also, in the case of a zinc complex, come from the filled $3d$ shell [217]. The colours and some spectroscopic properties of several 2,2'-bipyridyl complexes are listed in Table 8, in which the transition energy is given in the last column.

Table 8   *Organozinc bipyridyl complexes*

R in R_2Zn bipy	Colour	λ_{max} (mμ)	log ε_{max}	E kcal. mole^{-1}
iso-C_3H_7	dark red	480	2·63	59
n-C_4H_9	red	425	2·56	67
C_2H_5	orange red	420	2·77	68
CH_3	yellow	(very sparingly soluble)		
C_6H_5	pale yellow	350	2·91	82
C_6F_5	colourless	309	4·15	92
Br	colourless	310	4·13	92

As the electron-attracting character of R increases, so the net charge on the metal atom would become more positive, leading in turn to an increase in the ionization potential of the $3d$ electrons. This would account for the increase in E in passing from the relatively electron-repelling isopropyl to the electron-attracting pentafluorophenyl group (similar in this respect to

[216] G. E. Coates and S. I. E. Green, *Proc. Chem. Soc.*, 1961, 376; *J. Chem. Soc.*, 1962, 3340.
[217] J. G. Noltes and J. W. G. van den Hurk, *J. Organometal. Chem.*, 1965, **3**, 222.

a bromine atom). The change in intensity could be related to changes in the radial parts of the $3d$ orbitals (i.e. polarization).

The 1,10-phenanthroline complexes [217] have absorption maxima at somewhat longer wavelengths than their 2,2'-bipyridyl analogues, consistent with the electronic transition involving the π-electron system of the heterocyclic bases.

Zinc alkyl adducts with non-chelating heterocyclic bases (pyridine and the quinolines) are less strongly coloured than the bipyridyl and o-phenanthroline complexes. Further, as observed for the latter, the colours of dimethylzinc complexes, e.g. Me_2Znpy_2, colourless [213], m.p. 44°, are paler than those of adducts formed by higher alkyls [218], e.g. Et_2Znpy_2, yellow, m.p. 28°, Bu^n_2Zn quinoline$_2$, orange-red, m.p. −25°.

Co-ordination complexes with ligands containing acidic hydrogen

The zinc alkyls readily react with substances containing acidic hydrogen, and one or both organic groups are displaced according to the nature of the acid and the reaction conditions. Only one ethyl group is displaced from diethylzinc by reaction with water at 0°, and the product has been formulated as a dimer [219]:

$$2Et_2Zn + 2H_2O \longrightarrow EtZn \overset{OH}{\underset{OH}{\diagdown\diagup}} ZnEt + 2C_2H_6$$

Crystalline products, $RZnOR'$, from zinc alkyls and alcohols have been mentioned from time to time, the methoxide $MeZnOMe$ having been described by Butlerow [220] in 1864. Reaction between diethylzinc and isopropanol in heptane at room temperature results in rapid displacement of one ethyl group, but the second remains unattacked by excess isopropanol under these conditions [219]. Unless very bulky groups are attached to the oxygen, the compounds derived from dimethyl- and diethyl-zinc are all tetramers in benzene solution, e.g. $(MeZnOMe)_4$, $(MeZnOBu^t)_4$, $(EtZnOPr^i)_4$ and $(MeZnOPh)_4$. Of these only the phenoxy compound yields a pyridine adduct:

$$\tfrac{1}{2}(MeZnOPh)_4 + 2py \longrightarrow \overset{Me \quad OPh \quad py}{\underset{py \quad OPh \quad Me}{Zn \diagup\diagdown Zn}}$$

The prevalence of tetramers among the alkylzinc alkoxides suggested the possibility of cubic or near-cubic structures in which both metal and oxygen atoms are four-co-ordinate [214]. The highly symmetrical crystal

[218] K. H. Thiele and S. Schröder, *Z. anorg. Chem.*, 1965, **337**, 14.
[219] R. J. Herold, S. L. Aggarwal and V. Neff, *Canad. J. Chem.*, 1963, **41**, 1368.
[220] A. Butlerow, *Jahresber.*, 1864, 467.

structure [221] of the methylzinc methoxide tetramer has been determined
by X-ray diffraction

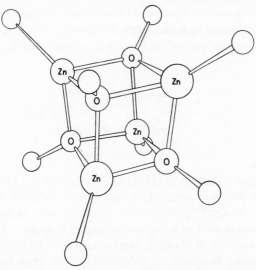

Fig. 15. (MeZnOMe)$_4$. Zn–C, 1·94; O–C, 1·46; Zn–O, 2·07 Å. Average angles in 'cube'.
96° at oxygen, 84° at zinc (after Shearer and Spencer [221])

Methylzinc t-butoxide eliminates isobutene when heated under atmospheric pressure, but sublimes unchanged in a vacuum. Most of the alkyl-zinc alkoxides, however, disproportionate to R$_2$Zn and [(R′O)$_2$Zn]$_x$ when heated, particularly at atmospheric pressure. Though (MeZnOPr^i)$_4$ and (MeZnOBu^t)$_4$ remain as tetramers in solution, the proton magnetic resonance spectra [222] of solutions of methylzinc methoxide change from the expected two lines, for freshly prepared solutions, to two unequal doublets. This effect is ascribed to a disproportionation forming dimethyl-zinc and a methylzinc methoxide Me$_6$Zn$_7$(OMe)$_8$, and dimethylzinc can be evaporated from the solution. Solutions resulting from the partial methanolysis of diphenylzinc behave similarly.

The presence of bulky groups attached to oxygen can result in degrees of association less than four. Thus methylzinc t-butoxide has a mean degree of association changing from four to just below three as the concentration of its solution in benzene is reduced from 0·7 to 0·12M (g. atoms zinc per litre) [222]. The trimeric diphenylmethoxy derivative, (EtZnOCHPh$_2$)$_3$, has already been mentioned. The triphenylmethoxy compound, (PhZnOCPh$_3$)$_2$

[221] H. M. M. Shearer and C. B. Spencer, *Chem. Comm.*, 1966, 194.
[222] G. Allen, J. M. Bruce, D. W. Farren and F. G. Hutchinson, *J. Chem. Soc.*, B, 1966, 799; J. M. Bruce, B. C. Cutsforth, D. W. Farren, F. G. Hutchinson, F. M. Rabagliati and D. R. Reed, ibid., p. 1020

from diphenylzinc and benzophenone, is a dimer [209], as is $(Bu^tZnOBu^t)_2$ [222a].

The production of reaction of dimethylzinc and 2-dimethylaminoethanol is a trimer. Though its structure is not known, a fused ring system (not, of course, co-planar) in which each zinc atom is four-co-ordinate and in which only one lone-pair of each oxygen is co-ordinated, is likely:

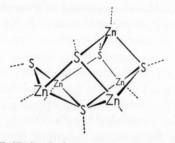

The trimethylsilyl derivative $(MeZnOSiMe_3)_4$ is also a tetramer [222b].

Reactions between zinc alkyls and thiols yield in some instances (MeZnSMe, $MeZnSPr^n$, MeZnSPh) insoluble and probably polymeric products, these doubtless being co-ordination polymers. They dissolve in benzene on addition of pyridine, but the latter can be removed at reduced pressure causing reversion to $(MeZnSR)_x$. The branched chain thiols isopropyl- and tertiary butyl-thiol, in contrast, yield the soluble oligomers $(MeZnSPr^i)_6$, $(MeZnSBu^t)_5$ and $(EtZnSBu^t)_5$. The zinc–sulphur framework of the pentamer $(MeZnSBu^t)_5$ is shown in Figure 16, in which

Fig. 16. Structure of $(MeZnSBu^t)_5$. Carbon atoms are omitted but dotted lines show the directions in which alkyl groups lie (after Adamson and Shearer [223])

dotted lines give the directions in which carbon atoms lie. The structure is that of a square-base pyramid of zinc atoms, in which the apical zinc lies over one side rather than over the centre of the pyramid. Though the co-ordination number of each zinc atom is four, that of one sulphur is three, of three sulphurs it is four, and that of the unique sulphur under the Zn_4

[222a] G. E. Coates and P. D. Roberts, *J. Chem. Soc.*, A, 1967, 1233.
[222b] F. Schindler, H. Schmidbaur and V. Krüger, *Angew. Chem. Internat. Edn.*, 1965, **4**, 876; see also H. Schmidbaur and G. Jonas, ibid., 1967, **6**, 449.
[223] G. W. Adamson and H. M. M. Shearer, unpublished observations.

square is five. An electron count, allowing a lone-pair for the three-co-ordinate sulphur, gives six electrons for the binding of the basal sulphur to four zinc atoms which may resemble the binding of the apical to the other boron atoms in B_5H_9, but it should be mentioned that one of the basal sulphur Zn–S bonds is rather longer than the other three. The butyl derivative $(MeZnSBu^t)_5$ adds pyridine giving a dimeric complex presenting no structural problems:

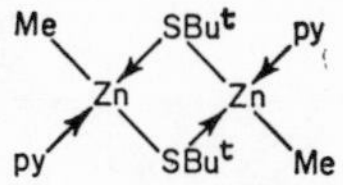

Though reactions between zinc alkyls and primary and secondary amines were reported some years ago [224], the nature of the zinc-containing products has only recently been examined. If dimethylamine is allowed to react with an equimolar proportion of dimethylzinc in the gas phase, only one half of the latter reacts:

$$2Me_2Zn + 2Me_2NH \longrightarrow \frac{1}{x}[(Me_2N)_2Zn]_x + Me_2Zn + CH_4$$

The insoluble and involatile bisamide could be formed either by the disproportionation of an intermediate, $MeZnNMe_2$, or reaction of the latter with more dimethylamine. The first of these is more likely to happen, since diphenylamine, which contains a more acidic hydrogen, yields the dimeric products $(MeZnNPh_2)_2$ and $(EtZnNPh_2)_2$. These dimers can only be formulated as containing three-co-ordinate zinc, e.g.

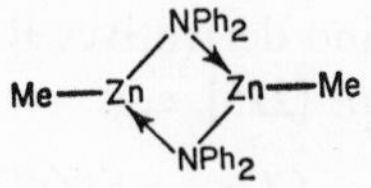

The co-ordination number of the metal could increase to four only by further association involving five-co-ordinate carbon (as in the dimethyl-beryllium polymer) or nitrogen (not yet observed). The three-co-ordination of the metal is, in fact, preserved in the crystalline state, as shown in Figure 17.

The dimer, $(MeZnNPh_2)_2$, adds pyridine as expected on account of its co-ordinative unsaturation, giving the bright yellow $Mepy_2ZnNPh_2$ or the pale yellow disproportionation product, $py_2Zn(NPh_2)_2$, according to the reaction conditions.

Trimethylethylenediamine reacts with dimethylzinc forming a dimeric product, $(MeZnNMeCH_2CH_2NMe_2)_2$, which can be formulated like the beryllium compound 2.11. The co-ordination number of the metal is

[224] E. Frankland, *Jahresber.*, 1867, 419.

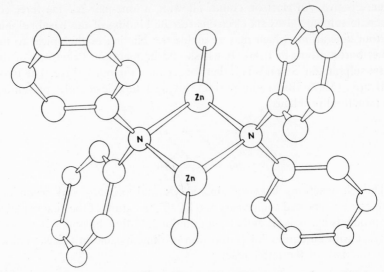

Fig. 17. Crystal structure of [MeZn NPh$_2$]$_2$ (after Shearer and Spencer [224a]). All the angles in the four-membered ring are right angles

brought up to four by means of the lone-pairs available on both nitrogen atoms [214].

A kinetic study of some reactions between amines and zinc alkyls has shown that in di-isopropyl ether the reaction is first order with respect to each reactant. The transition state is believed to involve both electrophilic attack by amino-hydrogen at the α-carbon and nucleophilic attack by nitrogen at the zinc atom [191a].

The Zn–N bond in the amino derivatives RZnNR′$_2$ adds readily across three-atom unsaturated groups [225], e.g.

$$EtZnNEt_2 + CO_2 \longrightarrow EtZnO{\cdot}CO{\cdot}NEt_2$$
$$EtZnNPh_2 + PhNCO \longrightarrow EtZnNPh{\cdot}CO{\cdot}NPh_2$$
$$EtZnNPh_2 + PhNCS \longrightarrow EtZnNPh{\cdot}CS{\cdot}NPh_2$$

The products of such reactions can act as catalysts for the trimerization of isocyanates. For example, EtZnNMe·CO·NPh$_2$ (from EtZnNPh$_2$ and MeNCO) is trimeric in benzene, and is believed to co-ordinate three molecules of MeNCO with the isocyanate-oxygen bound to zinc. In this complex there is likely to be strong interaction between the nitrogen of one isocyanate group and the carbon of the next; displacement by further MeNCO then results in the displacement of three MeNCO units at once as a 'pre-formed' trimer. This 'template-effect' in homogeneous catalysis is an important and promising development [225a].

[224a] H. M. M. Shearer and C. B. Spencer, personal communication.
[225] J. G. Noltes, *Rec. Trav. chim.*, 1965, **84**, 126.
[225a] J. G. Noltes and J. Boersma, *J. Organometal. Chem.*, 1967, **7**, P6.

The product derived from diethylzinc and t-butylamine, $EtZn(Bu^t)ZnEt$, is monomeric in benzene. It acts as a good catalyst for the stereoregular polymerization of propylene oxide, and the alkylaluminium oxide $Et_2AlOAlEt_2$ has somewhat similar properties [225b].

The expectation [209] that tetramers derivered from zinc alkyls and weak acids containing two donor atoms would have cage-like structures has been confirmed in the case of the tetramer derivered from dimethylzinc and acetoxime:

$$Me_2Zn + Me_2C:NOH \rightarrow (MeZnON:CMe_2)_4$$

The crystal structure of methylzinc acetoximate is shown in Figure 18.

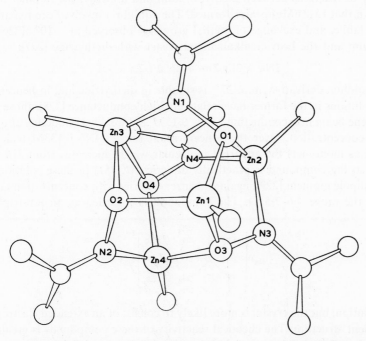

Fig. 18. Crystal structure of the methylzinc acetoximate tetramer, $(MeZnON:CMe_2)_4$ [224a]

Each metal atom is four-co-ordinate, and all nitrogen and oxygen atoms are three-co-ordinate. Thus each oxygen uses only one lone-pair for co-ordination, in contrast to the alkoxide tetramers (Figure 15). The structure consists of four five-membered and two six-membered rings fused together.

Some *azomethine* derivatives of zinc have been studied [225c]. Diphenyl-

[225b] H. Tani, T. Araki, N. Oguni and N. Ueyama, *J. Amer. Chem. Soc.*, 1967, **89**, 173.   [225c] I. Pattison and K. Wade, *J. Chem. Soc.*, A, 1967.

zinc forms a liquid adduct with phenyl cyanide, which rearranges at 100° giving the solid polymer $[(Ph_2C:N)_2Zn]_n$. Diphenylketimine, however, reacts at 30–65° with R_2Zn giving dimers $(Ph_2C:NZnR)_2$ (R = Me, Et, Ph) which are likely to resemble structurally the diphenylamino-compound (Figure 17).

Anionic complexes

The alkali metal alkyls dissolve in dialkyls of zinc to give conducting solutions containing the anions $(R_3Zn)_2^{2-}$ or R_4Zn^{2-}. The compound $Li_2ZnMe_4 \cdot OEt_2$ has been isolated from dimethylzinc and methyl-lithium in ether solution [226], and a detailed proton and ^7Li magnetic resonance study of reactions between methyl-lithium and dimethylzinc in ether has shown that Li_3ZnMe_5 is also formed. The equilibria involved are remarkably labile, and exchange of methyl groups is observed at $-107°$ [226a]. Sodium and the heavier alkali metals react with diethylzinc [227]:

$$2Na + 3Et_2Zn \longrightarrow 2NaEt_3Zn + Zn$$

The sodium derivative, m.p. 27°, is soluble in diethylzinc and in benzene. Its solutions in the former have relatively high conductance [228], those in benzene being non-conducting below 0·15M and weakly conducting above that concentration. Over the concentration range 0·046–0·133M (calculated as monomer) the apparent molecular weight increases from 314 to 362, so the compound is practically dimeric (M, 351) in these solutions. The dipole moment [229], again in benzene, varies with concentration and is in the range 4·6–7·5 D. The compound is regarded as an ion-triplet

in solution, but the crystal is more likely to consist of an extended electron-deficient structure. The chemical reactivity of these compounds is greater than that of diethylzinc, as might be expected if electron-deficient structures are involved.

The ethynyl complex, $K_2Zn(C:CH)_4$ is a strong electrolyte in liquid ammonia [230]; the anionic ethyl complexes would be instantly decomposed by that solvent.

[226] D. T. Hurd, *J. Org. Chem.*, 1948, **13**, 711.
[226a] L. M. Seitz and T. L. Brown, *J. Chem. Amer. Soc.*, 1966, **88**, 4140.
[227] J. A. Wanklyn, *Annalen*, 1858, **108**, 67; 1859, **111**, 234; 1866, **140**, 211.
[228] F. Hein, *Z. Elektrochem.*, 1922, **28**, 469.
[229] F. Hein, A. Schleede and H. Kallmeyer, *Z. anorg. Chem.*, 1961, **311**, 260.
[230] R. Nast and R. Müller, *Chem. Ber.*, 1958, **91**, 2861.

Diphenylzinc forms two complexes with phenyl-lithium [231]:

$$PhLi + Ph_2Zn \rightarrow LiPh_3Zn$$
$$3PhLi + 2Ph_2Zn \rightarrow Li_3Ph_7Zn_2$$

The first of these is more stable than the second and can be isolated, solvent-free from xylene, or as $LiPh_3Zn$ (dioxan)$_4$ from dioxan. The diphenyls of beryllium, magnesium and cadmium react similarly with phenyl-lithium, giving $LiPh_3M$. The relative stabilities of these compounds have been investigated by various methods, including ebullioscopic measurements, and the following stability sequence obtained:

$$LiPh_3Be > LiPh_3Zn > LiPh_3Mg > LiPh_3Cd > Li_3Ph_7Zn_2 > PhLi + Ph_2Hg$$
(i.e. no compound formed)

Diphenylzinc also reacts with lithium hydride, forming $LiPh_2HZn(OEt_2)$ [232]. Sodium hydride adds *two* mols. of diethylzinc in 1,2-dimethoxyethane or in 'diglyme' (but not in hydrocarbons nor in ether nor, curiously, in tetrahydrofuran), giving $NaH \cdot 2Et_2Zn$ which decomposes when attempts are made to isolate it from solution. The complex adds ethylene at 32 atmospheres and 100°. An even less stable complex, $NaH \cdot 2ZnCl_2$, is formed by zinc chloride [233].

The reaction between dimethylzinc and diborane gives an apparently polymeric mixed hydride [234], $(HZnBH_4)_x$, and with lithium aluminium hydride in ether solution the polymeric hydride, ZnH_2, is precipitated [235]:

$$Me_2Zn + 2LiAlH_4 \rightarrow ZnH_2 \downarrow + 2LiAlH_3Me$$

Zinc hydride has also been obtained [236] by the reduction of zinc iodide at $-40°$,

$$ZnI_2 + 2LiAlH_4 \rightarrow ZnH_2 \downarrow + 2AlH_3 + 2LiI$$

or, less satisfactorily, from zinc chloride and aluminium chlorohydride,

$$3ZnCl_2 + 2AlH_3 \cdot AlCl_3 \rightarrow 3ZnH_2 \downarrow + 4AlCl_3$$

CADMIUM

Owing to their conveniently mild reactivity, the organocadmium compounds have acquired some importance for ketone synthesis since they

[231] G. Wittig, F. J. Meyer and G. Lange, *Annalen*, 1951, **571**, 167; see also R. Waack and M. A. Doran, *J. Amer. Chem. Soc.*, 1963, **85**, 2861.
[232] G. Wittig and P. Hornberger, *Annalen*, 1952, **577**, 11.
[233] P. Kobetz and W. E. Becker, *Inorg. Chem.*, 1963, **2**, 859.
[234] H. I. Schlesinger and A. B. Burg, *Chem. Rev.*, 1942, **31**, 36.
[235] G. D. Barbaras, C. Dillard, A. E. Finholt, T. Wartik, K. E. Wilzbach and H. I. Schlesinger, *J. Amer. Chem. Soc.*, 1951, **73**, 4585.
[236] E. Wiberg, W. Henle and R. Bauer, *Z. Naturforsch.*, 1951, **6b**, 393.

can be made to react with acid chlorides without further reaction with the resulting ketones. Diethylcadmium has been studied as a catalyst for vinyl polymerization [237] (e.g. methyl methacrylate and styrene).

Preparation

The action of a Grignard reagent (or similar lithium compound) on an anhydrous cadmium halide is the usual method [238]:

$$2RMgX + CdCl_2 \longrightarrow R_2Cd + MgX_2 + MgCl_2$$

If the organocadmium compound is intended for reaction with acid chlorides it need not be separated from magnesium halides, and, indeed, the presence of the latter has been shown to be essential for reaction with acid chlorides to take place [239]. If the isolation of the lower dialkyls is required, they are distilled from the Grignard (or better, RLi) reaction mixture, first from a water-bath at atmospheric pressure and then from an oil-bath in vacuum. Two receivers are advisable, the first cooled in acetone– CO_2 and the second in liquid nitrogen; ether is subsequently removed by fractional distillation in an inert atmosphere.

Cadmium is chemically too close to mercury for the metal exchange reaction to be useful for preparative purposes, since equilibria,

$$R_2Hg + Cd \rightleftharpoons R_2Cd + Hg$$

result. A mixture of 75% diphenylcadmium and 25% diphenylmercury is obtained by heating cadmium with diphenylmercury [240], but diphenyl-cadmium, m.p. 173–174°, may be prepared by the addition of cadmium bromide to phenyl-lithium in ether [241] and can be separated by extraction and crystallization from benzene, or ether, followed by high vacuum sublimation [242]. The conversion of cadmium iodide into diethylcadmium by reaction with triethylaluminium is one step in a process for the manufacture of tetraethyl-lead from lead acetate and triethylaluminium: the diethylcadmium is used to alkylate metallic lead formed at one stage in the process [243].

$$3Pb + 6EtI + 3Et_2Cd \longrightarrow 3Et_4Pb + 3CdI_2$$

[237] J. Furukawa, T. Tsurata and T. Fueno, *J. Polymer Sci.*, 1958, **28**, 234.

[238] E. Krause, *Ber.*, 1917, **50**, 1813; P. L. de Benneville, *J. Org. Chem.*, 1941, **6**, 462; H. Gilman and J. F. Nelson, *Rec. Trav. chim.*, 1936, **55**, 518.

[239] J. Kollonitsch, *Nature*, 1960, **188**, 140; see also U.S.P. 3,065, 259 (to Merck), 1962.

[240] S. Hilpert and G. Grüttner, *Ber.*, 1913, **46**, 1682.

[241] A. N. Nesmeyanov and L. G. Makarova, *J. Gen. Chem. Russ.*, 1937, **7**, 2649; *Chem. Abs.*, 1938, **32**, 2095.

[242] W. Strohmeier, *Chem. Ber.*, 1955, **88**, 1218.

[243] U.S.P. 2,859,225–232 (to Ethyl Corporation), *Chem. Abs.*, 1959, **53**, 9149.

Bisethynylcadmium [244] is formed by the reversible reaction in liquid ammonia:

$$Cd(NH_2)_2 + 2C_2H_2 + (x-2)NH_3 \rightleftharpoons (HC{:}C)_2Cd(NH_3)_x$$

The bisethynyl remains in solution, but on evaporation of the solvent is converted into cadmium carbide:

$$(HC{:}C)_2Cd(NH_3)_x \rightleftharpoons CdC_2 + C_2H_2 + xNH_3$$

The bisethynyl is again formed if acetylene is bubbled into a suspension of the carbide in liquid ammonia.

Bisphenylethynylcadmium is formed by a similar reaction, from the amide and phenylacetylene, or from diphenylcadmium and phenyl-acetylene:

$$Ph_2Cd + 2PhC{:}CH \longrightarrow (PhC{:}C)_2Cd + 2C_6H_6$$

No PhCdC:CPh could be isolated. Bisphenylethynylcadmium is insoluble in ether, benzene, chloroform and dimethylformamide; it dissolves easily in ammonia at $-34°$ and crystallizes as an ammine when the temperature is reduced to $-78°$.

Diallylcadmium can be obtained by the exchange reaction,

$$3Me_2Cd + 2(CH_2{:}CH{\cdot}CH_2)_3B \longrightarrow 3(CH_2{:}CH{\cdot}CH_2)_2Cd + 2Me_3B$$

at low temperature. It is precipitated in the form of yellow crystals which decompose above $0°$. The methallyl compound $(CH_2{:}CMe{\cdot}CH_2)_2Cd$ is more stable thermally, and survives up to $10–12°$. These compounds form bright red bipyridyl complexes, but even these are thermally unstable. Diallylcadmium and related compounds are claimed to have ionic con-stitutions [244a]. For bispentafluorophenylcadmium see [244b].

Properties

The dialkyls are monomeric liquids which may be distilled at reduced pressure; thermal decomposition occurs above about 150° and may become explosive. It is a little surprising that dimethylcadmium, m.p. $-2.4°$ [245], b.p. $105.7°$ [246], is rather less volatile than dimethylmercury, b.p. $92.5°$. The heat of vaporization is 1.27 kcal. mole[-1] greater, but the Trouton constant is normal for a non-associated liquid. These effects are attributed [246] to enhanced van der Waals forces arising from the ano-malously long [247] Cd–C bond (2.112 ± 0.004 Å compared with 2.094 ± 0.005 Å for the Hg–C bond in Me_2Hg). The stretching force con-stant (2.05×10^5 dyne. cm[-1] [248] is less than that of Me_2Hg (2.45), and

[244] R. Nast and C. Richers, *Z. anorg. Chem.*, 1963, **319**, 320.

[244a] K. H. Thiele and J. Köhler, *J. Organometal. Chem.*, 1967, **7**, 365.

[244b] M. Schmeisser and M. Weidenbruch, *Chem. Ber.*, 1967, **100**, 2306.

[245] L. H. Long and R. G. W. Norrish, *Proc. Roy. Soc.*, 1949, **A241**, 596.

[246] L. H. Long and J. Cattanach, *J. Inorg. Nucl. Chem.*, 1961, **20**, 340.

[247] K. S. Rao, B. P. Stoicheff and R. Turner, *Canad. J. Phys.*, 1960, **38**, 1516.

[248] H. S. Gutowsky, *J. Amer. Chem. Soc.*, 1949, **71**, 3194.

the asymmetrical C–Cd–C stretching frequency is at 538 cm^{-1}, the symmetrical (Raman [249]) frequency being at 465 cm^{-1}. From a study of the homogeneous component of the pyrolysis of dimethylcadmium the dissociation energy for removal of the first methyl group is 49 kcal. [250].

The proton magnetic resonances of dimethyl-zinc, -cadmium and -mercury differ, but mixtures of the first two show a single rather broad resonance, and it is evident that an exchange of methyl groups takes place. Exchange appears to be facilitated in solvents of donor character such as pyridine or tetrahydrofuran. Both dimethyl-zinc and -cadmium exchange methyl groups rapidly with dimethylmagnesium and with trimethylaluminium, and electron-deficient intermediates are probably involved in the exchange process [251]. Dimethylmercury, on the other hand, undergoes exchange only very slowly.

The organocadmium compounds are considerably less reactive than those of zinc and do not normally take fire in the air, but they combine, with elimination of hydrocarbon, with compounds containing acidic hydrogen, e.g. water, alcohols. Alkyl and cadmium halides result from the action of halogens:

$$R_2Cd + 2X_2 \rightarrow 2RX + CdX_2$$

Alkylcadmium halides have been prepared by stirring R_2Cd with CdX_2 in ether. The ethyl compounds, EtCdX, described as white infusible powders which soften above 100°, are vigorously decomposed by water or alcohols and oxidized by air; they are insoluble in aromatic or saturated hydrocarbons and in ether. n-Butylcadmium bromide, in contrast, was crystallized from ether [252]. Phenylcadmium iodide [253], from Ph_2Cd + CdI_2 in ether, decomposes from about 150°. There is no information about the constitution of any of these compounds.

Diphenylcadmium is said to react with nitric oxide forming benzenediazonium nitrate, $PhN_2^+NO_3^-$, and it converts phenyliodidedichloride into diphenyliodonium chloride [241]. The reaction between dimethylcadmium and nitric oxide (similar to the reaction of zinc alkyls, p. 130) has been mentioned briefly [203].

The most important reaction of organocadmium compounds is with acid chlorides, when *ketones* are formed:

$$2RCOCl + R'_2Cd \rightarrow 2RCOR' + CdCl_2$$

[249] F. Feher, W. Kolb and L. Leverenz, *Z. Naturforsch.*, 1947, **2a**, 454.

[250] M. Krech and S. J. Price, *Canad. J. Chem.*, 1965, **43**, 1929.

[251] C. R. McCoy and A. L. Allred, *J. Amer. Chem. Soc.*, 1962, **84**, 912; R. E. Dessy, F. Kaplan, G. R. Coe and R. M. Salinger, ibid., 1963, **85**, 1191.

[252] N. I. Sheverdina, I. E. Paleeva, E. D. Delinskaya and K. A. Kocheshkov, *Doklady Akad. Nauk S.S.S.R.*, 1959, **125**, 348.

[253] Idem, ibid., 1962, **143**, 1123.

diamines and diethers. Although the dioxan complex is extensively dissociated in solution, it may reasonably be regarded as having a chelate structure in the crystalline state (m.p. 57°) [257].

Dimethylcadmium reacts with alcohols giving alkoxides very similar to those of zinc discussed earlier. The methoxide, $(MeCdOMe)_4$, is very sparingly soluble in organic solvents, but since it appears to be isomorphous with $(MeZnOMe)_4$, its structure is likely to be very similar. Several other alkoxides, $(MeCdOEt)_4$, $(MeCdOPr^i)_4$ and $(MeCdOPh)_4$, are tetramers in solution, and, as with the zinc series, only the phenoxide yields a pyridine adduct $(MepyCdOPh)_2$. The t-butoxide, $(MeCdOBu^t)_2$ is exceptional in being dimeric in solution, but even this one yields no pyridine adduct [258]. Trimethylsilanol however, gives the *tetrameric* product $(MeCdOSiMe_3)_4$ (Me_2Zn likewise gives $[MeZnOSiMe_3]_4$) which is believed to have a structure similar to that of $(MeZnOMe)_4$ (see Figure 15) [222*b*].

The thio-derivatives $(MeCdSMe)_x$ and $(MeCdSPh)_x$ are insoluble like their zinc analogues, and are regarded as polymeric. Though they dissolve in pyridine, evaporation of solvent yields only the original material. The isopropyl compound, $(MeCdSPr^i)_6$, resembles its zinc analogue, but the t-butyl sulphide, $(MeCdSBu^t)_4$, differs from the pentameric zinc compounds $[Me(or\ Et)ZnSBu^t]_5$ [258].

MERCURY

An enormous number of organomercury compounds has been prepared, largely in the earlier stages of the development of organometallic chemistry and to a great extent in the hope of finding substances of pharmacological value. The last factor was also responsible for much of the early work on the organic chemistry of arsenic and, to a lesser extent, of antimony. An additional factor facilitating the study of organomercury compounds is the low reactivity of mercury-carbon bonds to air and water, which is connected with the rather electronegative character of mercury and the low affinity of the element for oxygen.

Organomercury compounds may conveniently be considered in five categories:

(*a*) R—Hg—X, R being an alkyl, substituted alkyl or aryl, and X an electronegative radical,

[257] K. H. Thiele, *Z. anorg. Chem.*, 1964, **330**, 8.
[258] G. E. Coates and A. Lauder, *J. Chem., Soc.*, A, 1966, 264.

F

(b) R_2Hg,

(c) perhalo compounds (mainly perfluoro),

(d) vinyl and acetylenic compounds,

(e) mercarbides and similar substances.

The structural chemistry of mercury has been critically reviewed [259].

The alkyl- and aryl-mercury halides, etc. RHgX

Preparation

(i) ALIPHATIC SERIES. Some alkyl halides react directly with mercury, particularly when catalysed by sunlight. Methyl, benzyl, methylene and allyl *iodides* undergo this reaction [260], and allylmercury iodide is formed rapidly when mercury and allyl iodide are gently warmed together. Allyl-mercury iodide, $CH_2:CH \cdot CH_2HgI$, is believed to contain a π-bond between the olefin and mercury as well as a σ-bond between methylene and mercury [260a], though allylmercury systems are labile as shown by their n.m.r. spectra [260b].

The action of a Grignard reagent on mercury(II) chloride is a more general method, tetrahydrofuran often being a good solvent.

$$RMgX + HgCl_2 \longrightarrow RHgCl + MgXCl$$
$$RMgX + RHgCl \longrightarrow R_2Hg + MgXCl$$

The second stage is considerably slower than the first. Addition of the Grignard reagent to the mercury chloride (to avoid formation of R_2Hg) is not necessary, since the dialkyl compounds themselves react with mercury halides,

$$R_2Hg + HgX_2 \longrightarrow 2RHgX$$

For an n.m.r. study of this reaction, see [260c]. Normally it is more convenient to carry the reaction as far as R_2Hg and then convert to the desired halide.

The reaction between sodium amalgam and alkyl halides or sulphates, catalysed by methyl or ethyl acetate, gives both alkylmercury halides (or sulphates) and the dialkyls according to experimental conditions; mixtures are usually obtained.

A few special methods have been described for the preparation of methyl- and ethyl-mercury compounds. If $Me_3Al_2Cl_3$ and $Et_3Al_2Cl_3$ are readily available, these provide a convenient route to $MeHgCl$ or $EtHgCl$

[259] D. Grdenić, *Quart. Rev.*, 1965, **19**, 303.

[260] J. Maynard, *J. Amer. Chem. Soc.*, 1932, **54**, 2108.

[260a] M. M. Kreevoy, P. J. Steinwand and T. S. Straub, *J. Org. Chem.*, 1966, **31**, 4291.

[260b] Z. Rappoport, P. D. Sleezer, S. Winstein and W. G. Young, *Tetrahedron Letters*, 1965, 3719.

[260c] M. D. Rausch and J. R. van Wazer, *Inorg. Chem.*, 1964, **3**, 761.

by reaction with a suspension of $HgCl_2$ in methylene chloride; the preparations can be run on a several hundred gram scale [261]. Methylmercury compounds have also been prepared by reactions (10–18 hours) between methyl iodide and mercury(I) acetate or sulphate [262].

The halides may generally be converted into hydroxides, cyanides and other derivatives without great difficulty, by ion-exchange reactions [263] or the use of silver salts (e.g. MeHgCN from MeHgI using AgCN [264]). For methylmercury-fluoride, -thiocyanate (m.p. 125·5°) and -azide (m.p. 130·5°) see [265].

Diazomethane reacts with the covalent halides of several metals, forming halomethyl compounds. Mercury(II) chloride yields chloromethyl-mercury chloride, m.p. 131°, which is viciously vesicant, and bis(chloromethyl)mercury, m.p. 40° [266]:

$$HgCl_2 + CH_2N_2 \longrightarrow ClCH_2HgCl + N_2$$
$$ClCH_2HgCl + CH_2N_2 \longrightarrow (ClCH_2)_2Hg + N_2$$

2-Hydroxy- or 2-alkoxy-ethylmercury compounds are formed with considerable ease by the reaction between ethylene and mercury(II) salts, e.g.

$$C_2H_4 + Hg(NO_3)_2 + NaOH \longrightarrow HO \cdot CH_2CH_2HgNO_3 + NaNO_3$$

Often it is necessary to add alkali during the course of the reaction to neutralize acid as it is formed. The very easy regeneration of olefin, for example by reaction with acids, cyanides or thiocyanates, led to suggestions that the olefin was somewhat loosely bound to the mercury, perhaps like the olefin–platinum(II) complexes. On the other hand, there are reactions quite in accord with the 2-hydroxyethyl type of structure, for example HOC_2H_4HgI reacts with iodine in aqueous potassium iodide.

$$HOC_2H_4HgI + I_2 \longrightarrow HOC_2H_4I + HgI_2$$

and with sodium amalgam,

$$HOC_2H_4HgI + 2H \longrightarrow C_2H_5OH + Hg + HI$$

The extensive work done on these substances has been reviewed [267]. Doubts about their constitution have been resolved by measurement of the proton magnetic resonance spectra of 2-methoxyethylmercury acetate and 2-hydroxyethylmercury hydroxide ($HOCH_2CH_2HgOH$). The former

[261] Ger.P. 954,878 (to Hoechst); *Chem. Abs.*, 1959, **53**, 11226.
[262] V. N. Latyaeva, A. V. Malysheva and G. A. Razuvaev, *Zh. Vses. Khim. Obshchestva im. D. I. Mendeleeva*, 1962, **7**, 594; *Chem. Abs.*, 1963, **58**, 5709.
[263] T. D. Waugh, H. F. Walton and J. A. Laswick, *J. Phys. Chem.*, 1955, **59**, 395.
[264] J. E. Coates, L. E. Hinkel and T. H. Angel, *J. Chem. Soc.*, 1928, 540.
[265] A. Perret and R. Perrot, *Helv. Chim. Acta*, 1933, **16**, 848.
[266] L. Hellerman and M. D. Newman, *J. Amer. Chem. Soc.*, 1932, **54**, 2859.
[267] J. Chatt, *Chem. Rev.*, 1951, **48**, 7; N. S. Zefirov, *Uspekhi Khim.*, 1965, **34**, 527.

results when ethylene is passed into a suspension of mercury(II) acetate in methanol:

$$Hg(OAc)_2 + MeOH + C_2H_4 \longrightarrow MeOCH_2CH_2HgOAc + AcOH$$

The magnetic resonance spectra of these two compounds, measured in carbon tetrachloride and deuterium oxide respectively, clearly support their formulation as normal σ-bonded compounds rather than as π-complexes. The spectrum of the methylene group adjacent to mercury is clearly distinguishable from that of the methylene adjacent to methoxy or hydroxy [268].

It is quite possible that the formation of these compounds involves initial π-co-ordination of the olefin to mercury [267], followed by a $\pi \rightarrow \sigma$ transition of a kind now well established in the case of many olefin–transition metal complexes.

The facile elimination of olefin from these compounds, which has been the subject of detailed kinetic study [269], could be a reversal of the above process, i.e. a $\sigma \rightarrow \pi$ transition, but the detail of the transition state is not established with certainty.

The very easy oxymercuration of olefins, followed by borohydride reduction, provides a highly convenient method for the Markovnikov hydration of olefins under mild conditions. The method is nicely complementary to the anti-Markovnikov hydroboration process. The oxymercuration stage, in which the olefin is stirred at room temperature with a water–tetrahydrofuran solution of mercury(II) acetate, is normally complete in a few minutes. Sodium hydroxide is then added, followed by sodium borohydride, and reduction with precipitation of mercury is almost instantaneous.

$$Bu^n \cdot CH:CH_2 \xrightarrow{\text{Hg(OAc)}_2} Bu^n \cdot CHOH \cdot CH_2HgOAc \xrightarrow{\text{NaBH}_4} Bu^n \cdot CHOH \cdot CH_3$$

Since both stages are strongly exothermic, care should be taken in connexion with the scale of the reaction, and the temperature should be kept near 25° [269a].

[268] F. A. Cotton and J. R. Leto, *J. Amer. Chem. Soc.*, 1958, **80**, 4823.
[269] M. M. Kreevoy, J. W. Gilje, L. T. Ditsch, W. Batorewicz and M. A. Turner, *J. Org. Chem.*, 1962, **27**, 726; L. L. Schaleger, M. A. Turner, T. C. Chamberlin and M. M. Kreevoy, ibid., p. 3421.
[269a] H. C. Brown and P. Geoghegan, *J. Amer. Chem. Soc.*, 1967, **89**, 1522; H. C. Brown and W. J. Hammar, ibid., p. 1524; H. C. Brown, J. H. Kawakami and S. Ikegami, ibid., p. 1525.

The reaction between *carbon monoxide* and methanolic mercury(II) acetate also leads to the creation of a mercury–carbon bond:

$$Hg(OAc)_2 + MeOH + CO \longrightarrow CH_3 \cdot CO \cdot O \cdot Hg \cdot CO \cdot OCH_3$$

This structure for the product is preferred to the carbonyl co-ordination formula $AcOHg(\leftarrow C\equiv O)OMe$ on the basis of infrared and proton magnetic resonance spectra. The acetate group bound by the oxygen may easily be replaced by ions such as chloride, giving $ClHg \cdot CO \cdot OMe$ [270]. The chloride may itself be converted into biscarboxymethylmercury by the disproportionation brought about by triphenylphosphine (a type of reaction further discussed below),

$$2ClHg \cdot CO \cdot OMe + 2PPh_3 \longrightarrow (PPh_3)_2HgCl_2 \downarrow + Hg(CO \cdot OMe)_2$$

and into unsymmetrical di-organomercury compounds by very fast exchange reactions exemplified by [271]

$$ClHg \cdot CO \cdot OMe + Ph_2Hg \longrightarrow PhHgCl \downarrow + PhHg \cdot CO \cdot OMe$$

(*ii*) AROMATIC SERIES. The most generally useful preparative method is the reaction between a Grignard or organolithium reagent and a mercury halide. There are, however, several useful reactions available for the preparation of arylmercury compounds, which have no counterpart in the aliphatic series; these involve sulphinic acids, iodoxy and iodonium compounds, diazonium salts and the *mercuration* of aromatic compounds with mercury(II) acetate or perchlorate.

Various methods are available for obtaining arylmercury compounds from diazonium salts, and it appears likely that most of these involve a mechanism whereby the diazonium salt decomposes to an *aryl radical* (by an electron transfer process) which then attacks metallic mercury [272]; the latter should be finely divided and is conveniently obtained by reduction *in situ* of mercury(II) chloride. In the original method [273] the diazonium mercurichloride was reduced by copper powder:

$$ArN_2HgCl_3 + 2Cu \longrightarrow ArHgCl + 2CuCl_2 + N_2$$

The preparation of 2-naphthylmercury chloride by this method has been described in detail [274].

Alternatively the diazonium chloride may be stirred vigorously with finely divided mercury [275] at 0–5°,

$$ArN_2Cl + Hg \longrightarrow ArHgCl + N_2$$

[270] J. Halpern and S. F. A. Kettle, *Chem. and Ind.*, 1961, 668.
[271] F. E. Paulik and R. E. Dessy, ibid., 1962, 1650.
[272] W. A. Waters, *The Chemistry of Free Radicals*, Oxford, 1946.
[273] A. N. Nesmeyanov, *Ber.*, 1929, **62**, 1010, 1018.
[274] Idem, *Organic Syntheses*, Coll. Vol. II, p. 432, Wiley, New York, 1943.
[275] R. E. McClure and E. Lowry, *J. Amer. Chem. Soc.*, 1931, **53**, 319.

or the diazonium tetrafluoroborate may be stirred with precipitated mercury [276].

Diaryliodonium salts form mercurihalides which may be reduced by mercury to arylmercury halides, for example diphenyliodonium mercurichloride gives phenylmercury chloride in 70% yield. When this method is applied to mixed iodonium salts, the more negative aryl group becomes bonded to mercury [277]:

$$p\text{-ClC}_6\text{H}_4\text{IPh}\}\text{Cl} \longrightarrow p\text{-ClC}_6\text{H}_4\text{HgCl}$$
$$p\text{-MeOC}_6\text{H}_4\text{IPh}\}\text{Cl} \longrightarrow \text{PhHgCl}$$

Other reactions giving arylmercury compounds include the action of arylsulphinic acids on mercury(II) chloride [278],

$$\text{ArSO}_2\text{H} + \text{HgCl}_2 \longrightarrow \text{ArHgCl} + \text{SO}_2 + \text{HCl}$$

and that of iodoxy compounds on mercury oxide in alkaline solution [279]:

$$\text{ArIO}_2 + \text{HgO} \longrightarrow \text{ArHgIO}_3$$

Mercury(II) halides may be arylated by a variety of arylmetallic (and metalloid) compounds. These reactions, though of little value as preparative methods for arylmercury halides, are sometimes useful as analytical methods, an example being the reaction of arylboronic acids,

$$\text{ArB(OH)}_2 + \text{HgCl}_2 + \text{H}_2\text{O} \longrightarrow \text{ArHgCl} + \text{B(OH)}_3 + \text{HCl}$$

since the strong acid formed can be titrated.

Of particular interest are the 'mercuration' reactions between mercury salts (generally acetate or perchlorate) and aromatic compounds, in which mercury directly replaces hydrogen:

$$\text{ArH} + \text{Hg}^+\text{—X} \longrightarrow [\text{ArHHgX}]^+ \longrightarrow \text{ArHgX} + \text{H}^+$$

Proton transfer from the arylonium intermediate appears to be the rate-determining step, and there is a large isotope effect in that the C_6H_6 is mercurated six times faster than C_6D_6 under comparable conditions [280]. The relative rates of mercuration reactions are those expected for attack by a positive (electrophilic) reagent. Thus amines, phenols and aromatic ethers react rapidly, benzene more slowly (and toluene faster than benzene), and halo- and nitro-benzene very slowly. The orientation of the products is sometimes peculiar since *ortho* substitution has been reported (e.g. nitrobenzene [281]) in some cases when *meta* substitution might be

[276] M. F. W. Dunker, E. B. Starkey and G. L. Jenkins, *J. Amer. Chem. Soc.*, 1936, **58**, 2308.
[277] O. A. Reutov, O. A. Ptitsyna and Khun-Ven Khu, *Doklady Akad. Nauk S.S.S.R.*, 1958, **122**, 825; *Chem. Abs.*, 1959, **53**, 4177.
[278] W. Peters, *Ber.*, 1905, **38**, 2567.
[279] A. N. Nesmeyanov and L. G. Makarova, ibid., 1933, **66**, 199.
[280] A. J. Kresge and J. F. Brennan, *Proc. Chem. Soc.*, 1963, 215.
[281] O. Dimroth, *Annalen*, 1925, **446**, 148.

expected. These anomalies have for the most part been observed in reactions of mercury(II) *acetate* at relatively high temperatures. Further studies [282] on mercuration reactions have shown that addition of even small amounts of perchloric acid has the twofold effect of greatly increasing reaction rates and of making the orientation more specific and free from anomalies. The reason is the formation of positive ions Hg^{2+} or $HgOAc^+$ which are more active than the largely covalent acetate. The reaction between toluene and mercury(II) acetate is very slow at room temperature, but is practically complete after about two hours if carried out in glacial acetic acid containing about 1% perchloric acid; the products after treatment with sodium chloride are 17% *ortho*, 6% *meta* and 77% *para* tolylmercury chloride – together with a little dimercurated material. Addition of aniline to aqueous mercury(II) acetate at room temperature is followed in a few hours by separation of nearly pure *p*-aminophenylmercury acetate, m.p. 166–167°, some *ortho* isomer remaining in solution [283].

The mercuration of nitrobenzene, in contrast, is carried out in the presence of much perchloric acid [284]. Mercury(II) oxide and nitrobenzene are allowed to react in an excess of 70% perchloric acid for five days at room temperature; subsequent addition to aqueous sodium chloride gives *meta*-nitrophenylmercury chloride, m.p. 240–242°.

The fast mercuration of thiophen is the basis of a method for the removal of thiophen from benzene. If technical benzene is boiled with an aqueous solution of mercury(II) acetate a dimercurated product

$$\text{HO·Hg} \underset{S}{\overset{}{\bigsqcup}} \text{HgO·CO·Me}$$

is precipitated, and after about half an hour the benzene, itself scarcely attacked, is free from thiophen. The latter may be recovered from the above compound by boiling with 20% hydrochloric acid [285].

α-Chloromercuri-*thiophen*, and *-furan* may be prepared by adding thiophen or furan to an aqueous-alcoholic solution of mercury(II) chloride and sodium acetate, and leaving to stand at room temperature.

Properties

Alkyl- and aryl-mercury compounds, R·HgX, are crystalline solids, many of the former being sufficiently volatile to sublime under reduced pressure. The vapour pressures [286] of methyl- and ethyl-mercury halides (excluding fluorides) do not greatly depend on the halogen, e.g. at 0° MeHgCl,

[282] K. A. Kobe and P. F. Lueth, *Ind. Eng. Chem.*, 1942, **34**, 309; W. J. Klapproth and F. H. Westheimer, *J. Amer. Chem. Soc.*, 1950, **72**, 4461; H. C. Brown and C. W. McGary, ibid., 1955, **77**, 2300, 2306, 2310.
[283] O. Dimroth, *Ber.*, 1902, **35**, 2039.
[284] R. E. Dessy and J. Y. Kim, *J. Amer. Chem. Soc.*, 1960, **82**, 686.
[285] O. Dimroth, *Ber.*, 1899, **32**, 759.
[286] T. Charnley and H. A. Skinner, *J. Chem. Soc.*, 1951, 1921.

0·0040 mm., —Br, 0·0048 mm., —I, 0·0049 mm. (measured with a quartz fibre manometer). Mercury, in its two-covalent compounds, has long been assumed to use its $6s$ and $6p$ atomic orbital in the formation of two colinear bonds. The involvement of $5d$ orbitals [287] does not alter the stereochemistry. Methylmercury chloride and bromide, both symmetric top molecules, have relatively simple microwave spectra, and accurate dimensions have been measured [288].

$$H_3C \underset{2·061}{\text{———}} Hg \underset{2·282}{\text{———}} Cl \qquad H_3C \underset{2·074}{\text{———}} Hg \underset{2·406\,Å}{\text{———}} Br$$

The properties of the compounds R·HgX depend largely on the tendency of the atom or group X to form a covalent bond. When X is highly electronegative, like fluoride, nitrate, sulphate, phosphate or perchlorate, and has a strong tendency to exist in the anionic form, then the compounds RHgX behave largely as salts and are more soluble in water in which they dissolve as $[RHgOH_2]^+X^-$, than in organic, particularly non-polar, solvents. In some instances, e.g. $X = ClO_4^-$, BF_4^-, attempted isolation of the methylmercury salts gives the trismethylmercurioxonium salts [289], such as $[(MeHg)_3O]^+ClO_4^-$.

In certain instances, *nitrates* react with carbon monoxide under pressure (25–250 atm.) e.g. [289a]

$$Bu^nHgNO_3 + H_2O + CO \longrightarrow Bu^nCO_2H + Hg + HNO_3$$

Reaction between silver oxide, or alcoholic alkali, and alkylmercury halides gives substances earlier described [290] as alkylmercury hydroxides, RHgOH, but these consist of mixtures of $[(RHg)_3O]OH$ and $(RHg)_2O$. The methyl compounds $[(MeHg)_3O]OH$, m.p. 88°, and $(MeHg)_2O$, m.p. 139°, have been studied extensively [289] and a series of salts, $[(MeHg)_3O]X$ ($X = Br$, NO_3, OAc, CCl_3CO_2, MnO_4, ClO_4, BF_4, PF_6, SO_4, Cr_2O_7) prepared from them. The oxonium hydroxide loses water, even in dry air, giving the oxide $(MeHg)_2O$, and addition of acids to methanol or acetone solutions of the oxide results in the formation of the oxonium salts. The oxides dissolved in methanol absorb carbon dioxide forming alkylmercury carbonates:

$$(RHg)_2O + CO_2 \longrightarrow (RHg)_2CO_3$$

Methylmercury oxide also adds methylmercury bromide, giving the oxonium bromide $[(MeHg)_3O]Br$, m.p. 116°.

Methylmercury sulphide, $(MeHg)_2S$, m.p. 144°, from $MeHgBr + Na_2S$

[287] L. E. Orgel, *J. Chem. Soc.*, 1958, 4186.
[288] W. Gordy and J. Sheridan, *J. Chem. Phys.*, 1954, **22**, 92.
[289] D. Grdenić and F. Zado, *J. Chem. Soc.*, 1962, 521.
[289a] J. M. Davidson, *Chem. Comm.*, 1966, 126.
[290] K. H. Slotta and K. R. Jacobi, *J. prakt. Chem.*, 1929, **120**, 249.

[291] or MeHgCN + H$_2$S [264], is unstable and decomposes when heated [292]:

$$(RHg)_2S \rightarrow R_2Hg + HgS$$

It reacts with chromic acid giving a *sulphonium* salt,

$$3(MeHg)_2S + H_2Cr_2O_7 \rightarrow [(MeHg)_3S]_2Cr_2O_7$$

from which the nitrate (MeHg)$_3$SNO$_3$ has been obtained [291].

Though the oxonium salt [(MeHg)$_3$O]ClO$_4$ is obtained when the oxide is neutralized with perchloric acid, reaction between methylmercury iodide and silver perchlorate gives a solution in which the ion [Me—Hg$\leftarrow$OH$_2$]$^+$ was identified by its Raman spectrum [293], which includes v(Hg—Me) at 570 and v(Hg—O) at 463 cm^{-1}. Aqueous solutions of methylmercury nitrate contain both [Me—Hg$\leftarrow$OH$_2$]$^+$NO$_3^-$ and Me—Hg—O·NO$_2$, and dimethylsulphide displaces both H$_2$O and NO$_3$ giving the ion [MeHg$\leftarrow$SMe$_2$]$^+$, v(Hg—S) at 302 cm^{-1}. This agrees with the normal classification of mercury as a 'B' type acceptor, tending to combine with ligands capable of π back-co-ordination.

The relative affinities of a variety of ligands for the methylmercury group has been studied by measuring the partition (294):

$$\frac{[MeHgX]_{toluene}}{[MeHgX]_{water}} = 11, X = Cl: 45, X = Br: 300\text{-}500, X = I$$

Affinities decrease from RS$^-$ in the series:

$$RS^- > CN^- > OH^- > I^- > NH_3 > Br^- > SCN^- > Cl^- > \text{pyridine}$$

Tertiary phosphines are well-known ligands with π-bonding properties, but these along with some other ligands in the left-hand part of the above series commonly cause disproportionation. The use of cyanides and, more conveniently, iodides, for this purpose is a recognized way (mentioned below under R$_2$Hg) of preparing R$_2$Hg from RHgX:

$$2RHgX + 4I^- \rightarrow R_2Hg + HgI_4^{2-} + 2X^-$$

Neutral ligands, displacing halide ions, give cationic intermediates,

$$RHgX + PR'_3 \rightarrow [RHgPR'_3]^+ + X^-$$

but these rapidly decompose when R is aryl or another negative group such as ·CO$_2$Me [295] or ·CCl:CCl$_2$ [296]. Addition of triphenylphosphine to solutions of phenylmercury chloride results in an increase in electrical conductivity, but only PhHgCl was isolated from the mixture [297] presumably due to its low solubility. Addition of one mol. triphenylphosphine

[291] D. Grdenić and B. Markušić, *J. Chem. Soc.*, 1958, 2434.
[292] E. Dreher and R. Otto, *Ber.*, 1869, **2**, 542.
[293] P. L. Goggin and L. A. Woodward, *Trans. Faraday Soc.*, 1962, **58**, 1495.
[294] R. B. Simpson, *J. Amer. Chem. Soc.*, 1961, **83**, 4711.
[295] F. E. Paulik and R. E. Dessy, *Chem. and Ind.*, 1962, 1650.
[296] D. Seyferth and R. H. Towe, *Inorg. Chem.*, 1962, **1**, 185.
[297] R. E. Dessy, W. L. Budde and C. Woodruff, *J. Amer. Chem. Soc.*, 1962, **84**, 1176.

to an acetone solution (25°) of the more soluble m-tolylmercury chloride results in an immediate and large increase in conductivity followed by a steady fall during about six minutes as $(PPh_3)_2HgCl_2$ crystallizes:

$$m\text{-}MeC_6H_4HgCl + PPh_3 \longrightarrow [m\text{-}MeC_6H_4Hg \leftarrow PPh_3]^+Cl^- \longrightarrow$$
$$(m\text{-}MeC_6H_4)_2Hg + (PPh_3)_2HgCl_2 \downarrow$$

The corresponding bromide disproportionates even faster. Alkylmercury-phosphonium salts disproportionate more slowly, again in the order I (fastest) > Br > Cl, and the methyl compounds are sufficiently stable to allow their isolation as crystalline salts, e.g. $[MeHgPEt_3]Br$, m.p. 90–91°, $[MeHgPEt_3]BF_4$, dec. from 120°, $[MeHgPEt_3]ClO_4$, dec. from 137°, $[MeHgAsEt_3]ClO_4$, dec. from 120° and $[MeHgPPh_3]ClO_4$, m.p. 213° (decomp.) [298].

Few alkoxides have been described, but $(PhHgOMe)_3$ and $(PhHgOBu^n)_3$ are both regarded as containing Hg_3O_3 rings [298a].

The trimethylsiloxy derivative, $MeHgOSiMe_3$, is monomeric in dilute solution, in contrast to $(MeZnOSiMe_3)_4$ and $(MeCdOSiMe_3)_4$ on account of the relatively low acceptor character of mercury towards oxygen donors [299], but is tetrameric in the crystalline state [299a].

The electrolysis [300] of water–pyridine solutions of methylmercury acetate gives a good yield of dimethylmercury by the disproportionation reaction:

$$CH_3Hg^+ + e^- \longrightarrow CH_3Hg\cdot \longrightarrow \tfrac{1}{2}Hg + \tfrac{1}{2}(CH_3)_2Hg$$

The electrolysis of liquid ammonia solutions of alkylmercury halides at −33°, presumably containing $[RHg \leftarrow NH_3]^+$ cations, results in the deposition on the cathode of an electrically conducting solid of metallic appearance [301], which decomposes at room temperature into equimolar proportions of mercury and dialkylmercury. The substance is easiest to obtain when R = CH_3, and the products become increasingly unstable as R becomes more complex. The cathode product appears to be a *metal*, consisting, in the deposit from methylmercury compounds, of $CH_3\cdot Hg^+$ ions in a metallic lattice, together with the equivalent number of 'free' electrons, i.e. an *organic metal* [302]. The preparation of the methyl compound has been repeated [303], and a careful study of a series of these

[298] R. J. Cross, A. Lauder and G. E. Coates, *Chem. and Ind.*, 1962, 2013; G. E. Coates and A. Lauder, *J. Chem. Soc.*, 1965, 1857.

[298a] G. Holam, *Tetrahedron Letters*, 1966, 1985.

[299] H. Schmidbaur and F. Schindler, *Angew. Chem., Internat. Edn.*, 1965, **4**, 876.

[299a] E. Hellner and G. Dittmar, Lecture at 7th I.U.C. Crystallography Congress, Moscow 1966.

[300] J. L. Maynard and H. C. Howard, *J. Chem. Soc.*, 1923, 960.

[301] C. A. Kraus, *J. Amer. Chem. Soc.*, 1923, **35**, 1732; *Rec. Trav. chim.*, 1923, **42,** 588.   [302] G. E. Coates, *Quart. Rev.*, 1950, **4**, 217.

[303] F. O. Rice and B. L. Evering, *J. Amer. Chem. Soc.*, 1934, **56**, 2105.

experimentally rather difficult substances has been carried out [304] in which organomercury halides $RHgCl$ (R = Me, Et, Pr^n, Pr^i, Bu^n, Ph, $PhCH_2$ and trans-$ClCH{:}CH$) were electrolysed between platinum electrodes in liquid ammonia at $-78°$. Most of the cathode deposits are black, but those derived from Pr^n and Bu^nHgCl have a reddish-brown tinge and tend to grow out from the cathode in a tree-like manner. Decomposition occurs slowly even at $-50°$ and this unfortunately interferes with measurements of electrical conductivity and its temperature dependence. The products of decomposition are mercury and dialkyl (or diaryl) -mercury only, no products characteristic of radical disproportionation or dimerization being obtained. The substances are not free radicals since they interact neither with nitric oxide, nor with styrene, nor with diphenylpicrylhydrazyl, nor do they show an electron resonance absorption [305]. Their possible formulation as organic mercury(I) compounds, $RHgHgR$, is excluded by their relatively high electrical conductivity, in contrast to the insulating character of solid inorganic mercury(I) compounds. Their possible formulation as amalgams between mercury and organic free radicals is untenable since radicals are absent, since further addition of mercury does not cause further amalgamation, and, particularly, since their decomposition into R_2Hg + Hg and not R_2 shows that the organic groups are each bound to a mercury atom. If the 'organic metal' is prepared by the electrolysis of optically active sec.-butylmercury bromide, then the activity disappears. This, together with the other evidence, suggests that at the low temperatures at which the 'metals' are stable, R—Hg^+ units are present in a metallic kind of structure, but that as the temperature is allowed to rise the conduction electrons return to the mercury giving a non-metallic structure held together by C---Hg---C half-bonds (as pictured by Gowenlock and Trotman [304]). Decomposition to R_2Hg and mercury would then result in complete racemization.

The dialkyls and diaryls of mercury, R_2Hg

Preparation

There are three groups of preparative methods, (*i*) alkylation or arylation of inorganic mercury(II) compounds, (*ii*) alkylation or arylation of metallic mercury, (*iii*) reduction or disproportionation of $RHgX$.

(*i*) *Alkylation of Hg(II)*. The most commonly used procedure is the action of a slight excess of Grignard or lithium reagent on a mercury(II) halide. Optimum experimental details for several such preparations have been investigated [306].

[304] B. G. Gowenlock and J. Trotman, *J. Chem. Soc.*, 1957, 2114.
[305] B. G. Gowenlock, P. Pritchard-Jones and D. W. Ovenall, ibid., 1958, 535.
[306] H. Gilman and R. E. Brown, *J. Amer. Chem. Soc.*, 1930, **52**, 3314.

Reaction between mercury(II) chloride and aluminium alkyls or alkyl-aluminium halides results in the transfer of only one alkyl group to mercury (giving RHgCl, see p. 148) unless an excess of R_3Al is used, or unless sodium chloride is added [307]. Red mercury(II) oxide is converted to diethylmercury in 95% yield when stirred with triethylborane and aqueous sodium hydroxide at 75°. In this reaction [308] two of the three ethyl groups of the triethylborane are transferred to mercury. Similarly diethyl-mercury is obtained, in rather lower yield, when triethylborane is heated with mercury(II) acetate in boiling 1,2-dimethoxyethane.

Acetylenic mercury compounds (see p. 174) are formed from acetylenes $RC\text{:}CH$ and mercury(II) in *alkaline solution*.

The phosphorane reaction with mercury(II) bromide, giving a cation which has been isolated as mercuribromide, reineckate or tetraphenyl-borate, is an unusual type of alkylation process [309]:

$$Ph_3P\text{:}CH_2 + HgBr_2 \longrightarrow [Ph_3PCH_2HgCH_2PPh_3]^{2+} \longrightarrow$$
$$[Ph_3PCH_2HgCH_2PPh_3][Ph_4B]_2$$
$$\text{m.p. } 101\text{--}104°$$

Several mixed dialkyls, diaryls and alkyl aryls have been obtained [310], mainly by the action of R'MgX or R'Li on RHgX:

$$RHgX + R'MgX \longrightarrow RHgR' + MgX_2$$

For example, PhHgEt (b.p. 107–108°/5 mm.) has been prepared from EtHgCl + PhLi for dipole moment [311] and kinetic [312] studies. Dimethyl- and diphenyl-mercury undergo a statistical exchange of groups when heated together even without a catalyst, similarly PhHgMe gives an equilibrium mixture of PhHgMe, Ph_2Hg and Me_2Hg. Redistribution equilibria for a variety of organomercury compounds have been examined by gas chromatography and n.m.r. techniques. A near statistical exchange is observed only when the organic groups are fairly similar, e.g. both aryl or saturated alkyl. When vinyl, allyl or perfluoro mercurials exchange with dialkyls, the resulting distribution is far from statistical [260c, 313]. The exchange of alkyl and aryl groups is catalysed by peroxides and other radical sources, and particularly strongly by mercury(I) salts [314]. Mixed alkyl-mercury carborane derivatives, such as $MeHgB_{10}C_2H$ (m.p. 200–201°)

[307] H. Jenkner, Ger.P. 1,048,481 (to Kali-Chemie).
[308] J. B. Honeycutt and J. M. Riddle, *J. Amer. Chem. Soc.*, 1959, **81**, 2593.
[309] S. O. Grim and D. Seyferth, *Chem. and Ind.*, 1959, 849; N. A. Nesmeyanov, V. M. Novikov and O. A. Reutov, *J. Organometal. Chem.*, 1965, **4**, 202.
[310] M. S. Kharasch and A. L. Flenner, *J. Amer. Chem. Soc.*, 1932, **54**, 674.
[311] H. Sawatzky and G. F. Wright, *Canad. J. Chem.*, 1958, **36**, 1555.
[312] R. E. Dessy, Y. K. Lee and J. Y. Kim, *J. Amer. Chem. Soc.*, 1961, **83**, 1163.
[313] G. F. Reynolds and S. R. Daniel, *Inorg. Chem.*, 1967, **6**, 480.
[314] W. E. French, N. Inamoto and G. F. Wright, *Canad. J. Chem.*, 1964, **42**, 2228.

from MeHgCl and $B_{10}C_2HLi$, are of interest in showing no tendency to disproportionate [315].

(*ii*) *Alkylation of mercury*. Both dialkyls and diaryls can be prepared from sodium amalgam and the appropriate halide or sulphate [316] conveniently diluted with xylene; the addition of a little methyl or ethyl acetate or dimethylformamide [317] has a catalytic effect.

$$2RX + 2Na,Hg \longrightarrow R_2Hg + 2NaX$$

The mechanism of this reaction is unknown, but is likely to involve conversion of RX into $R \cdot + X^-$ followed by attack of the radical on the metal.

(*iii*) *Reduction or disproportionation of RHgX*. The electrolytic reduction of MeHgOAc has already been mentioned (p. 156). Arylmercury compounds can readily be converted to $Ar_2Hg + Hg$ by reduction with sodium, sodium stannite, or, very cleanly, by hydrazine hydrate and sodium carbonate in aqueous ethanol [318]. The disproportionation $RHgX \rightarrow R_2Hg + HgX_2$ brought about by tertiary phosphines has been discussed (p. 155); similar reactions occur with substances that form particularly stable anionic mercury complexes, notably iodide and cyanide, e.g.

$$2EtHgI + 2KCN \longrightarrow Et_2Hg + K_2HgI_2(CN)_2$$

Reaction with excess sodium iodide dissolved in alcohol [319] or better in acetone [284] is a standard procedure, the product R_2Hg crystallizing as the reaction mixture cools or being precipitated when it is poured into water.

Properties

The dialkyls are mostly monomeric volatile liquids, e.g. Me_2Hg, b.p. 92·5 (for vapour pressure see [320]), Et_2Hg, b.p. 159°, Pr^n_2Hg, b.p. 189°. They are dangerously toxic and vary considerably in stability. Dimethylmercury undergoes no perceptible decomposition at room temperature, but diethylmercury very slowly deposits metallic mercury. Most of the dialkyls can be kept unchanged in a refrigerator, one of the least stable being di-isopropylmercury [321]. Diaryls are generally less liable to decompose though some are affected by light. Diallylmercury is particularly

[315] L. I. Zakharkin, V. I. Bregadze and O. Y. Okhlobystin, *J. Organometal. Chem.*, 1965, **4**, 211.
[316] F. Fuchs, *J. prakt. Chem.*, 1928, **119**, 209.
[317] G. A. Razuvaev, G. G. Petukhov, V. P. Khripunov, Z. F. Timoshenko and E. M. Sergeeva, U.S.S.R.P. 113, 714 (1958); *Chem. Abs.*, 1959, **53**, 6082.
[318] H. Gilman and M. M. Barnett, *Rec. Trav. chim.*, 1936, **55**, 563.
[319] F. C. Whitmore and R. J. Sobatzki, *J. Amer. Chem. Soc.*, 1933, **55**, 1128; R. W. Beattie and F. C. Whitmore, ibid., p. 1567.
[320] L. H. Long and J. Cattanach, *J. Inorg. Nucl. Chem.*, 1961, **20**, 340.
[321] H. T. J. Chilton and B. G. Gowenlock, *Trans. Faraday Soc.*, 1953, **49**, 1451.

unstable and decomposes to mercury and diallyl [322]. The diaryls are mostly solids, Ph_2Hg, m.p. 125°, di-1-naphthylmercury, m.p. 243°. Bis-cyclopentadienylmercury, $(C_5H_5)_2Hg$, m.p. 83–85° (decomp. from about 60°) is formed from cyclopentadienylsodium and mercury(II) chloride in tetrahydrofuran, or, rather more easily, from C_5H_5Tl and $HgCl_2$ [323]. Its infrared spectrum and its reactions with maleic anhydride suggest a σ-bonded constitution [324]. As its proton magnetic resonance spectrum at room temperature consists of a single sharp resonance, it belongs to the now extensive class of stereochemically non-rigid compounds. The C_5 ring can rotate, probably through a relatively low energy π-bound intermediate, so that on average each carbon is bound to the metal for the same fraction of time. The effect has been discussed by F. A. Cotton [325].

The infrared and Raman spectra [195, 196] of dimethylmercury show that the mercury-carbon bonds are collinear, freely rotating methyls, with stretching frequencies 515 and 550 cm^{-1}. A medium to low intensity absorption in the range 515 to 550 cm^{-1} is characteristically found in compounds containing a $Hg–CH_3$ bond [258]. The pure rotation Raman spectra of Me_2Zn, Me_2Cd and Me_2Hg and their fully deuterated analogues have been measured, and lead to the following metal–carbon bond lengths: Zn–C, $1·929 \pm 0·004$; Cd–C, $2·112 \pm 0·004$; Hg–C, $2·094 \pm 0·005$ Å [326] (only $0·02–0·03$ Å longer than in MeHgBr and MeHgCl). Symmetrical mercury compounds, R_2Hg, have total polarizations in solution which apparently indicate non-zero dipole moments. Apparent moments [327] of ca. $0·4–0·5$ D for diphenylmercury in benzene and in decalin at 25° and 142° were originally interpreted as indicating a bent structure, i.e. the C–Hg–C bond being less than 180°. At about the same time de Laszlo concluded, from the electron diffraction of bis(p-bromphenyl)mercury vapour, that in the vapour state the C–Hg–C bonds in different molecules were bent by varying amounts up to about 30° away from the collinear [328]. Shortly afterwards several classes of compound, expected to have balanced dipoles and therefore zero permanent dipole moments, were shown to have quite appreciable apparent moments when measured in solution but zero moments when measured by the temperature variation of dielectric constant of the gas. The apparent moments in solution were ascribed to abnormally high atom polarization [329].

[322] K. V. Vijayaraghavan, *J. Indian Chem. Soc.*, 1943, **20**, 318.

[323] A. N. Nesmeyanov, R. B. Materikova and N. S. Kochetkova, *Bull. Acad. Sci. U.S.S.R.*, 1963, 1211 (Russ. p. 1334).

[324] G. Wilkinson and T. S. Piper, *J. Inorg. Nucl. Chem.*, 1956, **2**, 32.

[325] F. A. Cotton, Ch. 8 in *Proceedings of the 9th Robert A. Welch Foundation Conference on Chemical Research*, Nov. 15–17, 1965.

[326] K. S. Rao, B. P. Stoicheff and R. Turner, *Canad. J. Phys.*, 1960, **38**, 1516.

[327] G. C. Hampson, *Trans. Faraday Soc.*, 1934, **30**, 877.

[328] H. de Laszlo, ibid., p. 884.

[329] J. W. Smith and W. R. Angus, *Proc. Roy. Soc.*, 1932, *A* **137**, 372; A. E. Finn,

Compounds in question included various metal acetylacetonates and, for another example, benzoquinone. For the last, recent developments in far infrared spectroscopy have allowed the discovery of a strong absorption at 108 cm^{-1}, and this low frequency vibration itself accounts for two-thirds of the anomalously large atom polarization [330]. That high atom polarization is responsible for the apparent moments of mercury compounds, R_2Hg, has been denied by Wright [331] who found low atom polarizations by dielectric constant measurements on the compressed solid compounds. The molecules would not, however, be expected to be quite as flexible when constrained in a crystal lattice as in the dissolved or gaseous states. It is fairly clear that at least a significant proportion of these molecules are bent in the dissolved state. If the bending is mainly due to the electric field applied in order to measure the dipole moment, then the apparent moment can be ascribed to atom polarization. If it is due to thermal agitation, and the thermally bent molecules remain in that condition long enough to orient in the applied field, then the moments can reasonably be ascribed to orientation polarization and are thus 'real'. The effect of temperature on the apparent moments is not understood: for Ph_2Hg Hampson [327] found a very slight increase on changing from decalin at 25° to decalin at 142°, whereas Wright [331] found the apparent moment in CCl_4 decreased as the temperature was raised and an opposite effect in benzene.

Dicovalent mercury compounds whose crystal structures have been determined all contain C–Hg–C bonds which are collinear or nearly so. In mercury(II) cyanide there is evidently an appreciable degree of coordination between nitrogen and mercury, which distorts the environment of the mercury part way towards the tetrahedral, and the C–Hg–C angle [332] is 171°. On the other hand the compound described in early chemical literature as 2.17 has in fact the structure 2.18 in which the shorter Hg–O distances (2·2 Å) are those expected for a chemical bond. Even so the C–Hg–C angle is given [333] as 176°.

2.17   2.18

G. C. Hampson and L. E. Sutton, *J. Chem. Soc.*, 1938, 1254; I. E. Coop and L. E. Sutton, ibid., p. 1269; for review see J. W. Smith, *Electric Dipole Moments*, Butterworths, London, 1955.

[330] E. Charney and E. D. Becker, *J. Amer. Chem. Soc.*, 1961, **83**, 4468.

[331] H. Sawatzky and G. F. Wright, *Canad. J. Chem.*, 1958, **36**, 1555; W. C. Horning, F. Lautenschlaeger and G. F. Wright, ibid., 1963, **41**, 1441.

[332] J. Hvoslef, *Acta Chem. Scand.*, 1958, **12**, 1568.

[333] D. Grdenić, *Acta Cryst.*, 1952, **5**, 367.

Diphenylmercury is linear and centrosymmetric in the crystalline state [334], and X-ray structure analyses have been completed for di(p-tolyl)- and bispentafluorophenyl-mercury. The di-p-tolyl compound is linear and planar [335], but the perfluoro-aryl compound $(C_6F_5)_2Hg$ is not quite linear (176°) and the aryl rings are twisted 60° apart [336]. Numerous organomercury compounds have been assigned structures involving decidedly bent C–Hg–C bonds, and which are unlikely to be correct. In some instances later investigations have shown that particular compounds are associated to an extent which allows collinear C–Hg–C bonds (e.g. 2.18). The substance 'o-phenylenemercury', decomp. 326°, from o-di-

2.19

brombenzene and sodium amalgam in the presence of ethyl acetate [337], was given the structure 2.19, but was later shown to be hexameric and to

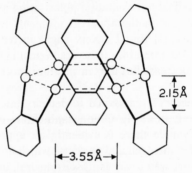

Fig. 19. o-Phenylenemercury (Grdenić [338], *Chem. Ber.*, 1959, **92**, 232, Fig. 1a, Verlag Chemie G.m.b.H.)

have the structure [338] shown in Figure 19. Similarly 2,2'-biphenylenemercury, m.p. 335–336°, from 2,2'-dilithiobiphenyl and mercury(II) chloride [339], was originally assigned the structure 2.20 but was later shown [340]

2.20

[334] B. Ziolkowska, *Roczniki Chem.*, 1962, **36**, 1341.
[335] N. R. Kunchur and M. Mathew, *Proc. Chem. Soc.*, 1964, 414.
[336] N. R. Kunchur and M. Mathew, *Chem. Comm.*, 1966, 71.
[337] L. Vecchiotti, *Ber.*, 1930, **63**, 2275; see also H. Gilman and E. A. Zuech, *J. Amer. Chem. Soc.*, 1960, **82**, 3605.
[338] D. Grdenić, *Chem. Ber.*, 1959, **92**, 231.
[339] G. Wittig and W. Herwig, ibid., 1954, **87**, 1511.
[340] G. Wittig and G. Lehmann, ibid., 1957, **90**, 875.

to be tetrameric, consistent with the structure shown in Figure 20, in which it should be understood that the phenyl groups are twisted relative to each other.

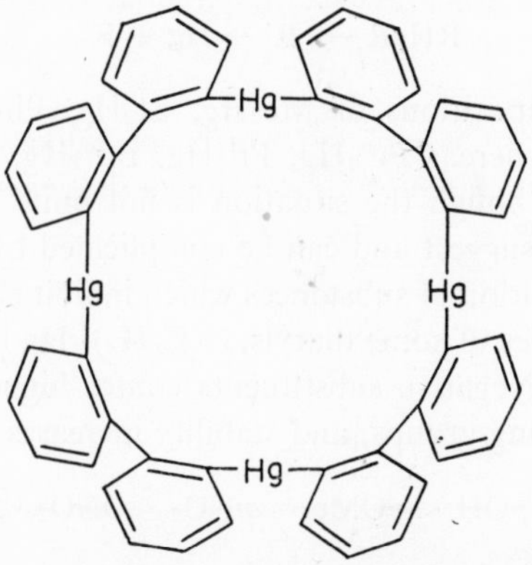

Fig. 20. Biphenylmercury (Wittig and Lehmann [340], *Chem. Ber.*, 1957, **90**, 876, Fig. 1, Verlag Chemie G.m.b.H.)

The *thermal decomposition* of mercury dialkyls has been the subject of numerous studies. The interest in these decompositions lies not only in the formation of free radicals, but also in the change in the valency state of the mercury from sp bivalent in R_2Hg to s^2 zerovalent in the product (mercury). The energy (D_1) required to detach a methyl group from dimethylmercury is 51 ± 2 kcal. mole^{-1}, and this process gives a radical CH_3—$Hg^{\cdot}$ in which the nature of the bonding is somewhat uncertain, but is lucidly discussed by Mortimer [341]. The energy (D_2) required to dissociate CH_3—$Hg^{\cdot}$ is only about 8 kcal. mole^{-1}. For all divalent Group IIb compounds D_1 is much bigger than D_2, examples being: Me_2Zn, D_1 47, D_2 35; Me_2Cd, D_1 45, D_2 22; $PhHgCl$, D_1 ~60, D_2 ~23; $PhHgI$, D_1 ~55, D_2 ~8.

Two classes of thermal decomposition of organomercury compounds are now recognized [342]. In class I the frequency factor A is about 10^{13} sec^{-1} and the activation energy is equal to D_1, so the decomposition takes place in two primary steps:

$$RHgR \longrightarrow RHg^{\cdot} + R^{\cdot} \text{ (slow)}$$
$$RHg^{\cdot} \longrightarrow Hg + R^{\cdot} \text{ (fast)}$$

[341] C. T. Mortimer, *Reaction Heats and Bond Strengths*, Pergamon, Oxford, 1962; see also H. A. Skinner in *Advances in Organometallic Chemistry*, Vol. 2, Academic Press, 1964.
[342] H. V. Carter, E. I. Chappell and E. Warhurst, *J. Chem. Soc.*, 1956, 106; M. Cowperthwaite and E. Warhurst, ibid., 1958, 2429; E. Warhurst, *Trans. Faraday Soc.*, 1958, **54**, 1769; H. T. J. Chilton and B. G. Gowenlock, ibid., 1953, **49**, 1451; 1954, **50**, 824; *J. Chem. Soc.*, 1954, 3174; B. H. M. Billinge and B. G. Gowenlock, *Trans. Faraday Soc.*, 1963, **59**, 690; H. O. Pritchard, *J. Chem. Phys.*, 1956, **25**, 267.

In class II, $A \approx 10^{15}$ sec^{-1} and the activation energy is equal to or greater than $D_1 + D_2$, so the molecule decomposes into three fragments at the same time:

$$RHgR \longrightarrow R^{\cdot} + Hg + R^{\cdot}$$

The thermal decompositions of Me_2Hg, Et_2Hg, $PhHgCl$ and $PhHgBr$ belong to class I, whereas Pr^n_2Hg, Pr^i_2Hg, Bu^n_2Hg, Ph_2Hg and $PhHgI$ belong to class II, though the situation is not quite so clear-cut as this classification might suggest and can be complicated by effects due to surfaces and by the addition of substances which inhibit chain reactions [343]. The relative stabilities of some diaryls, $(XC_6H_4)_2$ Hg have been examined qualitatively [344]. Negative substituents confer higher thermal stability than electron-donating groups, and stability increases in the order:

$$pNH_2 < pOH < pOMe < mNO_2 < oNO_2 < pCO_2H$$

It is well known that urea forms crystalline inclusion compounds with a number of unbranched-chain paraffin hydrocarbons, and similar compounds have been prepared from urea and *normal* dialkyls of mercury by mixing alcoholic solutions of the components [345]. These adducts are more stable to heat, light and X-rays than the dialkyls which they contain, and their vapour pressures are less. No adduct is formed with dimethylmercury, nor with 5,10-dimercura-n-tetradecane $C_4H_9Hg(CH_2)_4HgC_4H_9$. Neither are adducts formed by alkylmercury halides and this provides a means for separating R_2Hg from $RHgX$; such separations can be troublesome when R is a C_4 to C_7 radical. Adducts have been obtained from $R = C_2H_5$ to $C_{12}H_{25}$.

The dialkyl and diaryl derivatives of mercury are chemically less reactive than those of zinc and cadmium, and are the only dialkyl derivatives of Group II inert to water and oxygen. With the exception of some highly halogenated compounds, mentioned below, they do not form co-ordination complexes either with amines [346] or with tertiary phosphines.

Considerable effort has been devoted to find the mechanism of several reactions involving R_2Hg or $RHgX$. In view of the time needed to sort out reactions involving substitution at a saturated carbon atom, and the electronic versatility of the heavy elements as compared with carbon, it is not surprising that an altogether clear and agreed picture has been slow to emerge.

The reactions between R_2Hg and hydrogen chloride, mainly in dioxan-

[343] A. S. Kallend and J. H. Purnell, *Trans. Faraday Soc.*, 1964, **60**, 93, 103.

[344] M. M. Koton and V. G. Martynova, *Zhur. Obshchei Khim.*, 1954, **24**, 2177; *Chem. Abs.*, 1956, **50**, 217.

[345] G. Bähr and G. Meier, *Z. anorg. Chem.*, 1958, **294**, 22.

[346] J. Lile and R. C. Menzies, *J. Chem. Soc.*, 1950, 617.

dimethylsulphoxide, are faster when R is cyclopropyl than when it is methyl:

$$\text{cyclopropyl} > \text{vinyl} > \text{Ph} >> \text{Et} > \text{Pr}^i > \text{Pr}^n > \text{Me}$$

The fission of substituted aryl groups

$$(\text{X·C}_6\text{H}_4)_2\text{Hg} + \text{HCl} \longrightarrow \text{X·C}_6\text{H}_4\text{HgCl} + \text{C}_6\text{H}_5\text{X}$$

is accelerated when X is an electron-releasing group and retarded when it is electron attracting (as in di-m-nitrophenylmercury). The mechanism is believed to involve simultaneous attack by proton and halide ion (either as closely associated ion-pairs or as covalent HCl) giving a four-centre intermediate [347]:

$$
\begin{array}{ccccc}
\text{R—Hg—R} & & \text{R····Hg—R} & & \text{ClHgR} \\
& \rightarrow & \vdots \quad\; \vdots & \rightarrow & \\
\text{H}^+ \text{Cl}^- & & \text{H····Cl} & & + \text{RH}
\end{array}
$$

Considerable attention has been paid to the three redistribution reactions:

$$\text{X}_2\text{Hg} + \text{RHgX} \rightleftharpoons \text{XHgR} + \text{HgX}_2 \quad \text{(one-alkyl)}$$
$$\text{X}_2\text{Hg} + \text{RHgR}' \rightleftharpoons \text{XHgR} + \text{HgR}'\text{X} \quad \text{(two-alkyl)}$$
$$\text{XRHg} + \text{R}'\text{HgR}'' \rightleftharpoons \text{RHgR}' + \text{HgR}''\text{X} \quad \text{(three-alkyl)}$$

Kinetic studies, which have included the use of optically active and isotopically labelled substrates, have revealed the operation of three different mechanisms, but the results and conclusions only are outlined below as a recent review is available [348, see also 348a].

A single-stage synchronous bimolecular process, S_E2, appears to be most commonly found. All the reactions by this mechanism are accompanied by complete retention of optical configuration, showing that the attacking entity approaches the seat of substitution at a position adjacent to the leaving group. The rate of the two-alkyl reaction increase with the case of ionization of HgX_2 ($\text{HgCl}_2 > \text{HgBr}_2 > \text{HgI}_2 > \text{Hg(CN)}_2$ [349], $\text{Hg(NO}_3)_2 > \text{Hg(OAc)}_2 > \text{HgBr}_2$ [348a]). Bromide ions substantially retard the reaction with HgBr_2, probably because the formation of the complex ion reduces the electrophilic character of the mercury atom. Substitution via a cyclic transition state [349] is now regarded as very unlikely in the two-alkyl system [348].

One-alkyl exchange by mechanism S_E2 occurs more rapidly with MeHgX than EtHgX in ethanol, and the reaction is greatly accelerated by X⁻ ions.

[347] R. E. Dessy, G. F. Reynolds and J. Y. Kim, *J. Amer. Chem. Soc.*, 1959, **81**, 2683; R. E. Dessy and J. Y. Kim, ibid., 1960, **82**, 686; 1961, **83**, 1167.

[348] F. G. Thorpe in *Studies on Chemical Structure and Reactivity* (J. H. Ridd, Ed.), Methuen, London, 1965, ch. 12; N. A. Nesmeyanov and O. A. Reutov, *Tetrahedron*, 1964, **20**, 2803.

[348a] H. B. Charman, E. D. Hughes and C. K. Ingold, *J. Chem. Soc.*, 1959, 2523, 2530; H. B. Charman, E. D. Hughes, C. K. Ingold and F. G. Thorpe, ibid., 1961, 1121; E. D. Hughes, C. K. Ingold, F. G. Thorpe and H. C. Volger, ibid., p. 1133; E. D. Hughes and F. C. Volger, ibid., p. 2359.

[349] R. E. Dessy and Y. K. Lee, *J. Amer. Chem. Soc.*, 1960, **82**, 689; R. E. Dessy, Y. K. Lee and J. Y. Kim, ibid., 1961, **83**, 1163.

It is assumed that the anion complexes only weakly with RHgX, strongly with HgX_2, and even more strongly with the transition state where it acts as a bridge between a partially formed HgX_2 molecule and a partially formed HgX^-_3 ion:

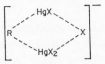

The analogues of this transition state for two- and three-alkyl exchange are considered to possess a much smaller stability and it is therefore thought unlikely that this cyclic mechanism, $S_E i$, will be observed for these systems.

The rate of one-alkyl exchange of $PhCH(CO_2Me)HgBr$ in dimethyl-sulphoxide is independent of the concentration of $HgBr_2$ and a uni-molecular mechanism, $S_E 1$, has therefore been proposed for this reaction:

$$RHgBr \longrightarrow R^- + Hg^+Br \quad \text{(slow)}$$
$$R^- + Hg^*Br_2 \longrightarrow RHg^*Br + Br^- \quad \text{(rapid)}$$
$$Br^- + Hg^+Br \longrightarrow HgBr_2 \quad \text{(rapid)}$$

Racemization occurs at the same rate in the absence of $HgBr_2$ and is catalysed by bromide ions, probably because the complex $RHgBr_3^{2-}$ (in equilibrium with RHgBr) produces the carbonium, R^-, more rapidly than RHgBr.

Perhalo compounds

Trifluoro-iodomethane reacts with mercury at about 260–290°, or, better, when irradiated with ultraviolet light at temperatures up to 150°, forming CF_3HgI (m.p. 112·5° in a sealed tube). This gives CF_3HgOH with silver oxide, in contrast to CH_3HgI which forms mixtures of $(MeHg)_2O$ and $[(MeHg)_3O]OH$ [350]. The perfluoro-alkylmercury hydroxides and halides are rather less ionized in solution than their hydrocarbon analogues, some pK values [351] being given in Table 9. Cadmium amalgam reduces the

Table 9 *pK values for methyl and perfluoro-alkymercury compounds, 25°*

	OH	Cl	Br	I
CH_3Hg	9·51	5·46	6·70	8·7
CF_3Hg	10·76	5·78	7·24	9·63
C_2F_5Hg	10·58	5·64	7·16	9·66
$n\text{-}C_3F_7Hg$	10·50	5·56	7·16	9·96

[350] H. J. Emeléus and R. N. Haszeldine, *J. Chem. Soc.*, 1949, 2948.
[351] H. B. Powell and J. J. Lagowski, ibid., 1962, 2047.

iodide to $(CF_3)_2Hg$ [352], m.p. $163°$, which has a linear structure in the crystalline and gaseous states. The $Hg–CF_3$ symmetrical and unsymmetrical stretching frequencies [353] are at 226 and 273 cm⁻¹, the CF_3 group behaving rather like an atom of atomic weight about 70. Changes of solvent have little effect on the spectrum of $(CF_3)_2Hg$; the linear structure seems always to be retained. Aqueous solutions of $(CF_3)_2Hg$ are about as electrically conducting as those of $Hg(CN)_2$, and this is believed to be due to hydration, and to ionization of the hydrate:

$$(CF_3)_2Hg \rightleftharpoons [(CF_3)_2HgOH_2] \rightleftharpoons (CF_3)_2HgOH^- + H_3O^+$$

The equilibrium constant for this reaction is about 3.10^{-15} mole litre⁻¹ [354]. Fluoroform is produced at both anode and cathode during electrolysis in an undivided cell [355].

Bistrifluoromethylmercury is also formed in the reaction between $(CF_3)_3P$ and HgO [356]. Higher perfluoro-alkylmercury iodides have also been obtained from mercury and the perfluoro-alkyl iodide [350, 357], but the addition of fluoro- or chlorofluoro-olefins to mercury(II) fluoride is a more convenient method particularly for larger scale preparations. Reaction between HgF_2 and $CF_2:CFCl$ gives $CF_3·CFClHgF$ [358], and $[(CF_3)_2CF]_2Hg$ is formed from HgF_2 and $CF_3·CF:CF_2$ [359]. The thermal stability of these compounds *increases* with chain branching, the perfluorotertiary butyl and -isopropyl being more stable than the corresponding primary compounds [360].

Fission of the Hg–C bond occurs readily in most cases, and reagents that bring about disproportionation of $RHgX$ to R_2Hg cannot be used since only hydrolysis products are obtained. Addition of potassium iodide to aqueous CF_3HgI is an example:

$$CF_3HgI + 3I^- + H_2O \longrightarrow CHF_3 + OH^- + HgI_4^{2-}$$

Similarly $(CF_3)_2CFH$ is formed from $[(CF_3)_2CF]_2Hg$ and aqueous potassium iodide, or sodium stannite, or sodium sulphide, though the mercurial in unaffected by acids or bases alone [360]. Attempts to transfer perfluoroalkyl groups from mercury to other metals have met with little success, but

[352] H. J. Emeléus and R. N. Haszeldine, ibid., 1949, 2953.
[353] A. J. Downs, ibid., 1963, 5273.
[354] Idem, *J. Inorg. Nucl. Chem.*, 1964, **26**, 41.
[355] H. J. Emeléus, Lecture at Chemical Society Symposium on Fluorine Chemistry, Birmingham, July 1959.
[356] J. E. Griffiths and A. B. Burg, *J. Amer. Chem. Soc.*, 1960, **82**, 5759.
[357] H. J. Emeléus and J. J. Lagowski, *J. Chem. Soc.*, 1959, 1497.
[358] H. Goldwhite, R. N. Haszeldine and R. N. Mukherjee, ibid., 1961, 3825.
[359] W. T. Miller, M. B. Freedman, J. H. Fried and H. F. Koch, *J. Amer. Chem. Soc.*, 1961, **83**, 4105.
[360] P. E. Aldrich, E. G. Howard, W. J. Linn, W. J. Middleton and W. H. Sharkey, *J. Org. Chem.*, 1963, **28**, 184.

tetrakispentafluorophenyltin has been obtained from bispentafluoro-phenylmercury and metallic tin [360a].

Though $(CF_3)_2Hg$ decomposes from 160°, and is less thermally stable than $(CH_3)_2Hg$, the perfluoro-*aryl* compound $(C_6F_5)_2Hg$ is unchanged after five hours' heating at 250°. Bispentafluorophenylmercury [361], m.p. 142°, from mercury(II) chloride and C_6F_5MgBr, or by the thermal decarboxylation of mercury(II) pentafluorobenzoate [362], differs sharply from dialkyl- and diaryl-mercurials in its resistance to protonic acids: it crystallizes unchanged from concentrated sulphuric acid. It reacts relatively slowly with bromine, rapidly with mercury(II) bromide and apparently not at all with mercury(II) iodide. In its reaction with dimethyl-mercury, catalysed by a trace of C_6F_5HgBr, giving the stable mixed mercurial C_6F_5HgMe, the pentafluorophenyl group takes on the character of a halogen atom rather than that of an aryl group. Some reactions of pentafluorophenylmercury compounds are summarized in the chart below.

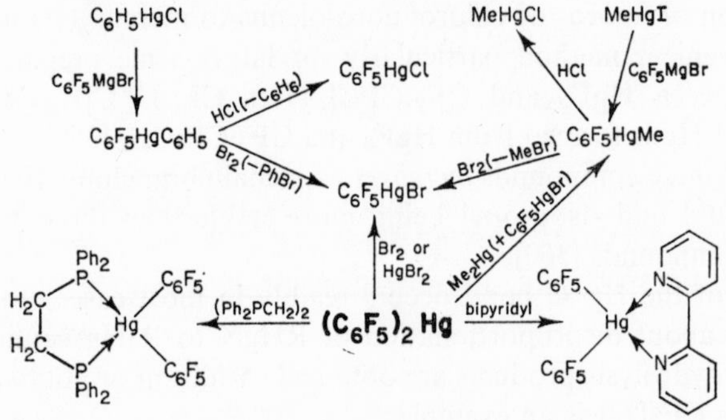

As shown in the chart, the pentafluorophenyl group is sufficiently electron-attracting to allow the formation of colourless crystalline neutral co-ordination complexes. Dimethyl-, diphenyl- and diphenylethynyl-mercury have yielded no isolable complexes. Bipyridyl forms brightly coloured complexes with Group II dimethyls, and though Me_2Cd forms a solid yellow complex, Me_2Hg dissolves bipyridyl without the development of any colour. The cleavage reactions of pentachlorophenyl mercury compounds (e.g. $C_6Cl_5HgCH_3$) resemble those of the C_6F_5 series [363]. Both bispentachlorophenylmercury and bis(2,4,5,6-tetrafluoropyridyl)

[360a] J. Burdon, P. L. Coe and M. Fulton, *J. Chem. Soc.*, 1965, 2094.

[361] R. D. Chambers, G. E. Coates, J. G. Livingstone and W. K. R. Musgrave, *ibid.*, 1962, 4367; R. D. Chambers and T. Chivers, *Organometal. Chem. Rev.*, 1966, **1**, 279.

[362] J. E. Connett, A. G. Davies, G. B. Deacon and J. H. S. Green, *Chem. and Ind.*, 1965, 512; *J. Chem. Soc.*, C, 1966, 106; J. E. Connett and G. B. Deacon, ibid., p. 1058.

[363] F. E. Paulik, S. I. E. Green and R. E. Dessy, *J. Organometal. Chem.*, 1965, **3**, 229; G. B. Deacon and P. W. Felder, *Austral. J. Chem.*, 1966, **21**, 2381.

mercury (from the mercury salt of the perfluoronicotinic acid [363a]) form co-ordination complexes.

Bistrifluoromethylmercury forms 1 : 1 and 1 : 2 complexes in solution with ligands such as pyridine, piperidine, triphenylphosphine and dimethyl sulphide, as indicated by changes in the dielectric constant of the solutions on addition of ligand [364]. This method reveals the formation in solution of complexes between diphenylmercury and piperidine. Several anionic complexes containing the CF_3 group bound to mercury have been identified by the conductimetric titration of $(CF_3)_2Hg$, and of CF_3HgX, with potassium halides (particularly iodide) and thiocyanate. The formation of ions such as $[HgCF_3BrI]^-$ and $[Hg(CF_3)_2I_2]^{2-}$ was deduced, and crystalline salts with large cations were obtained, formulated as $[Zn\,en_3][Hg(CF_3)_2I_2]$, $[Cd\,en_3][HgCF_3I_3]$ and $[Ni\,en_3][Hg(CF_3)_2I_2]$. These compounds are decomposed by hot water or aqueous potassium iodide, with evolution of fluoroform. However, the Raman spectra of solutions of $(CF_3)_2Hg$ in methanol to which various halides have been added (even in large excess) reveal no species other than uncomplexed $(CF_3)_2Hg$ [353]. The formation constants K for 1 : 1 complex formation

$$K = \frac{[\text{complex}^-]}{[(CF_3)_2Hg][X^-]}$$

between $(CF_3)_2Hg$ and Cl^-, Br^- and I^- in water have been measured by a freezing point method [354] and are $0\cdot3 \pm 0\cdot05$, $1\cdot6 \pm 0\cdot4$ and $9\cdot6 \pm 0\cdot8$ litre mole^{-1} respectively. In view of these figures there is some doubt whether the solid salts mentioned above really contain $[(CF_3)_2HgI_2]^{2-}$ anions. Complexes such as $(CF_3)_2Hg$ bipy are rather less dissociated in solution than their pentafluorophenyl analogues [364a].

Though mercurials containing a perfluoro-*alkyl* and a hydrocarbon group bound to the same mercury atom have not yet been described (cf. C_6F_5HgMe mentioned earlier), various compounds containing phenyl and CCl_nBr_{3-n} bound to mercury are known and they undergo some remarkable reactions.

Reaction between a phenylmercury halide, potassium t-butoxide and $CHCl_3$ (or $CHBr_3$) gives $PhHgCCl_3$ (or $PhHgCBr_3$) [365]. The reaction involves displacement of Cl by CX_3^-:

$$CHCl_3 + Bu^tO^- \longrightarrow Cl_3C^- + Bu^tOH$$
$$Cl_3C^- + PhHgBr \longrightarrow PhHgCCl_3 + Br^-$$

[363a] R. D. Chambers, F. G. Drakesmith, J. Hutchinson and W. K. R. Musgrave, *Tetrahedron Letters*, 1967, 1705.

[364] H. B. Powell, M. T. Maung and J. J. Lagowski, *J. Chem. Soc.*, 1963, 2484.

[364a] J. E. Connett and G. B. Deacon, ibid., C, 1966, 1058.

[365] A. N. Nesmeyanov, R. K. Freidlina and F. K. Velichko, *Doklady Akad. Nauk S.S.S.R.*, 1957, **114**, 557; O. A. Reutov and A. N. Lovtsova, *Izvest. Akad. Nauk S.S.S.R.*, 1960, 1716; *Doklady Akad. Nauk S.S.S.R.*, 1961, **139**, 622.

It is not a carbene insertion or PhHgCCl$_2$Br would be formed [366]. The inconvenient preparation of potassium tert-butoxide may be avoided, since the trihalomethyl anion can be produced from sodium methoxide and ethyl trichloracetate [367].

$$Cl_3C \cdot CO_2Et + NaOMe \rightarrow [Cl_3C^-] \xrightarrow{\text{PhHgBr}} PhHgCCl_3$$

The decomposition of *dry* sodium trichloroacetate in 1,2-dimethoxyethane also gives Cl$_3$C$^-$ anions, and has been applied to the easy preparation, not only of phenyltrichloromethylmercury, but of ClHgCCl$_3$ and (Cl$_3$C)$_2$Hg. The first results when the HgCl$_2$: Cl$_3$C·CO$_2$Na ratio is 1 : 1, and the second when it is 1 : 2 [368]. Bistrichloromethylmercury, m.p. 141°, forms a bipyridyl complex [369], m.p. 139° (with sudden decomposition).

The most significant reaction of the trichloro (and bromo) mercury compounds is the transfer of a CX$_2$ group to olefins. If PhHgCBr$_3$ is boiled with a mixture of benzene with a little cyclohexene, then PhHgBr is precipitated during two hours and dibromonorcarane may be isolated in 88% yield:

$$PhHgCBr_3 \longrightarrow PhHgBr + [CBr_2] \xrightarrow{\text{cyclohexene}} \langle\text{structure}\rangle CBr_2$$

The transfer of CCl$_2$ from PhHgCCl$_3$ is much slower (36–48 hours) under these conditions, and the reaction is believed to involve dichlorocarbene (either free or transferred in a concerted bimolecular process) as an intermediate [370]. The insertion of a CCl$_2$ group is better accomplished with the use of PhHgCCl$_2$Br (from PhHgCl, CHCl$_2$Br and KOBu^t), which reacts much faster than PhHgCCl$_3$, the bromine remaining attached to the mercury [366]. Cyclopropanes can be prepared from various other trihalomethyl compounds, but the reactions always require basic conditions [371]. The great advantage of the HgCX$_3$ method is that basic conditions are not needed; this has allowed the preparation of various cyclopropanes in yields stated, C$_3$Cl$_6$ (74%) from C$_2$Cl$_4$, CBr$_2$CH$_2$CH$_2$ (53%) from

[366] D. Seyferth and J. M. Burlitch, *J. Amer. Chem. Soc.*, 1962, **84**, 1757; *J. Organometal. Chem.*, 1965, **4**, 127.

[367] E. E. Schweizer and G. J. O'Neill, *J. Org. Chem.*, 1963, **28**, 851.

[368] T. J. Logan, ibid., p. 1129.

[369] G. E. Coates and D. Ridley, unpublished observation.

[370] D. Seyferth, J. M. Burlitch and J. K. Heeren, *J. Org. Chem.*, 1962, **27**, 1491; see also D. Seyferth and J. M. Burlitch, *J. Amer. Chem. Soc.*, 1964, **86**, 2730; D. Seyferth, J. M. Burlitch, R. J. Minasz, J. Y. Mui, H. D. Simmons, A. J. H. Treiber and S. R. Dowd, ibid., 1965, **87**, 4259. See also D. Seyferth, ch. 5. in *Proceedings of the 9th Robert A. Welch Foundation Conference on Chemical Research*, 15–17th Nov., 1965.

[371] E. Chinoporos, *Chem. Rev.*, 1963, **63**, 235.

C_2H_4, and

$$Me_2ClSi \cdot CH \overset{CCl_2}{\underset{CH_2}{\diamond}} \quad (58\%) \underline{\text{ from }} Me_2ClSiCH{:}CH_2 \quad [372]$$

Since 1,1-dichlorocyclopropanes can be converted into *allenes*, by reaction with methyl-lithium, the development of an easy preparative route will have a considerable effect on the growth of allene chemistry. The CClBr group is transferred to olefins starting from $PhHgCClBr_2$.

Perhaps the most surprising reaction of trihalomethylmercurials is the insertion of CX_2 into a C–H bond. Thus $PhHgCl_2Br$ reacts exothermically with ethylbenzene giving $PhHgBr$ and $PhCH(Me) \cdot CCl_2H$ in 35% yield. Similarly isopropylbenzene gives 58% $PhCMe_2 \cdot CCl_2H$ and, most surprising of all, cyclohexane gives 32% dichloromethylcyclohexane ($C_6H_{11} \cdot CCl_2H$) together with some $C_6H_{11}Br$ and C_2Cl_4. CX_2 groups may similarly be inserted between Si (or Ge) and H in Ph_3SiH and Ph_3GeH [373]. Dichlorocarbene may also be inserted between Hg and alkyl groups [374]. For example, when CCl_2 is generated from ethyl trichloracetate in the presence of di-isopropylmercury, the insertion product may be isolated in nearly 60% yield. It readily decomposes:

$$Pr^i_2Hg + {:}CCl_2 \rightarrow Me_2CHCCl_2HgCHMe_2$$

$$\downarrow \text{100-120}°$$

$$Me_2C{:}CHCl + Me_2CHHgCl$$

Vinyl and acetylenic compounds
These have a long and rather confused history dating from attempts to identify intermediates in the mercury-catalysed hydration of acetylene to acetaldehyde, a reaction discovered in 1881 [375] and for a long time the basis of the industrial production of acetaldehyde and acetic acid from acetylene. Latterly, however, ethylene has become a commercially more attractive source of C_2 organic compounds.

Vinylmercury halides are readily prepared by the rapid exchange reaction [376]

$$Bu^n_3SnCH{:}CH_2 + HgX_2 \rightarrow Bu^n_3SnX + CH_2{:}CHHgX$$

[372] D. Seyferth, R. J. Minasz, A. J. H. Treiber, J. M. Burlitch and S. R. Dowd, *J. Org. Chem.*, 1963, **28**, 1163.
[373] D. Seyferth and J. M. Burlitch, *J. Amer. Chem. Soc.*, 1963, **85**, 2667; see also E. K. Fields, ibid., 1962, **84**, 1744.
[374] J. A. Landgrebe and R. D. Mathis, ibid., 1964, **86**, 524.
[375] M. Kutscheroff, *Ber.*, 1881, **14**, 1540.
[376] D. Seyferth, *J. Org. Chem.*, 1957, **22**, 478.

They may be reduced to divinylmercury by sodium stannite [377]. Both $CH_2:CHHgX$ and $(CH_2:CH)_2Hg$ can be made by the direct vinylation of mercury halide and vinylmagnesium bromide [378]. Divinylmercury, b.p. $59\cdot5°/20$ mm., $156-157°/760$ mm., has a nasty smell ('very objectionable odor' [379]) and is toxic. More sensitive to acids than most diaryls or dialkyls, it is decomposed by 10% aqueous sulphuric acid.

Divinylmercury undergoes some novel reactions with carboxylic acids, phenols and thiols [380]. Whereas dialkyl or diarylmercury compounds are cleaved to hydrocarbon RH, and to $RHgO\cdot CO\cdot R$, divinylmercury reacts in two stages:

$$RCO_2H + (CH_2:CH)_2Hg \longrightarrow C_2H_4 + R\cdot CO\cdot O\cdot HgCH:CH_2$$
$$R\cdot CO\cdot O\cdot HgCH:CH_2 \longrightarrow R\cdot CO\cdot O\cdot CH:CH_2 + Hg$$

The reaction rates increase with the acid strength and in the case of trichloracetic acid the intermediate vinylmercury ester could not be isolated. Phenols react quickly giving vinyl aryl ethers

$$PhOH + (CH_2:CH)_2Hg \longrightarrow PhOCH:CH_2 + C_2H_4 + Hg$$

and a vinylmercury intermediate was isolated only from the reaction with pentachlorophenol. Thiols (even aliphatic) give vinyl thioethers:

$$PhSH + (CH_2:CH)_2Hg \longrightarrow PhSHgCH:CH_2 + C_2H_4$$
$$PhSHgCH:CH_2 \longrightarrow PhSCH:CH_2 + Hg$$

Bistrifluorovinylmercury [381], b.p. $65-66°/17$ mm., from $CF_2:CFMgI$ and $HgCl_2$ at $-10°$, has been used in the preparation of the relatively inaccessible trifluorovinyl aluminium compounds. The chloride, $CF_2:CFHgCl$, is formed from $Bu^n_3SnCF:CF_2$ and $HgCl_2$ [382] and is converted into $(CF_2:CF)_2Hg$ by even *one* equivalent of sodium iodide in acetone [383].

$$2CF_2:CFHgCl + 2NaI \longrightarrow (CF_2:CF)_2Hg + Na_2HgCl_2I_2$$

Bistrichlorovinylmercury, $(CCl_2:CCl)_2Hg$, m.p. $72-73°$, is among the earlier vinyl-metallics to have been described [384], and is readily obtained

[377] A. N. Nesmeyanov, A. E. Borisov, I. S. Saveleva and E. I. Golubeva, *Izvest. Akad. Nauk S.S.S.R.*, 1958, 1490; *Chem. Abs.*, 1959, **53**, 7973.

[378] B. Bartocha, F. E. Brinckman, H. D. Kaesz and F. G. A. Stone, *Proc. Chem. Soc.*, 1958, 116; G. F. Reynolds, R. E. Dessy and H. H. Jaffe, *J. Org. Chem.*, 1958, **23**, 1217.

[379] H. D. Kaesz and F. G. A. Stone, *Organometallic Chemistry*, Ch. 3, Reinhold, New York, 1960.

[380] D. J. Foster and E. Tobler, *J. Amer. Chem. Soc.*, 1961, **83**, 851; see also idem, *J. Org. Chem.*, 1962, **27**, 834.

[381] R. N. Sterlin, V. G. Li and I. L. Knunyants, *Izvest. Akad. Nauk S.S.S.R.*, 1959, 1506; *Chem. Abs.*, 1960, **54**, 1273.

[382] D. Seyferth, G. Raab and K. A. Brändle, *J. Org. Chem.*, 1961, **26**, 2934.

[383] D. Seyferth and R. H. Towe, *Inorg. Chem.*, 1962, **1**, 185.

[384] K. A. Hofmann and H. Kirmreuther, *Ber.*, 1908, **41**, 314.

by the reaction:

$$Hg(CN)_2 + 2CCl_2:CClH + 2KOH \longrightarrow (CCl_2:CCl)_2Hg + 2KCN + 2H_2O$$

Reaction with chlorine and bromine results in the formation of mercury halide even when a deficiency of $(CCl_2:CCl)_2Hg$ is used. The chloride and bromide may be obtained by the slow reactions with HgX_2,

$$(CCl_2:CCl)_2Hg + HgBr_2 \longrightarrow 2CCl_2:CClHgBr$$

but attempts to prepare the iodide or thiocyanate gave only disproportionation products (cf. the trifluorvinyl reaction mentioned above). Triphenylphosphine causes immediate disproportionation of the chloride [383].

$$2CCl_2:CClHgCl + 2PPh_3 \longrightarrow (PPh_3)_2HgCl_2 \downarrow + (CCl_2:CCl)_2Hg$$

2-Chlorovinylmercury compounds were first prepared in 1898 by bubbling acetylene through a solution of mercury(II) chloride and containing concentrated hydrochloric acid. Some acetaldehyde is formed. The product $C_2H_2HgCl_2$, m.p. 124°, was converted by ammonia (in chloroform) to another compound $C_4H_4HgCl_2$, m.p. 70°. The nature of these compounds, which was not established with certainty until 1945, became the subject of considerable uncertainty in view of the ease with which acetylene could be regenerated from them.

The compound $C_2H_2HgCl_2$, m.p. 124°, displays some versatility in its reaction with bases. The effect of ammonia has been mentioned; pyridine yields a 1 : 1 adduct, but alkali cyanide or thiosulphate, or triphenylphosphine causes elimination of acetylene:

$$C_2H_2HgCl_2 + 2PPh_3 \longrightarrow (PPh_3)_2HgCl_2 + C_2H_2$$

Acetylene is also produced by the action of diazomethane and by heating to its melting point. The easy elimination of acetylene, considered along with the rather similarly easy elimination of ethylene from the series of compounds XC_2H_4HgY (which, however, differ in being readily decomposed by acids) resulted in both series being regarded for some time as acetylene or olefin co-ordination complexes. On the other hand reaction of the compounds derived from acetylene with anhydrous hydrogen halides or with halogens gives vinyl halides or 1-chloro-2-halo-ethylene:

$$C_2H_2HgCl_2 + HCl \longrightarrow CH_2:CHCl + HgCl_2$$
$$C_2H_2HgCl_2 + Br_2 \longrightarrow CHCl:CHBr + HgCl_2$$

These reactions suggest the presence of a normal mercury–carbon bond. An X-ray structure analysis [385] showed that $C_2H_2HgCl_2$, m.p. 124°, is *trans*-2-chlorovinylmercury chloride (2.21).

[385] A. I. Kitaigorodsky, *Izvest. Akad. Nauk S.S.S.R.*, 1945, 170; *Chem. Abs.*, 1946, **40**, 3451. Idem, ibid., 1947, 259; *Chem. Abs.*, 1948, **42**, 5846.

2.21 m.p. 124°   2.22 m.p. 79°

2.23 m.p. 70°   2.24 liquid

The lower melting *cis* isomer (2.22) was obtained from mercury(II) chloride and the lower melting of the two isomers of (ClCH:CH)₃Sb, from SbCl₅ + C₂H₂ followed by reduction, the *trans* isomer being formed from HgCl₂ and the higher melting (*trans*) isomer of (ClCH:CH)₃Sb. *Cis*-2-chlorovinylmercury chloride is also produced when mercury(II) chloride reacts with acetylene in the vapour phase in the complete absence of moisture.

The reactions of these compounds proceed with *retention of configuration*, though isomerization results from the action of peroxides or of ultra-violet light (as with many organic *cis–trans* isomers). Thus the compound formed by the action of ammonia on 2.21 is the *trans–trans* isomer (2.23); similarly the action of ammonia on the *cis* isomer 2.22 gives the *cis–cis* compound (2.24). Numerous *trans*-metallation reactions have been carried out, giving 2-chlorovinyl derivatives of, for example, boron, thallium, tin and lead; geometrical configuration is retained in all cases. The ready elimination of acetylene, which caused so much bother some years ago, is probably due (as with the 'olefin complexes') to the provision of a low activation energy reaction pathway involving a $\sigma(Hg–C) \rightarrow \pi(Hg–$ acetylene) transition followed by loss of a chloride ion and of the co-ordinated acetylene.

The chemistry of the 2-chlorovinylmercury compounds, largely developed by Nesmeyanov and his school, has been very clearly reviewed [379].

True acetylenic derivatives of mercury, i.e. compounds containing —C:C·Hg— groups, are very easily prepared directly from an acetylene RC:CH and inorganic mercury(II) compounds in the presence of a base, a useful reaction for the characterization of monosubstituted acetylenes. The acetylene dissolved in ethanol is conveniently added to an alkaline solution of K₂HgI₄ [386]:

$$2RC:CH + K_2HgI_4 + 2KOH \rightarrow (RC:C)_2Hg + 4KI + 2H_2O$$

[386] J. R. Johnson and W. L. McEwen, *J. Amer. Chem. Soc.*, 1926, **48**, 468.

Similar reactions applied to RHgX lead to RHgC:CHgR (easily hydro-lysed) when acetylene is used [387]:

$$2RHgX + C_2H_2 + 2KOH \rightarrow RHgC\text{:}CHgR + 2KX + 2H_2O$$

and to unsymmetrical mercurials when an aryl acetylene is used:

$$PhHgBr + PhC\text{:}CH + Et_3N \rightarrow PhHgC\text{:}CPh \quad \text{m.p. } 96\text{--}97°$$

The kinetics of reactions between acetylenes RC:CH and RHgX or K_2HgX_4 in the presence of triethylamine have been studied by Dessy [388] who concludes that the rate-determining step is a $\pi \rightarrow \sigma$ transition:

$$RC\equiv CH + Et_3N \rightleftharpoons RC\equiv C\text{---}H\cdots NEt_3$$

$$RC\equiv C\text{---}H\cdots NEt_3 + PhHgX \rightarrow \underset{\underset{Ph\text{---}Hg\text{---}X}{\downarrow}}{R\text{---}C\equiv C\text{---}H\cdots NEt_3}$$

$$\downarrow$$

$$RC\equiv CHgPh + Et_3N\overset{+}{H} + X^- \leftarrow \quad \underset{Ph\text{---}Hg\cdots X}{R\text{---}C\equiv C\cdots H\cdots NEt_3}$$

Unsymmetrical mercurials containing the HC:CHg— group can be obtained by the use of HC:CMgBr in tetrahydrofuran [389],

$$MeHgI + HC\text{:}CMgBr \rightarrow MeHgC\text{:}CH \quad \text{m.p. } 117\text{--}118°$$

The mechanism of the mercury-catalysed hydration of acetylenes is still not clear, but it is becoming increasingly likely that π-co-ordination is involved followed by a $\pi \rightarrow \sigma$ transition and hydrolysis of the Hg–C σ-bond along the lines [390]:

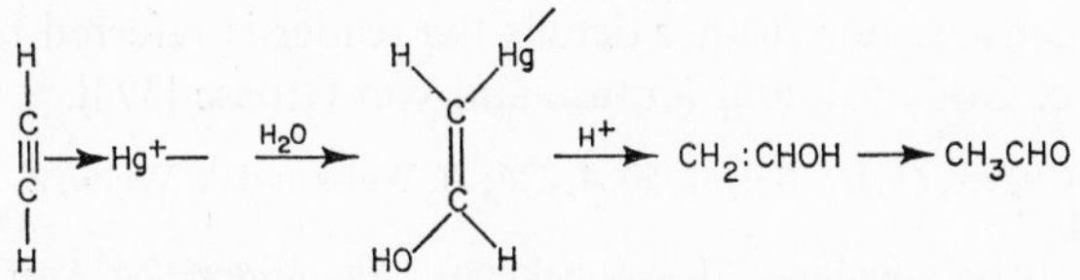

Dessy has obtained clear indication of the formation of bright yellow $[(PhC\text{:}CPh)_2Hg]^{2+}$ complexes in acid solutions of mercury(II) perchlorate and believes much acid is necessary to displace co-ordinated water from the mercury(II) ions. Phenylacetylene forms similar complexes, but in contrast to those of diphenylacetylene which are stable in solution for several days, the yellow colour quickly disappears with the concurrent formation of acetophenone [391].

[387] R. J. Spahr, R. R. Vogt and J. A. Nieuwland, ibid., 1933, **55**, 2465, 3728.
[388] R. E. Dessy, W. L. Budde and C. Woodruff, ibid., 1962, **84**, 1172.
[389] M. Kraut and L. C. Leitch, *Canad. J. Chem.*, 1963, **41**, 549.
[390] See E. G. Rochow, D. T. Hurd and R. N. Lewis, *The Chemistry of Organo-metallic Compounds*, Wiley, New York, 1957, p. 112.
[391] W. L. Budde and R. E. Dessy, *Chem. and Ind.*, 1963, 735.

Mercarbides and similar substances

A large number of compounds containing mercury, mostly prepared from aliphatic alcohols, glycols, aldehydes, ketones and acids has been described. Most of these are insoluble and almost certainly have polymeric constitutions. The structures given for most of them in early works are not compatible with present knowledge of stereochemistry and cannot be correct.

A typical member of this class is the compound known as ethane hexa-mercarbide, $(C_2H_2Hg_6O_4)_n$, which is obtained as a yellowish insoluble powder by the prolonged action of yellow mercury(II) oxide and boiling aqueous alkali on ethyl, propyl, allyl or amyl alcohol, acetaldehyde, cellulose, starch or sucrose. It behaves as a somewhat inefficient anion-exchange resin and a polymeric structure has been suggested [392]. Several interesting derivatives have been prepared from it: prolonged heating of the 'base', $C_2H_2Hg_6O_4$, with ethyl iodide and ether gives an orange-coloured crystalline substance, $C_2Hg_6I_6$. The nitrate, $[C_2Hg_6O_2(NO_3)_2]_n$, gives a cyanide, $C_2Hg_4(CN)_2$, with potassium cyanide, and the action of hot concentrated hydrochloric acid on this first gives a chloride, $C_2H_2Hg_4Cl_4$, and finally a soluble somewhat volatile substance once believed to be $ClHgCH_2CH_2HgCl$, but recently identified [393] as methylmercury chloride.

A polymeric acid which forms soluble salts is hydroxymercuri-acetic acid $(-Hg \cdot CH_2 \cdot CO_2 -)_n$, obtained, for example, from mercury(II) oxide and sodium malonate. The salts probably are of the type $HO \cdot Hg \cdot CH_2 \cdot CO_2^- M^+$.

Space does not permit the description or discussion of more of the vast number of organomercury compounds which have been mentioned in the chemical literature. For further details the reader is referred to the works of Whitmore, Goddard, and Krause and von Grosse [394].

[392] G. E. Coates, *Quart. Rev.*, 1950, **4**, 226; A. Weiss and A. Weiss, *Z. anorg. Chem.*, 1955, **282**, 324.

[393] S. V. Belshinskii and M. Usubakunov, *Sb. Materialov Konf. Posvyashch. 100-Letiyu sodyna Rozhdeniya Akademika N. S. Kurnakova, Akad. Nauk Kirg. S.S.R.*, 1963, 90; *Chem. Abs.*, 1964, **60**, 539.

[394] F. C. Whitmore, *Organic Compounds of Mercury*, Chem. Cat. Co., New York, 1921; A. E. Goddard, and D. Goddard, *A Text Book of Inorganic Chemistry*, ed. by J. Newton Friend, Vol. XI, Part I, Griffin, 1928; E. Krause and A. von Grosse, *Die Chemie der Metallorganischen Verbindungen*, Borntraeger, Berlin, 1937.

CHAPTER THREE

Group III

BORON

The organic chemistry of boron has developed remarkably rapidly during the last twenty years, to a considerable extent because the Government of the United States invested millions of dollars in research into many aspects of boron chemistry during the nineteen-fifties when it seemed likely that the high energies of oxidation of boron hydrides or organoboranes would make them suitable for use as 'superfuels' for jet aircraft or rockets [1]. Interest in these applications subsided when a combination of factors such as high cost, high toxicity and difficulties in exploiting the full oxidation energy due to incomplete combustion contributed to reduce the advantages of boron fuels [2], but the attention of many research groups had by this time been directed to several aspects of organoboron chemistry which are being actively pursued today. Other possible uses of boron compounds which are still being explored are as thermally stable polymers, for which boron–nitrogen, –phosphorus and –oxygen systems in particular have been studied, and as biologically active materials. In this last capacity a particular feature of boron compounds, quite apart from their specifically chemical properties, is the high neutron capture cross-section of ^{10}B, the less abundant of the two natural boron isotopes. The capture of slow thermal neutrons converts this isotope into a source of alpha particles which could be used to destroy surrounding (malignant) tissue if the boron compound were taken up into the appropriate part of a living organism [3, 4]. The high neutron cross-section of ^{10}B may also be utilized in the detection of neutrons in scintillation counters, for which purpose fluorescent boron compounds, e.g. certain aryl borazines, have been studied [5].

Particularly important developments have occurred in several branches of organoboron chemistry. Heterocyclic organic boron compounds have received a lot of attention [6]. For example, M. J. S. Dewar and his co-workers have prepared a whole range of heteroaromatic compounds, containing boron atoms as components of six-membered rings, of a different

[1] P. F. Winternitz, *Advanc. in Chem. Series*, 1961, **32**, 174.
[2] T. Wartik, ibid., preface.
[3] A. H. Soloway, 'Boron compounds in cancer therapy', Ch. 4 of ref. [4].
[4] H. Steinberg and A. L. McCloskey (eds.), *Progress in Boron Chemistry*, Vol. 1, Pergamon, 1964.
[5] M. A. Molinari and P. A. McCusker, *J. Org. Chem.*, 1964, **29**, 2094.
[6] P. M. Maitlis, *Chem. Rev.*, 1962, **62**, 223.

order of stability from that of most previously known organoboron compounds [7]; the scope of the general organic chemistry of boron had been obscured earlier by the high reactivity of many of the simpler compounds towards oxygen. Information continues to accumulate on borazine derivatives, which are 'pseudo-organic' systems, though many of these compounds contain no boron–carbon bonds and thus fall only marginally within the scope of this book. H. C. Brown and his school have discovered and developed the hydroboration reaction, the addition of B–H across olefinic or acetylenic multiple bonds to form organoboranes, a reaction of considerable importance in synthetic organic chemistry, providing a route to other hydrocarbons, alcohols and ketones [8]. The same group used volatile trialkyls of boron in studying the electronic and steric effects which influence the formation of co-ordination compounds. Boron alkyls have attracted some attention as catalysts for the polymerization of negatively substituted vinyl compounds, and in the aryl series the salt $NaBPh_4$ has become a valuable gravimetric reagent for potassium and a number of other ions.

Studies on alkyl and other derivatives of the higher boranes, particularly decarborane, $B_{10}H_{14}$, have largely verified predictions concerning the nature of the bonding and the charge distribution in these molecules. Also in the field of the chemistry of the higher boranes, a particularly interesting development has been the preparation of various carboranes, $B_nC_2H_{n+2}$, in which the carbon atoms are involved in the electron-deficient skeleton of the molecule [8a]. These compounds are isoelectronic with the anions $B_mH_m{}^{2-}$ whose existence was predicted several years before actual examples were prepared [9].

The increasing interest in organoboron chemistry is reflected in the welter of reviews it has elicited lately. The subject as a whole was reviewed in 1956 [10] and 1967 [11, 12] by Lappert, and in 1961 by Gerrard [13]. A comprehensive literature survey was launched in 1964 by the publication of a volume on boron–oxygen and boron–sulphur compounds [14], and the

[7] M. J. S. Dewar, *Advanc. in Chem. Series*, 1964, **42**, 227; idem, 'Heteroaromatic boron compounds', Ch. 5 of ref. [4].

[8] H. C. Brown, *Hydroboration*, W. A. Benjamin, N.Y., 1962; idem, Ch. 4 in *Organometallic Chemistry*, ed. H. Zeiss, Reinhold, N.Y., 1960.

[8a] T. P. Onak, *Advances in Organometallic Chemistry*, ed. F. G. A. Stone and R. West, 1965, **3**, 263; R. Köster and M. A. Grassberger, *Angew. Chem., Internat. Edn.*, 1966, **5**, 218.

[9] W. N. Lipscomb, *Advances in Inorganic Chemistry and Radiochemistry*, ed. Eméleus and Sharpe, Academic Press, 1961, Vol. 3; idem, *Boron Hydrides*, W. A. Benjamin, N.Y., 1963.   [10] M. F. Lappert, *Chem. Rev.*, 1956, **56**, 959.

[11] M. F. Lappert, Ch. X of ref. [12].

[12] E. L. Muetterties (ed.), *The Chemistry of Boron and Its Compounds*, Wiley, 1967.

[13] W. Gerrard, *The Organic Chemistry of Boron*, Academic Press, London and New York, 1961.

[14] H. Steinberg (ed.), *Organoboron Chemistry*, Wiley, 1964: Vol. 1, 'Boron–Oxygen and Boron–Sulphur compounds'.

same year saw the publication of the first volume in a series containing reviews on many aspects of the subject [4, 3, 7, 15–22]. Other recent reviews have covered borazines [23], organoboranes [8], carboranes [8a], hydroboration [8], boron hydrides [24], heterocyclic organic boron compounds [6], heteroaromatic boron compounds [7], boron-nitrogen compounds [25], organofunctional boronic esters [26], and boron–sulphur compounds [27].

In the following pages an attempt is made to survey the main aspects of organoboron chemistry and to indicate some recent developments. References to recent work are generally given as a lead into the literature, which currently runs to several hundred papers a year.

The formation of boron–carbon bonds

Three different types of reaction have proved useful for the preparation of compounds containing boron-carbon bonds; these are reactions between

(a) another organometallic compound and a boron halide or a borate ester,

(b) an olefin or acetylene and a boron hydride,

(c) a hydrocarbon and a boron halide.

Preparations using other organometallic compounds

This method is the most useful and convenient for the preparation of trialkyls or triaryls of boron either on a laboratory or a large scale. On the laboratory scale the reaction between Grignard reagents and boron trifluoride (conveniently used as its ether complex) is often satisfactory:

$$Et_2O \cdot BF_3 + 3RMgX \longrightarrow R_3B + 3MgXF + Et_2O$$

The formation of magnesium fluoride can result in a reaction mixture

[15] R. J. Brotherton, 'Chemistry of compounds with B–B bonds', Ch. 1 of ref. [4].
[16] T. D. Coyle and F. G. A. Stone, 'Some aspects of the co-ordination chemistry of boron', Ch. 2 of ref. [4].
[17] G. W. Campbell, 'The structures of the boron hydrides', Ch. 3 of ref. [4].
[18] A. G. Davies, 'Organoperoxyboranes', Ch. 6 of ref. [4].
[19] R. Köster, 'Organoboron heterocycles', Ch. 7 of ref. [4].
[20] C. E. H. Bawn and A. Ledwith, 'The reactions of diazoalkanes with boron compounds', Ch. 8 of ref. [4].
[21] K. Torssell, 'The chemistry of boronic and borinic acids', Ch. 9 of ref. [4].
[22] R. Schaeffer, 'NMR spectroscopy of boron compounds', Ch. 10 of ref. [4].
[23] J. C. Sheldon and B. C. Smith, *Quart. Rev.*, 1960, **14**, 200; E. K. Mellon and J. J. Lagowski, *Advances in Inorganic Chemistry and Radiochemistry*, ed. Emeléus and Sharpe, 1963, **5**, 259.
[24] R. M. Adams (ed.), *Boron, Metallo-boron Compounds and Boranes*, Wiley, 1964.
[25] K. Niedenzu and J. W. Dawson, *Boron–Nitrogen Compounds*, Springer-Verlag, 1965.
[26] D. S. Matteson, *Organometal. Chem. Reviews*, 1966, **1**, 1.
[27] R. H. Cragg and M. F. Lappert, ibid., 1966, **1**, 43.

which is difficult to work up, and the use of boron trichloride is satisfactory only if the reaction is carried out carefully, in view of the instability of the $Et_2O \cdot BCl_3$ complex. *Alkyl orthoborates* appear to be the most generally satisfactory reagents:

$$B(OMe)_3 + 3RMgX \longrightarrow R_3B + 3MgXOMe$$
$$3MgXOMe + 3HCl \longrightarrow 1\tfrac{1}{2}MgCl_2 + 1\tfrac{1}{2}MgX_2 + 3MeOH$$

In the aryl series it is important to avoid excess of Grignard reagent which results in the formation of BAr_4^- anions, and this occurs easily in both aryl and alkyl series when organolithium compounds are used as the arylating or alkylating agents.

The dialkyls and diaryls of zinc have been applied to the preparation of organoboron compounds, but the reaction, at least with boron trihalides, is rather violent and less satisfactory than the Grignard method. The carefully controlled reaction between dimethylzinc and boron trichloride has been used to prepare the unstable halides $MeBCl_2$ and Me_2BCl [28], which readily disproportionate to Me_3B and BCl_3. Various trialkylboranes have been prepared by bubbling BF_3 gas through a solution of the appropriate alkylzinc bromide in dimethylformamide at 90–95° under nitrogen [29].

Even the relatively unreactive organomercury compounds have been used to prepare certain arylboron halides [30]:

$$BBr_3 + PhHgCl \longrightarrow PhBClBr + HgBr_2$$

although the reverse reaction, e.g. between triethylborane and mercury(II) oxide or chloride, has been described as a route to diethylmercury [31]:

$$2Et_3B + 3HgO + 3H_2O \longrightarrow 3Et_2Hg + 2B(OH)_3$$

A preferred synthesis of phenyldichloroborane, however, makes use of tetraphenyltin. The equation usually written for this reaction is:

$$Ph_4Sn + 2BCl_3 \longrightarrow 2PhBCl_2 + Ph_2SnCl_2$$

although yields of $PhBCl_2$ are often higher than this equation implies, possibly because $PhSnCl_3$ or even $SnCl_4$ is formed, or else because there is Friedel–Crafts attack on the benzene solvent [32]. Alkylboron halides may be prepared by a similar reaction from a tetra-alkyltin and boron tri-

[28] E. Wiberg and W. Ruschmann, *Ber.*, 1937, **70**, 1583.

[29] R. Bucourt and R. Joly, *Compt. rend.*, 1962, **254**, 1655; R. Joly and R. Bucourt, Fr.P. 1, 240,097; *Chem. Abs.*, 1962, **56**, 1480.

[30] W. Gerrard, M. Howarth, E. F. Mooney and D. E. Pratt, *J. Chem. Soc.*, 1963, 1582; G. C. Brown, B. E. Deuters, W. Gerrard and D. B. Green, *Chem. and Ind.*, 1965, 1634.

[31] J. B. Honeycutt and J. M. Riddle, *J. Amer. Chem. Soc.*, 1959, **81**, 2593; 1960, **82**, 3051.

[32] J. E. Burch, W. Gerrard, M. Howarth and E. F. Mooney, *J. Chem. Soc.*, 1960, 4916; K. Niedenzu and J. W. Dawson, *J. Amer. Chem. Soc.*, 1960, **82**, 4223; K. Niedenzu, H. Beyer and J. W. Dawson, *Inorg. Chem.*, 1962, **1**, 738.

chloride or tribromide [33]. Tetramethyl-lead in the absence of solvent readily replaces boron-attached halogen atoms by methyl groups [33a]. For example, conversion of boron trichloride into trimethylborane is effectively quantitative. An advantage of this reagent is that the other product is trimethyl-lead chloride which, being very stable, non-volatile and water-soluble is readily separated from the organoborane.

The most satisfactory alkylating agents for the preparation of organo-boron compounds now appear to be the alkyls of aluminium [34]; no quaternary salts are formed and the fact that many of these reactions require no solvent or diluent is a particularly attractive feature for large-scale preparations. The reaction

$$BF_3 + Alk_3Al \longrightarrow AlF_3 + Alk_3B$$

does not readily go to completion. The use of ether complexes is more satisfactory, but not all the alkyl is transferred,

$$2BF_3 \cdot OEt_2 + 3Et_3Al \cdot OEt_2 \longrightarrow 2Et_3B + 3EtAlF_2 + 5Et_2O$$

although about 90% yields of triethylborane are obtained relative to the boron trifluoride used. The reaction mixture is gradually taken to 200° and both ether and triethylborane distil off. The use of amine complexes is rather better, and, for example, yields of over 90% of tripropylborane are obtained when a mixture of tripropylaluminium and triethylamine-boron trifluoride is heated at 150–160°:

$$Et_3N \cdot BF_3 + Pr^n_3Al \longrightarrow Pr^n_3B + Et_3N + AlF_3$$

Alternatively dry powdered potassium borofluoride may be suspended in an inert solvent (1-methylnaphthalene has been used) and triethyl-aluminium gradually added at 175–195°; most of the triethylborane distils away as it forms. Tetra-alkylaluminates [35] and alkylaluminium halides have also been used as sources of alkyl groups. The use of the latter to pre-pare alkylchloroboranes is an adaptation of the usual preparation of boron trichloride [36]:

$$EtAlCl_2 + BF_3 \rightleftharpoons EtBCl_2 + AlF_{3(s)}$$

Both ethyl- and methyl-dichloroboranes have been prepared by the gas-phase reaction between boron trifluoride and the appropriate alkyl-aluminium dichloride. Methylaluminium dichloride may even be prepared from aluminium carbide [37]:

$$Al_4C_3 + HCl/BCl_3 \text{ mixture} \longrightarrow AlCl_3 + MeBCl_2 \text{ (via MeAlCl}_2)$$

[33] W. Gerrard, E. F. Mooney and R. G. Rees, *J. Chem. Soc.*, 1964, 740.
[33a] A. K. Holliday and G. N. Jessop, *J. Chem. Soc. (A)*, 1967, 889.
[34] R. Köster, *Annalen*, 1958, **618**, 31.
[35] H. Jenkner, Kali-Chemie A.-G. Brit.P. 900,132, July 4, 1962.
[36] B. Lengyel and B. Csákvári, *Z. anorg. Chem.*, 1963, **322**, 103.
[37] R. L. Barnes and T. Wartik, *J. Amer. Chem. Soc.*, 1963, **85**, 360.

Although boron halides are normally more readily alkylated than borate esters, which in turn are more reactive than aminoboranes towards carbanionic reagents [37a], the most satisfactory method of preparing alkylboranes is probably the reaction between an aluminium alkyl and a borate ester, no solvent being necessary [38]. A mixture of triethylaluminium and ethyl orthoborate spontaneously heats to over 100°, and triethylborane can be distilled off in over 90% yield:

$$B(OEt)_3 + Et_3Al \longrightarrow Et_3B + Al(OEt)_3$$

A useful variation of this method is the preparation of boronic esters by the use of appropriate reactant ratios:

$$Et_3Al + 3B(OBu^n)_3 \longrightarrow 3EtB(OBu^n)_2 + Al(OBu^n)_3$$

Alkyl 'metaborates' (alkoxyboroxines) also give good yields of trialkylboranes when allowed to react with aluminium alkyls, or, more conveniently in some instances, alkylaluminium sesquihalides. The exothermic reaction is conveniently carried out in a mineral oil diluent [38]:

$$3Et_3Al_2Cl_3 + (MeOBO)_3 \longrightarrow 3Et_3B + Al(OMe)_3 + Al_2O_3 + 3AlCl_3$$

Even boric oxide [39] or sodium borate [40] may be alkylated by alkylaluminium sesquichlorides provided the starting materials are vigorously dried at up to 260° *in vacuo*. For example, anhydrous sodium borate, $Na_2B_4O_7$, prepared by dehydrating borax, suspended in ethylaluminium sesquichloride for three hours at 200–210° yields 94% triethylborane [40]. Incompletely alkylated diboranes may be obtained by the reaction [41]:

$$Me_3Al + 2LiBH_4 + 5HCl \longrightarrow 2LiCl + AlCl_3 + 5H_2 + B_2H_3Me_3$$

Addition of B–H bonds to olefins or acetylenes: hydroboration
Under mild experimental conditions, compounds containing B–H bonds react with olefins or acetylenes to form organoboron compounds; e.g.

$$R^1R^2C{=}CH_2 + H{-}B{\Big<} \longrightarrow R^1R^2CHCH_2B{\Big<}$$

$$RC{:}CH + H{-}B{\Big<} \longrightarrow RCH{=}CHB{\Big<}$$

This method of forming boron–carbon bonds, the *hydroboration reaction*, is one of the most important developments in boron chemistry and is of considerable significance in synthetic organic chemistry, as the resulting organoboron compound can be used as an intermediate in the con-

[37a] M. F. Lappert and M. K. Majumdar, *J. Organometal. Chem.*, 1966, 6, 316.
[38] E. C. Ashby, *J. Amer. Chem. Soc.*, 1959, 81, 4791; U.S.P. 3,023, 248. R. Long and H. B. Silver, Brit.P. 897,485, May 30, 1962.
[39] H. Jenkner, Kali-Chemie A.-G., Ger.P. 1,121,048, Jan. 4, 1962.
[40] Idem, Ger.P. 1,127,356, April 12, 1962.
[41] L. H. Long and A. C. Sanhueza, *Chem. and Ind.*, 1961, 588.

version of olefins or acetylenes into other hydrocarbons, alcohols, aldehydes or ketones. The scope of the reaction is evident from the recent
authoritative reviews by H. C. Brown, [8], whose group has been responsible for much of the work in this field. As a way of preparing simple
organoboron compounds, the hydroboration reaction is not as generally
useful as the reactions already described. However, the factors involved in
forming boron–carbon bonds by this method are important because of
their relevance to its application in organic syntheses.

The reaction between diborane and aliphatic olefins and styrene, whereby
organoboron compounds are formed, was reported some years ago [42].
The successful development of such reactions as useful laboratory methods
resulted from improvements in processes for the convenient laboratory
preparation of diborane, by adding a solution of sodium borohydride
in diglyme (2,5,8-trioxanonane, $(CH_3OCH_3CH_2)_2O$, i.e. diethyleneglycol
dimethyl ether) *to* a solution of boron trifluoride–ether complex in the
same solvent [43],

$$3NaBH_4 + 4BF_3 \longrightarrow 2B_2H_6 + 3NaBF_4$$

and from the discovery that the addition of diborane to olefins is strongly
catalysed by ethers. One convenient procedure is to bubble diborane in a
stream of nitrogen through a solution of the olefin in an appropriate ether,
such as diglyme (b.p. 162°), triglyme (b.p. 216°), diethyl ether or tetrahydrofuran, the last being preferred as it is the best solvent for diborane.
Reaction is rapid at room temperature, and excess diborane is conveniently removed by washing exit gases with acetone. In this way tri-n-
hexylborane, b.p. 185–188°/30 mm., was obtained in 91% yield from
1-hexene [44]:

$$6Bu^nCH:CH_2 + B_2H_6 \longrightarrow 2(C_6H_{13})_3B$$

Alternatively, diborane or some other active B–H compound may be
generated *in situ*, for example boron trifluoride–ether complex may be
added to a mixture of the olefin and sodium borohydride in diglyme:

$$12RCH{=}CH_2 + 3NaBH_4 + 4BF_3,OEt_2 \longrightarrow 4(RCH_2CH_2)_3B + 3NaBF_4 + 4Et_2O$$

The reaction mixture is poured into water, in which solvents like diglyme
are soluble, and the product selectively extracted into ethyl ether.

Although these two procedures are the most generally useful, many
variations have proved practicable though less efficient [45]. The essential
ingredients are a *hydride*, which need not contain boron (e.g. $LiBH_4$,

[42] D. T. Hurd, *J. Amer. Chem. Soc.*, 1948, **70**, 2053; A. T. Whatley and R. N.
Pease, ibid., 1954, **76**, 835.
[43] H. C. Brown and P. A. Tierney, ibid., 1958, **80**, 1552; H. C. Brown and B. C.
Subba Rao, *J. Org. Chem.*, 1957, **22**, 1135.   [44] Idem, ibid., p. 1136.
[45] H. C. Brown, K. J. Murray, L. J. Murray, J. A. Snover and G. Zweifel, *J. Amer.
Chem. Soc.*, 1960, **82**, 4233.

$NaBH_4$, KBH_4, $LiAlH_4$, LiH, NaH, C_5H_5N,BH_3 or Me_3N,BH_3); an *acid*, which should contain boron if the hydride does not (e.g. BF_3, BCl_3, $AlCl_3$, $AlCl_3 + B(OMe)_3$, $TiCl_4$, HCl or H_2SO_4); and a suitable *ethereal solvent* having a boiling point which allows easy separation from the product. As sources of boron hydride, amine-boranes R_3N,BH_3 are less convenient than metal hydrides or double hydrides for the hydroboration of olefins, requiring temperatures in the range of 100–200°, although trimethylamine-t-butylborane, Me_3N,BH_2Bu^t, is a useful reagent [46] achieving the hydroboration of olefins, dienes and acetylenes in two hours at 60°. This reagent is prepared by treating t-butylboroxine $(Bu^tBO)_3$ (from t-butylmagnesium chloride and methyl borate at low temperatures) with lithium aluminium hydride in the presence of trimethylamine. Its superiority over simple amine-boranes is presumably due to its greater dissociation brought about by the inductive and steric requirements of the t-butyl group.

The *direction of addition* of B–H bonds to olefins is highly specific, the boron atom generally becoming attached to the *less substituted* of the two carbon atoms of the double bond [47]. For example, tri-n-pentylborane, b.p. 94–95°/2 mm., has been prepared in 88% yield from 1-pentene [48].

$$6CH_3(CH_2)_2CH:CH_2 + B_2H_6 \longrightarrow 2(n\text{-}C_5H_{11})_3B$$

The direction of hydroboration is conveniently determined by oxidation of the organoborane by alkaline hydrogen peroxide, which places a hydroxyl group in the position formerly occupied by boron, and by identification of the resulting alcohol:

$$(n\text{-}C_5H_{11})_3B \xrightarrow{H_2O_2} n\text{-}C_5H_{11}OH + H_3BO_3$$

The hydroboration of cyclic olefins [49] such as norbornene and of acetylenes [50] has been shown to involve *cis* addition of B–H, and it has therefore been suggested that the addition involves a four-centre transition state, the relative orientation of the molecules being determined by the slightly polar character of the B–H and C=C bonds:

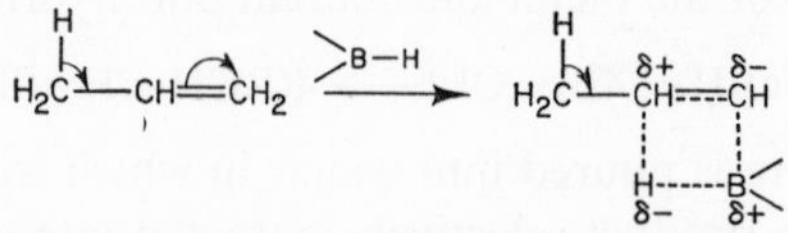

The same explanation holds for the enhanced preference of boron for the less substituted carbon atom of 2,2-dialkylethylenes and trialkylethylenes. Styrene differs from alkyl substituted olefins in that its hydroboration leads

[46] M. F. Hawthorne, *J. Amer. Chem. Soc.*, 1959, **81**, 5836; 1960, **82**, 748; 1961, **83**, 2541.

[47] H. C. Brown and G. Zweifel, ibid., 1960, **82**, 4708.

[48] H. C. Brown and B. C. Subba Rao, ibid., 1956, **78**, 5694; 1959, **81**, 6423, 6428, 6434.　　　[49] H. C. Brown and G. Zweifel, ibid., 1959, **81**, 247; 1961, **83**, 2544.

[50] Idem, ibid., 1959, **81**, 1512.

to significant quantities (20%) of the derivative having boron attached to the more highly substituted carbon atom [51]:

$$\text{PhCH=CH}_2 \xrightarrow{\text{HB}<} 20\% \text{ PhCHCH}_3 + 80\% \text{ PhCH}_2\text{CH}_2\text{B}<$$
$$\overset{|}{\underset{\text{B}<}{}}$$

Here the phenyl group can either withdraw or release electrons, allowing polarization of the olefinic bond in either direction:

$$\longrightarrow \beta\text{-B-derivative} \qquad \longrightarrow \alpha\text{-B-derivative}$$

It is possible that the four-centre transition state itself is reached via an intermediate in which there is donation of π-electrons from the double bond to the boron atom, which subsequently moves to the more negative end of the double bond.

Although no simple compounds are known in which a boron atom is bound to the π-electrons of an olefin, the bonding in the C-dimethyl derivative of dihydrocarborane-4, $B_4H_6C_2Me_2$, is best explained in such terms [52] (see 3.17), and complexes between boron trifluoride and unsymmetrical olefins have been considered to be formed at low temperatures [53]. (See also ref. [85].)

Because of the preference of the boron atom for the less substituted carbon atom of a double bond, the addition of B–H bonds to terminal olefins is faster than addition to non-terminal olefins, and treatment of a mixture of 1- and 2-pentene with a deficiency of diborane results in the selective conversion of the terminal olefin into tri-n-pentylborane. The addition of diborane to 2-pentene gives a mixture of products, since oxidation of the resulting organoborane yields a roughly 2 : 1 mixture of 2- and 3-pentanol [54]:

$$\text{Pr}^{\text{n}}\text{CH:CH}_2 \xrightarrow{\text{B}_2\text{H}_6} (\text{C}_5\text{H}_{11})_3\text{B} \xrightarrow[\text{OH}^-]{\text{H}_2\text{O}_2} 95\% \text{ n-C}_5\text{H}_{11}\text{OH}$$

$$\text{EtCH:CHMe} \xrightarrow{\text{B}_2\text{H}_6} (\text{C}_5\text{H}_{11})_3\text{B} \xrightarrow[\text{OH}^-]{\text{H}_2\text{O}_2} 63\% \text{ Pr}^{\text{n}}\text{CHOHCH}_3 + 37\% \text{ Et}_2\text{CHOH}$$

[51] Idem, ibid., 1960, **82**, 4708; H. C. Brown and R. L. Sharp, ibid., 1966, **88**, 5851.

[52] W. E. Streib, F. P. Boer, and W. N. Lipscomb, ibid., 1963, **85**, 2331; idem, *Inorg. Chem.*, 1964, **3**, 1666.

[53] R. Nakane, T. Watanabe, O. Kurihara and T. Oyama, *19th Int. Congress IUPAC*, London, July 1963, Abstracts AB4-79.

[54] H. C. Brown and B. C. Subba Rao, *J. Org. Chem.*, 1957, **22**, 1137.

Various attempts at the preparation of mixed trialkylboranes, RR'_2B, have shown that these compounds tend to disproportionate and more particularly, to *isomerize* in the sense that compounds are favoured in which chain branching is absent or relatively remote from the boron atom. If the mixed alkylboranes resulting from the reaction of diborane with 2-pentene are boiled for four hours in diglyme solution, they are converted into tri-n-pentylborane:

$$EtCHCH_2CH_3 + EtCH_2CHCH_3 \xrightarrow[\text{reflux 4 hr.}]{\text{diglyme}} (n\text{-}C_5H_{11})_3B$$
$$\underset{B/3}{|} \qquad\qquad \underset{B/3}{|}$$

This reaction provides not only a method for obtaining primary alcohols from non-terminal olefins but also for obtaining terminal olefins from their non-terminal isomers. (Usually, *terminal olefins* may be converted into *non-terminal olefins* under the influence of acid catalysts.) The reaction probably involves reversible dissociation of the alkylboranes [55], although intramolecular rearrangement of intermediate alkylboron hydrides may also be involved [56]. A trialkylborane whose alkyl chains are three or more carbon atoms long reversibly dissociates when heated:

$$2(RCH_2CH_2)_3B \rightleftharpoons (RCH_2CH_2)_2BH \cdot BH(CH_2CH_2R)_2 + 2RCH:CH_2$$

Consequently, addition of a less volatile longer-chain olefin will displace a more volatile shorter-chain olefin [54, 55, 57, 58]. These reactions resemble those of alkylaluminium compounds discovered a few years earlier. They must be carried out at elevated temperatures (above 120°) for the dissociation rate to be appreciable. For example, if a mixture of tri-isobutyl-borane and 3–4 mols. 1-decene is heated, isobutene evolution begins at 120°, is vigorous between 140° and 170°, and is complete by 210°. Removal by distillation of the excess decene from the residue affords a practically quantitative yield of tri-n-decylborane:

$$Bu^i_3B + 3C_8H_{17}CH:CH_2 \longrightarrow (C_{10}H_{21})_3B + 3Me_2C:CH_2$$

Attempted distillation of tri-n-decylborane, even at 10^{-3} mm., yields 1-decene and (mainly) tetradecyldiborane:

$$2(C_{10}H_{21})_3B \longrightarrow (C_{10}H_{21})_2BHBH(C_{10}H_{21})_2 + 2C_8H_{17}CH:CH_2$$

An important distinction between alkylboron and alkylaluminium compounds is that the former react with both terminal and non-terminal olefins, whereas the latter react at useful rates only with terminal olefins

[55] H. C. Brown and G. Zweifel, *J. Amer. Chem. Soc.*, 1960, **82**, 1504; 1966, **88**, 1433; 1967, **89**, 561; H. C. Brown and M. V. Bhatt, ibid., 1966, **88**, 1440; H. C. Brown, M. V. Bhatt, T. Munekata and G. Zweifel, ibid., 1967, **89**, 567.

[56] R. E. Williams, *Inorg. Chem.*, 1962, **1**, 971; F. M. Rossi, P. A. McCusker and G. F. Hennion, *J. Org. Chem.*, 1967, **32**, 450.

[57] R. Köster, *Annalen*, 1958, **618**, 31.

[58] H. C. Brown and M. V. Bhatt, *J. Amer. Chem. Soc.*, 1960, **82**, 2074.

(containing the C:CH$_2$ group). The addition of olefins to trialkylboranes is catalysed by small amounts of trialkylaluminium [59].

The directing influences in hydroboration are not always strong enough to cause formation of only one of the two theoretically possible isomers (see, for example, 2-pentene and styrene). *Selective hydroboration* may, however, be facilitated by use of a substituted diborane, particularly a tetra-alkyldiborane, R$_2$BHBHR$_2$, in which the groups R are bulky alkyl groups. One such reagent which has been found to have wide application [60] is the dimer of bis-(3-methyl-2-butyl)-borane or 'disiamylborane' (from 'di-sec-isoamyl-borane'), prepared by the hydroboration of 2-methyl-2-butene with diborane, a reaction which effectively stops at this stage:

$$B_2H_6 + \text{excess } Me_2C{=}CHMe \xrightarrow{\text{fast}}$$

$$[(Me_2CHCHMe)_2BH]_2 \xrightarrow[\text{slow}]{\text{very}} (Me_2CHCHMe)_3B$$

The bulky alkyl groups prevent reaction with sterically hindered olefins at any appreciable rate, but still allow the boron atom to become attached to an easily accessible carbon atom. For example, diborane reacts with styrene to place 20% of the boron on the secondary position, whereas disiamylborane reduces this to 2%. Another hydroborating reagent [61] which makes use of a bulky alkyl substituent on the boron atom is the trimethylamine adduct of t-butylborane, Me$_3$N,BH$_2$Bu^t. Optically active alcohols and olefins may be synthesized via hydroboration reactions using bis(isopinocamphenyl)borane as the reagent, itself readily obtained from diborane and α-pinene [62]. Use of mono- or di-*chloro*borane in tetrahydrofuran affords alkylchloroboranes R$_2$BCl or RBCl$_2$ [62a].

Both boron [63] and aluminium [64] hydrides react with *acetylenes* by *cis*-addition, forming vinyl derivatives, which provide a good route to *cis*-olefins:

[59] M. F. Hawthorne, ibid., p. 748.

[60] H. C. Brown and G. Zweifel, ibid., pp. 3222, 3223, 4708; 1961, **83**, 1241. G. Zweifel, K. Nagase and H. C. Brown, ibid., 1962, **84**, 190; F. Sondheimer and M. Nussim, *J. Org. Chem.*, 1961, **26**, 630; H. C. Brown, K. P. Singh and B. J. Garner, *J. Organometal. Chem.*, 1963, **1**, 2; H. C. Brown and K. A. Keblys, *J. Amer. Chem. Soc.*, 1964, **86**, 1791, 1795; H. C. Brown and V. Varma, ibid., 1966, **88**, 2871.

[61] M. F. Hawthorne, ibid., 1961, **83**, 2541.

[62] H. C. Brown, N. R. Ayyanger and G. Zweifel, ibid., 1964, **86**, 397, 1071; G. Zweifel, N. R. Ayyanger, T. Munekata and H. C. Brown, ibid., p. 1076.

[62a] D. J. Pasto and P. Balasubramaniyan, ibid., 1967, **89**, 295.

[63] H. C. Brown and G. Zweifel, ibid., 1959, **81**, 1512; L. I. Zakharkin and A. I. Kovredov, *Izvest. Akad. Nauk S.S.S.R.*, 1964, 393; *Chem. Abs.*, 1964, **60**, 12038.

[64] G. Wilke and M. Müller, *Chem. Ber.*, 1956, **89**, 444.

The direct reaction with diborane is unsatisfactory when applied to terminal acetylenes, since complete reduction occurs by addition of two B–H bonds, although disiamylborane [65] or trimethylamine-t-butylborane [61] can be used:

$$(Pr^iCHMe)_2BH + Bu^nCH{:}CH \longrightarrow Bu^nCH{:}CHB(CHMePr^i)_2$$

HOAc↙   ↘H₂O₂

$$Bu^nCH{:}CH_2 \qquad\qquad Bu^nCHO$$

The dihydroboration of acetylenes occurs preferentially to place two boron atoms on the same carbon atom [65a] (although acetylene itself also gives 1,2-diboroethane derivatives, as indicated by the isolation of the hydrolysis product $(HO)_2BC_2H_4B(OH)_2$ [66]). The products are very sensitive to hydrolytic cleavage, and are of less use as intermediates than the vinylboranes obtained by monohydroboration [67]. Difficulties with the direct hydroboration of acetylenes may be avoided by the use of a trialkylborane as a source of boron hydride [68]:

$$3RC{:}CR + Et_3B \longrightarrow (RCH{:}CR)_3B + 3CH_2{:}CH_2 \uparrow$$

Each acetylenic bond becomes linked to only one boron atom. In the hydroboration of allenes the boron generally becomes attached to the central carbon atom [69].

The hydroboration of dienes has been used to prepare organoboron ring compounds, described below, and to prepare unsaturated alcohols [70].

The uses to which hydroboration may be put may therefore be summarized as follows. It is a convenient route to many trialkylboranes or alkylboron hydrides [71]. The steric and directing influences commonly enable H–B to be added across a particular carbon–carbon multiple bond in a molecule, the boron atom becoming attached to the *less substituted* carbon atom, i.e. the carbon atom to which *hydrogen* becomes attached when HX is added to a multiple bond. Addition is *cis*, and so allows stereochemical control, and, for example, asymmetric syntheses [72]. Sub-

[65] H. C. Brown and G. Zweifel, *J. Amer. Chem. Soc.*, 1961, **83**, 3834.

[65a] G. Cainelli, G. Dal Bello and G. Zubiani, *Tetrahedron Letters*, 1966, 4315; G. Zweifel and H. Arzoumanian, *J. Amer. Chem. Soc.*, 1967, **89**, 291.

[66] G. F. Clark and A. K. Holliday, *J. Organometal. Chem.*, 1964, **2**, 100.

[67] A. Hassner and B. H. Braun, *J. Org. Chem.*, 1963, **28**, 261; D. S. Matteson and J. G. Shdo, ibid., 1964, **29**, 2742; D. J. Pasto, *J. Amer. Chem. Soc.*, 1964, **86**, 3039; G. Cainelli, G. D. Bello and G. Zubiani, *Tetrahedron Letters*, 1965, 3429.

[68] A. J. Hubert, *J. Chem. Soc.*, 1965, 6669.

[69] D. Devaprabhakara and P. D. Gardner, *J. Amer. Chem. Soc.*, 1963, **85**, 1458.

[70] G. Zweifel, K. Nagase and H. C. Brown, ibid., 1962, **84**, 190.

[71] R. Köster, G. Griasnow, W. Larbig and P. Binger, *Annalen*, 1964, **672**, 1.

[72] H. C. Brown and G. Zweifel, *J. Amer. Chem. Soc.*, 1961, **83**, 486; H. C. Brown, N. R. Ayyanger and G. Zweifel, ibid., 1962, **84**, 4341, 4342.

sequent reactions of the organoboron intermediate lead to a range of products.

(*i*) Alkaline hydrogen peroxide yields an alcohol, i.e. overall *cis anti-Markownikov hydration.*

(*ii*) Protonation by acetic or propionic acid yields a hydrocarbon, i.e. overall *hydrogenation* [73].

(*iii*) Heating, followed by treatment with an involatile olefin, yields an isomer of the parent olefin, i.e. '*contra-thermodynamic* isomerization' [57].

(*iv*) Oxidation with chromic acid yields *ketones* [74] or acids.

(*v*) Treatment with alkaline silver nitrate solution causes *coupling* of the alkyl groups [75].

(*vi*) Treatment with an N-chlorodialkylamine such as Et_2NCl gives an alkyl chloride, i.e. overall *anti-Markownikov addition* of *hydrogen chloride* [76].

(*vii*) Treatment with chloramine or hydroxylamine-O-sulphonic acid gives an *alkyl amine* [77].

(*viii*) Treatment with $PhHgCCl_2Br$ effects *coupling through an extra carbon atom* ([77a]:

$$RCH{:}CH_2 \xrightarrow{B_2H_6} (RCH_2CH_2)_3B \xrightarrow{PhHgCCl_2Br} RCH_2CH_2CH{:}CHCH_2R$$

(*ix*) Treatment of the diglyme solution of the organoborane at $100-125°$ with carbon monoxide at 1 atmosphere affords a route to *carbinols* [77b]:

$$R_3B + CO \xrightarrow{100-125°} [R_3CBO] \xrightarrow[NaOH]{H_2O_2} R_3COH$$

(*x*) Carbonylation at atmospheric pressure in the presence of water affords *ketones* after oxidation [77c]:

$$R_3B + CO \xrightarrow[100°]{H_2O} [RB(OH)CR_2OH] \xrightarrow[NaOH]{H_2O_2} R_2CO$$

[73] H. C. Brown and K. Murray, ibid., 1959, **81**, 4108.

[74] H. C. Brown and C. P. Garg, ibid., 1961, **83**, 2951.

[75] H. C. Brown, N. C. Hébert and C. H. Snyder, ibid., p. 1001; H. C. Brown, C. Verbrugge and C. H. Snyder, ibid., p. 1001; H. C. Brown and C. H. Snyder, ibid., p. 1002.

[76] J. G. Sharefkin and H. D. Banks, *J. Org. Chem.*, 1965, **30**, 4313.

[77] H. C. Brown, W. R. Heydkamp, E. Breuer and W. S. Murphy, *J. Amer. Chem. Soc.*, 1964, **86**, 3565; M. W. Rathke, N. Inoue, K. R. Varma and H. C. Brown, ibid., 1966, **88**, 2870.

[77a] D. Seyferth and B. Prokai, ibid., 1966, **88**, 1834.

[77b] H. C. Brown and M. W. Rathke, ibid., 1967, **89**, 2737.

[77c] Idem, ibid., p. 2738.

(*xi*) Carbonylation at atmospheric pressure in the presence of a borohydride effects *oxymethylation* of the parent olefin [77*d*]:

$$R_3B + CO \xrightarrow[\text{or LiBH}_4/\text{THF; 45°}]{\text{NaBH}_4/\text{diglyme}} \xrightarrow{\text{KOH}} RCH_2OH$$

It should be pointed out that the hydroboration reaction is applicable to a wide range of multiply-bonded functional groups other than olefinic or acetylenic linkages such as carboxylic acids, carbonyl compounds, nitriles, amides and esters [78], but as the products have the boron atom attached to the element other than carbon, these reactions do not fall into the category at present being discussed in the sense that boron–carbon bonds are not formed.

Reaction between a hydrocarbon and a boron halide
This third method for the preparation of organoboron compounds appears to be more limited in scope than the other methods, although its possibilities are still being explored. There are two types of reaction between a hydrocarbon and a boron halide:

(*i*) *addition* of B–X to an olefin or acetylene, analogous to the hydroboration reaction, and termed for example 'chloroboration'; and

(*ii*) *substitution* reactions in which a BX₂ group is substituted in an aromatic hydrocarbon, hydrogen halide being eliminated, essentially a Friedel–Crafts reaction.

(*i*) Olefins react less readily with boron trichloride than with diborane, many being polymerized [85], although boron trichloride adds to norbornadiene [79, 79*a*]. Acetylenes react with boron trichloride under mild conditions to form 2-chlorovinylboranes [80, 81], and more vigorously with boron tribromide to form 2-bromovinylboranes [81]. 2-Chlorovinyldichloroborane, a liquid b.p. 34°/70 mm., has been obtained in 90% yield from the vapour-phase reaction of boron trichloride with acetylene,

$$BCl_3 + CH:CH \rightarrow Cl_2BCH{=}CHCl$$

although in the presence of an excess of acetylene and a catalyst of mercuric

[77*d*] M. W. Rathke and H. C. Brown, *J. Amer. Chem. Soc.*, 1967, **89**, 2740; see also J. J. Tufariello, P. Wojtkowski and L. T. C. Lee, *Chem. Comm.*, 1967, 505.

[78] H. C. Brown and W. Korytnyk, *J. Amer. Chem. Soc.*, 1960, **82**, 3866; H. C. Brown and P. Heim, ibid., 1964, **86**, 3566.

[79] F. Joy and M. F. Lappert, *Proc. Chem. Soc.*, 1960, 353; M. F. Lappert, *Angew. Chem.*, 1960, **72**, 36.

[79*a*] F. Joy, M. F. Lappert and B. Prokai, *J. Organometal. Chem.*, 1966, **5**, 506.

[80] E. Gipstein, P. R. Kippur, M. A. Higgins and B. F. Clark, *J. Org. Chem.*, 1961, **26**, 2947.

[81] M. F. Lappert and B. Prokai, *J. Organometal Chem.*, 1963, **1**, 384; see also J. J. Eisch and L. J. Gonsior, *J. Organometal. Chem.*, 1967, **8**, 53.

chloride on activated carbon, further reaction at 100° yields bis-(2-chloro-vinyl)chloroborane,ClB(CH:CHCl)$_2$, and some tris-(2-chlorovinyl)borane, B(CH:CHCl)$_3$ [80].

Chloroboration and related reactions of unsaturated compounds like isocyanates RNCO, isothiocyanates RNCS, carbodiimides RNCNR and certain ketones have been shown to occur [82], but as these invariably place the boron on an atom other than carbon they do not fall within the scope of reactions being discussed here.

No examples of fluoroboration have been reported although there is some evidence [53] of weak complex formation between polar olefins and boron trifluoride at temperatures below −100°. Boron tribromide adds across the double bond of certain olefins at 100° [83].

(*ii*) The Friedel–Crafts reaction involving a boron chloride has been used extensively by Dewar and co-workers as the key cyclization step in the preparation of derivatives of 10,9-borazarophenanthrene and related compounds [7]. For example, condensation of 2-aminobiphenyl with boron trichloride and aluminium chloride gives 10-chloro-10,9-borazarophenan-threne [84], presumably via an intermediate arylaminodichloroborane, ArNHBCl$_2$:

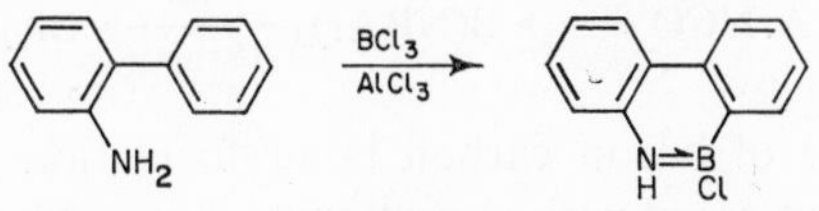

Benzene reacts with boron trichloride at 120–150° (1 hour) or 30–50° (1–2 days) in the presence of aluminium powder and a little aluminium chloride, iodine or methyl iodide, to give a 60–72% yield of phenyldichloro-borane after filtration and distillation [85]. Toluene gives a mixture of *m*- and *p*-MeC$_6$H$_4$BCl$_2$. The Friedel–Crafts reaction with *boron tribromide* and aluminium bromide is more convenient on a laboratory scale; after 15 hours' reflux in benzene at atmospheric pressure, phenyldibromo-borane has been obtained in 50% yield. Some diphenylbromoborane is also formed [86]. Boron tribromide and tri-iodide have also been shown to react with benzene under ultraviolet irradiation in the absence of catalyst [87].

[82] M. F. Lappert and B. Prokai, *J. Chem. Soc.*, 1963, 4223; G. W. Parshall, *Inorg. Chem.*, 1965, **4**, 52; R. Jefferson, M. L. Lappert, B. Prokai and B. P. Tilley, *J. Chem. Soc. (A)*, 1966, 1584.

[83] B. M. Mikhailov and M. E. Nikolaeva, *Izvest. Akad. Nauk S.S.S.R.*, 1963, 1368; *Chem. Abs.*, 1963, **59**, 15296.

[84] M. J. S. Dewar, V. P. Kubba and R. Pettit, *J. Chem. Soc.*, 1958, 3073.

[85] E. L. Muetterties, *J. Amer. Chem. Soc.*, 1959, **81**, 2597; 1960, **82**, 4163.

[86] Z. J. Bujwid, W. Gerrard and M. F. Lappert, *Chem. and Ind.*, 1959, 1091.

[87] R. A. Bowie and O. C. Musgrave, *Proc. Chem. Soc.*, 1964, 15.

Other methods of forming boron–carbon bonds

Some reactions which have resulted in boron–carbon compounds do not fall into the three main categories discussed above. The autoclave reaction at 180–200° between benzene and an alkyldiborane or triethylamine-borane has been shown to form triphenylborane [88]. Diazomethane has been used to insert methylene groups between a halogen atom and the boron of a boron halide [20, 89, 90];

$$BX_3 + nCH_2N_2 \longrightarrow X_2B(CH_2)_nX + nN_2$$

The boron content of the products of such reactions is generally low, however, and they are more realistically regarded as polymethylene with boron-containing end groups. For example, diborane (1 mol.) and diazomethane (16 mols.) give a highly crystalline polymethylene m.p. 136° containing 1% boron [91].

An interesting sequence of reactions has been described as leading to alkyls of boron or other elements starting from the appropriate alkoxide: boron alkoxides react with aryl isocyanates with evolution of carbon dioxide to form tris-(arylalkylamino)boranes, which are converted into trialkylboranes by reaction with carbon monoxide under pressure [92].

$$B(OR)_3 + ArNCO \xrightarrow{-CO_2} B(NRAr)_3 \xrightarrow[150\,\text{p.s.i.}]{CO} BR_3 + ArNCO$$

A further example of boron–carbon bond formation is the reaction of diborane with an excess of carbon monoxide in an autoclave at 90°, which results in borane carbonyl, BH_3CO [93]. The same reactants combine in THF at room temperature in the presence of sodium borohydride to give trimethylboroxine [93a]:

$$3[BH_3] + 3CO \xrightarrow{NaBH_4/THF} (MeBO)_3$$

Properties and reactions of the organoboranes

In this section, the simple trialkyls and triaryls of boron will be described, together with those compounds in which interest is centred mainly on the organic part of the molecule, such as alkenyl, alkynyl and fluorocarbon derivatives and alicyclic boron compounds. Derivatives in which one or

[88] R. Köster, K. Reinert and K. H. Mueller, *Angew. Chem.*, 1960, **72**, 78.
[89] J. Goubeau and K. H. Rohwedder, *Annalen*, 1957, **604**, 168.
[90] A. G. Davies, D. G. Hare, O. R. Khan and J. Sikora, *Proc. Chem. Soc.*, 1961, 172; idem, *J. Chem. Soc.*, 1963, 4461.
[91] G. H. Dorion, S. E. Polchlopek and E. H. Sheers, *Angew. Chem., Internat. Edn.*, 1964, **3**, 447.
[92] R. S. Aries, U.S.P. 3,053,871, Sept. 11, 1962; *Chem. Abs.*, 1963, **58**, 12602.
[93] A. B. Burg and H. I. Schlesinger, *J. Amer. Chem. Soc.*, 1937, **59**, 780; M. E. Garabedian and S. W. Benson, ibid., 1964, **86**, 176.
[93a] M. W. Rathke and H. C. Brown, ibid., 1966, **88**, 2606.

more of the bonds to boron are occupied by elements other than carbon, and in which the chemistry tends to be dominated by these functional groups, will be described in the next section, being classified according to that element.

Trialkylboranes

Trimethylborane, Me_3B, m.p. $-159·85°$, b.p. $-21·8°$, is conveniently obtained by the slow addition, in a nitrogen atmosphere, of a solution of boron trifluoride in di-n-butyl ether to methyl magnesium bromide in the same solvent. The trimethylborane is evolved as a gas and the use of di-n-butyl ether avoids extensive contamination of the product with the much more volatile ethyl ether normally used for Grignard reactions. In the event of trimethylaluminium being conveniently available, then reaction with tributyl borate provides the easiest route [34] to trimethylborane. Trimethylborane, which is spontaneously inflammable, may safely be stored in combination with trimethylamine; the solid complex $Me_3B·NMe_3$ can readily be purified by sublimation and the trimethylborane regenerated by treatment with slightly less than the theoretical amount of dry hydrogen chloride [94]:

$$Me_3B·NMe_3 + HCl \rightarrow Me_3B + Me_3NHCl$$

Trimethylborane, unlike trimethylaluminium, does not associate; nor of course do the boron halides. The quadrupole resonance spectra of various trialkylboranes indicate that their monomeric nature (and low Lewis acidity) may be explained in terms of a hyperconjugation effect, in which the attached alkyl groups release electrons into the vacant $2p$ orbital of the boron, an effect which is greatest with trimethylborane [95]. For calculations indicating the magnitude of this effect, see ref. [152]. It is the most stable (thermally) of the boron alkyls, but decomposes at $400-600°$ and $1-6$ atm. with the formation of methane, hydrogen, polymeric material, and the interesting liquid product [96] (3.1):

$$CH_3\!-\!B\!-\!CH_2\!-\!B\!-\!CH_3$$
$$CH_2 \qquad CH_2$$
$$CH_3\!-\!B\!-\!CH_2\!-\!B\!-\!CH_3$$

3.1

Though unaffected by water under ordinary conditions it is slowly (7 hours) hydrolysed at $180°$ with loss of one methyl group. Still more

[94] H. C. Brown, ibid., 1945, **67**, 375; H. C. Brown and R. B. Johannesen, ibid., 1953, **75**, 19; J. Chatt, *J. Chem. Soc.*, 1949, 3340.
[95] P. Love, *J. Amer. Chem. Soc.*, 1963, **85**, 3044.
[96] J. Goubeau and R. Epple, *Chem. Ber.*, 1957, **90**, 170.

resistant to hydrogen sulphide, it reacts at 280° giving boron sulphide:

$$B_2S_3 + CH_4 \xleftarrow[280°]{H_2S} Me_3B \xrightarrow[180°]{H_2O} Me_2BOH + CH_4$$

Several other high-temperature reactions of trimethylborane have afforded a variety of heterocyclic products [97]:

Triethylborane, Et_3B, m.p. $-92.5°$, b.p. 95°, from ethylmagnesium bromide and methyl borate, or from triethylaluminium and butyl borate [34], is spontaneously inflammable like all the volatile boron alkyls and can be purified and stored as the ammonia complex, which may be distilled and then decomposed with hydrogen chloride. *Tri-n-propylborane*, Pr^n_3B, b.p. 156°, and *tri-n-butylborane*, Bu^n_3B, b.p. 90–91°/9 mm., are most readily prepared on the laboratory scale by the Grignard method. Tri-isopropylborane has probably never been obtained in a pure state. When the product from isopropylmagnesium bromide and boron trichloride is fractionally distilled in a 60-cm. column, the boiling range remains 148–154°. It is probable that isomerization occurs quite rapidly [98].

The branched-chain butylboranes have been the subject of a certain amount of confusion. *Tri-isobutylborane*, b.p. 68°/7 mm., 188–188·5°/ 745–750 mm., can be obtained without difficulty by the Grignard or the aluminium methods [Bu^i_3 Al + $(Bu^nO)_3B$]; it is stable to distillation at atmospheric pressure. *Tri-s-butylborane*, b.p. 59·7–60°/2·5 mm., from s-butylmagnesium bromide and boron trifluoride, slowly isomerizes to tri-n-butylborane when boiled with reflux at atmospheric pressure [99]. *Tri-t-butylborane*, though frequently described, does not and apparently cannot exist. Attempts to prepare it from t-butylmagnesium chloride and boron trifluoride have resulted in tri-isobutylborane or $Bu^i_2Bu^tB$, identified by hydrogen peroxide oxidation and analysis of the resulting alcohols [99]. *Di-isobutyl-t-butylborane* was later prepared from di-isobutylfluoro-

[97] D. Ulmschneider and J. Goubeau, *Chem. Ber.* 1957, **90**, p. 2733.
[98] P. A. McCusker, G. F. Hennion and E. C. Ashby, *J. Amer. Chem. Soc.*, 1957, **79**, 5192; P. A. McCusker, F. M. Rossi, J. H. Bright and G. F. Hennion, *J. Org. Chem.*, 1963, **28**, 2889.
[99] G. F. Hennion, P. A. McCusker, E. C. Ashby and A. J. Rutkowski, *J. Amer. Chem. Soc.*, 1957, **79**, 5190.

borane (Bu^i_2BF) and t-butylmagnesium chloride and by four other methods [100]; it may be distilled without disproportionation or re-arrangement if the boiling point does not exceed 60°, otherwise Bu^i_3B is formed. It seems that not more than two t-butyl groups may be attached to the same boron atom, and then only when the remaining group is unbranched. n-Butyl-di-t-butylborane, b.p. 47·7°/1·7 mm., and n-pentyl-di-t-butylborane, b.p. 42·5–42·7°/0·5 mm., have been prepared, the first from boron trifluoride and t-butylmagnesium chloride in ether containing a large excess of 1-butene; both compounds rearrange rapidly when heated, $(n-C_5H_{11})Bu^t_2B$ giving a 2 : 1 mixture of Bu^i_3B and $(n-C_5H_{11})_3B$ [101]. It has been possible to prepare a compound n-amyl-isobutyl-t-butylborane, b.p. 43·5–44°/0·5 mm., with three different alkyl groups; it gave the correct alcohols in equal amounts when oxidized with alkaline hydrogen peroxide [102]. The discovery that the co-ordination complex t-butylborane-trimethylamine reacts unusually rapidly with olefins at 50–60° provided an improved route to t-butyldialkylboranes [59].

$$Bu^tBH_2·NMe_3 + 2CH_2{:}CHEt \rightarrow Bu^tBu^n_2B + NMe_3$$

The exchange of alkyl radicals between different trialkyl boranes

$$R_3B + R'_3B \rightleftharpoons R_2R'B + RR'_2B$$

does not take place at an appreciable rate below about 100°, unless R is α-branched (e.g. Pr^i, Bu^s). The exchange is, however, strongly catalysed by traces of trialkylaluminium through the formation of bridged inter-mediates [103]:

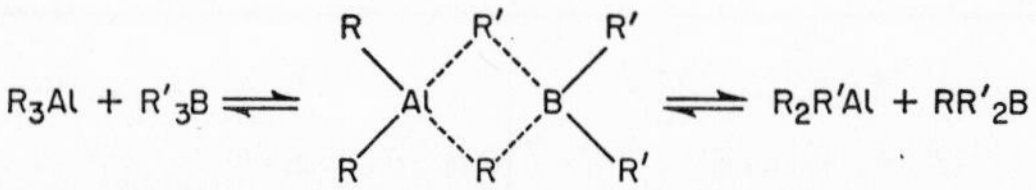

Experiments on the use of organoboron compounds as polymerization catalysts have usually been conducted with tri-n-butylborane, though ethyl and propyl derivatives have also been tried. Polymers and co-polymers have been obtained from vinyl chloride, vinyl cyanide, methyl acrylate and methacrylate and styrene [104].

Although three tertiary butyl groups have not been attached directly to boron, there is evidently room for them to be attached via methylene

[100] G. F. Hennion, P. A. McCusker and A. J. Rutkowski, ibid., 1958, **80**, 617.
[101] G. F. Hennion, P. A. McCusker and J. V. Marra, ibid., 1959, **81**, 1768.
[102] Idem. ibid., 1958, **80**, 3481.
[103] R. Köster and G. Bruno, *Annalen*, 1960, **629**, 89.
[104] G. S. Kolesnikov and N. V. Klimentova, *Izvest. Akad. Nauk S.S.S.R.*, 1957, 652; *Chem. Abs.*, 1957, 15458; G. S. Kolesnikov and L. S. Fedorova, *Izvest. Akad. Nauk S.S.S.R.*, 1957, 236; *Chem. Abs.*, 1957, 11291; N. Ashikari, *J. Polymer Sci.*, 1958, **28**, 250; idem, *Bull. Chem. Soc. Japan*, 1958, **31**, 229; J. Furukawa and T. Tsuruta, *J. Polymer Sci.*, 1958, **28**, 227.

groups in *trineopentylborane*, $(Me_3CCH_2)_3B$, b.p. $227°/747$ mm. *without decomposition*, which can be prepared by the Grignard route [104a]. The remarkable thermal stability of this compound is evidently a consequence of its quaternary β carbon atoms which prevent dissociation into alkene and $H—BR_2$. Unlike other primary alkylboranes, it does not react with boron trichloride up to $175°$. In the absence of B–H species to facilitate alkyl–halogen exchange, the bulk of the alkyl groups clearly prevents close enough approach of BCl_3 and $(Bu^tCH_2)_3B$ to allow direct exchange by a four-centre mechanism with transiently bridging chlorine and neopentyl groups.

Reactions of the trialkylboranes
These are summarized in the following diagram.

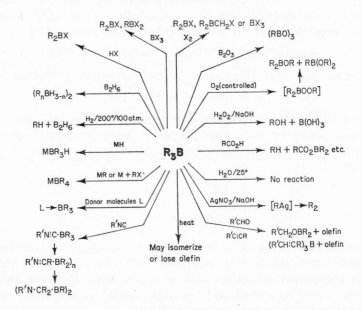

HYDROLYSIS. Boron is the only element of Group III whose trialkyls (or triaryls) are not decomposed by water under normal conditions. This has been exploited in the preparation of mercury alkyls by an aqueous reaction as already mentioned [31],

$$3HgO + 2Et_3B + 3H_2O = 3Et_2Hg + 2H_3BO_3$$

and has allowed the electrolysis of aqueous solutions of alkali metal tetra-alkyl borates $MBAlk_4$, with a mercury cathode and an anode of lead,

[104a] F. M. Rossi, P. A. McCusker and G. F. Hennion, *J. Org. Chem.*, 1967, **32**, 1233.

antimony, bismuth or mercury, to be used to prepare alkyls of these elements [105].

OXIDATION. The trialkylboranes are very sensitive to oxygen, a property shared by all the other Group III trialkyls. The lower trialkyls are spontaneously inflammable and burn with a green-tinged flame. Controlled oxidation [106] leads to the formation of esters of alkylboric acids as if oxygen atoms were inserted between the boron and the alkyl groups, e.g.

$$2Bu^n_3B + O_2 \longrightarrow 2Bu^n_2BOBu^n$$

An early step in the reaction is the formation of a peroxide R_2BOOR [107, 108], itself possibly formed via a complex $R_3B.O_2$ [109]. For example, in the oxidation of trimethylborane at pressures below the explosion limit Me_2BOOMe is obtained; this explosive substance is reduced to methoxydimethylborane ($MeOBMe_2$) by sodium iodide in isopropanol–glacial acetic acid or by hydrogen iodide at $-78°$. In a sealed tube at room temperature it rearranges to give about 90% dimethoxymethylborane, $(MeO)_2BMe$ [107]. The higher trialkyls form more stable peroxides [18], and have been used as intermediates in the formation of alkylhydroperoxides from olefins [110].

$$Et_3N·BH_3 + olefin \longrightarrow BR_3 \xrightarrow{\text{dry } O_2} RB(OOR)_2$$

$$\downarrow \text{peracids}$$

$$ROOH \xleftarrow{\text{hydrolysis}} ROB(OOR)_2$$

The oxidation of organoboron compounds with alkaline (or alkaline-alcoholic) hydrogen peroxide smoothly breaks the B–C bonds, with quantitative formation of an alcohol and a boric acid. This is a general reaction of importance in analysis and in synthetic organic chemistry following hydroboration. Alternatively, oxidation with chromic acid converts branched alkyl groups into ketones [74].

All the boron–carbon links of organoboranes are smoothly converted into B–O–C links by anhydrous N-oxides of tertiary amines. For example, when trimethylamine-N-oxide is used, the trimethylamine evolved can be

[105] K. Ziegler and O. W. Steudel, *Annalen*, 1962, **652**, 1.
[106] E. Frankland, *J. Chem. Soc.*, 1862, **15**, 363; J. R. Johnson and M. G. van Campen, *J. Amer. Chem. Soc.*, 1938, **60**, 121; C. H. Bamford and D. M. Newitt, *J. Chem. Soc.*, 1946, 695.
[107] R. C. Petry and F. H. Verhoek, *J. Amer. Chem. Soc.*, 1956, **78**, 6416.
[108] A. G. Davies, D. G. Hare and R. F. M. White, *J. Chem. Soc.*, 1961, 341; A. G. Davies, D. G. Hare and O. R. Khan, ibid., 1963, 1125.
[109] S. B. Mirviss, *J. Amer. Chem. Soc.*, 1961, **83**, 3051; R. L. Hansen and R. R. Hamann, *J. Phys. Chem.*, 1963, **67**, 2868; L. Parts and J. T. Miller, *Inorg. Chem.*, 1964, **3**, 1483; but see A. G. Davies and B. P. Roberts, *Chem. Comm.*, 1966, 298.
[110] G. Wilke and P. Heimbach, *Annalen*, 1962, **652**, 7.

determined acidimetrically, thus providing a convenient quantitative determination of the boron–carbon bonds [110a]:

$$R_3B + Me_3NO \longrightarrow B(OR)_3 + 3Me_3N$$

HALOGENS. The lower trialkylboranes tend to inflame in chlorine or bromine, but tripropylborane reacts smoothly with iodine at about 150°, giving iododipropylborane:

$$Pr^n_3B + I_2 \longrightarrow Pr^n_2BI + Pr^nI$$

The corresponding chloride and bromide have been obtained by the action of antimony trichloride (or SbBr₃) on the iodide [111]. The gas-phase reaction between chlorine and trimethylborane at −95° yields *chloromethyldimethylborane* [112, 113], $ClCH_2BMe_2$, v.p. 43 mm./0°:

$$Me_3B + Cl_2 \xrightarrow{-95°} ClCH_2BMe_3 + HCl$$

The product may be converted into azidomethyldimethylborane, $Me_2BCH_2N_3$, v.p. 4 mm./0°, by treatment with lithium azide, and the azide in turn may be catalytically (Pd/C) reduced to *aminomethyldimethylborane*, $Me_2BCH_2NH_2$ a white very volatile solid, apparently dimeric in solution in carbon disulphide at low temperatures [113].

HYDROGEN HALIDES. When hydrogen chloride is passed into tri-butylborane at 110°, dibutylchloroborane (b.p. 173°) is formed almost quantitatively [114*]:

$$Bu^n_3B + HCl \longrightarrow Bu^n_2BCl + C_4H_{10}$$

Further reaction with hydrogen chloride takes place between 180° and 210°, but mixtures of products result. The dichloroborane (b.p. 108°) can be obtained by the aluminium chloride catalysed reaction at 110°:

$$Bu^n_2BCl + HCl \xrightarrow{AlCl_3} Bu^nBCl_2 + C_4H_{10}$$

Much better preparative methods for alkylchloroboranes are described below under reactions with boron halides.

BORON HALIDES. Mixtures of trimethylborane and boron halides come to equilibrium when heated to 380–390°, and methylboron halides Me_2BCl, b.p. 4·9°, $MeBCl_2$, b.p. 11·1°, Me_2BBr, b.p. 31·3°, and $MeBBr_2$, b.p. 60·0°, have been prepared in this way as well as from trimethyl-

[110a] R. Köster and Y. Morita, *Angew. Chem., Internat. Edn.*, 1966, 5, 580.
[111] L. H. Long and D. Dollimore, *J. Chem. Soc.*, 1953, 3902, 3906.
[112] L. Zeldin and P. R. Girardot, *140th A.C.S. Meeting, Chicago, Ill.*, 1961, Abstracts p. 15-N; U.S.P. 3,083,230, March 26, 1963; *Chem. Abs.*, 1963, 59, 10116.
[113] R. Schaeffer and L. J. Todd, *J. Amer. Chem. Soc.*, 1965, 87, 488.
[114] R. B. Booth and C. A. Kraus, ibid., 1952, 74, 1415.

* Reference [114] contains useful information on analyis for boron.

borane and hydrogen halides, and from boron halides and zinc or aluminium methyls [115].

Reaction between trialkylboranes and (mainly) boron trichloride is an excellent method for the preparation of alkylhaloboranes *without loss of alkyl* groups. Triethylborane and boron trichloride heated together for four hours at 200° give good yields of *dichloroethylborane*, $EtBCl_2$, b.p. $+1°/100$ mm., and *chlorodiethylborane*, Et_2BCl, b.p. $25°/100$ mm. which can be separated by distillation at reduced pressure. In a similar way, *butyldifluoroborane*, Bu^nBF_2, b.p. $35°/760$ mm., and *dibutylfluoroborane*, Bu^n_2BF, b.p. $-5°/100$ mm., were prepared from tributylborane and boron trifluoride [116] (200°, 20 hours).

The rapid reaction, at atmospheric pressure, between trialkylboroxines and boron trichloride is also a good method for the preparation of alkyldihaloboranes [117],

$$(RBO)_3 + 2BCl_3 \longrightarrow 3RBCl_2 + B_2O_3$$

but the slow disproportionation of dialkylchloroboranes at temperatures above 180° can be used as well, the more volatile $RBCl_2$, being taken off from the top of a column [118]. The *alkyldifluoroboranes* are conveniently obtained from the dichloro compounds and antimony trifluoride.

Certain dialkylchloroboranes are quite readily accessible, since they are formed in excellent yield simply by bubbling boron trichloride into the appropriate trialkylborane at about 160°. They are relatively stable to disproportionation, and the equilibrium

$$2R_2BCl \rightleftharpoons RBCl_2 + R_3B$$

lies sufficiently far to the left, at least at temperatures up to 180°, to allow dialkylchloroboranes to be purified by vacuum distillation [118]. The direct syntheses of alkylboron chlorides by the reaction between boron trifluoride and the appropriate alkylaluminium halide [36] or from alkenes and H_nBCl_{3-n} [62a] have already been mentioned.

Redistribution and exchange reactions of derivatives of Main Group elements, including boron, were reviewed in 1965 [119].

BORIC OXIDE. Trialkylboranes react reversibly with boric oxide at about 200°:

$$R_3B + B_2O_3 \rightleftharpoons RB\begin{matrix} O-BR \\ \diagup \quad \diagdown \\ \quad \quad O \\ \diagdown \quad \diagup \\ O-BR \end{matrix} \qquad 3.2$$

[115] FIAT Review of German Science (1939–46), *Inorganic Chemistry*, Vol. I, 1948, pp. 226–38; J. Goubeau and R. Link, *Z. anorg. Chem.*, 1951, **267**, 27; W. Schabacher and J. Goubeau, ibid., 1958, **294**, 183.
[116] V. W. Buls, O. L. Davis and R. I. Thomas, *J. Amer. Chem. Soc.*, 1957, **79**, 337.
[117] P. A. McCusker, E. C. Ashby and H. S. Makowski, ibid., p. 5182.
[118] P. A. McCusker, G. F. Hennion and E. C. Ashby, ibid., p. 5192.
[119] J. C. Lockhart, *Chem. Rev.*, 1965, **65**, 131.

For example, heating equimolar quantities of tri-n-butylborane and boric oxide at reflux (200°) for 40 hours and vacuum distillation of the product gives a nearly 70% yield of tri-n-butyl boroxine (3.2, $R = Bu^n$). Tri-ethyl, -n-propyl, -isobutyl, -cyclohexyl and -phenyl boroxines have been prepared by this method, but α-branched-chain trialkylboranes rearrange (tri-s-butylborane and boric oxide yield tri-n-butylboroxine) [120]. As a route to trialkylboroxines (which are described below on p. 255) a better procedure uses the following sequence of reactions [121]:

$$B_2O_3 + (MeO)_3B \longrightarrow (MeOBO)_3 \xrightarrow[130-207°;\, 2\,hr.]{R_3B} (RBO)_3 + (MeO)_3B$$

ALKALI METALS. Although the triarylboranes form well-defined addition compounds with alkali metals, no analogous alkyl compounds are known. Tri-n-butylborane in ether solution very slowly develops a colour on standing in contact with liquid sodium–potassium alloy, but no reaction product has been identified. However, both trimethyl- and tri-n-butyl-borane react with alkali metals in liquid ammonia giving salts, derivatives of the ammonia co-ordination compounds $R_3B \cdot NH_3$:

$$R_3B \cdot NH_3 + M \longrightarrow M^+[R_3B \cdot NH_2]^- + \tfrac{1}{2}H_2$$

The same salts are obtained with sodamide in liquid ammonia:

$$R_3B \cdot NH_3 + NaNH_2 \longrightarrow Na^+[R_3B \cdot NH_2]^- + NH_3$$

They can be crystallized from ether, but are only slightly soluble in benzene and are insoluble in light petroleum. Similar compounds are formed in ethylamine solution [122] e.g.

$$Me_3B \cdot NH_2Et + Li \longrightarrow Li^+[Me_3B \cdot NHEt]^- + \tfrac{1}{2}H_2$$

When the potassium salt $K[H_2NBMe_3]$ is heated, two mols. of methane are evolved leaving a residue described as a polyanionic salt which yields hydrogen and methane on hydrolysis [123]:

$$nK[H_2NBMe_3] \longrightarrow K_n[HNBMe_2]_n \longrightarrow K_n[NBMe]_n$$

It is suggested that the product may have the structure $K_n[(\cdot N:BH \cdot CH_2 \cdot)_n]$. These compounds appear to deserve further study, as well as the products from the reaction between tetramethyldiborane and calcium in liquid ammonia, which are reported [124] to include a salt $CaHBMe_2 \cdot NH_3$, a material 'Ca(BMe_2)_2', and Li_2HBMe_2.

[120] G. F. Hennion, P. A. McCusker, E. C. Ashby and A. J. Rutkowski, *J. Amer. Chem. Soc.*, 1957, **79**, 5194.
[121] P. A. McCusker and J. H. Bright, *J. Org. Chem.*, 1964, **29**, 2093.
[122] J. E. Smith and C. A. Kraus, *J. Amer. Chem. Soc.*, 1951, **73**, 2751.
[123] A. K. Holliday and N. R. Thompson, *J. Chem. Soc.*, 1960, 2695.
[124] G. W. Campbell, *J. Amer. Chem. Soc.*, 1957, **79**, 4023; idem, *Advanc. in Chem. Series*, 1961, **32**, 195; A. Burg and G. W. Campbell, *J. Amer. Chem. Soc.*, 1952, **74**, 3744.

Boron–phosphorus compounds related to these amides are also known. For example, potassium phosphinide in ether takes up one mol. of diborane to give $K[H_3BPH_2BH_3]$, while $KPMe_2$ with Me_3B affords $K[Me_3BPMe_2BMe_3]$. Both products are sensitive to hydrolysis, particularly by acids, and to oxygen [125].

LITHIUM ALUMINIUM HYDRIDE. Trimethylborane undergoes a remarkable reaction with lithium aluminium hydride at room temperature (24 hours), in which dimethylaluminium hydride is formed [126]:

$$LiAlH_4 + Me_3B \longrightarrow LiBH_3Me + Me_2AlH$$

Similar reactions take place with trimethylaluminium and trimethylgallium, dimethylaluminium hydride being formed in each case, though the lithium salts have not been fully studied.

ALKALI METAL HYDRIDES. Alkali metal hydrides react with trialkylboranes very rapidly in ethereal solution at room temperature [127, 128], or less rapidly in paraffin solvents [129] at a temperature between 50 and $200°$, to form hydridotrialkylborates, MBR_3H. For example, when a slight excess of a solution of triethylborane in diethyl ether was added to sodium hydride suspended in the same solvent, reaction was effectively instantaneous. The product, $NaBEt_3H$ [128], a dark viscous oil, was left after evaporation of the solvent and removal of unchanged triethylborane at $75°$. Hydridotrialkylborates react with water to form hydrogen and trialkylboranes, and with olefins to form tetra-alkylborates [130, 131]; for example, sodium tetra-ethylborate, $NaBEt_4$, m.p. $143°$, is obtained from $NaBEt_3H$ and ethylene [131]. The tetra-alkylborate is stable to water but decomposed by mineral acids.

LITHIUM ALKYLS. Trimethylborane reacts with ethyl-lithium, most conveniently in benzene solution, forming a crystalline compound $LiBMe_3Et$. This compound would normally be regarded as a salt $Li^+[BMe_3Et]^-$; however, its solubility in benzene, a suitable solvent for recrystallization, may indicate a structure similar to those of analogous aluminium compounds (see p. 314) or the isoelectronic beryllium alkyls (p. 104), with alkyl bridges linking adjacent lithium and boron atoms, a structure nevertheless unusual in view of the absence of association in the boron alkyls themselves. The compound dissolves in water to form a clear solution, but gas is evolved in a few seconds [132]. A similar compound,

[125] N. R. Thompson, J. Chem. Soc., 1965, 6290.
[126] T. Wartik and H. I. Schlesinger, J. Amer. Chem. Soc., 1953, 75, 835.
[127] J. B. Honeycutt, Jr, and J. M. Riddle, ibid., 1961, 83, 369.
[128] J. B. Honeycutt, Jr (Ethyl Corp.), U.S.P. 3,055, 943, 1962; Chem. Abs., 1963, 58, 7974.
[129] Idem, U.S.P. 3,055,944, 1962; Chem. Abs., 1963, 58, 7974.
[130] Idem, Ger.P. 1,121,612, Jan. 11, 1962; Chem. Abs., 1962, 57, 11232.
[131] K. Ziegler, Brit.P. 911,387, Nov. 28, 1962; Chem. Abs., 1963, 58, 10236.
[132] H. I. Schlesinger and H. C. Brown, J. Amer. Chem. Soc., 1940, 62, 3429.

LiBMe₄, has been prepared from methyl-lithium and trimethylborane in ether [133]. Hydrogen chloride reacts with these tetra-alkylborates to regenerate trialkylborane [134]. Aqueous solutions of LiBMe₄ are conducting and on electrolysis yield hydrocarbon mixtures containing methane, ethane and cyclopropane. The electrolysis of aqueous solutions of MBR₄ with a mercury cathode and various anodes has already been mentioned [105].

The tetra-alkylammonium salt (isoamyl)₄NB(isoamyl)₄, in which the cation and anion are large symmetrical ions of virtually the same size and presumably similar mobilities, has been used as a reference electrolyte for the evaluation of single ion conductivities in the solvents acetonitrile, nitromethane and nitrobenzene [135].

Recent methods of preparing alkali metal tetra-alkyl borates themselves have used the reaction between sodium (as a dispersion) and a solution of alkyl halide and trialkylborane in a hydrocarbon–ether medium at or near room temperature [134]. Examples include some cyclopentadienyl derivatives: NaB(C₅H₅)Et₃, LiB(C₅H₅)₄, NaB(C₅H₅)H₃, NaB(C₅H₅)₃CN, RbB(C₅H₅)₃H, and Sr[B(C₅H₅)₃Br]₂ [136].

The corresponding *aryl* derivatives are more stable and are discussed below. As long ago as 1862 alkali hydroxide solutions were found to absorb trimethylborane, but no crystalline product was isolated on evaporation of the solvent [137].

ALDEHYDES. Triethylborane in ether solution reduces aldehydes with elimination of ethylene forming a borinic ester, e.g.

$$PhCHO + Et_3B \xrightarrow{100-200°} PhCH_2OBEt_2 + C_2H_4$$

This provides quite a convenient method for the preparation of diethylborinic acid (obtained by hydrolysis of the ester) [138].

CARBOXYLIC ACIDS. Alkyl groups may be cleaved as alkanes from boron by the action of carboxylic acids, affording a route for the non-catalytic conversion of olefins into saturated compounds via hydroboration and protonolysis [73]:

$$3RCH:CH_2 \xrightarrow{NaBH_4/BF_3} (RCH_2CH_2)_3B \xrightarrow{EtCO_2H} 3RCH_2CH_3$$

[133] D. T. Hurd, *J. Org. Chem.*, 1948, **13**, 711; R. A. Damico, ibid., 1964, **29**, 1971.
[134] K. Ziegler and H. Hoberg, *Angew. Chem.*, 1961, **73**, 577; E. C. Ashby (Ethyl Corp.), U.S.P. 3,007,970; *Chem. Abs.*, 1962, **56**, 6000.
[135] J. F. Coetzee and G. P. Cunningham, *J. Amer. Chem. Soc.*, 1964, **86**, 3403; 1965, **87**, 2529.
[136] H. Shapiro, E. G. de Witt and J. E. Brown (Ethyl Corp.), U.S.P. 3,030, 398, April 17, 1962; *Chem. Abs.*, 1963, **58**, 1489.
[137] E. Frankland and D. Duppa, *Annalen*, 1862, **124**, 129.
[138] H. Meerwein, G. Hinz, H. Majert and H. Sönke, *J. prakt. Chem.*, 1936, **147**, 226; H. Meerwein and H. Sönke, ibid., p. 251.

Controlled cleavage of alkyl groups affords borinic esters [139], e.g.

$$Me_3B + MeCO_2H \longrightarrow MeCO_2BMe_2$$

The readier cleavage of alkyl groups from boron by carboxylic acids than by hydrogen halides may well reflect the co-ordinating or potentially chelating ability of the former [140].

For the *complete* removal of all three alkyl groups of a trialkylborane the suggested procedure is to reflux the sample in diglyme with a slight excess of propionic acid for 2–3 hours. Substituted vinylboranes, $(RCH:CH)_3B$, intermediates derived from alkynes by hydroboration, are best cleaved by acetic acid at or even below room temperature, the products in this case being olefins [65].

ACETYLACETONE reacts with trialkylboranes at 70–75° to form cyclic dialkylboronium acetylacetonates, affording a convenient route to borinic acids and their derivatives [141]:

$$R_3B + MeCOCH:C(OH)Me \longrightarrow RH + R_2B \underset{O-CMe}{\overset{O=CMe}{\bigwedge}} CH$$

QUINONES. Alkyl hydroquinones are obtained when solutions of equimolar proportions of 1,4-benzoquinone and a trialkylborane in ether are boiled for 30 minutes [142].

ALKYLBORANES AS ALKYLATING AGENTS. Triethylborane, tri-n-hexylborane and triphenylborane have been shown to alkylate or arylate mercuric salts in aqueous or ethereal solution, forming the bis-organo-mercurial R_2Hg, while tetra-alkyl-lead derivatives have been prepared from lead(II) salts, metallic lead being a by-product of the latter reaction [31]. A useful application of the alkylating properties of alkylboranes is provided by the reaction with silver oxide:

$$Et_3B + 3AgOH + NaOH \xrightarrow{25°} 3EtAg + NaB(OH)_4$$
$$\downarrow$$
$$C_4H_{10} + C_2H_6 + C_2H_4$$

The unstable silver alkyls, RAg, decompose to form alkyl radicals R·, which couple to form R_2. In this way the hydroboration reaction can be applied to the coupling of olefins [75].

$$R_3B + R'_3B + AgNO_3 + NaOH \longrightarrow R_2 + RR' + R'_2$$

With suitable reaction conditions relatively little olefin is formed.

[139] A. K. Holliday, G. N. Jessop and F. B. Taylor, *J. Chem. Soc.*, 1965, 1551.

[140] L. H. Toporcer, R. E. Dessy and S. I. E. Green, *J. Amer. Chem. Soc.*, 1965, **87**, 1236.

[141] M. F. Hawthorne and M. Reintjes, ibid., 1964, **86**, 5016; *J. Org. Chem.*, 1965, **30**, 385; R. Köster and G. W. Rotermund, *Annalen*, 1965, **689**, 40.

[142] M. F. Hawthorne and M. Reintjes, *J. Amer. Chem. Soc.*, 1964, **86**, 951; 1965, **87**, 4585.

DIBORANE. The volatile trialkylboranes react with diborane at room temperature with the formation of *alkyldiboranes*, e.g.

$$2R_3B + B_2H_6 \longrightarrow 2R_2BHBH_2R$$

This reaction and the products are discussed in some detail on p. 231.

HYDROGEN. Trialkylboranes R_3B react with hydrogen at a pressure of 1000–2000 p.s.i. and a temperature of 150–250° to form alkanes RH and alkyldiboranes, or ultimately diborane, no catalyst being required. Since the trialkylboranes themselves can be prepared from diborane and an olefin, this reaction affords a method for the hydrogenation of olefins, with diborane serving the function of a catalyst [143].

CO-ORDINATION COMPOUNDS. Studies on the co-ordination compounds of boron (mainly its halides, alkyls and hydrides) have contributed quite substantially to our understanding of the factors which influence the stability of co-ordination compounds. The factors which particularly concern boron complexes are *inductive* and *steric* effects and *reorganization energies*.

Inductive effects. The formation of a co-ordination compound between, for example, boron and nitrogen as represented by the equation

$$R_3B + NR'_3 \longrightarrow R_3B{\leftarrow}NR'_3$$

involves the transfer of electronic charge from nitrogen to boron. In this reaction the more electronegative element, nitrogen, loses negative charge to the more electropositive boron, a circumstance not likely to enhance stability. This is quite a general impediment to the formation of co-ordination compounds since donor atoms, e.g. N, P, O, S, Cl are always fairly electronegative, while acceptor atoms are usually metals or relatively electropositive non-metals.

Thus it is reasonable to suppose that the stability of a co-ordination compound will be enhanced by the extent to which

(a) negative charge is removed from the (electropositive) acceptor atom, and

(b) positive charge is removed from the (electronegative) donor atom.

For example, in a compound $R_3B{\leftarrow}NR'_3$, if the bonds R–B were polar in the sense R←B, the negative charge would to some extent be distributed over the three groups R by *induction* instead of being concentrated on the boron atom. This would occur to a greater extent as R became more electron-attracting. Consequently, if this effect were the only factor influ-

[143] R. Köster, G. Bruno and P. Binger, *Annalen*, 1961, **644**, 1; R. Klein, A. Bliss, L. Schoen and H. G. Nadeau, *J. Amer. Chem. Soc.*, 1961, **83**, 4131; E. J. de Witt, F. L. Ramp and L. E. Trapasso, ibid., p. 4672.

encing the stability of co-ordination complexes, BF_3 should form more stable co-ordination complexes than BCl_3. and so on in the order $BF_3 > BCl_3 > BBr_3 > BH_3 > BMe_3$. In fact, towards such donor molecules as pyridine, trimethylamine, phosphorus halides and acetonitrile [144], the order of acceptor strength is $BBr_3 > BCl_3 > BF_3 \sim BH_3 > BMe_3$, showing that factors other than the inductive effect must also be taken into consideration (see below). However, by a similar consideration of inductive effects alone, NMe_3 should be (and is) a stronger donor than NCl_3 or NF_3, while acceptor strengths should (and do) decrease in the sequence $BF_3 > MeBF_2 > Me_2BF > Me_3B$. Whereas the complex $F_3B \leftarrow NMe_3$ is not perceptibly dissociated below $180°$, substitution of methyl for fluorine diminishes the stability considerably; $MeBF_2 \leftarrow NMe_3$ is 24% dissociated at 100 mm. and $135°$ and $Me_2BF \leftarrow NMe_3$ is almost wholly dissociated under these conditions. The trimethylborane compound $Me_3B \leftarrow NMe_3$ is still less stable [145].

Similarly, in the series of adducts formed between ammonia or amines and Me_3B for which dissociation data and heats of formation are listed in Table 10, the electron-releasing effect of the methyl group is seen in the increasing donor strength of the series $NH_3 < MeNH_2 < Me_2NH$ [146]. However, Me_3N is a less strong donor towards Me_3B than it should be considering only inductive effects. Inductive effects are shown by the ionization potentials of the amines, also listed in Table 10.

Table 10   *Dissociation data on Me₃B-amine compounds* [146]

Amine	Kp (atm.) at 100°C	ΔH (kcal./mole)	I.P. of amine (eV)
NH_3	4·6	13·75	10·15
$MeNH_2$	0·035	17·64	8·97
Me_2NH	0·021	19·26	8·24
Me_3N	0·472	17·62	7·82
$EtNH_2$	0·075	18·00	8·86
Et_2NH	1·22	16·31	8·01
Et_3N	Too highly dissociated to be measured		7·50
Pyridine	0·301	17·00	9·27
α-Picoline	Too highly dissociated to be measured		9·02
Quinuclidine	0·020	19·94	?

Steric effects. The figures quoted in Table 10 are typical of many accurate measurements, due mainly to H. C. Brown and his collaborators, which

[144] H. C. Brown and R. R. Holmes, *J. Amer. Chem. Soc.*, 1956, **78**, 2173; J. M. Miller and M. Onyszchuk, *Canad. J. Chem.*, 1964, **42**, 1518; 1965, **43**, 1877; 1966, **44**, 899; A. F. Armington, J. R. Weiner and G. H. Moates, *Inorg. Chem.*, 1966, **5**, 483; A. Finch, P. J. Gardner and K. K. Sen Gupta, ibid., 1967, **6**, 386.
[145] A. B. Burg and A. A. Green, *J. Amer. Chem. Soc.*, 1943, **65**, 1838.

threw much light on both inductive and steric effects [146]. Gas-phase equilibria have the advantage that complications due to solvents, solubilities, lattice-energies etc. can be avoided. The interpretation of the anomalously low heat of formation of Me_3B,NMe_3 is that, despite the electron-releasing properties of the *three* methyl groups of Me_3N, as a donor towards Me_3B trimethylamine is less effective than dimethylamine because when three methyl groups are attached to nitrogen they interfere sterically with those attached to boron. Towards the *proton* as acceptor, that is, towards a very small acceptor which will not obstruct the groups attached to nitrogen, the donor strengths of alkyl amines increase throughout the series $NH_3 < RNH_2 < R_2NH < R_3N$, as has been shown by studies on the interaction between, e.g., the butyl amines and acids *in inert solvents* [147]. As it happens, the basic strengths of alkyl amines measured in *aqueous* solution change in a similar manner to their donor properties towards Me_3B, i.e. $NH_3 < MeNH_2 < Me_2NH > Me_3N$. ($pK_b$ values: NH_3, 4·75; $MeNH_2$, 3·36; Me_2NH, 3·23; Me_3N, 4·20.) In aqueous solution, the alkylammonium cations are stabilized by solvation involving hydrogen bonding, which is least for the ion Me_3NH^+, and most for NH_4^+. Me_3N accordingly appears to be a weaker base than Me_2NH in aqueous solution, not for reasons of steric crowding, but because the greater solvation energy of $Me_2NH_2^+$ compared with Me_3NH^+ offsets the difference between Me_2NH and Me_3N noted in inert solvents.

Steric effects in boron complexes are more clearly shown in the ethylamine series, since the ethyl group is larger than the methyl group. In this series the strongest donor to trimethylborane is ethylamine, whereas the strongest base in aqueous solution is diethylamine, and in an inert solvent triethylamine.

The inductive effect of the methyl group makes α-picoline a stronger base than pyridine, but the steric effect makes it a much weaker donor to trimethylborane [148].

Perhaps the most striking demonstration of the effect of steric hindrance on donor strength is the comparison between the trimethylborane adducts of triethylamine and quinuclidine [149]. The compound with triethylamine is too unstable to allow its dissociation constant to be measured, due to steric interference between the ethyl groups and the trimethylborane molecule. In the compound with quinuclidine the carbon atoms are held back from the nitrogen and do not interfere with the trimethylborane, and the compound has a smaller dissociation constant and a larger heat of formation than any of the others in Table 10.

[146] H. C. Brown, M. Gerstein and M. D. Taylor, *J. Amer. Chem. Soc.*, 1944, **66**, 431; H. C. Brown and M. D. Taylor, ibid., 1947, **69**, 1332.

[147] R. P. Bell and J. W. Bayles, *J. Chem. Soc.*, 1952, 1518.

[148] H. C. Brown and G. K. Barbaras, *J. Amer. Chem. Soc.*, 1947, **69**, 1137.

[149] H. C. Brown and S. Sujishi, ibid., 1948, **70**, 2878.

```
     H2C————CH2
      |        |
 HC———C———C———N——►BMe3
         H2  H2 /
      |        |
     H2C————CH2
```

The effect of bulky alkyl groups attached to boron is illustrated by experiments with tri-isobutylborane or di-isobutyl-t-butylborane (earlier described as tri-t-butylborane). In this case the donor strength of the ethylamines is in the order [150]

$$NH_3 > EtNH_2 \gg Et_2NH > Et_3N$$

which contrasts with the order of basic strength in aqueous solution,

$$NH_3 < EtNH_2 < Et_2NH \gg Et_3N$$

Reorganization energies. One electronic effect which accompanies co-ordination, the transfer of charge from donor to acceptor, has already been discussed in considering inductive effects. There are other important electronic consequences of adduct formation by boron compounds R_3B. On co-ordination, the shape of the R_3B acceptor changes from the planar unco-ordinated molecule, with bond angles $\angle RBR = 120°$, to the pyramidal co-ordinated form in which the bond angles are about $109°$. In the unco-ordinated form, the boron may be regarded as sp^2 hybridized, the third p orbital being available for π-bonding between boron and the groups R. In the co-ordinated form, however, the boron may be regarded as sp^3 hybridized; three of the sp^3 hybrid orbitals are used in σ-bonding between boron and the groups R, but the fourth is involved in the new bond to the donor atom and consequently not available for π-bonding between boron and the groups R to any great extent. Co-ordination thus results in both the loss of probably most of the π-bond energy of the molecule R_3B, and in a modification in the σ-bond energy as the character of the R–B bonds changes with the hybridization of the boron. The overall energy change is referred to as the reorganization energy. Some small energy of reorganization of the *donor molecule* on co-ordination may also need to be taken into account, but it should be noted that the donor molecule does not normally undergo any major change in shape on co-ordination, although some restriction may be imposed on the conformation of bulky groups.

Attempts have been made to assess the reorganization energies of boron compounds. Cotton and Leto used simple MO theory to estimate the strength of π-bonding in the planar boron halides [151]. They suggested that the loss of this π-bond energy accounted for most of the reorganization

[150] H. C. Brown, ibid., 1945, 67, 1452.
[151] F. A. Cotton and J. R. Leto, *J. Chem. Phys.*, 1959, 30, 993.

energy of the halides, the changes in σ-bond strengths being small, and obtained the following reorganization energy values:

$$BF_3, 48\cdot3; \quad BCl_3, 30\cdot3; \quad BBr_3, 26\cdot2 \text{ kcal. mole}^{-1}$$

These values represent maximum values in that complete absence of multiple bonding is assumed for the co-ordinated form. It is suggested that unless a reorganized BF_3 molecule forms a bond to a particular donor with the release of at least $18\cdot0$ kcal. mole^{-1} *more* energy than is released when reorganized BCl_3 forms a bond to the same donor, it will be the weaker Lewis acid. Clearly, the reorganization energies of the boron halides are the reason for the observed sequence of acceptor strengths, $BF_3 < BCl_3 < BBr_3$.

Comparatively high values for the reorganization energy of a molecule BX_3 are likely when boron is bound to fluorine, oxygen or nitrogen, as the size of these atoms is such as to allow considerable π-bonding to boron. Trimethylborate is consequently a very weak acceptor, and $B(NMe_2)_3$ appears devoid of acceptor properties. The size disparity between boron and the heavier elements of Groups V and VI should lead to less π-bonding, and accordingly lower reorganization energies for derivatives of these heavier elements compared with the first-row elements, giving group trends similar to that observed with the halogens.

Multiple bonding between boron and *carbon* may also be significant in certain organoboranes. Estimates of the reorganization energies of a number of organoboranes using an L.C.A.O.–S.C.F.–M.O. approach have been made recently by Perkins and co-workers [152]. Their method affords figures significantly higher than those of Cotton and Leto for the loss of π-bonding energy, but a compensating gain in σ-bonding energy ultimately gives similar values. In particular, the reorganization energy of Me_3B is calculated to be $\sim$22 kcal. mole^{-1}, and of vinyl$_3$B 23 kcal. mole^{-1}. The closeness of these figures is a striking illustration of the hyperconjugative effect of the methyl group, implying a similar amount of B–C multiple bonding in these two compounds.

Borane complexes. Apart from the factors considered above, complexes of borane (BH_3) are frequently exceptional; thus diborane displaces BF_3 from its trimethylphosphine complex [153],

$$F_3B,PMe_3 + \tfrac{1}{2}B_2H_6 \longrightarrow H_3B,PMe_3 + BF_3$$

and BH_3 alone of BX_3-type compounds forms a complex with PF_3 and CO

[152] D. R. Armstrong and P. G. Perkins, *Theoretica chim. Acta*, 1966, **4**, 69, 352; **5**, 11; P. G. Perkins and D. H. Wall, *J. Chem. Soc.(A)*, 1966, 1207; P. G. Perkins, private communication.
[153] W. A. G. Graham and F. G. A. Stone, *J. Inorg. Nucl. Chem.*, 1956, **3**, 164.

[154], ligands which normally utilize suitable vacant orbitals for π-bonding in their complexes, the electrons for this bonding originating on the Lewis acid. The heats of formation of adducts $Ph_nPH_{3-n}BH_3$ (n = 1, 2 or 3), the ready exchange of hydrogen for deuterium in the system $Ph_3P,BD_3/$ HCl, and the formation of Ph_3P,BI_3 from Ph_3P,BH_3 and ICl are all consistent with multiple phosphorus–boron bonding (and consequent drift of electronic charge away from the borane hydrogen atoms) in these complexes [155]. The exceptional behaviour of BH_3 in this respect in apparently being able to act as a source of electrons allowing some degree of back donation, is reminiscent of the hyperconjugative effect of methyl groups and of the exceptional behaviour of NH_3 as a donor, particularly to transition metals [156].

The co-ordination compounds of Group III elements were reviewed in 1958, [157], in 1963 (halides only) [158], and in 1964 [16]; aspects of their thermochemistry were discussed in 1962 [159].

Miscellaneous co-ordination compounds. Some complexes with rather unusual structures have recently been prepared, and deserve brief mention here. Borane–carbonyl, $BH_3\cdot CO$, already mentioned, reacts with ammonia, methylamine or dimethylamine to form solid adducts $H_3B.CO.2NR_2H$ (R = H or Me) which are stable to air, and may be recovered from aqueous solution undecomposed. An X-ray diffraction study of the methylamine complex reveals the structure $MeN\overset{+}{H_3} MeH\overset{-}{N}.CO.BH_3$ in which the anion is isoelectronic with methylacetamide, the O, N, C, B skeleton being very nearly planar [160]. Trimethylamine forms an adduct $H_3BCO.NMe_3$, presumed to have the zwitterionic structure $Me_3\overset{+}{N}.CO.\overset{-}{B}H_3$. Some related phosphorus compounds $Ph_3P.CHR.BX_3$ have been prepared by reaction between alkylidene triphenylphosphoranes, $Ph_3\overset{+}{P}—\overset{-}{C}HR$ and diborane [161, 162](X = H), boron trifluoride(X = F)[162, 163] or trichloride [162]

[154] T. P. Fehlner and W. S. Koski, *J. Amer. Chem. Soc.*, 1965, **87**, 409; A. B. Burg and Y.-C. Fu, ibid., 1966, **88**, 1147; R. W. Rudolph and R. W. Parry, ibid., 1967, **89**, 1621; L. J. Malone and R. W. Parry, *Inorg. Chem.*, 1967, **6**, 176.

[155] M. A. Frisch, H. G. Heal, H. Mackle and I. O. Madden, *J. Chem. Soc.*, 1965, 899.   [156] J. Chatt and G. A. Gamlen, ibid., 1956, 2371.

[157] F. G. A. Stone, *Chem. Rev.*, 1958, **58**, 101.

[158] D. R. Martin and J. M. Canon, Ch. 6 in *Friedel–Crafts and Related Reactions*, Vol. I, ed. G. A. Olah, Interscience, New York and London, 1963; N. N. Greenwood and K. Wade, ibid., Ch. 7.

[159] C. T. Mortimer, *Reaction Heats and Bond Strengths*, Pergamon Press, 1962.

[160] R. W. Parry, C. E. Nordman, J. C. Carter and G. TerHaar, *Advan. in Chem. Series*, 1964, **42**, 302; J. C. Carter and R. W. Parry, *J. Amer. Chem. Soc.*, 1965, **87**, 2354; J. Grotewold E. A. Lissi and A. E. Villa, *J. Chem. Soc. (A)*, 1966, 1034.

[161] M. F. Hawthorne, *J. Amer. Chem. Soc.*, 1958, **80**, 3480; 1961, **83**, 367.

[162] D. Seyferth and S. O. Grim, ibid., 1961, **83**, 1613.

[163] S. O. Grim and D. Seyferth, *Chem. and Ind.*, 1959, 849; D. Seyferth, *Angew. Chem.*, 1960, **72**, 36.

(X = Cl) or triphenylborane (X = Ph) [162]. Reaction of $Ph_3\overset{+}{P}CH_2\overset{-}{B}F_3$ with Grignard reagents yields trialkyl derivatives, e.g. $Ph_3\overset{+}{P}CH_2\overset{-}{B}Me_3$. Triphenylphosphinimines $Ph_3P:NR$ form adducts $Ph_3\overset{+}{P}:NR.BX_3$ both with boron trifluoride and with triphenylborane [164].

The isoelectronic relationship between borane BH_3 and an oxygen atom prompted Malone and Parry [164a] to look for similarities between the reactions of borane-carbonyl and carbon dioxide. In fact, borane-carbonyl is absorbed by alcoholic alkali, moist calcium oxide, or even by NaOH/ asbestos such as is used to absorb carbon dioxide in gas analysis with formation of salts of the anion $H_3BCO_2^{2-}$ (cf. CO_3^{2-}).

The acceptor properties of $F_2BCH_2CH_2BF_2$ have been studied recently [164b]. This compound can function as a chelate acceptor, e.g.

Triarylboranes

The new and improved methods for the preparation of trialkylboranes (e.g. use of aluminium alkyls, addition of olefins to B–H) are not in general applicable or convenient for the triarylboranes, and the method generally used is reaction between a Grignard reagent and BF_3OEt_2 or a borate ester. Many members of the aromatic series are sensitive to oxygen, and this together with their low volatility can make their separation from reaction mixtures difficult. Further, the reaction can proceed beyond the triarylborane stage, with the formation of tetra-arylborate anions:

$$3ArMgBr + BF_3OEt_2 \rightarrow Ar_3B + 3MgBrF + Et_2O$$
$$ArMgBr + Ar_3B \rightarrow MgBr^+Ar_4B^-$$

Tetra-arylborates are described below.

Triphenylborane, m.p. 142°, b.p. 203°/15 mm. Although large quantities are perhaps best prepared by the direct Grignard method, the product being distilled from the reaction mixture at 250° and about 5–6 mm [165, 166], and purified by crystallization from ether in an inert atmosphere,

[164] H. Zimmer and G. Singh, *Advan. in Chem. Series*, 1964, **42**, 17; *J. Org. Chem.*, 1964, **29**, 3412.
[164a] L. J. Malone and R. W. Parry, *Inorg. Chem.*, 1967, **6**, 817.
[164b] M. J. Biallas and D. F. Shriver, *J. Amer. Chem. Soc.*, 1966, **88**, 375; D. F. Shriver and M. J. Biallas, ibid., 1967, **89**, 1078.
[165] E. Krause and H. Polack, *Ber.*, 1926, **59**, 777; E. Krause and R. Nitsche, ibid., 1922, **55**, 1261.
[166] G. Wittig, G. Keicher, A. Rückert and P. Raff, *Annalen*, 1949, **563**, 110.

small amounts are most easily obtained by the thermal decomposition of trimethylammonium tetraphenylborate [167].

Addition of an ether solution of the boron–trifluoride–ether complex to a slight excess of phenylmagnesium bromide gives a solution containing Ph_4B^- ions: after treatment with water and removal of magnesium as carbonate, addition of trimethylamine hydrochloride precipitates the insoluble salt $Me_3NH^+Ph_4B^-$. This decomposes smoothly when heated to 200° in a stream of nitrogen:

$$Me_3NH^+Ph_4B^- \longrightarrow Me_3N + C_6H_6 + Ph_3B$$

The triphenylborane is distilled in vacuum after the trimethylamine and benzene have been swept away; the yield (from the tetraphenylborate) is about 90%.

Triphenylborane has also been prepared from tetra-ethyldiborane, $Et_4B_2H_2$, and an excess of benzene at 180° and 20 atm. [168]. The use of tetra-phenyltin to attach one phenyl group to a boron atom has already been mentioned [32].

Tri-p-tolylborane, m.p. 175°, and *tribenzylborane*, m.p. 47°, are examples of triarylboranes which have been prepared by the Grignard method.

Tri-1-naphthylborane, m.p. 206–207°, crystallizes with 1 mol. of benzene, $(1\text{-}C_{10}H_7)_3B\cdot C_6H_6$, and has been prepared from 1-naphthylmagnesium bromide and $BF_3\cdot OEt_2$. Its isolation is facilitated by its insensitivity to oxygen, a characteristic it shares with compounds with similarly bulky aryl groups, such as trimesitylborane [169], $(Me_3C_6H_2)_3B$, m.p. 193°.

In the preparation of mixed triarylboranes, disproportionation is suppressed by working with amine (particularly pyridine) complexes. For example, p-tolyl-lithium and the pyridine complex Bu^iOBPh_2,py yields $p\text{-}CH_3C_6H_4BPh_2,py$, m.p. 156–158°. The pyridine can be removed from triarylborane complexes by the action of aqueous sulphuric acid, ethereal hydrogen chloride, or picric acid in benzene. These methods have yielded the mixed aryls $p\text{-}CH_3C_6H_4BPh_2$, b.p. 170–173°/3 mm., $(1\text{-}C_{10}H_7)_2BPh$, m.p. 146–148°, b.p. 230–240°/2 mm., and $(1\text{-}C_{10}H_7)_2BC_6H_4OCH_3$, b.p. 197–199°/0·08 mm. [170]. Once prepared the mixed arylboranes are relatively stable to disproportionation. There is evidence that organolithium and Grignard reagents and other electron-deficient compounds catalyse this kind of disproportionation (aluminium alkyls have been mentioned above in connexion with the disproportionation of trialkylboranes),

[167] G. Wittig and P. Raff, ibid., 1951, **573**, 195.
[168] R. Köster, K. Reinert and K. H. Müller, *Angew. Chem.*, 1960, **72**, 78.
[169] H. C. Brown and V. H. Dodson, *J. Amer. Chem. Soc.*, 1957, **79**, 2302; I. I. Lapkin and G. A. Yuzhakova, *Zhur. obshchei Khim.*, 1962, **32**, 1967; *Chem. Abs.*, 1963, **58**, 4589.
[170] B. M. Mikhailov and V. A. Vaver, *Izvest. Akad. Nauk S.S.S.R.*, 1957, 812; *Chem. Abs.*, 1958, **52**, 3667; cf. ibid., 1957, **51**, 15440; 1956, **50**, 11964.

so the essential point is the co-ordinative saturation of the boron during preparative stages involving such reagents.

Boron has been attached to aromatic rings other than benzene; e.g. to the 2-position of the thiophene, furan and pyridine rings, via the lithium derivative of the aromatic compound [171]. The compounds in which boron is incorporated in an aromatic ring are discussed below.

Reactions of the triarylboranes

The triarylboranes are rather less sensitive to oxygen than their alkyl analogues, but must still be handled in an inert atmosphere with the exception of tri-1-naphthylborane and trimesitylborane. Their reactivity is, of course, considerably diminished by co-ordination to strong donor substances. They are not sensitive to water, but alcohol converts triphenylborane into ethyl diphenylborinate:

$$Ph_3B + EtOH \longrightarrow Ph_2BOEt + C_6H_6$$

REACTION WITH ALKALIS. Triphenylborane reacts with tetramethyl ammonium hydroxide in alcoholic solution:

$$Ph_3B + Me_4N^+OH^- \longrightarrow Me_4N^+[Ph_3BOH]^-$$

The product, which crystallizes with water or alcohol, contains four-covalent boron [172]. Fusion with sodium hydroxide gives the sodium salt $Na^+[Ph_3BOH]^-$, which crystallizes from ether with solvent of crystallization (lost at 100° in vacuum). The salt is soluble in water, but is slowly hydrolysed. Acetic acid causes immediate precipitation of triphenylborane,

$$Na[Ph_3BOH] + HOAc \longrightarrow Ph_3B + NaOAc + H_2O$$

while the ammine of triphenylborane results from the slow reaction with ammonium chloride:

$$Na[Ph_3BOH] + NH_4Cl \longrightarrow NaCl + Ph_3B \cdot NH_3 + H_2O$$

A rather similar compound is formed from sodium cyanide, $Na[Ph_3BCN]$, and this is more stable to acids than the hydroxy salt. Aqueous solutions of this salt are neutral. The lithium, sodium, potassium and ammonium salts are soluble, the rubidium salt slightly soluble and the caesium salt insoluble (70 mg. Cs in 100 c.c. water at 0°) [167]. Tri-1-naphthylborane can be titrated accurately in alcoholic solution with sodium methoxide, ethoxide or isopropoxide, using phenolphthalein as indicator [173]:

$$(C_{10}H_7)_3B + Na^+OCH_3^- \longrightarrow Na^+[(C_{10}H_7)_3BOCH_3]^-$$

[171] B. M. Mikhailov and T. K. Kozminskaya, *Bull. Akad. Sci. U.S.S.R.*, 1959, 72 (English trans.); A. N. Nesmeyanov, V. A. Sazonova and V. N. Drozd, ibid., p. 147.

[172] D. L. Fowler and C. A. Kraus, *J. Amer. Chem. Soc.*, 1940, **62**, 1143; see also C. A. Kraus and W. W. Hawes, ibid., 1933, **55**, 2776.

[173] H. C. Brown and Sei Sujishi, ibid., 1948, **70**, 2793.

REACTION WITH ALKALI METALS. The acceptor properties of the triaryl derivatives of boron should be greater than those of the trialkyls, since aryl groups are more electronegative. This effect is largely offset, however, by the steric requirements of the relatively large aryl groups and by back-donation from aryl to boron, but the acceptor character of the triaryls is well shown in reaction with alkali metals, even as amalgams, when the metal acts as donor and transfers an electron to the boron compound:

$$Ar_3B + Na \longrightarrow Ar_3B^{\cdot-} + Na^+$$

The resulting compounds [174], which are prepared in ether solution with rigorous exclusion of moisture, oxygen and carbon dioxide, are necessarily radicals (if monomeric). The triphenylborane anion-radical is isoelectronic with the triphenylmethyl *neutral* radical, and in fact the colours of the two series are similar.

Triphenylborane-sodium reacts with triphenylmethyl with the formation of the triphenylmethyl anion:

$$Ph_3\overset{\cdot}{B}^-Na^+ + Ph_3C^{\cdot} \longrightarrow Ph_3B + Ph_3C^-Na^+$$

A brilliant red compound results from triphenylmethyl and triphenylborane; this may well be a radical of constitution $(Ph_3B—CPh_3)^{\cdot}$ There is some evidence [175] that triphenylborane-sodium has the dimeric formula $[Ph_3B\cdot BPh_3]^=Na_2^+$, since it is diamagnetic. The conductance of these compounds in ether solution is very small, indicating extensive ion-association.

Table 11

Sodium complex	Solvent	Association	Magnetic susceptibility
Ph_3BNa	Diethyl ether	+	dia
,,	Tetrahydrofuran	+	dia
$(1\text{-}C_{10}H_7)_3BNa$	Diethyl ether[a]	+	dia
,,	Tetrahydrofuran[b]	−	para
,,	None (i.e. solid)	+	dia
$(1\text{-}C_{10}H_7)_3BNa_2$	Tetrahydrofuran[c]	−	dia
$(2\text{-}C_{10}H_7)_3BNa$	Tetrahydrofuran	−	para
$(mesityl)_3BNa$	Tetrahydrofuran	−	para

Notes: a, orange colour; b, green; c, violet-black.

Tri-1-naphthylborane can add successively one atom of sodium to give the brown-yellow compound $(C_{10}H_7)_3\overset{\cdot}{B}^-Na^+$ (or its dimer) and then a

[174] E. Krause and A. Von Grosse, *Die Chemie der Metallorganischen Verbindungen*, Borntraeger, Berlin, 1937, pp. 207–11.
[175] T. Li Chu, *J. Amer. Chem. Soc.*, 1953, **75**, 1730.

second to give the deep violet $(C_{10}H_7)_3B^=Na_2^{++}$ [176]. Studies on the molecular weights of solutions of these addition compounds, and on their magnetic susceptibilities, have shown a marked dependence of the position of monomer–dimer equilibria on (a) the aromatic groups bonded to boron, and (b) the solvent [177].

The tendency to form monomeric anions (which, however, exist largely as ion-pairs) increases with the degree of steric hindrance about the boron, in the order:

$$\text{phenyl} < \text{1-naphthyl} < \text{2-naphthyl} < \text{mesityl}$$

The effect of tetrahydrofuran in dissolving sodium-tri-1-naphthyl-borane as the green monomeric form, in contrast to diethyl ether dissolving it as the orange dimeric form, has been attributed to the stronger donor character of tetrahydrofuran resulting in a covalent B–O bond, $[^-(1\text{-}C_{10}H_7)_3B{-\!\!\!}^+O(CH_2)_4]Na^+$, in which case the unpaired electron must occupy orbitals on the naphthyl groups. The electron would doubtless pass rapidly between neighbouring naphthyl groups (cf. the paracyclophane anions), so the difference in appearance between the spectra of sodium-naphthalene and sodium-tri-1-naphthylborane is not surprising.

The triarylborane–alkali metal compounds are very reactive; iodine in ether is immediately decolorized:

$$2Ph_3B^{\cdot-}Na^+ + I_2 \longrightarrow 2Ph_3B + 2NaI$$

The reaction with methanol gives a boron hydride derivative [166]:

$$2Ph_3B^{\cdot-}Na^+ + MeOH \longrightarrow Na^+[Ph_3BOMe]^- + Na^+[Ph_3BH]^-$$

Sodium (or lithium) triphenylborohydride can also be obtained by the direct addition (in ether) of triphenylborane to sodium or lithium hydride, though a better method [178] is to add, say, LiH to Ph_3B and heat at 180° until the melt solidifies. It is moderately readily hydrolysed by water, but vigorously evolves hydrogen with acids;

$$Na^+[Ph_3BH]^- + H_3O^+ \longrightarrow Na^+ + Ph_3B + H_2 + H_2O$$

Arylboron free radicals related to those just described result from the reduction of dimesitylfluoroborane with sodium amalgam or sodium/potassium alloy [179].

CO-ORDINATION COMPOUNDS. Like the trialkylboranes, the triaryls

[176] H. E. Bent and M. Dorfman, J. Amer. Chem. Soc., 1932, 54, 2132; 1935, 57, 1259, 1924.

[177] T. Li Chu and T. J. Weissmann, ibid., 1956, 78, 23, 3610; idem, J. Phys. Chem., 1956, 60, 1020; C. W. Moeller and W. K. Wilmarth, J. Amer. Chem. Soc., 1959, 81, 2638.

[178] G. Wittig and A. Rückert, Annalen, 1950, 566, 101.

[179] J. E. Leffler, E. Dolan and T. Tanigaki, J. Amer. Chem. Soc., 1965, 87, 927, 928; S. I. Weissman and H. van Willigen, ibid., p. 2285.

do not co-ordinate to ethers, but form compounds with a variety of amines, e.g. $Ph_3B\cdot\overset{-}{N}\overset{+}{H}_3$, m.p. 212°, $Ph_3B\cdot\overset{-}{N}\overset{+}{M}e_3$, m.p. 136°.

When three large groups are bonded to boron, as in tri-1-naphthyl-borane, steric effects become very important. There is evidence [173] that this compound can exist in two isomeric forms differing in the relative positions of the naphthalene rings (which cannot rotate readily about the B–C bonds). The order of donor strength of the methylamines to tri-1-naphthylborane is

$$NH_3 > MeNH_2 > Me_2NH > Me_3N$$

The steric strain is so great that the least sterically hindered amine (NH_3) forms the most stable compound, and trimethylamine does not combine at all. The ammonia complex melts at 200–205° if heated slowly in a capillary tube, but if the tube is plunged in a bath at 170–172° the compound melts, then solidifies, and finally melts again at 200–205°. Further, the ammonia dissociation pressure, which increases with temperature in the usual way, decreases rapidly at about 140°, and then increases again with temperature. These and other observations point to the ammonia complex showing hindered rotation dimorphism.

With trimesitylborane, $(Me_3C_6H_2)_3B$, the steric effects of the three mesityl groups are so large as to prevent the formation even of an ammonia complex [169].

THE TETRAPHENYLBORATES. Addition of phenyl-lithium to an ether solution of triphenylborane gives, with heat evolution, the salt $Li^+[BPh_4]^-$, which is stable to boiling water and is decomposed by acids only at 80° or more [166]. It crystallizes from ether as $LiBPh_4.8Et_2O$, the ether being lost in high vacuum. The salt is virtually fully dissociated in water in which, as in alcohol, it is freely soluble; it is insoluble in the non-polar solvents benzene, cyclohexane and carbon tetrachloride.

The sodium salt may be prepared by the reaction between boron tri-fluoride [167] or sodium tetrafluoroborate [180] and excess phenylmag-nesium bromide, the product being treated with excess aqueous sodium chloride. Sodium tetraphenylborate is soluble in both ether and chloro-form, the solubility diminishing with rise of temperature, an effect attri-buted to the increasing ionic solvation at lower temperatures.

Sodium tetraphenylborate is now a valuable analytical reagent,* par-ticularly for potassium, rubidium, caesium, thallium, various nitrogen bases, and a number of other cations whose tetraphenylborates are

[180] A. N. Nesmeyanov and V. A. Sazonova, *Izvest. Akad. Nauk S.S.S.R.*, 1955, 187; K. R. Kozlova and V. A. Pal'm, *Zhur. obshchei Khim.*, 1961, **31**, 2922; H. Holtzapfel and K. Richter, ibid., 1962, **32**, 1358; *Chem. Abs.*, 1963, **58**, 1481.

* Some 350 references to the subject will be found in ref. [13], pp. 234–51.

sufficiently insoluble to allow gravimetric application, e.g. $[Ph_4P][BPh_4]$, $[Co(C_5H_5)_2][BPh_4]$.

Both ammonia and the methylamines form insoluble salts which decompose on heating:

$$NH_4BPh_4 \xrightarrow{240°} Ph_3B + C_6H_6 + NH_3$$

$$Me_3NHBPh_4 \xrightarrow{200°} Ph_3B + C_6H_6 + Me_3N$$

In contrast, the tetramethylammonium salt is stable to 340°.

The phenyldiazonium salt, $PhN_2^+BPh_4^-$, is only slightly soluble, and explodes when dry. A suspension in aqueous sodium acetate decomposes at about 50° with the transient formation of phenyl radicals, since both biphenyl and terphenyl are among the products. The formation of biphenyl during anodic oxidation of a tetraphenylborate has been shown to be an intramolecular process [181].

Kinetic studies on the acid decomposition of tetraphenylborates have shown no evidence for a molecular species $HBPh_4$, in contrast to earlier reports, although an activated complex

may be formed transiently [182].

The reaction between sodium tetraphenylborate and mercuric chloride is rapid and quantitative, and suitable for analytical purposes:

$$NaBPh_4 + 4HgCl_2 + 3H_2O \rightarrow 4PhHgCl + NaCl + 3HCl + B(OH)_3$$

Copper(II) chloride is reduced:

$$2NaBPh_4 + 2CuCl_2 \rightarrow 2CuCl + 2NaCl + 2Ph_3B + Ph_2$$

but quite a different reaction takes place with the chlorides of Mn^{++}, Fe^{++}, Co^{++} and Ni^{++}:

$$2NaBPh_4 + MCl_2 + 6H_2O \rightarrow M(OH)_2 \downarrow + 2NaCl + 2PhB(OH)_2 + 6PhH$$

When sodium tetraphenylborate is heated with boron halides, phenylboron dihalides result [183], e.g.

$$NaBPh_4 + 3BBr_3 \rightarrow NaBr + 4PhBBr_2$$

With the sulphonium salt $[(Me_2N)_2SBr]Br$, sodium tetraphenylborate gives the triphenylborane adduct, $Ph_3B \cdot S(NMe_2)_2$ [184].

[181] D. H. Geske, *J. Phys. Chem.*, 1962, **66**, 1743.
[182] J. N. Cooper and R. E. Powell, *J. Amer. Chem. Soc.*, 1963, **85**, 1590.
[183] M. Bloom and R. M. Washburn, U.S.P. 3,096,370; *Chem. Abs.*, 1964, **60**, 546.
[184] H. Nöth and G. Mikulaschek, *Chem. Ber.*, 1964, **97**, 202.

PHENYLBORON. A material of apparent composition $(PhB)_n$ has been obtained from the reaction between sodium and phenyldichloroborane in toluene [185]. The product, a yellow-brown amorphous powder which ignites in air, is soluble in benzene or dioxan to give yellow-brown solutions in which the molecular weight corresponds to a formula $(PhB)_{9-12}$. Hydrolysis in neutral solution yields phenylboronic acid, $PhB(OH)_2$, but only 10% of the hydrogen expected from the equation:

$$PhB + 2H_2O \longrightarrow PhB(OH)_2 + H_2$$

Phenylboron is oxidized by permanganate or silver nitrate, and reacts with ammonia to give a product $[(PhB)_2.NH_3]_n$.

Alkenyl derivatives of boron

Vinylboranes. PREPARATION. Vinylboron compounds and their derivatives are generally prepared from the appropriate vinyl derivative of another metal. For example, dimethylbromoborane and vinylsodium react at a low temperature to form *dimethylvinylborane* [186, 187], $Me_2BCH:CH_2$, v.p. 126 mm. at 0°, which disproportionates slowly at room temperature to a mixture of trimethylborane, methyldivinylborane and trivinylborane. The Grignard method has been used for the preparation of *tri(2-phenylvinyl)borane* [188], $(PhCH:CH)_3B$, m.p. 64–65°, and for the preparation of *vinylboronic acid* [189], $CH_2:CHB(OH)_2$, from trimethylborate. Vinylmercury, -zinc and -tin compounds [30, 190] have been used to prepare vinylhaloboranes $(CH_2:CH)_2BX$ and $CH_2:CHBX_2$ (X = F or Cl), while the *perfluorovinylboranes* [191] $CF_2:CFBF_2$, b.p. $-14°$, $CF_2:CFBCl_2$, b.p. 48°, $(CF_2:CF)_2BCl$, b.p. 100·5°, and $(CF_2:CF)_3B$, b.p. 104·9° have been prepared from the appropriate boron halide and bis(perfluorovinyl)-dimethyltin, $Me_2Sn(CF:CF_2)_2$.

Other methods of preparation involve addition reactions of acetylenic compounds. The hydroboration of acetylenes leads to vinylboranes [65]:

$$12RC:CR' + 3NaBH_4 + 4BF_3 \longrightarrow 4(RCH:CR')_3B + 3NaBF_4$$

although as a preparative method this is limited to compounds with large groups R and R', or to $(RCH:CH)BR''_2$, again where R and R'' are large.

[185] W. Kuchen and R. D. Brinkmann, *Angew. Chem.*, 1960, **72**, 564; *Z. anorg. Chem.*, 1963, **325**, 225.

[186] T. D. Parsons and D. M. Ritter, *J. Amer. Chem. Soc.*, 1954, **76**, 1710.

[187] T. D. Parsons, M. B. Silverman and D. M. Ritter, ibid., 1957, **79**, 5091.

[188] A. V. Topchiev, A. A. Prokhorova and M. V. Kurashev, *Doklady Akad. Nauk S.S.S.R.*, 1961, **141**, 1386.

[189] H. Normant and J. Braun, *Compt. rend.*, 1959, **248**, 828; G. W. Willcockson and J. K. Sandie, U.S.P. 3,045,039, July 17, 1962; *Chem. Abs.*, 1963, **59**, 1680.

[190] F. E. Brinckmann and F. G. A. Stone, *J. Amer. Chem. Soc.*, 1960, **82**, 6218; J. Braun, *Compt. rend.*, 1963, **256**, 2422; P. Fritz, K. Niedenzu and J. W. Dawson, *Inorg. Chem.*, 1964, **3**, 626.

[191] S. L. Stafford and F. G. A. Stone, *J. Amer. Chem. Soc.*, 1960, **82**, 6238.

The chloroboration of acetylenes affords 2-chlorovinylboranes [192]; for example, *2-chlorovinyldichloroborane*, $Cl_2BCH:CHCl$, v.p. 70 mm. at 34°, may be obtained in 90% yield from boron trichloride and acetylene. The product may be refluxed unchanged, but disproportionates into BCl_3 and $ClB(CH:CHCl)_2$ in the presence of activated carbon.

An interesting reaction involving addition of a diazo compound to an acetylenic boron compound is the synthesis of a pyrazoleboronic acid from dibutylethynylboronate and diazoacetic ester [193]:

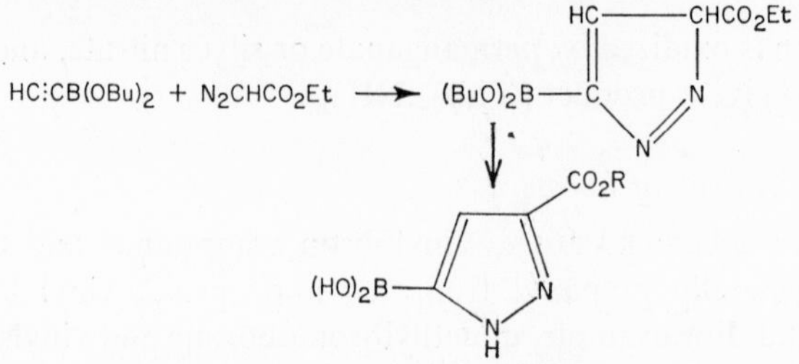

PROPERTIES. In the vinylboranes, the vacant p orbital of the boron may be utilized in a delocalization of the π-electrons of the ethylenic bond, so that the structure may be written $CH_2\!\cdots\!CH\!\cdots\!BR_2$ rather than $CH_2:CH—BR_2$. The extent of this delocalization has been studied by spectroscopic (mass, infrared, u.v., ^{11}B and ^{19}F n.m.r.) and chemical (Lewis acid strength) methods [194–197], and a bond order of 1·33 has been estimated for the B-vinyl bond in the methylvinylboranes $MeB(CH:CH_2)_2$ and $Me_2BCH:CH_2$ [198]. More recent calculations indicate that the B-vinyl bond order may be nearer 1·2, similar in fact to the B-methyl bond order [152].

Addition reactions of the ethylenic bond of vinylboron compounds, now becoming promising synthetic reagents, have been studied recently by Matteson [26] (using vinylboronic esters) and Seyferth (using B-vinyl borazines). Hydroboration of dibutylvinylboronate gives a diboronic acid with both boron atoms attached to the same carbon [199]:

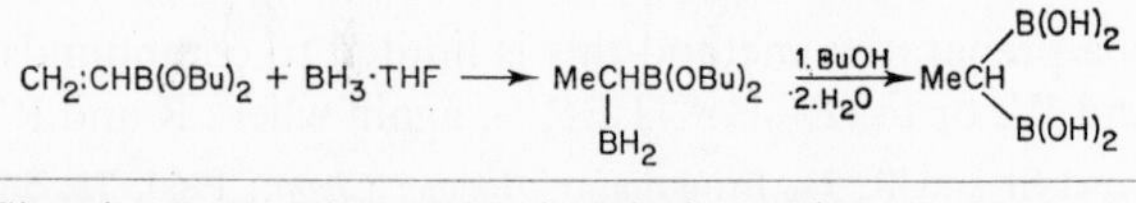

[192] E. Gipstein, P. R. Kippur, M. A. Higgins and B. F. Clark, *J. Org. Chem.*, 1961, **26**, 2947; P. R. Kippur, U.S.P. 3,045, 044, July 17, 1962.

[193] D. S. Matteson, *J. Org. Chem.*, 1962, **27**, 4293.

[194] T. D. Coyle and F. G. A. Stone, *J. Amer. Chem. Soc.*, 1960, **82**, 6223.

[195] T. D. Coyle, S. L. Stafford and F. G. A. Stone, *J. Chem. Soc.*, 1961, 3103.

[196] W. C. Steele, L. D. Nichols and F. G. A. Stone, *J. Amer. Chem. Soc.*, 1962, **84**, 1154.

[197] S. L. Stafford, *Canad. J. Chem.*, 1963, **41**, 807.

[198] C. D. Good and D. M. Ritter, *J. Amer. Chem. Soc.*, 1962, **84**, 1162.

[199] D. S. Matteson and J. D. Liedtke, *Chem. and Ind.*, 1963, 1241; D. S. Matteson and J. G. Shdo, *J. Org. Chem.*, 1964, **29**, 2742. See also B. M. Mikhailov and P. M. Aronovich, *Izvest. Akad. Nauk S.S.S.R.*, 1963, 1233; *Chem. Abs.*, 1963, **59**, 14011.

The direction of addition may be explained by the polarization of the vinyl group $\overset{\delta+}{CH_2}\text{---}\overset{}{CH}\text{---}\overset{\delta-}{B(OBu)_2}$. However $H^{\delta+}$—$Br^{\delta-}$ in the form of liquid hydrogen bromide adds the opposite way, e.g.:

$$MeCH:CMe.B(OBu)_2 + HBr \longrightarrow MeCH_2CBrMe.B(OBu)_2$$

The *β-bromo derivative* may, however, be obtained by radical-initiated addition of HBr [200]:

$$CH_2:CHB(OBu)_2 + HBr \overset{hv}{\longrightarrow} BrCH_2CH_2B(OBu)_2$$

Similar radical-catalysed addition of H_2S to butyldivinylborinate, $(CH_2:CH)_2BOBu$, affords 4-butoxy-1-thia-4-boracyclohexane [201]:

$$(CH_2:CH)_2BOBu + H_2S \longrightarrow \text{<image: hexagonal ring with S at top and BOBu>}$$

Various other radical-initiated addition reactions or polymerizations of vinylboronic esters have been studied [202].

Related reactions with B-vinyl borazines have been used to prepare borazines with large groups attached to boron as possibly hydrolytically stable materials. For example, addition of various silanes (such as $MeSiHCl_2$, Me_2SiHCl, $Me_3SiOSiMe_2H$, and $(Me_3SiO)_2SiHMe$) to $(CH_2:CHBNPh)_3$ gives the respective B-tris-(β-silylethyl)-N-triphenyl-borazines, $(R_3SiCH_2CH_2BNPh)_3$, and similar tin derivatives are formed from triphenyl- and triethyl-stannane [203]. Compounds exemplified by $(X_3C.CH_2.CHBr.BNPh)_3$, where $X = Cl$ or Br, may be prepared by addition of CCl_3Br or CBr_4 to the vinylborazine [204]. The product from addition of HBr, $(BrCH_2CH_2BNPh)_3$, undergoes elimination of ethylene when treated with a Grignard reagent:

$$(BrCH_2CH_2BNPh)_3 + 3PhMgBr \longrightarrow (PhBNPh)_3 + 3C_2H_4 + 3MgBr_2$$

B-Trivinyl-N-triphenylborazine can itself be polymerized [205].

Vinylated aminoboranes such as $Me_2N{=}BMeCH:CH_2$ have attracted some interest as examples of BN analogues of dienes; for a survey of such systems see ref. [206].

[200] D. S. Matteson and J. D. Liedtke, *J. Org. Chem.*, 1963, **28**, 1924.
[201] D. S. Matteson, ibid., 1962, **27**, 275.
[202] D. S. Matteson, *J. Amer. Chem. Soc.*, 1960, **82**, 4228; idem, *J. Org. Chem.*, 1962, **27**, 3712; D. S. Matteson and J. O. Waldbillig, ibid., 1963, **28**, 366.
[203] D. Seyferth and M. Takamizawa, *Inorg. Chem.*, 1963, **2**, 731; D. Seyferth, H. P. Kögler, W. R. Freyer, M. Takamizawa, H. Yamazaki and Y. Sato, *Advan. in Chem. Series*, 1964, **42**, 259; see also D. Seyferth, Y. Sato and M. Takamizawa, *J. Organometal. Chem.*, 1964, **2**, 367; J. Braun, *Compt. rend.*, 1965, **260**, 218.
[204] D. Seyferth and M. Takamizawa, *J. Org. Chem.*, 1963, **28**, 1142.
[205] J. Pellon, W. G. Deichert and W. M. Thomas, *J. Polymer Sci.*, 1961, **55**, 153.
[206] K. Niedenzu, P. Fritz and J. W. Dawson, *Inorg. Chem.*, 1964, **3**, 778.

Allylboranes. Triallylborane [207], $(CH_2:CHCH_2)_3B$, b.p. 44–46°/10 mm., 62–65°/15 mm., prepared by the Grignard method, is unusual in its hydrolysis by water,

$$(CH_2:CHCH_2)_3B + H_2O \rightarrow CH_2:CHCH_2B(OH)_2 + CH_2:CHCH_3$$

in its reaction with alcohols,

$$(CH_2:CHCH_2)_3B + EtOH \rightarrow CH_2:CHCH_2B(OEt)_2 + CH_2:CHCH_3$$

and in being able to add to the carbonyl group of aldehydes and ketones ('allylboration') [208]:

$$(CH_2:CHCH_2)_3B + EtCHO \rightarrow B(OCHEtCH_2CH:CH_2)_3$$

Reaction with the appropriate amount of ethyl mercaptan gives the ethyl esters of diallylthioborinic acid or allylthioboronic acid [209],

$$(CH_2:CHCH_2)_2BSEt \qquad CH_2:CHCH_2B(SEt)_2$$
$$\text{b.p. } 67\text{–}70°/11 \text{ mm.} \qquad \text{b.p. } 62\text{–}64°/2 \text{ mm.}$$

When an excess of ethyl mercaptan is used, some addition across the ethylenic bond occurs to form $(EtS)_2BCH_2CH_2CH_2SEt$, b.p. 118–121°/ 1·5 mm.

Hydroboration of triallylborane gives polymeric materials [210] containing B—$(CH_2)_3$—B linkages from which it has been possible to isolate compounds containing 1,5-diboracyclo-octane rings, including the highly reactive *1,5-diborabicyclo[3,3,3]undecane* [211] (3.2a):

---

[207] B. M. Mikhailov and F. B. Tutorskaya, *Doklady Akad. Nauk S.S.S.R.*, 1958, **123,** 479; *Chem. Abs.*, 1959, **53,** 6990; A. V. Topchiev, A. A. Prokhorova, Ya. M. Paushkin and M. V. Kurashev, *Tr. Inst. Nefti, Akad. Nauk S.S.S.R.*, 1960, **14,** 85; *Chem. Abs.*, 1963, **58,** 3452; K. H. Thiele and P. Zdunneck, *J. Organometal. Chem.*, 1965, **4,** 10; B. M. Mikhailov and Yu N. Bubnov, *Izvest Akad. Nauk S.S.S.R.*, 1965, 1310; *Chem. Abs.*, 1965, **63,** 13303.

[208] B. M. Mikhailov and Yu. N. Bubnov, *Izvest. Akad. Nauk S.S.S.R.*, 1964, 1874; *Chem. Abs.*, 1965, **62,** 11840.

[209] B. M. Mikhailov and F. B. Tutorskaya, *Zhur. obshchei Khim.*, 1962, **32,** 833; *Chem. Abs.*, 1963, **58,** 3452.

[210] B. M. Mikhailov and V. F. Pozdnev, *Izvest. Akad. Nauk S.S.S.R.*, 1962, 1475, 1698; B. M. Mikhailov, V. F. Pozdnev and V. G. Kiselev, *Doklady Akad. Nauk S.S.S.R.*, 1963, **151,** 577; *Chem. Abs.*, 1963, **58,** 3451, 6850; **59,** 12830. B. M. Mikhailov, A. N. Blokhina and V. F. Pozdnev, *Izvest. Akad. Nauk S.S.S.R.*, 1965, 197; *Chem. Abs.*, 1965, **62,** 11841c.

[211] N. N. Greenwood, J. H. Morris and J. C. Wright, *J. Chem. Soc.*, 1964, 4753; see also G. B. Butler and G. L. Statton, *J. Amer. Chem. Soc.*, 1964, **86,** 518.

Hydroboration of triallyl*amine* leads to the related *1-aza-5-boratricyclo-[3,3,3,0]undecane* (3.2b), which contains an internal B–N link, and is therefore much less reactive [211]:

$$(CH_2:CHCH_2)_3N + Et_3N \cdot BH_3 \longrightarrow N \underset{(CH_2)_3}{\overset{(CH_2)_3}{\underset{}{\overset{}{\longleftrightarrow}}}} B \quad \text{m.p. } 123° \quad 3.2b$$

In contrast to the labile allylboranes, the tribut-3-enyl compound, $(CH_2:CH.CH_2CH_2)_3B$, b.p. 98–103°/17 mm., is relatively stable to hydrolysis and alcoholysis [212].

Alkynyl derivatives of boron

Alkynylboron compounds may be prepared by the reaction between a boron halide or alkoxide and the appropriate Grignard reagent or sodium acetylide. For example, phenylethynylsodium reacts with boron tribromide or trichloride in benzene at −60°, or with boron trifluoride in boiling ether, to form sodium tetraphenylethynylborate [213], $NaB(C:CPh)_4$, which may be extracted from the reaction mixture with ether or tetrahydrofuran. The product, like sodium tetraphenylborate, forms many water-insoluble salts with cations such as NH_4^+, K^+, Li^+, and Ca^{2+}.

$$4PhC:CNa + BX_3 \longrightarrow 3NaX + NaB(C:CPh)_4$$

The reaction between sodium acetylide and boron trifluoride–pyridine complex in pyridine, followed by recrystallization of the product from acetone–water, gives purple crystals of triethynylborane–pyridine complex [214], $(HC:C)_3B \cdot py$, m.p. 153°. Similar reactions with dialkyl- or diaryl-boron halides have been used to prepare a variety of compounds $R_2BC:CR'$ [215] or their pyridine adducts [216].

Alkynylboranates $Na[R_3BC:CR']$ or $Na_2[R_3BC:CBR_3]$ are also accessible through reactions of alkynes with a borohydride $NaBR_3H$, e.g. [217]

$$NaBR_3H + HC:CR' \longrightarrow NaR_3BC:CR' + H_2 \uparrow$$

[212] R. E. Lyle, E. J. DeWitt and I. C. Pattison, *J. Org. Chem.*, 1956, **21**, 61.

[213] U. Krüerke, *Z. Naturforsch.*, 1956, **11b**, 364.

[214] E. C. Ashby, W. E. Foster, J. R. Maugham and T. H. Pearson (Ethyl Corp.), U.S.P. 2,961,443; *Chem. Abs.*, 1961, **55**, 21053; E. C. Ashby and W. E. Foster, *J. Org. Chem.*, 1964, **29**, 3225.

[215] H. Hartmann and K. H. Birr, *Angew. Chem.*, 1956, **68**, 247; A. A. Petrov, S. V. Zavgorodnii and V. A. Kormer, *Zhur. obshchei Khim.*, 1962, **32**, 1349; *Chem. Abs.*, 1963, **58**, 1481.

[216] J. Soulié and A. Willemart, *Compt. rend.*, 1960, **251**, 727; D. Giraud, J. Soulié and P. Cadiot, ibid., 1962, **254**, 319.

[217] P. Binger and R. Köster, *Tetrahedron Letters*, 1965, 1901.

Subsequent reaction of the product with alkyl halides affords a route from alkynes to *cis*- and *trans*-alkenes:

$$\text{HC:CR}' \xrightarrow[\substack{\text{(i)NaBR}_3\text{H} \\ \text{(ii) R}''\text{X} \\ \text{(iii)H}_2\text{O}}]{} \begin{array}{c} \text{R} \\ \diagdown \\ \text{C}\!=\!\text{C} \\ \diagup \\ \text{H} \end{array}\!\!\begin{array}{c} \text{R}' \\ \diagup \\ \\ \diagdown \\ \text{R}'' \end{array}$$

Esters of ethynylboronic acids [218, 219] may be prepared by the reaction at $-70°$ between equimolar quantities of trimethylborate and the Grignard reagent:

$$\underset{\text{in THF}}{\text{HC:CMgBr}} + \underset{\text{in Et}_2\text{O}}{(\text{MeO})_3\text{B}} \xrightarrow{-70°} [\text{HC:CB(OMe)}_2] \xrightarrow[\substack{+\ \text{BuOH}}]{\text{HCl + aq. H}_3\text{PO}_4} \text{HC:CB(OBu)}_2$$

Care is needed in working up the product, as although the :C–B link is stable in neutral or acidic solution, it is rapidly cleaved by bases as mild even as sodium bicarbonate [218].

Free radicals add to HC:CB(OBu)_2 without disturbing the C–B bond; reaction with CBrCl_3 gives $\text{Cl}_3\text{CCH:CBrB(OBu)}_2$, HBr forms BrCH:CHB(OBu)_2, bromine forms BrCH:CBrB(OBu)_2, while mercaptans give RSCH:CHB(OBu)_2. The reactivity of the ethynylboron group $\text{HC:CB}\diagdown$ towards free radicals is lower than that of the vinylboron group $\text{CH}_2\text{:CHB}\diagdown$, but high enough to be of considerable synthetic use, a limitation being the sensitivity of the group towards bases [218].

Addition of cyanates to ethynylboronic esters affords 5-isoxazoleboronic acids [218a]:

$$\text{PhCNO} + \text{CH:CB(OBu)}_2 \xrightarrow{\text{Et}_2\text{O}} \underset{\substack{}}{\overset{\text{Ph}}{\diagup}}\!\!\!\!\begin{array}{c} \\ \text{N} \\ \diagdown \\ \text{O} \end{array}\!\!\!\!\text{-B(OH)}_2$$

Halocarbon derivatives of boron

Chloroalkyl derivatives, $\text{Cl(CH}_2)_n\text{BR}_2$. Chloromethyldimethylborane [112, 113], $\text{ClCH}_2\text{BMe}_2$, has been described earlier as the product from the gas-phase reaction between chlorine and trimethylborane at $-95°$. *β-Chloroethyldichloroborane*, in the form of its complex with dimethylether,

[218] D. S. Matteson and K. Peacock, *J. Amer. Chem. Soc.*, 1960, **82**, 5759; *J. Org. Chem.*, 1963, **28**, 369; *J. Organometal. Chem.*, 1964, **2**, 190, 192.
[218a] G. Bianchi, A. Cogoli and P. Grünanger, ibid., 1966, **6**, 598.
[219] V. S. Zavgorodnii and A. A. Petrov, *Zhur. obshchei Khim.*, 1961, **31**, 2433; *Chem. Abs.*, 1962, **56**, 2464; U.S. Borax and Chemical Corp., Brit.P. 884, 547, Dec. 13, 1961; *Chem. Abs.*, 1962, **57**, 7308; see also J. Soulié and P. Cadiot, *Bull. Soc. Chim. France*, 1966, 3846; W. G. Woods and P. L. Strong, *J. Organometal. Chem.*, 1967, **7**, 371.

$ClCH_2CH_2BCl_2.OMe_2$, m.p. 54–56°, may be prepared by the hydroboration of vinyl chloride in dimethylether [220]. It is quantitatively decomposed by water or bases into boric and hydrochloric acids and ethylene. Analogous *β-bromoethylboron* compounds, obtained by radical addition of hydrogen bromide to vinylboron compounds, are also decomposed by bases with elimination of ethylene [200, 204].

Hydroboration of allyl chloride in ether affords a mixture of *tris-γ-chloropropylborane*, $(ClCH_2CH_2CH_2)_3B$, and *bis-γ-chloropropylchloroborane*, $(ClCH_2CH_2CH_2)_2BCl$, which are decomposed by bases with quantitative evolution of cyclopropane [220]. (Cyclopropane is also evolved when γ-chloropropylboron compounds are mixed with alkylaluminium compounds, since alkyl exchange forms the unstable γ-chloropropyl aluminium compound, see p. 324 [221].) Use of this reaction with derivatives of allyl chloride has been suggested as a route to substituted cyclopropanes [222]:

$$RCH{:}CHCH_2Cl \xrightarrow{B_2H_6} RCH{\cdot}CH_2CH_2Cl \xrightarrow{OH^-} \triangle$$

An interesting application of this reaction, using a dialkylboryl allyl chloride, has led to cyclopropylboranes [223]:

$$R_4B_2H_2 + CH{:}CCH_2Cl \longrightarrow [R_2BCH{:}CHCH_2Cl] \longrightarrow (R_2B)_2CHCH_2CH_2Cl$$

$$\downarrow \begin{array}{c} NaBR_4 \\ \text{non aqueous} \\ \text{solvent} \end{array}$$

$$R_2B{-}\triangleleft$$

Diethylcyclopropylborane, $Et_2B(C_3H_5)$, b.p. 75–76°/150 mm., prepared in this way, disproportionates in the presence of catalytic amounts of B–H compounds into triethylborane and *tricyclopropylborane*, $(C_3H_5)_3B$, b.p. 65–66°/10 mm. The cyclopropyl group attached to boron is very stable to boron hydrides, is not displaced by olefins, and the ring remains intact at 100°.

Fluorocarbon derivatives

It is only recently that attempts to prepare fluorocarbon derivatives of boron have been successful. The gas-phase reaction between diazomethane and boron trifluoride at low pressures and −40° yields *fluoromethyldifluoroborane* [89], FCH_2BF_2, m.p. −47°, b.p. (extrapolated) +7°. Monomeric in the gas phase, this compound appears, on the evidence of its

[220] M. F. Hawthorne and J. A. Dupont, *J. Amer. Chem. Soc.*, 1958, **80**, 5830.
[221] P. Binger and R. Köster, *Tetrahedron Letters*, 1961, 156.
[222] M. F. Hawthorne, *J. Amer. Chem. Soc.*, 1960, **82**, 1886.
[223] P. Binger and R. Köster, *Angew. Chem.*, 1962, **74**, 652.

Trouton constant and infrared spectrum, to be associated in the liquid and solid phases; there is clearly strong interaction between one molecule and another involving bridging fluorine (see p. 338 for fluorine bridging in aluminium alkyls). This contrasts with the lack of association of the boron alkyls and halides themselves, and indicates the probable mode of decomposition of fluoroalkylboron compounds, which are generally unstable, decomposing to form boron trifluoride, which was often the product when their preparation was attempted [224].

The first successful attachment of a trifluoromethyl group to boron to form a stable compound significantly involved a co-ordinatively saturated boron [225]. The reaction between BF_3 and trifluoromethyltrimethyltin, Me_3SnCF_3, in CCl_4 gave a white solid, $Me_3Sn[CF_3BF_3]$, stable in neutral aqueous solution, which reacted with KF to form trimethyltin fluoride and potassium trifluoromethyltrifluoroborate, $K^+[CF_3BF_3]^-$:

$$Me_3SnCF_3 \xrightarrow{BF_3} Me_3SnCF_3BF_3 \xrightarrow{KF} Me_3SnF + KCF_3BF_3$$

Amine adducts of trifluoromethyldifluoroborane, $R_3N \cdot BF_2CF_3$, are formed in a series of reactions starting from $KBBu_2$ and CF_3I in triethylamine solvent [226],

$$KBBu_2 + CF_3I \rightarrow [Bu_2BCF_3] \xrightarrow{BF_3} [CF_3BF_2] \xrightarrow{R_3N} R_3N \cdot BF_2CF_3$$

and a poorly characterized dimethyl ether complex, $CF_3BF_2 \cdot OMe_2$, was isolated from the products of the reaction between diborane and CF_3SCl.

The preparation of the *perfluorovinyl* compounds $CF_2{:}CFBF_2$, b.p. $-14°$, $CF_2{:}CFBCl_2$, b.p. $48°$, $(CF_2{:}CF)_2BCl$, b.p. $100\cdot5°$, and $(CF_2{:}CF)_3B$, b.p. $104\cdot9°$, from BX_3 (X = F,Cl) and $Me_2Sn(CF{:}CF_2)_2$ has already been mentioned [191]. These do not require co-ordination for stabilization; possibly C–B π-bonding reduces the electrophilic character of the boron atom. All are air-sensitive, and react with hot water with evolution of trifluoroethylene. Even perfluorovinylborazines are hydrolytically unstable [226a].

Alkylboranes with a trifluoromethyl group attached to boron through either one or two carbon atoms, e.g. $CF_3CH_2CH_2BF_2$ [227], $CF_3CHMeBMe_2$ [228] and $(CF_3CH_2CH_2BO)_3$ [229], have been prepared

[224] J. J. Lagowski and P. G. Thompson, *Proc. Chem. Soc.*, 1959, 301; B. Bartocha, W. A. G. Graham and F. G. A. Stone, *J. Inorg. Nucl. Chem.*, 1958, **6**, 119.

[225] R. D. Chambers, H. C. Clark and C. J. Willis, *Proc. Chem. Soc.*, 1960, 114; idem. *J. Amer. Chem. Soc.*, 1960, **82**, 5298; R. D. Chambers, H. C. Clark, L. W. Reeves and C. J. Willis, *Canad. J. Chem.*, 1961, **39**, 258.

[226] T. D. Parsons, E. D. Baker, A. B. Burg and G. L. Juvinall, *J. Amer. Chem. Soc.*, 1961, **83**, 250.

[226a] A. J. Klanica, J. P. Faust and C. S. King, *Inorg. Chem.*, 1967, **6**, 840.

[227] J. R. Phillips and F. G. A. Stone, *J. Chem. Soc.*, 1962, 94.

[228] J. M. Birchall, R. N. Haszeldine and J. F. Marsh, *Chem. and Ind.*, 1961, 1080.

[229] V. F. Gridina, A. L. Klebanskii and V. A. Bartashev, *Zh. Vses. Khim. Obshestva im. D. I. Mendeleeva*, 1962, **7**, 230; *Chem. Abs.*, 1963, **58**, 541.

either by hydroboration reactions with $CF_3CH:CH_2$ or by the Grignard method. The *β-fluorinated* compound is thermally unstable, losing $CF_2:CHMe$ to form Me_2BF, possibly by an intramolecular mechanism. The *γ-fluorinated* compounds on the other hand are thermally stable, and do not lose cyclopropane derivatives on basic hydrolysis [227], as do γ-chloropropylboron compounds.

Fluoroarylboron compounds are more thermally stable than are fluoroalkylboranes. *Tris(pentafluorophenyl)borane*, $(C_6F_5)_3B$, an air-sensitive white solid which may be sublimed at 150° *in vacuo* with some decomposition, has been prepared by the Grignard route [230] or by the reaction between boron trichloride and a suspension of pentafluorophenyl-lithium in pentane at $-78°$; the product was obtained by evaporation of the solvent after lithium chloride had been filtered off [231]:

$$BCl_3 + 3C_6F_5Li \longrightarrow 3LiCl \downarrow + (C_6F_5)_3B$$

Tris(pentafluorophenyl)borane reacts with various ligands to form adducts such as $H_3N \cdot B(C_6F_5)_3$, $Me_3N \cdot B(C_6F_5)_3$, $Ph_3P \cdot B(C_6F_5)_3$, and $Li[(C_6F_5)_4B]$; potassium and tetraethylammonium salts of the tetrakis-(pentafluorophenyl)borate anion have been prepared from the lithium salt in aqueous solution.

Another route to pentafluorophenylboranes is via pentafluorophenyltin compounds. *Pentafluorophenylboron difluoride*, $C_6F_5BF_2$, is obtained from $Me_3SnC_6F_5$ and BF_3 in CCl_4 (in contrast to the reaction of Me_3SnCF_3, which gives $Me_3SnCF_3BF_3$):

$$Me_3SnC_6F_5 + 2BF_3 \longrightarrow Me_3SnBF_4 + C_6F_5BF_2$$

The difluoride decomposes slowly (40% in 1 month) at room temperature, evolving BF_3. With aqueous potassium fluoride it forms the salt $K^+C_6F_5BF_3^-$. The *dichloride* $C_6F_5BCl_2$, prepared by a similar reaction but without use of a solvent, can be distilled (b.p. 123–124°/760 mm.) with but slight decomposition. It reacts with water in acetone at $-80°$ to form *pentafluorophenylboronic acid*, $C_6F_5B(OH)_2$, m.p. 290°, which differs from other boronic acids in that it does not dehydrate to a boroxine, forms no diethanolamine ester, and loses pentafluorophenyl groups when treated with aqueous ethanol [232]. With 90% hydrogen peroxide it gives pentafluorophenol, C_6F_5OH.

Heterocyclic compounds containing boron and carbon
Although boron–carbon ring compounds were first described as recently

[230] J. L. W. Pohlmann and F. E. Brinckmann, *Z. Naturforsch.*, 1965, **20b**, 5.
[231] A. G. Massey, A. J. Park and F. G. A. Stone, *Proc. Chem. Soc.*, 1963, 212; A. G. Massey and A. J. Park, *J. Organometal. Chem.*, 1964, **2**, 245; 1966, **5**, 218.
[232] R. D. Chambers and T. Chivers, *Proc. Chem. Soc.*, 1963, 208; *J. Chem. Soc.*, 1965, 3933; R. D. Chambers, T. Chivers and D. A. Pyke, *J. Chem. Soc.*, 1965, 5144.

as 1954 [233], many examples are now known, as will be apparent from recent reviews [6, 19, 238]. Boracycloalkanes having 5-, 6- and 7-membered rings (borolanes, borinanes and borepanes) have been prepared, and examples of the unsaturated boroles and borepins have been described, together with fused-ring systems and rings containing two or more boron atoms.

borolane   borinane   borepane   borole   borepin

9-boradecalin   perhydro-9b-boraphenalene   boroindan   borotetralin

1,5-diboracyclo-octane   1,5 diborabicyclo[3,3,3]undecane   1,3,5-triboracyclohexane

Reactions used to prepare these compounds have included (*i*) the reaction between organoboron dihalides and α,ω-dilithioalkanes or di-Grignard reagents, (*ii*) the hydroboration of dienes, and (*iii*) condensation reactions, particularly of alkylboranes with alkyl chains longer than C_3.

The alicyclic boranes 1-phenyl-borolane and 1-phenyl-borinane were first prepared from phenyldifluoroborane and 1,4-dilithiobutane or 1,5-dilithiopentane [233]; 1-phenyl-borolane can also be prepared from butadiene and $PhBH_2 \cdot NEt_3$ [234]. 1-Butyl analogues were prepared by the Grignard method, and were also unexpectedly obtained in attempts to prepare $Bu^n_2B(CH_2)_nBBu^n_2$ ($n = 4$ or 5) from Bu^n_2BCl and $BrMg(CH_2)_nMgBr$ [235]:

$$Bu^n_2B(CH_2)_nBBu^n_2 \longrightarrow Bu^nB \underset{CH_2}{\overset{CH_2}{\diagdown}}(CH_2)_{n-2} + Bu^n_3B$$

The hydroboration of 1,3-butadiene with diborane, alkylboranes or their adducts with tertiary bases at moderate temperatures affords boro-

[233] K. Torssell, *Acta Chem. Scand.* 1954, **8**, 1779.
[234] N. N. Greenwood and J. C. Wright, *J. Chem. Soc.*, 1965, 448.
[235] S. L. Clark, J. R. Jones, and H. Stange, *Advan. in Chem. Series*, 1961, **32**, 228.

lanes (boracyclopentanes): [61, 234, 236, 237]:

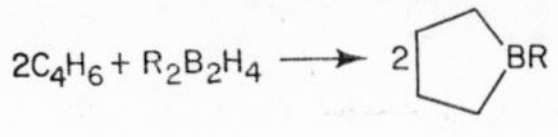

$$2C_4H_6 + R_2B_2H_4 \longrightarrow 2 \quad \text{BR}$$

Diborane itself reacts with an excess of butadiene to form a polymeric product from which compounds such as 1,1'-tetramethylene-bisborolane may be isolated [236]:

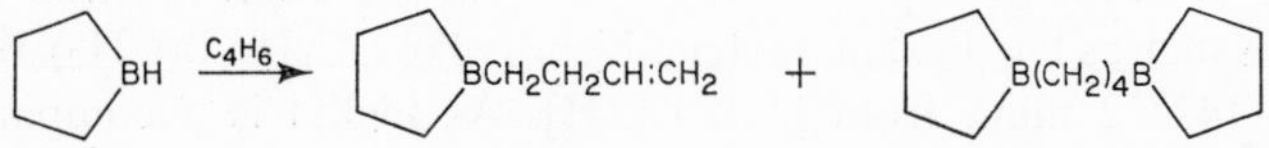

$$\text{BH} \xrightarrow{C_4H_6} \text{BCH}_2\text{CH}_2\text{CH:CH}_2 + \text{B(CH}_2)_4\text{B}$$

3.3

There is some spectroscopic evidence that the 1-butenylborolane intermediate (3.3), in this reaction sequence has a structure in which there is interaction between the C=C double bond and the boron atom. The infrared spectrum of the dimethyl derivative (3.4) has two clearly separated absorption maxima for the C=C bond, at 1645 and 1610 cm^{-1}, the latter

3.4

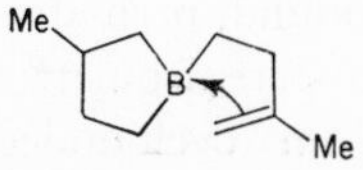

disappearing completely on addition of certain donor molecules [238]. Bisborolane itself, $(C_4H_8BH)_2$, may be recovered only after destructive distillation of the polymeric product. There has been some uncertainty about the structure of this compound, which would normally be written (3.5), since the simple bisborolanes themselves show a surprising lack of reactivity compared with tetra-alkyldiboranes $R_4B_2H_2$. The B–H bonds

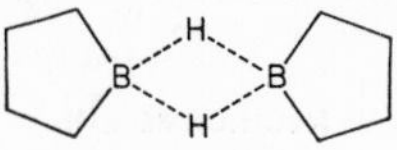

3.5 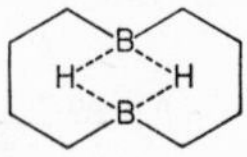   3.6

do not undergo hydrolysis or alcoholysis at room temperature, and the compounds do not readily react with hydrogen peroxide or oxygen. A transannular structure 3.6 was therefore suggested [239], and evidence has been presented for the intermediate formation of 1,2-tetramethylene-

[236] R. Köster, *Angew. Chem.*, 1959, **71**, 520; 1960, **72**, 626; B. M. Mikhailov, A. Ya. Bezmenov, L. S. Vasil'ev and V. G. Kiselev, *Doklady. Akad. Nauk S.S.S.R.*, 1964, **155**, 141; A. I. Kovredov and L. I. Zakharkin, *Izvest. Akad. Nauk S.S.S.R.*, 1964, 50; *Chem. Abs.*, 1964, **60**, 10704, 13263.
[237] K. A. Saegebarth, *J. Amer. Chem. Soc.*, 1960, **82**, 2081; U.S.P. 3,008,997.
[238] R. Köster, *Angew. Chem.*, 1963, **75**, 1079; *Internat. Edn.*, 1964, **3**, 174.
[239] G. Zweifel, K. Nagase and H. C. Brown, *J. Amer. Chem. Soc.*, 1962, **84**, 183.

diborane (3.7) and 1,2(1'-methyltrimethylene)-diborane (3.8) in the reaction between butadiene and diborane [240]:

3.7   3.8

Other boracycloalkanes prepared by the hydroboration reaction include borepanes such as 1,1'-hexamethylene-bisborepane, $C_6H_{12}B(CH_2)_6BC_6H_{12}$, b.p. 141–142°/2 mm., from biallyl [241]. As biallyl is a comparatively involatile diene, it can be used to displace more volatile olefins from trialkylboranes, in the same way that n-decene is used to displace a more volatile olefin after a hydroboration–isomerization reaction [242]; e.g.

The interesting tricyclic compound, perhydro-9b-boraphenalene, has been prepared in the form of two stereoisomers together with some isomeric boraperhydrobenzazulene from cyclododecatriene and triethylamine-borane [243].

Trialkylboranes with four or more carbon atoms in an unbranched chain disproportionate when heated to form cyclic compounds, olefins and hydrogen [244].

[240] H. G. Weiss, W. J. Lehmann and I. Shapiro, *J. Amer. Chem. Soc.*, 1962, **84**, 2840; H. Lindner and T. Onak, ibid., 1966, **88**, 1886, 1890.

[241] B. M. Mikhailov, L. S. Vasil'ev, and E. N. Safonova, *Doklady Akad. Nauk S.S.S.R.*, 1962, **147**, 630; *Chem. Abs.*, 1963, **58**, 9108; T. A. Shchegoleva, E. M. Shashkova, V. G. Kiselev and B. M. Mikhailov, *Izvest. Akad. Nauk S.S.S.R.*, 1964, 365; *Chem. Abs.*, 1964, **60**, 12037.

[242] Studiengesellschaft Kohle m.b.H., Ger.P. 1,109,682; *Chem. Abs.*, 1962, **56**, 10188.

[243] R. Köster, *Angew. Chem.*, 1957, **69**, 684; N. N. Greenwood and J. H. Morris, *J. Chem. Soc.*, 1960, 2922; G. W. Rotermund and R. Köster, *Angew. Chem.*, 1962, **74**, 329; idem, *Annalen*, 1965, **686**, 153.

[244] R. Köster and G. Rotermund, *Angew. Chem.*, 1960, **72**, 138; R. Köster, W. Larbig and G. W. Rotermund, *Annalen*, 1965, **682**, 21; H. C. Brown, K. J. Murray, H. Müller and G. Zweifel, *J. Amer. Chem. Soc.*, 1966, **88**, 1443.

This method has been used to prepare 5-, 6- and 7-membered boracyclo-alkanes [237, 244]. The reaction probably goes via an alkylboron hydride intermediate [245], as alkyldiboranes and olefins are also products of the pyrolysis of trialkylboranes [246] and can themselves be converted into cyclic compounds provided the alkyl groups are long enough.

The boracycloalkanes are thermally more stable than acyclic mixed alkylboranes and can be distilled above 100° without disproportionation. At higher temperatures isomerization may occur. The 6-membered borinane ring is the most stable, and may be formed by thermal isomeriza-tion of borepanes (7-membered rings) or of alkyl substituted borolanes (5-membered rings) [237].

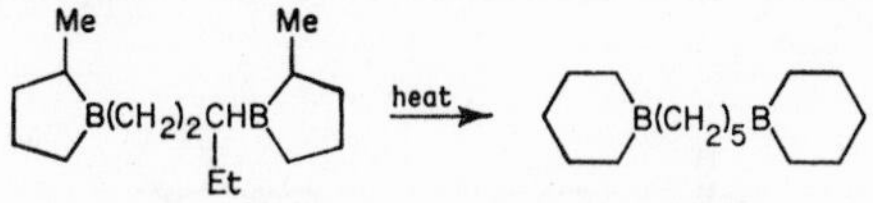

Esters, halides or hydrides result from exchange with alkyl borates, boron halides or alkylboranes respectively at elevated temperatures [247]:

Other heterocyclic boron compounds result from heating certain trialkyl-boranes at 180–200° [247a]:

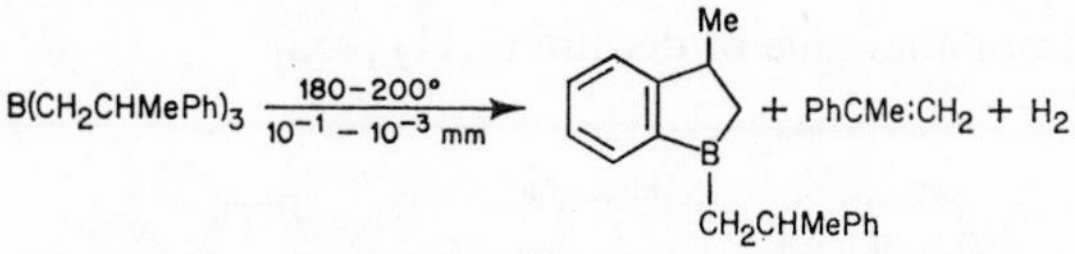

This dehydrogenating ring closure can be carried out with mixtures of boranes; for example a mixture of 2 mols. tri-isobutylborane and 1 mol. tri(2-phenylpropyl)borane affords 90% B-isobutyl-3-methyl-boro-indane, b.p. 109°/11 mm., when heated at about 200° (at atmospheric pressure).

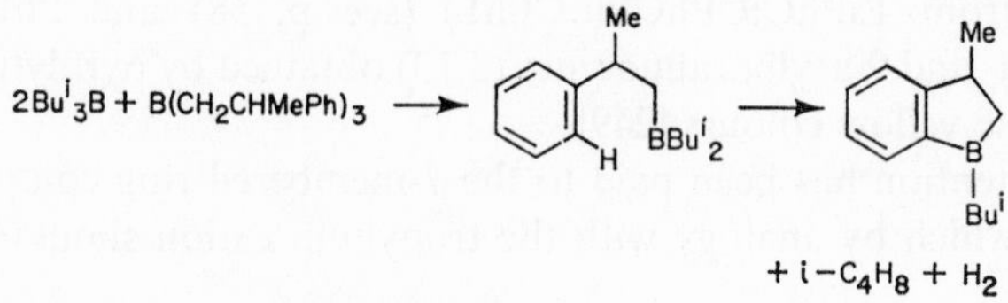

[245] P. F. Winternitz and A. A. Carotti, ibid, 1960, **82**, 2430.
[246] L. Rosenblum, ibid., 1955, **77**, 5016.
[247] B. M. Mikhailov, T. K. Kozminskaya and A. Ya. Bezmenov, *Izvest. Akad. Nauk S.S.S.R.*, 1965, 355; *Chem. Abs.*, 1965, **62**, 14710.
[247a] R. Köster, G. Benedikt, W. Fenzl and K. Reinert, *Annalen*, 1967, **702**, 197.

Several examples of this type have been prepared: the alkyl groups attached to boron may be removed by hydrogenation at 160° under pressure and in this way the following dimeric (cf. alkyl$_4$B$_2$H$_2$) heterocyclic compounds were obtained [248, 249]:

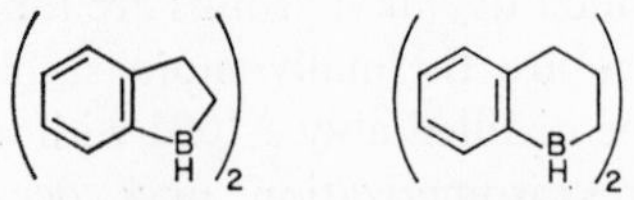

Boro-indane,
m.p. 132°

Boro-tetralin,
m.p. 103–104°

Dehalogenation of 1-chloroborolanes has led to compounds in which two or more borolane rings are linked through B–C bonds, such as (3.9) and (3.10) [250]:

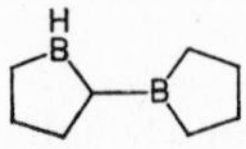

3.9 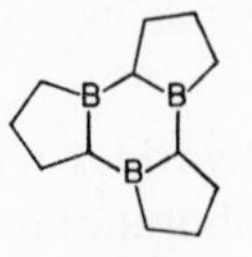   3.10

Reference has already been made to derivatives of 1,5-diboracyclo-octane, prepared from diborane and triallylborane [210, 211]. 1,4-Diboracyclohexane rings are present in the products of pyrolysis of Me$_2$BCH$_2$CH$_2$BMe$_2$ [251] and 1,3,5,7-tetraboracyclo-octane derivatives have been obtained from the pyrolysis of trimethylborane [96]. Pyrolysis of tri-n-nonylborane yields the 9-bora analogue of decalin (3.11) [252].

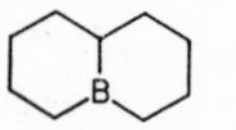

3.11 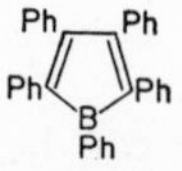   3.12 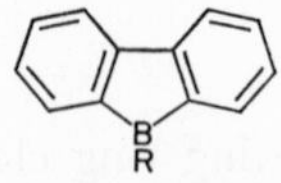   3.13

Little is known about unsaturated boron–carbon ring compounds. Pentaphenylborole (3.12), a pale yellow solid, m.p. 175° (decomp.), was obtained from LiPhC:CPhCPh:CPhLi (see p. 58) and PhBCl$_2$ [253]. The 9-alkyl- and 9-arylborafluorenes (3.13) obtained by pyrolytic methods, have intense yellow colours [249].

More attention has been paid to the 7-membered ring compounds, the borepins, which by analogy with the tropylium cation should have some

[248] R. Köster and K. Reinert, Angew. Chem., 1959, 71, 521.
[249] R. Köster and G. Benedikt, ibid., 1963, 75, 419.
[250] Idem. ibid., p. 346.
[251] G. Urry, J. Kerrigan, T. D. Parsons and H. I. Schlesinger, J. Amer. Chem. Soc., 1954, 76, 5299.
[252] R. Köster and G. Rotermund, Angew. Chem., 1960, 72, 563.
[253] E. H. Braye, W. Hübel and I. Caplier, J. Amer. Chem. Soc., 1961, 83, 4406.

aromatic character. A dihydro derivative of a dibenzoborepin was prepared from o,o'-dilithiobibenzyl and butyl borate [254]:

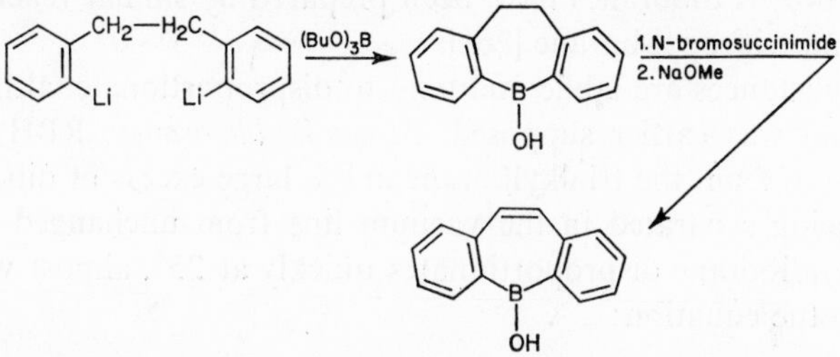

This was dehydrogenated as indicated, the borinic acid being isolated as the ethanolamine complex [255]. Derivatives proved to be unstable, and it was deduced that the hetero-ring has no aromatic character. An attempt to prepare a monobenzoborepin failed [256].

The reaction between diphenylacetylene, phenylboron dibromide and potassium affords a material of composition $Ph_6C_4B_2$, which may be a diboracyclohexadiene or an organocarborane (cf. 3.19, p. 245) [79a]:

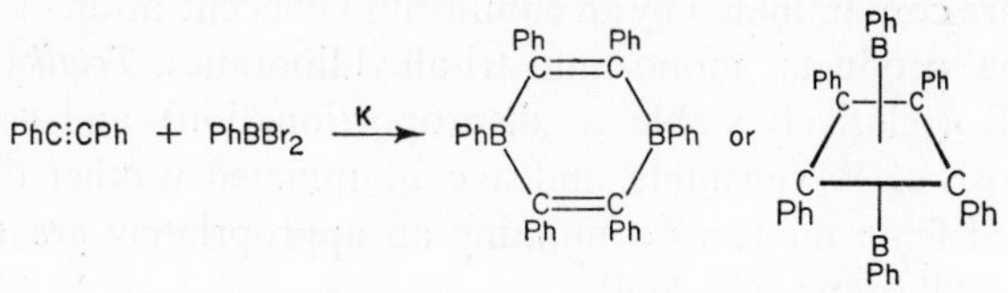

$$PhC:CPh + PhBBr_2 \xrightarrow{K} PhB \cdots BPh \text{ or }$$

Organoboron hydrides [8, 9, 17, 24, 257]

Derivatives of diborane

The importance of organodiboranes as reagents or intermediates in the hydroboration reaction has already been mentioned. In this section the properties of the simpler compounds will be outlined.

The volatile *trialkylboranes* react with diborane at room temperature to form alkyldiboranes, e.g.

$$2R_3B + B_2H_6 \rightleftharpoons 2R_2BHBH_2R$$

All five of the possible methyldiboranes have been prepared [258, 259].

[254] R. L. Letsinger and I. M. Skoog, ibid., 1955, **77**, 5176.
[255] E. E. Van Tamelen, G. Brieger and K. G. Untch, *Tetrahedron Letters*, 1960, **8**, 14.
[256] P. M. Maitlis, *J. Chem. Soc.*, 1961, 3149.
[257] T. Onak, *Advances in Organometallic Chemistry*, eds. F. G. A. Stone and R. West, 1965, Vol. 3, p. 263.
[258] H. I. Schlesinger and A. O. Walker, *J. Amer. Chem. Soc.*, 1935, **57**, 621.
[259] H. I. Schlesinger, N. W. Flodin and A. B. Burg, ibid., 1939, **61**, 1078.

The failure to obtain penta- and hexa-methyldiborane provided early chemical evidence in favour of the bridge model of diborane [260]. Various ethyl and propyl diboranes have been prepared by similar reactions with triethyl- and tripropyl-borane [261].

These substances are labile and tend to disproportionate, although less readily than was earlier supposed. *Monoalkyldiboranes*, RBH_2BH_3, are best prepared from the trialkylborane and a large excess of diborane, the product being separated in the vacuum line from unchanged diborane. Mono-ethyldiborane disproportionates quickly at 25°, almost wholly according to the equation:

$$2EtBH_2BH_3 \rightleftharpoons EtBH_2BH_2Et + B_2H_6 \quad (K_p = 0.039 \pm 0.006)$$

For the analogous methyl compounds $K_p = 0.070$ [262]. This reaction can be used to prepare *sym-dialkyldiboranes*, RBH_2BH_2R, themselves quite stable to disproportionation [259, 263]. *Unsymmetrical* or *1,1-dialkyldiboranes*, R_2BHBH_3, are the major product (80%) of the reaction between equimolar quantities of diborane and trialkylborane,

$$2B_2H_6 + 2R_3B \longrightarrow 3R_2BHBH_3$$

but at 25° are contaminated by an equilibrium concentration of the disproportionation products, mono- and tri-alkyldiboranes. *Trialkyldiboranes*, R_2BHBH_2R (relatively stable to disproportionation), and *tetra-alkyldiboranes*, R_2BHBHR_2 (unstable, and so contaminated by other derivatives), are prepared from mixtures containing an appropriately greater proportion of trialkylborane [258, 264].

The alkyldiboranes may be identified by their infrared spectra [263, 265] and by the products of their hydrolysis, e.g.

$$EtBH_2BH_2Et + H_2O \longrightarrow EtB(OH)_2$$
$$Et_2BH.BH_3 + H_2O \longrightarrow Et_2BOH + H_3BO_3$$

Recent preparative methods for alkyldiboranes make use of borohydride or lithium aluminium hydride as starting material. Sodium borohydride in tetraethylene glycol dimethyl ether (chosen because of its low vapour pressure) reacts at room temperature with vinyl and with allyl

[260] R. P. Bell and H. J. Emeléus, *Quart. Rev.*, 1948, **2**, 141.

[261] H. I. Schlesinger, L. Horvitz and A. B. Burg, *J. Amer. Chem. Soc.*, 1936, **58**, 407.

[262] L. Van Alten, G. R. Seely, J. Oliver and D. M. Ritter, *Advan. in Chem. Series*, 1961, **32**, 107.

[263] I. J. Solomon, M. J. Klein and K. Hattori, *J. Amer. Chem. Soc.*, 1958, **80**, 4520; idem, U.S.P. 3,053,899, Sept. 11, 1962; *Chem. Abs.*, 1963, **58**, 9136.

[264] B. M. Mikhailov, A. A. Akhnazaryan and L. S. Vasil'ev, *Doklady Akad. Nauk S.S.S.R.*, 1961, **136**, 828.

[265] W. J. Lehmann, C. O. Wilson and I. Shapiro, *J. Chem. Phys.*, 1960, **32**, 1088, 1786; 1960, **33**, 590; 1961, **34**, 476, 783; but see M. J. D. Low, R. Epstein and A. C. Bond, *Chem. Comm.*, 1967, 226.

bromide, forming unsym-diethyl- and di-n-propyl-diboranes [266]:

$$NaBH_4 + CH_2{:}CHBr \longrightarrow NaBr + \tfrac{1}{2}Et_2B_2H_4$$
$$NaBH_4 + CH_2{:}CHCH_2Br \longrightarrow NaBr + \tfrac{1}{2}Pr^n_2B_2H_4$$

Alkyldiboranes are also obtained from suitable combinations of a boro-hydride, a trialkyl-borane or -alane, and a boron halide or hydrogen halide, e.g. [41, 267]:

$$4AlR_3 + 3LiBH_4 + 5BX_3 \longrightarrow 3LiX + 4AlX_3 + 4B_2H_3R_3$$

Amine adducts of alkylboranes, $RBH_2{\cdot}NR'_3$, may conveniently be prepared by the reduction of boronic anhydrides, $(RBO)_3$, using $LiAlH_4$ in presence of NR'_3 in ether solution [268]. This method avoids the use of the more reactive halide, RBX_2, or diborane itself, and affords alkylboranes in a suitable form for use in selective hydroboration reactions. Alternatively, symmetrical dialkyldiboranes with bulky alkyl groups may be prepared by the hydroboration of a suitable olefin [269]. Tetra-alkyldiboranes have also been prepared from borinic esters and diborane [270].

Although alkylboron hydrides have been known [258] since 1935, arylboron hydrides were reliably characterized only in 1958. Symmetrical *diphenyldiborane*, $PhBH_2BH_2Ph$, m.p. 85°, was prepared from diphenylborane and diborane at 80° and 2·2 atm. pressure, and by the reduction of phenyldichloroborane ($PhBCl_2$) with lithium aluminium hydride. It forms a series of amine complexes, $PhBH_2{\cdot}NR_3$, and adds lithium hydride in ether:

$$2LiH + PhBH_2BH_2Ph \longrightarrow 2Li[BH_3Ph]$$

The salt $Li[BH_3Ph]$ is also obtained from phenyl-lithium and diborane [271].

The pyridine complex, $PhBH_2{\cdot}py$, m.p. 80–83°, and various other compounds of the type $ArBH_2NR_3$ result from the lithium aluminium hydride reduction of the appropriate boronic esters in ether in the presence of the amine at $-70°$ or below; they are stable in dry air [272]. The diaryl hydride complexes are less stable [273]; they are similarly prepared by lithium aluminium hydride reduction of borinic esters in the presence of pyridine at $-70°$, e.g. $Ph_2BH{\cdot}py$, m.p. 106–107°, $(p\text{-}BrC_6H_4)_2BH{\cdot}py$, m.p. 122–124°. In the absence of amine, the diaryl hydrides apparently disproportionate into diaryldiborane and triarylborane, since 1,2-diaryldiboranes

[266] T. Wartik and R. K. Pearson, *J. Inorg. Nuclear Chem.*, 1958, **5**, 250.
[267] L. H. Long and M. G. H. Wallbridge, *Chem. and Ind.*, 1959, 295; idem, *J. Chem. Soc.*, 1963, 2181; 1965, 3513.
[268] M. F. Hawthorne, *J. Amer. Chem. Soc.*, 1959, **81**, 5836; 1961, **83**, 831.
[269] H. C. Brown and G. J. Klender, *Inorg. Chem.*, 1962, **1**, 204.
[270] B. M. Mikhailov and L. S. Vasil'ev, *Izvest. Akad. Nauk S.S.S.R.*, 1962, 628; *Chem. Abs.*, 1962, **57**, 16643.
[271] E. Wiberg, J. E. F. Evans and H. Nöth, *Z. Naturforsch.*, 1958, **13b**, 263.
[272] M. F. Hawthorne, *J. Amer. Chem. Soc.*, 1958, **80**, 4291.
[273] Idem. ibid., p. 4293.

are formed when diborane is passed through solutions of diarylborinic esters in ether, e.g. [274]:

$$(p\text{-}CH_3C_6H_4)_2BOBu + B_2H_6 \rightarrow (p\text{-}CH_3C_6H_4BH_2)_2 \quad \text{m.p. } 128\text{-}132° \text{ (decomp.)}$$

Derivatives of higher boranes

Much work has been done on alkyl derivatives of penta- and deca-borane, but publication was delayed because of the interest in these materials as high energy fuels; the purpose of alkylation was to obtain fuels with more suitable physical properties (liquid range, vapour pressure, density) than the parent borane without too great a decrease in the calorific value.

The main methods of attaching alkyl groups to boron involve reactions between a nucleophile (carbanion, olefin, acetylene) and a boron Lewis acid (boron halide, diborane). With the higher boranes, in which theoretical considerations indicate that some boron atoms are surrounded by a greater electron density than others (see diagram, p. 236) [9], attack by carbonium ions is possible, and in fact Friedel–Crafts reactions have been used for the alkylation of e.g. pentaborane and decaborane. It has been possible to establish the position of attachment of alkyl groups in derivatives of pentaborane and decaborane, using mass, infrared and n.m.r. spectroscopic techniques, and so to investigate how far predictions, concerning which of the boron atoms were the most likely to be attacked by nucleophiles or electrophiles, are borne out in practice. The development of the higher boron hydrides is an area of chemistry in which theory has advanced more rapidly than experiment.

Tetraborane, B_4H_{10}, reacts with ethylene forming hydrogen and *2,4-dimethylenetetraborane* [275]:

$$B_4H_{10} + C_2H_4 \rightarrow C_2H_4B_4H_8 + H_2$$

The reaction may be carried out in a sealed tube at low temperature or by passing the gas mixture through a heated tube, and is catalysed by aluminium chloride. Hydrolysis of the product affords ethylene glycol, boric acid and hydrogen, and its infrared, proton and [11]B nuclear magnetic resonance spectra are consistent with the structure 3.14.

3.14.

[274] B. M. Mikhailov and V. A. Dorokhov, *Doklady Akad. Nauk S.S.S.R.*, 1960, **130**, 782; **133**, 119; *Zhur. obshchei Khim.*, 1961, **31**, 4020; *Chem. Abs.*, 1962, **57**, 10991; *Izvest. Akad. Nauk S.S.S.R.*, 1962, 623.

[275] B. C. Harrison, I. J. Solomon, R. D. Hites and M. J. Klein, *J. Inorg. Nuclear*

Pentaborane-9, B_5H_9, reacts slowly with ethylene or butene at 150° in a sealed vessel, giving 5–10% conversion into alkylpentaboranes, RB_5H_8, in which the alkyl group is attached to a *basal* boron atom. It is suggested that reaction proceeds via nucleophilic attack by the olefin [276]. In the presence of aluminium chloride, however, pentaborane-9 reacts with ethylene at room temperature to form 1-ethylpentaborane, i.e. B_5H_9 with the *apical* hydrogen substituted [277, 278].

$$B_5H_9 + C_2H_4 \xrightarrow{AlCl_3} 1\text{-}EtB_5H_8$$

Other catalysts, e.g. $FeCl_3$ or $SnCl_4$, have proved effective, and higher olefins give similar reactions. Alkyl halides may be used instead [277, 278, 279].

$$MeCl + B_5H_9 \xrightarrow[100°]{AlCl_3} 1\text{-}MeB_5H_8$$

Substitution occurs mainly at the apical position of the molecule, where the negative charge density is highest [280], although subsequent rearrangement may occur at higher temperatures [278] or under the influence of amines [281]. Amines have also been shown to catalyse the reaction between pentaborane and olefins [282].

Ethyl derivatives of pentaborane, $B_5H_{9-n}Et_n$ (where n = 2–5), and of decaborane, $B_{10}H_{14-m}Et_m$ (m = 1–4), have also been isolated from the mixture obtained when ethylene and diborane are heated together [283], and alkyl derivatives of pentaborane-11 or tetraborane have been prepared by exchange reactions using alkyldiboranes [284]:

$$B_4H_{10} + B_2H_5Me \rightleftharpoons MeB_4H_9 + B_2H_6$$

The Friedel–Crafts alkylation of *decaborane*, $B_{10}H_{14}$, using alkyl

Chem., 1960, **14**, 195; I. Shapiro, R. E. Williams and S. G. Gibbons, *J. Phys. Chem.*, 1961, **65**, 1061.

[276] G. E. Ryschkewitsch, E. J. Mezey, E. R. Altwicker, H. H. Sisler and A. B. Garrett, *Inorg. Chem.*, 1963, **2**, 893.

[277] G. E. Ryschkewitsch, S. W. Harris, E. J. Mezey, H. H. Sisler, E. A. Weilmuenster and A. B. Garrett, ibid. p. 890; E. R. Altwicker, G. E. Ryschkewitsch, A. B. Garrett and H. H. Sisler, ibid., 1964, **3**, 454.

[278] T. P. Onak and F. J. Gerhart, ibid., 1962, **1**, 742.

[279] E. R. Altwicker, A. B. Garrett, E. A. Weilmuenster and S. W. Harris, U.S.P. 3,038,012, June 5, 1962; U.S.P. 3,052,725, Sept. 4, 1962.

[280] N. J. Blay, I. Dunstan and R. L. Williams, *J. Chem. Soc.*, 1960, 430; see also M. G. H. Wallbridge, J. Williams and R. L. Williams, *J. Chem. Soc. (A)*, 1967, 132.

[281] T. P. Onak, *J. Amer. Chem. Soc.*, 1961, **83**, 2584; W. V. Hough, L. J. Edwards and A. F. Stang, ibid., 1963, **85**, 831; A. B. Burg and J. S. Sandhu, ibid., 1965, **87**, 3787; T. Onak, L. B. Friedman, J. A. Hartsuck and W. N. Lipscomb, ibid., 1966, **88**, 3439; L. B. Friedman and W. N. Lipscomb, *Inorg. Chem.*, 1966, **5**, 1752.

[282] G. E. Ryschkewitsch, U.S.P. 3,030,417, April 17, 1962.

[283] N. J. Blay, J. Williams and R. L. Williams, *J. Chem. Soc.*, 1960, 424.

[284] C. A. Lutz and D. M. Ritter, *Canad. J. Chem.*, 1963, **41**, 1344; I. J. Solomon, M. J. Klein, R. G. Maguire and K. Hattori, *Inorg. Chem.*, 1963, **2**, 1136.

halides [280, 285], olefins [286] or acetylenes [287], generally in the presence of aluminium halides, has been widely studied. Again, substitution occurs primarily at the apical (2,4) boron atoms where the charge density is highest [280, 288]. On the other hand, *nucleophilic* substitution of deca-borane, by lithium alkyls, does *not* give the 2(4) derivative; the preferred point of attack in this case is the 6-position, followed by the 5-position. The order of decreasing electron density deduced from such substitution reactions [289] is 2- > 1- > 5- > 6-. This differs slightly from the order

B_5H_9
Predicted charge
distribution[290]

$B_{10}H_{14}$
Numbering of
B atoms

$B_{10}H_{14}$
Predicted charge
distribution[291]

2- > 1- > 6- > 5- predicted by Lipscomb and his co-workers [290] who however had neglected the effect of the bridging hydrogen atoms between borons 5 and 6 and equivalent positions. When these are allowed for the calculated order is the same as that deduced from experiments (see dia-gram) [9, 291]. The order of charge distribution in decaborane has also been deduced from ^1H and ^{11}B magnetic resonance studies and shows good, though not complete, agreement with the chemical evidence [292].

With methylmagnesium iodide in ether, decaborane reacts to form a novel kind of Grignard reagent [293]:

$$B_{10}H_{14} + MeMgI \longrightarrow B_{10}H_{13}MgI + CH_4$$

Hydrolysis yields decaborane, and reaction with benzyl chloride, alkyl fluorides [294] and alkyl sulphates [295] affords 5- or 6-alkyl derivatives.

[285] E. R. Altwicker, A. B. Garrett, E. A. Weilmuenster and S. W. Harris, U.S.P. 2,999,117; *Chem. Abs.*, 1962, **56**, 1478; S. L. Clark and D. A. Fidler, U.S.P. 3,030,422; *Chem. Abs.*, 1962, **57**, 6201.
[286] J. A. Neff and E. J. Wandel, U.S.P. 2,987,552; *Chem. Abs.*, 1962, **57**, 14078.
[287] S. K. Alley and O. Fuchs, U.S.P. 3,030,423; *Chem. Abs.*, 1962, **57**, 7512.
[288] R. L. Williams, I. Dunstan and N. J. Blay, *J. Chem. Soc.*, 1960, 5006.
[289] I. Dunstan, R. L. Williams and N. J. Blay, ibid., p. 5012.
[290] W. H. Eberhardt, B. L. Crawford and W. N. Lipscomb, *J. Chem. Phys.*, 1954, **22**, 989.
[291] E. B. Moore, *U.S. Dept. Comm., Office Tech. Serv., AD* 274,090 (1962); *Chem. Abs.*, 1963, **59**, 4554.
[292] R. L. Williams, N. N. Greenwood and J. H. Morris, *Spectrochim. Acta.*, 1965, **21**, 1579.
[293] B. Siegel, J. L. Mack, J. U. Lowe and J. Gallaghan, *J. Amer. Chem. Soc.*, 1958, **80**, 4523.
[294] J. Gallaghan and B. Siegel, ibid., 1959, **81**, 504.
[295] I. Dunstan, N. J. Blay and R. L. Williams, *J. Chem. Soc.*, 1960, 5016.

The sodium derivative, $NaB_{10}H_{13}$, prepared from sodium hydride and decaborane, has similar properties to the magnesium compound [296, 297]. The reactions of these have been studied to determine the probable structure of the $B_{10}H_{13}$ group, in which the electron distribution differs significantly from that in $B_{10}H_{14}$ [297].

The chemistry of decaborane-14 was reviewed in 1963 [298]. For recent SCF–MO calculations on diborane and a number of higher boranes see [298a].

The carboranes [257]

The derivatives described above retain the boron framework of the parent borane, but have one or more of the terminal hydrogen atoms replaced by alkyl groups attached by normal two-electron bonds. Recently, borane derivatives have been made in which carbon atoms are themselves involved in the electron-deficient framework of the molecule. Most of these belong to a series of general formula $B_nC_2H_{n+2}$, the *carboranes*, of which examples having values of n from 3 to 10 inclusive are known, but some other dicarbapolyboranes $B_nC_2H_{n+4}$, and their derivatives have also been prepared. These compounds are isoelectronic with borane anions $B_mH_m^{2-}$ or $B_mH_{m+2}^{2-}(m = n + 2)$, the existence and structures of which were predicted by Eberhardt, Crawford and Lipscomb [290] several years before actual samples were prepared. They suggested that ions $B_mH_m^{2-}$ should have compact structures based on cages of boron atoms, each boron having one terminal hydrogen attached, there being no bridging hydrogen atoms. Such structures have in fact been found for borane anions $B_mH_m^{2-}$ and carboranes $B_nC_2H_{n+2}$. The relative stabilities of a number of known and hypothetical carboranes have also been discussed by Hoffman and Lipscomb [299]. A useful survey of boron polyhedra, both anionic and neutral, is given in [299a].

The most readily accessible carboranes are derivatives of $B_{10}H_{10}C_2H_2$, which can be prepared from decaborane, $B_{10}H_{14}$, and which, decomposing only at high temperatures, being resistant to oxidation and hydrolysis, and affording scope for the study of an effectively three-dimensional electron-delocalized system, are currently attracting much attention. A standardized system of naming and numbering cage boranes, using the prefix 'clovo'-(= cage) in those cases where there are no bridging hydrogen atoms, has

[296] R. J. F. Palchak, J. H. Norman and R. E. Williams, *J. Amer. Chem. Soc.*, 1961, **83**, 3380.

[297] N. J. Blay, R. J. Pace and R. L. Williams, *J. Chem. Soc.*, 1962, 3416.

[298] M. F. Hawthorne, *Advances in Inorganic Chemistry and Radiochemistry*, ed. Eméleus and Sharpe, 1963, **5**, 308.

[298a] F. P. Boer, M. D. Newton and W. N. Lipscomb, *J. Amer. Chem. Soc.*, 1966, **88**, 2361; W. E. Palke and W. N. Lipscomb, ibid., p. 2384.

[299] R. Hoffmann and W. N. Lipscomb, *Inorg. Chem.*, 1963, **2**, 231.

[299a] F. K. Klanberg and E. L. Muetterties, *Inorg. Chem.*, 1966, **5**, 1955.

been recommended for use and largely adopted in western publications [300]; this numbering system is indicated in 3.15, 3.16, 3.19 and 3.20 below. Russian workers use the name 'barene' for $B_{10}H_{10}C_2H_2$.

1,2-Dicarbaclovododecaborane-(12) ('carborane'), $B_{10}H_{10}C_2H_2$, and its C-substituted derivatives are readily prepared by the reaction between decaborane-14 derivatives $B_{10}H_{12}L_2$ (where L is a donor molecule such as acetonitrile or diethyl sulphide) and acetylenes [301]:

$$B_{10}H_{14} + HC\!:\!CH \xrightarrow[C_6H_6]{2Et_2S;\ 90°} B_{10}H_{10}C_2H_2 + 2H_2$$

m.p. 320°

Thus diacetylenes, e.g. $HC\!:\!C\!\cdot\!C\!:\!CH$ give C–C linked bicarboranyls, $(B_{10}H_{10}C_2H)_2$ [302], while the use of substituted acetylenes has led to a wide range of compounds having functional groups attached to the carbon atoms, which occupy adjacent (ortho) positions on the icosahedral framework of the nucleus [301] (3.15a). Such a structure has been confirmed in the case of several derivatives by X-ray crystallographic studies [303], and is consistent with electron-diffraction data for the parent compound [304].

$o\text{-}B_{10}H_{10}C_2H_2$.

3.15a*

The carborane nucleus is not attacked by compounds with active hydrogen such as water, alcohols and acids, and is very resistant to oxidation, which is probably best effected with chromium trioxide after treatment with alcoholic alkali; the last removes one boron atom from the icosahedron

[300] R. Adams, *Inorg. Chem.*, 1963, **2**, 1087.

[301] T. L. Heying *et al.*, ibid., pp. 1089, 1097, 1105; 1964, **3**, 1444; M. M. Fein *et al.*, ibid., 1963, **2**, 1111, 1115, 1120, 1125; 1965, **4**, 661; *J. Amer. Chem. Soc.*, 1964, **86**, 4210; L. I. Zakharkin *et al.*, *Izvest. Akad. Nauk S.S.S.R.*, 1963, pp. 2236, 2238; 1964, pp. 582, 772, 944, 2208, 2210; 1965, pp. 158, 1114, 1464; *Chem. Abs.*, 1964, **60**, 9301, 15898; 1965, **62**, 7787, 9161, 11840; 1965, **63**, 8388, 16374; V. I. Stanko *et al.*, *Zhur. obshchei Khim.*, 1965, **35**, 394, 753, 1139, 1141, 1433, 1503; *Chem. Abs.*, 1965, **62**, 13165; **63**, 4318, 11596, 14892; H. D. Smith, C. O. Obenland and S. Papetti, *Inorg. Chem.*, 1966, **5**, 1013.

[302] J. A. Dupont and M. F. Hawthorne, *J. Amer. Chem. Soc.*, 1964, **86**, 1643.

[303] J. A. Potenza and W. N. Lipscomb, ibid., p. 1874; idem, *Inorg. Chem.*, 1964, **3**, 1673; 1966, **5**, 1471, 1478, 1483; D. Voet and W. N. Lipscomb, ibid., 1964, **3**, 1679; L. I. Zakharkin, V. I. Stanko, V. A. Brattsev, Yu. A. Chapovskii and Yu. T. Struchkov, *Izvest. Akad. Nauk. S.S.S.R.*, 1963, 2069; *Chem Abs.*, 1964, **60**, 5531.

[304] L. V. Vilkov, V. S. Mastryukov, P. A. Akishin and A. F. Zhigach, *Zhur. Strukt. Khim.*, 1965, **6**, 447; *Chem. Abs.*, 1965, **63**, 14891.

* The lines in 3.15, 3.16, 3.18, 3.19 and 3.20 are construction lines to clarify the geometry of the molecules, whereas the lines in 3.17 represent the bonding.

leaving a more reactive molecule [305]. The nucleus of $B_{10}H_{10}C_2H_2$ is unaffected by chlorine in carbon tetrachloride, which causes successive replacement first of the B-attached hydrogen atoms by chlorine atoms, and finally one of the C-hydrogens, giving the undecachloro derivative, $B_{10}Cl_{10}C_2HCl$, m.p. 279°, as the final product [306]. This in turn may be converted into perchlorocarborane, $B_{10}Cl_{10}C_2Cl_2$ by treatment with N-chlorosuccinimide [307]. Studies on the position of stepwise substitution on the boron cage have revealed the distribution of charge over the icosahedral surface [308].

Substitution at the *carbon* atoms of the parent carborane may be effected through the lithium derivatives, which are obtained by reactions with lithium amide or butyl-lithium [301], e.g.

$$
\begin{array}{ccc}
 & \xrightarrow{CO_2} & H_{10}B_{10} \underset{CCO_2H}{\overset{CCO_2H}{\big\langle}} \\
H_{10}B_{10}\underset{CH}{\overset{CH}{\big\langle}} & \xrightarrow{Ph_2PCl} & H_{10}B_{10}\underset{CPPh_2}{\overset{CPPh_2}{\big\langle}} \\
\big\downarrow {\scriptstyle BuLi} & & \\
H_{10}B_{10}\underset{CLi}{\overset{CLi}{\big\langle}} & \xrightarrow{PCl_3} & H_{10}B_{10}\langle\underset{C-PCl}{\overset{C-PCl}{}}\rangle B_{10}H_{10} \\
 & \xrightarrow[(ii)\,NH_3]{(i)\,R_2SiCl_2} & H_{10}B_{10}\langle\underset{C-SiR_2}{\overset{C-SiR_2}{}}\rangle NH
\end{array}
$$

The ready formation of exocyclic derivatives affords further evidence of the *ortho* structure of the carborane, as does the ability of such derivatives as $B_{10}H_{10}C_2(SH)_2$ and $B_{10}H_{10}C_2(PPh_2)_2$ to function as chelating ligands towards transition metals [309].

[305] L. I. Zakharkin, *Zhur. obshchei Khim.*, 1964, **34**, 4121; L. I. Zakharkin, V. I. Stanko and V. A. Brattsev, *Izvest. Akad. Nauk S.S.S.R.*, 1964, 2091; *Chem. Abs.*, 1965, **62**, 7787, 9160.

[306] H. Schroeder, T. L. Heying and J. R. Reiner, *Inorg. Chem.*, 1963, **2**, 1092; L. I. Zakharkin, V. I. Stanko and A. I. Klimova, *Izvest. Akad. Nauk S.S.S.R.*, 1964, 771; *Chem. Abs.*, 1964, **61**, 3131.

[307] H. Schroeder, J. R. Reiner, R. P. Alexander and T. L. Heying, *Inorg. Chem.*, 1964, **3**, 1464.

[308] H. D. Smith, T. A. Knowles and H. Schroeder, ibid., 1965, **4**, 107; L. I. Zakharkin, and V. N. Kalinin, *Izvest. Akad. Nauk S.S.S.R.*, 1965, 1311; L. I. Zakharkin, V. N. Kalinin and L. S. Podvistotskaya, ibid., p. 1713; *Chem. Abs.*, 1965, **63**, 13302, 18135; J. A. Potenza, W. N. Lipscomb, G. D. Vickers and H. Schroeder, *J. Amer. Chem. Soc.*, 1966, **88**, 628.

[309] H. D. Smith, *J. Amer. Chem. Soc.*, 1965, **87**, 1817; F. Röhrocheid and R. H. Holm, *J. Organometal. Chem.*, 1965, **4**, 335; H. D. Smith, M. A. Robinson and S. Papetti, *Inorg. Chem.*, 1967, **6**, 1014.

When *ortho*-carborane, $1,2\text{-}B_{10}H_{10}C_2H_2$, is held at $465\text{-}500°$ for one day, it rearranges to the *meta* isomer *neocarborane*, 1,7-dicarbaclovododeca-borane-(12), m.p. $264\text{-}266°$ (3.15*b*) [310], which is less polar [311] and even more thermally stable than the 1,2 isomer. The chemical reactions of the two compounds are similar [307, 312] except that neocarboranes under-standably do not readily form exocyclic derivatives [313]. Bromination in the presence of aluminium bromide gives the dibromo derivative $m\text{-}B_{10}H_8Br_2C_2H_2$ in which an X-ray crystallographic study has shown the two bromine atoms to be attached to borons 9 and 10, those furthest from the two carbons and calculated by a non-empirical molecular orbital approach to be the most negatively charged borons [313*a*]. Substitution at carbon is again conveniently effected via lithium derivatives, e.g. [313*b*, 313*c*]:

$$2m\text{-}MeCB_{10}H_{10}CLi + HgCl_2 \longrightarrow (m\text{-}MeCB_{10}H_{10}C)_2Hg + 2LiCl$$
$$m\text{-}LiCB_{10}H_{10}CLi + Ph_2SnX_2 \longrightarrow (\cdot CB_{10}H_{10}CSnPh_2\cdot)_n + 2LiX$$

This last reaction exemplifies a route to potentially thermally stable polymers.

$m\text{-}B_{10}H_{10}C_2H_2$

3.15*b*

$p\text{-}B_{10}H_{10}C_2H_2$

3.15*c*

The 'para' or 1,12-dicarba-compound, m.p. $259\text{-}261°$ (structure 3.15*c*) is obtained in 6% yield by the rearrangement of neocarborane during 17 hours at $615°$ [314]. As expected, it has zero dipole moment [311] and its ^{11}B n.m.r. spectrum shows only one doublet from the 10 equivalent boron atoms, each coupled with a single proton.

Generally, the chemical shifts of ^{11}B in icosahedral carboranes can be satisfactorily explained on the basis of differences primarily in the para-

[310] D. Grafstein and J. Dvorak, *Inorg. Chem.*, 1963, **2**, 1128; H. Schroeder and G. D. Vickers, ibid., p. 1317; R. M. Salinger and C. L. Frye, ibid., 1965, **4**, 1815.

[311] A. W. Laubengayer and W. R. Rysz, *Inorg. Chem.*, 1965, **4**, 1513; see also R. Maruca, H. Schroeder and A. W. Laubengayer, ibid., 1967, **6**, 572.

[312] M. F. Hawthorne, T. E. Berry and P. A. Wegner, *J. Amer. Chem. Soc.*, 1965, **87**, 4746; L. I. Zakharkin and A. V. Kazantsev, *Zhur. obshchei Khim.*, 1965, **35**, 1123; *Chem. Abs.*, 1965, **63**, 9974; R. P. Alexander and H. Schroeder, *Inorg. Chem.*, 1966, **5**, 493.

[313] S. Papetti and T. L. Heying, *Inorg. Chem.*, 1964, **6**, 1448; J. R. Reiner, R. P. Alexander and H. Schroeder, ibid., 1966, **5**, 1460.

[313*a*] H. Beall and W. N. Lipscomb, ibid., 1967, **6**, 874.

[313*b*] L. I. Zakharkin and L. S. Podvisozkaya, *J. Organometal. Chem.*, 1967, **7**, 385.

[313*c*] S. Bresadola, F. Rossetto and G. Tagliavini, *Chem. Comm.*, 1966, 623.

[314] S. Papetti and T. L. Heying, *J. Amer. Chem. Soc.*, 1964, **86**, 2295.

magnetic shielding of boron atoms in different chemical environments [314a].

Lower carboranes. Treatment of $1,2\text{-}B_{10}H_{10}C_2H_2$ with potassium hydroxide in methanol, followed by addition of a tetramethylammonium salt, gives the salt $Me_4N^+B_9C_2H_{12}^-$, which with ethereal hydrogen chloride gives dicarbaundecaborane-(13), $B_9C_2H_{13}$, m.p. $110°$ (decomp.), a much less thermally stable and more reactive compound than the carboranes $B_{10}C_2H_{12}$ already described [315]. This degradation reaction of $1,2\text{-}B_{10}H_{10}C_2H_2$, which is also effected by amines [316] and is applicable to C-substituted derivatives $B_{10}H_{10}C_2R_2$, affords a route into the chemistry of carboranes and related compounds having 6, 7, 8 or 9 boron atoms in the molecule. Some key reactions are indicated in the following diagram:

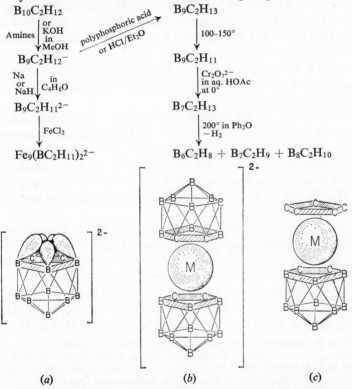

Fig. 21 (a)–(c). Structures of $B_9C_2H_{11}^{2-}$, $Fe(\pi-B_9C_2H_{11})_2^{2-}$, and $\pi-C_5H_5$ $Fe(\pi-B_9C_2H_{11})$ with H-atoms omitted and showing the sp^3 hybrid atomic orbitals assumed to be present in $B_9C_2H_{11}^{2-}$ (after Hawthorne and Andrews [319])

[314a] F. P. Boer, R. A. Hegstrom, M. D. Newton, J. A. Potenza, and W. N. Lipscomb, ibid., 1966, **88**, 5340; G. D. Vickers, H. Agahigian, E. A. Pier and H. Schroeder, *Inorg. Chem.*, 1966, **5**, 693.

[315] R. A. Wiesboeck and M. F. Hawthorne, *J. Amer. Chem. Soc.*, 1964, **86**, 1642.

[316] M. F. Hawthorne, P. A. Wegner and R. C. Stafford, *Inorg. Chem.*, 1965, **4**, 1675.

The $B_9C_2H_{12}^-$ anion is thought to have the geometry of an eleven-particle icosahedral fragment and is readily converted into $B_9C_2H_{11}^{2-}$ by the abstraction of a proton with sodium metal or sodium hydride in tetrahydrofuran [317]. The structure of $B_9C_2H_{11}^{2-}$ (with the hydrogen atoms omitted) is illustrated in Figure 21(a), which shows the sp^3 hybrid atomic orbitals assumed to project in the direction of the empty icosahedral corner. The pentagonal face exposed is capable of bonding to a transition metal in a similar manner to the cyclopentadienyl anion, and a range of carbametallic boron hydride derivatives is known [317–319]. For example the complex anion $Fe(B_9C_2H_{11})_2^{2-}$, presumed to have the sandwich structure also shown in Figure 21(b), can be prepared from $FeCl_2$ and $Na_2B_9C_2H_{11}$ [317]. An X-ray diffraction study on the mixed sandwich compound $\pi\text{-}C_5H_5Fe(\pi\text{-}B_9C_2H_{11})$, m.p. 181–182°, prepared from NaC_5H_5, $Na_2B_9C_2H_{11}$ and $FeCl_2$, has shown the structure to be that illustrated in Figure 21(c) (M = Fe), in which the Fe–C and Fe–B distances are essentially equivalent, all lying in the range 2·03–2·09 Å [320]. The rhenium compound $Cs[(CO)_3Re(\pi\text{-}B_9C_2H_{11})]$ has a similar structure [320a]. For a suggested system of naming and numbering of these transition metal derivatives see ref. [318].

In the transition metal derivatives of $B_9C_2H_{11}^{2-}$, the metal completes the icosahedron. The icosahedron may also be regenerated by reaction of $Na_2B_9C_2H_{11}$ with $PhBCl_2$, giving $PhB_{10}C_2H_{11}$ [321]. The combination of alkaline degradation and reaction with $PhBCl_2$ thus effects substitution at a boron of $B_{10}C_2H_{12}$. Alkaline degradation of $1,7\text{-}B_{10}C_2H_{12}$ gives anions $B_9C_2H_{12}^-$ in which the carbon atoms are no longer adjacent in the icosahedral fragment [322].

Several lower carboranes $B_nC_2H_{n+2}$ (n = 6, 7, 8 or 9) are accessible through the compound $B_9C_2H_{13}$. Pyrolysis of derivatives of $B_9C_2H_{13}$ at 110–150° in an organic solvent gives derivatives of $B_9C_2H_{11}$ which have decarborane-like frameworks with a boron bridging the 6 and 9 positions, themselves occupied by carbon atoms (3.15d) [324a].

More reactive than their B_{10} analogues [323], derivatives of $B_9C_2H_{11}$ can be degraded to derivatives of dicarbananonaborane (13), $B_7C_2H_{13}$, m.p.

[317] M. F. Hawthorne, D. C. Young and P. A. Wegner, *J. Amer. Chem. Soc.*, 1965, **87**, 1818.   [318] M. F. Hawthorne and R. L. Pilling, ibid., p. 3987.

[319] M. F. Hawthorne and T. D. Andrews, *Chem. Comm.*, 1965, 443; idem, *J. Amer. Chem. Soc.*, 1965, **87**, 2496; A. H. Maki and T. E. Berry, ibid., p. 4437.

[320] A. Zalkin, D. H. Templeton and T. E. Hopkins, ibid., p. 3988.

[320a] A. Zalkin, T. E. Hopkins and D. H. Templeton, *Inorg. Chem.*, 1966, **5**, 1189.

[321] M. F. Hawthorne and P. A. Wegner, *J. Amer. Chem. Soc.*, 1965, **87**, 4392.

[322] P. M. Garrett, F. N. Tebbe and M. F. Hawthorne, ibid., 1964, **86**, 5016; L. I. Zakharkin and V. N. Kalinin, *Zhur. obshchei Khim.*, 1965, **35**, 1691; *Chem. Abs.*, 1965, **63**, 18135.

[323] F. N. Tebbe, P. M. Garrett and M. F. Hawthorne, *J. Amer. Chem. Soc.*, 1964, **86**, 4222; T. E. Berry, F. N. Tebbe and M. F. Hawthorne, *Tetrahedron Letters*, 1965, 715.

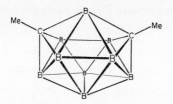

3.15*d* Structure of $B_9C_2H_9Me_2$ (H atoms omitted) [324*a*].

60·5–61° by the action of dichromate ion in aqueous acetic acid at 0° [324]. Although $B_7C_2H_{13}$ is not itself a carborane – the B_7C_2 unit of $B_7C_2H_{11}Me_2$ is an icosahedral fragment with two adjacent bridge hydrogen atoms and two MeCH groups in the open face [324*b*] – when $B_7C_2H_{13}$ or its derivatives are heated to about 200° in diphenyl ether the carboranes $B_6C_2H_8$, $B_7C_2H_9$ and $B_8C_2H_{10}$ (or their derivatives) are formed in proportions which can be varied by suitable adjustment of the reaction conditions [325]. The compound $B_6C_2H_6Me_2$ can also be prepared from hexaborane-10, B_6H_{10}, and dimethylacetylene [326]. The structures of these lower carboranes are also believed to be based on B_nC_2 polyhedra [323, 325].

Carboranes containing three, four or five boron atoms can be prepared via dicarbahexaborane-(8), $B_4C_2H_8$, which results from the reaction between B_5H_9 and acetylene at elevated temperatures:

$$B_5H_9 \xrightarrow{\text{RC}\vdots\text{CR}} B_4C_2H_6R_2 \xrightarrow[\text{or electric discharge}]{\text{pyrolysis, U.V.}} \begin{array}{c} 1,5\text{-}B_3H_3C_2R_2 \\ + \\ 1,2\text{- and } 1,6\text{-}B_4H_4C_2R_2 \\ + \\ 2,4\text{-}B_5H_5C_2R_2 \end{array}$$

The structures of the derivatives $B_4C_2H_6R_2$, as deduced from their [11]B n.m.r. spectra [327], are related to the pentagonal pyramid of hexaborane-10, B_6H_{10}, with two carbon atoms replacing two boron atoms and two bridge hydrogen atoms in the base (3.16). Such a structure has been confirmed in the case of the dimethyl derivative $B_4H_6C_2Me_2$, by an X-ray crystallographic study which showed the C–C distance to be only 1·43 Å,

[324] F. N. Tebbe, P. M. Garrett and M. F. Hawthorne, *J. Amer. Chem. Soc.*, 1966, **88**, 607.

[324*a*] C. Tsai and W. E. Streib, ibid., p. 4513.

[324*b*] D. Voet and W. N. Lipscomb, *Inorg. Chem.*, 1967, **6**, 113.

[325] F. N. Tebbe, P. M. Garrett, D. C. Young and M. F. Hawthorne, *J. Amer. Chem. Soc.*, 1966, **88**, 609.

[326] R. E. Williams and F. J. Gerhart, ibid., 1965, **87**, 3513.

[327] R. E. Williams and T. P. Onak, ibid., 1964, **86**, 3159.

I

comparable to that in graphite [52]. A plausible bonding scheme for this structure is shown in (3.17)

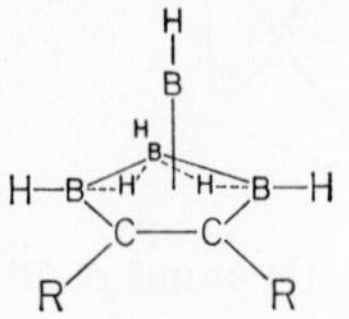

$B_4H_6C_2R_2$
3.16

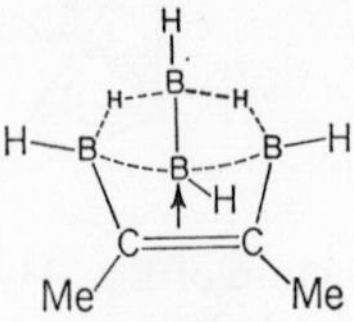

$B_4H_6C_2Me_2$
3.17

With sodium hydride, $B_4C_2H_8$ gives $Na^+B_4C_2H_7^-$ which with deuterium chloride gives the bridge-deuterated $B_4C_2H_7D$. Deuteration of terminal B–H in $B_4C_2H_8$ is achieved by exchange with B_2D_6 at 100° [327a].

Pyrolysis, u.v. irradiation and electric discharge of derivatives $B_4C_2H_6R_2$ or of diborane–acetylene mixtures afford routes to carboranes with three, four or five boron atoms, the relative proportions of which vary considerably with the reaction conditions. Thus u.v. irradiation [328], or electric discharge [329], at or near room temperature gives mixtures of $1,5\text{-}B_3H_3C_2R_2$ (3.18), $1,2\text{-}B_4H_4C_2R_2$ (3.19a) and $1,6\text{-}B_4H_4C_2R_2$ (3.19b), while thermal decomposition [330] of $B_4H_6C_2R_2$ gives $2,4\text{-}B_5H_5C_2R_2$ (3.20) and $1,6\text{-}B_4H_4C_2R_2$.

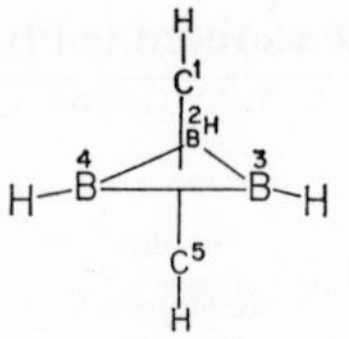

$B_3H_3C_2H_2$
3.18

Carborane-3 or 1,5-dicarbaclovopentaborane-(5), $B_3H_3C_2H_2$, a colourless gas, b.p. $-4°$, apparently has a trigonal bipyramidal structure, the equatorial positions being occupied by boron and the apical by carbon atoms (3.18) [328–330]. This compound is thermally stable and does not react with acetone, trimethylamine, air or water at 20°, in striking contrast to the lower boranes. An alkyl derivative, $B_3Et_3C_2Me_2$, is a minor product of the reaction between $Et_4B_2H_2$ and acetylene at 200° [331].

[327a] T. Onak and G. B. Dunks, *Inorg. Chem.*, 1966, **5**, 439.
[328] J. R. Spielman and J. E. Scott, *J. Amer. Chem. Soc.*, 1965, **87**, 3512.
[329] T. Onak, R. P. Drake and G. B. Dunks, *Inorg. Chem.*, 1964, **3**, 1686; R. N. Grimes, *J. Amer. Chem. Soc.*, 1966, **88**, 1070, 1895; *J. Organometal. Chem.*, 1967, **8**, 45.
[330] T. P. Onak, F. J. Gerhart and R. E. Williams, *J. Amer. Chem. Soc.*, 1963, **85**, 3378.
[331] R. Köster and G. W. Rotermund, *Tetrahedron Letters*, 1964, 1667; R. Köster

cis-$B_4H_4C_2R_2$	trans-$B_4H_4C_2R_2$	$B_5H_5C_2R_2$
3.19a	3.19b	3.20

The structures of the dicarbaclovohexaborane-(6) isomers, 1,2- and 1,6-$B_4H_4C_2R_2$ (3.19a and b) [332] are based on an octahedral cage related to that of the anion $B_6H_6^{2-}$, the structure of which has been confirmed by an X-ray crystallographic study of the salt $(Me_4N)_2B_6H_6$ [333]. Apart from these cis- and trans- dicarba-derivatives of this anion, a monocarbahexaborane-(7), B_5H_6CH is also known, being formed in trace quantities by the passage of an electric discharge through 1-methylpentaborane [334]. The seventh hydrogen atom in this compound is thought to occupy a bridging position on one edge of the octahedron of borons and carbon.

The pentagonal bipyramidal structure (3.20) shown for the dicarbaclovoheptaboranes-(7), $B_5H_5C_2R_2$, is supported by a microwave study on the parent compound (3.20; R = H) [335]. Fully alkylated carboranes $B_5R_5C_2R'_2$ have been isolated from reactions between ethyldiboranes and acetylene [331, 336].

Derivatives of monocarbahexaborane-(9), B_5H_8CH, in which the one carbon atom and three bridging hydrogens are believed to be located in the base of a pentagonal pyramidal structure, are among the products of the reaction between acetylene and pentaborane-(9) at 215° [336a]. Derivatives of B_5H_8CH have also been isolated from reactions between organoboron halides (particularly $EtBF_2$) and alkali metals, followed by treatment of the reaction mixture with ethylene under pressure [336b]. Carboranes with two carbon atoms (such as $B_5Et_5C_2Me_2$) are also formed in such dehalogenations [336c], possibly even with four carbons [79a]. The tri-carbahexa-

and M. A. Grassberger, Angew. Chem., Internat. Edn., 1965, 4, 439; R. Köster, H.-J. Horstschäfer and P. Binger, ibid., 1966, 5, 730.

[332] I. Shapiro, B. Keilin, R. E. Williams and C. D. Good, J. Amer. Chem. Soc., 1963, 85, 3167.

[333] R. Schaeffer, Q. Johnson and G. S. Smith, Inorg. Chem., 1965, 4, 917.

[334] T. Onak, R. Drake and G. Dunks, J. Amer. Chem. Soc., 1965, 87, 2505.

[335] R. A. Beaudet and R. L. Poynter, ibid., 1964, 86, 1258; T. Onak, G. B. Dunks, R. A. Beaudet and R. L. Poynter, ibid., 1966, 88, 4622.

[336] R. Köster and G. W. Rotermund, Tetrahedron Letters, 1965, 777.

[336a] T. P. Onak, G. B. Dunks, J. R. Spielman, F. J. Gerhart and R. E. Williams, J. Amer. Chem. Soc., 88, 2061.

[336b] R. Köster and M. A. Grassberger, Angew. Chem. Internat. Edn., 1966, 5, 580.

[336c] R. Köster, M. A. Grassberger, E. G. Hoffman and G. W. Rotermund, Tetrahedron Letters, 1966, 905.

borane-(7) $B_3C_3H_7$ and several derivatives have been isolated from reactions between tetraborane, B_4H_{10}, and acetylene [336d]. Indeed, it appears probable that an extensive range of compounds incorporating varying numbers of borons and carbons in an electron-deficient framework remains to be discovered. For further examples, see [336e].

Organoboron–oxygen compounds [14]

(i) Borinic acids and esters [21]

Dialkylborinic acids, R_2BOH, are easily obtained from the halides R_2BX, but are probably most conveniently prepared by hydrolysis of the acetylacetonates $R_2B(MeCOCHCOMe)$, which themselves result from the smooth cleavage of one alkyl group from the trialkylborane R_3B by acetylacetone [141].

Dimethylborinic acid, Me_2BOH, v.p. 36 mm. at $0°$ and diethylborinic acid, Et_2BOH, b.p. $96°$, are very weak acids and easily form anhydrides R_2BOBR_2. With potassium hydroxide, dimethylborinic acid forms the salt $K^+Me_2B(OH)_2^-$, a colourless very hygroscopic solid which decomposes at $130°$ with evolution of methane and trimethylborane [337]. Mixed alkylborinic acids and their esters may be prepared from boronic esters and lithium alkyls, e.g. [338].

$$EtLi + BuB(OBu)_2 \rightarrow EtBuBOBu$$

The rapid *exchange* of alkoxy groups between borinic and boronic esters R_2BOR' and $RB(OR')_2$ has been demonstrated by proton magnetic resonance techniques [339].

The allyl ester of dibutylborinic acid undergoes an interesting cyclization reaction when heated to $150°$ in the presence of tributylborane [340]:

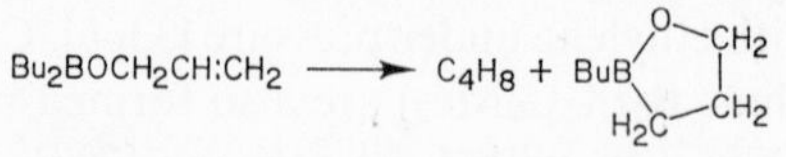

A convenient general method for the preparation of *diaryl borinic acids* is by the action of the appropriate Grignard reagent on diphenylaminodichloroborane, Ph_2NBCl_2 (from diphenylamine and boron trichloride),

[336d] C. L. Bramlett and R. N. Grimes, *J. Amer. Chem. Soc.*, 1966, **88**, 4269.

[336e] D. E. Hyatt, D. A. Owen and L. J. Todd, *Inorg. Chem.*, 1966, **5**, 1749; W. H. Knoth, *J. Amer. Chem. Soc.*, 1967, **89**, 1274.

[337] J. Goubeau and J. W. Ewers, *Z. anorg. Chem.*, 1960, **304**, 230; idem, *Z. phys. Chem.*, 1960, **25**, 276.

[338] B. M. Mikhailov and T. A. Shchegoleva, *Zhur. obshchei Khim*, 1959, **29**, 3124; *Chem. Abs.*, 1960, 13035.

[339] P. A. McCusker, P. L. Pennartz and C. R. Pilger, *J. Amer. Chem. Soc.*, 1962; **84**, 4362.

[340] B. M. Mikhailov and V. A. Dorokhov, *Izvest. Akad. Nauk S.S.S.R.*, 1964, 946; *Chem. Abs.*, 1964, **61**, 5677.

the product being isolated as the ethanolamine ester, which is air-stable and readily crystallized [341]:

$$BCl_3 + Ph_2NH \longrightarrow Cl_2BNPh_2 \xrightarrow{2ArMgX} Ar_2BNPh_2$$

$$\Big\downarrow H_2O + H_2N(CH_2)_2OH$$

$$Ar_2BOH \xleftarrow{HCl} Ar_2B\overset{O-CH_2}{\underset{H_2N-CH_2}{\Big\langle}}$$

The advantages of this method are that only a slight excess of Grignard reagent is needed, giving yields of between 51 and 93% with no contamination by *boronic* acids [341].

Another possible route to diarylborinic acids is the disproportionation of arylboronic acids or arylboroxines in the presence of bases [342]:

$$(PhBO)_3 \xrightarrow{\text{KOBu in xylene}} Ph_2BOH$$

Diphenylborinic acid, Ph_2BOH, has also been prepared by the partial hydrolysis of sodium tetraphenylborate [343]. For example, tetraphenylborate salts of various aminoalcohols such as ethanolamine give very good yields of diphenylborinic esters when heated

$$HOC_2H_4NH_3BPh_4 \longrightarrow Ph_2B\overset{O-CH_2}{\underset{H_2N-CH_2}{\Big\langle}}$$

Another method is the low-temperature reaction between phenyl-magnesium bromide and borate esters [344], although better (60%) yields are obtained from trimethoxyboroxine ('methyl metaborate') at 25° [345].

$$(MeOBO)_3 + 9PhMgBr \longrightarrow Ph_2BOMgBr \xrightarrow{H^+} Ph_2BOH \xrightarrow{HOC_2H_4NH_2} Ph_2B\overset{O-CH_2}{\underset{H_2N-CH_2}{\Big\langle}}$$

The acid is precipitated as an oil when hydrochloric acid is added to a solution of the ethanolamine ester; it loses water when it is pumped, even at room temperature, forming the anhydride $(Ph_2B)_2O$, m.p. 116°, which has been used as an analytical reagent for various types of flavones and related compounds [346].

[341] G. E. Coates and J. G. Livingstone, *J. Chem. Soc.*, 1961, 4909; G. N. Chremos, H. Weidmann and H. K. Zimmerman, *J. Org. Chem.*, 1961, **26**, 1683.
[342] M. J. S. Dewar and R. C. Dougherty, *Tetrahedron Letters*, 1964, 907.
[343] R. Neu, *Naturwiss.*, 1960, **47**, 304.
[344] R. Neu, *Chem. Ber.*, 1954, **87**, 802; 1955, **88**, 1761; *Naturwiss.*, 1959, **46**, 262; B. M. Mikhailov and V. A. Vaver, *Izvest. Akad. Nauk S.S.S.R.*, 1957, 989; 1958, 419; *Chem. Abs.*, 1958, **52**, 3667, 4532.
[345] T. P. Povlock and W. T. Lippincott, *J. Amer. Chem. Soc.*, 1958, **80**, 5409.
[346] R. Neu, *Z. anal. Chem.*, 1954, **142**, 335; 1956, **151**, 328; *Mikrochim. Acta*, 1956, 1169.

For thermochemical studies on diphenylborinic acid, phenylboronic acid, and their anhydrides see [346a].

Borinic anhydrides have also been obtained by the action of sulphur dioxide on aminoboranes [347]:

$$2Bu_2B\cdot NMe_2 + SO_2 \xrightarrow{50-60°} (Bu_2B)_2O + OS(NMe_2)_2$$

Diaminoboranes, $RB(NMe_2)_2$, give boronic anhydrides (boroxines).

Mixed arylborinic acids may be prepared by the Grignard method from boronic acids [348] e.g.

$$PhB(OBu)_2 + 1\text{-}C_{10}H_7MgBr \longrightarrow 1\text{-}C_{10}H_7PhBOBu$$

The reverse process, the deboronation of borinic acids to form boronic acids, is achieved by heating the borinic acid with an acid amide [349]

$$Ph_2BOH \xrightarrow[(ii) \text{ azeotropic distillation}]{(i) \text{ MeCONH}_2 \text{ in toluene}} (PhBO)_3$$

The ethanolamine esters of borinic acids are examples of *boroxazolidines* (3.21), derivatives which owe their air-stability to their cyclic structure and the four-co-ordinate boron atom which is not readily attacked by bases. The presence of a boron–nitrogen link in these compounds has been confirmed by studies of their rate of esterification and of their 'delayed basicity' [350]. The rate of formation of such esters from aminoalcohols can be a guide to the structures of the latter, and has been used to determine the constellations of the ephedrine bases PhCHOHCHMeNHMe [351]. The ease of hydrolysis of boroxazolidines in acidic solutions increases with their degree of substitution [352]. Some borinic acids do not react readily with ethanolamine itself, and 8-hydroxyquinoline has been suggested as a useful alternative reagent for preparing stable crystalline derivatives [353]. Cyclic derivatives of borinic acids may also be obtained using α and β amino acids (3.22 and 3.23) [354] or even from the dimethylglyoxime derivatives of nickel, palladium, copper and iron; these last are believed [355] to

[346a] A. Finch and P. J. Gardner, *Trans. Faraday Soc.*, 1966, **62**, 3314.
[347] H. Nöth and P. Schweizer, *Chem. Ber.*, 1964, **97**, 1464.
[348] B. M. Mikhailov and N. S. Fedotov, *Zhur. obshchei Khim.*, 1959, **29**, 2244; *Chem. Abs.*, 1960, 10966; for thienylborinic acids see H. J. Roth and B. Miller, *Naturwiss.*, 1963, **50**, 732.
[349] H. K. Zimmerman, *J. Org. Chem.*, 1961, **26**, 5214.
[350] Y. Rasiel and H. K. Zimmerman, *Annalen*, 1961, **649**, 111; H. K. Zimmerman, *Advan. in Chem. Series*, 1964, **42**, 23.
[351] H. J. Roth and N. N. El Din, *Arch. Pharm.*, 1962, **295**, 679.
[352] H. K. Zimmerman and D. A. Jones, *Rec. Trav. chim.*, 1964, **83**, 123.
[353] J. E. Douglass, *J. Org. Chem.*, 1961, **26**, 1312.
[354] Farbenfabriken Bayer A.-G., Ger.P. 1,097,446, Jan. 19, 1961; 1,130, 445, May 30, 1962; *Chem. Abs.*, 1962, **56**, 1478; 1963, **58**, 1488; I. H. Skoog, *J. Org. Chem.*, 1964, **29**, 492.
[355] F. Umland and D. Thierig, *Angew. Chem.*, 1962, **74**, 388.

3.21 Boroxazolidines   3.22 Boroxazolidones   3.23 Boroxazones

3.24   3.25

have the structure (3.24). Cyclic esters which are particularly resistant to hydrolysis are formed by β-keto enols or β-keto esters such as ethyl acetoacetate; an important feature of these derivatives (3.25) is the conjugation of the ring [356]. (See also ref. [141]). Extended conjugation also exists in the related curcumin complexes of borinic acids which, having characteristic colours, lend themselves to the spectrophotometric estimation of borinic acids [357].

For other cyclic derivatives of borinic acids see ref. [358].

(ii) Boronic acids and esters [21]

Boronic acids $RB(OH)_2$ can be prepared by the addition of the correct quantity of Grignard reagent to trimethyl borate [359].

$$RMgX + (MeO)_3B \longrightarrow RB(OMe)_2 + MgXOMe$$

Hydrolysis then affords the acids; the lower alkyl acids are in some cases difficult to isolate. An alternative preparation utilizes the hydrolysis of boroxines, $(RBO)_3$, prepared from R_3B and boric oxide [120] or better trimethoxyboroxine [121].

[356] W. Gerrard, M. F. Lappert and R. Shafferman, *Chem. and Ind.*, 1958, 722; *J. Chem. Soc.*, 1958, 3648; R. Neu, *Experientia*, 1963, **19**, 68; A. T. Balaban, E. Barabas and A. Arsene, *Tetrahedron Letters*, 1964, 2721; I. Bally, A. Arsene, M. Bacescu-Roman and A. T. Balaban, ibid., 1965, 3929.

[357] H. J. Roth and B. Miller, *Arch. Pharm.*, 1964, **297**, 617; *Chem. Abs.*, 1965, **62**, 579.

[358] H. J. Roth, R. Brandes and C. Schwenke, *Arch. Pharm.*, 1964, **297**, 766; *Chem. Abs.*, 1965, **62**, 7786d; F. Umland and C. Schleyerbach, *Angew Chem.*, 1965, **77**, 169; G. Zinner, W. Ritter and W. Kliegel, *Pharmazie*, 1965, **20**, 291; *Chem. Abs.*, 1965, **63**, 13302; L. H. Toporcer, R. E. Dessy and S. I. E. Green, *Inorg. Chem.*, 1965, **4**, 1649.

[359] H. R. Snyder, J. A. Kuck and J. R. Johnson, *J. Amer. Chem. Soc.*, 1938, **60**, 105; P. B. Brindley, W. Gerrard and M. F. Lappert, *J. Chem. Soc.*, 1955, 2956. J. P. Laurent, *Compt. rend.*, 1961, **253**, 1812; 1962, **254**, 866; D. S. Matteson, *J. Org. Chem.*, 1964, **29**, 3399.

Methylboronic acid, $MeB(OH)_2$, m.p. 96–100° (decomp.), dehydrates readily and reversibly to trimethylboroxine [360, 361]:

$$3MeB(OH)_2 \rightleftharpoons MeB\left\langle\begin{array}{c}O\text{---}BMe \\ \\ O\text{---}BMe\end{array}\right\rangle O + 3H_2O$$

The acid is volatile, but the vapour contains an equilibrium mixture of acid, boroxine and water. The higher alkylboronic acids are readily oxidized by molecular oxygen, and the sensitivity to oxygen increases when the boron is bonded to a secondary carbon atom, and is very marked in tertiary butylboronic acid, $Bu^tB(OH)_2$. In contrast, the arylboronic acids are insensitive to oxygen.

Derivatives of methylboronic acid are accessible via the iodomethyl compound $ICH_2B(OBu)_2$, itself prepared from iodomethyl mercury iodide and boron tribromide [361*a*]:

$$ICH_2HgI \xrightarrow[\text{BuOH}]{BBr_3 + NaI} BrCH_2B(OBu)_2 \xrightarrow[\text{BuOH/Me}_2CO]{NaI} ICH_2B(OBu)_2$$

The boronic acids are easily dehydrated to boroxines, the Dean and Stark method being quite satisfactory except for the volatile methyl and ethyl compounds. Many boronic esters are known, being obtained directly from trialkylboranes and alkyl borates [362].

$$R_3B + 2B(OR')_3 \xrightarrow{\sim 200°} 3RB(OR')_2$$

In this reaction, for which diborane or its alkyl derivatives have been suggested as catalysts [363], most of the R_2BOR' also formed decomposes into R_3B and $RB(OR')_2$.

Boronic esters can also be prepared by the hydroboration of olefins using diborane and controlled quantities of olefin [364], or by using a dialkoxyborane $HB(OR)_2$ as the hydroborating agent [365]. The *diboronic acids* $(HO)_2B(CH_2)_nB(OH)_2$, where n = 3, 4, 5 or 6, and their esters have been prepared via hydroboration reactions using triallylborane [366] (for

[360] A. B. Burg, *J. Amer. Chem. Soc.*, 1940, **62**, 2228.
[361] P. A. McCusker, E. C. Ashby and H. S. Makowski, ibid., 1957, **79**, 5179.
[361*a*] D. S. Matteson and T.-C. Cheng, *J. Organometal. Chem.*, 1966, **6**, 100.
[362] R. Köster, *Angew. Chem.*, 1959, **71**, 31.
[363] B. M. Mikhailov and L. S. Vasil'ev, *Doklady Akad. Nauk S.S.S.R.*, 1961, **139**, 385; *Izvest. Akad. Nauk S.S.S.R.*, 1962, 628, 827, 1756; *Chem. Abs.*, 1962, **56**, 1467; **57**, 16643; 1963, **58**, 5706; **59**, 648.
[364] H. C. Brown and A. Tsukamoto, *J. Amer. Chem. Soc.*, 1960, **82**, 746.
[365] Callery Chemical Co., Ger.P. 1,111,181; *Chem. Abs.*, 1962, **56**, 8742.
[366] L. I. Zakharkin and A. I. Kovredov, *Izvest. Akad. Nauk S.S.S.R.*, 1962, 1564; B. M. Mikhailov and V. F. Pozdnev, ibid., p. 1861; *Chem. Abs.*, 1963, **58**, 9107, 9109.

$n = 3$) or appropriate dienes C_nH_{2n}, [367] e.g.

$$(CH_2{:}CHCH_2)_3B \xrightarrow[\text{THF}]{B_2H_6} \quad \searrow B(CH_2)_3B \swarrow \quad \xrightarrow[200°]{BCl_3} \quad Cl_2B(CH_2)_3BCl_2$$

(polymeric)

$$\downarrow ROH$$

$$(RO)_2B(CH_2)_3B(OR)_2$$

The more direct method would be to use the di-Grignard reagent $BrMg(CH_2)_nMgBr$ or dilithium reagent and trimethyl borate. The hydroboration of N-alkenylcarbamates leads to aminoalkylboronic acids, $NH_2(CH_2)_nB(OH)_2$ [368].

Phenylboronic acid, $PhB(OH)_2$, m.p. 216°, may be prepared by the addition of a mol. of phenylmagnesium bromide in ether to boron trifluoride or an alkyl borate in ether at $-30°$ or lower. The acid can readily be ether-extracted after hydrolysis of the reaction mixture [369]. An alternative preparation is the hydrolysis of dichlorophenylborane, $PhBCl_2$, readily obtained from tetraphenyltin and boron trichloride [32].

Phenylboronic acid is decomposed by halogens under quite mild conditions, in aqueous solution [370]

$$PhB(OH)_2 + Br_2 + H_2O \rightarrow PhBr + HBr + H_3BO_3$$

and by mercuric halides, conveniently mercuric chloride in sodium chloride solution.

$$PhB(OH)_2 + HgCl_2 + H_2O \rightarrow PhHgCl + HCl + H_3BO_3$$

Reactions with mercuric chloride [371] and with hydrogen peroxide [370, 372],

$$RB(OH)_2 + H_2O_2 \rightarrow ROH + H_3BO_3$$

have been used in quantitative analytical procedures. Phenylboronic acid is cleaved by water at 150° or at lower temperatures in the presence of catalysts such as concentrated acids or bases or salts of zinc, cadmium and silver:

$$PhB(OH)_2 + H_2O \rightarrow PhH + B(OH)_3$$

[367] L. I. Zakharkin and A. I. Kovredov, *Izvest. Akad. Nauk S.S.S.R.*, 1962, 357, 362; *Zhur. obshchei Khim.*, 1962, **32**, 1421; *Chem. Abs.*, 1962, **57**, 11219, 12519; 1963, **58**, 4589.
[368] D. N. Butler and A. H. Soloway, *Chem. Comm.*, 1965, 333; idem, *J. Amer. Chem. Soc.*, 1966, **88**, 484.
[369] R. F. Bean and J. R. Johnson, ibid., 1932, **54**, 4415.
[370] A. D. Ainley and F. Challenger, *J. Chem. Soc.*, 1930, 2171.
[371] A. Michaelis and P. Becker, *Ber.*, 1882, **15**, 180.
[372] H. R. Snyder, J. A. Kuck and J. R. Johnson, *J. Amer. Chem. Soc.*, 1938, **60**, 105.

The kinetics of these and related cleavage and substitution reactions of alkyl- and aryl-boronic acids have been widely studied [373]. The disproportionation of arylboronic acids or arylboroxines to diarylborinic acids has already been described [342].

For calculations by the Pariser–Parr–Pople method of electron densities and bond orders in phenylboronic acid and some derivatives see [373a].

Derivatives of phenylboronic acid having amine groups close to the acid group (e.g. 3.26, 27, 28) have been synthesized, and their spectroscopic properties and chemical reactions have been used to determine the extent of boron–nitrogen interaction [374].

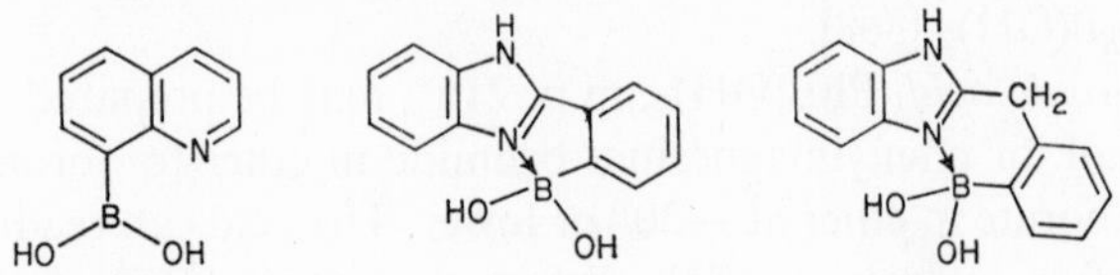

3.26   3.27   3.28

Aprotic diazotization of ortho-aminophenylboronic acid generates benzyne [374a]:

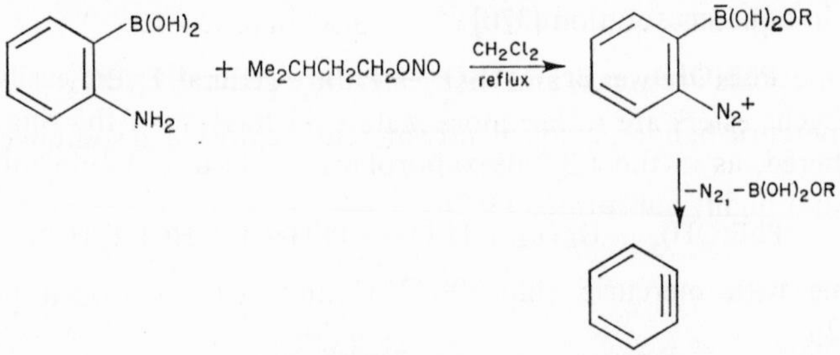

[373] H. G. Kuivila and K. V. Nagabedian, *J. Amer. Chem. Soc.*, 1961, **83**, 2159, 2164, 2167; H. G. Kuivila and T. C. Muller, ibid., 1962, **84**, 377; H. G. Kuivila, L. E. Benjamin, C. J. Murphy, A. D. Price and J. H. Polevy, *J. Org. Chem.*, 1962, **27**, 825; H. Minato, J. C. Ware and T. G. Traylor, *J. Amer. Chem. Soc.*, 1963, **85**, 3024; J. C. Ware and T. G. Traylor, ibid., p. 3026; D. R. Harvey and R. O. C. Norman, *J. Chem. Soc.*, 1962, 3822; H. G. Kuivila, J. F. Reuwer and J. A. Mangravite, *Canad. J. Chem.*, 1963, **41**, 3081; D. S. Matteson and J. O. Waldbillig, *J. Amer. Chem. Soc.*, 1964, **86**, 3778; D. S. Matteson, J. O. Waldbillig and S. W. Peterson, ibid., p. 3781; D. S. Matteson and J. D. Liedtke, ibid., 1965, **87**, 1526; D. S. Matteson and R. A. Bowie, ibid., p. 2587; D. S. Matteson and M. L. Talbot, ibid., 1967, **89**, 1119, 1123; R. D. Brown, A. S. Buchanan and A. A. Humffray, *Austral. J. Chem.*, 1965, **18**, 1521, 1527.
[373a] D. R. Armstrong and P. G. Perkins, *J. Chem. Soc. (A)*, 1967, 123.
[374] R. L. Letsinger, S. Dandegaonker, W. J. Vullo and J. D. Morrison, *J. Amer. Chem. Soc.*, 1963, **85**, 2223; R. L. Letsinger and J. D. Morrison, ibid., p. 2227; R. L. Letsinger and D. B. MacLean, ibid., p. 2230; R. L. Letsinger and A. J. Wysocki, *J. Org. Chem.*, 1963, **28**, 3199; R. L. Letsinger, *Advan. in Chem. Series*, 1964, **42**, 1; J. D. Morrison and R. L. Letsinger, *J. Org. Chem.*, 1964, **29**, 3405; R. L. Letsinger, J. M. Smith, J. Gilpin and D. B. MacLean, ibid., 1965, **30**, 807.
[374a] L. Verbit, J. S. Levy, H. Rabitz and W. Kuralwasser, *Tetrahedron Letters*, 1966, 1053.

Paraphenylene diboronic acid, $(HO)_2BC_6H_4B(OH)_2$, and several of its esters have been prepared from methyl or butyl borate and *para*-phenylenedimagnesium bromide in tetrahydrofuran or by the use of *para*-phenylene dilithium [375]. Other aromatic diboronic acids have been synthesized for possible use in the therapeutic treatment of brain tumours by neutron-capture irradiation, for which a high percentage of boron is required [376]. Derivatives of ethylboronic acid, $X(CH_2)_2B(OH)_2$ (where X = e.g. cysteinyl), prepared by radical catalysed addition of HX to a vinylboronic ester, appear to have similar biological potential [377]. Diboronic acids of both the aliphatic and aromatic series have been used as polymer intermediates [378], and polymers have also been prepared from vinylphenylboronic acids [379].

Boronic acids are readily characterized as diethanolamine esters [380] (e.g. 3.29), as the pyridine complexes of the corresponding boroxines [381] (e.g. 3.30), or as the benzodiazaboroles (see 3.79, p. 279).

3.29, m.p. 214–215°   3.30, m.p. 154–156°

Boronic acids are weak, and their esters are generally very easily hydrolysed. Cyclic esters are rather more stable, particularly if the ring is 5- or 6-membered, as in the 1,3,2-dioxaborolans (3.31) or 1,3,2-dioxaborinans (3.32), and highly substituted [382].

1,3,2-Dioxaborolans   1,3,2-Dioxaborinans

3.31   3.32

[375] O. C. Musgrave, *Chem. and Ind.*, 1957, 1152; D. R. Nielsen and W. E. McEwen, *J. Amer. Chem. Soc.*, 1957, **79**, 3081.

[376] A. H. Soloway, ibid., 1960, **82**, 2442; J. F. Cairns and H. R. Snyder, *J. Org. Chem.*, 1964, **29**, 2810.

[377] D. S. Matteson, A. H. Soloway, D. W. Tomlinson, J. D. Campbell and G. A. Nixon, *J. Med. Chem.*, 1964, **7**, 640.

[378] W. R. Bamford and S. Fordham, *Soc. Chem. Ind. Monograph*, 1961, **13**, 320.

[379] W. J. Lennarz and H. R. Snyder, *J. Amer. Chem. Soc.*, 1960, **82**, 2169; W. J. Dale and J. E. Rush, *J. Org. Chem.*, 1962, **27**, 2598.

[380] O. C. Musgrave and T. O. Park, *Chem. and Ind.*, 1955, 1552; R. L. Letsinger and I. Skoog, *J. Amer. Chem. Soc.*, 1955, **77**, 2491.

[381] H. R. Snyder, M. S. Konecky and W. J. Lennarz, ibid., 1958, **80**, 3611.

[382] R. A. Bowie and O. C. Musgrave, *J. Chem. Soc.*, 1963, 3945; A. Finch and J. C. Lockart, ibid., 1962, 3723; H. Piotrowska, B. Serafin and T. Urbanski, *Tetrahedron*, 1963, **19**, 379; A. Finch, P. J. Gardner and E. J. Pearn, *Rec. Trav. chim.*, 1964, **83**, 1314; A. Finch and P. J. Gardner, *J. Chem. Soc.*, 1964, 2985.

Such esters may be prepared either by alkylation or arylation of the B-chloro ring compound (e.g. 3.32, R = Cl) [383] or directly from the boronic acid or boroxine and an appropriate diol, in which case some linear polymeric ester may also result, the amount of the latter depending on the reaction conditions and on the stereochemistry of the diol [383, 384]. Hexosides, for example, give cyclic esters. Boronic acids in fact appear likely to prove useful reagents in carbohydrate chemistry [385]. Butyl-boronic acid is a convenient reagent for the separation of isomeric *cis-trans*-cycloalkanediols; the volatile cyclic boronates formed by the *cis*-diols are easily separated by distillation from the non-volatile polymeric boronates formed by the *trans*-diols. Transesterification of the esters with ethylene glycol regenerates the diols [386].

The unsaturated 1,3,2-dioxaboroles (3.33) are prepared from acyloins and boronic acids or organoboron dichlorides [387, 388]; 5-oxo derivatives may be prepared from α-hydroxy esters [294], and benzo derivatives (3.34) from catechol [97].

1, 3, 2-Dioxaboroles

3.33   3.34

The products are sensitive to air and moisture, but may have slight aromatic character, as may the cyclic derivatives formed by amidoximes [388a]:

$(PhBO)_3$ + RC(NHR'):NOH ⟶

Cyclic esters of boronic acids thus have a substantial resistance to hyd-

[383] A. Finch, P. J. Gardner, J. C. Lockhart and E. J. Pearn, *J. Chem. Soc.*, 1962, 1428.
[384] V. Karnojitzky, S. Kohn and P. Schneebeli, *Compt. rend.*, 1961, **253**, 1463; S. Kato, M. Wada and Y. Tsuzuki, *Bull. Chem. Soc. Japan*, 1962, **35**, 1124; *Chem. Abs.*, 1962, **57**, 9866; B. Serafin and G. Milkowska, *Roczniki Chem.*, 1964, **38**, 897; *Chem. Abs.*, 1965, **62**, 16286.
[385] R. J. Ferrier, *J. Chem. Soc.*, 1961, 2325; R. J. Ferrier, D. Prasad, A. Rudowski and I Sangster, ibid., 1964, 3330; R. J. Ferrier, D. Prasad and A. Rudowski, ibid., 1965, 858; E. J. Bourne, E. M. Lees and H. Weigel, ibid., p. 3798; R. J. Ferrier and D. Prasad, ibid., p. 7425.
[386] H. C. Brown and G. Zweifel, *J. Org. Chem.*, 1962, **27**, 4708.
[387] G. Smolinsky, ibid., 1961, **26**, 4915.
[388] K. A. Jensen and T. Pederson, *Acta Chem. Scand.*, 1961, **15**, 1780.
[388a] A. Dornow and K. Fischer, *Chem. Ber.*, 1966, **99**, 68.

rolysis only when the boron is co-ordinatively saturated and particularly when it also is four-co-ordinate, as in the diethanolamine esters.

(iii) Boroxines
The cyclic anhydrides of boronic acids are known as boroxines, boroxine itself being the substance 3.35.

3.35   3.36   3.37

Their interest derives partly from their possibly aromatic structure. Trichloroboroxine (3.36 and 3.37, R = Cl) is stable only above about 200°, and is the cause of the apparent volatility of boric oxide in the presence of boron trichloride:

$$B_2O_3 + BCl_3 \rightleftharpoons B_3O_3Cl_3$$

Boroxine itself is unstable with respect to boric oxide and diborane at ordinary temperatures, but can be obtained by treating diborane with oxygen and caution at low pressure, the reaction being initiated by a spark from a Tesla coil [388b]. An alternative synthesis is to pass steam over a mixture of boron and boric oxide at 1100° [388c]. With carbon monoxide it forms borane carbonyl.

The alkylboroxines, most of which are liquids at room temperature, were formerly prepared by dehydration of alkylboronic acids [361]. A convenient method for the preparation of normal trialkylboroxines is the reaction between trialkylboranes and boric oxide [120] or trimethoxy-boroxine (MeOBO)$_3$ [389].

$$R_3B + B_2O_3 \rightarrow R_3B_3O_3$$

It should be noted that isomerization can occur in this reaction: tri-n-butylboroxine results from tri-s-butylborane and boric oxide. Triorgano-boroxines have also been obtained from the borates of alkali metals or alkaline earths by their reaction with a mixture of a boron halide and a trialkyl- or triaryl-borane [390]. Some B–C cleavage reactions of trialkyl-boranes stop at the stage where one alkyl group remains attached to boron, in which case the product is frequently a boroxine or boronic acid; e.g. tributylboroxine is said to be formed in 67–96% yield from tributylborane

[388b] L. Barton, F. A. Grimm and R. F. Porter, *Inorg. Chem.*, 1966, 5, 2076.
[388c] S. K. Wason and R. F. Porter, ibid., p. 161.
[389] P. M. Iloff, U.S.P. 3,010,989; *Chem. Abs.*, 1962, 57, 9880.
[390] E. H. Dobratz, U.S.P. 3,078,305; *Chem. Abs.*, 1963, 59, 1679.

and formic or acetic acid [391]:

$$3Bu_3B + 3HCO_2H \longrightarrow (BuBO)_3 + 6BuH + 3CO$$

The tri-alkyl and -aryl boroxines are readily hydrated to the boronic acids, and they form 1 : 1 co-ordination complexes, those between triaryl-boroxines and pyridine being suitable for identification purposes [381]. The sterically hindered mesitylboronic acid $Me_3C_6H_2B(OH)_2$ forms a *dimeric* anhydride, $(Me_3C_6H_2BO)_2$, which does not form a complex with pyridine [392]. (The bulky mesityl groups can modify properties considerably – trimesitylborane with nitric acid gives a *hexanitro* derivative, $[(O_2N)_2Me_3C_6]_3B$.)

Calculations by the Pople S.C.F. technique of the π-electronic structures of boroxine, triphenylboroxine, tristyrylboroxine and dimesitylboronic anhydride have shown the six electrons of the boroxines to be more localized than in borazines, although the π-electron delocalization in the six-membered ring is greater than in the four-membered ring of the mesityl compound [392a].

The trialkylboroxines are slowly oxidized by atmospheric oxygen. Tri-n-butylboroxine yields n-butyldichloroborane on treatment with aluminium chloride,

$$BuBCl_2 \xleftarrow{\text{AlCl}_3} Bu_3B_3O_3 \xrightarrow{\text{Me}_3\text{Al}} BuBMe_2$$

and the mixed trialkylborane $BuBMe_2$ is said to be formed with trimethyl-aluminium or methylaluminium sesqui-iodide [393], a surprising result in view of the strong catalytic effect of aluminium alkyls on alkyl exchange in alkylboranes.

(iv) Boroxarenes

Although the parent compound has yet to be prepared, many derivatives of 2,1-*boroxarobenzene*, or *boroxarene* (3.38) are now known. The extra

3.38   3.39   3.40   3.41

[391] M. Kumada, M. Ishikawa and K. Yoshida, *Mem. Fac. Eng., Osaka City Univ.*, 1962, **3**, 201; *Chem. Abs.*, 1962, **57**, 2238.
[392] R. T. Hawkins, W. J. Lennarz and H. R. Snyder, *J. Amer. Chem. Soc.*, 1960, **82**, 3053.
[392a] D. R. Armstrong and P. G. Perkins, *J. Chem. Soc. (A)*, 1967, 790.
[393] J. C. Perrine and R. N. Keller, *J. Amer. Chem. Soc.*, 1958, **80**, 1823.

prefix 'aro-' in the names of these compounds and of the corresponding nitrogen compounds, the *borazarenes*, is used to stress the aromatic character of the ring, which would not be apparent from the systematic name (e.g. 1,2-azabora*dihydro*benzene for borazarene).

10-Hydroxy-10,9-boroxarophenanthrene (3.39, R = OH) has been prepared by heating 2-hydroxybiphenyl with boron trichloride and aluminium chloride, followed by hydrolysis [394]. It is also obtained by diazotization of a nitrogen analogue, 10-methyl-10,9-borazarophenanthrene again followed by hydrolysis [395]. The benzo derivatives 3.40 and 3.41 have been prepared by similar methods. The aromatic character of these compounds is less than that of the borazarophenanthrenes described below, some derivatives being quite rapidly oxidized by air, so that the canonical structures shown (3.38–41) contribute probably only to a small extent. With derivatives of *4,1-boroxarene* (3.42), the greater separation of charges in the aromatic ring and consequently higher energy of such a zwitterionic form relative to the uncharged diene structure (3.43) means that the aromatic character of such a ring will be negligible.

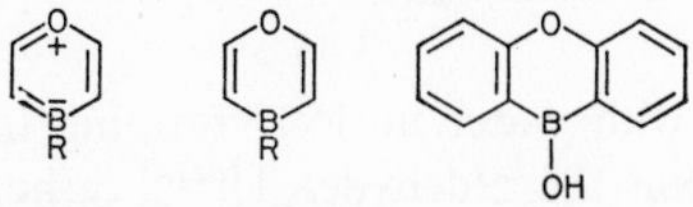

3.42   3.43   3.44

In fact, 10-hydroxy-10,9-boroxaroanthracene (3.44), prepared from 2,2′-dilithiodiphenyl ether and boron trichloride followed by hydrolysis, shows pronounced Lewis acid character [396].

The carbonylation of organoboranes
High-pressure reactions between carbon monoxide and trialkylboranes in the presence of water, diols or aldehydes have been shown to produce various boron–oxygen–carbon ring compounds. Carbonylation of trialkylboranes at 50° in the presence of *water* affords hexa-alkyl-2,5-diboradioxanes (3.45), which at 150° isomerize to trialkylcarbinylboroxines or boronic acids [397].

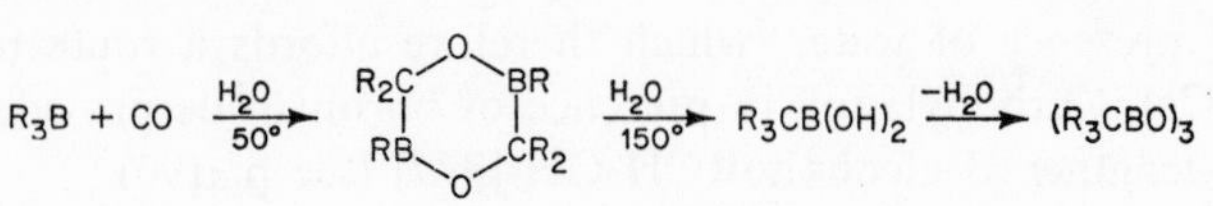

3.45

[394] M. J. S. Dewar and R. Dietz, *J. Chem. Soc.*, 1960, 1344.
[395] M. J. S. Dewar and P. M. Maitlis, *Chem. and Ind.*, 1960, 1626.
[396] J. M. Davidson and C. M. French, *J. Chem. Soc.*, 1960, 191.
[397] M. E. D. Hillman, *J. Amer. Chem. Soc.*, 1962, **84**, 4715.

This provides a novel route to trialkylcarbinols, obtained on oxidation of the product.

Carbonylation of trialkylboranes at about 800 atmospheres in the presence of *diols* gives cyclic or polymeric esters of trialkylcarbinylboronic acids, substances which are unusually stable to hydrolysis and oxidation in contrast to the sensitivity to oxidation of such boronic acids as $Bu^tB(OH)_2$ and $Pr^iB(OH)_2$ [398].

$$R_3B + HOCH_2CH_2OH + CO \longrightarrow R_3CB\overset{O}{\underset{O}{\diagdown}}\hspace{-0.5em}\rceil$$

The product from polyvinylalcohol is a hydrolytically stable polymer, insoluble in water, soluble in organic solvents, which can be cast into colourless transparent films and drawn into fibres.

Carbonylation in the presence of *aldehydes* leads to a new type of ring, the 4-bora-1,3-dioxolans (3.46) [399]:

$$R_3B + CO + R'CHO \longrightarrow \begin{array}{c} RB\!\!-\!\!O \\ | \hspace{1.5em} \diagdown CHR' \\ R_2C\!\!-\!\!O \end{array} \xrightarrow[150°]{H_2O} (R_3CBO)_3 + R'CHO$$

3.46

The products react with water at 150° forming trialkylcarbinylboronic acids and regenerating the aldehyde. These carbonylation reactions of trialkylboranes apparently proceed via an adduct $R_3B{\leftarrow}CO$ which subsequently rearranges to a boryl ketone $R_2B.CO.R$, and this either rearranges further and is isolated as the dimer (3.45) or undergoes further reaction with the other species present.

The considerable potential of these carbonylation reactions in organic syntheses has recently been demonstrated by H. C. Brown and M. W. Rathke [77b, 77c, 77d], who have shown that the use of certain ethereal solvents (preferably diglyme) allows the carbonylation of organoboranes to be carried out at atmospheric pressure. The diglyme solutions of organoboranes which result from the hydroboration of olefins absorb carbon monoxide smoothly at 100–125° giving trialkylcarbinylboroxines $(R_3CBO)_3$ which when oxidized afford carbinols [77b]. The number of alkyl groups which migrate from boron to carbon may be limited to two by carbonylation in presence of water, which therefore affords a route to ketones R_2CO [77c]. Carbonylation in presence of borohydride provides a route to chain-lengthened alcohols RCH_2OH [77d] (see p. 190)

Organoboron–nitrogen compounds [25]
Boron–nitrogen systems have received particular attention because of their relationship to organic systems. When a C–C link in an organic

[398] M. E. D. Hillman, *J. Amer. Chem. Soc.*, 1963, **85**, 982.
[399] Idem, ibid., p. 1626.

compound is replaced by a B–N link, the resulting compound is iso-electronic with, but more polar than, the original (e.g. compare CH_3CH_3 with BH_3NH_3). Attention has been directed, therefore, to finding ways of preparing boron–nitrogen analogues of known organic materials, and to comparing the properties of the two series. For example, derivatives of the benzene analogues borazine and borazarene have been investigated for their aromatic character, and boron–nitrogen polymers have been studied for possibly greater thermal stability than their organic counterparts.

In the following pages, organoboron–nitrogen compounds are treated under the following headings:

Aminoboranes $(RR'BNR''R''')_n$;
Boronium salts $(R_2BL_2)^+X^-$ where L is generally an amine;
Borazines $(RBNR')_3$ including related oligomers $(RBNR')_2$ and $(RBNR')_4$;
Borazarenes derivatives of the benzene analogue C_4BNH_6; and
Miscellaneous ring compounds

Aminoboranes [400]
Several methods have been used for the preparation of aminoboranes, $(RR'BNR''R''')_n$. Adducts of alkylboranes with ammonia or a primary or secondary amine eliminate hydrogen when heated, e.g.

$$Me_2BH \cdot NH_3 \longrightarrow Me_2BNH_2 + H_2$$

Dialkyl- or diaryl-chloroboranes react with ammonia or a primary or secondary amine to liberate hydrogen chloride, conveniently removed as trie*thyl*amine hydrochloride [401, 402]:

$$R_2BCl + R'_2NH + Et_3N \longrightarrow R_2BNR'_2 + Et_3NHCl$$

Use of tertiary amines other than triethylamine (e.g. Me_3N or py) generally leads not to aminoboranes but to boronium salts [402a]:

$$Me_2NH + BCl_3 + Me_3N \longrightarrow [Me_3N(Me_2NH)BCl_2]^+Cl^-$$

A lithium amide may be used instead of the secondary amine [401]:

$$Ph_2BCl + LiNR_2 \longrightarrow Ph_2BNR_2 + LiCl$$

or the organic groups may be attached to the boron after formation of the amino–boron link. Aminodichloroboranes, Cl_2BNR_2, from boron tri-

[400] K. Niedenzu, *Angew. Chem.*, 1964, **76**, 165; *Internat. Edn.*, 1964, **3**, 86.
[401] G. E. Coates and J. G. Livingstone, *J. Chem. Soc.*, 1961, 1000.
[402] W. Gerrard, H. R. Hudson and E. F. Mooney, ibid., 1960, 5168; K. Niedenzu, D. H. Harrelson, W. George and J. W. Dawson, *J. Org. Chem.*, 1961, **26**, 3037.
[402a] H. Nöth, P. Schweizer and F. Ziegelgänsberger, *Chem. Ber.*, 1966, **99**, 1089.

chloride and a secondary amine, are treated with a suitable Grignard reagent [401, 403, 404]:

$$2RMgBr + Cl_2BNR'_2 \rightarrow R_2BNR'_2 + MgCl_2 + MgBr_2$$

The amino group of one aminoborane may be replaced by another amino group by reaction with an excess of a suitable amine. This method, the *transamination* reaction, is convenient for the preparation of derivatives of comparatively involatile amines; the volatile displaced amine is distilled from the reaction mixture [405]:

$$R_2BNR'_2 + HNR''_2 \rightleftharpoons R_2BNR''_2 + HNR'_2$$

Aminosilanes can be used to attach amino groups to boron; this method has the advantage of involving no strong acid or base in the reaction mixture [406], e.g.

$$Me_3SiNR_2 + R'_2BCl \rightarrow Me_3SiCl + R_2NBR'_2$$
$$3(Me_3Si)_2NMe + PhBCl_2 \rightarrow (PhBNMe)_3 + 6Me_3SiCl$$

Aminoboranes, having the general formula $(RR'BNR''R''')_n$, are sometimes referred to as 'borazenes', since when $n = 1$ they are formally analogous to alkenes. For example in monomeric aminodimethylborane the boron makes use of internal co-ordination to achieve a covalency of four:

$$Me_2B—NH_2 \rightarrow Me_2B\!\leftharpoondown\!NH_2 \quad \text{or} \quad Me_2\overset{-}{B}\!=\!\overset{+}{NH_2}$$
$$\text{3.47} \qquad\qquad\qquad \text{3.48}$$

Formula 3.47 is preferred to 3.48 as it avoids the misleading suggestion of extensive charge separation in the latter; the polarity of the molecule is less than that implied by 3.48 since the electronegativity difference between boron and nitrogen causes the bond between these two elements to be polarized in the sense B→N [407].

Co-ordination saturation can also be achieved by association, usually dimerization, and the compound just mentioned can be obtained in two forms, a monomeric gas (b.p. $\sim1°$) and colourless crystals (m.p. $9°$) [115].

$$2Me_2B\!\leftharpoondown\!NH_2 \;\rightleftharpoons\; Me_2B\diamond BMe_2$$

[403] C. E. Erickson and F. C. Gunderloy, *J. Org. Chem.*, 1959, **24**, 1161.

[404] K. Niedenzu and J. W. Dawson, *J. Amer. Chem. Soc.*, 1959, **81**, 5553; K. Niedenzu, J. W. Dawson, P. Fritz and J. Jenne, *Chem. Ber.*, 1965, **98**, 3050.

[405] H. Nöth, *Z. Naturforsch.*, 1961, **16b**, 470; W. D. English, A. L. McCloskey and H. Steinberg, *J. Amer. Chem. Soc.*, 1961, **83**, 2122.

[406] E. W. Abel, D. A. Armitage, R. P. Bush and G. R. Willey, *J. Chem. Soc.*, 1964, 62.

[407] R. Hofmann, *Advan. in Chem. Series*, 1964, **42**, 78; J. J. Kaufman and J. R. Hamann, ibid., p. 95.

In this particular case a reversible equilibrium can be observed in the gas phase at about room temperature. In other similar substances the attainment of co-ordinative saturation by double bonding, or by dimerization, is determined mainly by the size of the atoms or groups bound to the boron or nitrogen. If these are very bulky, association may be hindered or impossible. Thus, reactions between boron trichloride (or BBr_3) and secondary amines with relatively large alkyl or cycloalkyl groups give aminoboron halides which remain monomeric, e.g. $Pr^n_2NBCl_2$, $Bu^n_2NBCl_2$, and (3.49).

| 3.49 | 3.50 | 3.51 |

In contrast, piperidino- and morpholino-dichloroborane gradually form the dimers 3.50 and 3.51 [408]. Among aminodiarylboranes, the only dimers are those containing NH_2 or $NHMe$ groups, as in $(Ph_2BNHMe)_2$. Any larger groups attached to the nitrogen would cause substantial steric interference even with the hydrogen atoms in *ortho*-positions on the aryl groups, and so the dimethylamino derivative, Ph_2BNMe_2 is monomeric [401]. Studies on the association of aminoboranes are complicated by the exceedingly slow rate of dimerization at normal temperatures in certain cases where the dimer is the thermodynamically more stable form [409].

Association to form trimers, which have a chair-shaped ring (3.52) like that of cyclohexane, involves even greater crowding of the groups attached to boron and nitrogen, and is found in only a few examples such as cyclotriborazane itself [410], $(H_2BNH_2)_3$, the methyl derivatives $(H_2BNHMe)_3$ [411] and $(H_2BNMe_2)_3$ [412], and some adducts of borazine, e.g. $(ClHBNH_2)_3$ [413].

3.52

[408] O. C. Musgrave, *J. Chem. Soc.*, 1956, 4305.

[409] F. C. Gunderloy and C. E. Erickson, *Inorg. Chem.*, 1962, **1**, 349.

[410] G. H. Dahl and R. Schaeffer, *J. Amer. Chem. Soc.*, 1961, **83**, 3032; S. G. Shore and C. W. Hickam, *Inorg. Chem.*, 1963, **2**, 638.

[411] T. C. Bissot and R. W. Parry, *J. Amer. Chem. Soc.*, 1955, **77**, 3481; D. F. Gaines and R. Schaeffer, ibid., 1963, **85**, 395.

[412] L. M. Trefonas, F. S. Matthews and W. N. Lipscomb, *Acta Cryst.*, 1961, **14**, 273; G. W. Campbell and L. Johnson, *J. Amer. Chem. Soc.*, 1959, **81**, 3800.

[413] A. W. Laubengayer, O. T. Beachley and R. F. Porter, *Inorg. Chem.*, 1965, **4**, 578.

Where the size of substituents is such as to allow degrees of association greater than two it is not necessarily the thermodynamically most stable oligomer that is obtained as a reaction product. For example, cycloborazanes $(H_2BNH_2)_n$ with n = 2, 3, 5 and possibly also 4 have been obtained from sodium amide and the diammoniate of diborane $[(NH_3)_2BH_2^+BH_4^-]$ in liquid ammonia [413a]. The state of association of the product appears to be governed by the reaction mechanism; for example, the formation of the trimer $(H_2BNHMe)_3$ from the adduct H_3B,NH_2Me has been shown to involve the boronium borohydride $(MeNH_2)_2BH_2^+BH_4^-$ and subsequently $[MeH_2N\cdot BH_2\cdot NHMe\cdot BH_2\cdot NH_2Me]^+BH_4^-$ as intermediates [413b] (see also [413c] for studies on $(H_2BNMe_2)_n$).

Apart from these steric and mechanistic factors, *electronic effects* also appear to influence the state of association of aminoboranes [414]. When relatively electro-positive groups are bound to boron, double bonding is favoured; for example Me_2BNMe_2 is *monomeric* [115, 415] and the B–N force constant (from its Raman spectrum [416]) indicates a double $B \Leftarrow N$ bond. The B–N absorption frequency in the infrared spectra of monomeric aminoboranes is generally found in the region 1330–1530 cm^{-1}, while dimeric aminoboranes have a characteristic band around 900 cm^{-1} [401, 404, 417]. Dipole moment measurements on monomeric aminodiarylboranes indicate that N-methyl compounds have polarities of different sign from those of N-aryl compounds:

$$\overset{\leftarrow +}{Ph_2B\text{—}NMe_2} \quad \text{and} \quad \overset{+\rightarrow}{Ph_2B\text{—}NPh_2} \quad [401]$$

In trisdimethylaminoborane, $(Me_2N)_3B$, which is monomeric, coordinative saturation is evidently achieved by partial multiple bonding [152]. This compound does not react with amines and is only slowly hydrolysed [418]. Monomeric dimethylaminodichloroborane, Cl_2BNMe_2, on the other hand, is a very reactive liquid, violently hydrolysed by cold water, which slowly changes into a remarkably unreactive solid dimer [419].

A consequence of the multiplicity of the $B \Leftarrow N$ bond in monomeric

[413a] K. W. Böddeker, S. G. Shore and R. K. Bunting, *J. Amer. Chem. Soc.*, 1966, **88**, 4396.
[413b] O. T. Beachley, *Inorg. Chem.*, 1967, **6**, 870.
[413c] M. P. Brown, R. W. Heseltine and D. W. Johnson, *J. Chem. Soc. (A)*, 1967, 597; A. B. Burg and J. S. Sandhu, *J. Amer. Chem. Soc.*, 1967, **89**, 1626.
[414] J. Goubeau, H. J. Becher and F. Griffel, *Z. anorg. Chem.*, 1955, **282**, 86.
[415] G. E. Coates, *J. Chem. Soc.*, 1950, 3481.
[416] H. J. Becher and J. Goubeau, *Z. anorg. Chem.*, 1952, **268**, 133.
[417] M. F. Lappert, M. K. Majumdar and B. P. Tilley, *J. Chem. Soc. (A)*, 1966, 1590.
[418] J. K. Ruff, *J. Org. Chem.*, 1962, **27**, 1020; D. W. Aubrey, M. F. Lappert and M. K. Majumdar, *J. Chem. Soc.*, 1962, 4088.
[419] E. Wiberg and K. Schuster, *Z. anorg. Chem.*, 1933, **213**, 77.

aminoboranes is that rotation about this bond is hindered. Evidence for this has been obtained from proton magnetic resonance studies on $Me_2BNMePh$, which showed [420] the two boron-attached methyl groups to differ (3.53), and on $PhClBNMe_2$ and vinyl$(Br)BNMe_2$, in each of which the methyl groups attached to nitrogen were found to be non-equivalent [421]. The energy barriers to rotation in these compounds are in the region 14–18 kcal. mole^{-1}. Similar studies on $MePhBNMePh$, combined with infrared and Raman spectroscopic evidence, indicated a *trans* structure (3.54) with the phenyl groups twisted out of the plane of the molecule [422].

3.53   3.54

The appearance of two peaks due to boron-attached methyl groups in the proton magnetic resonance spectrum of a compound such as $MePhBNMePh$ is not necessarily indicative of *cis–trans*-isomers, but can arise from different orientations of the rings with respect to each other and to the plane of the molecule [423].

X-Ray diffraction studies on three dimeric aminoboranes $(X_2BNMe_2)_2$ have been reported, where X = H [424], Cl [425] or F [425a]. All three molecules have symmetry *mmm*, with a planar ring having all B–N bonds of equal length, 1·61 Å in the hydride, 1·59 Å in the chloride and 1·60 Å in the fluoride. Ring angles at nitrogen are 86·9° (chloride) and 88·3° (fluoride). Unsymmetrical substitution of opposite corner atoms of such a ring, as in the dimeric ethylideneaminodialkylboranes, $(R_2BN=CHMe)_2$, leads to opportunities for *cis–trans*-isomerism, and two isomers of $(Me_2BN=CHMe)_2$, prepared from methyl cyanide and tetramethyldiborane, $(Me_2BH)_2$, have been isolated. The proton magnetic resonance

[420] G. E. Ryschkewitsch, W. S. Brey and A. Saji, *J. Amer. Chem. Soc.*, 1961, **83**, 1010; W. S. Brey, M. E. Fuller, G. E. Ryschkewitsch and A. S. Marshall, *Advan. in Chem. Series*, 1964, **42**, 100; see also T. Totani, H. Watanabe, T. Nakagawa, O. Ohashi and M. Kubo, ibid., p. 108.

[421] P. A. Barfield, M. F. Lappert and J. Lee, *Proc. Chem. Soc.*, 1961, 421; K. Neidenzu, J. W. Dawson, G. A. Neece, W. Sawodny, D. R. Squire and W. Weber, *Inorg. Chem.*, 1966, **5**, 2161.

[422] H. Baechle, H. J. Becher, H. Beyer, W. S. Brey, J. W. Dawson, M. E. Fuller and K. Niedenzu, ibid., 1963, **2**, 1065.

[423] H. J. Becher and H. Diehl, *Chem. Ber.*, 1965, **98**, 526; H. J. Becher and H. T. Baechle, ibid., p. 2159; H. T. Baechle and H. J. Becher, *Spectrochim. Acta*, 1965, **21**, 579.

[424] P. J. Schapiro, *Dissertation Abstracts*, 1962, **22**, 2607.

[425] H. Hess, *Int. Union of Cryst. 6th Int. Congress and Symposia*, Abstracts of Communications, Rome, Sept. 1963, A77.

[425a] A. C. Hazell, *J. Chem. Soc. (A)*, 1966, 1392.

spectra of these isomers have been interpreted in terms of the *cis*- and *trans*- structures 3.55 and 3.56, which differ in that 3.55 has two types of boron-attached methyl, for which two peaks occur in the spectrum, whereas

3.55   3.56

3.56 has only one type of B-methyl, and one appropriate peak in the spectrum [426]. The structure of the *trans*-isomer (3.56) has been determined by an X-ray diffraction study [427], which has shown that, despite the exocyclic double bonds to the nitrogen atoms, the $(BN)_2$ ring is very nearly square. $\angle BNB = 93.5°$. Similar isomerism is possible in alkylideneamino t-butylboranes $(Bu^tHBN{=}CHR)_2$ [428], while the three peaks due to the Me_2N groups in the proton magnetic resonance spectra of dimethyl-aminochloroboranes $(RClB \cdot NMe_2)_2$ show both *cis*- and *trans*- forms to be present in these compounds, which are prepared from the appropriate dichloride, $RBCl_2$, and diaminoborane, $RB(NMe_2)_2$ [429].

The reaction between diphenylketimine and trimethylborane at about 200° gives an azomethine derivative $Ph_2C{:}NBMe_2$ which in the solid phase may well have a dimeric structure like 3.55 and 3.56 above, but which in the vapour phase appears to be monomeric (mass spectroscopy) and so formally analogous to the allene $Ph_2C{:}C{:}CMe_2$ [429a]

Interaction of aminoboranes with donor or acceptor molecules is a further way in which co-ordinative saturation of the boron or nitrogen can be achieved. The Lewis acidity of aminoboranes is most pronounced when electronegative groups or atoms are attached to boron; chlorides R_2NBCl_2 form adducts R_2NBCl_2py, $[R_2NClBpy_2]^+Cl^-$ and $[R_2NBpy_3]^{2+}2Cl^-$ when treated with increasing proportions of pyridine [429b]. On the other hand, aminoboranes such as Me_2NBMe_2 or $Me_2NBPr^n_2$ act as amine donors towards iodine in carbon tetrachloride [429c].

Diaminoboranes, $RB(NR'_2)_2$, are obtained by methods similar to those used for aminoboranes. Thus bis-dimethylaminoboranes, $RB(NMe_2)_2$,

[426] J. E. Lloyd and K. Wade, *J. Chem. Soc.*, 1964, 1649.
[427] H. M. M. Shearer and J. Willis, personal communication.
[428] M. F. Hawthorne, *Tetrahedron*, 1962, **17**, 117.
[429] H. Nöth and P. Fritz, *Z. anorg. Chem.*, 1963, **324**, 270.
[429a] I. Pattison and K. Wade, *J. Chem. Soc. (A)*, 1967, 1098.
[429b] M. F. Lappert and G. Srivastava, ibid., 1967, 602.
[429c] I. D. Eubanks and J. J. Lagowski, *J. Amer. Chem. Soc.*, 1966, **88**, 2425.

may be prepared by the solvolysis of $RBCl_2$ in Me_2NH or by alkylation of $(Me_2N)_2BCl$ with RLi, e.g. [430]

$$RBCl_2 + 4HNMe_2 \rightarrow RB(NMe_2)_2 + 2Me_2NH\cdot HCl$$

This reaction may be partially reversed by hydrogen chloride,

$$PrB(NMe_2)_2 + 2HCl \rightarrow PrClBNMe_2 + Me_2NH\cdot HCl$$

possibly via an intermediate boronium salt $[(Me_2NH)_2BClPr]^+Cl^-$.

The mass spectra of the aminoboranes $PhB(NMe_2)_2$, $Ph\overline{B\cdot NMe\cdot C_2H_4\cdot NMe}$ and $(Me_2N)_3B$ show an unusual feature in that the largest peaks correspond to the loss of *two* electrons from the parent molecule, and it has been suggested that salts of the cation $[(Me_2N)_3B]^{2+}$ might be preparable [431].
For silylaminoboranes and other aminoboranes, see ref. [432].

Boronium salts

Many examples are now known of boronium salts, $(R_2BL_2)^+X^-$ in which the boronium cation R_2B^+ (where R can $=$ H, F, Cl, Br, alkyl or aryl) is stabilized by two donor molecules L (generally amines) or a single bidentate ligand such as bipyridyl or phenanthroline. In the hydride series (R $=$ H), although the hydrated boronium cation $(H_2O)_2BH_2^+$ appears capable of existence only at low temperatures [432a], the thermally more stable diammoniate of diborane [433] has the structure $(NH_3)_2BH_2^+BH_4^-$, and halides such as $(Me_2NH)_2BCl_2^+Cl^-$ have been described [434]. Among cationic organoboron complexes, the aryl derivatives appear to be the most stable. These were first obtained by the reaction between chlorodiphenylborane and aluminium chloride in ethyl methyl ketone, when solvated diphenylboronium, Ph_2B^+, ions were apparently

[430] H. Nöth and P. Fritz, *Z. anorg. Chem.*, 1963, **322**, 297; H. Nöth and H. Vahren-kamp, *Chem. Ber.*, 1966, **99**, 2757.

[431] M. J. S. Dewar and P. Rona, *J. Amer. Chem. Soc.*, 1965, **87**, 5510.

[432] H. Jenne and K. Niedenzu, *Inorg. Chem.*, 1964, **3**, 68; K. Niedenzu, H. Beyer, J. W. Dawson and H. Jenne, *Chem. Ber.*, 1963, **96**, 2653; V. V. Korshak, N. I. Bekasova, L. M. Chursina and V. A. Zamyatina, *Izvest. Akad. Nauk S.S.S.R.*, 1963, 1645; *Chem. Abs.*, 1963, **59**, 15296.

[432a] W. L. Jolly and T. Schmitt, *Inorg. Chem.*, 1967, **6**, 344.

[433] D. R. Schultz and R. W. Parry, *J. Amer. Chem. Soc.*, 1958, **80**, 4; S. G. Shore and R. W. Parry, ibid., pp. 8, 12 and 15; S. G. Shore, P. R. Giradot and R. W. Parry, ibid., p. 20; R. W. Parry, G. Kodama and D. R. Schultz, ibid., p. 24; B. Z. Egan and S. G. Shore, ibid., 1961, **83**, 4717; C. E. Nordman, C. Reimann and C. R. Peters, *Advan. in Chem. Series*, 1961, **32**, 204; see also O. T. Beachley, *Inorg. Chem.*, 1965, **4**, 1823; 1967, **6**, 870; S. G. Shore, C. W. Hickham and D. Cowles, *J. Amer. Chem. Soc.*, 1965, **87**, 2755; G. E. McAchran and S. G. Shore, *Inorg. Chem.*, 1965, **4**, 125; S. G. Shore and C. L. Hall, *J. Amer. Chem. Soc.*, 1966, **88**, 5346.

[434] W. Gerrard, H. R. Hudson and E. F. Mooney, *J. Chem. Soc.*, 1960, 5168; H. Nöth and S. Lukas, *Chem. Ber.*, 1962, **95**, 1505; B. M. Mikhailov, V. D. Sheludyakov and T. A. Shchegoleva, *Izvest. Akad. Nauk S.S.S.R.*, 1962, 1698; N. E. Miller and E. L. Muetterties, *J. Amer. Chem. Soc.*, 1964, **86**, 1033.

formed. Addition of silver perchlorate to a solution of chlorodiphenyl-borane in nitrobenzene causes immediate precipitation of silver chloride and the solution contains diphenylboronium perchlorate [435]:

$$Ph_2BCl + AgClO_4 \rightarrow AgCl + Ph_2B^+ClO_4^-$$

If the reaction between chlorodiphenylborane and silver perchlorate is carried out in nitromethane, and bipyridyl is added after removal of silver chloride, the compound 2,2'-bipyridyldiphenylboronium perchlorate crystallizes [436]:

$$Ph_2BCl + AgClO_4 \rightarrow Ph_2B^+ClO_4^- \xrightarrow{\text{bipy}} [Ph_2B \text{ bipy}]^+ClO_4^-$$

The ionic structures of these compounds have been confirmed by conductivity measurements [437].

Diphenylbipyridylboronium chloride may be prepared in quantitative yield from bipyridyl and chlorodiphenylborane in benzene solution, and is conveniently crystallized from hot water. Its stability to air and mild aqueous acid conditions is shown by its preparation in 50–55% yields by boiling diphenylborinic acid or its ethanolamine ester with bipyridyl and 5N hydrochloric acid for 2–3 hours [438].

$$Ph_2BOH + bipy + HCl \rightarrow (Ph_2B \text{ bipy})Cl + H_2O$$

The ion is, however, readily decomposed by alkali, apparently through nucleophilic attack on the bipyridyl. Salts other than the chloride are obtained by metathetical reactions in aqueous solution.

Phenanthroline [438] or primary aliphatic amines [439] have been used instead of bipyridyl to stabilize the diphenylboronium cation. The yellow or orange colours of the iodides and some other salts of the $[Ph_2B \text{ bipy}]^+$ and $[Ph_2B \text{ phenan}]^+$ cations are considered to be due to charge-transfer transitions from the anion to the co-ordinated amine in the cation. The aqueous solutions of these salts are colourless. The ability of such cations to take up electrons to furnish neutral species is illustrated by the isolation of materials $(Me_2N)_2B$ bipy, Me_2NB bipy and even $(bipy)_2B$ from reactions between lithium-bipyridyl adducts and appropriate boron chlorides [439a].

In the alkyl series, dimethylboronium salts of such cations as $Me_2B(NH_3)_2^+$ or Me_2B en$^+$ are accessible via unsymmetrial cleavage reactions of tetramethyldiborane [439b], while dibutylboronium chlorides,

[435] J. M. Davidson and C. M. French, *J. Chem. Soc.*, 1958, 114.
[436] Idem, *Chem. and Ind.*, 1959, 750.
[437] Idem, *J. Chem. Soc.*, 1962, 3364.
[438] L. Banford and G. E. Coates, ibid., 1964, 3564.
[439] B. M. Mikhailov and N. S. Fedotov, *Izvest. Akad. Nauk S.S.S.R.*, 1959, 1482; 1961, 1913; *Chem. Abs.*, 1960, **54**, 1376; 1962, **56**, 7341.
[439a] M. A. Kuck and G. Urry, *J. Amer. Chem. Soc.*, 1966, **88**, 426.
[439b] P. C. Moews and R. W. Parry, *Inorg. Chem.*, 1966, **5**, 1552.

(Bu$_2$BL$_2$)$^+$Cl$^-$, have been prepared from dibutylchloroborane and various amines [438, 440]. The iodide (Bu$_2$B bipy)I is yellow in colour, again because of charge transfer from the anion. Colours attributed to *intra-ionic* charge transfer occur with salts of the phenylenedioxybipyridylboronium cation (3.57); for example the perchlorate has a yellow colour. It is suggested that electron transfer occurs from the 'lone-pairs' of the oxygen atoms of the catechol residue into the π-electron system of the bipyridyl [438].

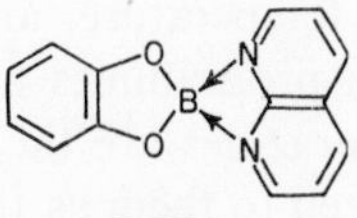

3.57

Heterocyclic boronium salts result from the action of amines on 1-chloroboracycloalkanes, e.g. [441]

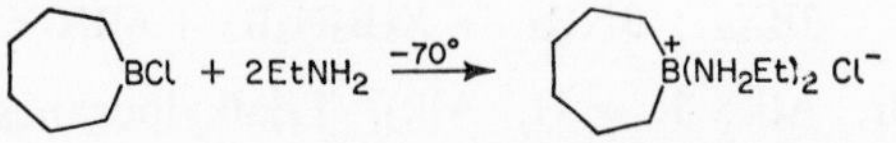

Further routes to boronium salts are exemplified by the following equations [442, 443]:

$$PhBH_2,py + I_2 + 2\,py \longrightarrow [PhBH\,py_2]^+I^- + py\,H^+I^-$$
$$\text{m.p. } 199\text{–}202°$$
$$PhB(NMe_2)_2 + 2HCl \longrightarrow [(Me_2NH)_2BClPh]^+Cl^-$$

Borazines

The chemistry of this class of cyclic B–N compounds has been greatly extended, particularly in recent years, since the preparation of the parent compound *borazine* (formerly known as *borazole*), B$_3$N$_3$H$_6$ (3.58), b.p. 53°, by A. Stock [444] in 1926. The compound was originally obtained by the thermal decomposition of the diborane-diammonia complex, (NH$_3$)$_2$BH$_2$$^+BH_4$$^-$. The planar structure of borazine has been

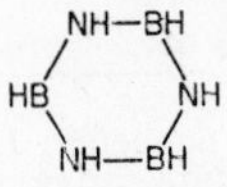

3.58 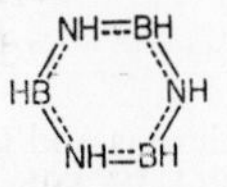   3.59

[440] W. Gerrard, M. F. Lappert and R. Schafferman, *J. Chem. Soc.*, 1957, 3828; H. Nöth, *Z. Naturforsch.*, 1961, **16b**, 471; T. A. Schegoleva and B. M. Mikhailov, *Izvest. Akad. Nauk S.S.S.R.*, 1965, 714; *Chem. Abs.*, 1965, **63**, 2992.

[441] B. M. Mikhailov and T. K. Kozminskaya, *Izvest. Akad. Nauk S.S.S.R.* 1963, 1703; *Chem. Abs.*, 1963, **59**, 15294; B. M. Mikhailov, T. K. Kozminskaya and L. V. Tarasov, *Doklady. Akad. Nauk S.S.S.R.*, 1965, **160**, 615; *Chem. Abs.*, 1965, **62**, 14714.

[442] J. E. Douglass, *J. Amer. Chem. Soc.*, 1964, **86**, 5431.

[443] H. Nöth, S. Lukas and P. Schweizer, *Chem. Ber.*, 1965, **98**, 962.

[444] A. Stock and E. Pohland, *Ber.*, 1926, **59**, 2215.

confirmed by various electron-diffraction and spectroscopic studies [445]. The aromatic character of the ring (3.59) is, however, slight, the electron density alternating round the ring because of the different electronegativities of the boron and nitrogen atoms, although substituents may have a marked effect on the electronic distribution in the ring, as various theoretical treatments have shown [446]. Though borazine itself decomposes slowly at room temperature, many of its derivatives with alkyl or aryl groups substituted for hydrogen (either on boron or nitrogen atoms) are stable when kept at room temperature, and some derivatives have been studied as part of research programmes aimed at materials resistant to high temperatures [447]. Borazines are the subject of two recent reviews [23], and the reader is referred to them as the main sources of references.

The main methods available for the synthesis of borazines are condensation reactions between amines and boron hydrides or halides at about 200°, with the elimination of hydrogen or hydrogen halide,

$$3BX_3 + 3NR_3 \longrightarrow X_3B_3N_3R_3 + 6RX$$

(X = H, Cl, Br, Alk; R = H, Alk). Trialkylboranes condense with amines at temperatures higher than 300° to form B-trialkylborazines and alkanes. Choice of appropriate starting materials can therefore lead directly to borazines with the required substituent groups.

The reaction most widely used for the synthesis of borazines is that between boron halides and amines, which normally leads to the B-trihalogeno derivative, a useful intermediate in that the halogen may readily be replaced by hydrogen or organic groups. For example, B-trichloroborazine is obtained in about 50% yield by the passage of boron trichloride over ammonium chloride supported on asbestos at 200°, or by reaction between the same materials in chlorobenzene solution [448, 449, 450].

---

[445] J. R. Platt, H. B. Klevens and G. W. Schaeffer, *J. Chem. Phys.*, 1947, **15**, 598; L. E. Jacobs, J. R. Platt and G. W. Schaeffer, ibid., 1948, **16**, 116; C. W. Rector, G. W. Schaeffer and J. R. Platt, ibid., 1949, **17**, 460.

[446] R. Hoffmann, *Advan. in Chem. Series*, 1964, **42**, 78; O. Chalvet, R. Daudel and J. J. Kaufman, ibid., p. 251; J. Goubeau, ibid., p. 87; D. R. Shriver, D. E. Smith and P. Smith, *J. Amer. Chem. Soc.*, 1964, **86**, 5153; O. Chalvet, R. Daudel and J. J. Kaufman, ibid., 1965, **87**, 399; D. F. Shriver and P. M. Kuznesof, *Inorg. Chem.*, 1965, **4**, 434; P. G. Perkins and D. H. Wall, *J. Chem. Soc.*, 1966A, 235.

[447] H. C. Newsom, W. D. English, A. L. McCloskey and W. G. Woods, *J. Amer. Chem. Soc.*, 1961, **83**, 4134.

[448] E. F. Rothgery and L. F. Hohnstedt, *Inorg. Chem.*, 1967, **6**, 1065.

[449] G. Dahl and R. Schaeffer, *J. Inorg. Nucl. Chem.*, 1960, **12**, 380.

[450] C. A. Brown and A. W. Laubengayer, *J. Amer. Chem. Soc.*, 1955, **77**, 3699.

In the solution method, acetonitrile can be used to complex with the boron trichloride until the latter has reacted with the ammonium chloride [448]; otherwise a low-temperature condenser is needed to return boron trichloride continuously to the solution. Borazine itself is then prepared by reduction of the chloro derivative using sodium borohydride in diglyme or triglyme solution [449, 451]. Use of amine hydrochlorides instead of ammonium chloride affords N-substituted derivatives [452].

A particularly thorough study of the dehydrohalogenation reactions of adducts RNH_2,BX_3 (R = alkyl or aryl, X = Cl or Br) has been carried out by Turner and co-workers [453, 454], who have examined the effects on the reaction path of variations of conditions and of the nature and bulk of the groups R. Tetrameric borazynes $(RNBX)_4$ result from reactions in which alkyl groups R are very bulky (see below). The dehydrohalogenation of arylamine adducts $ArNH_2,BCl_3$ using Et_3N surprisingly leads to *di*chloroborazines $Ar_3N_3B_3HCl_2$; apparently Et_3N may function as a reducing agent as well as a scavenger for hydrogen halide in such reactions.

If B-alkyl or -aryl borazines are required, these may be obtained from the B-chloro compound by the Grignard reaction [455]

$$2Cl_3B_3N_3R_3 + 6R'MgBr \rightarrow 2R'_3B_3N_3R_3 + 3MgBr_2 + 3MgCl_2$$

Difficulties in isolating the product from such Grignard reactions are reduced if the borazine–magnesium halide mixture is treated with water after the ether has been removed by distillation [456], or if the mixture is refluxed with a tertiary amine [457]. Although alkylaluminium halides and related compounds are described as being useful for the alkylation of N-alkyl-B-chloroborazines [458], the reaction between triethylaluminium and B-trichloroborazine apparently results in complete breakdown of the borazine ring [459]:

$$Cl_3B_3N_3H_3 + 3AlEt_3 \rightarrow 3BEt_3 + (ClAlNH)_x$$

Phenylation of B-trichloroborazine has been effected by a Friedel–Crafts reaction [460]:

$$Cl_3B_3N_3H_3 + AlCl_3 + C_6H_6 \rightarrow Ph_3B_3N_3H_3$$

[451] D. T. Haworth and L. F. Hohnstedt, ibid., 1960, **82**, 89.

[452] I. M. Butcher and W. Gerrard, *J. Inorg. Nucl. Chem.*, 1965, **27**, 823, 2114.

[453] H. S. Turner and R. J. Warne, *J. Chem. Soc.*, 1965, 6421.

[454] R. K. Bartlett, H. S. Turner, R. J. Warne, M. A. Young and I. J. Lawrenson, ibid., 1966A, 479.

[455] D. T. Haworth and L. F. Hohnstedt, *J. Amer. Chem. Soc.*, 1960, **82**, 3860; S. J. Groszos and S. F. Stafiej, ibid., 1958, **80**, 1357.

[456] U. S. Borax and Chemical Corp., Ger.P. 1,131,673, June 20, 1962; *Chem. Abs.* 1962, **57**, 13801.

[457] Idem, Ger.P. 1,131,672, June 20, 1962; *Chem. Abs.*, 1962, **57**, 13801; U.S.P. 3,000,937; *Chem. Abs.*, 1962, **56**, 1479.

[458] Kali Chemie A.-G., Ger.P. 1,138,052; *Chem. Abs.*, 1963, **58**, 5722.

[459] W. G. Woods and A. L. McCloskey, *Inorg. Chem.*, 1963, **2**, 861.

[460] K. Niedenzu and J. W. Dawson, *Angew. Chem.*, 1959, **71**, 651.

Unsymmetrically substituted borazines are obtained either by exchange reactions, e.g. [461]

$$Me_3B_3N_3Me_3 + Cl_3B_3N_3Me_3 \underset{}{\overset{250-350°}{\rightleftharpoons}} ClMe_2B_3N_3Me_3 + Cl_2MeB_3N_3Me_3$$

or by the use of suitably limited quantities of a lithium or Grignard reagent [462]:

$$H_3B_3N_3H_3 \xrightarrow{PhMgBr} PhH_2B_3N_3H_3 + Ph_2HB_3N_3H_3 + \text{some } Ph_3B_3N_3H_3$$

The products may be separated by sublimation. Partial chlorination of borazine (to $H_3N_3B_3H_2Cl$ and $H_3N_3B_3HCl_2$) is conveniently effected by mercury(II) chloride [462a].

Many B-organofunctional borazines have been prepared by addition reactions with B-vinylborazines, e.g. [203, 463]

$$3Ph_3SnH + (CH_2{:}CH)_3B_3N_3Ph_3 \rightarrow (Ph_3SnCH_2CH_2)_3B_3N_3Ph_3$$

The B-vinylborazines themselves are normally preparable by the Grignard route, although specific derivatives are accessible only by hydrogenation of B-ethynylborazines [464]:

$$(RC{:}C)_3B_3N_3R'_3 \xrightarrow[\text{catalyst}]{H_2} (cis\text{-}RCH{:}CH)_3B_3N_3R'_3$$

Apart from their preparation from alkylamines, certain N-trialkyl-borazines may be obtained by bubbling diborane in nitrogen through a suitable refluxing nitrile, e.g. [1, 465]

$$MeCN + B_2H_6 \rightarrow H_3B_3N_3Et_3$$

Condensed borazines analogous to naphthalene ('borazanaphthalene', 3.60) and biphenyl ('biborazinyl', 3.61) have been prepared in small

3.60   3.61

[461] H. C. Newsom, W. G. Woods and A. L. McCloskey, *Inorg. Chem.*, 1963, **2**, 36; V. Gutmann, *Angew. Chem., Internat. Edn.*, 1965, **4**, 891.
[462] P. C. Moews and A. W. Laubengayer, *Inorg. Chem.*, 1963, **2**, 1072; J H. Smalley and S. F. Stafiej, *J. Amer. Chem. Soc.*, 1959, **81**, 582; V. Gutmann, A. Meller and R. Schleger, *Monatsh.*, 1963, **94**, 1071; P. Powell, J. A. Semlyen, R. E. Blofeld and C. S. G. Phillips, *J. Chem. Soc.*, 1964, 280; A. Grace and P. Powell, *J. Chem. Soc.* (*A*), 1966, 673.
[462a] R. Maruca, O. T. Beachley and A. W. Laubengayer, *Inorg. Chem.*, 1967, **6**, 575.
[463] D. Seyferth and H. P. Kögler, *J. Inorg. Nucl. Chem.*, 1960, **15**, 99.
[464] H. Watanabe, T. Totani and T. Yoshizaki, *Inorg. Chem.*, 1965, **4**, 657; T. Yoshizaki, H. Watanabe, K. Nagasawa, T. Totani and T. Nakagawa, ibid., p. 1016.
[465] H. J. Eméleus and K. Wade, *J. Chem. Soc.*, 1960, 2614; J. R. Jennings and K. Wade, unpublished observations; A. J. Leffler, *Inorg. Chem.*, 1964, **3**, 145.

quantities by the dehydrogenation of borazine by pyrolysis [466] or in a silent electrical discharge [467]. B-alkylated biborazinyls are also by-products in the alkylation of B-trichloroborazines, e.g. [468]

The coupling is accompanied by evolution of butane, and probably takes place via an N–MgX derivative. Reaction between N-*lithio borazines* (from the N–H compound and methyl lithium) and *haloborazines* has been used to prepare B–N linked borazine polymers with up to ten rings in a chain [469]. Other borazine polymers are obtained by controlled hydrolysis of B-chloro compounds, which forms chains of borazine rings linked by B–O–B units [469], or by reactions between BH or BCl compounds and diamines [470] or di-Grignard reagents such as $ClMg(CH_2)_4MgCl$, whereby B–$(CH_2)_4$–B linkages result [463]. Biborazinyls with B–B linkages may be prepared by the action of sodium on B-chloroborazines [471], while polymers containing such links appear to be formed from $Ph_3N_3B_3H_3$ at 420° [472].

Borazines are much more reactive than analogous benzene compounds towards most chemical reagents. A marked difference from benzene, which reflects the polarity of the bonds in the ring, is that borazine itself adds water, methanol, alkyl iodides and hydrogen halides, the negative parts of these reagents becoming attached to the boron atoms.

The products are cycloborazines, analogous to cyclohexane derivatives, and may be reduced to cycloborazane by sodium borohydride [473]. In

[466] A. W. Laubengayer, P. C. Moews and R. F. Porter, *J. Amer. Chem. Soc.*, 1961, **83**, 1337; G. Mamantov and J. L. Margrave, *J. Inorg. Nucl. Chem.*, 1961, **20**, 348.

[467] A. W. Laubengayer and O. T. Beachley, *Advan. in Chem. Series*, 1964, **42**, 281.

[468] J. J. Harris, *J. Org. Chem.*, 1961, **26**, 2155.

[469] R. I. Wagner and J. L. Bradford, *Inorg. Chem.*, 1962, **1**, 93, 99.

[470] J. M. Turner, *J. Chem. Soc.* (*A*), 1966, 401, 410, 415; V. V. Korshak, N. I. Bekasova and L. G. Komarova, *Izvest. Akad. Nauk S.S.S.R.*, 1965, 1462; *Chem. Abs.*, 1965, **63**, 16375.

[471] R. J. Brotherton and A. L. McCloskey, U.S.P. 3,101,369; *Chem. Abs.*, 1964, **60**, 547.

[472] V. V. Korshak, V. A. Zamyatina, N. I. Bekasova and L. G. Komarova, *Izvest. Akad. Nauk S.S.S.R.*, 1964, 2223; *Chem. Abs.*, 1965, **62**, 7786.

[473] G. H. Dahl and R. Schaeffer, *J. Amer. Chem. Soc.*, 1961, **83**, 3032; D. F. Gaines and R. Schaeffer, ibid., 1963, **85**, 3592.

contrast to earlier reports, the adducts with hydrogen halides do *not* form B-halogenated borazines on heating, but instead dissociate to the parent borazine and hydrogen halide, with concurrent decomposition to involatile material and hydrogen [413]. The reactivity of borazines to such addition reactions and consequently to hydrolysis is reduced markedly if bulky substituents are attached to boron and nitrogen [473a].

Borazines have recently been shown to be capable of forming π-complexes with transition metals [473b]. For example, hexamethylborazine displaces the nitrile ligands from $(MeCN)_3Cr(CO)_3$ in dioxan solution at 30°, to form $(\pi-Me_3N_3B_3Me_3)Cr(CO)_3$. This compound appears likely to be the first example of many such complexes, which however are expected to prove less stable than their benzene analogues [473c].

The borazines $(RBNR')_3$ are examples of *trimeric borazynes*. Oligomers other than trimers are obtained if the substitents R and R' are too bulky to be accommodated about a planar six-membered ring. For example *tetrameric* borazynes or *borazocines* are obtained from t-butylamine and boron trichloride [453, 474]:

$$4Bu^tNH_2 + 4BCl_3 \longrightarrow (Bu^tNBCl)_4 + 8HCl$$

The products have a boat-shaped ring (3.62) like that of cyclo-octatetraene.

In the borazyne system $(Bu^iNBPh)_n$ which results from the elimination of HCl from $Bu^iNH_3^+PhBCl_3^-$ or $Bu^iNH_2,PhBCl_2$ using Et_3N, both the borazocine $(Bu^iNBPh)_4$, m.p. 232°, and borazine $(Bu^iNBPh)_3$, m.p. 134° have been prepared [475]. The tetramer changes into the trimer at 250°. An earlier report of more highly polymeric species in the same system, prepared by the pyrolytic elimination of isobutylamine from $(Bu^iNH)_2BPh$, has not been confirmed by subsequent work [476].

3.62   3.63   3.64

[473a] K. Nagasawa, *Inorg. Chem.*, 1966, **5**, 442.
[473b] R. Prinz and H. Werner, *Angew. Chem., Internat. Edn.*, 1967, **6**, 91.
[473c] D. A. Brown and C. G. McCormack, *Chem. Comm.*, 1967, 383.
[474] H. S. Turner and R. J. Warne, *Proc. Chem. Soc.*, 1962, 69; *Advan. in Chem. Series*, 1964, **42**, 290; *J. Chem. Soc.*, 1965, 6421; J. H. S. Green, W. Kynaston and H. M. Paisley, *Advan. in Chem. Series*, 1964, **42**, 301; P. T. Clarke and H. M. Powell, *I.U.P.A.C. 19th Int. Conf. London, July 1963*, abstracts AB4–78.
[475] B. R. Currell, W. Gerrard and M. Khodabocus, *Chem. Comm.*, 1966, 77.
[476] J. E. Burch, W. Gerrard and E. G. Mooney, *J. Chem. Soc.*, 1962, 2200; J. A. Semlyen and P. J. Flory, *J. Chem. Soc. (A)*, 1966, 191.

Dimeric borazynes (1,3-diaza-2,4-boretanes, 3.63) may be obtained by condensation reactions from t-butylaminoboron compounds [477], or by a rearrangement reaction of azidodiphenylborane [478]:

$$\text{LiN}_3 + \text{Ph}_2\text{BCl} \rightarrow \text{Ph}_2\text{BN}_3 \xrightarrow{-\text{N}_2} [\text{PhBNPh}] \rightarrow (\text{PhBNPh})_2 \qquad (3.64)$$

Thermal decomposition of the *pyridine adduct* of azidodiphenylborane, Ph_2BN_3.py, leads to trimers, i.e. borazines, through the intermediates Ph_2BN and PhB=NPh, detected by reactions with Me_2NH and PhCN_2Ph [478]:

Monomeric borazynes $\text{C}_6\text{F}_5\text{B}\equiv\text{NR}$ (R = p-anisyl or mesityl) have been prepared from pentafluorophenylboron dichloride and the aryl amine in boiling benzene [478a]. These compounds are formal analogues of alkynes, and the high BN bond order is reflected in the high frequency (1703 cm^{-1}, with a ^{10}B subsidiary at 1710 cm^{-1}) of the boron–nitrogen stretching vibration of the anisyl derivative. This is Raman but not infrared active, a feature attributed to the electron-withdrawing properties of the pentafluorophenyl group which is considered to strengthen the two possible BN π bonds and render the BN link effectively non-polar. The anisyl derivative forms a pyridine adduct $\text{C}_6\text{F}_5\text{BNC}_6\text{H}_4\text{OMe}$,py and appears capable of Diels–Alder type reactions.

Borazarenes

One of the most important recent advances in organoboron chemistry has been the development in the chemistry of heteroaromatic boron compounds during the last few years, which has opened up a whole new field

[477] M. F. Lappert and M. K. Majumdar, *Proc. Chem. Soc.*, 1963, 88; *Advan. in Chem. Series*, 1964, **42**, 208. See also C. R. Russ and A. G. MacDiarmid, *Angew. Chem., Internat. Edn.*, 1964, **3**, 509.

[478] P. I. Paetzold, *Z. anorg. Chem.*, 1963, **326**, 53, 58, 64; P. I. Paetzold, P. P. Habereder and R. Müllbauer, *J. Organometal. Chem.*, 1967, **7**, 45, 51; P. I. Paetzold and P. P. Habereder, ibid., p. 71.

[478a] P. I. Paetzold and W. M. Simson, *Angew. Chem., Internat. Edn.*, 1966, **5**, 842.

of heteroaromatic chemistry. Most of the compounds obtained have resembled normal organic compounds in their chemical stability, in marked contrast to the air-sensitivity of many simpler organoboron compounds. Most of the work in this field has been carried out by M. J. S. Dewar and his co-workers, and the subject has recently been reviewed by Dewar [7]. Only the main features can be outlined here.

Most of the borazarenes so far described have been multi-ring systems such as the 10,9-borazarophenanthrenes (3.65), the 2,1-borazaronaphthalenes (3.66) and various benzo derivatives of these. Compounds have also been prepared with heteroatoms at bridgeheads (e.g. 3.67) as well as boron-containing analogues of quinoline and isoquinoline (3.68).

Condensation of 2-aminobiphenyl with boron trichloride and aluminium chloride gives *10-chloro-10,9-borazarophenanthrene* (3.65, R′ = Cl), apparently through Friedel–Crafts cyclization of an intermediate aryl-

| 3.65 | 3.66 | 3.67 | 3.68 |
| 10,9– | 2,1– | 10,9– | 4,3– |

| borazarophenanthrenes | borazaronaphthalenes | borazaroisoquinolines |

aminodichloroborane, ArNHBCl₂ [479]. Treatment of the product with water, Grignard reagents or lithium aluminium hydride gives the B-hydroxy, -alkyl or -aryl derivatives, or the parent heterocycle. Although the B–Cl and B–H compounds are readily hydrolysed, B-alkyl or -aryl derivatives are particularly resistant to hydrolytic attack, the phenyl compound being unchanged by boiling 40% potassium hydroxide or concentrated hydrochloric acid [480].

Substitution of the benzene rings of 10,9-borazarophenanthrenes occurs with the usual electrophilic reagents, and the positions of substitution in nitration [481], chlorination [482] and Friedel–Crafts acetylation [483] reactions agree with predictions of reactivity derived from a molecular orbital treatment [7, 484]. Substitution at the nitrogen atom is effected through the N-lithio derivative (3.65, R = Li), obtained by the action of

[479] M. J. S. Dewar, V. P. Kubba and R. Pettit, *J. Chem. Soc.*, 1958, 3073; M. J. S. Dewar, J. Hashmall and V. P. Kubba, *J. Org. Chem.*, 1964, **29**, 1755.
[480] M. J. S. Dewar, R. Dietz, V. P. Kubba, and A. R. Lepley, *J. Amer. Chem. Soc.*, 1961, **83**, 1754.
[481] M. J. S. Dewar and V. O. Kubba, *Tetrahedron*, 1959, **7**, 213.
[482] Idem, *J. Org. Chem.*, 1960, **25**, 1722.
[483] Idem, *J. Amer. Chem. Soc.*, 1961, **83**, 1757.
[484] J. J. Kaufman and J. R. Hamann, *Advan. in Chem. Series*, 1964, **42**, 273.

methyl-lithium on the N–H compound. The B–N bond is broken by treatment of 10-hydroxy-10,9-borazarophenanthrene with sodium nitrite in acetic acid, apparently through decomposition of the N-nitroso derivative [485].

Benzo derivatives of borazarophenanthrene such as the pyrene 3.69 may be prepared by heating appropriate derivatives of 2-aminobiphenyl with boron trichloride or dichlorophenylborane in the presence of aluminium chloride [486]. Use of 2,6-diaminobiphenyl with two moles of dichlorophenylborane in the presence of aluminium chloride gives a compound with two boron atoms, 5,9-diphenyl-5,9-dibora-4,10-diazaropyrene (3.70) [487]:

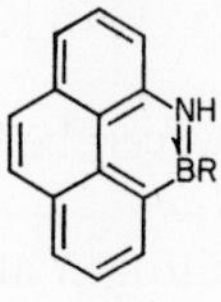

3.69 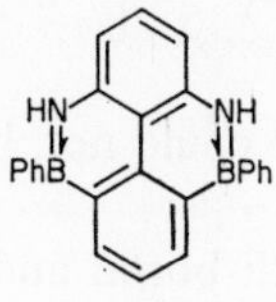   3.70

Compounds containing only *one* ring fused with borazarene are obtained from *o*-aminostyrene or its derivatives. When *o*-aminostyrene is heated with boron trichloride or dichlorophenylborane in the absence of a catalyst, 2-chloro- or 2-phenyl-2,1-borazaronaphthalene is formed in good yield [479, 488].

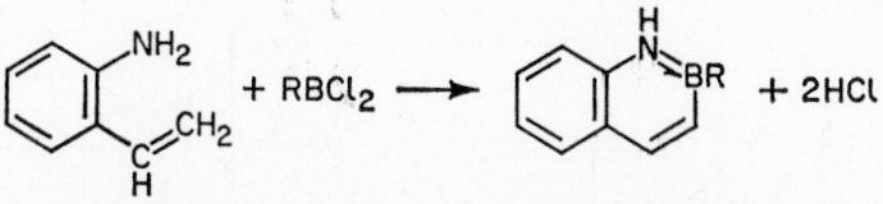

The 2,1-borazaronaphthalenes have properties similar to those of the 10,9-borazarophenanthrenes. Substituent groups can be attached to the boron or nitrogen in the same way, and the products are very stable to hydrolysis by hot strong acid or alkali. That this stability is associated primarily with the aromatic nature of the ring is shown by the ready hydrolysis of the dihydro derivative 3.71 [489]:

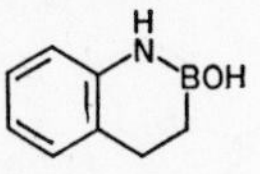

3.71

[485] M. J. S. Dewar and P. M. Maitlis, *J. Amer. Chem. Soc.*, 1961, **83**, 187; idem, *Tetrahedron*, 1961, **15**, 35.

[486] M. J. S. Dewar, J. Hashmall and V. P. Kubba, *J. Org. Chem.*, 1964, **29**, 1755; M. J. S. Dewar and W. H. Poesche, ibid., p. 1757.

[487] S. S. Chissick, M. J. S. Dewar and P. M. Maitlis, *Tetrahedron Letters*, 1960, **23**, 8.

[488] M. J. S. Dewar and R. Dietz., *J. Chem. Soc.*, 1959, 2728.

[489] Idem, *Tetrahedron*, 1961, **15**, 26.

K

10,9-Borazaronaphthalene has been prepared in very low yield by the following sequence of reactions [490]:

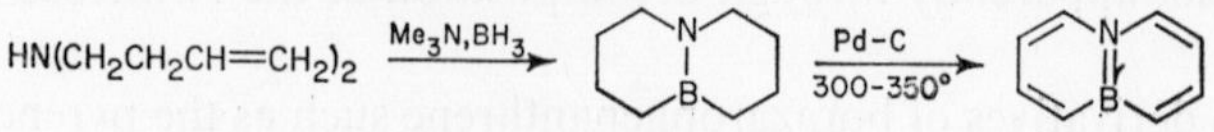

If the Friedel–Crafts cyclization procedure is applied to heterocyclic amines, the resulting borazarene has a nitrogen atom at a bridgehead, e.g.:

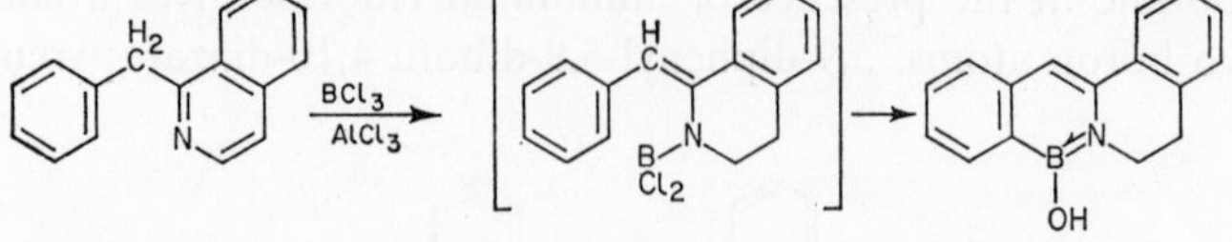

The product in this case could not, however, be hydrogenated to the fully aromatic system [491].

Compounds with both boron and nitrogen at bridgeheads can be obtained from other borazarenes. For example, 12,11-borazarophenanthrene (3.72) is obtained by the following sequence of reactions [491]:

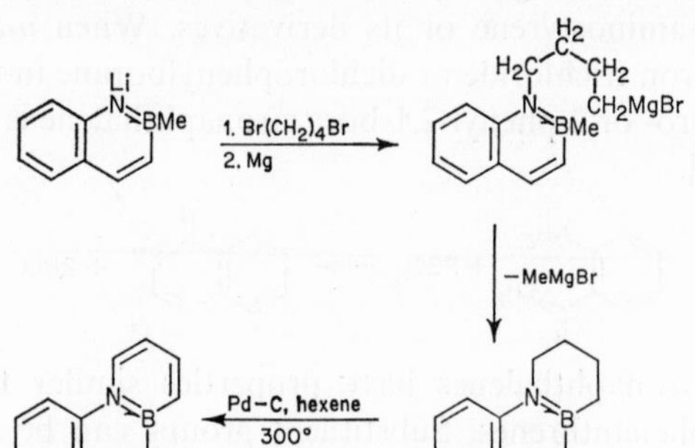

3.72

A fused-ring system (3.73) may also be obtained by heating 4-amino-1-butene hydrochloride with lithium borohydride under pressure [492]:

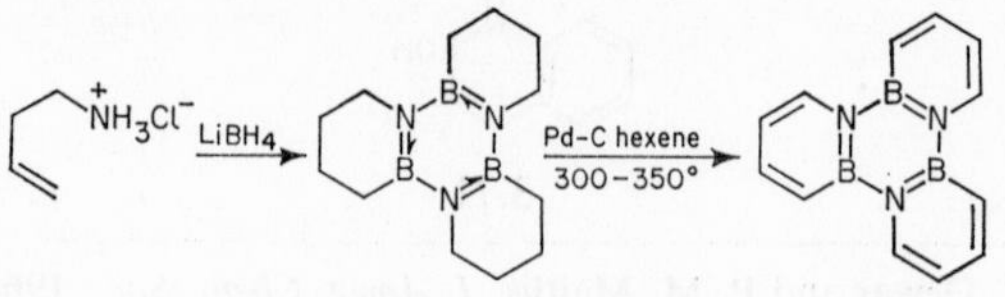

3.73

[490] M. J. S. Dewar, G. J. Gleicher and B. P. Robinson, *J. Amer. Chem. Soc.*, 1964, **86**, 5698.
[491] M. J. S. Dewar, C. Kaneko and M. K. Bhattachargee, ibid., 1962, **84**, 4884.
[492] G. C. Culling, M. J. S. Dewar and P. A. Marr, ibid., 1964, **86**, 1125.

This particular reaction sequence would afford a route to the parent borazarene if the product could be hydrolysed to three molecules of 2-hydroxyborazarene.

A more complex fused-ring system based on three borazarophenanthrene units has also been described [493].

2-Phenyl-2,1-borazarene has been prepared by a modification of this last route, using 4-amino-1-butene and the trimethylamine complex of phenylborane as starting materials [494]:

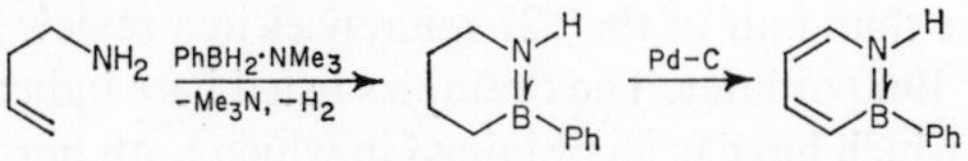

Compounds related to *isoquinoline* have been prepared from hydrazine or phenylhydrazine and o-formylphenylboronic acid [495],

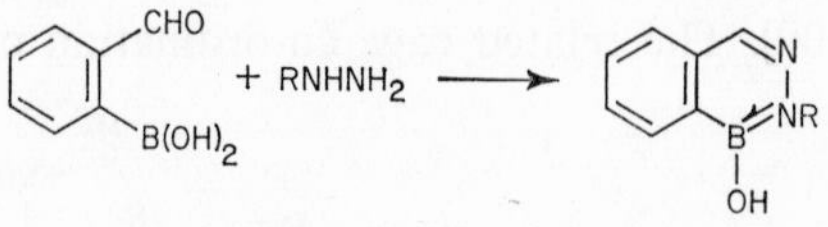

while use of hydroxylamine instead of hydrazine leads to the analogous boroxaroisoquinoline, 3.74 [496]. This last compound shows only weak

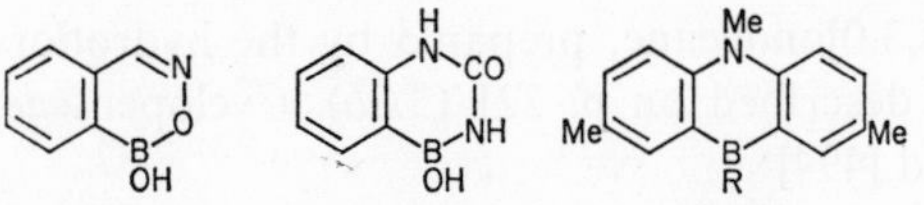

3.74   3.75   3.76

aromatic character, as do the *quinoline* analogue 3.75 (from phenylurea and boron tribromide in the presence of aluminium bromide [497]) and the *10,9-borazaroanthracenes* 3.76 (from *bis*-(2'-lithio-*p*-tolyl)-N-methylamine and dichlorophenylborane or boron trichloride [498]).

Most of the borazarenes already mentioned have a boron atom and a nitrogen atom in place of a pair of carbon atoms in known 6-membered

[493] R. Köster, S. Hattori and Y. Morita, *Angew. Chem., Internat. Edn.*, 1965, **4**, 695.

[494] D. G. White, *J. Amer. Chem. Soc.*, 1963, **85**, 3634; see also G. B. Butler and G. L. Statton, ibid., 1964, **86**, 518; B. M. Mikhailov, V. A. Dorokhov and N. V. Mostovoi, *Izvest. Akad. Nauk S.S.S.R.*, 1964, 201, 202; *Chem. Abs.*, 1964, **60**, 13261.

[495] M. J. S. Dewar and R. C. Dougherty, *J. Amer. Chem. Soc.*, 1962, **84**, 2648; 1964, **86**, 433; P. Tschampel and H. R. Snyder, *J. Org. Chem.*, 1964, **29**, 2168; M. J. S. Dewar and J. L. Von Rosenberg, *J. Amer. Chem. Soc.*, 1966, **88**, 358.

[496] H. R. Synder, A. J. Reedy and W. I. Lennarz, ibid., 1958, **80**, 835.

[497] M. J. S. Dewar and R. C. Dougherty, unpublished work quoted in ref. [7].

[498] P. M. Maitlis, *J. Chem. Soc.*, 1961, 425.

aromatic ring systems. Systems in which *four* carbon atoms have been replaced by two boron–nitrogen pairs are also known, e.g. [499]

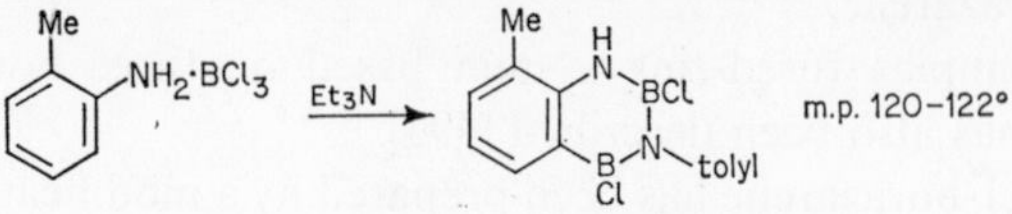

m.p. 120–122°

Miscellaneous heterocyclic organoboron–nitrogen compounds
Heterocyclic organic boron compounds are currently receiving much attention; more than half of the 127 references in a review [6] published in 1962 are dated 1960 or later. The examples listed here indicate the diversity of the systems which have been obtained in which both boron and nitrogen atoms occur in the ring.

Cyclic *co-ordination compounds*, which have already been exemplified by the alkanolamine esters of borinic and boronic acids, are also illustrated by the cyclopentane analogue 3.77, obtained by the hydroboration of allyl-dimethylamine [500]. The related cage co-ordination compound 1-aza-5-

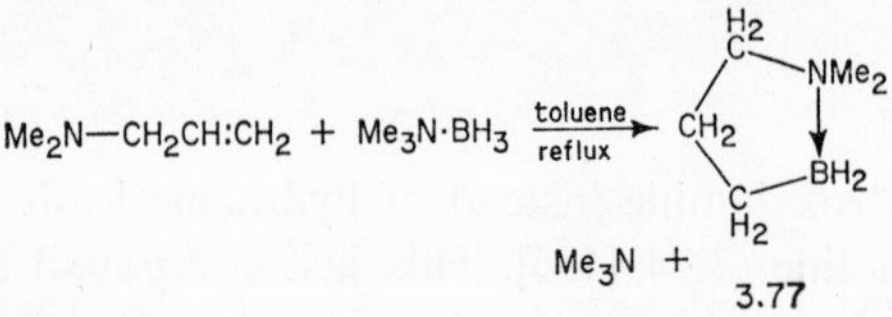

$$\text{Me}_2\text{N}-\text{CH}_2\text{CH:CH}_2 + \text{Me}_3\text{N}\cdot\text{BH}_3 \xrightarrow[\text{reflux}]{\text{toluene}}$$

$$\text{Me}_3\text{N} +$$

3.77

boratricyclo[3,3,3,0]undecane, prepared by the hydroboration of triallyl-amine [211], is described on p. 221 (3.2*b*). Cyclopent*ene* analogues may also be prepared [494]:

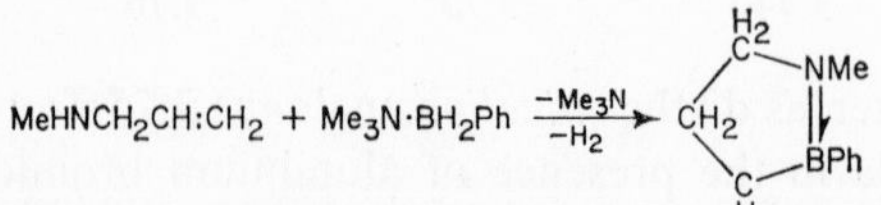

$$\text{MeHNCH}_2\text{CH:CH}_2 + \text{Me}_3\text{N}\cdot\text{BH}_2\text{Ph} \xrightarrow[-\text{H}_2]{-\text{Me}_3\text{N}}$$

The preparation of *cyclic diaminoboranes* (e.g. 3.78) is conveniently achieved by transamination reactions [501]:

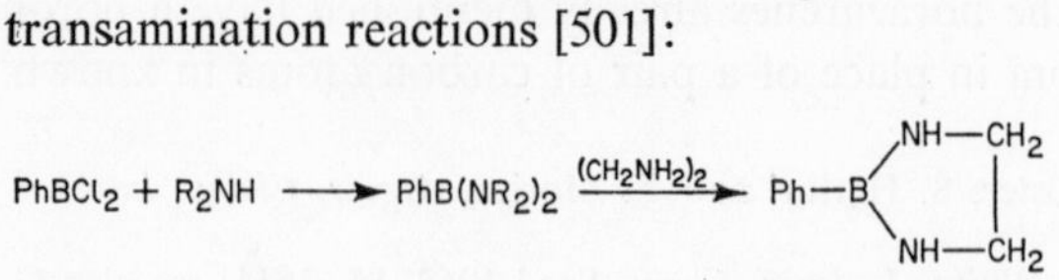

$$\text{PhBCl}_2 + \text{R}_2\text{NH} \longrightarrow \text{PhB(NR}_2)_2 \xrightarrow{(\text{CH}_2\text{NH}_2)_2}$$

3.78

[499] H. S. Turner, R. J. Warne and I. K. Lawrenson, *Chem. Comm.* 1965, 20.
[500] R. M. Adams and F. D. Poholsky, *Inorg. Chem.*, 1963, **2**, 640; B. M. Mik-hailov, V. A. Dorokhov and N. V. Mostovoi, *Izvest. Akad. Nauk S.S.S.R.*, 1964, 199; *Chem. Abs.*, 1964, **60**, 9301; G. B. Butler, G. L. Statton and W. S. Brey, *J. Org. Chem.*, 1965, **30**, 4194.
[501] K. Niedenzu, H. Beyer and J. W. Dawson, *Inorg. Chem.*, 1962, **1**, 738; see

A similar ring system to the example above is said to result from the curious reaction [502]:

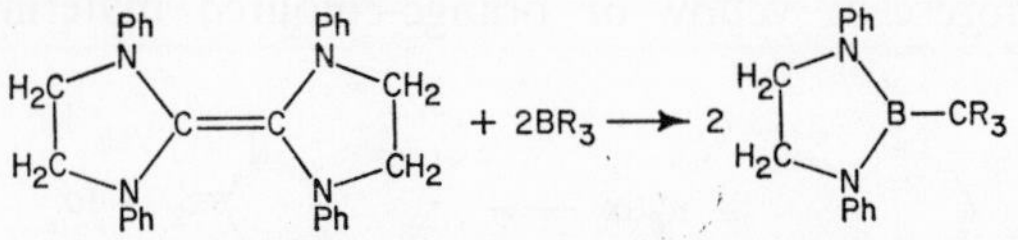

The unsaturated *1,3,2-benzodiazaboroles* (3.79) are obtained by the reaction between *o*-phenylenediamine and a boronic acid, ester or boroxine [503, 504, 505], or an organoboron-dichloride [506] or -dihydride [507]. The transamination reaction has also been used [508].

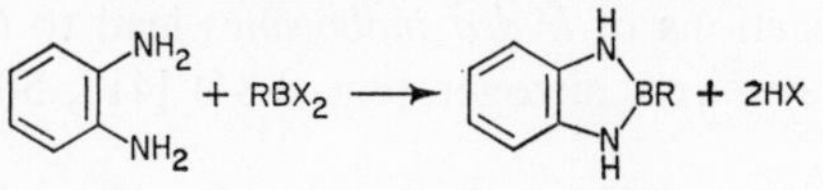

3.79

(X = OH, OR', Cl, H or NR'₂). The parent compound (R = H) can be prepared from *o*-phenylenediamine monohydrochloride and sodium borohydride [509]. Their electronic spectra resemble those of benziminazoles, and indicate some multiple B–N bonding. Being quite stable to hydrolysis, these compounds have been used for isolating and characterizing alkylboronic acids. The melting points of many of these derivatives, and of some benzodioxaboroles, are tabulated in reference [6]. A number of related systems, such as 3.79a [509a], 3.80 [504, 505], 3.81 [505] and 3.82 [510] have been prepared.

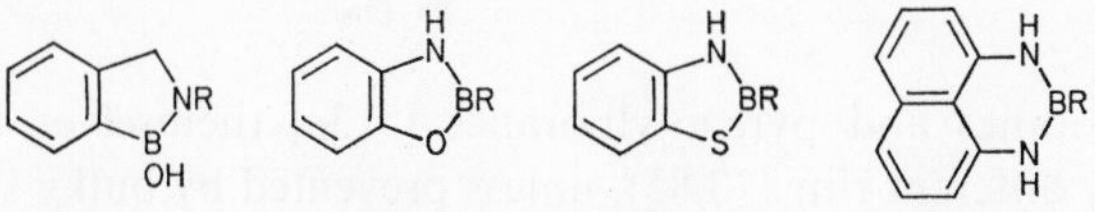

3.79a   3.80   3.81   3.82

also E. W. Abel and R. P. Bush, *J. Organometal. Chem.*, 1965, **3**, 245; W. Weber, J. W. Dawson and K. Niedenzu, *Inorg. Chem.*, 1966, **5**, 726; J. W. Dawson, P. Fritz and K. Niedenzu, *J. Organometal. Chem.*, 1966, **5**, 211.

[502] G. Hesse and A. Haag, *Tetrahedron Letters*, 1965, 1123.
[503] R. L. Letsinger and S. B. Hamilton, *J. Amer. Chem. Soc.*, 1958, **80**, 5411; E. Nyilas and A. H. Soloway, ibid., 1959, **81**, 2681; R. T. Hawkins and H. R. Snyder, ibid., 1960, **82**, 3863.
[504] R. J. Brotherton and H. Steinberg, *J. Org. Chem.*, 1961, **26**, 4632; R. Hemming and D. G. Johnston, *J. Chem. Soc.*, 1964, 466.
[505] M. Pailer and W. Fenzl, *Monatsh.*, 1961, **92**, 1294.
[506] L. F. Hohnstedt and A. M. Pellicciotto, *U.S. Dept. Comm., Office Tech. Serv.*, *AD* 256,420 (1962); *Chem. Abs.*, 1963, **58**, 7960.
[507] M. F. Hawthorne, *J. Amer. Chem. Soc.*, 1959, **81**, 5836; 1961, **83**, 831.
[508] H. Beyer, K. Niedenzu and J. W. Dawson, *J. Org. Chem.*, 1962, **27**, 4701.
[509] J. Goubeau and H. Schneider, *Annalen*, 1964, **675**, 1.
[509a] R. T. Hawkins and A. U. Blackham, *J. Org. Chem.*, 1967, **32**, 597.
[510] F. F. Caserio, J. J. Cavallo and R. I. Wagner, ibid., 1961, **26**, 2157.

The *2-bora-1,3-diaza-azulenes* (3.83), prepared by the reaction of 1-amino-7-imino-1,3,5 cycloheptatrienes with selected boron esters or halides are fluorescent yellow or orange-coloured materials which are

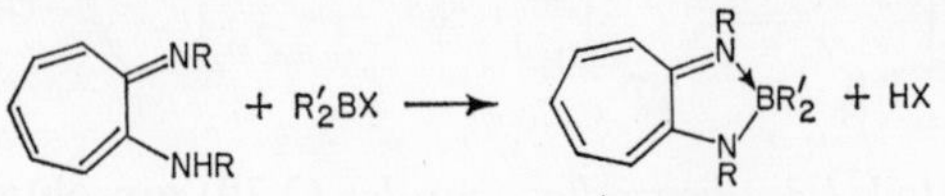

3.83

very stable to hydrolysis; aryl or alkoxy substituents on the boron are hydrolytically cleaved before the B–N bonds are ruptured [511].

Condensation reactions of *hydrazinoboranes* lead to 6-membered rings containing only boron and nitrogen (e.g. 3.84) [417, 501, 512, 513]. The

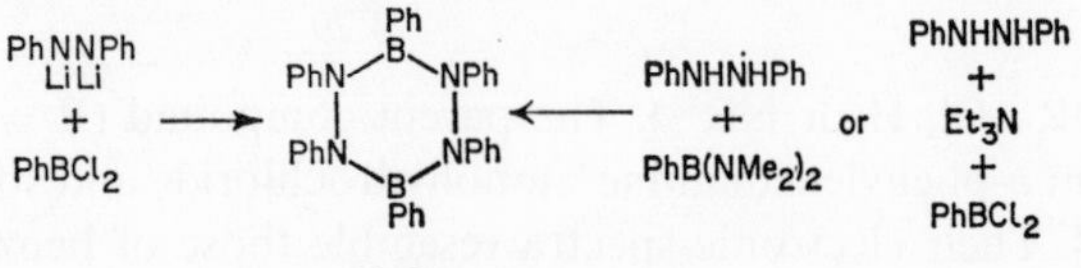

3.84

same ring system is obtained by the hydroboration of azobenzene [513]:

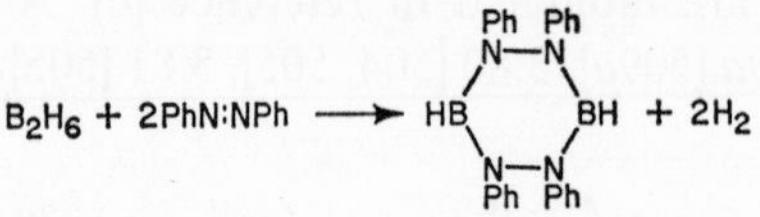

Hydrazinoboranes and pyrazolylboranes [513a] themselves dimerize to form slightly different rings (3.85), unless prevented by bulky substituents.

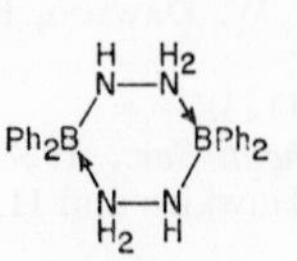

3.85a   3.85b   3.86

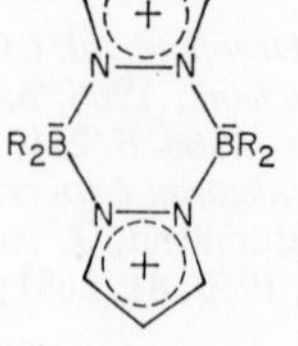

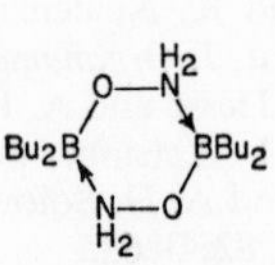

[511] H. E. Holmquist and R. E. Benson, *J. Amer. Chem. Soc.*, 1962, **84**, 4720.

[512] H. Nöth, *Angew. Chem.*, 1960, **72**, 40; M. F. Lappert, M. K. Majumdar and B. Prokai, *Int. Symp. on Boron–Nitrogen Chemistry, Durham, N.C.*, April, 1963, Preprints p. 161.

[513] H. Nöth and W. Regnet, *Advan. in Chem. Series*, 1964, **42**, 166.

[513a] S. Trofimenko, *J. Amer. Chem. Soc.*, 1966, **88**, 1842.

The related 'bon-bon' ring (3.86) is formed by the reaction between a boronic acid and hydroxylamine [514]:

$$Bu^n_2BOH + NH_2OH \xrightarrow{EtOH} (Bu^n_2BONH_2)_2 \text{ d. } 130°$$

Compounds of the type R_2BONR_2 were first isolated from the complex mixture of products of the reaction between nitric oxide and tributylborane [514], which apparently proceeds by rearrangement reactions involving an adduct R_3BNO when carried out at low temperatures, although at elevated temperatures the reaction seems to involve co-ordination through oxygen, R_3BON [515].

A 'bon-bon' cyclic structure has been proposed for crystalline dimethylboron acetoxime $Me_2BON:CMe_2$ (from trimethylborane and acetoxime) [515a].

$$Me_3B + Me_2C:NOH \longrightarrow \tfrac{1}{2}Me_2C = N \overset{\displaystyle O - BMe_2}{\underset{\displaystyle Me_2B - O}{\bigcirc}} N = CMe_2$$

This compound is partly dissociated in benzene solution, and completely dissociated in the gas phase. Pyridine-2-aldoxime $C_5H_4N \cdot CH:NOH$ gives a monomeric boron derivative $C_5H_4N \cdot CH:NOBMe_2$ [515b].

The reaction between trialkylboranes, triarylboranes or diborane and *hydrogen cyanide* or *isonitriles* leads to other cyclic compounds related to pyrazine, e.g.:

$$\begin{array}{c} 2Bu_3B \\ + \\ 2PhNC \end{array} \xrightarrow{Et_2O} \quad \underset{Ph}{BuC} \overset{N}{\underset{N}{\bigcirc}} BBu_2 \quad \xrightarrow{>200°} \quad Bu_2C \overset{Ph}{\underset{N}{\bigcirc}} BBu$$

The products are stable crystalline substances, readily soluble in non-polar solvents, and are unaffected by boiling aqueous acids or alkalies [516].

[514] L. P. Kuhn and M. Inatome, ibid., 1963, **85**, 1206; M. Inatome and L. P. Kuhn, *Advan. in Chem. Series*, 1964, **42**, 183. See also H. J. Roth and B. Miller, *Archiv. der Pharmazie*, 1964, **297**, 744.

[515] M. H. Abraham, J. H. N. Garland, J. A. Hill and L. F. Larkworthy, *Chem. and Ind.*, 1962, 1615; S. J. Brois, *Tetrahedron Letters*, 1964, 345.

[515a] J. R. Jennings and K. Wade, *J. Chem. Soc. (A)*, 1967, 1333.

[515b] I. Pattison and K. Wade, unpublished observations.

[516] G. Hesse and H. Witte, *Angew. Chem.*, 1963, **75**, 791; *Annalen*, 1965, **687**, 1; G. Hesse, H. Witte and G. Bittner, ibid., p. 9; J. Casanova and R. E. Schuster, *Tetrahedron Letters*, 1964, 405; S. Bresadola, G. Carraro, C. Pecile and A. Turco, ibid., p. 3185; J. Tanaka and J. C. Carter, ibid., 1965, 329; S. Bresadola, F. Rossetto and G. Puosi, ibid., p. 4775; G. Hesse, H. Witte, and H. Haussleiter, *Angew. Chem. Internat. Edn.*, 1966, **5**, 723.

They are capable of further isomerization, particularly in the presence of Lewis acids [517]:

$$R'_2C \begin{matrix} R \\ N \\ \end{matrix} BR' \longrightarrow R'_2C \begin{matrix} R \\ N \\ \end{matrix} B-CR'_3 \longrightarrow R'_3C-B \begin{matrix} \\ N \\ R \end{matrix} B-CR'_3$$

Related saturated compounds have been prepared from the boronium salt $H_2B(NMe_3)_2Cl$ [518]:

$$NaH + H_2B(NMe_3)_2Cl \longrightarrow \begin{matrix} & Me_2 & \\ & N & \\ H_2C & & BH_2 \\ & & \\ H_2B & & CH_2 \\ & N & \\ & Me_2 & \end{matrix}$$

Use of butyl-lithium instead of sodium hydride leads to a material believed to contain both boron and lithium in a six-membered ring [518a]:

$$2BuLi + H_2B(NMe_3)_2Cl \xrightarrow[\text{hexane}]{20°} \begin{matrix} & Me_2 & \\ & N & \\ H_2C & & Li \\ & & \\ H_2B & & CH_2 \\ & N & \\ & Me_2 & \end{matrix} \quad m.p.\ 112-114°$$

Rings containing *three* nitrogen atoms (e.g. 3.87) have been obtained by reactions between *isocyanates* and B-trialkylborazines [519]. Use of *ureas*

$$Me_3B_3N_3H_3 + 6\ RNCO \longrightarrow 3 \begin{matrix} & Me & \\ & B & \\ HN & & NR \\ & & \\ OC & & CO \\ & N & \\ & R & \end{matrix}$$

3.87

instead of isocyanates leaves a larger section of the borazine ring intact (3.88). The related sulphur and silicon compounds (3.89, 90) have been

$$\begin{matrix} & Me & \\ & B & \\ HN & & NMe \\ & & \\ MeB & & CO \\ & N & \\ & Me & \end{matrix} \qquad \begin{matrix} & Ph & \\ & B & \\ HN & & NH \\ & & \\ O_2S & & SO_2 \\ & N & \\ & H & \end{matrix} \qquad \begin{matrix} & Ph & \\ & B & \\ HN & & NH \\ & & \\ R_2Si & & SiR_2 \\ & N & \\ & R' & \end{matrix}$$

3.88   **3.89**   **3.90**

[517] J. Casanova, H. R. Kiefer, D. Kuwada and A. H. Boulton, *Tetrahedron Letters*, 1965, 703; H. Witte, ibid., p. 1127.

[518] N. E. Miller and E. L. Muetterties, *Inorg. Chem.*, 1964, **3**, 1196; N. E. Miller, M. D. Murphy and D. L. Reznicek, ibid 1966, **5**, 1832.

[518a] N. E. Miller, *J. Amer. Chem. Soc.*, 1966, **88**, 4284.

[519] J. L. Boone and G. W. Willcockson, *142nd A.C.S. Meeting, Atlantic City N.J.*, Sept. 1962, Abstracts, p. 6N; J. L. Boone, U.S.P. 3,060,234, Oct. 23, 1962; *Chem. Abs.*, 1963, **58**, 5704.

prepared by transamination reactions [520]. An unsaturated ring (3.91) is obtained from biguanide and an aminoborane [521]. Other systems, such

3.91   3.92   3.93   3.94

as 3.92, 93, and 94, have been prepared and shown to be biologically active [522].

The reaction between aminoboranes and isocyanates RNCO or iso-thiocyanates RNCS is similar to the hydroboration reaction of boron hydrides in that addition to the N=C bond occurs:

$$RN{=}C{=}O + R'_2BNR''_2 \rightarrow R'_2B.NR.CO.NR''_2$$

This *aminoboration* reaction appears to be much more limited in scope than the hydroboration reaction. When it is applied to *cyclic diamino-boranes*, a larger ring (e.g. 3.95) results [523]. For further recently described

3.95

boron–nitrogen ring systems see ref. [524]. One surprisingly innocuous example which deserves mention is the cyclotetrazenoborane system which

[520] J. W. Dawson, H. Beyer, H. Jenne and K. Niedenzu, *19th I.U.P.A.C. Congress*, *London*, July 1963, Abstracts AB4–71.

[521] J. E. Milks, G. W. Kennerly and J. H. Polevy, *J. Amer. Chem. Soc.*, 1962, **84**, 2529.

[522] H. L. Yale, F. H. Bergeim, F. A. Sowinski, J. Bernstein and J. Fried, ibid., p. 688.

[523] R. H. Cragg, M. F. Lappert and B. P. Tilley, *J. Chem. Soc.*, 1964, 2108; H. Beyer, J. W. Dawson, H. Jenne and K. Niedenzu, ibid., p. 2115; R. H. Cragg and M. F. Lappert, *Advan. in Chem. Series*, 1964, **42**, 220; T. L. Heying and H. D. Smith, ibid., p. 201.

[524] H. Watanabe, K. Nagasawa, T. Totani, T. Yoshizaki, and T. Nakagawa, ibid., p. 116; R. Köster and K. Iwasaki, ibid., p. 148; K. Niedenzu, P. Fritz and H. Jenne, *Angew. Chem.*, 1964, **3**, 506; M. Pailer and H. Huemer, *Monatsh.*, 1964, **95**, 373; K. Nagasawa, T. Yoshizaki and H. Watanabe, *Inorg. Chem.*, 1965, **4**, 275; P. Fritz, K. Niedenzu and J. W. Dawson, ibid., 1964, **3**, 1077; 1965, **4**, 886; F. G. Sherif and C. D. Schmulbach, ibid., 1966, **5**, 322.

results from reactions between organic azides and primary amine boranes [525]:

$$RN_3 + R'NH_2, BH_3 \longrightarrow$$

R = R' = Me, m.p. 11°

R = R' = Ph, m.p. 117°

Despite the chain of four nitrogen atoms in these compounds, the derivatives known at present (1966) are comparatively stable to heat and have proved insensitive to hammering.

Organoboron–sulphur compounds [14, 27]

Organoboron–sulphur compounds have been studied relatively little by comparison with their oxygen counterparts, although sulphur analogues of many of the simpler types of organoboron–oxygen compound are known, e.g. adducts $R_3B.SR'_2$, thioborinic esters R_2BSR', thioboronic esters $RB(SR')_2$ and 'borosulpholes' $(RBS)_3$.

The existence of a co-ordination compound $Me_3B.SMe_2$, m.p. $-42°$, which is stable only at low temperatures, may be contrasted with the non-existence of $Me_3B.OMe_2$. It is suggested that there is less crowding of the methyl groups in the sulphur compound than there would be in the ether adduct, rather than that trimethylborane can show a 'back-co-ordination' effect like borane [526].

Thioborinates R_2BSR' and thioboronates $RB(SR')_2$ may be prepared from the appropriate chloride and a sodium mercaptide [527]:

$$Bu_2BCl + EtSNa \rightarrow Bu_2BSEt + NaCl$$
$$PhBCl_2 + 2C_5H_{11}SNa \rightarrow PhB(SC_5H_{11})_2 + 2NaCl$$

If the mercaptan itself is used, reaction tends to be incomplete [528],

$$RBCl_2 + R'SH \rightarrow RBClSR' \xrightarrow{\text{distil}} RB(SR')_2 + RBCl_2$$

although disproportionation of the product affords some thioboronate. A preferred method makes use of an organoboron hydride [529]:

$$Me_3N.BH_2R + 2R'SH \xrightarrow{100°} Me_3N + 2H_2 + RB(SR')_2$$

[525] N. N. Greenwood and J. H. Morris, *J. Chem. Soc.*, 1965, 6205; J. H. Morris and P. G. Perkins, ibid., 1966A, 576, 580; A. J. Downs and J. H. Morris, *Spectrochim. Acta*, 1966, **22**, 957.

[526] W. A. G. Graham and F. G. A. Stone, *J. Inorg. Nuclear Chem.*, 1956, **3**, 164.

[527] N. Ashikari, *Bull. Chem. Soc. Japan*, 1959, **32**, 1157; *Chem. Abs.*, 1960, **54**, 18339; D. R. Nielsen, W. E. McEwen and C. A. Vanderwerf, *Chem. and Ind.*, 1957, 1069.

[528] B. M. Mikhailov and T. K. Kozminskaya, *Izvest. Akad. Nauk S.S.S.R.*, 1962, 256; *Chem. Abs.*, 1962, **57**, 16641.

[529] M. F. Hawthorne, *J. Amer. Chem. Soc.*, 1960, **82**, 748; 1961, **83**, 1345.

Alternatively, trialkylboranes and thioborates may be heated together in the presence of catalytic amounts of diborane [530]:

$$(MeS)_3B + 2BMe_3 \rightleftharpoons 3MeSBMe_2$$

Various organoboron-sulphur compounds, e.g. $MeSCR'R''B(SMe)_2$, have also been recovered from reactions between trimethylthioborate and diazoalkanes, $R'R''CN_2$ [531], and cyclic thioboronates have been prepared from dithiols and boron trichloride or dichlorophenylborane [532]:

$$HS(CH_2)_n\,SH + PhBCl_2 \longrightarrow (CH_2)_n \overbrace{}^{S}\underbrace{}_{S}BPh$$

The ready cleavage of Si–S bonds by chloroboranes affords a further route to boron–sulphur compounds [533], e.g.

$$Me_2Si\!\!\begin{array}{c}S{-}CH_2\\ \big|\\ S{-}CH_2\end{array}\!\! + PhBCl_2 \xrightarrow{-78^\circ} PhB\!\!\begin{array}{c}S{-}CH_2\\ \big|\\ S{-}CH_2\end{array} + Me_2SiCl_2$$

while the hydroboration of alkenyl mercaptans leads to novel ring compounds [534], e.g.

$$CH_2{:}CHCH_2SH + (PhBH_2)_2 \longrightarrow \begin{array}{c}H_2C\\ \big|\\ H_2C{-}C\\ H_2\end{array}\!\!\!\overbrace{}^{S}BPh \quad \text{m.p. } 38{-}41^\circ$$

Alkylthioborinates are unpleasant-smelling liquids which are oxidized slowly by air, but are stable to cold water [527]. Thioboronates are easily hydrolysed by water, and react with mercury(II) chloride to form the corresponding alkyldichloroborane [529]:

$$RB(SR')_2 + 2HgCl_2 \longrightarrow RBCl_2 + 2HgClSR'$$

The action of acetone converts the thioesters into borinic or boronic anhydrides [535]:

$$PhB(SBu)_2 + Me_2CO \longrightarrow (PhBO)_3 + Me_2C(SBu)_2$$

Sulphur analogues of boroxines, the 'borosulpholes' [536], $(RBS)_3$

[530] A. B. Burg and F. M. Graber, ibid., 1956, **78**, 1523.

[531] C. D. Gutsche and K. Kinoshita, *J. Org. Chem.*, 1963, **28**, 1762.

[532] A. Finch and J. Pearn, *Tetrahedron*, 1964, **20**, 173; see also B. Z. Egan, S. G. Shore and J. E. Bonnell, *Inorg. Chem.*, 1964, **3**, 1024.

[533] E. W. Abel, D. A. Armitage and R. P. Bush, *J. Chem. Soc.*, 1965, 3045.

[534] B. M. Mikhailov, N. V. Mostovoi and V. A. Dorokhov, *Izvest. Akad. Nauk S.S.S.R.*, 1964, 1358; *Chem. Abs.*, 1964, **61**, 12023.

[535] B. M. Mikhailov and N. S. Fedotov, *Izvest. Akad. Nauk S.S.S.R.*, 1961, 999; 1962, 827; *Chem. Abs.*, 1962, **57**, 16643.

[536] E. Wiberg and W. Sturm, *Z. Naturforsch.*, 1953, **8b**, 529, 530, 689; 1955, **10b**, 108–115; *Angew. Chem.*, 1955, **67**, 483.

3.96 3.97

appear to contain six-membered rings (3.96). The methyl compound $(MeBS)_3$ is obtained by the reaction of trimethylborane with meta-thioboric acid, 3.97:

$$BBr_3 + H_2S \xrightarrow[-40°]{CS_2} (HSBS)_3 \xrightarrow{Me_3B} (MeBS)_3$$

The phenyl derivative $(PhBS)_3$, m.p. 232°, can be prepared directly from dibromophenylborane and hydrogen sulphide:

$$3PhBBr_2 + 3H_2S \longrightarrow (PhBS)_3 + 6HBr$$

Use of hydrogen *di*sulphide in carbon disulphide gives five-membered rings [537]:

e.g. $2 PhBX_2 + 2H_2S_2 \longrightarrow$ [ring] $+ S + 2HX$ (X = Cl or Br)

Bulky substituents X in materials $(XBS)_n$ may cause the ring to be four-membered [537a]:

$$R_3N,BH_3 + H_2S \xrightarrow{200°} \frac{1}{n}(R_2NBS)_n + RH + 2H_2$$

$$n = 3 \text{ for } R = Me; \quad n = 2 \text{ for } R = Et$$

Organoboron–selenium compounds $R_2B_2Se_3$ are reported to be formed by reactions between trialkylboranes and selenium at 220–250°; a cyclic structure is suggested but not proved [538].

Organoboron–phosphorus compounds

Interest in organoboron–phosphorus compounds has been concentrated mainly on phosphinoboranes, $(R_2BPR'_2)_n$, which exist in the form of trimers, tetramers or polymers except when R = aryl, when they are monomeric. They may be prepared by condensation reactions of adducts of organoboranes with phosphines. For example, reaction between dimethylphosphine and bromodimethylborane in the presence of 1 mol. triethylamine gives the fully methylated trimeric phosphinoborane 3.98. This compound, m.p. 333–334°, is resistant to acid hydrolysis below 300°.

[537] M. Schmidt and W. Siebert, *Angew. Chem. Internat. Edn.*, 1964, **3**, 637; 1966, **5**, 597.
[537a] J. A. Forstner and E. L. Muetterties, *Inorg. Chem.*, 1966, **5**, 164.
[538] B. M. Mikhailov and T. A. Shchegoleva, *Bull. Akad. Sci. U.S.S.R.*, 1959, 331.

$$\text{Me}_2\text{PH} + \text{Me}_2\text{BBr} + \text{Et}_3\text{N} \longrightarrow \text{Me}_2\text{B} \overset{\overset{\displaystyle \text{Me}_2 \quad \text{Me}_2}{P-B}}{\underset{\underset{\displaystyle \text{Me}_2 \quad \text{Me}_2}{P-B}}{}} \text{PMe}_2$$

3.98

In contrast, $\text{Me}_2\text{B.PH}_2$ appears to be rather unstable, but $\text{H}_2\text{B.PMe}_2$, from $\text{H}_3\text{B.PHMe}_2$ at 150°, forms exceptionally stable cyclic trimers and tetramers [539]. The thermal stability and general resistance of these compounds to chemical attack directed attention to the possible development of linear (as opposed to cyclic) polymers of these general types. Dimethylphosphinoborane polymers $(\text{H}_2\text{BPMe}_2)_n$ have been obtained with n about 80 by the pyrolysis of $\text{H}_3\text{B.PHMe}_2$ in the presence of an amine (e.g. triethylamine) as a chain-end blocking group. These polymers melt at about 170° but at this temperature sometimes rearrange to form the thermodynamically (entropy factor) more stable cyclic trimers and tetramers [540]. Similar polymers $(\text{H}_2\text{BPR}'\text{R}'')_n$ have been prepared from other phosphines [541].

An X-ray study [542] of the tetramer $(\text{H}_2\text{BPMe}_2)_4$ has shown its structure to consist of a puckered eight-membered ring with bond angles BPB, 125° ± 1° and PBP 104° ± 2°.

Diphenylphosphinodiphenylborane, Ph_2BPPh_2, has been prepared by the addition of chlorodiphenylborane to diphenylphosphine and triethylamine (addition of the phosphine to the other reactants gives the salt $\text{Et}_3\text{NH}^+\text{Ph}_2\text{BCl.PPh}_2{}^-$, and omission of the amine leads to formation of the adduct $\text{Ph}_2\text{BCl.PHPh}_2$). Other phosphinodiarylboranes have been obtained using the sodium derivative of the phosphine [401]:

$$\text{Ph}_2\text{BCl} + \text{NaP}(\text{C}_6\text{H}_4\text{Me})_2 \longrightarrow \text{Ph}_2\text{BP}(\text{C}_6\text{H}_4\text{Me})_2 + \text{NaCl}$$

All the known phosphinodiarylboranes are monomeric, and their infrared spectra have a very strong absorption (doublet) in the range 1400–1500 cm^{-1} attributed to a B–P stretching vibration, i.e. at a *higher* frequency than the B–N band in related aminoboranes, apparently indicating pronounced double bond character. The presence of π-bonding between boron and phosphorus would lead to a polarity $\text{Ar}_2\overset{-}{\text{B}} \Leftarrow \overset{+}{\text{P}}\text{R}_2$, whereas dipole moment studies show the phosphino group to be the *negative* end of the dipole. It is concluded, therefore, that phosphorus is not acting as a π

[539] A. B. Burg and R. I. Wagner, *J. Amer. Chem. Soc.*, 1953, **75**, 3872; see also R. I. Wagner and C. O. Wilson, *Inorg. Chem.*, 1966, **5**, 1009.

[540] R. I. Wagner and F. F. Caserio, *J. Inorg. Nuclear Chem.*, 1959, **11**, 259.

[541] A. B. Burg and R. I. Wagner, U.S.P. 2,925,440; 3,065,271; 3,071,553; *Chem. Abs.*, 1960, **54**, 15408; 1963, **58**, 9140; 1963, **59**, 5198; A. B. Burg and P. J. Slota, U.S.P. 2,877,272; *Chem. Abs.*, 1959, **53**, 16062; idem, *J. Amer. Chem. Soc.*, 1960, **82**, 2145, 2148; C. P. Haber and C. O. Wilson, U.S.P., 2,892,873; *Chem. Abs.*, 1960, **54**, 3203.

[542] P. Goldstein and R. A. Jacobson, *J. Amer. Chem. Soc.*, 1962, **84**, 2457.

donor to boron in these systems, the boron atom being co-ordinatively saturated (or nearly so) by π-bonding with the *aryl groups* (3.99).

PhP——BPh

PhB——PPh

3.99   3.100

Other organoboron–phosphorus compounds have been prepared from *bifunctional* phosphines or boranes. Phenylphosphinidenebis(diphenylborane), $(Ph_2B)_2PPh$, from Ph_2BCl and $PhPH_2$, and the analogous compound phenylbis(diphenylphosphino)borane, $PhB(PPh_2)_2$, from $PhBCl_2$ and Ph_2PH, are colourless solids, sensitive to oxygen, and are monomeric in benzene solution. Dichlorophenylborane and phenylphosphine form a 1 : 1 complex, which slowly evolves hydrogen chloride when its solution in xylene is boiled. The reaction products include chloro(phenylphosphino)phenylborane, $PhClB.PPhH$, b.p. 98–100° at 10^{-3} mm., or its trimer, $(PhClB.PPhH)_3$, a waxy solid, a colourless compound $(PhBPPh)_2$, m.p. 89–91° (3.100) and a polymeric material, apparently of formula $PhClB(PPh.BPh)_nPPhH$ [543].

$$PhBCl_2 + PhPH_2 \longrightarrow PhCl_2B.PPhH_2 \xrightarrow{-HCl} PhClB.PPhH \xrightarrow{-HCl} (PhBPPh)_2$$

A more highly associated form of $(PhBPPh)_n$ is obtained from the same reactants with the addition of triethylamine to take up the hydrogen chloride. The product, a solid, m.p. 142–144°, is apparently a mixture of trimer and tetramer [544]. A similar product has been prepared from $PhBCl_2$ and $(Me_3Si)_2PPh$ [545]:

$$PhBCl_2 + (Me_3Si)_2PPh \xrightarrow{200°} (PhBPPh)_n + Me_3SiCl$$

It is unlikely that there is appreciable boron–phosphorus multiple bonding in these materials $(PhBPPh)_n$, despite their formal analogy to aromatic systems, although molecular orbital calculations have shown that B–P analogues of borazines might be capable of existence [546]; co-ordinative saturation may instead be achieved through interaction with the phenyl groups.

The gas-phase dissociation equilibria of complexes $Me_3B.PR_3$ show that the donor strengths of various phosphines towards trimethylborane

[543] G. E. Coates and J. G. Livingstone, *J. Chem. Soc.*, 1961, 5053; A. D. Tevebaugh, *Inorg. Chem.*, 1964, **3**, 302.
[544] W. D. English, U.S.P. 3,035,095, May 15, 1962; *Chem. Abs.*, 1962, **57**, 11239.
[545] H. Nöth and W. Schraegle, *Z. Naturforsch*, 1961, **16b**, 473.
[546] D. A. Brown and C. G. McCormack, *J. Chem. Soc.*, 1964, 5385.

decrease in the order $EtMe_2P > Me_3P > Me_2PCH:CH_2 >> Et_3P > (CH_2:CH)_3P$ [547]. The dimethylaminophosphines [548] $P(NMe_2)_3$,

$MeP(NMe_2)_2$ and Me_2PNMe_2 and polycyclic phosphites [549]

also form 1 : 1 adducts with trialkylboranes; the infrared spectra of the latter have B–P absorption frequencies in the region 750–870 cm^{-1}.

Organoboron-arsenic compounds have been relatively little studied. The arsinoboranes $Ph_2B.AsPh_2$, m.p. 202–204°, $(p\text{-}MeC_6H_4)_2B.AsPh_2$, m.p. 224–225°, and $(p\text{-}BrC_6H_4)_2B.AsPh_2$, m.p. 244–245°, have been prepared from the chlorodiarylborane and the sodium salt of the diphenylarsine in tetrahydrofuran [401]:

$$Ar_2BCl + NaAsPh_2 \rightarrow Ar_2BAsPh_2 + NaCl$$

Like their phosphino-analogues, the products are monomeric in benzene solution and are unaffected by dilute acids or alkalis at 100°. The B–As absorption bands are at lower frequencies than those of B–P bands in similar compounds, and the arsino group is also the *negative* end of the dipole. The electronic situation in the arsinoboranes is therefore considered to resemble that in the phosphinoboranes.

Miscellaneous organoboron compounds

Silicon and germanium compounds
Reaction between B-trichloroborazines and triphenylsilylpotassium gives B-silylborazines [550]:

$$Cl_3B_3N_3R_3 + 3KSiPh_3 \xrightarrow{\text{Et}_2\text{O}} (Ph_3Si)_3B_3N_3R_3$$

The products are oils or waxy solids, and are decomposed by 20% aqueous sulphuric acid, a reaction which is useful in analysis. The salts $Li(Ph_3BSiPh_3)$ and $Li(Ph_3BGePh_3)$ are obtained from triphenylsilyl- or triphenylgermyl-lithium and triphenylborane [551]:

$$Ph_3B + LiMPh_3 \rightarrow LiPh_3BMPh_3 \ (M = Si, Ge)$$

The products are easily hydrolysed, but stable enough in methanol for insoluble salts of large inorganic or organic cations to be precipitated.

[547] H. D. Kaesz and F. G. A. Stone, *J. Amer. Chem. Soc.*, 1960, **82**, 6213.
[548] R. R. Holmes and R. P. Wagner, ibid., 1962, **84**, 357; R. R. Holmes and R. P. Carter, *Inorg. Chem.*, 1963, **2**, 1146.
[549] C. W. Heitsch and J. G. Verkade, ibid., 1962, **1**, 392, 863; 1963, **2**, 512; J. G. Verkade, R. W. King and C. W. Heitsch, ibid., 1964, **3**, 884.
[550] A. H. Cowley, H. H. Sisler, G. E. Ryschkewitsch, *J. Amer. Chem. Soc.*, 1960, **82**, 501.
[551] D. Seyferth, G. Raab and S. O. Grim, *J. Org. Chem.*, 1961, **26**, 3034.

It has been possible to prepare compounds with *two* silyl groups attached to boron, but only when the third bond to boron is occupied by an amino group [552]:

$$2Ph_3SiLi + Cl_2BNEt_2 \longrightarrow (Ph_3Si)_2BNEt_2 + 2LiCl$$

Compounds with boron–tin and boron–lead bonds have been prepared by similar reactions, and the method appears capable of extension to linking boron to many other elements.

Transition metal compounds [552]

Chloroboranes react with sodium pentacarbonylmanganate (-1) to form boron–manganese compounds:

$$(Me_2N)_2BCl + NaMn(CO)_5 \longrightarrow NaCl + (Me_2N)_2BMn(CO)_5$$

With chlorodiphenylborane, the product is $(Ph_2BMn)_2$, m.p. 216–218°, a chemically inert diamagnetic solid obtained in the form of colourless needles.

$$Ph_2BCl + NaMn(CO)_5 \longrightarrow NaCl + \tfrac{1}{2}(Ph_2BMn)_2 + 5CO$$

A sandwich structure (3.101) has been suggested for this compound.

3.101

With $NaMn(CO)_4PPh_3$, evolution of carbon monoxide does not occur:

$$Ph_2BCl + NaMn(CO)_4PPh_3 \longrightarrow Ph_2BMn(CO)_4PPh_3$$

Related diphenylboryl derivatives of cobalt, platinum, molybdenum and tungsten are known [553].

Compounds related to B_2X_4

It is only recently that organoboron compounds of the type $(BXR)_2$ have been prepared. Boron subhalides and related compounds with boron–boron bonds were reviewed in 1962 [554] and in 1964 [15]. Early work on such compounds was mainly concerned with diboron tetrachloride, a thermally unstable material obtained in low yields by passage of a direct

[552] H. Nöth and G. Schmid, *Angew. Chem.*, 1963, **75**, 861; idem, *J. Organometal. Chem.*, 1966, **5**, 109; H. Nöth and K.-H. Hermannsdörfer, *Angew. Chem., Internat. Edn.*, 1964, **3**, 377.

[553] G. Schmid and H. Nöth, *Z. Naturforsch.*, 1965, **20b**, 1008; idem, *J. Organometal. Chem.*, 1967, **7**, 129.

[554] A. K. Holliday and A. G. Massey, *Chem. Rev.*, 1962, **62**, 303.

current discharge through boron trichloride. Diboron tetrachloride reacts with olefins, acetylenes [555] and aromatic compounds, but as the reaction involves addition of B_2Cl_4 across a carbon–carbon multiple bond the products do not contain B–B links:

$$B_2Cl_4 + CH_2{:}CH_2 \rightarrow Cl_2BCH_2CH_2BCl_2$$

The thermal stability of compounds B_2X_4 *decreases* in the order $X = R_2N > RO \backsimeq RS > F > Cl > R > H$, that is as the group X decreases in its ability to form π-bonds to boron and so relieve the co-ordinative unsaturation. *Organo*boron compounds of this type are stable, therefore, only if amino groups are also present, as in $Bu(Me_2N)BB(NMe_2)Bu$, prepared from $BuBCl(NMe_2)$ by the reaction with sodium-potassium alloy [556]:

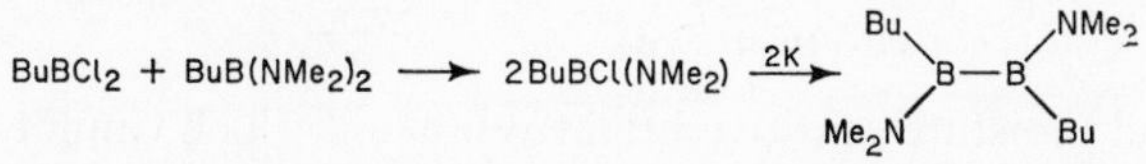

The product is a colourless oil, b.p. 69°/1 mm., monomeric in benzene solution. The analogous ethyl and phenyl compounds, obtained from the appropriate chlorides and sodium [557], are thermally stable to above 100°.

The boron–boron bond in such compounds is strong enough to be retained in transamination reactions with *o*-phenylenediamine, a novel ring resulting (e.g. 3.102) [558]:

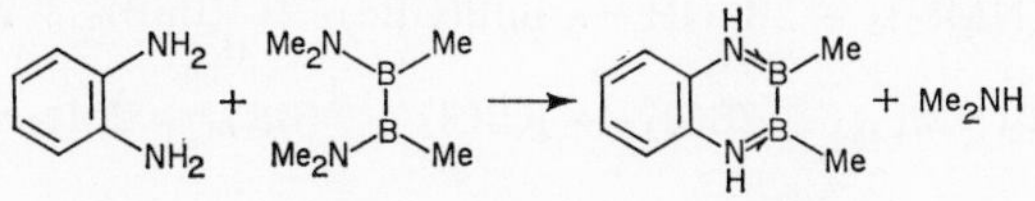

3.102

while the five-membered diazatriborolidine ring can be formed as follows [559]:

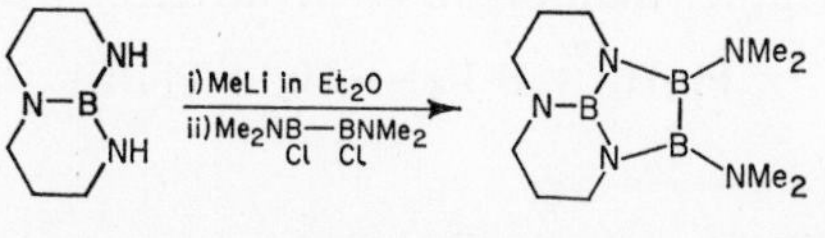

[555] A. K. Holliday and S. M. Walker, *Proc. Chem. Soc.*, 1964, 286; C. Chambers and A. K. Holliday, *J. Chem. Soc.*, 1965, 3459; M. Zeldin and T. Wartik, *J. Amer. Chem. Soc.*, 1966, **88**, 1336; H. K. Saha, L. J. Glicenstein and G. Urry, *J. Organometal. Chem.*, 1967, **8**, 37.

[556] H. Nöth and P. Fritz, *Angew Chem.*, 1961, **73**, 408; H. Nöth, ibid., *Internat. Edn.*, 1963, **2**, 270.

[557] R. J. Brotherton, H. M. Manasevit and A. L. McCloskey, *Inorg. Chem.*, 1962, **1**, 749; U.S. Borax and Chem. Corp., Brit.P. 921,179; *Chem. Abs.*, 1963, **59**, 10117.

[558] H. Nöth and P. Fritz, *Z. anorg. Chem.*, 1963, **324**, 129; R. J. Brotherton, U.S.P. 3,120,501; *Chem. Abs.*, 1964, **60**, 12050.

[559] H. Nöth and G. Abeler, *Angew. Chem., Internat. Edn.*, 1965, **4**, 522.

Compounds analogous to phenanthrene (3.103) and anthracene (3.104) may be prepared from diaminonaphthalenes. The boron–boron link in the

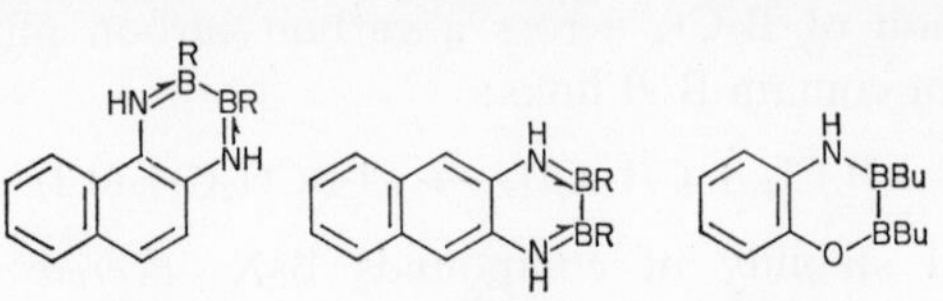

3.103   3.104   3.105

related oxygen compound 3.105 is weaker, and decomposition leads to a five-membered ring (3.80) and *polybutylboron*, $(BBu)_n$. Polybutylboron is also the reaction product from catechol and $Bu(Me_2N)BB(NMe_2)Bu$:

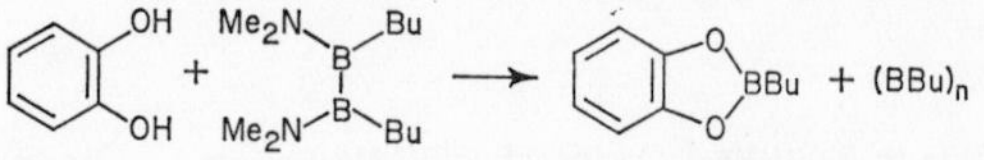

An air- and moisture-sensitive bright yellow oil which cannot be distilled without decomposition, polybutylboron as prepared from such reactions has a molecular weight corresponding to the formula $(BBu)_5$, although individual samples may have values of M falling in the range corresponding to the formulae $(BBu)_4$ to $(BBu)_6$. Their infrared spectra show no B–H absorptions. Similar materials are formed when the preparation of other unstable dibutyldiboron compounds RXB.BXR is attempted, e.g.

$$Bu_2B_2(NMe_2)_2 + 2BuOH \longrightarrow BuB(OBu)_2 + \frac{1}{n}(BuB)_n + 2HNMe_2$$

$$R_2B_2(NMe_2)_2 + 2BCl_3 \longrightarrow RBCl_2 + \frac{1}{n}(BR)_n + 2Me_2NBCl_2$$

These reactions illustrate the greater stabilizing influence of amino groups compared with alkoxy groups or chlorine atoms in compounds RXB.BXR.

Reactions between organomercury compounds and B_2F_4 lead to organoboron difluorides rather than organo derivatives of B_2F_4, e.g. [560],

$$Ph_2Hg + B_2F_4 \longrightarrow Hg + PhBF_2$$

Appendix

Infrared spectra of organoboron compounds [560a]
Assignments of characteristic group frequencies have been made for a number of groups which commonly occur in organoboron compounds. Some of these are listed in Table 10. Useful reviews are to be found in references [11, 13, 23, 560a, 561], which serve as an introduction to the

[560] A. K. Holliday and F. B. Taylor, *J. Chem. Soc.*, 1964, 2731.
[560a] A. Meller, *Organometal. Chem. Reviews*, 1967, **2**, 1.
[561] L. J. Bellamy, W. Gerrard, M. F. Lappert and R. L. Williams, *J. Chem. Soc.*, 1958, 2412.

considerable literature on this subject. References to a few of the more
recent publications are included in Table 12.

Table 12   *Infrared spectra of organoboron compounds; some group absorption frequencies*

Type of compound	Group	Vibration	Frequency (cm^{-1})	References
B-alkyl	B—Me	asym. deformation	1405–1460	[561, 562]
		sym. ,,	1280–1330	,,
	BC_2	asym. stretch	1110–1175	[265, 337]
		sym ,,	770–830	[561–3]
B-aryl	B-aryl	stretch	1125–1280	[561]
	aryl		1430–1440	[561]
$B(aryl)_2$	aryl CH	deformation	2 bands ~750	[561]
B—H	B—H$_{terminal}$	stretch	2500–2600	[265, 561 562a, 562b]
	B—H$_{bridge}$	,,	1500–1610	,,
	BH_2	deformation	1125–1165	,,
	BH_2	wag	920–975	,,
$R_2BNR'_2$	B—N	stretch	1330–1530	[401, 564–5, 565a, 565b]
$(R_2BNR'_2)_2$	B—N		~900	[417]
$R_3B.NR'_3$	B—N	,,	650–800	[562b, 566]
Borazines	B—N	,,	1375–1495	[13, 23, 567–8]
,,	B—N	deformation	~700	[569]
$R_2BPR'_2$	B—P	stretch	1410–1500	[401, 543]
$R_3BPR'_3$	B—P	,,	750–870	[549]
$R_2BAsR'_2$	B—As	,,	1365–1440	[401]
B—O	B—O	,,	1310–1380	[337, 561, 562]
B—S	B—S	,,	~930	[569a]
Boroxines	B_3O_3	skeletal	680–708	[567, 570]
BCl_2	B—Cl	asym. stretch	790–990	[13, 561, 565, 570a]
	B—Cl	sym. ,,	923	[565, 570a, 571]
BBr_2	B—Br	asym. ,,	830–880	[571]
	B—Br	sym. ,,	830–850	[571]
BI_2	B—I	asym. ,,	730–762	[571]
	B—I	sym. ,,	730–762	[571]

[562] D. Ulmschneider and J. Goubeau, *Z. phys. Chem. (Frankfurt)*, 1958, **14**, 56;
J. Goubeau and D. Hummel, ibid., 1959, **20**, 15.

[562a] H. Watanabe and K. Nagasawa, *Inorg. Chem.*, 1967, **6**, 1068.

[562b] J. N. G. Faulks, N. N. Greenwood and J. H. Morris, *J. Inorg. Nucl. Chem.*,
1967, **29**, 329.

[563] W. J. Lehmann, C. O. Wilson and I. Shapiro, *J. Chem. Phys.*, 1958, **28**, 781;
1959, **31**, 1071.

[564] K. Niedenzu and J. W. Dawson, *J. Amer. Chem. Soc.*, 1959, **81**, 5553; D. W.
Aubrey, M. F. Lappert and H. Pyszora, *J. Chem. Soc.*, 1960, 5239; G. M. Wyman, K.
Niedenzu and J. W. Dawson, ibid., 1962, 4068; H. J. Becher and H. T. Baechle, *Advan.
in Chem. Series*, 1964, **42**, 71; J. W. Dawson, P. Fritz and K. Niedenzu, *J. Organometal
Chem.*, 1966, **5**, 13.

[Continued overleaf

Nuclear magnetic resonance spectra of organoboron compounds

Nuclear magnetic resonance studies on boron compounds have been reviewed recently [22, 572, 572a]. The ^{11}B chemical shifts of the organo-boranes Me_3B, Et_3B, $PhBCl_2$, $BuB(OH)_2$, $PhB(OEt)_2$, $NaBPh_4$ and $LiB(C:CPh)_4$ are included among figures for a wide variety of boron compounds reported by W. D. Phillips and co-workers [573], and ^{11}B chemical shifts and spin–spin coupling values for many hydrides and halides have been determined [574]. Other useful sources of data are concerned with the methyldiboranes $Me_nB_2H_{6-n}$ (n = 1, 2, 3 or 4) [575], tetrahalo-borates [576, 577] and tetraorganoborates [577, 578], organodichloro-boranes $RBCl_2$, organodifluoroboranes and their adducts with trimethyl-amine [194], monomeric and dimeric aminoboranes [423, 565a, 579], B-organoborazines [580] and the vinylboranes $Me_2BCH:CH_2$, $MeB(CH:CH_2)_2$ and $B(CH:CH_2)_3$ [198]. As examples of the applications of

[565] A. J. Banister, N. N. Greenwood, B. P. Straughan and J. Walker, *J. Chem. Soc.*, 1964, 995.

[565a] M. R. Chakrabarty, C. C. Thompson and W. S. Brey, *Inorg. Chem.*, 1967, **6**, 518.

[565b] J. Dawson, P. Fritz and K. Niedenzu, *J. Organometal. Chem.*, 1966, **5**, 13; K. Niedenzu, J. W. Dawson, G. A. Neece, W. Sawodny, D. R. Squire and W. Weber, *Inorg. Chem.*, 1966, **5**, 2161.

[566] R. C. Taylor, *Advan. in Chem. Series*, 1964, **42**. 59.

[567] D. W. Aubrey, M. F. Lappert and H. Pyszora, *J. Chem. Soc.*, 1961, 1931.

[568] H. Watanabe, M. Narisda, T. Nakagwa and M. Kubo, *Spectrochim. Acta*, 1960, **16**, 78; R. E. Hester and C. W. J. Scaife, ibid., 1966, **22**, 455, 755; K. Niedenzu, J. W. Dawson and W. Weber, 152nd A.C.S. Meeting, Sept. 12–16, 1966, New York, Abstracts O 22.

[569] W. Gerrard, H. R. Hudson, E. F. Mooney, I. M. Stripp and H. A. Willis, ibid., 1962, **18**, 149; M. Goldstein and E. F. Mooney, *Chem. Comm.*, 1966, 104.

[569a] R. H. Cragg, M. F. Lappert and B. P. Tilley, *J. Chem. Soc.* (*A*), 1967, 947.

[570] W. J. Dale and J. E. Rush, *J. Org. Chem.*, 1962, **27**, 2598.

[570a] J. C. Lockhart, *J. Chem. Soc.* (*A*), 1966, 1552; T. A. Ford and W. J. Orville-Thomas, *Spectrochim. Acta*, 1967, **23A**, 579.

[571] A. Finch, P. J. Hendra, and E. J. Pearn, ibid., 1962, **18**, 51.

[572] J. W. Emsley, J. Feeney and L. H. Sutcliffe, *High Resolution Nuclear Magnetic Resonance*, Pergamon, Oxford, 1965–6.

[572a] H. Nöth and H. Vahrenkamp, *Chem. Ber.*, 1966, **99**, 1049.

[573] W. D. Phillips, H. C. Miller and E. L. Muetterties, *J. Amer. Chem. Soc.*, 1959, **81**, 4496.

[574] T. P. Onak, H. Landesman, R. E. Williams and I. Shapiro, *J. Phys. Chem.*, 1959, **63**, 1533.

[575] R. E. Williams, H. D. Fisher and C. O. Wilson, ibid., 1960, **64**, 1583.

[576] K. M. Harmon and F. E. Cummings, *J. Amer. Chem. Soc.*, 1965, **87**, 539.

[577] R. J. Thompson and J. C. Davis, *Inorg. Chem.*, 1965, **4**, 1464.

[578] A. G. Massey, E. W. Randall and D. Shaw, *Spectrochim. Acta*, 1965, **21**, 263.

[579] M. F. Hawthorne, *J. Amer. Chem. Soc.*, 1961, **83**, 2671; A. J. Banister and N. N. Greenwood, *J. Chem. Soc.*, 1965, 1534; N. N. Greenwood, K. A. Hooton and J. Walker, ibid., 1966A, 21.

[580] M. F. Hawthorne, *J. Amer. Chem. Soc.*, 1961, **83**, 833; I. M. Butcher, W. Gerrard, J. B. Leane and E. F. Mooney, *J. Chem. Soc.*, 1964, 4528.

nuclear magnetic resonance spectroscopy, the rate of exchange reactions such as those of alkoxy groups, between borinates R_2BOR' and boronates $RB(OR')_2$ has been measured using proton magnetic resonance spectra [581], ring-proton and ^{11}B resonance spectra of *para* substituted phenylboronic acids have been shown to be related to Hammett σ-functions for these acids [582], and the existence of the mixed halides PhBBrCl and BBrClI has been demonstrated [583]. Studies on BX_3 co-ordination compounds have shown the ^{11}B chemical shift to be an unreliable guide to the stability of adducts except where these adducts are members of a closely related series (562b, 584]. The ^{11}B chemical shift is nevertheless a useful guide to the co-ordination number of boron in certain classes of compound, and has for example revealed the association of dibenzyl phenylboronate $PhB(OCH_2Ph)_2$ in the liquid phase [584a] and of alkoxyboron difluorides $ROBF_2$, which appear to be trimeric as liquids [584b]. In the n.m.r. and infrared spectra of boron hydrides, a linear correlation has been found between $J(^{11}B\text{—}^1H)$ and $\nu(B\text{—}H)$ which reflects the dependence of both parameters on the hybridization of the boron orbital, and is analogous to the relationship found between $J(^{13}C\text{—}^1H)$ and $\nu(C\text{—}H)$ in organic compounds [562a]. Other applications of nuclear magnetic resonance spectroscopy to organoboron compounds, such as studies of the hindrance to rotation in aminoboranes have been mentioned earlier [423, 565a].

The ^{35}Cl *nuclear quadrupole resonance* spectra of a few B–Cl compounds have been reported [585].

ALUMINIUM

Although first prepared a century ago (Buckton and Odling [586], 1865, from aluminium and dimethylmercury; these authors also noted the association of trimethylaluminium), the organic compounds of aluminium

[581] P. A. McCusker, P. L. Pennartz and R. C. Pilger, *J. Amer. Chem. Soc.*, 1961, **83**, 4362; H. K. Hotmeister and J. R. Van Wazer, *J. Inorg. Nucl. Chem.*, 1964, **26**, 1209.

[582] H. C. Beachell and D. Beistel, *Inorg. Chem.*, 1964, **3**, 1028.

[583] A. Finch and J. C. Lockhart, *Chem. and Ind.*, 1964, 497; P. N. Gates, E. F. Mooney and D. C. Smith, *J. Chem. Soc.*, 1964, 3511; D. R. Armstrong and P. G. Perkins, *Chem. Comm.*, 1965, 337.

[584] C. W. Heitsch, *Inorg. Chem.*, 1965, **4**, 1019; P. N. Gates, E. J. McLauchlan and E. F. Mooney, *Spectrochim Acta*, 1965, **21**, 1445; E. J. McLauchlan and E. F. Mooney, ibid., 1967, **23A**, 1227.

[584a] E. F. Mooney and P. H. Winson, *Chem. Comm.*, 1967, 341.

[584b] J. E. De Moor and G. P. van der Kelen, *J. Organometal. Chem.*, 1966, **6**, 235; W. Gerrard, E. F. Mooney and W. G. Peterson, *J. Inorg. Nucl. Chem.*, 1967, **29**, 943.

[585] J. A. S. Smith and D. A. Tong, *Chem. Comm.*, 1965, 3.

[586] G. B. Buckton and W. Odling, *Annalen (Suppl.)*, 1865-6, **4**, 109; *Proc. Roy. Soc.*, 1865, **14**, 19.

have attracted much attention only during the last fifteen years. The confirmation (1941) of the dimerization of trimethylaluminium posed quite a problem for valency theory, and stimulated the study and theoretical interpretation of electron deficient molecules.

The large current interest in organoaluminium compounds derives mainly from the following developments:

(a) cheap processes, suitable for industrial operation, for making certain aluminium alkyls from aluminium, hydrogen and olefins;

(b) the reactions between aluminium alkyls and olefins, whereby it is possible to dimerize some olefins or to prepare paraffin polymers or various 1-alkenes which are significant in connexion with detergent manufacture;

(c) the formation from aluminium alkyls and some transition metal compounds of catalysts which are useful for olefin polymerization, sometimes giving isotactic (sterically regular) polymers;

(d) the use of aluminium alkyls for the preparation of alkyls of other elements, the point here being the possibility of dispensing with, or using cheap, diluents (cf. the large amounts of ether needed for Grignard alkylations).

The recent very extensive growth of organoaluminium chemistry is to a large extent due to K. Ziegler and his group, the development of catalysts for isotactic polymerization being associated also with G. Natta. Since organoaluminium compounds have been authoritatively reviewed [587], several aspects such as interaction with olefins, which are treated at length in the review, are discussed relatively briefly in this chapter. A supplementary detailed review has recently appeared [588].

With very few exceptions the aluminium alkyls and their derivatives are highly reactive to air and moisture, and many of them are spontaneously inflammable. Their controlled oxidation, giving alkoxides, provides an industrial route to some alcohols. Since several of the more reactive alkyls are readily available commercially, and in quantity, it should be emphasized that careful precautions against fire hazards should be taken, the kind and extent of the precautions advised [589] depending to a large extent on the quantities handled. Either in the laboratory or industrially the aluminium alkyls should be treated with great respect.

[587] K. Ziegler, Ch. 5 in *Organometallic Chemistry*, ed. H. Zeiss, Reinhold, New York, 1960.

[588] R. Köster and P. Binger, *Advances in Inorganic Chemistry and Radiochemistry*, 1965, **7**, 263.

[589] I. E. Knop, R. E. Leech, A. J. Reid and W. S. Tamplin, *Ind. Eng. Chem.*, 1957, **49**, 874.

The trialkyl derivatives of aluminium

General preparative methods

The original method of Buckton and Odling, whereby metallic aluminium is heated with an organic mercury compound,

$$2Al + 3R_2Hg \longrightarrow 2R_3Al + 3Hg$$

is convenient for the laboratory preparation of *small* quantities of tri-methylaluminium. An excess of aluminium turnings should be used, and the exothermic reaction goes readily at about 80–90°. Unless only a few grams of Me_3Al are needed, aluminium alkyls are not very suitable for laboratory preparation and are best obtained from industrial sources.

It is feasible to prepare some alkylaluminium halides in the laboratory and alkyls can be obtained from these. The reaction between aluminium metal, conveniently as turnings, and alkyl halides gives the *alkylaluminium sesquihalides* [590]:

$$2Al + 3RX \longrightarrow R_3Al_2X_3$$

The reaction is strongly exothermic and care must be taken to limit the temperature by the use of an inert volatile diluent such as methylcyclo-hexane. The reaction may also be carried out by leading the gaseous alkyl halide (MeCl, EtCl) into heated aluminium turnings previously activated by iodine or, better, some product from a previous reaction; when the reaction gets under way the temperature can be limited by control of the gas flow. This method is satisfactory for the preparation of *methyl* and *ethyl* aluminium sesquihalides, less satisfactory for propyl and useless for higher alkyl chlorides since these react very rapidly with aluminium alkyls or alkylaluminium chlorides giving hydrocarbons and $AlCl_3$ [591].

The alkylaluminium sesquihalides are air-sensitive liquids which do not have sharp boiling points ($Me_3Al_2Cl_3$ b.p. ca. 127–148°) on account of disproportionation:

$$R_3Al_2X_3 \rightleftharpoons R_2Al_2X_4 + R_4Al_2X_2$$

They do not react with carbon dioxide, in contrast to the trialkyls.

The conversion of sesquihalides to trialkyls is by *reduction* or *dispropor-tionation* processes. Reduction with alkali metal [590] can be vigorous and needs care; it can also be carried too far since alkali metals react with trialkyls (not with Me_3Al) forming more aluminium and the tetralkyl-aluminate [590, 592].

$$R_3Al_2X_3 + 3Na = R_3Al + Al + 3NaX$$
$$4R_3Al + 3Na = 3NaAlR_4 + Al \ (R \neq Me)$$

[590] A. von Grosse and J. M. Mavity, *J. Org. Chem.*, 1940, **5**, 106.

[591] A. G. Pozamantir and M. L. Genusov, *J. Gen. Chem. U.S.S.R.*, 1962, **32**, 1149 (Eng. trans.).

[592] L. I. Zakharkin and V. V. Gavrilenko, ibid., p. 688 (Eng. trans.).

Magnesium can be used similarly, preferably alloyed with the aluminium [593].

$$Al_2Mg_3 + 6EtCl \longrightarrow 2Et_3Al + 3MgCl_2$$

Disproportionation reactions are rather more satisfactory. If the mixed iodides from aluminium and methyl iodide are slowly distilled, best under somewhat reduced pressure (about 200 mm.), the most volatile component of the disproportionation equilibrium, trimethylaluminium, may be taken off from the top of a fractionating column. In this way over half of the methyl used can be recovered as Me_3Al, and this is quite a convenient way of preparing the compound on a medium laboratory scale [594].

Useful directions for carrying out many of these processes on a laboratory scale have been given [595].

Dimethylaluminium chloride, from the sesquichloride,

$$Me_3Al_2Cl_3 + Me_3Al \longrightarrow 3Me_2AlCl$$

reacts with sodium fluoride in two stages,

$$Me_2AlCl + NaF \longrightarrow Me_2AlF + NaCl$$
$$Me_2AlF + NaF \longrightarrow Na[Me_2AlF_2]$$

and the complex salt disproportionates when heated to 200–300° [596]:

$$3Na[Me_2AlF_2] \longrightarrow Na_3AlF_6 + 2Me_3Al$$

This has been suggested as a large-scale route to trimethylaluminium, since scarcely any methyl is lost and the olefin methods (see below) are not applicable.

The now well-known *direct synthesis* of trialkyls,

$$Al + \tfrac{3}{2}H_2 + 3(1\text{-olefin}) \longrightarrow alkyl_3Al$$

extensively used on the industrial scale for the manufacture, mainly, of *triethyl, tri-isobutyl-*, and to a lesser extent of *tri-n-propyl-aluminium* has its origin in the discovery that olefins containing terminal $=CH_2$ groups (1-olefins) react with aluminium hydride [597]. For example, if 2-ethylhex-1-ene in excess is heated with aluminium hydride, reaction sets in about 80°, with a rise of temperature and the disappearance of the hydride,

$$3Bu^nEtC:CH_2 + AlH_3 = (Bu^nEtCHCH_2)_3Al$$

[593] K. Ziegler, *Angew. Chem.*, 1952, **64**, 323, 330.

[594] K. S. Pitzer and H. S. Gutowsky, *J. Amer. Chem. Soc.*, 1946, **68**, 2204.

[595] C. J. Marsel, E. O. Kalil, A. Reidlinger and L. Kramer, *Metal-Organic Compounds*, p. 172, American Chemical Society, Washington, 1959.

[596] K. Ziegler and R. Köster, *Annalen*, 1957, **608**, 1.

[597] K. Ziegler, *Angew. Chem.*, 1952, **64**, 323; *Brennstoff-Chem.*, 1952, **33**, 193; K. Ziegler, H. G. Gellert, H. Martin, K. Nagel and J. Schneider, *Annalen*, 1954, **589**, 91.

Tri-iso-octylaluminium may be obtained by short-path high-vacuum distillation of the reaction mixture. The product is in this instance free from ether (aluminium hydride is not easy to prepare free from ether), but the more volatile alkylaluminium compounds are not readily obtained ether-free by this method. The more volatile olefins, for example propene and isobutene, combine under pressure with aluminium hydride forming tri-n-propyl- and tri-isobutyl-aluminium.

Lithium aluminium hydride as normally used in ether solution adds olefins only with difficulty and under high pressure, but in the absence of ether and of oxygen addition takes place easily:

$$LiAlH_4 + 4C_2H_4 \rightarrow LiAlEt_4$$

The crucial step in the development of the direct process was the discovery [598] that although aluminium hydride could not be made from aluminium and hydrogen, hydrogen was taken up by the metal *in the presence of aluminium alkyl*,

$$Al + \tfrac{3}{2}H_2 + 2\,alkyl_3Al \rightarrow 3\,alkyl_2AlH$$

and the dialkylaluminium hydrides thus formed take up a further olefin molecule giving the trialkyl. Tri-isobutylaluminium is made in a one-step process in which the two stages just mentioned are combined (200 atm. hydrogen, temperature from 80° up to not more than 110°), but triethyl- and tripropyl-aluminium are more satisfactorily made by a two-step process or by displacing isobutene with ethylene or propene [599]:

$$(Me_2CH\cdot CH_2)_3Al + 3C_2H_4 \rightarrow Et_3Al + 3Me_2C:CH_2$$

The aluminium metal must have an oxide-free surface, and this has generally been achieved by ball-milling aluminium powder under some preformed alkyl, though the liquid metal has also been sprayed into aluminium alkyl or a solution of this [600].

Physical properties
Trimethylaluminium, Me_6Al_2, m.p. 15·0°, b.p. 126°, is a clear mobile liquid at room temperature and may be distilled unchanged at atmospheric pressure. The higher alkyls have varying tendencies to evolve olefin (most marked among the type $[R_2CHCH_2]_3Al$) and should be distilled under reduced pressure. *Triethylaluminium*, m.p. −52·5°, b.p. 186°, 75–80°/2·5 mm., and *tri-isobutylaluminium*, m.p. 3·8°, b.p. 46°/0·05 mm., are the most commonly used trialkyls; the latter loses isobutene so readily that distillation yields much di-isobutylaluminium hydride unless care is taken to

[598] K. Ziegler, H. Gellert, K. Zosel, H. Lehmkuhl and W. Pfohl, *Angew. Chem.*, 1955, **67**, 424. The date of discovery was of course earlier than that of public disclosure as the authors wished to secure patent protection.

[599] K. Ziegler, H. Martin and F. Krupp, *Annalen*, 1960, **629**, 14.

[600] K. Ziegler, H. G. Gellert, H. Lehmkuhl, W. Pfohl and K. Zosel, ibid., p. 1.

keep the pressure low and to prevent the temperature exceeding about 50–60°. Di-isobutylaluminium hydride is usually present in amounts up to 10% in commercially produced Bu^i_3Al.

Trimethylaluminium is dimeric in benzene solution [601], and a mono-mer–dimer equilibrium has been observed in the vapour from 100° to 160°, the heat of dissociation to two moles of monomer being 20·4 kcal [602]. Tri-ethyl-, tri-n-propyl- and tri-n-butyl-aluminium are also dimeric in benzene or p-xylene, but some dissociation is apparent at very low concentration. In contrast, the branched-chain alkyls such as Pr^i_3Al, Bu^i_3Al and $(Me_3CCH_2)_3Al$ are monomeric [603] because of steric hindrance to dimerization.

Tri-isobutylaluminium has been studied as a solvent for cryoscopic molecular weight measurement, as it has a convenient freezing point (3·8°). In this solvent those alkyls which are monomeric in benzene give three times the freezing point depression expected for a monomer, on account of alkyl exchange:

$$(Me_3C \cdot CH_2)_3Al + 2Bu^i_3Al \rightleftharpoons 3Bu^i_2(Me_3C \cdot CH_2)Al$$

In the presence of excess solvent, the equilibrium lies wholly to the right. Not only is alkyl exchange rapid, by a mechanism involving alkyl bridges,

but the stability of the bridged species is greatest when the bridging group is methyl and decreases with chain branching. This is shown not only by the fact that Me_3Al, Et_3Al, Pr^n_3Al are dimeric in benzene whereas Pr^i_3Al and Bu^i_3Al are monomeric, but formation of a methyl-bridged species in solution (such as 3.106) is indicated by cryoscopic measurements on mixtures of Me_6Al_2 and Bu^i_3Al in benzene:

3.106

Since it appears that only the monomeric alkyls enter into the important reactions with olefins, the addition of Me_6Al_2 to other alkyls decreases their reactivity to olefins by converting them into dimeric species.

The bridge structure of trimethylaluminium, analogous to that of

[601] K. S. Pitzer and H. S. Gutowsky, *J. Amer. Chem. Soc.*, 1946, **68**, 2204.

[602] A. W. Laubengayer and W. F. Gilliam, ibid., 1941, **63**, 477; C. H. Henrickson and D. P. Eyman, *Inorg. Chem.*, 1967, **6**, 1461.

[603] E. G. Hoffmann, *Annalen*, 1960, **629**, 104.

diborane, was first indicated by Raman [604] and infrared [605] spectra, and was confirmed by an X-ray crystal analysis [606] (Figure 22). The dis-

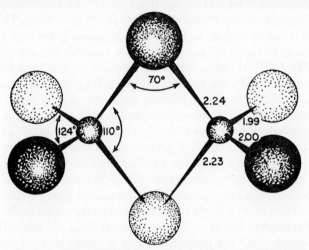

Fig. 22. Molecular structure of trimethylaluminium dimer [606]

tance, 1·99 Å, from aluminium to an *external* carbon atom, corresponds quite well with the calculated single bond length 2·03 Å. The bridge four-membered ring is quite symmetrical, the aluminium–carbon distance

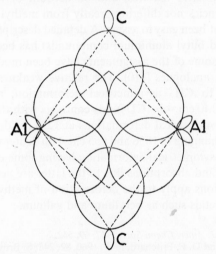

Fig. 23. Schematic representation of bonding atomic orbitals in the bridge [606]

[604] K. W. F. Kohlrausch and J. Wagner, *Z. physik. Chem.*, 1942, **B52,** 185.
[605] K. S. Pitzer and R. K. Sheline, *J. Chem. Phys.*, 1948, **16,** 552.
[606] P. H. Lewis and R. E. Rundle, ibid., 1953, **21,** 986.

being 2·24 Å, which corresponds with the distance, 2·21 Å, calculated for a *half-bond* by Pauling's rule [607].

The rather small Al–C–Al angle, 70° (cf. 66° in the Me_2Be polymer), is required for good overlap between the Al sp^3 and C sp^3 orbitals. The reason for the dimerization of trimethylaluminium is primarily the high tendency for aluminium to make use of all four of its available low-energy atomic orbitals. The Al–C–Al bridge bonds are regarded essentially as formed by bent three-centre molecular orbitals (Al sp^3 + C sp^3 + Al sp^3, see Figure 23). There would be two such orbitals, each occupied by a pair of electrons, so each Al–C–Al (three-centre) bond could be regarded as a single bond, or equivalently, each Al–C (bridge) bond as a half-bond. The Al–Al distance 2·55 Å, is only slightly greater than twice the Al single-bond covalent radius (1·26 Å), and there may be some degree of Al–Al bonding.

Proton magnetic resonance spectra of trimethylaluminium should distinguish between the two different kinds of methyl groups. However, at room temperature only a single resonance is observed owing to the rapidity of methyl exchange, but at −75° (in solution) there are two resonances [608]. At about −20° the mean lifetime of a particular configuration is only ca. 3 milliseconds.

As a consequence of the centrosymmetric structure of both Me_6Al_2 and $Me_4Al_2Cl_2$ (which has a μ-dichloro bridge) there are no Raman–infrared coincidences of fundamentals. The spectra of these and related compounds have several distinctive features, and on account of methyl-aluminium stretching frequencies not differing greatly from methyl rocking frequencies, they have not been easy to assign. A detailed description of the spectra (also of ethyl and butyl aluminium compounds) has been given by Hoffmann [609], but some of the assignments have been modified on the basis of data for CD_3 analogues [610]. The relative weakness of the infrared absorption due to CH_3 asymmetrical deformation, at 1440 cm⁻¹ in $(CH_3)_6Al_2$ and 1140 cm⁻¹ in $(CD_3)_6Al_2$ contrasts with the intense absorption due to the symmetrical deformations at 1255 (bridge CH_3) and 1208 (terminal CH_3) changing to 1036 and 955 cm⁻¹ on deuteration. This results, in part, from the symmetrical deformation having some of the character of Al–C stretching, and absorptions due to the latter are very intense indeed. Similar observations apply to the deformation of methyl bound to other electropositive metals such as beryllium and gallium.

[607] L. Pauling, *J. Amer. Chem. Soc.*, 1947, **69**, 542.
[608] N. Muller and D. E. Pritchard, ibid., 1960, **82**, 248; S. Brownstein, B. C. Smith, G. Ehrlich and A. W. Laubengayer, ibid., p. 1000; E. G. Hoffmann and G. Schomburg, *Advances in Molecular Spectroscopy*, p. 804, Pergamon, 1962; E. G. Hoffmann, *Trans., Faraday Soc.*, 1962, **58**, 642.
[609] Idem., *Z. Elektrochem.*, 1960, **64**, 616.
[610] A. P. Gray, *Canad. J. Chem.*, 1963, **41**, 1511; see also T. Onishi and T. Shimanouchi, *Spectrochim. Acta*, 1964, **20**, 325.

The vibrations mainly having the character of stretching of the bonds between aluminium and terminal methyl groups are shown below (Table 13), with numbers as used by several authors [611, 609, 610]. The Al–Me

Table 13   *Infrared AlMe₂ stretching frequencies, cm⁻¹*

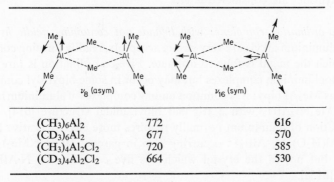

	ν_8 (asym)	ν_{16} (sym)
$(CH_3)_6Al_2$	772	616
$(CD_3)_6Al_2$	677	570
$(CH_3)_4Al_2Cl_2$	720	585
$(CD_3)_4Al_2Cl_2$	664	530

stretching frequencies in the above compounds are intense, and co-ordination complexes containing the Me_2Al group have a very strong absorption at about 680 cm⁻¹ due to the unsymmetrical vibration and a rather weaker, though still strong, absorption about 580 cm⁻¹ due to the symmetrical mode, the last being rather variable.

From the heat of reaction between trimethylaluminium and acetic acid, the mean Al–C bond dissociation energy in liquid Me_6Al_2 is 64·5 ± 2 kcal. mole⁻¹, which is fairly high for a metal-carbon bond [612] (compare B, 89; Si, 77; Sn, 53; Pb, 35; Zn, 41; Sb, 50; Bi, 38). The mean Al–C bond dissociation energy of the monomer would be about 70 kcal. mole⁻¹. Thermodynamic functions for trimethylaluminium have been calculated [613].

Chemical reactions

These are grouped in the following way:

(*a*) formation of co-ordination complexes with ligands *not* containing acidic hydrogen, e.g. with Me_3N giving $R_3Al{\leftarrow}NMe_3$;

(*b*) formation of co-ordination complexes with ligands containing acidic hydrogen, e.g. with Me_2NH giving $(R_2Al{\cdot}NMe_2)_2 + 2RH$;

(*c*) anionic co-ordination complexes, e.g. $K[Et_6Al_2F]$;

(*d*) thermal decomposition;

(*e*) reaction with olefins;

[611] R. P. Bell and H. C. Longuet-Higgins, *Proc. Roy. Soc.*, 1945, **A183**, 357.
[612] C. T. Mortimer and P. W. Sellars, *J. Chem. Soc.*, 1963, 1978.
[613] J. P. McCullough, J. F. Messerly, R. T. Moore and S. S. Todd, *J. Phys. Chem.*, 1963, **67**, 677.

(*f*) reaction with acetylenes;

(*g*) aluminium alkyls as reducing agents;

(*h*) aluminium alkyls as alkylating agents.

Unsaturated organoaluminium compounds, heterocyclics, aryls, halides and hydrides are considered later.

(*a*) *Co-ordination complexes with ligands not containing acidic hydrogen.* The aluminium alkyls are very strong acceptors, readily forming complexes in which the metal is four-co-ordinate. Five-co-ordination is rare among organoaluminium complexes but may occur in some bipyridyl compounds such as Me_3Al bipy; it is common among complexes of aluminium hydride, e.g. $(Me_3N)_2AlH_3$ with a trigonal bipyramidal structure [614]. Six-co-ordination of aluminium normally requires more electronegative ligands, e.g. $Al(H_2O)_6^{3+}$, AlF_6^{3-} occurring also in gaseous $[\{CH_2NMe_2)_2AlH_3]_2$ [615], but not in the crystal which has five co-ordinate $N\cdot AlH_3\cdot N$ units [615*a*].

The formation of co-ordination compounds between trimethylaluminium and various Group V and VI methyls has been studied by displacement and vapour-phase dissociation methods [616]. The trimethylamine complex, $Me_3Al{\leftarrow}NMe_3$, m.p. 105°, and its phosphorus analogue, $Me_3Al{\leftarrow}PMe_3$, m.p. 62·5°, are not appreciably dissociated in the vapour phase, but the relative co-ordination affinities have been established by showing that the reaction

$$Me_3Al{\leftarrow}PMe_3 + Me_3N \rightleftharpoons Me_3Al{\leftarrow}NMe_3 + Me_3P$$

goes wholly to the right. Dissociation equilibria have been studied for some weaker donors (the equilibrium is complicated by the simultaneous $Me_6Al_2 \rightleftharpoons Me_3Al$ reaction), and the following order of donor character established:

$$NMe_3 > PMe_3 > OMe_2 > SMe_2 > SeMe_2 > TeMe_2$$
$$\Delta H > 19 \qquad\quad 19 \qquad\quad 16 \qquad\quad < 16$$

The dissociation heats given are for the reaction

$$\underset{\text{monomer, gas}}{Me_3Al} + \underset{\text{gas}}{donor} \rightleftharpoons \underset{\text{gas}}{complex}$$

Methyl chloride does not co-ordinate to trimethylaluminium, though it does so to aluminium chloride and gallium chloride. The ether complexes

[614] C. W. Heitsch, C. E. Nordman and R. W. Parry, *Inorg. Chem.*, 1963, **2**, 508; C. W. Heitsch and R. N. Knisely, *Spectrochim. Acta*, 1963, **19**, 1385; G. W. Fraser, N. N. Greenwood and B. P. Straughan, *J. Chem. Soc.*, 1963, 3742.

[615] J. M. Davidson and T. Wartik, *J. Amer. Chem. Soc.*, 1960, **82**, 5506.

[615*a*] G. J. Palenik, *Acta Cryst.*, 1964, **17**, 1573.

[616] H. C. Brown and N. R. Davidson, *J. Amer. Chem. Soc.*, 1942, **64**, 316. See also G. Bähr and G. E. Müller, *Chem. Ber.*, 1965, **88**, 251; C. H. Hendrickson and D. P. Eyman, *Inorg. Chem.*, 1967, **6**, 1461.

$Me_3Al \leftarrow OMe_2$, m.p. $-30°$, b.p. $159°$, $Me_3Al \leftarrow OEt_2$, b.p. $68°/15$ mm., and $Et_3Al \leftarrow OEt_2$, b.p. $122°/12$ mm., are spontaneously inflammable but less reactive than the alkyls themselves.

The diethylether complex of tri-tertiarybutylaluminium, from $AlCl_3$ and Bu^tMgCl in ether, is a crystalline solid, m.p. $120–124°$, which isomerizes when heated [617]:

$$Bu_3^tAl \cdot OEt_2 \xrightarrow[24 \text{ hr.}]{170°} Bu_3^iAl \cdot OEt_2$$

The heats of formation of several triethylaluminium complexes, measured by an ingenious calorimetric technique [618], are given in Table 14. Further data are given in ref. [620].

Table 14   *Heats of formation of triethylaluminium complexes*

	$-\Delta H$ kcal. mole^{-1}		$-\Delta H$ kcal. mole^{-1}
Diethyl ether	11·2	Thiophen	0
Di-n-butyl ether	11·0	Dimethylaniline	11·5
Tetrahydrofuran	14·0	Dimethylcyclohexylamine	17·2
1,4-Dioxan	10·7	Pyridine	19·4
Diphenyl ether	2·7	Quinoline	20·1
Anisole	2·3	iso-Quinoline	20·7

The high heats of formation of the tetrahydrofuran complex and those of the pyridine bases should be noted. Owing to aluminium having a larger covalent radius (1·26 Å) than boron (0·88 Å), the effect of 2-, and 2,6-methyl substitution decreases the stability of pyridine–$AlEt_3$ complexes much less than those of analogous pyridine–BMe_3 complexes. The heat of formation of the triethylaluminium complex of 2,6-dimethylpyridine is only about 3 kcal. mole^{-1} less than that of the pyridine complex, whereas the former (sterically hindered) base does not combine with BMe_3 and the latter forms a stable complex ($\Delta H = -15$ kcal. mole^{-1} [619]).

Since much heat may be evolved when complexes are formed, and since the complexes have large dipole moments (about 5–6 D), the process of complex formation may be followed calorimetrically [620] and by dielectric constant measurement [621]. The heats of formation of dialkylaluminium hydride complexes are considerably less than those of the corresponding trialkylaluminium complexes, and calorimetric titration allows mixtures, for example, of $Et_3Al + Et_2AlH$ to be analysed.

[617] H. Lehmkuhl, *Angew. Chem., Internat. Edn.*, 1964, **3**, 640.
[618] E. Bonitz, *Chem. Ber.*, 1955, **88**, 742.
[619] D. F. Hoeg, S. Liebman and L. Schubert, *J. Org. Chem.*, 1963, **28**, 1554.
[620] E. G. Hoffman and W. Tornau, *Z. anal. Chem.*, 1962, **188**, 321.
[621] Idem, ibid., 1962, **186**, 231.

Monomeric phosphine oxide complexes have also been described [622], for example, $Me_3POAlMe_3$, m.p. 89°.

Bipyridyl and o-phenanthroline form coloured 1 : 1 complexes with Me_3Al (yellow) and Et_3Al (red). The phenanthroline complexes are very sparingly soluble, but the bipyridyl compounds, e.g. bipy $AlEt_3$, are monomeric in solution [623]. These complexes could contain five-co-ordinate aluminium, though no structural data are available. The colours are probably due to electron-transfer transitions as discussed in connexion with similarly coloured dialkylberyllium complexes (p. 112). The aliphatic chelating amine, tetramethylethylenediamine adds two mols. of alkyl, $R_3Al{\leftarrow}NMe_2{\cdot}CH_2CH_2{\cdot}Me_2N{\rightarrow}AlR_3$ [623].

The complex formed from trimethylaluminium and tetramethylhydrazine [624] is monomeric and could be

$$Me_3Al\overset{\nearrow}{\underset{\searrow}{\big|}}\begin{matrix}NMe_2\\ \\NMe_2\end{matrix}\quad \text{or, more likely,}\quad Me_3Al \leftarrow NMe_2{\cdot}NMe_2\ [624a]$$

Tetramethyltetrazene, $Me_2N{\cdot}N{:}N{\cdot}NMe_2$, which might act as a chelate ligand giving pentaco-ordinate complexes, displaces trimethylamine from its triethylaluminium complex, but the structure of the product is not known.

$$Et_3Al{\cdot}NMe_3 + Me_2N{\cdot}N{:}N{\cdot}NMe_2 \longrightarrow Et_3Al(Me_2N{\cdot}N{:}N{\cdot}NMe_2) + NMe_3$$

Direct reaction between tetramethyltetrazene and Me_3Al, Et_3Al, $Me_3Al{\cdot}NMe_3$ or $H_3Al{\cdot}NMe_3$ results in evolution of nitrogen and formation of dimeric products of a type discussed later [625]:

$$2Me_3Al{\cdot}NMe_3 + Me_2N{\cdot}N{:}N{\cdot}NMe_2 \longrightarrow (Me_2Al{\cdot}NMe_2)_2 + N_2 + 2NMe_3 + 2CH_4$$

similarly

$$\tfrac{1}{2}Me_2N{\cdot}N{:}N{\cdot}NMe_2 + H_3Al{\cdot}NMe_3 \longrightarrow \tfrac{1}{3}(H_2Al{\cdot}NMe_2)_3 + \tfrac{1}{2}N_2 + \tfrac{1}{2}H_2 + NMe_3$$

The reaction between trimethylaluminium and $(Me_2N)_2B{\cdot}B(NMe_2)$ proceeds according to the equation:

$$3B_2(NMe_2)_4 + 4Me_6Al_2 \longrightarrow$$
$$Al_4B(NMe_2)_3Me_6 + 5Me_2BNMe_2 + 2(Me_2AlNMe_2)_2$$

The Al_4B product is monomeric in cyclopentane and is believed to contain Al–Al bonds [625a].

[622] F. Schindler, H. Schmidbaur and G. Jonas, *Angew. Chem., Internat. Edn.*, 1965, **4**, 153.

[623] W. Brüser, K. H. Thiele and H. K. Müller, *Z. Chem.*, 1962, **2**, 342.

[624] N. R. Fetter and B. Bartocha, *Canad. J. Chem.*, 1961, **39**, 2001; see also N. R. Fetter, F. E. Brinckman and D. W. Moore, ibid., 1962, **40**, 2184; N. R. Fetter, B. Bartocha, F. E. Brinckman and D. W. Moore, ibid., 1963, **41**, 1359.

[624a] T. Mole, *Chem. and Ind.*, 1964, 281.

[625] N. R. Fetter and B. Bartocha, *Canad. J. Chem.*, 1962, **40**, 342; D. F. Clemens, W. S. Brey and H. H. Sisler, *Inorg. Chem.*, 1963, **2**, 1251.

[625a] E. P. Schram, ibid., 1966, **5**, 1291.

(b) *Co-ordination complexes with ligands containing acidic hydrogen.*
Organoaluminium compounds are not only stronger acceptors than their
boron analogues, but are also much more reactive to protonic acids,
probably on account of the higher polarity of aluminium–carbon
bonds. Trimethylaluminium forms a 1 : 1 complex with dimethylamine,
$Me_3Al \leftarrow NHMe_2$, m.p. 49·1°, which eliminates methane when heated
at 110°:

$$2Me_3Al \leftarrow NHMe_2 = (Me_2Al \cdot NMe_2)_2 + 2CH_4$$

The dimeric amino compound $(Me_2Al \cdot NH_2)_2$, from $Me_3Al \leftarrow NH_3$, has
also been described [616]. The monomer, $Me_2Al\!-\!NR_2$, formed by methane
elimination, would contain co-ordinatively unsaturated aluminium and
nitrogen. Co-ordinative unsaturation could be relieved by the formation of
a double bond (as in the boron analogue $Me_2B \rightleftharpoons NMe_2$), or by the formation by each element of an additional single bond. There is no evidence for
double bonding in any of these compounds formed by aluminium, or (see
below) any of the similar compounds formed by the Group IIIB elements.
In all cases the products of these reactions are associated (except certain
instances where chelation is possible). Association normally leads to
dimers or *trimers*, polymers resulting only when more than one alkyl is
displaced from the metal. Ligands containing hydrogen more acidic than
that present in secondary amines often eliminate alkane so rapidly on
reaction with trialkylaluminium that the intermediate complex is not
isolated:

$$3Me_3Al + 3MeOH \rightarrow (Me_2AlOMe)_3 + 3CH_4$$
$$2Me_3Al + 2MeSH \rightarrow (Me_2AlSMe)_2 + 2CH_4$$

These compounds are formulated with cyclic structures:

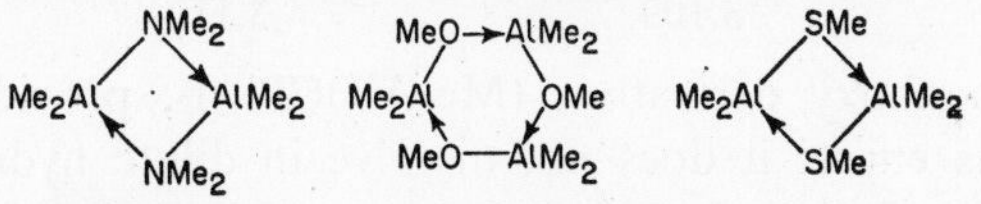

The question whether a dimer or trimer is formed is probably decided by a
balance between entropy factors (favouring the formation of the maximum
number of molecules, hence dimers) and steric factors. The valency angles
in a four-membered ring must average 90° and involve some strain from
the tetrahedral angle, 109·5°, and a puckered six-membered ring could be
strainless in this respect; hence this factor favours *trimer* formation. On
the other hand steric interference between substituent groups is more
severe in a trimer than in the corresponding dimer, and this factor favours
dimer formation*.

Dimerization sometimes occurs even though a chelate monomer might

---

*The possibly polymeric constitution of the *glassy* form of $Me_2Al \cdot NMe_2$ is discussed
later in connexion with the analogous gallium compound (p. 352).

L

be formed. Thus reaction between Et_3Al and $EtOCH_2CH_2OH$ gives 3.107 instead of 3.108. This happens because the polar $\overset{\delta+}{Al}-\overset{\delta-}{O}$ bond makes

$$\text{3.107} \qquad\qquad \text{3.108}$$

the Al–O–C oxygen a stronger donor than the ether C–O–C oxygen [626].

Dimers are more numerous than trimers in this group of compounds and include $(Me_2Al\cdot NMe_2)_2$ [616], $(Et_2Al\cdot NEt_2)_2$, $(Bu_2Al\cdot NMe_2)_2$ [634], $(Me_2Al\cdot NPh_2)_2$, $(Me_2Al\cdot PPh_2)_2$, $(Me_2Al\cdot AsPh_2)_2$ [627], $(Et_2Al\cdot PEt_2)_2$, $(Et_2Al\cdot PPh_2)_2$ [628], $(Et_2Al\cdot OEt)_2$, $(Et_2Al\cdot OBu)_2$ [626] and $(Me_2Al\cdot SMe)_2$ [616]. Trimers are mostly less sterically hindered methyl compounds and hydrides; cyclic trimers include $(Me_2Al\cdot PMe_2)_3$, $(Me_2Al\cdot OMe)_3$ [616], $(Et_2Al\cdot OMe)_3$ [626], $(H_2Al\cdot NMe_2)_3$ [629], $(H_2Al\cdot PEt_2)_3$ [630] and also $(Et_2Al\cdot NH_2)_3$ [631].

A bulky group such as tertiary butoxy not only gives a dimer but also greatly reduces the rate of attack on the metal by air or water. After 100 hours exposure to moist air $(Bu_2^iAlOBu^t)_2$ is less than 2% decomposed; $(Et_2AlOEt)_2$ in contrast is very sensitive to air [632]. A similar effect is observed with the even bulkier trimethylsilyl group, 3.109 and 3.110 being relatively unreactive [633].

$$\text{3.109} \qquad\qquad\qquad \text{3.110}$$

The triphenylmethoxy derivative, $(Me_2AlOCPh_3)_2$, provides a striking example of this effect: it does not dissolve in dilute hydrochloric acid [633a]. A series of dialkylmetal derivatives, $(R_2MN{:}PR_3')_2$ [633b], and $[R_3MN(SiMe_3){:}PR_3']_2$ (M = Al, Ga, In) [633c] has been investigated.

[626] E. G. Hoffmann, *Annalen*, 1960, **629**, 104.
[627] G. E. Coates and J. Graham, *J. Chem. Soc.*, 1963, 233.
[628] K. Issleib and H. J. Deylig, *Z. Naturforsch.*, 1962, **17b**, 198.
[629] J. K. Ruff, *J. Amer. Chem. Soc.*, 1961, **83**, 1798.
[630] G. Fritz and G. Trenczek, *Z. anorg. Chem.*, 1964, **331**, 206.
[631] M. Cohen, J. K. Gilbert and J. D. Smith, *J. Chem. Soc.*, 1965, 1092.
[632] E. G. Hoffmann and W. Tornau, *Angew. Chem.*, 1961, **73**, 578.
[633] H. Schmidbaur and M. Schmidt, *Angew. Chem., Internat. Edn.*, 1962, **1**, 327; *J. Amer. Chem. Soc.*, 1962, **84**, 1069; H. Schmidbaur, *Angew. Chem., Internat. Edn.*, 1965, **4**, 152.   [633a] T. Mole, personal communication.
[633b] H. Schmidbaur, G. Kuhr and V. Kröger, *Angew. Chem., Internat. Edn.*, 1965, **4**, 877.
[633c] H. Schmidbaur and W. Wolfsberger, *Chem. Ber.*, 1967, **100**, 1000, 1016, 1023.

These cyclic compounds are split open by reaction with a stronger donor if this is able to compete successfully for co-ordination positions around the metal. Sulphur is a relatively weak donor to aluminium, and the methyl-thio derivative reacts reversibly with trimethylamine [616]:

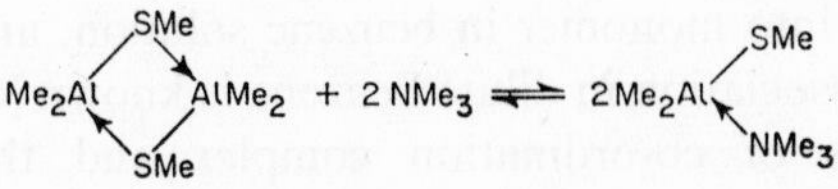

Dialkylphosphino- are stronger donors than diarylphosphino- groups, and $(Me_2Al \cdot PPh_2)_2$ reacts reversibly with trimethylamine [627], though $(Me_2Al \cdot PMe_2)_3$ does not [616]. Though $(Me_2Al \cdot NMe_2)_2$ is not split by trimethylamine, many di-isobutylaluminium derivatives react exothermically with amines. The products obtained by adding Bu_2^iAlH to azomethines have been extensively studied [634]:

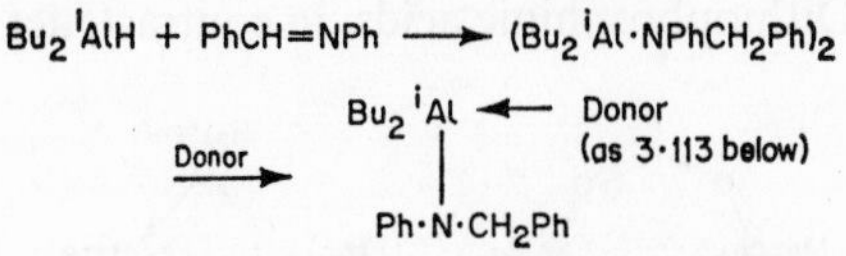

This dimer reacts with methyl aniline (4·4), benzalaniline (4·4), diethylether (4·9), tetrahydrofuran (8·9) and isoquinoline (11·9 kcal. mole^{-1}), the reaction heats being given. When the donor atom is nitrogen, and when it is part of an aromatic system or conjugated with an aromatic system, then the adducts are coloured.

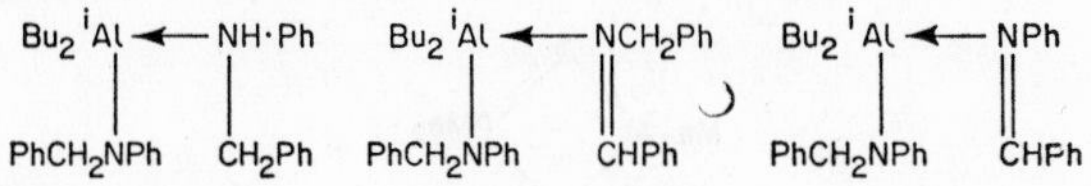

3.111 colourless   3.112 yellow-orange   3.113 deep red

The isoquinoline complex is deep red. These colours are attributed to charge-transfer transitions [635]. The origin of the colour of beryllium bipyridyl complexes has been discussed in an earlier chapter; the electron transfer is into the lowest unoccupied molecular orbital of the aromatic π-electron system, and the more extended is the latter the smaller is the gap between highest occupied and lowest unoccupied levels. Consequently more complex aromatic donors give complexes which absorb at longer wavelengths. This is apparent in the group of compounds 3.111–3.113; in 3.111 the (saturated) nitrogen is conjugated with only one benzene ring, in 3.112 it is part of a Ph·CH=N—system, and in 3.113 the entire benzalani-

[634] W. P. Neumann, *Annalen*, 1963, 667, 1.   [635] Idem, ibid., p. 12.

line system is involved. The 9,10-dihydrophenanthridine complex, in which the donor atom is an —NH—group, is colourless, whereas the phenanthridine complex, in which the donor atom is part of a tricyclic aromatic system, is deep red.

Not all complexes of the type $R_2Al \cdot NR_2'$ are dimeric: $(Bu^i_2Al \cdot NPh_2)_2$ is partly dissociated into monomer in benzene solution, and an example of about sevenfold association in dilute benzene is known [634].

Both this class of co-ordination complex and the simpler type, $R_3Al \leftarrow Donor$, can be prepared by the alkylation or arylation of aluminium hydride complexes [629], examples being as follows:

$$H_3Al \cdot NMe_3 + \tfrac{3}{2}Bu^n_2Hg \rightarrow Bu^n_3Al \cdot NMe_3 + \tfrac{3}{2}Hg + \tfrac{3}{2}H_2$$
$$(H_2Al \cdot NMe_2)_3 + 6Bu^nLi \rightarrow \tfrac{3}{2}(Bu^n_2Al \cdot NMe_2)_2 + 6LiH$$

Reactions between trimethylaluminium and phosphinic acids give dimers, formulated 3.114, in which the phosphinic group acts as a three-atom bridging group, rather than as 3.115, on the basis of the P–O infrared absorption [636]. Dithiophosphinic acids, in contrast, act as chelate groups

3.114   3.115

and give monomeric derivatives, 3.116, evidently because sulphur can accommodate a considerably smaller valency angle than oxygen.

3.116

Hydrazines containing NH groups react with Me_3Al or its trimethylamine complex forming either *dimers* or, if more than one methyl is displaced, *polymers*, e.g. [624]

$$Me_3Al + HNMe \cdot NMe_2 \rightarrow Me_3Al \leftarrow HNMe \cdot NMe_2 \rightarrow (Me_2Al \cdot NMe \cdot NMe_2)_2$$
m.p. 80–83°   m.p. 125–126°
$$Me_3Al + H_2N \cdot NMe_2 \rightarrow (Me_2Al \cdot NH \cdot NMe_2)_2$$
m.p. 77–78·5°
$$Me_3Al + HNMe \cdot NHMe \rightarrow polymer$$
$$+ H_2N \cdot NHMe \rightarrow polymer$$

The *cyanide* group acts as a bridging ligand and its stereochemical

[636] G. E. Coates and R. N. Mukherjee, *J. Chem. Soc.*, 1964, 1295.

requirements result in tetramer formation [637] as in the gold compounds $(R_2AuCN)_4$:

$$Me_3Al + HCN \longrightarrow$$

$$\begin{array}{ccc} Me_2Al-C\equiv N\rightarrow AlMe_2 \\ \uparrow \quad\quad | \\ N \quad\quad C \\ ||| \quad\quad ||| \\ C \quad\quad N \\ | \quad\quad \downarrow \\ Me_2Al\leftarrow N\equiv C-AlMe_2 \end{array}$$

Oligomers, $(Me_2AlCN)_{\sim 7}$ and $(Et_2AlCN)_{\sim 7}$ have also been isolated [638].

Though cyanides such as MeCN or EtCN containing α-CH react to some extent as acids, alkyl transfer also takes place. For example, ethyl cyanide and trimethylaluminium form a dimer, m.p. 73° [639]

$$EtCN + Me_3Al \longrightarrow MeEtC=N\overset{\overset{\displaystyle AlMe_2}{\diagup}}{\underset{\underset{\displaystyle AlMe_2}{\diagdown}}{}}N=CMeEt$$

Dimeric aldimine derivatives $(RCH:N\cdot AlMe_2)_2$ are obtained from nitriles and dimethylaluminium hydride, and similar compounds $(Ph_2C:N\cdot AlR_2)_2$ can be prepared by elimination of alkane from adducts $Ph_2C:NH,AlR_3$ [639a]. An X-ray crystallographic study of the compound $(Bu^tCMe:N\cdot AlMe_2)_2$ (from Bu^tCN and Me_3Al) has shown the ring geometry to be very similar to that of the related boron compound $(MeCH:N\cdot BMe_2)_2$ (3.56, p. 264 [427]).

$$\begin{array}{c} \overset{But}{\diagdown}\underset{Me}{\diagup}C=N\overset{94\cdot6°}{\underset{}{}}\underset{\underset{Me_2}{Al}}{\overset{\overset{Me_2}{Al}}{}}\overset{1\cdot96Å}{\underset{1\cdot27Å}{}}N\overset{}{\diagup}\underset{Bu^t}{\overset{Me}{\diagup}}C \end{array}$$

Reactions with oximes give derivatives believed to have related structures [639b]:

$$Me_2C:NOH + Me_3Al \longrightarrow \overset{Me}{\underset{Me}{\diagup}}C=N\overset{\overset{\overset{Me_2}{Al}-O}{}}{\underset{O-Al}{}}\underset{Me_2}{}N=C\overset{Me}{\underset{Me}{\diagdown}}$$

[637] Idem, ibid., 1963, 229.

[638] R. Ehrlich and A. R. Young, *J. Inorg. Nucl. Chem.*, 1966, **28**, 674.

[639] J. E. Lloyd and K. Wade, *J. Chem. Soc.*, 1965, 2662; J. R. Jennings, J. E. Lloyd and K. Wade, ibid., p. 5083.

[639a] K. Wade and B. K. Wyatt, *J. Chem. Soc. (A)*, 1967, 1339.

[639b] J. R. Jennings and K. Wade, ibid., 1967, 1333.

In the pyridine-2-aldoxime derivative, the pyridine nitrogen may raise the metal co-ordination number to five [639c]:

Rather similar compounds are formed by gallium, indium and thallium.

The formation of polymers when two of the alkyl groups have been displaced is illustrated by the progressive elimination of ethane in the reactions [640]:

$$MeNH_3Cl + Et_3Al \longrightarrow MeNH_2 \cdot AlEt_2Cl + C_2H_6$$
m.p. $-11 \cdot 5°$, monomeric

$\downarrow$ heat

$$(MeN \cdot AlCl)_n \xleftarrow{\quad 210-220° \quad} (MeNH \cdot AlEtCl)_2$$
polymer $\qquad$ m.p. 91° (d.), dimer as vapour

Whereas reactions between aluminium alkyls and primary amines normally result in the formation of insoluble polymers once two alkyl groups have been displaced from the metal, crystalline soluble *tetramers* can be obtained if the reaction is carried out in high-boiling hydrocarbon solvents.

$$Et_3Al + PhNH_2 \rightarrow \tfrac{1}{4}(EtAl \cdot NPh)_4 + 2C_2H_6$$

Other examples are $(ClAl \cdot NMe)_4$ and $(ClAl \cdot NPh)_4$, which are believed to have the cubane-type structure found by crystallographic analysis for the phenyl compound $(PhAl \cdot NPh)_4$ discussed below (p. 335). These tetramers add hydrogen chloride [641]:

$$\tfrac{1}{4}(EtAl \cdot NPh)_4 \xrightarrow{\text{HCl}} \tfrac{1}{2}(EtClAl \cdot NHPh)_2 \xrightarrow{\text{HCl}} EtAlCl_2 \cdot PhNH_2$$

Just as reactions with amines containing two or more acidic hydrogen atoms readily lead to complex polymeric products, so also are complex products formed from aluminium alkyls and *water*. Evidence for the formation of oxides R_4Al_2O has been obtained from controlled low-temperature reactions [642]. These substances are associated, Et_4Al_2O being trimeric in benzene solution [643]. Diethylaluminium oxide, as prepared from Et_2AlOLi and Et_2AlCl, catalyses the polymerization of propylene

[639c] I. Pattison and K. Wade, unpublished observations.

[640] A. W. Laubengayer, J. D. Smith and G. G. Ehrlich, *J. Amer. Chem. Soc.*, 1961, **83**, 542.

[641] J. K. Gilbert and J. D. Smith, *J. Chem. Soc.* (to be published).

[642] G. B. Sakharovskaya, N. N. Korneev, A. F. Popov, E. I. Larikov and A. F. Zhigach, *Zhur. obshchei Khim.*, 1964, **34**, 3435.

[643] A. Storr and A. W. Laubengayer, Lecture to Organometallic Symposium, Madison, 1965.

oxide, much of the polymer being stereoregular [225*b*]. It is doubtful if $(Et_2Al)_2O$ has been obtained in a pure form [643*a*].

Diethylaluminium azide, $(Et_2AlN_3)_3$, is believed to have a *planar* Al_3N_3 ring on the basis of its infrared and Raman spectra [643*b*].

(*c*) *Anionic co-ordination complexes.* These are of interest on account of certain structural features such as electron-deficient bonding involving alkali metal, 'fluorine-bonding', and the formation of metal alkyls by means of electrolytically produced alkyl radicals.

Lithium and sodium tetra-ethylaluminate were studied some time ago by Hein [644], who found they are electrically conducting in the fused state [specific conductances about 0·06 (130°,Na) and 10^{-3} (100°,Li)ohm^{-1} cm^{-1}]. The lithium compounds were prepared from the lithium alkyl and the trialkylaluminium–ether complex [645], but preparations of the sodium compounds required hydrocarbon solvents to avoid attack of ether by sodium alkyl. In their early work on aluminium alkyls, Grosse and Mavity [590] mentioned that sodium reacts with triethylaluminium,

$$3Na + 4Et_3Al \longrightarrow 3Na[Et_4Al] + Al$$

but not with trimethylaluminium. This type of reaction has recently been more widely explored by Zakharkin and Gavrilenko [646], who find the alkali metals increase in reactivity Li < Na < K. When the metals are finely divided reaction begins at room temperature and is completed at 60–80° in hydrocarbon solvents. Trimethylaluminium reacts with lithium in the presence of ether, and ether may be removed from the product $Li[Me_4Al]$, m.p. 260° (dec.), at 100–120° in vacuum. Lithium tetramethyl-aluminate has been investigated as a methylating agent [647]. Sodium and potassium react with Me_3Al in the presence of tetrahydrofuran, and the complex, $Na[AlMe_4]THF$, loses THF at 120° giving $Na[AlMe_4]$, m.p. 221–225° (dec.). The ethyl complexes are lower melting, $Li[AlEt_4]$, m.p. 163–165°, $Na[AlEt_4]$, m.p. 122–124°, $K[AlEt_4]$, m.p. 80–82°, and $K[AlPr_4^n]$ is a liquid at room temperature. The potassium compounds are practically insoluble in saturated hydrocarbons, and may reasonably be

[643*a*] S. Ishida, *J. Polymer Sci.*, 1962, **62**, 10; T. Saegusa, Y. Fujii, H. Fujii and J. Furukawa, *Makromol. Chem.*, 1962, **55**, 232.

[643*b*] K. Dehnicke, J. Strähle, D. Seybold and J. Müller, *J. Organometal. Chem.*, 1966, **6**, 298; J. Müller and K. Dehnicke, *Z. anorg. Chem.*, 1966, **348**, 261; M. I. Prince and K. Weiss, *J. Organometal. Chem.*, 1966, **5**, 584.

[644] F. Hein, E. Petzchner, K. Wagler and F. A. Seglitz, *Z. anorg. Chem.*, 1924, **141**, 161.

[645] D. T. Hurd, *J. Org. Chem.*, 1948, **13**, 711; E. B. Baker and H. H. Sisler, *J. Amer. Chem. Soc.*, 1953, **75**, 5193.

[646] L. I. Zakharkin and V. V. Gavrilenko, *J. Gen. Chem. U.S.S.R.*, 1962, **32**, 688 (Eng. trans.).

[647] D. J. Pasto and R. Snyder, *J. Org. Chem.*, 1965, **30**, 1634.

regarded as salts $K^+[AlR_4]^-$, but the sodium and more particularly the lithium compounds are appreciably soluble. For example $Li[AlEt_4]$ may be recrystallized from a benzene–hexane mixture, and it can be sublimed in vacuum. In the crystalline state it has a polymeric structure [648] resembling that of dimethylberyllium; each lithium and each aluminium is tetrahedrally surrounded by CH_2 groups.

The ion aggregates which must be present in solutions of $LiAlR_4$ and $NaAlR_4$ in hydrocarbons and in the vapour of $LiAlEt_4$ presumably contain units in which Al–C bonds are polarized by the alkali metal ion to the point at which the bonding may more appropriately be described as three-centre electron-deficient (as in the crystal of $LiAlEt_4$):

The reaction between sodium and triethylaluminium is believed to take place by the ionization of the triethylaluminium,

$$(Et_3Al)_2 \rightleftharpoons Et_2Al^+ + AlEt_4^-$$

followed by electron transfer from sodium, giving the tetra-ethy, aluminate and the diethylaluminium radical – which decomposes [648a]

$$Et_2Al^+ + Na \longrightarrow Et_2Al^· + Na^+$$

The use of the sodium-naphthalene adduct allows the isolation of a naphthalene–$AlEt_2$ complex, which is precipitated as bright yellow crystals.

No metallic aluminium is precipitated. The diamagnetic naphthalene

[648] R. L. Gerteis, R. E. Dickerson and T. L. Brown, *Inorganic Chemistry*, 1964, **3**, 872.

[648a] H. Lehmkuhl, *Tetrahedron Letters*, 1966, 2811.

complex loses tetrahydrofuran when heated at 60–80° in vacuum, and reacts with Et_2AlCl giving an unstable complex $(C_{10}H_8)$ $(Et_2Al)_2$ which is regarded as a salt $(C_{10}H_8)^{2-}(Et_2Al^+)_2$ [648b].

Dimethyl- and diethyl-magnesium, which are polymeric insoluble substances, are slowly dissolved by Me_3Al or Et_3Al forming viscous complexes $MgAl_2R_8$. These are easily soluble in aliphatic hydrocarbons and would be expected to have an electron-deficient structure analogous to that of $LiAlEt_4$, i.e.

Attempted distillation of $MgAl_2Me_8$ results in separation of Me_3Al and formation of the crystalline complex $MeMgAlMe_4$, m.p. 88·5°, which can be distilled in high vacuum at 70–75° but itself loses Me_3Al on further heating, with reversion to polymeric Me_2Mg [649]. Alkali earth complexes $Ca(AlEt_4)_2$, m.p. 40°, b.p. 90–95°/10⁻³ mm., $Sr(AlEt_4)_2$, m.p. 109°, b.p. 122–123°/10⁻³ mm., and $Ba(AlEt_4)_2$, m.p. 38°, b.p. >160°/10⁻³ mm. result from the reactions

$$4Et_3Al + M(OR)_2 \rightarrow M(AlEt_4)_2 + 2Et_2AlOR \ (M = Ca, Sr, Ba)$$

The sodium complex can be obtained by a similar reaction [650].

$$2Et_3Al + NaOR \rightarrow NaAlEt_4 + Et_2AlOR$$

Electrolysis of fused $NaAlEt_4$ gives sodium at the cathode and Et_3Al + C_2H_4 + C_2H_6 (from the decomposition of ethyl radicals) at the anode. Unless the Et_3Al is continuously removed by volatilization at low pressure, it reacts with the sodium in the way described earlier giving metallic aluminium in spongy form. If an aluminium *anode* is used, then it is attacked by the ethyl radicals with formation of triethylaluminium:

$$NaAlEt_4 \rightarrow Na + Et_3Al + (Et^{\cdot} \xrightarrow{Al} \tfrac{1}{3}Et_3Al)$$

Since the sodium can be converted to NaH and combined with Et_3Al + C_2H_4 giving back $NaAlEt_4$, the net result of the electrolysis is the formation of one-third of a mole of Et_3Al (from H_2, C_2H_4 and Al). This electrolytic alternative to the direct synthesis avoids the need to use finely divided oxide-free aluminium, and requires only moderate (10 atm.) instead of high pressures. The disadvantages are the need to remove

[648b] Idem, *Angew. Chem., Internat. Edn.*, 1965, **4**, 600.
[649] K. Ziegler and E. Holzkamp, *Annalen*, 1957, **605**, 93.
[650] H. Lehmkuhl and W. Eisenbach, *ibid.*, 1967, **705**, 42.

Et_3Al from the cell before it can react with the sodium, and to recycle three-quarters of the product.

The use of a *lead anode* gives a mixture of $4Et_3Al + Et_4Pb$, and this is the basis of a possible electrolytic route to tetra-ethyl-lead [587, 650a].

Aluminium alkyls react readily with alkali metal hydrides, giving adducts of the type exemplified by $LiAl_2HEt_6$ [651, 652], and $NaAlHMe_3$. Sodium hydride reacts more readily than lithium hydride, and potassium hydride still more readily and with considerable heat evolution [646]. The difference is mainly due to the hydride of the smallest cation (Li^+) having the highest lattice energy, and the lattice has to be broken down for the reaction to take place. The hydride complexes are commonly soluble in hydrocarbons, e.g. $NaAlHEt_3$, m.p. 64°, $KAlHEt_3$, m.p. 46–50° (both crystallized from benzene + hexane).

Dihydro complexes, $M[AlR_2H_2]$, are formed by direct addition of MH to the dialkylaluminium hydride,

$$Bu_2^iAlH + NaH \longrightarrow Na[AlBu_2^iH_2], \text{ m.p. } 180\text{–}184° \text{ from xylene}$$

or the chloride may be used as starting material. The chloride is added to a stirred suspension of alkali metal hydride in hydrocarbon or ether solvents containing a little R_2AlH or R_3Al to keep some MH in solution [646, 653, 654]:

$$Et_2AlCl + NaH \longrightarrow Et_2AlH + NaCl$$
$$Et_2AlH + NaH \longrightarrow Na[AlEt_2H_2], \text{ m.p. } 85\text{–}87° \text{ from hexane}$$

This reaction can equally well be used to prepare the hydride, R_2AlH. The potassium salt, $K[AlEt_2H_2]$, is a liquid at room temperature. The hydride complexes readily add olefin, e.g.

$$Na[AlEt_3H] + C_2H_4 \longrightarrow Na[AlEt_4]$$

The hydride complexes $Na[AlEt_3H]$ and $Na[AlEt_2H_2]$, but not $Na[AlEtH_3]$, may be prepared by heating $NaAlH_4$ and $NaAlEt_4$ together in the right proportion for about 10 minutes at 80–100° [655].

All the alkali metal hydrides examined add to aluminium alkyls, but, as mentioned earlier, the addition of LiH is relatively sluggish on account of its higher lattice energy. Similar effects dominate the addition of *halides* to aluminium alkyls [652], and in several instances high lattice energies pre-

[650a] H. Lehmkuhl and W. Grimme, *Annalen*, 1967, **705**, 1.

[651] K. Ziegler, H. Lehmkuhl and E. Lindner, *Chem. Ber.*, 1959, **92**, 2320.

[652] K. Ziegler, R. Köster, H. Lehmkuhl and K. Reinert, *Annalen*, 1960, **629**, 33.

[653] H. Jenkner, Ger.P. 1,058,478 (to Kali-Chemie); see also idem, Ger.P. 1,116,664.

[654] L. I. Zakharkin, V. V. Gavrilenko and I. M. Khorlina, *Izvest. Akad. Nauk S.S.S.R.*, 1962, 438.

[655] P. Kobetz, W. E. Becker, R. C. Pinkerton and J. B. Honeycutt, *Inorg. Chem.*, 1963, **2**, 859.

vent the formation of complexes, e.g. sodium fluoride (lattice energy 218 kcal. mole^{-1}) adds to Et$_3$Al whereas lithium fluoride (lattice energy 247 kcal. mole^{-1}) does not. The reaction

$$R_3Al + X^- \rightarrow [R_3AlX]^- + Q$$

becomes less exothermic as the size of the ion X$^-$ increases, so the addition of alkali metal halides to R$_3$Al is determined mainly by a balance between lattice energy (involving the sizes of both M$^+$ and X$^-$) and Q (involving mainly the radius of X$^-$). Thus the formation of complexes is favoured when the *cation is large* and the *anion is small*, as shown in Table 15 in which the existence of a complex is indicated by +.

Table 15   *Stability of 1 : 1 MX, Et$_3$Al complexes*

	H$^-$	F$^-$	Cl$^-$	Br$^-$	I$^-$
Li$^+$	+	−	−	−	−
Na$^+$	+	+	−	−	−
K$^+$	+	+	+	−	−
Rb$^+$	(+)	+	+	+	−
Cs$^+$	(+)	+	+	+	−
Et$_4$N$^+$	(+)	(+)	+	+	+

(+) Formation of these not investigated.

Substitution of alkyl by halogen also favours complex formation. Sodium chloride, for example, forms a complex with MeAlCl$_2$ but not with Me$_2$AlCl, and this allows the easy separation of the latter from methylaluminium sesquichloride [587, 656]:

$$Me_3Al_2Cl_3 + NaCl \rightarrow Na[AlMeCl_3] + Me_2AlCl$$

The fluoride complexes are of particular interest because two series are formed, e.g. Na[AlEt$_3$F], m.p. 72–74°, K[AlEt$_3$F], m.p. 56–58°, and Na[Al$_2$Et$_6$F], m.p. ca. 35°, K[Al$_2$Et$_6$F], m.p. 127–129°. The 1 : 1 complexes are the more soluble in saturated hydrocarbons and have lower conductances in the fused state, compare Na[AlEt$_3$F], 1·9.10^{-4} ohm^{-1} cm^{-1} at 100° with Na[Al$_2$Et$_6$F], 0·042 ohm^{-1} cm^{-1} at 100°. The fluorine atom in the 1 : 2 KF complex is symmetrically placed between the aluminium atoms, as shown by an X-ray structure analysis, the Al–F distance being 1·80 Å and the Al···F···Al system linear.

[656] G. J. Sleddon, *Chem. and Ind.*, 1961, 1492.

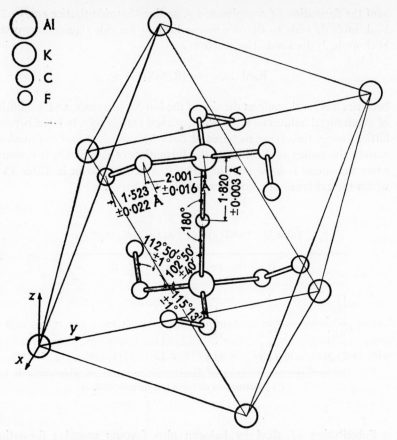

Fig. 24. Axonometric projection of the $[(C_2H_5)_3Al—F—Al(C_2H_5)_3]^-$ ion, and of the six nearest octahedrally disposed K^+ ions. Hydrogen atoms have been omitted. Bond lengths and valence angles have also been represented, together with the corresponding standard deviations (after Allegra and Perego [657])

The 1 : 2 complexes dissociate when heated, giving 1 : 1 complexes and R_3Al, and since $K[Al_2Et_6F)$ may be obtained from KF (or $KAlEt_3F$) and Et_3Al even in ether solution this allows the separation of Et_3Al from its ether complex. Trimethylamine decomposes the 1 : 2 complexes [652]:

$$Na[Al_2Et_6F] + 2Me_3N \longrightarrow NaF + 2Et_3Al{\leftarrow}NMe_3$$
$$K[Al_2Et_6F] + Me_3N \longrightarrow K[AlEt_3F] + Et_3Al{\leftarrow}NMe_3$$

The enhancement of the donor strength of oxygen bound to aluminium has already been mentioned, and the di- or tri-meric alkoxides $(R_2AlOR')_2$ do not react with alkali halides.

[657] G. Allegra and G. Perego, *Acta Cryst.*, 1963, **16**, 185.

The lithium derivatives, R_2AlOLi, which are soluble in toluene, act as donors towards R'_3Al:

$$R_2AlOLi + R'_3Al \longrightarrow Li\left[R_2Al{\overset{\displaystyle R'}{\underset{\displaystyle O}{\diamond}}}AlR'_2\right]$$

Some of these products, e.g., $Li[Et_2AlOAlEt_3]$ and the amino complex $Li[Et_2AlNPhAlEt_3]$, catalyse the polymerization of acetaldehyde [658] and yield about 80% isotactic polymer at $-78°$.

The co-ordination chemistry of organoaluminium compounds is critically discussed in a review by Lehmkuhl [659]; see also Köster and Binger's review [588].

(d) *Thermal decomposition* [660]. Triethylaluminium decomposes with loss of ethylene at about 200°, but the tri-isobutyl loses isobutene extremely easily giving the hydride Bu^i_2AlH which itself decomposes in the gas phase in contact with a surface at about 300° depositing a film of aluminium, though it is difficult to avoid slight contamination by aluminium carbide.

The pyrolysis of trimethylaluminium at 200–250° proceeds by the elimination of methane and formation of aluminium carbide, though cross-linked polymeric matter containing $-CH_2-$, $-\overset{\centerdot}{C}H-$, and $\cdot\overset{\centerdot}{C}\cdot$ as well as some $-CH_3$ groups is formed at an intermediate stage, since hydrolysis with D_2O gives a mixture of CH_3D, CH_2D_2, CHD_3 and CD_4.

The thermal decomposition of triethylaluminium in glass vessels has been studied in detail [660a], and is complicated. The rate-controlling step is believed to be ethylene elimination occurring at the glass surface, and involving a four-centre transition state (the activation energy is less than half the Al–C bond energy). Subsequent significant processes are ethylene insertion into Et_3Al and subsequent elimination of butene, and similarly ethylene insertion into $Al-Bu^n$ accounting for the observed small amount of hex-1-ene. Aluminium was deposited as a mirror, with simultaneous formation of methane and hydrogen, only after an appreciable amount of decomposition had already occurred. In fact the concentration of Et_2AlH went through a maximum at the time aluminium was first deposited, and the processes leading to metal deposition are believed to be the following, occurring in rapid succession:

$$2Et_2AlH \longrightarrow Et_3Al + EtAlH_2$$
$$2EtAlH_2 \longrightarrow Et_2AlH + AlH_3$$
$$AlH_3 \longrightarrow Al + \tfrac{3}{2}H_2$$

[658] H. Tani, T. Araki, N. Oguni, T. Aoyagi and H. Yasuda, reported in *Chem. and Eng. News*, 9 Aug. 1965, p. 40.

[659] H. Lehmkuhl, *Angew. Chem., Internat. Edn.*, 1964, **3**, 107.

[660] K. Ziegler, K. Nagel and W. Pfohl, *Annalen*, 1960, **629**, 210.

[660a] W. L. Smith and T. Wartik, *J. Inorg. Nucl. Chem.*, 1967, **29**, 629.

(e) *Reaction with olefins.** Tri-isobutylaluminium loses isobutene when heated at 120–150°, and the Bu_2^iAlH produced recombines with isobutene if heated with an excess of the olefin at 60–70°:

$$Bu_3^iAl \rightleftharpoons Bu_2^iAlH + CH_2{:}CMe_2$$

If Bu_3^iAl is heated with propene, then isobutyl are displaced by n-propyl groups, and ethylene similaily displaces propene. The affinities of the three types of olefin for addition to Al–H are

$$C_2H_4 > MeCH{:}CH_2 > Me_2C{:}CH_2$$

Equilibrium constants for the reactions in which propene (or $RCH{:}CH_2$ in general) displace isobutene (or $R_2C{:}CH_2$ in general), by reversible processes involving the dialkylaluminium hydride intermediate, are about 40, and the equilibrium constants for displacement of $RCH{:}CH_2$ by ethylene are about the same.

Since Al–H bonds are polarized, all three types of olefin give alkyls containing α-CH_2 groups:

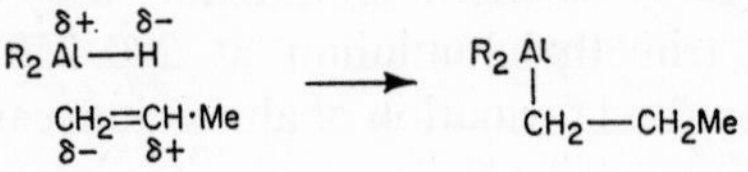

1,2-Disubstituted olefins add to Al–H about 100 times more slowly than α-olefins. The displacement reaction allows the preparation of aluminium alkyls of the type $(RCH_2CH_2)_3Al$ simply by heating Bu_3^iAl or Bu_2^iAlH (or in practice a mixture of these) with an excess of $RCH{:}CH_2$ under pressure.

If *ethylene* is heated with tri*ethyl*-aluminium at 90–120° and about 100 atmospheres pressure then olefin molecules are slowly inserted into the Al–C bonds in the trialkyl:

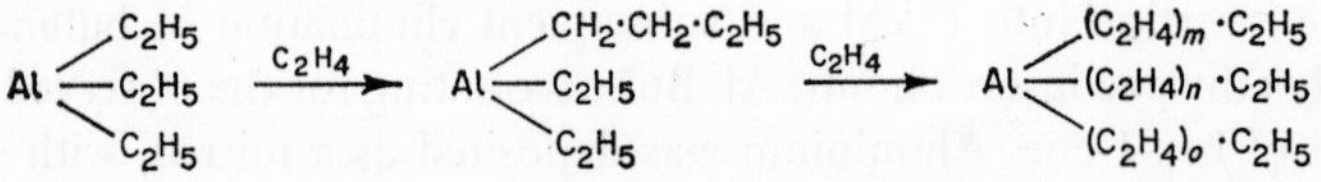

This process is in competition with fission into al–H + olefin, a process whose rate does not depend appreciably on pressure and which results in immediate conversion of al–H into al–C_2H_5 on account of the very high affinity of C_2H_4 for al–H (it is convenient to represent $\frac{1}{3}$Al as al). The 'growth' reaction goes faster as the pressure is raised, so high pressures favour larger values of m, n and o in the resulting trialkyl. At about 100 atmospheres the alkyl chain length grows to about C_{200} before it becomes detached as a long-chain olefin, and this is possible only with careful exclusion of impurities some of which (particularly nickel) strongly

---

* Few references are given under this heading. The reader is referred to the reviews by Ziegler, [587] and by Köster and Binger [588]. See also P. E. M. Allen, J. N. Hay, G. R. Jones and J. C. Robb, *Trans. Faraday Soc.*, 1967, **63**, 1636.

catalyse the displacement reaction. Hydrolysis of the high-molecular-weight aluminium alkyls made this way gives unbranched long-chain hydrocarbons containing an *even* number of carbon atoms. Hydrolysis of the product from ethylene and tri-n-propylaluminium gives unbranched long-chain hydrocarbons with an *odd* number of carbon atoms, though the displacement of propene by ethylene always gives some al–Et and hence some even hydrocarbon. Trimethylaluminium does not add olefins in the above manner. The addition of ethylene to aluminium alkyls can advantageously be carried out faster at temperatures up to 160° if the residence time at the high temperature is kept short.

Medium- to high-molecular-weight 'linear' polyethylene is more satisfactorily obtained by the use of the aluminium–alkyl–transition metal catalysts (discussed briefly below). The growth reaction could be used to make straight-chain hydrocarbons in the range C_4 to C_{30}, a distribution of products being obtained depending on the ratio $C_2H_4 : Et_3Al$. Hydrolysis of the reaction product gives the hydrocarbons, $CH_3(C_2H_4)_nCH_3$, and controlled oxidation with atmospheric oxygen gives the primary alcohols $CH_3(C_2H_4)_nCH_2OH$, after hydrolysis of the aluminium alkoxide.

Straight-chain α-olefins, $C_2H_5(C_2H_4)_nCH{:}CH_2$, can be obtained from C_2H_4 and Et_3Al at about 200° since at the higher temperatures fission of the al–C bond occurs after relatively short chain growth:

$$al{\cdot}C_2H_5 \xrightarrow{\,C_2H_4\,} al(C_2H_4)_nC_2H_5$$

$$al(C_2H_4)_nC_2H_5 \longrightarrow alH + C_2H_5(C_2H_4)_{n-1}CH{:}CH_2$$

$$alH \xrightarrow{\,C_2H_4\,} al{\cdot}C_2H_5$$

However, this process gives a rather broader distribution of chain length than the lower temperature growth reaction, and it is better to allow the latter to proceed until the maximum proportion of desired chain length is present, and then to add nickel. This catalyses the displacement reaction, re-forming triethylaluminium:

$$al{\cdot}(C_2H_4)_nC_2H_5 \xrightarrow[\text{Ni}]{\,C_2H_4\,} alC_2H_5 + C_2H_5(C_2H_4)_{n-1}CH{:}CH_2$$

Nickel and olefin are then separated from the Et_3Al, which is re-cycled.

Quite different results are obtained from reactions between aluminium alkyls and olefins other than ethylene. If propene and Pr_3^nAl are heated at 140–200° under pressure, then a growth reaction takes place as with ethylene though rather more slowly.

$$Pr_2^n Al{-}Pr^n + MeCH{:}CH_2 \longrightarrow Pr_2^n AlCH_2CH\begin{smallmatrix}\nearrow Me\\ \searrow Pr^n\end{smallmatrix}$$

In this case only *one* olefin molecule is added because the product, being similar to Bu^i-al, very rapidly loses olefin of the type $CH_2:CR_2$,

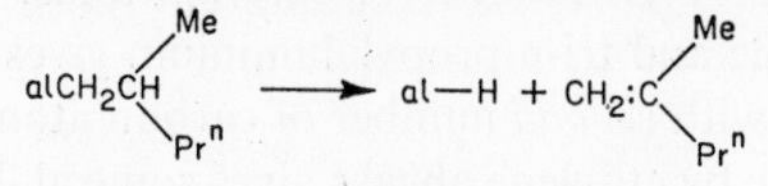

$$alCH_2\underset{\displaystyle Pr^n}{\overset{\displaystyle Me}{CH}} \longrightarrow al{-}H + CH_2{:}\underset{\displaystyle Pr^n}{\overset{\displaystyle Me}{C}}$$

and this step is followed by the addition of propene to al–H:

$$al{-}H + MeCH{:}CH_2 \longrightarrow al{\cdot}CH_2CH_2CH_3$$

The overall process therefore consists of the *catalytic dimerization* of the propene. Triethyl- or tri-isobutyl-aluminium would give the same result since both would quickly be converted into Pr^n_3Al by the excess propene. All α-olefins can be dimerized this way:

$$2RCH{:}CH_2 \longrightarrow RCH_2CH_2{\cdot}C(R){:}CH_2$$

The aluminium-alkyl-catalysed dimerization of propene, followed by thermal elimination of methane, is one of the major industrial processes for making isoprene (itself subsequently polymerized by a transition metal-aluminium alkyl catalyst):

$$2MeCH{:}CH_2 \longrightarrow CH_3CH_2CH_2\underset{\displaystyle \overset{|}{C}H_3}{C}{:}CH_2 \longrightarrow CH_2{:}CH{\cdot}\underset{\displaystyle \overset{|}{C}H_3}{C}{:}CH_2$$

Tri-t-butylaluminium is exceptional in that it adds three mols. of ethylene, even when it reacts in the form of the ether complex (m.p. 120–124°) [661]:

$$Bu^t_3Al{\cdot}OEt_2 + 3C_2H_4 \xrightarrow[\text{24 hr. 60 atm.}]{100\text{–}110°} (Me_3C{\cdot}CH_2CH_2)_3Al{\cdot}OEt_2$$

Non-terminal olefins add to al–H much less readily than terminal olefins, and until recently the preparation of secondary organoaluminium compounds by processes such as

$$Bu^i_3Al + 2C_5H_{11}{\cdot}CH{:}CH{\cdot}C_6H_{13} \longrightarrow (sec\text{-}C_{13}H_{27})_2AlH$$

was not regarded as feasible. However, displacements such as that shown above occur slowly, over a period of about 15 hours for 90% reaction in the temperature range 135–150°. At higher temperatures, 170–220°, isomerization to n-alkyl derivatives takes place. Di-sec-alkylaluminium hydrides can also be made by the direct reaction between aluminium, the olefin (e.g. 3-heptene, 4-nonene, 6-dodecene and cyclohexene) and hydrogen at 200–300 atm. and 120°.

The displacement of isobutene from Bu^i_2AlH by a *tri*alkylethylene has also been observed [662]:

$$(n\text{-}C_5H_{11})_2C{:}CHBu^n + Bu^i_2AlH \longrightarrow (sec\text{-}C_{16}H_{33})Bu^iAlH$$

[661] H. Lehmkuhl, *Angew. Chem., Internat. Edn.*, 1964, **3**, 640.
[662] G. Bruno, *J. Org. Chem.*, 1965, **30**, 623.

The *catalytic polymerization* of α-olefins by transition metal catalysts is rather a different process. A typical catalyst is obtained by reaction between Et_3Al and $TiCl_4$ in heptane; the resulting chocolate-brown suspension absorbs a large amount of ethylene at room temperature and atmospheric pressure with the formation of 'linear' polyethylene, m.p. about 135°, similar to the polymethylene derived from diazomethane. The titanium(IV) is reduced and the catalyst is a compound of titanium in a lower valency state. Catalysts can be prepared from $TiCl_3$ (and various other transition metal compounds) and many of these cause the stereoregular polymerization of propene and other α-olefins. The crystalline *isotactic* polypropene, in which successive C_3 units have the same stereochemical configuration, melts at about 170° whereas the disordered (or atactic) polymer is an oil at room temperature. The mechanism of this type of polymerization has been the subject of much discussion, and has been lucidly reviewed [663]. The scheme proposed by Cossee [664] appears to be gaining wide acceptance; the function of the aluminium alkyl (or alkylaluminium halide) is to maintain some alkylated titanium atoms at the *surface* of, say, a $TiCl_3$ crystal. The olefin then co-ordinates by a π-bond and the σ-Ti-alkyl grows by a $\pi \rightarrow \sigma$ slip.

The reactions between aluminium alkyls and halides of iron, cobalt, nickel, copper and silver commonly result in reduction to the metal by processes such as:

$$al \cdot C_2H_5 + CoCl_2 \rightarrow Co + \tfrac{1}{2}C_2H_4 + \tfrac{1}{2}C_2H_6$$
$$al \cdot C_2H_5 + 2CuCl \rightarrow 2Cu + al \cdot Cl + C_2H_5Cl$$

Both types of reaction can take place concurrently and some higher hydrocarbons are also formed [665].

Quite another result follows from the addition of the al–CH_2X group to an olefin, a process that leads to the formation of *cyclopropanes*. The exceptionally high reactivity of the Zn–C bond in halomethylzinc compounds, —$ZnCH_2X$, has been mentioned in connexion with the preparation of cyclopropanes from these compounds and olefins (p. 126). Halomethylaluminium compounds are similarly reactive [666]. Aluminium alkyls react with diazomethane mainly yielding longer-chain alkyls and

[663] C. E. H. Bawn and A. Ledwith, *Quart. Rev.*, 1962, **16**, 361.
[664] P. Cossee, *Trans. Faraday Soc.*, 1962, **58**, 1226.
[665] C. Eden and H. Feilchenfeld, *Tetrahedron*, 1962, **18**, 233; M. I. Prince and K. Weiss, *J. Organometal. Chem.*, 1964, **2**, 166.
[666] H. Hoberg, *Annalen*, 1962, **656**, 1; see also idem, ibid., 1967, **703**, 1.

nitrogen:

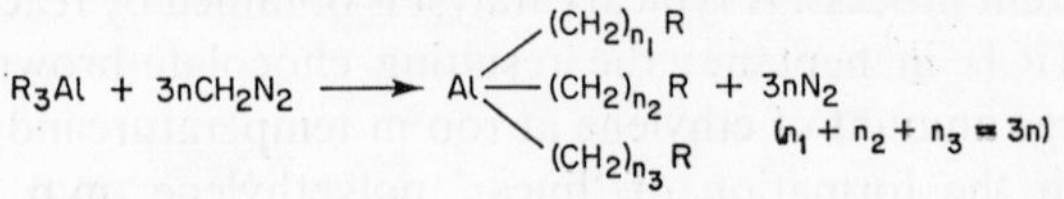

$$R_3Al + 3nCH_2N_2 \longrightarrow Al\Big\langle {{(CH_2)_{n_1}R}\atop{(CH_2)_{n_2}R}\atop{(CH_2)_{n_3}R}} + 3nN_2 \qquad (n_1 + n_2 + n_3 = 3n)$$

In hydrocarbon solvents at room temperature, dialkylaluminium halides yield nitrogen, ethylene, a little cyclopropane, and the aluminium compound remains unchanged, but at $-80°$ iodomethyldiethylaluminium may be isolated:

$$Et_2AlI + CH_2N_2 \xrightarrow[-80°]{\text{pentane}} Et_2AlCH_2I \downarrow + N_2$$

If this substance, which is thermally unstable, is stirred in cyclohexene at $-80°$ and the temperature allowed to rise, it slowly dissolves at $-50°$ and hydrolysis then gives norcarane in 100% yield. The halomethylaluminium alkyls are more stable in ether, in which they exist as co-ordination complexes $R_2AlCH_2X\cdot OEt_2$.

The formation of norcarane at temperatures well *below* those at which Et_2AlCH_2I is thermally decomposed (a process that might yield carbene, CH_2, as an intermediate) suggests that the olefin adds to the aluminium compound, and this is followed by the decomposition of the 3-halopropyl-aluminium alkyl:

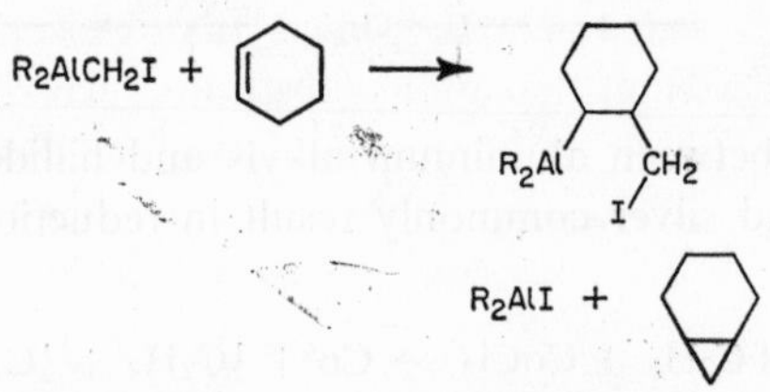

This mechanism implies that 3-halopropylaluminium compounds are exceptionally unstable, and the truth of this is apparent from the immediate evolution of cyclopropane when an aluminium alkyl is mixed with a 3-chloropropylborane [667]:

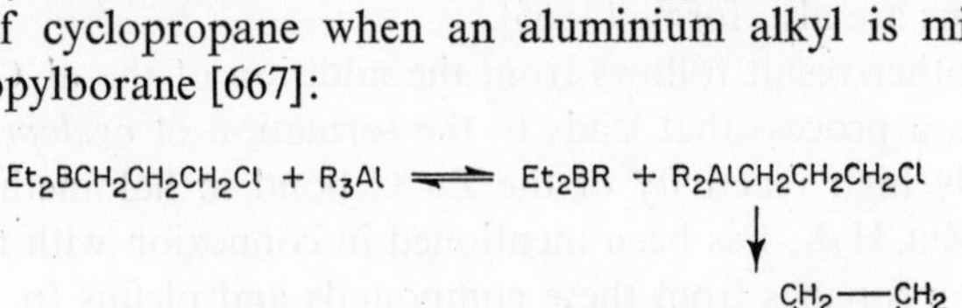

Diethylzinc behaves very similarly, and there is reason to believe that 3-halopropyl derivatives of any electropositive acceptor element would decompose to cyclopropane in this way. A further indication of the for-

[667] P. Binger and R. Köster, *Tetrahedron Letters*, 1961, 156.

mation of 3-haloalkylaluminium compounds in the cyclopropane synthesis was obtained by a study of the reaction of 2-butyne with Et_2AlCH_2Cl. The intermediate was expected to undergo cyclopropene elimination

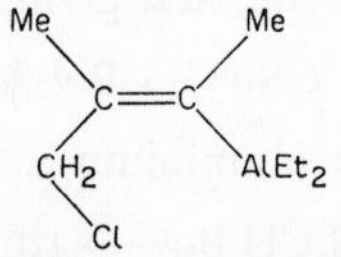

rather more slowly than the 3-chloropropyl derivatives, and, in fact, both dimethylcyclopropene (33%) and $MeCH:CMe·CH_2Cl$ were isolated from the reaction between Et_2AlCl, $MeC:CMe$ and CH_2N_2 at $-50°$.

There seems to be no reason to believe that carbene plays a part in these cyclopropane syntheses, and Hoberg has shown that alkoxymethyllithium, in which the C–Li bond is similarly activated, can also add to an olefin with elimination of a cyclopropane:

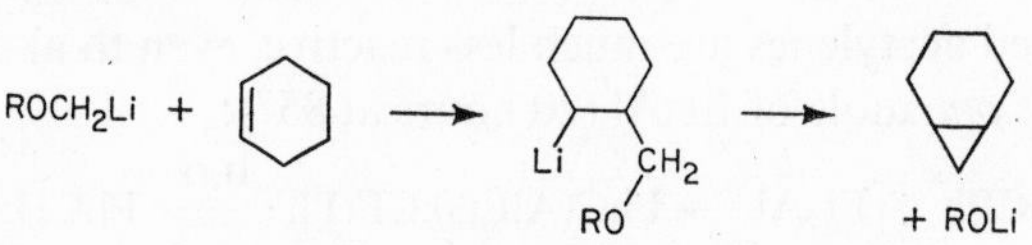

(*f*) *Reaction with acetylenes* [668]. Both al–H and al–C bonds *add* to acetylenes, generally at temperatures lower than those required for additions to olefins. The claim that monosubstituted acetylenes do not react as acids, displacing alkane or hydrogen, in contrast to reactions $RC:CH$ + Et_3Ga (see p. 345), has been shown to be incorrect. For example, phenylethynyl(dimethyl)aluminium has been made in about 60% yield by the reaction

$$PhC:CH + Me_3Al \rightarrow PhC:CAlMe_2 + CH_4$$

in toluene at $110°$ for $1\frac{1}{2}$ hours. Other examples of this type of reaction have also been found [669].

However, the most extensively studied reactions of acetylenes with aluminium alkyls involve *addition* to the triple bond [668]. Acetylene itself adds Bu^i_3Al at room temperature,

$$Bu^i_2Al·Bu^i + HC:CH \rightarrow Bu^i_2Al·CH:CH·Bu^i$$

but the resulting vinyl compound, m.p. $55–60°$, is unstable like all vinylaluminium compounds and it decomposes above its melting point. The lower reactivity of Et_3Al (higher temperatures needed), and the apparent failure of Me_3Al to react by addition (it tends to eliminate CH_4), provides

[668] G. Wilke and H. Müller, *Annalen*, 1960, **629**, 222.
[669] T. Mole and J. R. Surtees, *Chem. and Ind.*, 1963, 1727; J. J. Eisch and W. C. Kaska, *J. Organometal. Chem.*, 1964, **2**, 184.

further indication that these addition processes involve the *monomeric* alkyl; Bu^i_3Al reacts quickly because it is monomeric. The Al–H bond is particularly reactive towards acetylenes, and in spite of the association of Bu^i_2AlH it adds *twice* to hex-1-yne, first giving a vinyl compound,

$$Bu^i_2AlH + HC:CBu^n \rightarrow Bu^i_2AlCH:CH \cdot Bu^n$$

and then a product with two aluminium atoms bound to one carbon:

$$Bu^i_2AlH + Bu^i_2AlCH:CH \cdot Bu^n \rightarrow (Bu^i_2Al)_2CH \cdot CH_2 \cdot Bu^n$$

This forms $Bu^iCH_2CHD_2$ on reaction with D_2O and Bu^nCH_2CHO on oxidation followed by hydrolysis. Addition of two molecules of Et_2AlH to an acetylenic compound,

$$2Et_2AlH + Et_2AlC:CEt \rightarrow (Et_2Al)_3C \cdot CH_2Et,$$

gives a product with three aluminium atoms bound to one carbon (hydrolysis gives mainly $C_2H_6 + n\text{-}C_4H_{10}$) which is something of a chemical curiosity.

Disubstituted acetylenes are much less reactive, even to al–H. Diphenylacetylene adds *one* mole of Et_3Al (20 hours at $85°$):

$$PhC:CPh + Et_3Al \rightarrow PhC(AlEt_2):CEtPh \xrightarrow{H_2O} PhCH:CEtPh$$

(g) Aluminium alkyls as reducing agents [587, 588]. Displacement of $Me_2C:CH_2$ from Bu^i_3Al by an olefin followed by hydrolysis to alkane constitutes reduction of the olefin,

$$Bu^i_3Al + CH_2:CHR \rightarrow al\text{—}CH_2CH_2R \xrightarrow{H_2O} CH_3CH_2R,$$

and this is suggested as a means for selectively reducing α-olefins, since non-terminal olefins react so very much more slowly [670, 671].

Long before the recent revival of interest in aluminium alkyls, Meerwein [672] showed that Et_3Al reduces chloral with elimination of *ethylene*, and a rather similar reaction takes place with Et_3B.

$$Et_3Al + 3CCl_3 \cdot CHO \rightarrow (CCl_3CH_2O)_3Al + 3C_2H_4$$
$$(CCl_3CH_2O)_3Al + 3H_2O \rightarrow 3CCl_3CH_2OH + Al(OH)_3$$

The very ready displacement of $Me_2C:CH_2$ from Bu^i_3Al makes this a more convenient reagent for such reductions, and either Bu^i_3Al or Bu^i_2AlH will reduce carbonyl compounds, esters, cyanides and azomethines, though each molecule of Bu^i_3Al yields only *one* hydrogen:

$$Ph_2CO + Bu^i_3Al \rightarrow Ph_2CHOAlBu^i_2 + Me_2C:CH_2$$
$$PhCN + 2Bu^i_3Al \xrightarrow{80\text{–}90°} [PhCH_2N(AlBu^i_2)_2] \xrightarrow{H_2O} PhCH_2NH_2 \text{ [671]}$$

[670] K. Ziegler, H. G. Gellert, H. Martin, K. Nagel and J. Schneider, *Annalen*, 1954, **589**, 91.   [671] K. Ziegler, K. Schneider and J. Schneider, ibid., 1959, **623**, 9. [672] H. Meerwein, G. Hinz, H. Majert and H. Sönke, *J. prakt. Chem.*, 1937, **147**, 226.

Triethylaluminium has been found to be a convenient reducing agent in the preparation of metal carbonyls from metal halides and carbon monoxide. Hexacarbonylchromium is formed in ether solution at 110–115° and at 3500 lb. pressure of CO [673]:

$$CrCl_3 + Et_2O + Et_3Al \xrightarrow{CO} Cr(CO)_6$$

Care should be taken when aluminium alkyls are used in the presence of polyhalo-compounds: a mixture of Et_3Al and CCl_4 has exploded violently [674]. In reaction with halohydrocarbons, aluminium alkyls can act both as reducing and alkylating agents; these reactions go more smoothly in the presence of ether [675].

(h) *Aluminium alkyls as alkylating agents.* Reactions of the type

$$al\text{–}R + M\text{–}X \longrightarrow al\text{–}X + M\text{–}R$$

in which X is halogen or some other relatively electronegative group are sometimes quite attractive methods for preparing other metal alkyls. The main difficulty is in transferring *all* the alkyl from aluminium to the other element. The alkylation of borate esters or boroxines goes particularly well and gives excellent yields of R_3B [676, 677]:

$$B(OEt)_3 + Et_3Al \longrightarrow Al(OEt)_3 + Et_3B \; (>90\%)$$
$$3Et_3Al_2Cl_3 + (MeOBO)_3 \longrightarrow 3Et_3B + Al(OMe)_3 + Al_2O_3 + 3AlCl_3$$

Reaction between borate esters and R_2AlH results in transfer of alkyl only [587]:

$$2B(OEt)_3 + 3Et_2AlH \longrightarrow 2Et_3B + 3Al(OEt)_2H$$

The alkylation of $SnCl_4$ illustrates the problem of achieving complete alkyl transfer. Reaction between Et_3Al and $SnCl_4$ gives a most complex mixture containing all the ethyl-chlorstannanes, Et_nSnCl_{4-n}, together with Et_2AlCl and $EtAlCl_2$. Complete alkylation in this and several other similar reactions is achieved by the addition of complexing agents, particularly sodium chloride [678]:

$$3SnCl_4 + 4Et_3Al + 4NaCl \longrightarrow 3Et_4Sn + 4NaAlCl_4$$

Ethers and tertiary amines give similar results [587]. The ethylation of lead compounds by means of Et_3Al has been closely studied with the object of

[673] H. E. Podall, *J. Amer. Chem. Soc.*, 1958, **80**, 5573; H. E. Podall, J. H. Dunn and H. Shapiro, ibid., 1960, **82**, 1325.

[674] H. Reinheckel, *Angew. Chem., Internat. Edn.*, 1964, **3**, 65.

[675] D. B. Miller, *J. Org. Chem.*, 1966, **31**, 908.

[676] R. Köster, *Annalen*, 1958, **618**, 31.

[677] E. C. Ashby, *J. Amer. Chem. Soc.*, 1959, **81**, 4791.

[678] H. Jenkner and H. W. Schmidt, Ger.P. 1,048,275 (to Kali-Chemie); see also ref. [587].

developing better routes to tetra-ethyl-lead. Alkylation of $PbCl_2$ with Et_3Al gives Et_4Pb and metallic lead, but only part of the ethyl is transferred from the aluminium. Alkylation of lead(II) oxide, sulphide or carboxylates results in transfer of all the ethyl, but half of the lead appears as metal. This difficulty is overcome by use of the fact that an ethyl iodide–diethylcadmium mixture reacts with the finely divided lead as produced in these processes:

$$6Pb(OAc)_2 + 4Et_3Al \longrightarrow 3Pb + 3Et_4Pb + 4Al(OAc)_3$$
$$3Pb + 6EtI + 6Et_2Cd \longrightarrow 3Et_4Pb + 3CdI_2$$

The cadmium is recycled, and the overall reaction is,

$$3Pb(OAc)_2 + 3Et_3Al + 3EtI \longrightarrow 3Et_4Pb + 2Al(OAc)_3 + AlI_3$$

and the iodine in the AlI_3 is used to make ethyl iodide [679].

A process has also been developed whereby metal powders are converted into their ethyl derivatives (e.g. Sn, Zn) by reaction with $NaAlEt_4$ and ethyl chloride at 50–60° [680].

Reaction between trimethylaluminium and titanium(IV) chloride under controlled conditions gives the unstable methyltitanium chlorides. These, e.g. $MeTiCl_3$, are not catalysts for olefin polymerization, but some of their decomposition products are active catalysts [681].

One of the most interesting alkylation applications is the reaction between silica, as dry silica gel or as various forms of naturally occurring silica, with methylaluminium sesquichloride. Once started, the methylation of a silicon atom tends to go all the way to Me_4Si:

$$4Me_3Al_2Cl_3 + 3SiO_2 \longrightarrow 3Me_4Si + 4AlCl_3 + 2Al_2O_3$$

A similar reaction takes place between silica and $NaAlMeCl_3$ at 310°. These processes [682] provide very convenient routes to both tetramethyl- and tetra-ethyl-silane, and the former is of considerable interest as a possible heat-exchange fluid in view of its low critical pressure and its thermal stability to at least 500°C.

Aluminium alkyls are capable of acting as alkylating agents in reactions with functional groups such as ketones, these reactions resembling those of Grignard reagents. However, only one alkyl group is transferred. The reaction resembles that of Grignard reagents in respect of complications due to enolization or reduction. The relative extent of these reactions depends on the individual alkyl and ketone, and on the reactant ratio [683].

[679] L. L. Sims, U.S.P. 2,859,225–232 (to Ethyl Corporation); *Chem. and Eng. News*, 28 April 1958, p. 66.
[680] G. C. Robinson, U.S.P. 3,057,894 (to Ethyl); *Chem. Abs.*, 1963, **58**, 6858.
[681] A. P. Gray, A. B. Callear and F. H. C. Edgecombe, *Canad. J. Chem.*, 1963, **41**, 1502.
[682] R. C. Anderson and G. J. Sleddon, *Chem. and Ind.*, 1960, 1335.
[683] S. Pasynkiewicz and E. Sliwa, *J. Organometal. Chem.*, 1965, **3**, 121; S. Pasynkiewicz, L. Kozerski and B. Grabowski, ibid., 1967, **8**, 233.

For example, for reaction between Et_3Al and Et_2CO in 1 : 1 molar ratio at 25° the products (after hydrolysis) are triethylcarbinol (addition) 56%, diethylcarbinol (reduction) 26% and diethylketone (enolization) 19%.

$$Et_3Al + Et_2CO \nearrow \begin{array}{l} Et_2AlOCEt_3 \longrightarrow Et_3COH \quad \text{addition} \\ Et_2AlOCHEt_2 \longrightarrow Et_2CHOH \quad \text{reduction} \\ \quad + C_2H_4 \\ Et_2AlOCEt{:}CHMe \longrightarrow Et_2CO \quad \text{enolization} \\ \quad + C_2H_6 \end{array}$$

Naturally reduction does not take place so readily when trimethyl or triphenylaluminium is used. Esters react only by reduction and addition.

Unsaturated organoaluminium compounds

Some vinyl derivatives have already been mentioned in connexion with the addition of aluminium alkyls and alkyl hydrides to acetylenes, $RC{:}CH$. Trivinylaluminium is unstable at room temperature and soon polymerizes to a glass, but various derivatives have been obtained in which there is some stabilization due to co-ordination [684]:

$$AlCl_3 + CH_2{:}CHMgCl \xrightarrow{\text{THF}} (CH_2{:}CH)_3Al(THF) \text{ b.p. } 86°/2 \text{ mm.}$$
$$AlH_3{\cdot}NMe_3 + \tfrac{3}{2}(CH_2{:}CH)_2Hg \longrightarrow (CH_2{:}CH)_3Al{\cdot}NMe_3 \text{ b.p. } 45°/10^{-3} \text{ mm.}$$

The pyridine complex, $(CH_2{:}CH)_3Al\,py$, melts at 43·8°, but lithium tetravinyl aluminate polymerizes at room temperature. Trifluorovinyl derivatives are at least as unstable, since reaction between $CF_2{:}CFMgBr$ and aluminium chloride in tetrahydrofuran gives only polymeric material. Trifluorovinylation by the mercury method

$$3(CF_2{:}CF)_2Hg + 2H_3Al{\cdot}NMe_3 \rightarrow 2(CF_2{:}CF)_3Al{\cdot}NMe_3 + 3H_2 + 3Hg$$

gives a liquid product which may be kept some weeks at $-20°$ but it decomposes at room temperature [685].

Compounds in which a single vinyl-type of group is attached to aluminium are more stable, though these readily decompose when heated. A cyclopentadienyl derivative has also been described:

$$Et_2AlCl + C_5H_5K \text{ suspended in } C_6H_6 \rightarrow C_5H_5AlEt_2 \text{ b.p. } 47°/0·005 \text{ mm.}$$

The constitution of this compound is not known with certainty. It is somewhat associated (cryoscopically in benzene), and forms a 1:1 ether complex [686]. The di-isobutyl compound $Bu^i_2AlC_5H_5$ adds ethylene at all three aluminium–carbon bonds.

[684] B. Bartocha, A. J. Bilbo, D. E. Bublitz and M. Y. Gray, Z. Naturforsch., 1961, **16b**, 357.

[685] B. Bartocha and A. J. Bilbo, J. Amer. Chem. Soc., 1961, **83**, 2202; see also Chem. Abs., 1963, **58**, 12588.

[686] V. Giannini and S. Cesca, Gazzetta, 1961, **91**, 597; W. R. Kroll, Trans. New York Acad. Sci., 1965, **27**, 337.

Those *acetylenic* derivatives which have been studied appear to be rather more stable (thermally) than the vinyls. Several monoacetylenic derivatives have been made by the reaction

$$RC:CH + R_3'Al \rightarrow RC:CAlR_2' + R'H$$
$$(R = Ph, 1\text{-}C_{10}H_7, CH_3(CH_2)_7: R' = Me, Et, Pr^n, Bu^i),$$

an example being 1-naphthylethynyl(dimethyl)-aluminium, m.p. 190° (decomp.) [669]. A monoacetylenic compound has also been prepared by the reaction:

$$Et_2AlCl + NaC:CEt \xrightarrow{\text{hexane}} Et_2AlC:CEt \text{ b.p. } 70\text{–}75°/10^{-3} \text{ mm.}$$

It is noteworthy that this evolves little heat when mixed with ether, and the ether can be pumped off at 10–20 mm. [668]. A series of tri-acetylenic derivatives has also been described [687],

$$3NaC:CH + AlCl_3 \xrightarrow{\text{dioxan}} (HC:C)_3Al(\text{dioxan}) \text{ m.p. } 165\text{–}170° \text{ (d.)}$$

and all are co-ordination complexes. Derivatives include anionic complexes, $K[Al(C:CH)_3F]$, and the tetra-ethynylaluminate, see also [687a]:

$$4PhC:CH + LiAlH_4 \rightarrow LiAl(C:CPh)_4$$

The last reaction contrasts with the *addition* of al–H, in R_2AlH, across acetylenic bonds. An amine complex was obtained by the transmetalation reaction:

$$Al + NMe_3 + OEt_2 + (PhC:C)_2Hg \xrightarrow{2°} (PhC:C)_3Al \cdot NMe_3 \text{ m.p. } 176\text{–}178°$$

A bis-pyridine complex $(HC:C)_3Al \text{ py}_2$ is of interest as possibly containing five-co-ordinate aluminium.

The hydride complexes $Na[AlEt_3H]$ and $Na[AlBu^i_3H]$ react vigorously with acetylene in hydrocarbon solvents [655]:

$$2Na[AlEt_3H] + C_2H_2 \rightarrow Na_2[Et_3Al \cdot C:C \cdot AlEt_3] + 2H_2$$

The product from reaction between this sodium salt and diethylaluminium chloride,

$$Na_2[Et_3Al \cdot C:C \cdot AlEt_3] + 2Et_2AlCl \rightarrow Et_2Al \cdot C:C \cdot AlEt_2 + 2Et_3Al + 2NaCl,$$

is insoluble in hydrocarbons and is regarded as a polymer [688].

Both $R_2AlCH:CHR'$ and $R_2AlC:CR'$ are dimeric, even if R is Bu^i (compare monomeric Bu^i_3Al) [588]. Possibly bridging is favoured by the

[687] P. Chini, A. Baradel, E. Pauluzzi and M. de Malde, *Chim. Ind.* (Milan), 1962, **44**, 1220.
[687a] L. I. Zakharkin, V. V. Gavrilenko and L. L. Ivanov, *Zhur. obshchei Khim.*, 1965, **35**, 1676.
[688] P. Binger, *Angew. Chem., Internat. Ed.*, 1963, **2**, 686.

higher s content (therefore less directional character) of the sigma orbital of the bridging carbon atom (sp^2 or sp).

Cyclic organoaluminium compounds

These are formed from cyclic boron compounds by exchange with trialkyl-aluminium, for example 1-propylalumina-indane [689],

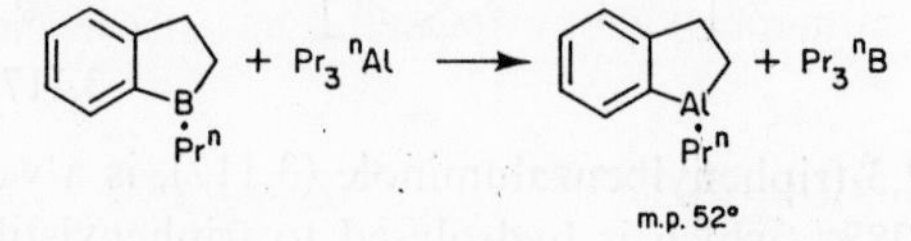

m.p. 52°

The use of trimethylaluminium can lead to a bridged product:

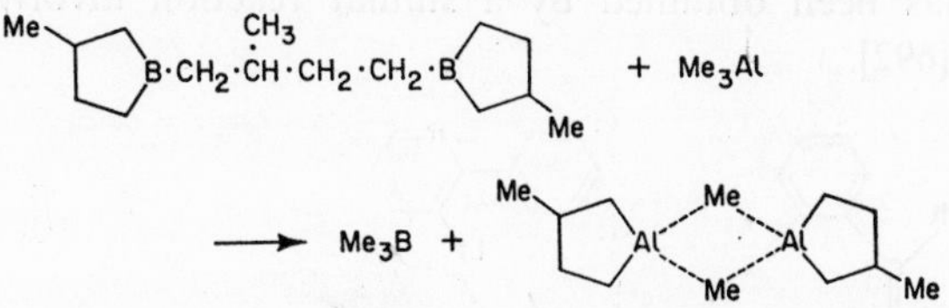

Addition of Bu^i_2AlH to diallyl gives cyclopentylmethyl derivatives [690],

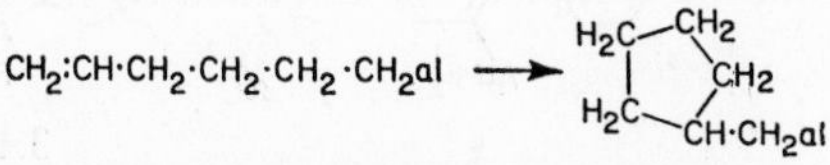

but a cyclic aluminium compound is formed in the reaction [691]:

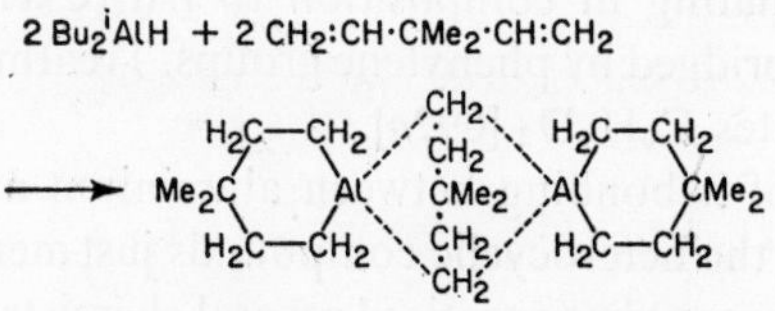

$$2 Bu^i_2AlH + 2 CH_2:CH \cdot CMe_2 \cdot CH:CH_2$$

The product, b.p. 132–140°/10^{-4} mm., condenses to a colourless glass and is evidently extensively associated in that state, though the vapour probably consists of molecules with the above structure. It reacts in benzene solution with $SnCl_4$ and $Bu_2^nSnCl_2$ giving

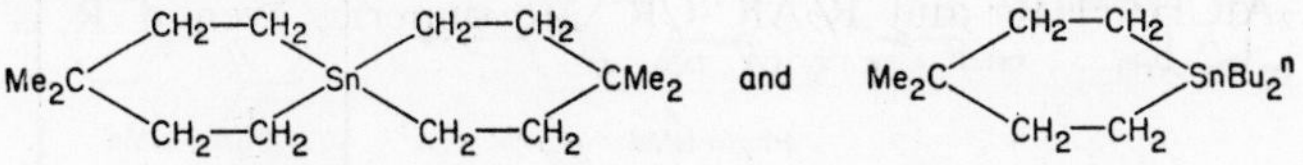

---

[689] R. Köster and G. Benedikt, ibid., 1962, 1, 507.
[690] K. Ziegler, Angew. Chem., 1956, 68, 721.
[691] R. Polster, Annalen, 1962, 654, 20.

It was mentioned earlier that aluminium alkyls do not react very readily with non-terminal acetylenes, but at 200° Ph_3Al eliminates benzene in reaction with PhC:CPh:

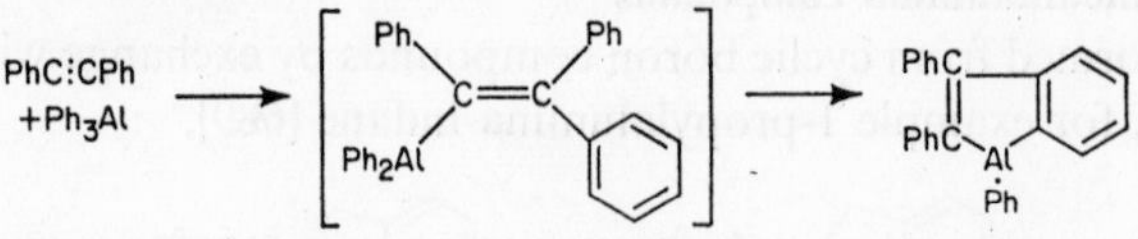

PhC:CPh +Ph₃Al

3.117

The product, 1,2,3-triphenylbenzaluminole (3.117), is a yellow crystalline solid, m.p. 285–288°, which is hydrolysed to triphenylstilbene and gives 3.118 on reaction with iodine. A colourless dibenzaluminole (3.119), m.p. 225–230°, has been obtained by a similar reaction involving benzene elimination [692].

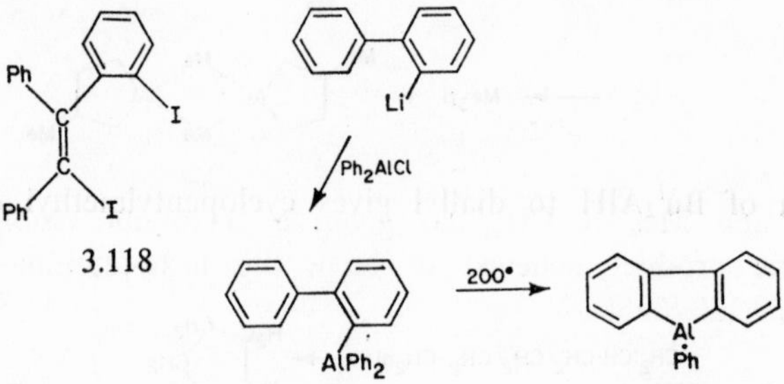

3.118

3.119

Triphenylaluminium itself loses benzene at about 250° to give involatile materials approximating in composition to $[Al_2(C_6H_4)_3]_n$ in which aluminium atoms are bridged by phenylene groups. Treatment with DCl/D_2O, for example, liberates $C_6H_4D_2$ [692a].

The possibility of π-bonding between aluminium and carbon (as conceivably in some of the heterocyclic compounds just mentioned, or between aluminium and nitrogen) has exercised several chemists. However, the sizes (radial parts) of the Al$3p$ and C$2p$ wave functions differ so much that effective π-bonding is not likely to occur. Lack of such bonding is very well shown in the Al–N analogue of a phenanthrene:

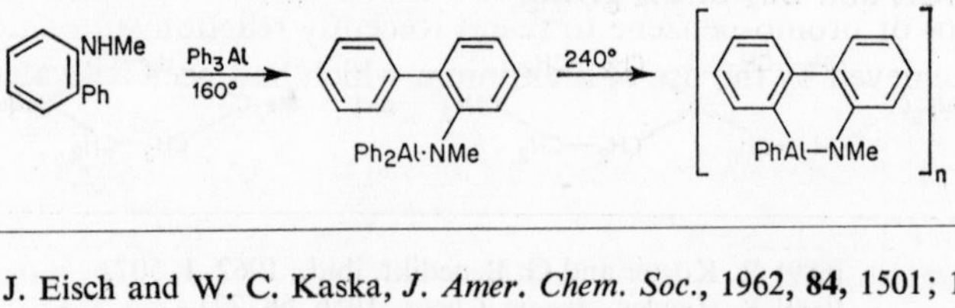

[692] J. J. Eisch and W. C. Kaska, J. Amer. Chem. Soc., 1962, **84**, 1501; 1966, **88**, 2976.
[692a] J. C. Kotz, A. W. Laubengayer and K. Wade, unpublished observations.

The product is at least dimeric and may be even more associated, so the co-ordination of both Al and N is raised to four by the formation of additional σ-bonds (as is normal for amino-aluminium compounds) rather than by means of an Al–N double bond forming part of the aromatic system [693]. The *boron analogue* of this compound is monomeric and its ultraviolet spectrum confirms the presence of B–N conjugation involving the entire ring system (see pp. 273–77).

A similar elimination of benzene from a trimethylsilyltriphenylphos-phinimine complex results in the formation of another heterocyclic system containing aluminium [694]:

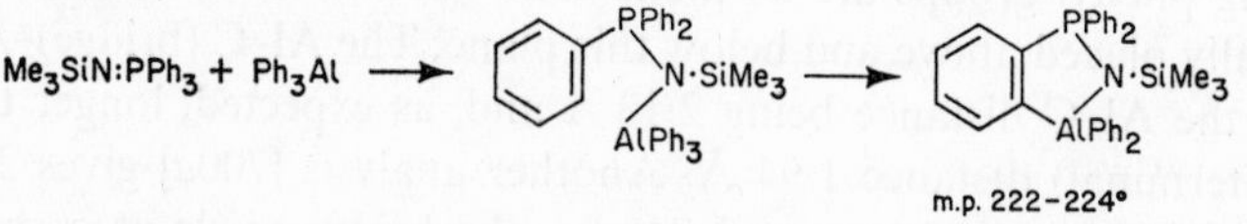

$$Me_3SiN:PPh_3 + Ph_3Al \longrightarrow \quad \longrightarrow$$

m.p. 222–224°

The formation of $(Et_2Al)_3C\cdot CH_2Et$ by addition of Et_2AlH to $Et_2AlC:CEt$ has been mentioned earlier (p. 326). Such compounds disproportionate when distilled, even at low pressure, forming trialkylaluminium and cyclic compounds. A reaction of this type, starting from Me_2AlH and $Me_2AlC:CH$, has given a crystalline, sublimable, and monomeric product believed to have the hexa-alumina-adamantane structure, 3.120 [695].

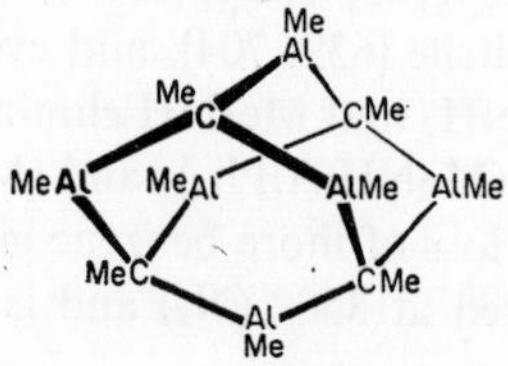

3.120

Aryls [696]

So far the aluminium aryls have received less attention than the alkyls since they have not been easily accessible by low cost methods similar to those which have been developed for the alkyls. Grosse and Mavity prepared $Ph_3Al_2I_3$ from iodobenzene and aluminium but could not get chloro- or bromo-benzene to react. Recently reaction with chlorobenzene was achieved by the use of aluminium which had been activated by grinding with $AlCl_3$. Chlorobenzene is used as the solvent, and reaction for about 22 hours gives a solution about 1M in $Ph_3Al_2Cl_3$; this has been used

[693] J. J. Eisch and M. E. Healy, *J. Amer. Chem. Soc.*, 1964, **86**, 4221.
[694] H. Schmidbaur and W. Wolfsberger, *Chem. Ber.*, 1967, **100**, 1016.
[695] G. Wilke and W. Schneider, *Bull. Soc. Chim. France*, 1963, 1462.
[696] J. R. Surtees, *Rev. Pure Appl. Chem.*, 1963, **13**, 91–109.

for the arylation of PCl_3 and $SnCl_4$. If the reaction with aluminium is carried out with salt present, a mixture of $Na[AlPhCl_3]$ and $Na[AlPh_2Cl_2]$ is obtained [697], though $PhAlCl_2$ complexes preferentially.

Triphenylaluminium, Ph_3Al, m.p. 225–228°, has been prepared from aluminium and diphenylmercury either alone at about 140°, or better, in boiling toluene [698]. It can also be obtained from the chloride,

$$3PhLi + AlCl_3 \cdot OEt_2 \longrightarrow Ph_3Al \cdot OEt_2 \xrightarrow{160-170°} Ph_3Al$$

It is about 80% associated to dimer, as a 2% solution in boiling benzene [699]. Its crystal structure [700] is similar to that of Me_6Al_2. The two bridging phenyl groups are co-planar and the two metal atoms are symmetrically placed above and below this plane. The Al–C (bridge)–Al angle is 77°, the Al–C distance being 2·13 Å and, as expected, longer than the Al–C (terminal) distance 1·94 Å. Another analysis [700a] gives 2·18 and 1·96 Å for these distances, and 74° for the bridge angle at carbon. Triphenylaluminium differs from the majority of the trialkyls in that ether can be removed from its complex, m.p. 127–128°, by pumping at 160–170° and finally at 200° [699, 701].

The triaryls are extremely sensitive to air and moisture. Triphenylaluminium forms 1 : 1 co-ordination complexes with ether, ammonia (m.p. 112°), methylamine, dimethylamine [698] (m.p. 125–130°) and trimethylamine [629] (m.p. 227–229°, but there is some doubt about this complex [698]), pyridine [702] (m.p. 133°), triphenylphosphine [703], tetrahydrofuran, benzonitrile [639, 704], and cyclohexylisocyanide [704a]. The complexes with $MeNH_2$ and Me_2NH eliminate benzene when heated, giving dimeric products $(MeNH \cdot AlPh_2)_2$ and $(Me_2N \cdot AlPh_2)_2$. The first of these melts at 170° with loss of more benzene giving $(MeN \cdot AlPh)_x$, which is unchanged when heated at 350° (N_2) and is very sparingly soluble in benzene [698].

Co-ordination complexes between Ph_3Al and aromatic primary amines eliminate one mol. of benzene, giving dimeric products $(ArNH \cdot AlPh_2)_2$ if the amine has an *ortho* substituent, and a dimer is also obtained from benzylamine. Primary aromatic amines without an *ortho* substituent

[697] D. Wittenberg, *Annalen*, 1962, **654**, 23.
[698] A. W. Laubengayer, K. Wade and G. Lengnick, *Inorg. Chem.*, 1962, **1**, 632.
[699] T. Mole, *Austral. J. Chem.*, 1963, **16**, 794.
[700] R. A. Jacobson, personal communication.
[700a] J. F. Malone and W. S. McDonald, *Chem. Comm.*, 1967, 444.
[701] G. Wittig and D. Wittenberg, *Annalen*, 1957, **606**, 13.
[702] A. N. Nesmeyanov and N. N. Novikova, *Izvest. Acad. Sci. U.S.S.R.*, 1942, 372 (this paper describes several other complexes, and some substituted aryls).
[703] O. Neunhoeffer and W. Weigel, *J. prakt. Chem.*, 1957, **4**, 201.
[704] T. Mole, *Austral. J. Chem.*, 1963, **16**, 801.
[704a] G. Hesse, H. Witte and P. Mischke, *Angew. Chem., Internat. Edn.*, 1965, **4**, 355.

eliminate *two* moles of benzene, giving tetramers (ArNAlPh)$_4$. Tetramers have been obtained from aniline, *m*-toluidine, *p*-toluidine, *p*-anisidine, *p*-chloraniline and *p*-iodaniline; they are soluble in benzene and are extremely sensitive to oxygen and moisture. An X-ray study of the phenyl tetramer, (PhNAlPh)$_4$ indicates a structure based on a N$_4$Al$_4$ cube, the N–Al distances being 1·93 Å [705]. The tert-butylamine complex Ph$_3$Al·NH$_2$Bu^t does not eliminate benzene even at 110° [706].

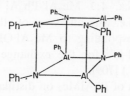

Useful information about the mechanism of the displacement of one ligand by another has been obtained from proton magnetic resonance spectra. The spectrum of a mixture of Ph$_3$Al·NEt$_3$ and free triethylamine shows the characteristic patterns of both free and complexed amine, indicating an average life for the complex well in excess of a tenth of a second. Addition of a little diethyl ether causes collapse to a single broad resonance, this being due to catalysis of the exchange process by means of the ether. A mixture of Ph$_3$Al·NMe$_3$ and free trimethylamine has only a single resonance due to trimethylamine, in between those characteristic of free and complexed amine. These results are interpreted in terms of an S$_N$2 mechanism, in which the transition state contains five-co-ordinate aluminium:

$$R_3N \cdot AlPh_3 + NR'_3 \rightleftharpoons R_3N \cdots AlPh_3 \cdots NR'_3 \rightleftharpoons R_3N + Ph_3Al \cdot NR'_3$$

The ease of attainment of the transition state is believed to be very sensitive to the steric requirements of the ligands, exchange rates increasing, Et$_3$N < Et$_2$O < Me$_3$N, as the ligand molecules become smaller. The observations are not consistent with dissociation of the complex,

$$Ph_3Al \cdot NR_3 \rightleftharpoons Ph_3Al + NR_3$$

being a rate-determining step [707]. In the case of tri*methyl*aluminium complexes, as might be expected if steric considerations were important, exchange is fast with either Me$_3$N or Et$_3$N. For example a mixture of Et$_3$N and Me$_3$Al in molar ratio 5 : 2 shows one quartet and one triplet in positions between those of free and complexed amine [708].

[705] J. Idris Jones and W. S. McDonald, *Proc. Chem. Soc.*, 1962, 366; T. R. R. McDonald and W. S. McDonald, ibid., 1963, 382.

[706] J. Idris Jones and W. S. McDonald, Lecture at I.U.P.A.C. Congress, London, July 1963.

[707] T. Mole, *Austral. J. Chem.*, 1963, **16**, 801.

[708] Idem, *Chem. and Ind.*, 1964, 281.

Reaction between triphenylaluminium and trimethylaluminium gives the crystalline mixed derivative, $PhAlMe_2$, m.p. 98–103°, which is dimeric in benzene. Other similar compounds, $PhAlEt_2$, $PhAlBu^i_2$ and Ph_2AlBu^i have also been described. Attempted distillation of $PhAlMe_2$ at 0·01 mm. has resulted in disproportionation, and the proton magnetic resonance spectrum of its solution in hydrocarbons contains only a single methyl resonance even at −40°. The presence of *bridging phenyl* is shown by the −75° spectrum of ca. 4:1 Me_3Al–Ph_3Al mixtures in toluene. In ether solution, however (i.e. with an excess of ether), three methyl resonances are observed corresponding to $Me_3Al\cdot OEt_2$, $Me_2PhAl\cdot OEt_2$ and $MePh_2Al\cdot OEt_2$. The half-life for the exchange process in ether must exceed 0·1 seconds (at 40°) [709].

The disproportionation of $PhAlMe_2$ on distillation provides a route to triphenylaluminium [588]:

$$Me_2AlCl + PhNa \rightarrow PhAlMe_2 \rightarrow \tfrac{1}{3}Ph_3Al + \tfrac{2}{3}Me_3Al$$

The phenylation of benzophenone by triphenylaluminium is not greatly affected by co-ordinated ether, but is completely inhibited by strong donors such as pyridine or quinoline, and proceeds only slowly in the presence of tetrahydrofuran. The phenylation of benzaldehyde follows the course,

since about equal amounts of benzyl alcohol, diphenylcarbinol and benzophenone are formed after hydrolysis. This is rather similar to the Meerwein–Pondorff reduction. The hydrogen transfer responsible for benzyl alcohol formation may be avoided if only one mole of benzaldehyde is allowed to react with triphenylaluminium in the absence of ether or other base [710]. In the reaction between triphenylaluminium and benzophenone (benzene, 80°), the dimer $(Ph_2AlOCPh_3)_2$ is formed very rapidly. However, prolonged reaction gives mixtures of hydrocarbons, particularly Ph_3CH. These arise from a radical reaction ($Ph_3C^•$ having been

[709] T. Mole and J. R. Surtees, *Austral. J. Chem.*, 1964, **17**, 310; E. A. Jeffery, T. Mole and J. K. Saunders, *Chem. Comm.*, 1967, 696.
[710] T. Mole, *Austral. J. Chem.*, 1963, **16**, 807.

identified by e.s.r.), which is catalysed by ultraviolet light [710a]:

$$[Ph_2AlOCPh_3)_2 \rightarrow 2Ph_3C^{\cdot} + [PhAlO] + 2Ph^{\cdot}$$

Acetylacetone yields the chelate complex 3.121 [711].

$$Ph_2Al \begin{array}{c} O-C\cdot Me \\ \diagdown \quad CH \\ O=C\cdot Me \end{array}$$

3.121

Triphenylaluminium resembles triphenylborane in combining with sodium; the reaction is carried out in ether solution and a brown micro-crystalline powder is deposited:

$$Ph_3Al + Na \rightarrow Ph_3Al^{-} \}Na^{+}$$

No magnetic properties of the complex have been reported, so it may be dimeric. Like the analogous boron compound it is very sensitive to air [712].

Phenyl-lithium reacts exothermically with Ph_3Al in ether; a lower layer separates and slowly crystallizes. *Lithium tetraphenylaluminate* [713] $LiAlPh_4 2-3Et_2O$, is sparingly soluble in ether and in dioxan but very soluble in tetrahydrofuran. It is very easily hydrolysed, in contrast to $LiBPh_4$. The hydride, $LiAlPh_3H$, is also known.

Phenylaluminium sesquichloride has already been mentioned; the mono- and di-chlorides Ph_2AlCl [692], m.p. 145–148°, and $PhAlCl_2$ [590], m.p. 94–95°, are obtained by mixing Ph_3Al and $AlCl_3$ in suitable proportions; they are dimeric in benzene solution [714].

The alkylaluminium halides

The sesquichlorides, $Me_3Al_2Cl_3$ and $Et_3Al_2Cl_3$, are readily made from the metal and the alkyl chloride, and the sesqui-bromides and -iodides are equally accessible [590].

For laboratory purposes Me_2AlCl, b.p. 119·4°, is conveniently obtained from the sesquichloride,

$$Me_3Al_2Cl_3 + NaCl \rightarrow Na[AlMeCl_3] + Me_2AlCl$$

or by addition of the correct amount of $AlCl_3$ to Me_3Al if the last is readily available. The chlorine-bridged structure of the monochloride has been confirmed by electron diffraction [715] and by the Raman spectrum

[710a] C. Harris, T. Mole and F. D. Looney, *Tetrahedron Letters*, 1966, 4195.
[711] G. Costa and R. Calcinari, *Gazzetta*, 1959, **89**, 1415.
[712] E. Krause and H. Polack, *Ber.*, 1926, **59**, 1428.
[713] L. I. Zakharkin and L. L. Ivanov, *Izvest. Akad. Nauk S.S.S.R.*, 1964, 196 (Eng. p. 182); see also H. Lehmkuhl and R. Schäfer, *Annalen*, 1967, **705**, 32.
[714] P. G. Perkins and M. E. Twentyman, *J. Chem. Soc.*, 1965, 1038.
[715] L. O. Brockway and N. R. Davidson, *J. Amer. Chem. Soc.*, 1941, **63**, 3287.

[716]. The infrared spectrum [609, 610] is relatively simple and has been

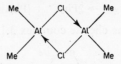

assigned in detail. The bridge is readily split by stronger electron donors, such as ethers and trimethylamine, giving, for example, $Me_2ClAl \leftarrow NMe_3$, m.p. 124° (see [717a]).

Methylaluminium dichloride, m.p. 72·7°, b.p. 97–100°/100 mm., has a *trans* structure,

as shown both by its spectrum [610] and an X-ray crystal structure analysis [717]. The Cl–Al–Cl angle is about 90°, the Al–bridge Cl distance 2·25 ± 0·01 Å, and the Al–terminal Cl 2·05 ± 0·01 Å. The dichloride is normally obtained from the sesquichloride and $AlCl_3$, but is also formed from hydrogen chloride and aluminium carbide at 300°:

$$Al_4C_3 + 9HCl \longrightarrow 3MeAlCl_2 + AlCl_3$$

It is interesting that Al–CH₃ bonds survive long enough in the presence of hydrogen chloride to allow the isolation of $MeAlCl_2$ [718].

The alkylaluminium *fluorides* [596] differ from the other halides in their physical properties. Whereas the other halogens form two bonds more or less at an angle of 90°, two-co-ordinate fluorine seems to prefer much larger angles (cf. 180° in the ion $Et_3Al \cdots F \cdots AlEt_3$) (see Figure 21 p. 318), and this causes *oligomer* and *polymer* formation in the fluorides R_2AlF.

These are prepared by heating the chlorides in xylene solution with dry finely ground sodium fluoride:

$$R_2AlCl + NaF \longrightarrow R_2AlF + NaCl$$

They are evidently much more associated than the dimeric chlorides, since Me_2AlF (b.p. 68–70°/15 mm.) and Et_2AlF (b.p. 90–91°/0·4 mm.) are very viscous glass-like liquids. The propyl and higher dialkyl fluorides are mobile and not so much associated. The degree of association of all these is much reduced when they are dissolved in inert solvents. Diethylaluminium fluoride is tetrameric in benzene solution, a result [719] compatible

[716] O. Yamamoto, *Bull. Chem. Soc. Japan*, 1962, **35**, 619.
[717] G. Allegra, G. Perego and A. Immirzi, *Makromol. Chem.*, 1963, **61**, 69.
[717a] C. A. Smith and M. G. H. Wallbridge, *J. Chem. Soc.*, (*A*), 1967, 7.
[718] R. L. Barnes and T. Wartik, *J. Amer. Chem. Soc.*, 1963, **85**, 360.
[719] G. F. Lengnick and A. W. Laubengayer, *Inorg. Chem.*, 1966, **5**, 503.

with two-co-ordinate fluorine forming co-linear or nearly co-linear bonds; compare $(Me_2AlCN)_4$ also containing a linear co-ordinating group. The fluorine-bonding is so strong that the tetramer is depolymerized neither by ethers nor by trimethylamine. The reluctance of $(Et_2AlF)_4$ to crystallize has been attributed to the possibility of various different conformations, but the pure liquid may contain aggregates other than or additional to tetramers.

Alkylaluminium fluorides are formed from the trialkyls and aluminium fluoride only if the last is in a particularly reactive form (e.g. as obtained from the reaction $Et_3Al + BF_3 \rightarrow AlF_3 + Et_3B$). Alkylaluminium *difluorides* are described as being rather similar to aluminium fluoride itself in respect of being insoluble and involatile polymers.

The organoaluminium hydrides

Methylaluminium hydrides were first obtained [720] by the action of an electric discharge on a mixture of trimethylaluminium with excess hydrogen; the products varied from $(Me_3Al_2H_3)_n$ to $(Me_2AlH)_n$. Dimethylaluminium hydride was later prepared [721] from $LiAlH_4$ and some Group III trimethyls:

$$LiAlH_4 + Me_3M = Me_2AlH + LiMH_3Me \quad (M = B, Al, Ga)$$

It is a colourless very viscous liquid at room temperature, its vapour pressure, $\log_{10}(mm.) = 8.92 - 2575/T$, being 2 mm. at $25°$ so it can be transferred within a vacuum apparatus at room temperature.

A more convenient and general preparative method starts from the trialkyls, which are split by hydrogen under pressure at $150–200°$ [722, 723]:

$$R_3Al + H_2 \rightarrow R_2AlH + RH$$

Di-isobutylaluminium hydride is commercially available, is practically always present as an impurity in Bu^i_3Al, and can very easily be obtained from the latter by pumping it (ca. 20 mm.) at $140°$. It can be distilled at ca. $90–110°$ in a diffusion pump vacuum. Most of the studies on dialkylaluminium hydrides have been carried out with Bu^i_2AlH on account of its ready availability.

Diethylaluminium hydride can be prepared from the chloride and sodium hydride in hexane (this should not be attempted without a careful study of the literature), or by the two-stage reaction in ether [670]:

$$Et_2AlCl + 2LiH \rightarrow LiCl + LiAlEt_2H_2$$
$$LiAlEt_2H_2 + Et_2AlCl \rightarrow LiCl + 2Et_2AlH$$

[720] O. Stecher and E. Wiberg, *Ber.*, 1942, **75**, 2003.
[721] T. Wartik and H. I. Schlesinger, *J. Amer. Chem. Soc.*, 1953, **75**, 835.
[722] T. Köster, G. Bruno and H. Lehmkuhl, Ger.P. (DDR) 16,650 (1957).
[723] H. E. Podall, H. E. Petree and J. R. Zietz, *J. Org. Chem.*, 1959, **24**, 1222.

M

Ether can be removed from R_2AlH solutions simply by pumping, and finally the hydride is distilled, Et_2AlH, b.p. $65-75°/0.7$ mm. Disproportionation resulting in the precipitation of aluminium hydride can be troublesome, but is largely inhibited by the use of a benzene–ether mixture as solvent, instead of ether alone.

The three hydrides most studied, viz. dimethyl-, diethyl- and di-isobutyl-, are all trimeric in solution in inert solvents [603, 721], as in 3.122 in which dotted lines represent half-bonds. Both Et_2AlH and $Bu_2{}^iAlH$ are liquids

3.122

of normal viscosity, so the very high viscosity of Me_2AlH suggests further association in the pure liquid state. Though $Bu_2{}^iAlH$ is trimeric in benzene, it is *monomeric* in $Bu^i{}_3Al$ in which it must dissolve as a 1 : 1 complex 3.123 [603]. There is evidence for such 1 : 1 association in other cases and

3.123

the 1 : 1 complex has a distinctly higher conductance (ca. $1.8 \cdot 10^{-8}$ ohm^{-1} cm^{-1} in the case of $Et_3Al \cdot Et_2AlH$) than that of the trialkyl. The lowest conductance recorded for Et_3Al (10^{-10}) is attributed to traces of Et_2AlH [587].

The heat of association of these hydrides is 15–20 kcal. mole^{-1} per H-bridge, which is greater than the 10 kcal. mole^{-1} per CH_3-bridge for the heat of association of Me_3Al. The infrared spectra of alkylaluminium hydrides and their co-ordination complexes have been intensively studied [724, 725], largely by Hoffmann who refers to the 'anionic–hydrogen bonding' in these compounds in contrast to the more familiar 'cationic–hydrogen bonding' in water or ammonia [726]. Bands due to Al–H stretching are strong and rather broad in compounds such as $(Bu_2{}^iAlH)_3$ containing hydrogen bridges, as are the OH or NH bands in 'cationic–hydrogen bonded' compounds, and have maxima just under 1800 cm^{-1}. These bands remain broad even when the trimer is in dilute solution in an inert solvent, in contrast to the band sharpening normally observed when, say, phenols are dissolved in inert solvents. If $Bu^i{}_2AlH$ is dissolved in

[724] W. Zeil, R. Dautel and W. Honsberg, Z. *Elektrochemie*, 1956, **60**, 1131.
[725] E. G. Hoffmann and G. Schomburg, ibid., 1957, **61**, 1101, 1110.
[726] Idem, *Hydrogen Bonding*, p. 509, Pergamon Press, 1959.

hexane containing increasing proportions of dibutylether, the Al–H stretching band gradually becomes sharper as an increasing proportion of the hydride is in the form of co-ordination complex, $Bu^i_2HAl \cdot OBu^n_2$, containing a *free* Al–H group. For the pure complexes, v(Al–H) is sharp and at slightly lower frequencies than in the associated compounds.

A complete spectroscopic assignment of all the Al–H and Al–N vibrations of $H_3Al \cdot NMe_3$ and $D_3Al \cdot NMe_3$ is given in Table 16 [727]. Similar

Table 16   *Infrared bands of $H_3Al \cdot NMe_3$ and $D_3Al \cdot NMe_3$*

$H_3Al \cdot NMe_3$	$D_3Al \cdot NMe_3$	Vibration
1792 cm^{-1}	1304	v_1, v_4 sym. and asym. Al–H stretch
773	567	v_5 asym. H–Al–H deformation
768	562	v_2 sym. H–Al–H deformation
533	540	v_3 Al–N stretch

data are available for the trigonal biprismatic bisamine complexes, $H_3Al(NMe_3)_2$ and $D_3Al(NMe_3)_2$ [728].

Though mono-alkylaluminium hydrides have not been described, some trimethylamine complexes have been prepared from $H_3Al \cdot NMe_3$ either by reaction with R_2Hg [729] or by equilibration with $R_3Al \cdot NMe_3$ (20 min., 35–40°, no solvent). The chloro complexes may also be reduced [730]:

$$\tfrac{1}{2}R_2Hg + H_3Al \cdot NMe_3 \longrightarrow RAlH_2 \cdot NMe_3 + \tfrac{1}{2}H_2 + \tfrac{1}{2}Hg$$

$$H_3Al \cdot NMe_3 + 2R_3AlNMe_3 \longrightarrow 3R_2AlH \cdot NMe_3$$

$$R_2AlCl \cdot NMe_3 + LiH \xrightarrow{Et_2O} R_2AlH \cdot NMe_3$$

Both $EtAlH_2 \cdot NMe_3$ and $MeAlH_2 \cdot NMe_3$ have been described, and the latter is dimeric in cyclohexane.

The proton magnetic resonance of hydrogen directly bound to aluminium is greatly broadened on account of the quadrupole moment of the aluminium nucleus [731].

Several of the chemical reactions characteristic of alkylaluminium hydrides have already been mentioned, including the important addition to olefins and the very fast addition to acetylenes. Di-isobutylaluminium hydride has been compared to lithium aluminium hydride as a reducing

[727] G. W. Fraser, N. N. Greenwood and B. P. Straughan, *J. Chem. Soc.*, 1963, 3742.
[728] I. R. Beattie and T. Gilson, ibid., 1964, 3528.
[729] J. K. Ruff, *J. Amer. Chem. Soc.*, 1961, **83**, 1798.
[730] F. M. Peters, B. Bartocha and A. J. Bilbo, *Canad. J. Chem.*, 1963, **41**, 1051.
[731] E. G. Hoffmann, *Z. anal. Chem.*, 1959, **170**, 177.

agent: its action is rather similar [732]. It reduces carbonyl groups and azomethines,

$$R_2CO + Bu^i_2AlH \longrightarrow (R_2CH—O·AlBu^i_2)_2$$
$$RCH:NR + Bu^i_2AlH \longrightarrow (RCH_2(R)N·AlBu^i_2)_2$$

and the addition of a second mole of azomethine forming coloured adducts, in the case of aromatic azomethines, has been discussed earlier. The reduction of esters may be stopped at the *aldehyde* stage (50–90% yields) when hydrocarbons are used as solvents and the reactions are carried out at −70°. Ether promotes the formation of alcohols by further reduction [733]. Similarly the reduction of cyanide may be stopped at the azomethine stage [639]. Quinoline and isoquinoline are reduced,

and reaction of a second molecule of base gives coloured adducts suitable for spectrophotometric analysis of Al–H groups [734]. Addition of Bu^i_2AlH to various ω-substituted olefins gives five- or six-membered cyclic products exemplified by [735]

the latter being formed from Bu^i_3Al and $CH_2:CH·CH_2·NH·Et$, giving $Bu^i_2Al·NEt·CH_2·CH:CH_2$ which eliminates isobutene when heated with a small proportion of Bu^i_2AlH; the molecular weight of this product was not reported.

Relatively little is known about *aryl*aluminium hydrides. Diphenylaluminium chloride does not appear to react with sodium hydride, but phenylaluminium hydrides have been prepared from the aluminium hydride–ether complex:

$$2Ph_3Al + AlH_3 \longrightarrow 3Ph_2AlH$$
$$Ph_3Al + 2AlH_3 \longrightarrow 3PhAlH_2$$

Diphenylaluminium hydride, m.p. 156–157·5° (decomp.), has a mean degree of association of about 2·4 (measured ebullioscopically). The dihydride, $PhAlH_2$ (decomp. 125–130°), is obtained as an amorphous

[732] G. Wilke and H. Müller, *Chem. Ber.*, 1956, **89**, 444.

[733] L. I. Zakharkin and I. M. Khorlina, *Izvest. Akad. Nauk S.S.S.R.*, 1963, 316 (Eng. trans., p. 288).

[734] W. P. Neumann, *Annalen*, 1960, **629**, 23.

[735] L. I. Zakharkin and L. A. Savina, *Izvest. Akad. Nauk S.S.S.R.*, 1959, 444; 1960, 1039; 1962, 824.

material which retains some diethyl ether. The exchange reactions between the triphenylaluminium trimethylamine complex and AlH_3, or between Ph_3Al and $LiAlH_4$ are less satisfactory as preparative methods [736].

The organic chemistry of the IIIB elements has been much less intensively studied than that of boron and aluminium; the elements are relatively scarce and costly.

Whereas displacement of the first alkyl group from R_3Al, by reaction with an alcohol for example, takes place more readily than that of the remaining alkyl groups, those that do remain are normally (but see p. 308) highly sensitive to air and moisture. The IIIB elements differ in that displacement of the second and third alkyl groups is *much* more difficult. Compounds such as $Me_3Ga \cdot OEt_2$ or $(Me_2GaCN)_4$ are readily hydrolysed, but the process stops at the dimethylgallium stage $(Me_2GaOH)_4$. This effect reaches a maximum with thallium, whose trialkyls are reactive and unstable, and the dialkyl compounds tend to be ionic (R_2Tl^+) and unreactive.

Other differences between the IIIB elements and aluminium are the comparative *instability* of the *hydrides* (hydrides of indium and thallium being virtually unknown or at least *extremely* unstable), and a contrast between relative ease of reaction with secondary amines, phosphines and arsines, giving methane and dimers, e.g. $(Me_2Ga \cdot PPh_2)_2$:

$$\underset{\text{most}}{Me_3Al + R_2NH} > R_2PH > \underset{\text{least reactive}}{R_2AsH}$$

$$\left.\begin{matrix} Me_3Ga \\ Me_3In \end{matrix}\right\} + \underset{\text{least}}{R_2NH} < R_2PH < \underset{\text{most reactive}}{R_2AsH}$$

Preparative methods

Metal exchange with organomercury compounds is a generally useful method, and is particularly useful for the preparation of Me_3Ga, $(CH_2:CH)_3Ga$, and Ph_3Ga. Reaction between a Grignard or organolithium compound and $GaCl_3$ gives ether complexes, but in some instances (e.g. Pr^n_3Ga) ether can be separated by distillation. Alkylation by dimethylzinc and by ethylaluminium compounds has also been used to prepare Me_3Ga and Et_3Ga.

Trimethylgallium, m.p. $-15 \cdot 7$ to $-15 \cdot 9°$, b.p. $56°$, v.p. $64 \cdot 5$ mm. at $0°$ [737] $(\log_{10} p \text{ (mm.)} = 8 \cdot 07 - 1705/T)$, is conveniently obtained by boiling dimethylmercury (b.p. $92°$) with gallium and a trace of methylmercury

[736] J. R. Surtees, *Chem. and Ind.*, 1964, 1260.
[737] E. Wiberg, T. Johannsen and O. Stecher, *Z. anorg. Chem.*, 1963, **251**, 114.

chloride as catalyst,

$$2Ga + 3Me_2Hg \rightarrow 2Me_3Ga + 3Hg$$

The vapour temperature soon begins to fall, and trimethylgallium can be taken off almost quantitatively (generally about two days) from the top of a fractionating column [738]. The reaction is inhibited by traces of tap-grease. The alkylation of $GaCl_3$ by Me_2Zn begins at room temperature but requires heating at 80–120° for its completion [739].

$$2GaCl_3 + 3Me_2Zn \rightarrow 2Me_3Ga + 3ZnCl_2$$

The ether complex [739, 740], $Me_3Ga \cdot OEt_2$, m.p. −76°, b.p. 98·3°, from $MeMgBr + GaCl_3$ in ether, is appreciably dissociated in the vapour state. Trimethylgallium, unlike trimethylaluminium, is monomeric as vapour and the Raman spectrum of the liquid shows that it, too, cannot be significantly associated. Both trimethyl- and triethyl-gallium are monomeric in benzene and in cyclopentane solution, and the proton magnetic resonance spectrum of Me_3Ga consists of a single resonance 1·48 p.p.m. upfield from solvent cyclopentane (i.e. τ ca. 9·97) [741]. The infrared spectrum of the vapour [742, 743], is remarkable in the very low intensity of the absorption due to unsymmetrical methyl deformation, whereas the absorption due to the symmetrical deformation is a very intense triplet (PQR) at 1211, 1205, 1198 cm⁻¹. The unsymmetrical GaC_3 stretching vibrations give rise to an intense triplet at 587, 577 and 571 cm⁻¹, and there is no absorption in the region 570–400 cm⁻¹ in which the symmetrical GaC_3 vibration would be expected, but in a planar molecule this would be infrared inactive. There is a very strong polarized line in the Raman spectrum at 521·5 cm⁻¹ due to ν sym GaC_3 [743]. Infrared spectra of the methyls and some other alkyls of both gallium and indium (4000–300 cm⁻¹) have been described [744].

Pyrolysis of Me_3Ga in toluene vapour in the range 410–510° occurs in two steps by homogeneous reactions, leading to the deposition of black polymeric material (MeGa) [745]. From the heat of its reaction with iodine, the heat of formation of Me_3Ga has been calculated, and the mean Ga–C bond dissociation energy, 56·7 ± 4 kcal. mole⁻¹, is rather less than that of the Al–C bonds in monomeric Me_3Al (∼70) [746].

[738] G. E. Coates, *J. Chem. Soc.*, 1951, 2003.
[739] C. A. Kraus and F. E. Toonder, *Proc. Nat. Acad. Sci.*, 1933, **19**, 292.
[740] G. Renwanz, *Ber.*, 1932, **65**, 1308.
[741] N. Muller and A. L. Otermat, *Inorg. Chem.*, 1965, **4**, 296.
[742] G. E. Coates and R. N. Mukherjee, *J. Chem. Soc.*, 1964, 1295.
[743] A. J. Downs and G. E. Coates, ibid., p. 3353; J. R. Hall, L. A. Woodward and E. A. V. Ebsworth, *Spectrochim. Acta*, 1964, **20**, 1249.
[744] F. Oswald, *Z. anal. Chem.*, 1963, **197**, 309.
[745] M. G. Jacko and S. J. W. Price, *Canad. J. Chem.*, 1963, **41**, 1650.
[746] P. A. Fowell and C. T. Mortimer, *J. Chem. Soc.*, 1958, 3734.

Triethylgallium [747], m.p. $-82.3°$, b.p. $143°$ ($\log_{10} p$ (mm.) = 8.083 $- 2162/T$), was first obtained from gallium and diethylmercury at $160°$ but is more conveniently prepared using Et_3Al as the source of ethyl [748]. Diethylzinc, from $2Et_3Al + ZnCl_2$, reacts with $GaBr_3$ in pentane giving 66% Et_3Ga, b.p. $43-44°/16$ mm.

The direct reaction between $GaBr_3$ and Et_3Al gives over 80% Et_3Ga:

$$GaBr_3 + 3Et_3Al \rightarrow Et_3Ga + 3Et_2AlBr$$

It is claimed that lower yields result when $GaCl_3$ is used, because about half the gallium forms a complex $Ga(Cl_2AlEt_2)_3$, b.p. $98-102°/2.5$ mm.:

$$GaCl_3 + 3Et_3Al \rightarrow Et_3Ga + 3Et_2AlCl$$
$$\text{and} \quad GaCl_3 + 3Et_2AlCl \rightarrow Ga(Cl_2AlEt_2)_3$$

The complex is split by KCl, so the ethylation of $GaCl_3$ is best conducted in the presence of KCl:

$$GaCl_3 + 3Et_3Al + 3KCl \rightarrow Et_3Ga + 3K[AlEt_2Cl_2]$$

The KCl is added *after* the initial reaction between $GaCl_3$ and Et_3Al is finished, and yields of about $80-90\%$ Et_3Ga and also Bu^i_3Ga (b.p. $67-69°/3$ mm.) may be obtained. Traces of Et_3Al or Bu^i_3Al in the product may be removed by distillation over NaF, which forms a complex with aluminium but not with gallium alkyls. Potassium fluoride forms a $1:1$ complex $K[GaEt_3F]$, m.p. $75-79°$, soluble in warm benzene. The direct reaction between Et_3Al and $GaCl_3$ in $1:1$ molar proportion has, however, been made to give Et_3Ga in 80% yield [749].

Triethylgallium is monomeric as vapour [750], but the liquid is described as 'somewhat viscous' [747]; however, in both benzene and cyclopentane the compound is monomeric [741]. The earlier report [751] that Et_3Ga is dimeric in solution is incorrect.

It undergoes the same types of reaction with olefins as Et_3Al, though less easily and the situation is complicated by the thermal instability of any hydrides formed. At $170°$ and 170 atmospheres, Et_3Ga absorbs ethylene and hydrolysis of the reaction product gives polyethylene, some *cis* and *trans* 2-butenes, a little 1-butene, as well as much unreacted ethylene. Triethylgallium reacts with terminal acetylenes,

$$Et_3Ga + HC:CBu^n \rightarrow Et_2GaC:CBu^n + C_2H_6$$

[747] L. M. Dennis and W. Patnode, *J. Amer. Chem. Soc.*, 1932, **54**, 182.
[748] J. J. Eisch, ibid., 1962, **84**, 3605.
[749] R. Doetzer and F. Englebrecht, Ger.P. 1,158,977 (1963); *Chem. Abs.*, 1964, **60**, 6867.
[750] A. W. Laubengayer and W. F. Gilliam, *J. Amer. Chem. Soc.*, 1941, **63**, 477.
[751] W. Strohmeier, K. Hümpfner, K. Miltenberger and F. Seifert, *Z. Elektrochem.*, 1959, **63**, 537.

Triethylaluminium more readily *adds* to triple bonds:

$$Et_3Al + HC:CH \rightarrow Et_2AlCH:CHEt$$

The mixed derivative $Et_2GaC:CBu^n$ is thermally unstable and attempted distillation has yielded tarry matter and a little Et_3Ga, which must be formed in a disproportionation process [752].

Tri-n-propylgallium, m.p. $-85°$, b.p. $75°/14$ mm., can be made from $GaCl_3$ and Pr^nMgCl in ether since it can be separated from ether by distillation [753], and Bu^n_3Ga (b.p. $113\cdot5°/12$ mm.) can be made the same way. They are monomeric in benzene solution. Both Pr^n_3Ga and Pr^i_3Ga have been obtained by the dialkylmercury route [754], and are monomeric as vapour.

Trivinylgallium is formed from gallium and divinylmercury *at room temperature*, in contrast to temperatures around $150°$ needed for the preparation of Pr^n_3Ga and Pr^i_3Ga by this method. Trivinylgallium, m.p. $-9°$, exists as a *dimer* in benzene solution, see $(Bu^i_2AlCH:CHEt)_2$ – p. 330. In addition to three-centre bonding as in the dimeric aluminium alkyls there is the possibility of association due to co-ordination between metal and olefin. Trivinylgallium ($\log_{10} p$ (mm.) $= 12\cdot12 - 3790/T$) decomposes from about $60°$ to a brown oil and a mixture of hydrocarbons, and the degree of association of the vapour has not been investigated with any success.

It is of interest that tri-*cis*-, tri-*trans*-, and tri-*iso*-propenylgallium may be prepared from the metal and the corresponding mercury compound (10 hours at room temperature in the presence of carbon tetrachloride) with complete retention of configuration. The tri-*trans* compound melts at about $40°$, the others being liquids [755].

$(ga = \frac{1}{3} Ga)$

The rates of exchange in the gallium–organomercury reaction decrease in the order vinyl, propenyl, allyl > cyclopropyl >> alkyl [756].

Triphenylgallium, m.p. $166°$, is the only uncomplexed triaryl yet described and is prepared by heating theoretical quantities of gallium and diphenylmercury at $130°$ for about three days [757]. It is monomeric in

[752] J. J. Eisch, *J. Amer. Chem. Soc.*, 1962, **84**, 3830.
[753] H. Hartmann and H. Lutsche, *Naturwiss.*, 1961, **48**, 601; 1962, **49**, 182.
[754] J. P. Oliver and L. G. Stevens, *J. Inorg. Nucl. Chem.*, 1962, **24**, 953.
[755] D. Moy, J. P. Oliver and M. T. Emerson, *J. Amer. Chem. Soc.*, 1964, **86**, 371.
[756] J. P. Oliver, personal communication.
[757] H. Gilman and R. G. Jones, *J. Amer. Chem. Soc.*, 1940, **62**, 980.

hydrocarbon solvents. It slowly reacts with benzoyl chloride, all three phenyl groups being replaced. The dioxan complexes of triphenyl- and tritolyl-gallium are known [758], as is the ether complex of trispentafluorophenylgallium [758a].

Properties

Hydrolysis is very rapid until the first organic group has been removed and then becomes slow, the removal of the second and third *methyl* groups being particularly slow.

Addition of a solution of water in ether to a well-cooled solution of trimethylgallium in ether gives an apparently polymeric and amorphous (by X-ray diffraction) substance $[(Me_2Ga)_2O]_x$. Freshly prepared ether solutions of this are rather viscous. The solid absorbs trimethylamine reversibly, with depolymerization and formation of a crystalline complex $(Me_2Ga)_2O(NMe_3)$ [759].

Reaction between Me_3GaOEt_2 and a slight excess of water gives a crystalline hydroxide [760]

$$4Me_3GaOEt_2 + 4H_2O \rightarrow (Me_2GaOH)_4 + 4Et_2O + 4CH_4$$

which can be sublimed in a good vacuum. The product has a sharp infrared band at $2\cdot8$ $\mu(OH)$ and it loses a mol. of methane at $150°$ (6 hours) giving a polymer $(MeGaO)_x$. X-ray diffraction shows the crystalline hydroxide is a tetramer (3.124) [761]. Addition of one mol. water to a

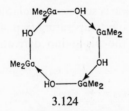

3.124

pentane solution of Et_3Ga results in lively gas evolution and the product, $(Et_2GaOH)_x$, remains in solution, and if this is heated one hour at $100°$ it gives polymeric $(EtGaO)_x$ [752]. The monohydroxide is said to give a weakly alkaline aqueous solution which can be titrated with hydrochloric acid [747]. The oxide $(MeGaO)_x$ is soluble in alkali, since hydrolysis of $Me_3Ga\cdot OEt_2$ with aqueous KOH gives one mol. CH_4 at room temperature and two mols. at $100°$ but the other products remain in solution at each stage [739].

[758] I. M. Viktorova, N. I. Sheverdina, E. D. Delinskaya and K. A. Kocheshkov, *Dokl. Akad. Nauk S.S.S.R.*, 1963, **152**, 609.
[758a] J. L. W. Pohlmann and F. E. Brinckman, *Z. Naturforsch.*, 1965, **20b**, 5.
[759] G. E. Coates and R. G. Hayter, unpublished observations.
[760] M. E. Kenney and A. W. Laubengayer, *J. Amer. Chem. Soc.*, 1954, **76**, 4839.
[761] G. S. Smith and J. L. Hoard, ibid., 1959, **81**, 3907.

Trimethyl- and triethyl-gallium take fire in the air, but if oxidation is restrained short of combustion then alkoxides are produced $(R_2GaOR)_2$, two of the alkyl groups remaining unaffected. These compounds are the cause of the characteristic sweet smell associated with the gallium alkyls; Et_2GaOEt is said to smell of vanilla and $Bu^i_2GaOBu^i$ of apricots [752].

Co-ordination compounds

Ammonia, trimethylamine, dimethyl sulphide and ether complexes of Et_3Ga have deen described, and the latter two dissociate extensively in the vapour state; all are liquids [747]. The complexes of trimethylgallium have been studied in rather greater detail. The diethyl ether complex $Me_3Ga \cdot OEt_2$, b.p. 98°, is less vigorously hydrolysed than Me_3Ga, and the ammine [739], $Me_3Ga \cdot NH_3$, m.p. 31–32°, though sensitive to water, is noticeably less reactive. Hydrolysis doubtless involves co-ordination to water as a preliminary step, and the hydrolysis of, for example, an ether complex would involve the displacement of ether (requiring activation energy).

$$Me_3Ga \cdot OEt_2 + OH_2 \rightarrow Me_3Ga \cdot OH_2 + Et_2O$$
$$Me_3Ga \cdot OH_2 \rightarrow Me_2GaOH + CH_4$$

The direct co-ordination of water to trimethylgallium is unlikely to require appreciable activation energy, and both the rate and heat of hydrolysis of the unco-ordinated trialkyl should thus be greater than those of its ether or ammine or other complexes.

Trimethylgallium ammine is sufficiently volatile to be transferred within a vacuum apparatus at room temperature (v.p. 4·4 mm. at 25°), but from 70° it decomposes into the bis-amino derivative [738], m.p. 97°, and methane:

$$2\,Me_3Ga \cdot NH_3 \longrightarrow Me_2Ga \underset{NH_2}{\overset{NH_2}{\diamondsuit}} GaMe_2 + 2CH_4$$

The ammine reacts with excess hydrogen chloride at 160° forming ammonium tetrachlorogallate [762],

$$Me_3Ga \cdot NH_3 + 4HCl \rightarrow NH_4[GaCl_4] + 3CH_4$$

Addition of one mol. of hydrogen chloride to an ether solution of trimethylgalliumammine causes immediate precipitation of ammonium chloride,

$$Me_3Ga \cdot NH_3 + HCl + Et_2O \rightarrow Me_3Ga \cdot OEt_2 + NH_4Cl$$

followed by re-solution of the precipitate,

$$Me_3Ga \cdot OEt_2 + NH_4Cl \rightarrow Me_2GaCl \cdot NH_3 + CH_4 + OEt_2$$

[762] C. A. Kraus and F. E. Toonder, *Proc. Nat. Acad. Sci.*, 1933, **19**, 298.

and formation of the ammine of dimethylgallium chloride, m.p. 54°. A *diammine* is also formed, m.p. 112°, which loses ammonia in vacuum at 60° and is a salt [Me$_2$Ga(NH$_3$)$_2$]Cl. It is more satisfactorily prepared by the addition of NH$_3$ to Me$_2$GaCl in hexane, and the ammonia may be displaced by ethylenediamine:

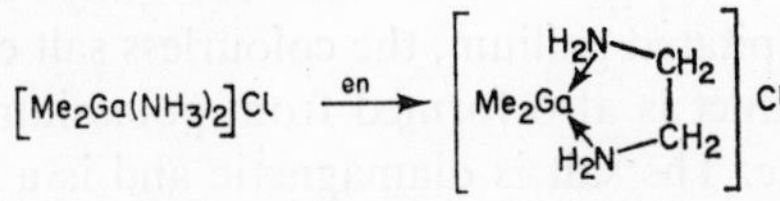

$$[Me_2Ga(NH_3)_2]Cl \xrightarrow{\ en\ } \left[Me_2Ga \begin{matrix} H_2N\!-\!CH_2 \\ | \\ H_2N\!-\!CH_2 \end{matrix} \right] Cl$$

The ethylenediamine complex is stable for short periods in aqueous solution and undergoes metathetic reactions with, for example, silver sulphate [763].

The reduction of Me$_3$Ga·NH$_3$ and Me$_2$GaCl·NH$_3$ by sodium in liquid ammonia has proved to be of great interest [764]. Trimethylgallium, in the form of its ammine in liquid ammonia, gives just under one atom of hydrogen for every two mols. of trimethylgallium. The following reactions appear to take place:

$$Na + 2Me_3Ga\cdot NH_3 \longrightarrow [Me_3Ga-NH_2 \rightarrow GaMe_3]^- + Na^+ + NH_3 + \tfrac{1}{2}H_2$$
$$2Na + 2Me_3Ga\cdot NH_3 \longrightarrow [Me_3Ga-GaMe_3]^{2-} + 2Na^+ + 2NH_3$$

It is significant that Me$_3$Ga·NH$_3$ can be recovered almost quantitatively after addition of ammonium bromide:

$$[Me_3Ga-NH_2 \rightarrow GaMe_3]^- + NH_4^+ \longrightarrow 2Me_3Ga\cdot NH_3$$
$$[Me_3Ga-GaMe_3]^{2-} + 2NH_4^+ \longrightarrow 2Me_3Ga\cdot NH_3 + H_2$$

The compound Na[Me$_3$GaNH$_2$→GaMe$_3$] can also be obtained directly from sodium amide:

$$2Me_3Ga\cdot NH_3 + NaNH_2 \longrightarrow Na[Me_3GaNH_2 \rightarrow GaMe_3]$$

The product from lithium in ethylamine is slightly different:

$$Li + Me_3Ga\cdot NH_2Et \longrightarrow Li[Me_3Ga\cdot NHEt] + \tfrac{1}{2}H_2$$

The substance Na$_2$[Me$_3$Ga·GaMe$_3$] and its lithium analogue are unstable above about −33°, and have not been isolated, unlike the potassium salt (next page). They are of interest since they are formulated with a metal–metal bond (not unknown in gallium chemistry, cf. GaS).

Addition of a mol. of sodium to Me$_2$GaCl in liquid ammonia results in the precipitation of sodium chloride and the appearance of an orange colour:

$$Me_2Ga(NH_3)_2Cl + Na \longrightarrow Me_2Ga(NH_3)\cdot Ga(NH_3)Me_2 + NaCl$$

The constitution of the product has not been investigated, but evaporation of the ammonia causes deposition of a brown solid which soon evolves

[763] D. F. Shriver and R. W. Parry, *Inorg. Chem.*, 1962, **1**, 835.
[764] C. A. Kraus and F. E. Toonder, *J. Amer. Chem. Soc.*, 1933, **55**, 3547.

hydrogen, forming $(Me_2Ga \cdot NH_2)_2$ (the same substance that is obtained by heating $Me_3Ga \cdot NH_3$ above 70°):

$$Me_2Ga(NH_3) \cdot Ga(NH_3)Me_2 \rightarrow Me_2Ga(NH_2)_2GaMe_2 + H_2$$

The potassium salt, $K_2Ga_2Me_6$, has been prepared by the reaction of potassium with trimethylgallium in 1,2-dimethoxyethane [764a]. After filtration from precipitated gallium, the colourless salt crystallizes solvent-free. The same product is also formed from potassium and $LiGaMe_4$ in 1,2-dimethoxyethane. Ths salt is diamagnetic and is a 2 : 1 electrolyte in dilute solution in 1,2-dimethoxyethane.

Reactions of $K_2Ga_2Me_6$ with methylchlorosilanes are of interest, since methyltrichlorosilane appears to break all the gallium–carbon bonds and leaves the metal–metal bond intact:

$$K_2Ga_2Me_6 + 2MeSiCl_3 \rightarrow 2Me_4Si + K_2Ga_2Cl_6$$

In contrast, trimethylchlorosilane causes Ga–Ga bond fission:

$$K_2Ga_2Me_6 + 8Me_3SiCl \rightarrow 6Me_4Si + Me_6Si_2 + 2KGaCl_4$$
$$K_2Ga_2Cl_6 + 2Me_3SiCl \rightarrow Me_6Si_2 + 2KGaCl_4$$

Trimethylgallium is a convenient acceptor with which the relative donor character of the Group VB and VIB elements can be studied. It is a stronger acceptor than trimethylborane,

$$Me_3B + NMe_3 = Me_3B \cdot NMe_3 + 17 \cdot 6 \text{ kcal. } [765]$$
$$Me_3Ga + NMe_3 = Me_3Ga \cdot NMe_3 + 21 \cdot 0 \text{ kcal. } [766]$$

It is weaker than trimethylaluminium,

$$Me_3Al + SMe_2 = Me_3Al \cdot SMe_2 + 19 \text{ kcal. } [767]$$
$$Me_3Ga + SMe_2 = Me_3Ga \cdot SMe_2 + 8 \text{ kcal. } [738]$$

but weak donors which co-ordinate to trimethylgallium often do not combine with trimethylaluminium on account of the 20 kcal. energy required to break the Me_6Al_2 dimer into monomeric Me_3Al. To trimethylgallium the heat of co-ordination, measured in the gas phase, of the Group VB trimethyls falls steadily from nitrogen to antimony; trimethylbismuth does not react.

$$NMe_3, 21 > PMe_3, 18 > AsMe_3, 10 > SbMe_3, \text{ too weak to measure}$$

Oxygen in dimethyl ether is a stronger donor to Me_3Ga than sulphur in dimethyl sulphide, but S, Se and Te are rather similar to each other. Towards Me_3Al the order is regular:

$$OMe_2 > SMe_2, 19 > SeMe_2, 16 > TeMe_2 \text{ (weak)}$$

The heat of dissociation of the trimethylamine complex of triethylgallium,

[764a] C. A. Wilkie and J. P. Oliver, personal communication.
[765] H. C. Brown and M. D. Taylor, *J. Amer. Chem. Soc.*, 1947, **69**, 1332.
[766] G. E. Coates and N. D. Huck, *J. Chem. Soc.*, 1952, 4511.
[767] H. C. Brown and N. Davidson, *J. Amer. Chem. Soc.*, 1942, **64**, 316.

17 kcal. mole^{-1}, is rather less than that of Me$_3$Ga·NMe$_3$; that of (CH$_2$:CH)$_3$Ga·NMe$_3$ (21) being the same. The increased acceptor character of gallium caused by substituting vinyl for ethyl has been attributed mainly to the electronegativity of the olefinic carbon being greater than that of saturated carbon. Any conjugation between vinyl groups and the gallium should *reduce* the acceptor strength of the metal [768].

The kinetics of the exchange reaction between Me$_3$Ga·NMe$_3$ and both free metal alkyl and base have been investigated by proton magnetic resonance. The exchange (unlike that of some BF$_3$ complexes) proceeds through a dissociative mechanism of activation energy (23 kcal. mole^{-1}) not very different from the heat of dissociation measured in the gas phase. The exchange of trimethylgallium with its dimethylamine complex also proceeds by means of a dissociation mechanism, of activation energy 18 kcal. mole^{-1}. In contrast, the exchange between trimethylgallium and its methylamine or ammonia complexes proceeds by an electrophilic displacement, with activation energies of 10 and 8·5 kcal. mole^{-1} respectively [769]. The chemical shift of the methyl protons in trimethylgallium complexes (and $\delta_{CH_2} - \delta_{CH_3}$ for Et$_3$Ga complexes) correlate so well with heats of dissociation where these are known, that they are likely to be useful in predicting heats of dissociation in cases in which this quantity is difficult to measure [770].

The thermal decomposition of Me$_3$Ga·NH$_3$ to (Me$_2$Ga·NH$_2$)$_2$ has already been mentioned; similar products are obtained from the methylamine and dimethylamine complexes:

$$2Me_3Ga\cdot NHMe_2 \longrightarrow Me_2Ga \underset{NMe_2}{\overset{NMe_2}{\diagup\diagdown}} GaMe_2 + 2CH_4$$

Similar compounds are formed by secondary aromatic amines, and dimers (Me$_2$Ga·MPh$_2$)$_2$, M = N, P, As, are formed from these as well as from phosphines and arsines. Trimethylgallium is relatively more reactive to secondary arsines than to secondary amines, the reverse of the behaviour of Me$_3$Al, as indicated by the temperatures at which the reactions Me$_3$Al(Ga) + Ph$_2$N(P,As)H → Me$_2$Al·NPh$_2$ etc. take place [771]:

	Ph$_2$NH	Ph$_2$PH	Ph$_2$AsH
Me$_3$Al	60–80°	140–160°	150–170°
Me$_3$Ga	120°	90–110°	0–30°

Trimethylindium resembles trimethylgallium in this respect.

[768] L. G. Stevens, B. Park and J. P. Oliver, *J. Inorg. Nucl. Chem.*, 1964, **26,** 97.

[769] J. B. DeRoos and J. P. Oliver, *Inorg. Chem.*, 1965, **4,** 1741; *J. Amer. Chem. Soc.*, 1967, **8,** 3970.

[770] A. Leib, M. T. Emerson and J. P. Oliver, *Inorg. Chem.*, 1965, **4,** 1825.

[771] G. E. Coates and J. Graham, *J. Chem. Soc.*, 1963, 233.

Reaction with secondary alkyl phosphines and arsines gives products such as $Me_2Ga·PMe_2$ and $Me_2Ga·AsMe_2$. Trimethyl-aluminium and -indium undergo similar reactions. Although the products are sufficiently volatile to allow of their sublimation under reduced pressure, in the condensed state they are glasses (as shown by their optical isotropy and by X-ray diffraction) and are regarded as mixtures of cyclic oligomers and polymers. They all dissolve in benzene as cyclic trimers, and the solutions have very simple proton magnetic resonance spectra.

The dimethylamino compounds, $Me_2Ga·NMe_2$ and its Al and In analogues, exhibit even more peculiar behaviour. These are dimeric in solution, as vapour, and in the case of the gallium compound in the crystalline state also. At temperatures in the range 50–80° all three compounds undergo a transition to the glassy form; material condensing from the vapour below the transition temperature range does so giving the crystalline form, and material condensing above the transition temperature forms the glass. The crystal–glass transitions are reversible, and again it is believed that the glassy forms of these substances consist of mixtures of cyclic oligomers and polymers. When these glasses are heated, they do not soften gradually over a wide temperature range but have the appearance of 'melting' to a normal liquid over a range of a few degrees only. This effect must be due to a relatively rapid change with temperature of the mean degree of polymerization [772].

	Crystal $\rightleftharpoons$ glass	Glass $\rightleftharpoons$ liquid
$Me_2Al·NMe_2$	50–70°	153–156°
$Me_2Ga·NMe_2$	55–80°	157–161°
$Me_2In·NMe_2$	70–80°	174–175°

Alcohols and thiols eliminate one mol. of methane from Me_3Ga, normally forming dimeric products [773]. The dimeric methoxide, m.p. 24·5–24·7°, is not detectably dissociated in the vapour up to 170° nor does it combine with trimethylamine. The sulphur (m.p. 113·3–113·7°) and selenium (m.p. 119–120°) analogues combine reversibly with trimethylamine, though they remain dimeric as vapour.

Phenols, thiophenols and selenophenol form similar dimeric dimethylgallium derivatives, e.g. $(Me_2Ga·OPh)_2$, m.p. 132°, $(Me_2Ga·SePh)_2$, m.p. 136°, all of which combine reversibly with trimethylamine. The dissociation

[772] O. T. Beachley and G. E. Coates, *J. Chem. Soc.*, 1965, 3241; O. T. Beachley, G. E. Coates and G. Kohnstam, ibid., p. 3248.
[773] G. E. Coates and R. G. Hayter, ibid., 1953, 2519.

pressures at 20° of the trimethylamine adducts of several such compounds are given in Table 17. A lower dissociation pressure indicates that NMe_3

Table 17 *Dissociation pressures at 20° of $Me_2GaR \cdot NMe_3$*

R	P (mm.)	R	P (mm.)	R	P (mm.)
OMe	No adduct	O·C₆H₄Buᵗ-p	14	SPhᶜ	0·4 (m.p. 51°)
SMeᵃ	10·3–10·4 (m.p. 26·0–26·2°)	OPh	6·1 (m.p. 39–40°)	SePh	0·1–0·2 (m.p. 48–50°)
SeMeᵇ	4·5 (m.p. 29·8–30·0°)	O·C₆H₄Cl-p	1·5	O·C₆H₄·CHO-o	11

ΔH (dissociation): $a = 7·5$; $b = 6·6$; $c = 9·3$ kcal./mole

more successfully competes with R as a donor to gallium; thus, for a group of reactions in which entropy changes would be similar, the donor properties of the group R should be in the same order as the dissociation pressures. Table 17 thus indicates that: (a) the order of donor character is O > S > Se both in the methyl and phenyl series, (b) substitution of phenyl for methyl diminishes the dissociation pressure and thus also decreases the donor character of the atom concerned, e.g. R = SMe, $p = 10$ mm., while for R = SPh, $p = 0·4$ mm.; and (c) substitution of an electropositive radical (Buᵗ) in a phenoxy-group increases the donor character of the oxygen, while an electronegative radical (Cl) decreases it.

Oxygen bound to an electropositive metal is a stronger donor than, say, ether oxygen and is stronger even than the nitrogen in the ·CH₂NMe₂ group. This is shown by the fact that dimethylethanolamine reacts with trimethylgallium giving the dimer (3.125), which forms a dimethiodide and *not* the chelate compound (3.126).

3.125   3.126

Chelate derivatives are, however, formed by acetylacetone and salicyl-aldehyde.

Acetic acid gives dimeric dimethylgallium acetate, m.p. 162°, but in this compound (3.127) the acetate acts as a three-atom bridging group, since

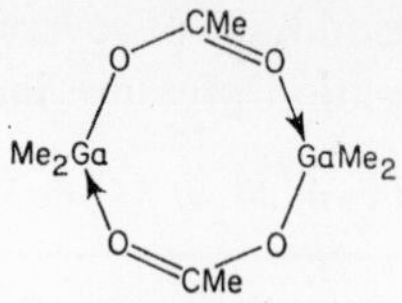

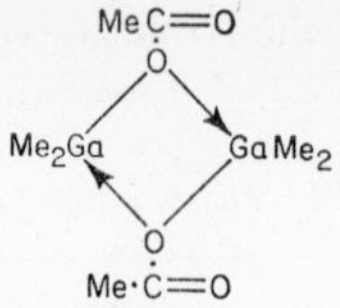

3.127   3.128

the infrared spectrum in the carbonyl region is that expected for either bridging or ionic acetate, and incompatible with the presence of free C=O groups as in (3.128). Chelate derivatives are not readily formed either by carboxylic or by other acids which would involve a four-membered ring containing oxygen. The formation of such rings is evidently prevented by the steric strain that would be imposed on the valency angles of the oxygen atoms. Instead these acids act as three-atom bridging groups, as in the phosphinic and thiophosphinic derivatives (3.129) and (3.130). The struc-

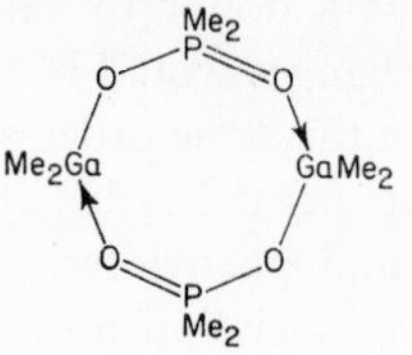

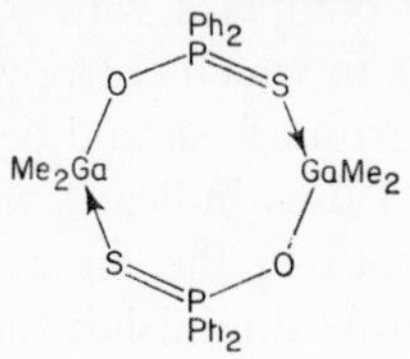

3.129   3.130

ture of (3.129) has been determined by X-ray diffraction [774]; the rela-

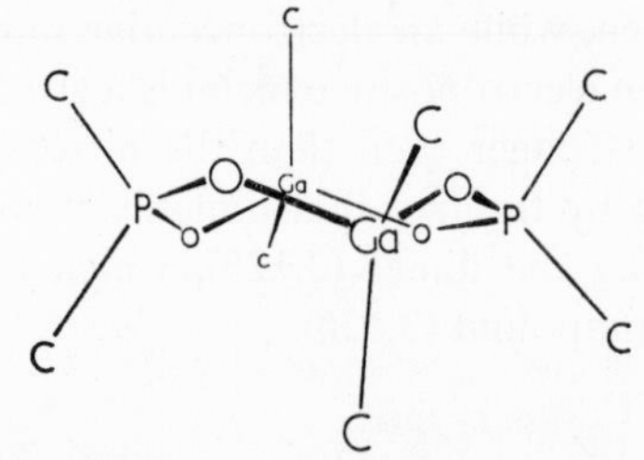

Fig. 25. Structure of dimethylgallium dimethylphosphinate (after Shearer and King [774]). Ring angles: P, 116°; Ga, 99°; O, 138°

tively flat ring and large oxygen angles are noteworthy. In contrast, the dithiophosphinic group forms monomeric chelate derivatives [775]. Hydrogen cyanide gives a tetrameric product $(Me_2GaCN)_4$, like its aluminium analogue (p. 311).

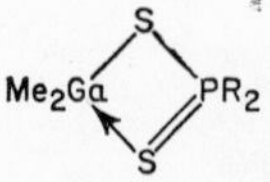

[774] H. M. M. Shearer and J. King, personal communication.
[775] G. E. Coates and R. N. Mukherjee, *J. Chem. Soc.*, 1964, 1295.

Organogallium halides

Trimethylgallium reacts with halogens, hydrogen halides or gallium tri-halides giving methylgallium halides, Me_nGaX_{3-n}. The reaction with iodine, in benzene or ether, removes two methyl groups at room temperature,

$$Me_3Ga + 2I_2 \rightarrow MeGaI_2 + 2MeI$$

but removal of the third methyl group is rather slow even at 55° [746]. Dimethylgallium chloride, $(Me_2GaCl)_2$, m.p. 45·3–45·6°, b.p. (extrapolated) 154°, is dimeric in the vapour state and is conveniently obtained from Me_3Ga and the appropriate amount of HCl or $GaCl_3$. It forms co-ordination complexes $Me_2GaCl\cdot NMe_3$, m.p. 111·5–112·5°, $Me_2GaCl\cdot PMe_3$, m.p. 93–93·5°, $Me_2GaCl\cdot OEt_2$, b.p. ∼160°/0·1 mm. The last is quantitatively hydrolysed by water, giving hydrochloric acid, but no methyl groups are detached from the gallium. The bromide $(Me_2GaBr)_2$, m.p. 58·7–59·0°, and the iodide $(Me_2GaI)_2$, m.p. 53·2–53·7°, also afford trimethylamine complexes $Me_2GaBr\cdot NMe_3$, m.p. 133·5–136°, and $Me_2GaI\cdot NMe_3$, m.p. 127·5–128° [759].

Methylgallium dichloride, $Me_2Ga_2Cl_4$, m.p. 75–76°, is formed in high yield by reaction between gallium(III) chloride and hexamethyldisiloxane or with tetramethyl-silane, -germane or -stannane, the order of reactivity being Si < Ge < Sn [776]. Ethylgallium dichloride is also formed when the hydride $(HGaCl_2)_2$ reacts with ethylene (rapidly at 0°):

$$(HGaCl_2)_2 + 2C_2H_4 \rightarrow (EtGaCl_2)_2$$

The hydride, which is prepared from gallium trichloride and trimethyl-silane, also adds across carbonyl bonds [776a]:

$$(HGaCl_2)_2 + 2Me_2CO \rightarrow (Me_2CHOGaCl_2)_2$$

Both diethylgallium-chloride (b.p. 60–62°/2 mm.) and -fluoride (b.p. 80–81°/1 mm.) have been described. The fluoride is made from the chloride and KF at 100–105°, and is viscous like Et_2AlF [752].

Phenylgallium chlorides and bromides are formed from triphenyl-gallium and the appropriate gallium(III) halide or the hydrogen halide (e.g. Ph_2GaCl, m.p. 197°, $PhGaCl_2$, m.p. 122·4–123·4°, Ph_2GaBr, m.p. 218–219°, $PhGaBr_2$, m.p. 129–130°). All these are dimeric in benzene solution. The monochloride is practically non-conducting both as solid and in the fused state, but the fused dichloride has quite an appreciable conductance ($2·1 \times 10^{-5}$ ohm^{-1} cm^{-1} at its m.p. [777]).

[776] H. Schmidbaur and W. Findeiss, *Angew. Chem., Internat. Edn.*, 1964, **3**, 696.
[776a] H. Schmidbaur and H. F. Klein, ibid., 1966, **5**, 312; *Chem. Ber.*, 1967, **100**, 1129; H. Schmidbaur, W. Findeiss and E. Gast, *Angew. Chem. Internat. Edn.*, 1965, **4**, 152; H. Schmidbaur and W. Findeiss, *Chem. Ber.*, 1966, **99**, 2187.
[777] P. G. Perkins and M. E. Twentyman, *J. Chem. Soc.*, 1965, 1038.

Alkylgallium hydrides

The isolation of $(Me_2GaH)_2$, extrapolated b.p. 172°, from the products of the action of an electric discharge on a mixture of $Me_3Ga + H_2$ was described some time ago [778]. It was claimed that triethylamine disproportionated this product into $Me_3Ga \cdot NEt_3$ and Ga_2H_6, m.p. $-21 \cdot 4°$, b.p. (extrap.) 139°. However, attempts to repeat this work, though giving a product yielding some hydrogen on pyrolysis, did not lead to digallane [779].

The trimethylamine complexes of GaH_3 and GaD_3 have been prepared from $LiGaH_4$ (or D_4) and Me_3NHCl, and have been studied spectroscopically [780], and an unstable viscous liquid hydride $(GaH_3)_x$ obtained by the reaction

$$Me_3N \cdot GaH_3 + BF_3 \xrightarrow{-15°} GaH_3 + Me_3N \cdot BF_3$$

It decomposes quantitatively at room temperature and has the remarkable property of being virtually insoluble in both saturated and aromatic hydrocarbons, possibly on account of polymerization due to hydrogen-bridging [781]. The gallium–hydrogen stretching frequency in $Me_3N \cdot GaH_3$, 1853 cm^{-1}, is higher than $v(Al–H)$ in $Me_3N \cdot AlH_3$, 1792 cm^{-1}, though $v(Ga–N)$, 482, is lower than $v(Al–N)$, 533 cm^{-1}.

Diethylgallium hydride [752], b.p. 40–42°/10^{-4} mm., has been prepared by the reaction:

$$Et_2GaCl + Et_2AlH + KCl \longrightarrow Et_2GaH + K[AlEt_2Cl_2]$$

It is evidently associated (like Et_2AlH), inflames in the air, reacts vigorously with water and decomposes fairly quickly above about 80°. The decomposition is accelerated by traces of gallium metal and to some extent inhibited by the presence of mercury, which acts as a gallium metal scavenger. Diethylgallium hydride resembles Et_2AlH in the ease with which it reacts with α-olefins, thus at 65° it adds 1-decene,

$$Et_2GaH + CH_2{:}CH \cdot C_8H_{17} \longrightarrow Et_2GaC_{10}H_{21}$$

but at 100° redistribution occurs and the triethylgallium can be pumped off leaving tri-n-decylgallium:

$$3Et_2GaC_{10}H_{21} \longrightarrow 2Et_3Ga \uparrow + (C_{10}H_{21})_3Ga$$

[778] E. Wiberg and T. Johannsen, *Naturwiss.*, 1941, **29**, 320; idem, *Angew. Chem.*, 1942, **55**, 38.

[779] D. F. Shriver, R. W. Parry, N. N. Greenwood, A. Storr and M. G. H. Wallbridge, *Inorg. Chem.*, 1963, **2**, 867.

[780] N. N. Greenwood, A. Storr and M. G. H. Wallbridge, *Proc. Chem. Soc.*, 1962, 249; *Inorg. Chem.*, 1963, **2**, 1036; D. F. Shriver and R. W. Parry, ibid., p. 1039.

[781] N. N. Greenwood and M. G. H. Wallbridge, *J. Chem. Soc.*, 1963, 3912.

It adds to non-terminal acetylenes,

$$Et_2GaH + EtC:CEt \longrightarrow Et_2GaCEt:CHEt$$

but the product is thermally unstable.

The thermal decomposition of tri-isobutylgallium [748] at 150–160° probably involves the splitting out of isobutene followed by decomposition of the resulting hydride,

$$Bu^i_3Ga \longrightarrow Bu^i_2GaH + CH_2:CMe_2$$
$$3Bu^i_2GaH \longrightarrow 2Bu^i_3Ga + [GaH_3 \longrightarrow Ga + \tfrac{3}{2}H_2]$$

If Bu^i_3Ga is heated at this temperature in the presence of 1-decene, then the latter adds to the Ga–H bond and the process continues until all the isobutyl is replaced by n-decyl.

The reaction between triethylgallium and phenyl cyanide, giving an azomethine derivative, is virtually a reaction of diethylgallium hydride [782]:

$$2PhCN + 2Et_3Ga \longrightarrow (PhCH:NGaEt_2)_2 + 2C_2H_4$$

INDIUM

In its organic derivatives, which have not yet been extensively studied, indium resembles gallium more than thallium.

The alkyls are somewhat weaker acceptors than those of gallium, but the element has a higher tendency to raise its co-ordination number above four. Low valency states become relatively more stable with increasing atomic weight in this group, and an organic compound of indium(I) is known, viz., cyclopentadienylindium(I). There are no known organic derivatives of gallium(I).

Trialkyl and triaryl derivatives
Preparative methods for the indium alkyls are, (a) exchange between indium metal and mercury alkyls, (b) the alkylation of indium trihalides by Grignard reagents or organo-lithium or -aluminium compounds, and (c) reaction between alkyl bromide and a Mg-In alloy.

Trimethylindium, m.p. 88·4°, b.p. 136°, has been obtained by all three methods. Reaction between indium and dimethylmercury [783] is rather slow at 100° and is better conducted at about 135° in a sealed tube, the initiation of the reaction being favoured by the presence of a little mercury. Its vapour pressure is 7·2 mm. at 30° and it can readily be transferred

[782] J. R. Jennings and K. Wade, ibid., 1967A, 1222.
[783] L. M. Dennis, R. W. Work and E. G. Rochow, *J. Amer. Chem. Soc.*, 1934, **56**, 1047.

within a vacuum apparatus at room temperature, condensing as beautifully refracting crystals. The vapour is monomeric and the In–C distance, 2.16 ± 0.04 Å, has been measured by electron diffraction [784].

The ether complex has been prepared from methylmagnesium iodide and ethereal indium trichloride [785]. The complex is relatively unstable and can be separated into its components by fractional condensation. This is rather a tedious process, however, and the separation of ether is greatly facilitated by the addition of benzene [786]. Distillation then results in separation of most of the ether with the benzene, and a repeated distillation gives ether-free Me_3In. A mixture of Et_2O and Me_3In is produced by the reaction between methyl bromide and an indium–magnesium alloy of composition about $InMg_{3-3.5}$ [786], and ether may subsequently be separated with the help of benzene. This method works very well.

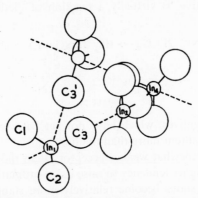

Fig. 26. The trimethylindium tetramer – weak bridge bonds to neighbouring tetramers are indicated by broken lines. (Amma and Rundle, 1958 [788]. Reproduced in modified form by permission)

Trimethylindium is monomeric in benzene, cyclopentane and methylene chloride solution [741, 787], though association in the solid state is suggested by its high melting point (88°, cf. Me_3Ga, $-16°$, and Me_3Tl, 38°). Association in the crystal has been confirmed by an X-ray analysis [788], which revealed a most unusual type of structure in which a polymeric network of tetramer units (Figure 26) is held together by long (3.6 Å) partial bonds.

The three nearest neighbours of each indium atom are three methyl groups in a plane (C_1, C_2 and C_3 of Figure 27), so little rearrangement

[784] L. Pauling and A. W. Laubengayer, *J. Amer. Chem. Soc.*, 1941, **63**, 480.

[785] F. Runge, W. Zimmermann, H. Pfeiffer and I. Pfeiffer, *Z. anorg. Chem.*, 1951, **267**, 39.

[786] E. Todt and R. Dötzer, ibid., 1963, **321**, 120.

[787] N. Muller and A. L. Otermat, *Inorg. Chem.*, 1963, **2**, 1075.

[788] E. L. Amma and R. E. Rundle, *J. Amer. Chem. Soc.*, 1958, **80**, 4141.

takes place when the crystal vaporizes into monomer. The $CH_3\cdots In—CH_3$ bridges are unsymmetrical, unlike the methyl bridges in Me_2Be and Me_3Al (q.v.). Within the tetramer unit the In–C distances in the In–C–In bridge (which is nearly linear) are 2·1 and 3·1 Å. This exceptional bonding is intelligible on the supposition that the methyl groups which take part in these bridges are somewhat flattened (in the xy plane) so that both lobes of the $C2p_z$ orbital overlap – unequally – with the vacant p orbitals of neighbouring indium atoms.

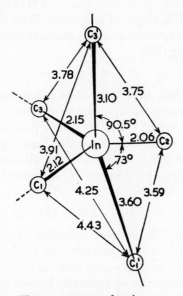

Fig. 27. Trimethylindium. The arrangement of carbon atoms about indium (Amma and Rundle, 1958 [788])

Triethylindium, b.p. 83–84°/12 mm., and several higher alkyls have been obtained by the Grignard method [785, 789] and from the alkyl bromide and Mg–In alloy [786]. They are all monomeric in benzene. Vapour pressure equations have been given for Et_3In (as well as Et_3Ga and $Pr_3{}^nGa$) [789]. Indium alkyls in which there is an α-branch in the chain are yellow, e.g. $Pr^i{}_3In$ and $Bu^s{}_3In$, and yellow colours also appear in the thallium alkyls. This curious effect deserves further consideration. Separation of ether from Et_3In and the higher alkyls merely requires distillation.

Both Et_3In and $Bu^i{}_3In$ have been prepared from the corresponding aluminium alkyls [748]. Reaction between $InCl_3$ and three mols. Et_3Al gives only Et_2AlCl and Et_3Al as volatile products, since the indium remains firmly complexed with Et_2AlCl groups. Addition of KCl to the reaction product before distillation allows recovery of Et_3In in about 70%

[789] H. Hartmann and H. Lutsche, *Naturwiss.*, 1962, **49**, 182.

yield. The alkylation of $InCl_3$ with Bu^i_3Al does not proceed so well, even when KCl has been used, and a mixture of Bu^i_3Al and Bu^i_3In is obtained. Tri-isobutylindium may be separated by taking advantage of the fact that Bu^i_3Al forms a complex with KF whereas Bu^i_3In does not. Tri-isobutyl-indium decomposes at $125°$ to indium metal, isobutane, isobutene and hydrogen. Displacement of isobutene by α-olefins goes rather slowly and is not a good preparative method for the higher indium alkyls because thermal decomposition of the higher alkyl is severe at the temperatures ($150°$) required for an appreciable rate of $CH_2{:}CMe_2$ evolution (using 1-decene). Isobutene is displaced less readily from Bu^i_3In than from the isobutyl derivatives of other Group III elements studied, the relative ease of displacement being [748]

$$Al > B > Ga > In$$

Triphenylindium [790], m.p. $208°$, from indium and diphenylmercury, forms colourless needles on crystallization from chloroform. It reacts slowly with CO_2 (in xylene solution) giving a poor yield of benzoic acid, and appears to be slightly more reactive than triphenylgallium.

The lower indium alkyls take fire in the air and the others oxidize rapidly. Slow oxidation of Me_3In at $-78°$ is reported to follow the course [783]:

$$4Me_3In + O_2 \rightarrow 2(Me_2In)_2O + 2C_2H_6$$

Ethane is also formed in the slow oxidation of liquid triethylindium, together with peroxides and acetaldehyde [791]. Trimethylindium is vigorously hydrolysed by cold water, with the formation of two mols. of methane. The resulting oxide or hydroxide has not been studied.

$$Me_3In + 2H_2O \rightarrow MeIn(OH)_2 + 2CH_4$$

Triethylindium, which loses one ethyl group with cold water (this is peculiar, since metal ethyls are normally more reactive than methyls), loses all three at $90°$. Ethanol, even at $70°$, liberates only one mol. of ethane [785],

$$Et_3In + EtOH \rightarrow Et_2In{\cdot}OEt + C_2H_6$$

Co-ordination compounds

Trimethylindium forms complexes with Me_2O and with Me_2S. The ether complex, $Me_3In{\cdot}OMe_2$, is a liquid at room temperature and almost wholly dissociated as vapour, as is the sulphur analogue, $Me_3In{\cdot}SMe_2$, m.p. $19{-}19{\cdot}5°$. Trimethyl-amine, -phosphine and -arsine form 1 : 1 complexes,

[790] H. Gilman and R. G. Jones, *J. Amer. Chem. Soc.*, 1940, **62**, 2353; W. C. Schumb and H. I. Crane, ibid., 1938, **60**, 306.
[791] C. F. Cullis, A. Fish and R. T. Pollard, *Trans. Faraday Soc.*, 1964, **60**, 2224.

$Me_3In \cdot NMe_3$, m.p. 66·2–66·4°, $Me_3In \cdot PMe_3$, m.p. 46·5°, and $Me_3In \cdot AsMe_3$, m.p. 24·2–24·8°. The stability of these appears to be a little less than that of the corresponding gallium compounds. The heat of co-ordination of Me_3N to Me_3In is 20·0 kcal. and to Me_3Ga 21·0 kcal. The Me_3P and Me_3As complexes are less stable.

Trimethylindium forms a dimethylamine complex which eliminates methane when heated, forming the dimer $(Me_2In \cdot NMe_2)_2$. Methanol yields a glass-like product $(Me_2In \cdot OMe)_n$ whose degree of association in benzene varies with concentration, but n is rather more than three. Methanethiol gives a dimer $(Me_2In \cdot SMe)_2$ [792], and a dimer is also formed from Me_3In and Ph_2AsH [771].

Phosphine forms a 1 : 1 adduct with Me_3In at −123°, but this decomposes into $Me_3In + PH_3$ as the temperature is raised. Above −78° irreversible decomposition takes place with formation of methane and polymeric material $(—MeIn—PH—)_n$, and the latter loses more methane between 95 and 275° giving InP [793].

Chelate complexes are formed by acetylacetone [792] and dithiophosphinic acids [775],

but phosphinic acids, R_2PO_2H, act as *bridging* groups (see p. 354) and yield dimers $(Me_2InO_2PR_2)_2$ [775].

Organo-indium halides

These have been relatively little investigated. Both diphenyl- and di-1-naphthyl-indium bromide have been made from the Grignard reagent and $InBr_3$. They are soluble in hydrocarbons (in contrast to the thallium compounds R_2TlX) and the dinaphthyl compound is said to be monomeric in benzene [785]. Bisperfluorophenylindium bromide in contrast is dimeric in benzene [758a], as might be expected.

Dimethyl-[791a] and diethyl-[791b] indium halides have only recently been described. If a mixture of methyl-lithium, lithium iodide and indium-(III) chloride in molar ratio 2 : 1 : 1 in ether is worked up after only half an hour, then trimethylindium is obtained, but after reaction for 2–3 days dimethylindium iodide is formed in over 70% yield. The chloride, Me_2InCl,

[791a] H. C. Clark and A. L. Pickard, *J. Organometal. Chem.*, 1967, **8**, 427.
[791b] K. Yasuda and R. Okawara, *Inorg. Nucl. Chem. Letters*, 1967, **3**, 135.
[792] G. E. Coates and R. A. Whitcombe, *J. Chem. Soc.*, 1956, 3351.
[793] R. Didchenko, J. E. Alix and R. H. Toeniskoetter, *J. Inorg. Nucl. Chem.*, 1960, **14**, 35.

can similarly be obtained by prolonged reaction between two moles of methyl-lithium and one of indium(III) chloride.

Both the dimethylindium halides are dimeric, and their infrared spectra indicate a bridged structure like that of $Me_4Al_2Cl_2$:

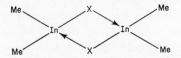

The halogen bridge may be broken by suitable bases, giving monomeric complexes exemplified by Me_2InIpy and $Me_2InClPPh_3$. Dimethylindium fluoride has also been prepared, and its crystal structure will be awaited with interest.

The diethylindium halides were formed from triethylindium and the appropriate halide; they are soluble in ether chloroform or bromoform, but no molecular weights were given. The sulphide $(EtInS)_x$, from Et_3In and $(Me_2SnS)_2$, is insoluble and probably a co-ordination polymer.

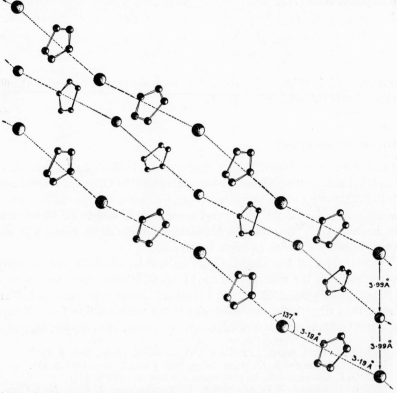

Fig. 28. Crystal structure of C_5H_5In (after Frasson, Menegus and Panattoni [795])

Cyclopentadienylindium

Though no other organoindium(I) compounds are known, the main product in the reaction between C_5H_5Na and $InCl_3$ is the pale yellow cyclopentadienylindium(I), C_5H_5In. This substance is stable to water but is rapidly decomposed by dilute sulphuric acid, and it is very sensitive to oxidation (far more so than C_5H_5Tl). The indium(III) compound, $(C_5H_5)_3In$, has been obtained in the above reaction only in very small yield; it decomposes above 160° forming the indium(I) compound [794].

The structure of crystalline C_5H_5In has been determined by X-ray diffraction, and is shown in Figure 28. The substance is a linear polymer. The metal–ring distance is 3·19 Å, and the metal–metal distance, 3·99 Å, is small enough to allow the possibility of some electronic interaction [795]. An electron-diffraction study of the vapour indicates a 'half-sandwich' structure similar to that of the thallium compound [796].

THALLIUM

The most distinctive feature of the organic chemistry of thallium is the peculiarly high stability of the type R_2TlX, these compounds commonly being salts $R_2Tl^+X^-$. The trialkyls, in contrast, are unstable and more liable to thermal decomposition than their gallium and indium analogues.

Trialkyl and triaryl derivatives

These unstable and reactive compounds are prepared with the use of organolithium reagents, since the action of the less reactive Grignard reagents in *diethyl ether* on thallium(III) chloride proceeds only as far as the introduction of two organic groups giving the well-known type R_2TlX. However, in *tetrahydrofuran* [797] the increased carbanion character of the ethyl group of ethylmagnesium bromide results in ethylation of Et_2TlCl to Et_3Tl in this solvent.

The exchange of alkyl between mercury alkyls and the Group IIIB elements becomes progressively less satisfactory as a preparative method as the atomic weight of the latter increases. The method is no use in the case of thallium, and in fact trimethylthallium reacts reversibly with mercury,

$$2Me_3Tl + 3Hg \rightleftharpoons 3Me_2Hg + 2Tl$$

Trimethylthallium [798], m.p. 38·5°, b.p. (extrap.) 147°, may be prepared from methyl-lithium and Me_2TlX (X = halide), or by an interesting re-

[794] E. O. Fischer and H. P. Hofmann, *Angew. Chem.*, 1957, **69**, 639.
[795] E. Frasson, F. Menegus and C. Panattoni, *Nature*, 1963, **199**, 1087.
[796] S. Shibata, L. S. Bartell and R. M. Gavin, *J. Chem. Phys.*, 1964, **41**, 717.
[797] O. Y. Okhlobystin, K. A. Bilevitch and L. I. Zakharkin, *J. Organometal. Chem.*, 1964, **2**, 281.
[798] H. Gilman and R. G. Jones, *J. Amer. Chem. Soc.*, 1946, **68**, 517; ibid., 1950, **72**, 1760.

action between methyl-lithium and thallium(I) iodide in the presence of methyl iodide. The overall reaction is

$$2MeLi + MeI + TlI \longrightarrow Me_3Tl + 2LiI$$

but the formation of Me_3Tl must take place in several stages, the first step probably being the transient formation of *monomethylthallium* followed by its immediate disproportionation,

$$MeLi + TlI \longrightarrow LiI + MeTl$$
$$3MeTl \longrightarrow Me_3Tl + 2Tl$$

As an ether solution of methyl-lithium is added to the suspension of thallium(I) iodide in ether and methyl iodide, a black cloud appears (no doubt due to finely divided thallium metal), and then gradually disappears. Low yields of triethylthallium have been obtained from ethyl chloride and thallium–sodium alloys [799], and although methyl iodide does not react with massive thallium or thallium–sodium alloy [800] it would seem to react with the metal in a finely divided state,

$$MeI + 2Tl \longrightarrow MeTl + TlI$$

The methylthallium could either react with methyl iodide,

$$MeTl + MeI \longrightarrow Me_2TlI$$

followed by

$$Me_2TlI + MeLi \longrightarrow Me_3Tl + LiI$$

or disproportionate into trimethylthallium and thallium metal.

Trimethylthallium can readily be separated from ether, so does not co-ordinate strongly with it (see below). It forms colourless crystals, quite volatile at room temperature (v.p. $\sim$5 mm. at 20°), which are very soluble in ether and in benzene (in which it is monomeric). It is stable if kept in the dark, but decomposes in the light (and can thereby make a horrible mess of a vacuum apparatus). Heating to about 90° or above can result in explosive decomposition, so some care is required in its manipulation. Trimethylindium, in contrast, is claimed to be stable at 250° [786].

Triethylthallium [799], m.p. −63°, b.p. (extrap.) 192°, from EtLi and Et_2TlCl at room temperature (heating the reaction mixture reduces the yield), is a bright yellow liquid which darkens when heated and becomes paler when cooled, being colourless in liquid nitrogen. The colourless Me_3Tl becomes pale yellow when warmed. Triethylthallium has also been made from EtLi, EtBr and TlCl [801] (cf. preparation of Me_3Tl), and from EtMgBr, EtBr and TlCl in tetrahydrofuran [797]. It is appreciably

[799] H. P. A. Groll, *J. Amer. Chem. Soc.*, 1930, **52**, 2998.
[800] E. G. Rochow and L. M. Dennis, ibid., 1935, **57**, 486.
[801] S. F. Birch, *J. Chem. Soc.*, 1934, 1132.

volatile at room temperature. Although it has not been reported to explode when heated, it decomposes very rapidly above about 125°. Triisobutylthallium [801], b.p. 74–76°/1·6 mm., is rather lighter in colour than the triethyl, and is sensitive to light.

Triphenylthallium [801, 802], m.p. 169–170°, from PhLi and Ph_2TlBr, crystallizes as colourless needles from benzene–light petroleum. When heated above its melting point it decomposes into thallium with formation of some biphenyl. It reacts with mercury giving thallium amalgam and diphenylmercury, and with reactive halides such as benzoyl chloride, giving Ph_2TlCl and, for example, benzophenone. Carbonation is inappreciable at room temperature, but a 70% yield of benzoic acid together with 73% biphenyl is obtained in boiling xylene.

$$Ph_3Tl + CO_2 \longrightarrow Ph \cdot Ph + PhCO_2Tl$$

Triphenylthallium is described as somewhat less reactive than triphenylgallium or -indium. Trispentafluorophenylthallium is monomeric in benzene [758a].

Triphenylthallium undergoes a rapid exchange reaction with n-butyllithium:

$$Ph_3Tl + 3Bu^nLi \longrightarrow 3PhLi + Bu_3^nTl$$

Rapid exchange of alkyl groups takes place between Me_3Tl and Et_3Tl in methylene chloride or toluene at room temperature, as shown by proton magnetic resonance. The activation energy for the exchange is about 6 kcal. $mole^{-1}$, and at −85° the species Me_2EtTl and $MeEt_2Tl$ can be detected [803]. A solution of Me_3Tl in $PhCD_3$ has two proton resonances at low temperature, separated by 250·4 cycles per second due to spin–spin coupling between the methyl protons and ^{203}Tl and ^{205}Tl. As the temperature is raised the resonances broaden and coalesce due to methyl exchange, requiring activation energy of 6·3 ± 0·5 kcal. $mole^{-1}$. The exchange reaction is second-order and observations are consistent with a dimeric transition state:

Exchange rates are lower in the donor solvents Me_2O and Me_3N. The phenyl groups of Ph_3Tl also exchange rapidly, and again the rate is reduced in solution in trimethylamine. Vinyl groups in mixed methyl vinyl thallium compounds (from $vinyl_2TlCl$ + MeLi, as $CH_2:CHLi$ apparently does not react with R_2TlCl) also undergo rapid exchange [804].

[802] H. Gilman and R. G. Jones, *J. Amer. Chem. Soc.*, 1939, **61**, 1513; 1940, **62** 2357.   [803] J. P. Maher and D. F. Evans, *Proc. Chem. Soc.*, 1961, 208.
[804] Idem, *J. Chem. Soc.*, 1963, 5534.

In contrast, the monomeric acetylenic derivative $Me_2TlC:CPh$ remains as such and does not appear to disproportionate. This compound behaves as a weak electrolyte in liquid ammonia, in which there may be some dissociation into solvated Me_2Tl cations and phenylethynyl anions. Other acetylenic derivatives prepared include the very explosive $Me_2TlC:CTlMe_2$, and the salts $M[Tl(C:CR)_4]$, (R = Me or Ph) [804a].

Although Me_3Tl is spontaneously inflammable, its slow oxidation has not been studied. Triethylthallium is less sensitive to oxygen, and phenol, biphenyl and diphenylthallium oxide have been found in the products of slow reaction of a benzene solution of Ph_3Tl with dry air.

Hydrolysis of R_3Tl proceeds only as far as R_2TlOH.

Co-ordination compounds

Although a decidedly weaker acceptor than Me_3In or Me_3Ga, Me_3Tl forms crystalline 1 : 1 complexes, $Me_3Tl·NMe_3$, m.p. $\sim 0°$, and $Me_3Tl·PMe_3$, m.p. 27–28°; these complexes are evidently extensively dissociated as vapours since the components can be partially separated by sublimation. Trimethylthallium does not complex appreciably with trimethylarsine, and only weakly with ether [792]. Triphenylthallium forms a 1 : 1 complex $Ph_3Tl·NMe_3$, whose dissociation pressure is negligible at room temperature ([804], and $(C_6F_5)_3Tl$ forms an ether complex stable at room temperature [758a].

The order of acceptor character of the Group III and IIIB elements in their trivalent states, as exemplified by the trimethyl derivatives, is:

$$B < Al > Ga > In > Tl$$

Dialkyl- and diaryl-thallium compounds

The first of this series was prepared in 1870 by the action of diethylzinc on an ether solution of thallium(III) chloride; they have long been recognized as among the most stable and least reactive organometallic compounds. They are more conveniently obtained by the use of Grignard reagents, but yields are sometimes poor owing to the oxidation of the Grignard reagent by the thallium(III) which is thereby reduced to thallium(I) chloride. Iodides and Grignard reagents derived from secondary alkyl groups are particularly prone to this trouble.

The solubilities of the lower dialkylthallium compounds (e.g. dimethyl and diethyl) are remarkably similar to those of the corresponding thallium(I) salts, and since a mixture of R_2TlX and TlX is almost invariably produced during the preparation of R_2TlX by the Grignard method, separation requires the use of special solvents such as pyridine, concentrated aqueous ammonia, or liquid ammonia in which the organic deriva-

[804a] R. Nast and K. Käb, *J. Organometal. Chem.*, 1966, **6,** 456.

tive is the more soluble (but see Me_2TlCl, below, for a way to avoid this difficulty). The presence of thallium(I) halides can be detected by means of an alkali sulphide since thallium(I) sulphide is black and the dialkyl-thallium sulphides are colourless.

Dialkyl- and diaryl-thallium compounds are with few exceptions (such as the $R_2Tl\cdot OR$ dimers) inert to hydrolysis and to atmospheric oxidation. The majority of them are salts, and Me_2TlI crystallizes with an ionic lattice [805], the $Me-Tl-Me^+$ group being linear and isoelectronic with $Me-Hg-Me$.

The hydroxides, R_2TlOH, obtained from the halides and silver oxide in aqueous suspension, are very soluble in water (like $TlOH$) and conductance measurements [806] indicate a high degree of dissociation, less than that of $TlOH$ but far more than those of $RHgOH$ or R_3PbOH. From a study of the hydroxide ion catalysis of the decomposition of diacetone alcohol [807] the dissociation constant of Me_2TlOH appears to be 0·09 at 25°. Experiments at relatively high concentration indicate the presence of a dimer, believed to have a hydroxy bridge. In a 0·2M-solution about 10%

of the thallium is present as the dimer, 36% as Me_2TlOH and 54% as Me_2Tl^+. However, a study of the Raman spectra [808] of aqueous solutions of Me_2TlOH gives no indication of an appreciable concentration of species containing Tl–O covalent bonds. The TlC_2 symmetrical stretching frequency in Me_2Tl^+ salts is at 498 cm^{-1} (the infrared-active asymmetrical stretching frequency in solid Me_2TlBr is at 541 cm^{-1}), and is only slightly different (490 cm^{-1}) in a 2·3M solution of Me_2TlOH. In fact the entire Raman spectrum is very similar to that of the free Me_2Tl^+ ion and it is concluded that the major species in concentrated aqueous Me_2TlOH consists of Me_2Tl^+ and OH^- ion-pairs.

An interesting consequence of the strength of dialkylthallium hydroxides as bases has been the preparation of crystalline Et_2TlHCO_3 from the hydroxide or carbonate and CO_2 [809].

Quite a large number of R_2TlX-type compounds has been described, but here it is appropriate to mention only a few representative examples.

[805] H. M. Powell and D. M. Crowfoot, *Z. Krist.*, 1934, **87**, 370; see also R. S. Tobias, *Organometal. Chem. Rev.*, 1966, **1**, 93.

[806] F. Hein and H. Meininger, *Z. anorg. Chem.*, 1925, **145**, 95.

[807] J. K. Lawrence and J. E. Prue, *Int. Conf. Co-ordination Chemistry, Chem. Soc. Special Publ.* No. 13, 1959, p. 186.

[808] P. L. Goggin and L. A. Woodward, *Trans. Faraday Soc.*, 1960, **56**, 1591.

[809] R. J. Meyer and A. Bertheim, *Ber.*, 1904, **37**, 2051.

Dimethylthallium chloride is obtained by the slow addition of methyl-magnesium chloride to a cooled ether solution of thallium(III) chloride. The resulting Me_2TlCl is separated from $TlCl$ by solution of the former in cold concentrated aqueous ammonia; it crystallizes as the ammonia evaporates or if the solution is heated. It decomposes about 280° without melting.

The *fluoride* is very soluble in water (from which it crystallizes as $Me_2TlF,12H_2O$) and methanol, less in ethanol and almost insoluble in ether and benzene. The *cyanide* is a salt and soluble in water [637] (contrast with tetrameric $Me_2Al,(Ga,In)CN$ and polymeric R_2BCN). The *nitrate, sulphate, chromate, carbonate* and *acetate* are typical examples of water-soluble Me_2Tl salts, and the *chloride, bromide, iodide* and *azide* are only very slightly soluble in water, the iodide being less soluble than the chloride.

The higher di-n-alkylthallium compounds call for little comment; they tend to have higher solubilities, and $(n-C_6H_{13})_2TlF$ dissolves in benzene forming ion-aggregates as revealed by high apparent molecular weights [810]. Dicyclohexylthallium fluoride has been used as a gravimetric reagent for nitrate.

Compounds with α-branched chains are less stable than the normal di-alkyls, thus Pr^i_2TlCl and Bu^s_2TlCl explode when heated to about 150° and are hydrolysed by boiling water.

Several *vinyl* compounds have been described, e.g. $(CH_2:CH)_2TlBr$ [811] and $(PhCH:CH)_2TlCl$ [812].

Diphenylthallium fluoride [813], m.p. 310°, is the most soluble of the known diphenylthallium salts, the nitrate and the other halides being practically insoluble in water. Diphenylthallium compounds are better made by the action of phenyl derivatives of elements other than magnesium, on $TlCl_3$, these include the phenyls of mercury, lead or bismuth but one of the most convenient to use is phenylboronic acid [814].

$$2PhB(OH)_2 + TlCl_3 + H_2O \rightarrow Ph_2TlCl + 2B(OH)_3 + 2HCl$$

Diphenylthallium bromide reacts with mercury,

$$Ph_2TlBr + Hg \rightarrow Ph_2Hg + TlBr$$

and is reduced by sodium in liquid ammonia to thallium and triphenyl-thallium [802].

Bispentafluorophenylthallium derivatives [815] differ from their phenyl

[810] E. Krause and P. Dittmar, *Ber.*, 1930, **63**, 1953.
[811] A. N. Nesmeyanov, A. E. Borisov, I. S. Saveleva and E. I. Golubeva, *Izvest. Akad. Nauk S.S.S.R.*, 1958, 1490.
[812] V. A. Sazonova and N. Y. Kronrod, *Zhur. obshchei Khim.*, 1956, **26**, 1876.
[813] E. Krause and A. von Grosse, *Ber.*, 1925, **58**, 272.
[814] F. Challenger and B. Parker, *J. Chem. Soc.*, 1931, 1462.
[815] G. B. Deacon and R. S. Nyholm, *Chem. and Ind.*, 1963, 1803; G. B. Deacon, J. H. S. Green and R. S. Nyholm, *J. Chem. Soc.*, 1965, 3411; G. B. Deacon and R. S. Nyholm, *ibid.*, p. 6107.

analogues in their much greater solubilities. The acetate, chloride, bromide and nitrate are virtually non-eletrolytes in acetone. The chloride and bromide are dimeric in benzene, and the presence of bridging halogen is

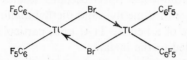

indicated by the infrared spectra. Bridging halogen gives rise to considerably lower frequency infrared absorptions than terminal halogen [815a]. These interesting pentafluorophenyl compounds provide a striking contrast to the essentially ionic hydrocarbon derivatives R_2TlX.

Co-ordination compounds

The solubility of otherwise rather insoluble dialkylthallium salts in pyridine or in concentrated aqueous ammonia may well be due to co-ordination:

$$R_2TlX + C_5H_5N \longrightarrow R_2Tl\begin{smallmatrix}NC_5H_5\\X\end{smallmatrix}$$

The pyridine complex of dimethylthallium perchlorate, [$Me_2Tl\,py$]ClO_4, has been isolated [816], and a number of internal co-ordination compounds have been prepared, of the type R_2TlD, where the group D possesses donor character. For example, Me_2TlBr and $(TlOMe)_4$ react as follows [817]:

$$2Me_2TlBr + \tfrac{1}{2}(TlOMe)_4 \longrightarrow Me_2Tl\begin{smallmatrix}OMe\\OMe\end{smallmatrix}TlMe_2 + 2TlBr$$

This dimeric methoxide, m.p. 177–181°, is analogous to the dimethylmethoxide of gallium. The ethoxide, $(Me_2Tl\cdot OEt)_2$, is a readily hydrolysed liquid [818]. The dimeric trimethylsiloxy compound is similarly constituted, $(Me_2Tl\cdot OSiMe_3)_2$ [819]. Other dimers, but with sulphur and selenium in the rings, are formed from Me_2TlF and $MeSNa$ (or $MeSeNa$) in methanol [792]. Though reaction between Me_2TlBr and $PhSNa$ gives $(Me_2Tl\cdot SPh)_2$, m.p. 188°, attempts to prepare $(Me_2Tl\cdot PPh_2)_n$ from Me_2TlBr and Ph_2PNa have yielded trimethylthallium and tetraphenyldiphosphine (isolated as

[815a] G. B. Deacon, J. H. S. Green and W. Kynaston, *J. Chem. Soc. (A)*, 1967, 158.
[816] I. R. Beattie and P. A. Cocking, *J. Chem. Soc.*, 1965, 3860.
[817] R. C. Menzies and A. R. P. Walker, ibid., 1934, 1131.
[818] R. C. Menzies, ibid., 1930, 1571.
[819] H. Schmidbaur and F. Schindler, *Angew. Chem., Internat. Edn.*, 1965, **4**, 876.

disulphide) [820]. Reaction between Me_3Tl and (1 mol.) Ph_2AsH similarly gives tetraphenyldiarsine, thallium metal and Me_3Tl.

The thallium atoms in several of these complexes have uncommon co-ordination environments. Spectroscopic studies on $[Me_2Tlpy]ClO_4$ [816] and on a range of dimethyl- and diethyl-thallium complexes [820a] suggest the presence of a bent C–Tl–C unit, particularly when a nitrogen donor is co-ordinated to the metal.

The crystal structure of the 1,10-phenanthroline complex of dimethyl-thallium perchlorate [820b] reveals a C–Tl–C unit which is bent 12° from linear, and the Tl-C bonds are slightly bent away from the phenanthroline unit. The TlN_2 bonds are short enough to permit partial covalent character. The overall co-ordination number of the thallium is six, but the remaining two co-ordination positions are taken up by perchlorate oxygen atoms at a distance appropriate for an electrostatic bond. Though the TlN_2O_2 group is co-planar, the co-ordination is far from octahedral, not only because of the 168° C–Tl–C unit, but also because of the O–Tl–O angle (135°).

Complexes of the type R_2TlX, in which R is a hydrocarbon radical, are derivatives of thallium(III). They could be regarded as containing Tl^{3+} ions bound to hydrocarbon anions, but the latter are so highly polarizable that the effective charge on the metal is unlikely to exceed $+1$. A different situation arises when Tl(III) is bound to electronegative groups such as pentafluorophenyl, which are not only highly negative but also are not very polarizable. This combination gives rise to higher co-ordination numbers than are typical of the dialkyl and diaryl complexes, in order to avoid the metal departing too far from electroneutrality. These considerations have been discussed by Nyholm [815, 820c].

The four-co-ordination present in $[(C_6F_5)_2TlBr]_2$ has already been mentioned. Numerous bispentafluorophenylthallium complexes have been prepared, in which the metal is four-co-ordinate. Examples are $[Et_4N][(C_6F_5)_2TlCl_2]$ and $(C_6F_5)_2TlBrL$ (L = Ph_3P, Ph_3PO, Ph_3As and Ph_3AsO). Perhaps the most interesting bispentafluorophenylthallium complexes are those in which the metal is five-co-ordinate. An example is the nitrate, $(C_6F_5)_2(Ph_3AsO)_2TlNO_3$, which is virtually a non-electrolyte in acetone, and has an infrared spectrum in the solid state consistent with a trigonal bipyramid structure with axial C_6F_5 groups (two As:O stretching frequencies are observed). This complex dissociates extensively in acetone, into Ph_3AsO and $(C_6F_5)_2(Ph_3AsO)TlNO_3$ [815]. The bipyridyl complex $(C_6F_5)_2(C_6F_5CO_2)Tlbipy$ is monomeric in benzene and in ace-

[820] G. E. Coates and J. Graham, unpublished observations.
[820a] G. D. Shier and R. S. Drago, *J. Organometal. Chem.*, 1966, **5**, 330.
[820b] T. L. Blundell and H. M. Powell, *Chem. Comm.*, 1967, 54.
[820c] R. S. Nyholm, *Proc. Chem. Soc.*, 1961, 273.

tone, and is another five-co-ordinate thallium compound. The carboxylate itself $[(C_6F_5)_2(C_6F_5CO_2)Tl]_2$ is a dimer, and is believed to contain bridging carboxylate groups in an eight-membered ring [820d].

Chelate derivatives, such as 3.131 from Me_2TlI and thallium(I) acetylacetonate, include compounds derived from benzoylacetone, ethyl acetoacetate, dibenzoylmethane and salicylic aldehyde [821]. Dimethyldithio-

3.131

phosphinic acid, which forms monomeric chelate derivatives with the Me_2Al, Me_2Ga and Me_2In groups, gives a dimethylthallium salt $[Me_2Tl^+][Me_2PS_2^-]$ whose infrared spectrum is virtually a superposition of those of Me_2TlBr and CsS_2PMe_2 [775].

Mono-alkyl and -arylthallium(III) compounds

The action of $TlCl_3$ on Me_2TlCl or Et_2TlCl gives $Tl_3(TlCl_6)$ [822], not mono-alkylthallium halides as claimed earlier. The only monomethylthallium compound to have been established is methylthallium diacetate. The formation of this was shown by following the proton magnetic resonance spectrum of a solution of Me_2TlOAc and $Hg(OAc)_2$ in D_2O. Transfer of methyl from thallium to mercury is apparent after an hour, since the characteristic CH_3–Hg spectrum appears and is identified with certainty by the satellite pattern.

$$Me_2TlOAc + Hg(OAc)_2 \longrightarrow MeTl(OAc)_2 + MeHgOAc$$

Methylthallium diacetate, m.p. 102–103°, slowly decomposes in solution giving methyl acetate and methanol [822a].

Reaction between phenylboronic acid and an excess of thallium(III) chloride gives phenylthallium dichloride [814], $PhTlCl_2$, m.p. 235° (decomp.).

$$PhB(OH)_2 + TlCl_3 + H_2O \longrightarrow PhTlCl_2 + B(OH)_3 + HCl$$

This resembles the formation of PhHgCl from $PhB(OH)_2$ and $HgCl_2$. Phenylthallium dichloride is much more soluble in water and organic solvents than Ph_2TlCl. It slowly disproportionates when heated in aqueous solution.

$$2PhTlCl_2 \longrightarrow Ph_2TlCl + TlCl_3$$

[820d] G. B. Deacon, *Austral. J. Chem.*, 1967, **20**, 459.
[821] R. C. Menzies, N. V. Sidgwick, E. F. Cutliffe and J. M. C. Fox, *J. Chem. Soc.*, 1928, 1288.
[822] D. Sarrach, *Z. anorg. Chem.*, 1962, **319**, 16.
[822a] H. Kurasowa and R. Okawara, *Inorg. Nucl. Chem. Letters*, 1967, **3**, 21, 93.

Addition of KCN gives the anionic complex $K[PhTl(CN)_3]$, which readily decomposes into Ph_2TlCN. Mercuric chloride is phenylated:

$$PhTlCl_2 + HgCl_2 \longrightarrow PhHgCl + TlCl_3$$

Reaction of $PhTlCl_2$, which is monomeric in methanol, with one mole of Me_4NCl gives the salt $Me_4N[PhTlCl_3]$, which behaves as a 1 : 1 electrolyte in methanol. However, reaction with two moles of Me_4NCl gives another salt $(Me_4N)_2[PhTlCl_4]$, whose i value in methanol changes rapidly with concentration but is consistent with the presence of the 1 : 2 salt (five-co-ordinate thallium) which may partly dissociate to Me_4NCl and $Me_4N[PhTlCl_3]$ [822b].

Phenylthallium dibromide, $PhTlBr_2$, m.p. 149°, from $PhB(OH)_2$ and $TlBr_3$, is less stable than the chloride and slowly disproportionates at room temperature. When heated it rapidly decomposes into $TlBr$ and $PhBr$, and addition of KI to either $PhTlCl_2$ or $PhTlBr_2$ results in the rapid formation of PhI. Both halides co-ordinate to pyridine, $PhTlCl_2py$, m.p. 172° (decomp.), and $PhTlBr_2py$, m.p. 85° [823]. The proton magnetic resonance spectra [824] of several arylthallium compounds have been studied with particular reference to changes in Tl–H coupling in the series R_3Tl, R_2Tl^+ and RTl^{++}.

*Aryl*thallium dicarboxylates are formed from Ph_2Hg and thallium(III) carboxylates:

$$Ph_2Hg + (Pr^iCO_2)_3Tl \longrightarrow PhHgO_2C \cdot Pr^i + PhTl(O_2C \cdot Pr^i)_2$$

The same compound results quantitatively when $Ph_2TlO_2CPr^i$ reacts with $(Pr^iCO_2)_3Tl$; it can be converted into $PhTlCl_2$ by treatment with NH_3 and then HCl (both in methanol) [825].

Similar substances are produced as by-products from the now extensively studied series of oxidations with thallium(III) acetate (cf. lead(IV) acetate) [826].

Thallium (II)

The probable ability of thallium(II) to form metal–metal bonds was discussed on electronic grounds some six years ago [820c]. Such a compound, $K_2[Tl_2Me_6]$, has been prepared [764a] by reduction of trimethylthallium in 1,2-dimethoxyethane with potassium. The chemical reactions of this salt are similar to those of its gallium(II) analogue mentioned above (p. 350). One of the more interesting properties of $K_2[Tl_2Me_6]$ is the absence of

[822b] G. Faraglia, L. R. Fiorani, B. C. L. Pepe and R. Barbieri, *Inorg. Nucl. Chem. Letters*, 1967, **3**, 277.
[823] F. Challenger and O. V. Richards, *J. Chem. Soc.*, 1934, 405.
[824] J. P. Maher and D. F. Evans, ibid., 1956, 637.
[825] V. P. Glushkova and K. A. Kocheskov, *Doklady Akad. Nauk S.S.S.R.*, 1957, **116**, 233; *Chem. Abs.*, 1958, 6236.
[826] H. J. Kabbe, *Annalen*, 1962, **656**, 204.

evidence for thallium–proton coupling in the proton magnetic resonance spectrum, which is temperature-independent down to $-50°$. The thallium(III) anion Me_4Tl^- shows the same effect.

Organothallium(I) compounds

The formation of benzoic acid and biphenyl in equivalent quantities when carbon dioxide is passed into a boiling solution of triphenylthallium in xylene suggests that the Ph_3Tl decomposes into $PhTl$ (immediately carbonated) and biphenyl:

$$Ph_3Tl \longrightarrow PhTl + Ph_2$$
$$PhTl + CO_2 \longrightarrow PhCO_2Tl$$

This is supported by the slow formation of biphenyl and deposition of metallic thallium when Ph_3Tl is boiled in xylene in the absence of CO_2. Further, no reaction with CO_2 occurs at room temperature, and no biphenyl is formed when diphenylthallium benzoate (a possible alternative intermediate) is boiled in xylene with CO_2 present. Mono-alkyl derivatives of thallium also appear to take part in the reactions in which thallium tri-alkyls are produced from $TlX + RLi$. Attempts, however, to prepare $PhTl$ from $TlCl$ and $PhLi$, even at $-70°$, have resulted in the rapid formation of metallic thallium and of triphenylthallium:

$$PhLi + TlCl \longrightarrow PhTl + LiCl$$
$$3PhTl \longrightarrow Ph_3Tl + 2Tl$$

Cyclopentadienylthallium(I) [827], in contrast, is one of the easiest organothallium compounds to prepare, being formed when cyclopentadiene is added to aqueous thallium(I) sulphate in the presence of sodium hydroxide. It is precipitated in colourless to pale yellow needles (depending on the temperature), is moderately soluble in most polar organic solvents, does not melt when heated but sublimes at about $100°$ in a good vacuum. It is hydrolysed by warm aqueous acids.

The relatively high hydrolytic stability of this compound has been attributed to its high symmetry, high lattice energy, and low solubility. It may be a salt $Tl^+C_5H_5^-$ [828a]. The methyl derivative $Tl^+C_5H_4CH_3^-$, m.p. 88–89°, can also be prepared in an aqueous medium, but differs from C_5H_5Tl in being sensitive to atmospheric oxidation [828]. The metal–ring distance in the vapour of C_5H_5Tl, 2·41 Å, is considerably less than in the crystal [829]. Crystalline C_5H_5Tl has a structure very similar to that of C_5H_5In (see Figure 28) and is a 'linear polymer'; the metal–ring distances

[827] E. O. Fischer, *Angew. Chem.*, 1957, **69**, 207; H. Meister, ibid., p. 533; F. A. Cotton and L. T. Reynolds, *J. Amer. Chem. Soc.*, 1958, **80**, 269.
[828] L. T. Reynolds and G. Wilkinson, *J. Inorg. Nucl. Chem.*, 1959, **9**, 86.
[828a] But see S. Shibata, L. S. Bartell and R. M. Gavin, *J. Chem. Phys.*, 1964, **41**, 717.
[829] J. K. Tyler, A. P. Cox and J. Sheridan, *Nature*, 1959, **183**, 1182.

would thus be at least 3·19 Å (this being the indium–ring distance in C_5H_5In).

Nothing is known of thallium–olefin complexes but these are considered to be formed in the initial step in the thallium(III) oxidation of olefins [830]:

$$RCH:CHR + Tl^{3+} + 2H_2O \rightarrow RCH(OH)\cdot CH(OH)R + Tl^+ + 2H^+$$

The oxidation of ethylene [831] is strongly accelerated by increasing salt concentration, perchlorate > sulphate > nitrate, and is first-order with respect both to ethylene and to thallium(III). The reaction is likely to proceed through a $\pi \rightarrow \sigma$ transition (compare the mercury catalysed hydration of olefins, p. 175).

[830] R. R. Grinstead, *J. Org. Chem.*, 1961, **26**, 238.
[831] P. M. Henry, *J. Amer. Chem. Soc.*, 1965, **87**, 990, 4423; 1966, **88**, 1597.

CHAPTER FOUR

Group IV

All the elements of Group IVB form a large number of organic derivatives. The fully substituted tetra-alkyl and tetra-aryl compounds differ from the fully alkylated (or arylated) derivatives of elements of the neighbouring groups in their *relatively* low chemical reactivity. Thus tetramethyltin is unreactive to air and water, in strong contrast to trimethylindium and trimethylstibine, both of which inflame in air. The high reactivity of Group III organic compounds may be attributed mainly to their vacant orbital and electron-deficient character. The high reactivity of Group V organic compounds (the trivalent compounds at least) is due to their unsaturated character and to the presence of a 'lone-pair' of electrons. The Group IVB alkyls and aryls behave as saturated compounds, and the elements show no tendency to expand their covalency above four unless they are bonded to strongly electronegative atoms or groups, e.g. whereas tetramethyltin is unreactive, tin(IV) chloride is readily hydrolysed and gives rise to compounds like ammonium chlorostannate, $(NH_4)_2SnCl_6$.

In making the above observations it is necessary to point out that compounds of the type R_4M, where M is Ge, Sn or Pb, are far more reactive than similar compounds of carbon R_4C or even of silicon R_4Si. In fact, as the group is descended the M–C bonds become more easily broken thermally (though thermal stability probably reaches a maximum at silicon), or chemically. Relative reactivities may be illustrated by the action of chlorine on the tetra-alkyls: Et_4C and Et_4Si undergo atomic chlorination with retention of the ethyl to C or Si bonds, Et_4Ge is easily broken down to $Et_3GeCl + EtCl$, Et_4Sn reacts so fast that care is needed to stop at Et_3SnCl, and Et_4Pb is completely broken down.

A special feature of the organic compounds of Group IVB is the occurrence of compounds containing metal–metal bonds. Though these are, of course, present in all metals themselves, they are comparatively unusual in chemical compounds, being limited outside Group IVB to the mercurous ion, arsenic, antimony and an increasing range of compounds in which transition metals are bound either to each other or to other metal atoms.* The stability of metal-to-metal bonds in the organic compounds of Group IVB increases towards the top of the group; Pb–Pb bonds are readily broken, Sn–Sn less so, Ge–Ge still less, until at the top the stability of C–C bonds is the basis for the existence of so many carbon compounds.

* Two or three instances of Ga–Ga and Tl–Tl bonds are known (see pp. 349, 372).

By far the largest-scale manufacture of organometallic compounds concerns this group. Though outside the scope of this book, organic silicon compounds are made on a large scale for the manufacture of silicone polymers: organic tin compounds are much in demand for biocidal and polymer-stabilization purposes, and the biggest organometallic production of all is of tetra-ethyl-lead as an anti-knock agent for petrol. The biggest industrial developments outside this group are in the organic compounds of aluminium, and possibly of manganese.

The group covalency of four makes for a wide range of possible derivatives, and this, coupled with ease of manipulation in comparison with most other types of organometallic compound, has resulted in the preparation of a very large number of organo derivatives. For the most part only representative types are considered in this chapter, along with their main reactions and principal features of interest.

GERMANIUM

Organogermanium compounds have been studied less than their silicon and tin counterparts, and similar large-scale commercial or industrial uses have not been found for them. Most of the compounds known may be regarded (and are named) as derivatives, $R_n GeX_{4-n}$, of germane, with one to four Ge-C bonds, and functional groups or atoms X occupying the remaining valences. Among such derivatives, the halides are valuable intermediates in the preparation of other compounds. Four-covalency is a feature of almost all of these compounds, including derivatives of the higher germanes, in which chains or rings of germanium atoms occur. The association of molecules through bridging alkyl groups, such a feature of many derivatives of elements in the first three Groups of the Periodic Table, is not observed at all with alkyl derivatives of germanium, tin or lead. Association through functional groups, involving co-ordination numbers greater than four, known to occur with a number of tin compounds, has not been demonstrated for germanium. Compounds which may ionize in solution, the alkali metal derivatives, R_3GeM, are known; these, too, are useful intermediates in syntheses. Di-lithium derivatives, R_2GeLi_2, have been detected in solution. Organogermyl groups have been attached to a number of other metals, including magnesium, tin, copper, silver, gold, platinum, iron and manganese.

The organic compounds of germanium are the subject of four recent reviews [1, 2, 3, 4], the third of which [3] supplements an earlier review [5]

[1] M. Dub, *Organometallic Compounds*. Vol. 2. *Organic Compounds of Germanium, Tin and Lead*, Springer-Verlag, Berling–Göttingen–Heidelberg, 1961.

[2] F. Rijken, *Organogermanium Compounds*, Germanium Research Committee, 1960.   [3] D. Quane and R. S. Bottei, *Chem. Rev.*, 1963, **63**, 403.

[4] F. Glockling, *Quart. Rev.*, 1966, **20**, 45.

[5] O. H. Johnson, *Chem. Rev.*, 1951, **48**, 259.

and covers much of the literature to the end of 1962. It contains useful tables of physical properties and spectroscopic data. Glockling's review [4] is a more critical account of the main features of organogermanium chemistry. Characteristic group frequencies in the infrared spectra of many organogermanium compounds are collected in ref. [6].

Tetra-alkyls and -aryls

Several methods are available for the preparation of these [7], but the most useful is the action of a *Grignard reagent* on *germanium tetrachloride*. The replacement of the first one or two chlorine atoms is easy, but an excess of Grignard reagent, or the use of a high-boiling solvent, may be necessary in certain cases (e.g. with bulky groups), to achieve complete substitution. They are stable to air, water, alcohol and dilute acids.

The action of a *dialkylzinc* on *germanium tetrachloride*, which was used to prepare the first organogermanium compound reported (tetra-ethylgermane [8]), is of value in some instances for small-scale preparations. The less reactive *diaryls* of *mercury* substitute only one chlorine; germanium tetrachloride and diphenylmercury at 140° (sealed tube) give phenyltrichlorogermane [9], $PhGeCl_3$. The more reactive *alkyls* or *aryls* of *lithium* are particularly useful and may give better yields of tetra substituted germanes than the Grignard reagents [10]. The Wurtz reaction has been used in the preparation of tetraphenyl- and other germanes [11]. The reaction goes rapidly in ether, e.g.

$$4PhBr + GeCl_4 + 8Na \longrightarrow Ph_4Ge + 4NaCl + 4NaBr$$

Organogermanium halides result from reactions between organic halides and powdered germanium [11a] or copper–germanium mixtures [12, 13, 13a], e.g.

$$MeCl + Cu + Ge \longrightarrow MeGeCl_3 + Me_2GeCl_2$$

The hydrogermylation reaction between, for example, trichloro- or

[6] R. J. Cross and F. Glockling, *J. Organometal. Chem.*, 1965, **3**, 146.

[7] O. H. Johnson, *Inorg. Syntheses*, **5**, 64.

[8] C. Winkler, *J. prakt. Chem.*, 1887, [2], **36**, 177.

[9] L. M. Dennis, W. K. Orndorff and D. L. Tabern, *J. Amer. Chem. Soc.*, 1927, **49**, 2512.

[10] O. H. Johnson and W. H. Nebergall, ibid., 1949, **71**, 1720.

[11] L. M. Dennis, W. K. Orndorff and D. L. Tabern, ibid., 1925, **47**, 2039.

[11a] M. Wieber, C. D. Frohning and M. Schmidt, *J. Organometal. Chem.*, 1966, **6**, 427.

[12] D. F. van de Vondel, ibid., 1965, **3**, 400.

[13] V. F. Mironov and T. K. Gar, *Izvest. Akad. Nauk S.S.S.R.*, 1964, 1887; *Chem. Abs.*, 1965, **62**, 2787.

[13a] K. Moedritzer, *J. Organometal. Chem.*, 1966, **6**, 282; J. J. Zuckerman, *Advances in Inorganic Chemistry and Radiochemistry*, ed. H. J. Emeléus and A. G. Sharpe, 1964, **6**, 383.

tribromo-germane $HGeX_3$ and an alkene or alkyne [14], and exchange reactions between $GeCl_4$ and an organolead [14a] or organotin compound [15, 16] are further routes to organogermanium compounds, particularly those containing only one Ge–C bond.

Germanium tetrachloride may be alkylated in the absence of solvent by aluminium alkyls, but because the formation of $RGeCl_3$ is slow compared with subsequent alkylation stages, the reaction is suitable for the preparation only of the tetra-alkyls R_4Ge [16a]. Di- and poly-germanes $R_{2n+2}Ge_n$ are side products in these reactions.

Tetramethylgermane, Me_4Ge, m.p. $-80°$, b.p. $43.4°$, is conveniently obtained on a laboratory scale by the Grignard reaction, provided that dibutyl ether is used as the solvent [12]. It has also been prepared from dimethylzinc and germanium tetrachloride [17]; any excess of the tetrachloride can be removed with potassium hydroxide, and the yield is quantitative.

$$2Me_2Zn + GeCl_4 \longrightarrow 2ZnCl_2 + Me_4Ge$$

It is monomeric as vapour and liquid and chemically very unreactive. The unsymmetrical molecular vibration [18] associated with Ge–CH_3 stretching is at 602 cm^{-1} (infrared), the symmetrical vibration (Raman) being at 558 cm^{-1}. The proton magnetic resonance spectrum of tetramethylgermane has been recorded [19, 20, 21]; the main interest of these measurements is in connexion with the relative electronegativities of the Group IV elements [19], although their significance in this respect has been questioned [21].

Tetra-ethylgermane, Et_4Ge, m.p. $-90°$, b.p. $163.5°$, is very easily obtained by the Grignard procedure [22], and may also be prepared from *triethylaluminium* and germanium tetrachloride [16a, 23]. Higher alkyls

[14] V. F. Mironov and T. K. Gar, *Izvest. Akad. Nauk S.S.S.R.*, 1965, 291, 755, 855; O. M. Nefedov, S. P. Kolesnikov and N. N. Novitskaya, ibid., p. 579; *Chem. Abs.*, 1965, **62**, 14715; **63**, 624, 2993, 5667; S. P. Kolesnikov and O. M. Nefedov, *Angew. Chem., Internat. Edn.*, 1965, **4**, 352.

[14a] K. Kühlein and W. P. Neumann, *Annalen*, 1967, **702**, 17.

[15] J. G. A. Luijten and F. Rijkens, *Rec. Trav. chim.*, 1964, **83**, 857.

[16] V. F. Mironov and A. L. Kravchenko, *Doklady Akad. Nauk S.S.S.R.*, 1964, **158**, 656; *Zhur. obshchei Khim.*, 1964, **34**, 1356; *Chem. Abs.*, 1964, **61**, 677; 1965, **62**, 580.

[16a] F. Glockling and J. R. C. Light, *J. Chem. Soc. (A)*, 1967, 623.

[17] J. H. Lengel and V. H. Dibeler, *J. Amer. Chem. Soc.*, 1952, **74**, 2683.

[18] H. Siebert, *Z. anorg. Chem.*, 1950, **263**, 82; 1952, **268**, 177; E. R. Lippincott and M. C. Tobin, *J. Amer. Chem. Soc.*, 1953, **75**, 4141.

[19] A. L. Allred and E. G. Rochow, *J. Inorg. Nucl. Chem.*, 1958, **5**, 264, 269; 1961, **20**, 167; C. R. McCoy and A. L. Allred, ibid., 1963, **25**, 1219.

[20] M. P. Brown and D. E. Webster, *J. Phys. Chem.*, 1960, **64**, 698.

[21] I. R. Beattie, *Quart. Rev.*, 1963, **17**, 382; R. S. Drago and N. A. Matwiyoff, *J. Organometal. Chem.*, 1965, **3**, 62.

[22] R. Schwarz and W. Reinhardt, *Chem. Ber.*, 1932, **65**, 1743.

[23] L. I. Zakharkin and O. Yu. Okhlobystin, *Zhur. obshchei Khim.*, 1961, **31**, 3662; *Chem. Abs.*, 1962, **57**, 8593.

are obtained similarly, although rarely in more than 80% yield and often with a complicated mixture of side products. For example, germanium tetrachloride and an excess of isopropylmagnesium chloride give as major products Pr^i_3GeH and Pr^i_3GeCl together with $Pr^i_3GePr^n$, as well as the expected Pr^i_4Ge, itself obtained in only 5–20% yield [23a]. Many other tetra-substituted germanes have been described, mixed alkyls or aryls being prepared from suitable organogermanium halides [3, 24].

Tetraphenylgermane, Ph_4Ge, m.p. 233·4°, from phenylmagnesium bromide and germanium tetrachloride in toluene [25], or, better, tetrahydrofuran, is stable to cold concentrated sulphuric acid, and is sulphonated on warming; it is resistant to boiling alkali and to catalytic hydrogenation conditions (H_2/Ni), [26], and requires particularly vigorous conditions, such as heating with mixed nitric and sulphuric acids, for degradation.

Tetrakispentafluorophenylgermane, $(C_6F_5)_4Ge$, a solid v.p. 760 mm. at 224–230°, and the pentafluorophenylgermanium halides $(C_6F_5)_nGeX_{4-n}$ (n = 2 or 3; X = Cl or Br) have been prepared by reactions between pentafluorophenyl-lithium and germanium halides [27]. The tetrakis compound can also be prepared by the direct reaction between germanium and iodopentafluorophenylbenzene at 325° [27a], and is in several respects even less reactive than tetraphenylgermane. The intensity of the peak assigned to the ion $(C_6F_5)_2^+$ in the mass spectrum of $(C_6F_5)_4Ge$ (it is in fact the base peak) has prompted the suggestion that controlled pyrolysis of the germane would yield octafluorobiphenylene [27b]. Fluorinated germafluorenes are also known [27a, 27c]:

Tetrabenzylgermane, $(PhCH_2)_4Ge$, m.p. 109–110°, from benzyl-magnesium chloride and germanium tetrachloride in xylene, is also relatively

[23a] A. Carrick and F. Glockling, *J. Chem. Soc.* (*A*), 1966, 623.
[24] M. Lesbre and P. Mazerolles, *Compt. rend.*, 1958, **246**, 1708; D. Seyferth, *J. Amer. Chem. Soc.*, 1957, **79**, 2738, J. A. Semlyen, G. R. Walker, R. E. Blofeld and C. S. G. Philipps, *J. Chem. Soc.*, 1964, 4948.
[25] O. H. Johnson and D. M. Harris, *J. Amer. Chem. Soc.*, 1950, **72**, 5564; *Inorg. Syntheses*, **5**, 70, 72, 74, 76.
[26] L. Spialter, G. R. Buell and C. W. Harris, *J. Org. Chem.*, 1965, **30**, 375.
[27] D. E. Fenton and A. G. Massey, *Chem. and Ind.*, 1964, 2100; C. Tamborski, E. J. Soloski and S. M. Dec, *J. Organometal. Chem.*, 1965, **4**, 446; D. E. Fenton, A. G. Massey and D. S. Urch, ibid., 1966, **6**, 352.
[27a] S. C. Cohen, M. L. N. Reddy and A. G. Massey, *Chem. Comm.*, 1967, 451.
[27b] J. M. Miller, *J. Chem. Soc.* (*A*), 1967, 828.
[27c] S. C. Cohen and A. G. Massey, *Tetrahedron Letters*, 1966, 4393.

unreactive. A tetrasulphonic acid derivative has been obtained by direct sulphonation [11]. Free radical bromination of benzylgermanes with N-bromosuccinimide in the presence of benzoyl peroxide involves attack on the methylene groups, giving $PhCBr_2GeR_3$, which can be hydrolysed to the benzoyl derivative $PhCOGeR_3$ [28]. Benzyl-germanium bonds are much more resistant to alkali cleavage than are benzyl-silicon or -tin bonds in analogous compounds [29].

The reaction of tetrabenzylgermane with lithium [30], giving the mono- and di-lithium derivatives $(PhCH_2)_3GeLi$ and $(PhCH_2)_2GeLi_2$, is described below (p. 403).

Many derivatives of phenyl- or benzyl-germanes, $R_3GeC_6H_4X$ or $R_3GeCH_2C_6H_4X$ have been prepared [31], and the relative rates of their hydrolytic [29, 32] or oxidative [33] cleavage reactions have shown the electronic effects of the substituent groups. When attached directly to a benzene ring, groups R_3M (R = Me or Ph; M = Si, Ge, Sn or Pb) appear to *withdraw* electrons, there apparently being some $d_\pi-p_\pi$ bonding between the metals and the aromatic ring [34]. When attached to a *saturated* carbon atom, however, as in the benzyl derivatives $Me_3MCH_2C_6H_4X$ (M = Si or Ge), the trimethylgermyl group *releases* electrons slightly more strongly than does the trimethylsilyl group [33].

Alkenyl- and alkynyl-germanes. Tetravinylgermane, $(CH_2:CH)_4Ge$, b.p. 52–54°/27 mm., and *hexavinyldigermane*, $[(CH_2:CH)_3Ge]_2$, b.p. 55°/0·3 mm., are the products when the vinyl Grignard reagent and germanium tetrachloride are heated for 20 hours in refluxing tetrahydrofuran [35]. Other ways of preparing unsaturated germanes are illustrated by syntheses of particular compounds, e.g. the Wurtz reaction applied to PhCH:CHBr

[28] A. G. Brook, M. A. Quigley, G. J. D. Peddle, N. V. Schwartz and C. M. Warner, *J. Amer. Chem. Soc.*, 1960, **82**, 5102.

[29] R. W. Bott, C. Eaborn and T. W. Swaddle, *J. Chem. Soc.*, 1963, 2342.

[30] R. J. Cross and F. Glockling, ibid., 1964, 4125.

[31] C. Eaborn and K. C. Pande, ibid., 1960, 3200; C. Eaborn, K. Leyshon and K. C. Pande, ibid., p. 3423; R. W. Bott, C. Eaborn and T. Hashimoto, ibid., 1963, 3906; H. Oikawa, *Nippon Kagaku Zasshi*, 1963, **84**, 272, 510; *Chem. Abs.*, 1963, **59**, 14013; 1964, **60**, 395; A. J. Leusink, J. G. Noltes, H. A. Budding and G. J. M. van der Kerk, *Rec. Trav. chim.*, 1964, **83**, 844.

[32] C. Eaborn and K. C. Pande, *J. Chem. Soc.*, 1961, 5082; R. W. Bott, C. Eaborn and D. R. M. Walton. *J. Organometal. Chem.*, 1964, **1**, 420; R. W. Bott, C. Eaborn and P. M. Greasley, *J. Chem. Soc.*, 1964, 4804.

[33] R. W. Bott, C. Eaborn, K. C. Pande and T. W. Swaddle, *J. Chem. Soc.*, 1962, 1217; R. W. Bott, C. Eaborn and D. R. M. Walton, *J. Organometal. Chem.*, 1964, **2**, 154.

[34] H. H. Freedman and T. A. Gosink, 'Current Trends in Organometallic Chemistry', Symposium, Cincinnati, June, 1963, Abstracts, p. 33; M. D. Curtis and A. L. Allred, *J. Amer. Chem. Soc.*, 1965, **87**, 2554; M. T. Ryan and W. L. Lehn, *J. Organometal. Chem.*, 1965, **4**, 455; J. Nagy, J. Reffy, A. Kuszmann-Borbely and K. Pálossy-Becker, ibid., 1967, **7**, 393.

[35] D. Seyferth, *J. Amer. Chem. Soc.*, 1957, **79**, 2738; for propenyl derivatives see D. Seyferth and L. G. Vaughan. *J. Organometal. Chem.*, 1963, **1**, 138.

and $GeCl_4$ leads to both alkenyl and alkynyl products [36]:

$$GeCl_4 + PhCH:CHBr + Na \xrightarrow{C_6H_6} \begin{matrix} 60\% \ (PhC:C)_4Ge, \ m.p. \ 187–188° \\ 17\% \ (PhCH:CH)_4Ge, \ m.p. \ 198–200° \\ + \ some \ [(PhCH:CH)_3Ge]_2, \ m.p. \ 230–232° \end{matrix}$$

For substituted phenylethynylgermanes $XC_6H_4C:CGeR_3$, see ref. [37].

Various germanium acetylides have been prepared recently by the action of the lithium [38], magnesium [39] or sodium [40] acetylide on a germanium halide in ether or tetrahydrofuran. Some of these compounds are explosive – for example, the residues from the preparation of the tetraethynyl compound $(HC:C)_4Ge$, m.p. 91–92°, are liable to detonate violently under friction [40]. In the vibrational spectra of $(HC:C)_4Ge$, $\nu(C:C)$ is 2057 cm^{-1} (Raman) and 2062 cm^{-1} (infrared) [40a].

An alternative route to alkenylgermanes is the abstraction of hydrogen halide from a saturated compound using an amine [41]:

$$Bu_3GeCHBrCH_2Br \xrightarrow[100°]{Et_2NH} Bu_3GeCBr:CH_2 \xrightarrow[150°]{NaNH_2} Bu_3GeC:CH$$

Alkenylgermanes are also obtained when compounds with Ge–H bonds add to acetylenes [14, 41, 42]:

$$Bu_3GeC:CH + Bu_3GeH \xrightarrow{H_2PtCl_6} Bu_3GeCH:CHGeBu_3$$

Perfluorovinylgermanes, e.g. $Ph_3GeCF:CF_2$, m.p. 84°, may be prepared by the Grignard method [43] or by the use of triphenylgermyl-lithium [44]:

$$Ph_3GeLi + Et_3SiCF:CF_2 \rightarrow Et_3SiCF:CFGePh_3, \ m.p. \ 64–66°$$

With iodomethylzinc iodide, vinylgermanes give cyclopropylgermanes [45]:

$$Me_3GeCH:CH_2 + ICH_2ZnI \rightarrow Me_3GeC_3H_5$$

[36] K. H. Birr and D. Kräft, *Z. anorg. Chem.*, 1961, **311**, 235.

[37] C. Eaborn and D. R. M. Walton, *J. Organometal. Chem.*, 1964, **2**, 95; 1965, **4**, 217.

[38] H. Hartmann and K. Meyer, *Naturwiss.*, 1965, **52**, 303; H. Hartmann and M. K. El A'ssar, ibid., p. 304.

[39] S. D. Ibekwe and M. J. Newlands, *J. Chem. Soc.*, 1965, 4608.

[40] W. Davidsohn and M. C. Henry, *J. Organometal. Chem.*, 1966, **5**, 29.

[40a] R. E. Sacher, D. H. Lemmon and F. A. Miller, *Spectrochim. Acta*, 1967, **23A**, 1169.

[41] P. Mazerolles, *Bull. Soc. chim. France*, 1960, 856; V. F. Mironov, A. L. Kravchenko and A. D. Petrov, *Doklady. Akad. Nauk S.S.S.R.*, 1964, **155**, 843; *Chem. Abs.*, 1964, **60**, 15899.

[42] J. G. Noltes and G. J. M. van der Kerk, *Rec. Trav. chim.*, 1962, **81**, 41.

[43] D. Seyferth, T. Wada and G. E. Maciel, *Inorg. Chem.*, 1962, **1**, 232.

[44] D. Seyferth and T. Wada, ibid., p. 78.

[45] D. Seyferth and H. M. Cohen, ibid., p. 913.

A number of halogenated cycloalkenyl- or cycloalkyl-germanes have been prepared by such routes as the following [45a]:

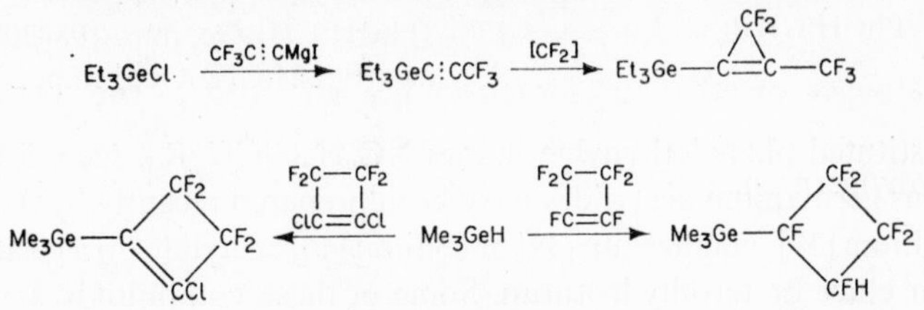

Several σ-bonded *cyclopentadienylgermanes*, e.g. $(C_5H_5)_2GeMe_2$, b.p. 71–73°/4 mm., are known [46], and triphenylgermyl substituted ferrocenes are formed from ferrocenyldisodium and triphenylbromogermane [47].

Heterocyclic compounds of germanium and carbon

Several germanium–carbon ring systems are now known. Cyclobutane, cyclopentane and cyclohexane analogues are readily obtained by the use of e.g. di-Grignard reagents [22, 48]:

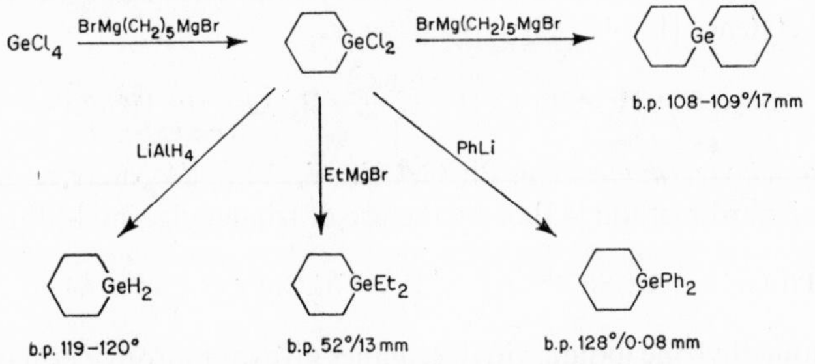

The strained ring of the cyclobutane analogues is cleaved by such reagents as silver nitrate, bromine, hydrogen halides and lithium aluminium hydride [48].

An unsaturated five-membered ring is formed by the reaction between trichlorogermane (as the ether complex, when it behaves as $GeCl_2$) and a

[45a] W. R. Cullen and W. R. Leeder, *Inorg. Chem.* 1966, **5**, 1004; W. R. Cullen and G. E. Styan, *J. Organometal. Chem.*, 1966, **6**, 633.

[46] V. F. Mironov, T. K. Gar and L. A. Leites, *Izvest. Akad. Nauk S.S.S.R.*, 1962, 1387; *Chem. Abs.*, 1963, **58**, 2464; M. Lesbre, P. Mazerolles and G. Manuel, *Compt. rend.*, 1962, **255**, 544; H. P. Fritz and C. G. Kreiter, *J. Organometal. Chem.*, 1965, **4**, 313.

[47] D. Seyferth, H. P. Hofmann, R. Burton and J. F. Helling, *Inorg. Chem.*, 1962, **1**, 227.

[48] P. Mazerolles, *Bull. Soc. chim. France*, 1962, 1907; F. J. Bajer and H. W. Post, *J. Org. Chem.*, 1962, **27**, 1422; P. Mazerolles and J. Dubac, *Compt. rend.*, 1963, **257**, 1103; P. Mazerolles, M. Lesbre and J. Dubac, ibid., 1965, **260**, 2255; P. Mazerolles, J. Dubac and M. Lesbre, *J. Organometal. Chem.*, 1966, **5**, 35.

twofold excess of butadiene [49] at $-50°$:

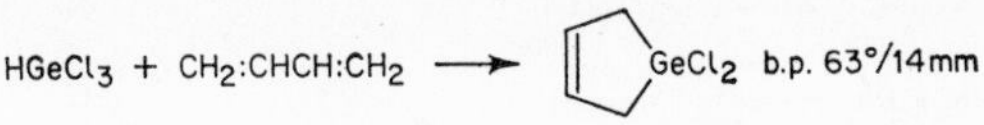

$$HGeCl_3 + CH_2:CHCH:CH_2 \longrightarrow \boxed{\quad} GeCl_2 \text{ b.p. } 63°/14mm$$

In the absence of ether, trichlorogermane adds 1,4 to the diene. Compounds with tin also in the ring result from addition of diphenylstannane to a divinylgermane [50]:

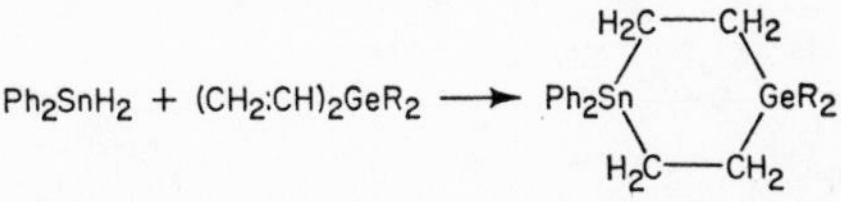

$$Ph_2SnH_2 + (CH_2:CH)_2GeR_2 \longrightarrow \underset{\text{Ph}_2\text{Sn}}{\overset{H_2C—CH_2}{\quad}} \underset{H_2C—CH_2}{GeR_2}$$

Unsaturated ring compounds may also be obtained by catalytic de-hydrogenation of the appropriate saturated compound [51]; thus germanacyclopentenes and germanacyclopentadienes are formed when germanacyclopentanes are passed over 10% platinum–carbon or a mixed oxide catalyst at 600°. A more direct route to the diene or germanole ring uses the di-lithium derivative of a butadiene (see also p. 59) [52]:

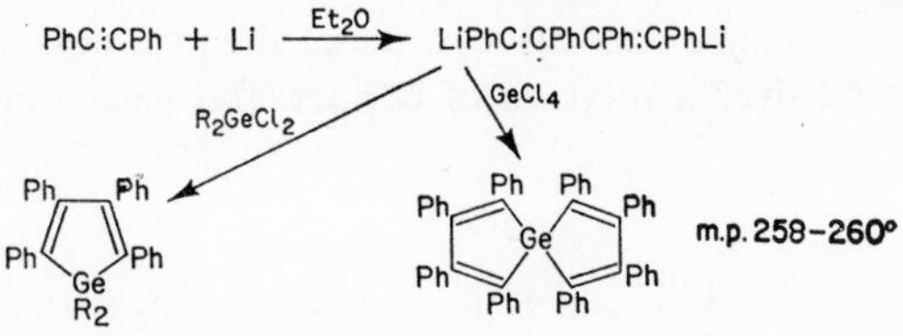

$$PhC:CPh + Li \xrightarrow{\text{Et}_2\text{O}} LiPhC:CPhCPh:CPhLi$$

m.p. 258–260°

Analogues of 5,10-dihydroacridine have been prepared similarly [53]:

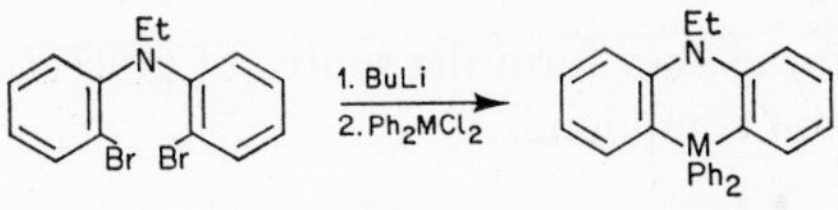

M = Si, Ge, Sn, Pb

Unsaturated compounds with *two* germanium atoms in a six-membered ring have been prepared recently. Germanium di-iodide and diphenyl-

[49] V. F. Mironov and T. K. Gar, *Izvest. Akad. Nauk S.S.S.R.*, 1963, 578; *Doklady Akad. Nauk S.S.S.R.*, 1963, **152**, 1111; O. M. Nefedov, S. P. Kolesnikov, A. S. Khachaturov and A. D. Petrov, ibid., 1964, **154**, 1389; *Chem. Abs.*, 1963, **59**, 3941; 1964, **60**, 1786, 12039.

[50] M. C. Henry and J. G. Noltes, *J. Amer. Chem. Soc.*, 1960, **82**, 561.

[51] O. M. Nefedov and M. N. Manakov, *Izvest. Akad. Nauk S.S.S.R.*, 1963, 769; *Chem. Abs.*, 1963, **59**, 8780.

[52] F. C. Leavitt, T. A. Manuel and F. Johnson, *J. Amer. Chem. Soc.*, 1959, **81**, 3163; F. C. Leavitt, T. A. Manuel, F. Johnson, L. U. Matternas and D. S. Lehman, ibid., 1960, **82**, 5099.

[53] H. Gilman and E. A. Zuech, ibid., 1960, **82**, 2522.

acetylene react at 200° to form a derivative of 1,4-digermin in 30% yield [54]:

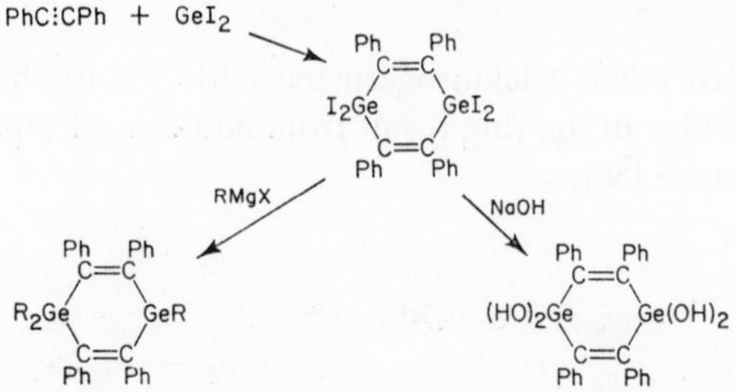

At first these compounds were assigned an unsaturated three-membered ring structure and called germirenes, apparently because of difficulties with molecular weight determinations. Their dimeric nature has, however, been confirmed by a mass spectroscopic investigation [55], and by an X-ray crystallographic and electron-diffraction study of two derivatives [56], which showed the ring to be planar, with bond angles CGeC 113 ± 4°, GeCC 123 ± 2° in the case of the diphenyl derivative.

A *trigermacyclohexane* derivative is one of the products when methylene chloride is passed over a mixture of copper and germanium powders at 370–390° [13]:

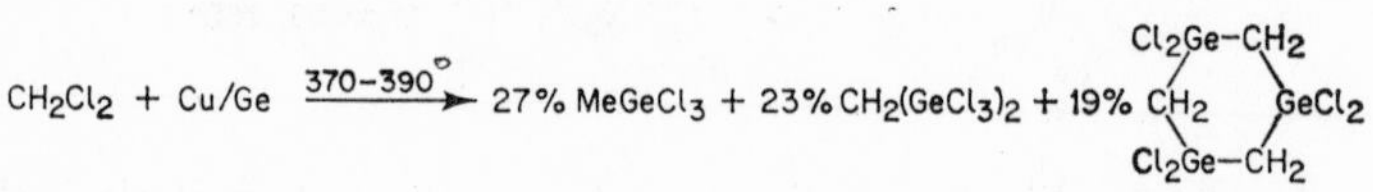

Halogen derivatives

These are important as they form the source of practically all other types of organogermanium compounds.

The Monohalides

The monobromides are best obtained by the action of bromine on the tetra-alkyls or -aryls. Other mono-halo derivatives are conveniently pre-

[54] M. E. Vol'pin, Yu. D. Koreshkov, V. G. Dulova and D. N. Kursanov, *Tetrahedron*, 1962, **18**, 107; M. E. Vol'pin and D. N. Kursanov, *Zhur. obschei Khim.*, 1962, **32**, 1455; *Chem. Abs.*, 1963, **58**, 9111; M. E. Vol'pin, V. G. Dulova and D. N. Kursanov, *Izvest. Akad. Nauk, S.S.S.R.*, 1963, 727; L. A. Leites, V. G. Dulova and M. E. Vol'pin, ibid., p. 731; *Chem. Abs.*, 1963, **59**, 10104.

[55] F. Johnson and R. S. Gohlke, *Tetrahedron Letters*, 1962, 1291; R. West and R. E. Bailey, *J. Amer. Chem. Soc.*, 1963, **85**, 2871; F. Johnson, R. S. Gohlke and W. A. Nasutavicus, *J. Organometal. Chem.*, 1965, **3**, 233.

[56] M. E. Vol'pin, Yu. T. Struchkov, L. U. Vilkov, V. S. Mastryukov, V. G. Dulova and D. N. Kursanov, *Izvest. Akad. Nauk S.S.S.R.*, 1963, 2067; *Chem. Abs.*, 1964, **60**, 5532; M. E. Vol'pin, V. G. Dulova, Yu. T. Struchkov, N. K. Bokiy and D. N. Kursanov, *J. Organometal. Chem.*, 1967, **8**, 87.

pared indirectly through the bromide. The choice of solvent is important for bromination. Germanium is intermediate between silicon and tin in the reactivity of its tetra-alkyls and -aryls to halogen, since silicon reacts only with difficulty and tin very easily. Germanium differs from tin in that mixed alkyl halides are not formed readily by uncatalysed rearrangement between the tetra-alkyls and tetrahalides [57], though phenyltrichlorogermane can be made this way. Rearrangement is catalysed by *aluminium halides* or *germanium(II) halides* [57a]. Mixtures of tetrabutylgermane and germanium tetrachloride equilibrate when heated 4–6 hours at 120–200° in Carius tubes in the presence of aluminium chloride; tributylchlorogermane and dibutyldichlorogermane may be prepared in over 80% yield in this way [58]:

$$3Bu_4Ge + GeCl_4 \xrightarrow{AlCl_3} 4Bu_3GeCl$$

Such redistribution reactions occur more readily with the bromides than with the chlorides [59]. Aluminium halides also catalyse the direct bromination or iodination of tetra-alkylgermanes [24].

Several special methods for the preparation of halogen derivatives are given under the compounds for which they are of particular use.

Trimethylbromogermane, Me_3GeBr, m.p. −25°, b.p. 113·7°, from tetramethylgermane and hydrogen bromide in the presence of aluminium bromide [25, 60],

$$Me_4Ge + HBr \xrightarrow{AlBr_3} Me_3GeBr + CH_4$$

or from the slow (several weeks at 20°) reaction between tetramethylgermane and bromine, is readily hydrolysed by water (unlike the tetramethyl, which is not hydrolysed by either concentrated sodium hydroxide or concentrated sulphuric acid) to trimethylgermanol, Me_3GeOH (isolated as the oxide $(Me_3Ge)_2O$).

Trimethylchlorogermane, Me_3GeCl, m.p. −14°, b.p. 97°, is obtained in the form of an azeotrope with ether when prepared from dimethyldichlorogermane and a methyl Grignard or lithium reagent, but may be separated chromatographically [61]. It can also be prepared by a method similar to

[57] G. M. Burch and J. R. Van Wazer, *J. Chem. Soc. (A)*, 1966, 586.
[57a] F. Rijkens, E. J. Bulten, W. Drenth and G. J. M. van der Kerk, *Rec. Trav. chim.*, 1966, **85**, 1223.
[58] G. T. M. van der Kerk, F. Rijkens and M. J. Janssen, ibid., 1962, **81**, 764; F. Rijkens and G. J. M. van der Kerk, ibid., 1964, **83**, 723; J. G. A. Luijten and F. Rijkens, ibid., p. 857.
[59] P. Mazerolles, *Compt. rend.*, 1960, **251**, 2041; *Bull. Soc. chim. France*, 1961, 1911; G. A. Razuvaev, N. S. Vyazankin, O. S. D'yachkovskaya, I. G. Kiseleva and Yu. I. Dergunov, *Zhur. obschei Khim.*, 1961, **31**, 4056; *Chem. Abs.*, 1962, **57**, 9875.
[60] L. M. Dennis and W. I. Patnode, *J. Amer. Chem. Soc.*, 1930, **52**, 2779.
[61] M. Schmidt and I. Ruidisch, *Z. anorg. Chem.*, 1961, **311**, 331.

that used for the bromide, from Me₄Ge and HCl in the presence of AlCl₃ [12]. For nuclear magnetic resonance and infrared spectroscopic data on these and related trimethylgermyl compounds, see refs [62] and [62a] respectively.

Triethylbromogermane, Et₃GeBr, b.p. 190·9°, may be prepared by the bromination of tetra-ethylgermane in ethyl bromide [63],

$$Et_4Ge + Br_2 \longrightarrow Et_3GeBr + EtBr$$

or by the reaction between tetra-ethylgermane and germanium tetra-bromide in the presence of aluminium bromide [59]. It is readily hydrolysed by water or aqueous alkali, giving bis-triethylgermanium oxide:

$$2Et_3GeBr + 2KOH \longrightarrow (Et_3Ge)_2O + 2KBr + H_2O$$

This substance, conveniently purified by distillation, b.p. 254°, serves as a very useful source of other triethylgermanium compounds.

Triethylfluorogermane, Et₃GeF, b.p. 149°, from the above oxide and hydrofluoric acid, is more resistant to hydrolysis than the other halides.

Triethylchlorogermane, Et₃GeCl, b.p. 176°, and *triethyliodogermane* [24], Et₃GeI, b.p. 212°, are prepared similarly. The reaction between bis-triethylgermanium oxide and sulphuric acid is reversible, the *sulphate*, (Et₃Ge)₂SO₄, b.p. 165°/3 mm., being formed in large proportion when the acid is more than 11 molar [64]. Ref. [64a] is a useful source of proton magnetic resonance and infrared spectroscopic data for ethylgermanium halides, hydrides and oxides Et$_n$GeX$_{4-n}$ (n = 1, 2, 3 or 4).

For the *tri-n-hexyl* series see ref. [65].

Triphenylbromogermane, Ph₃GeBr, m.p. 138·5°, is prepared by direct bromination of tetraphenylgermane in boiling ethylene dibromide [25, 60], or from the tetraphenyl and hydrogen bromide in chloroform at room temperature [66]. Like the triethyl compound, it is converted into bis-triphenylgermanium oxide by aqueous alkali, and the other halogen deriva-tives may be obtained by the action of the halogen hydracids on the oxide. The ease of hydrolysis of the triphenylhalogermanes increases in the order F < Cl < Br < I, the fluoride being by far the least readily hydrolysed. Kinetic studies of the rapid hydrolyses of triphenylchlorogermane and triphenylchlorosilane and some derivatives show the silanes to be more

[62] H. Schmidbaur and I. Ruidisch, *Inorg. Chem.*, 1964, **3**, 599.

[62a] D. F. van de Vondel and G. P. van der Kelen, *Bull. Soc. chim. Belges*, 1965, **74**, 453, 467.

[63] C. A. Kraus and E. A. Flood, *J. Amer. Chem. Soc.*, 1932, **54**, 1635; N. S. Vyazan-kin, E. N. Gladyshev, S. P. Korneva and G. A. Razuvaev, *Zhur. obschei Khim.*, 1964, **34**, 1645; *Chem. Abs.*, 1964, **61**, 5680.

[64] H. H. Anderson, *J. Amer. Chem. Soc.*, 1950, **72**, 194.

[64a] K. M. Mackay and R. Watt, *J. Organometal. Chem.*, 1966, **6**, 336.

[65] R. Fuchs and H. Gilman, *J. Org. Chem.*, 1958, **23**, 911.

[66] C. A. Kraus and H. S. Nutting, *J. Amer. Chem. Soc.*, 1932, **54**, 1622.

rapidly hydrolysed than the germanes, apparently because the five-co-ordinate transition state in the reaction is more stabilized by d-orbital participation at silicon than at germanium, a silicon–oxygen bond being stronger and more easily formed than a germanium–oxygen bond [67].

The Dihalides

These again are best obtained through the dibromides, with certain exceptions where direct preparation from the metal and an alkyl halide is possible.

Dimethyldichlorogermane, Me_2GeCl_2, m.p. $-22°$, b.p. 124°, can be prepared by the direct reaction between germanium and methyl chloride at 320° or above, copper being present as catalyst [68]; some *methyltrichloro-germane*, $MeGeCl_3$, b.p. 111°, is also formed. This is analogous to the well-known process for obtaining methylchlorosilanes, essential inter-mediates in the manufacture of silicone polymers. The reaction also serves to prepare diethyldichlorogermane, m.p. 37–39°, b.p. 175°, and diphenyl-dichlorogermane, m.p. 9°, but the use of n-propyl chloride [69] gives mainly n-propyltrichlorogermane, n.p. 167°. The hydrolysis of dimethyl-dichlorogermane does not produce polymers analogous to the silicones; it is reversible in aqueous solution [68]:

$$Me_2GeCl_2 + 2H_2O \rightleftharpoons Me_2Ge(OH)_2 + 2HCl$$

The oxide, $(Me_2GeO)_4$, is described below.

Diethyldibromogermane may be prepared from tetra-ethylgermane and tetrabromogermane in the presence of aluminium bromide [59]. The action of bromine on tetra-ethylgermane or triethylbromogermane cannot be used, since attempts to introduce a second bromine atom result in the elimination of hydrogen bromide instead of ethyl bromide. However, the chloride, Et_3GeCl, and particularly the fluoride, Et_3GeF, react readily with bromine; the crude product is best hydrolysed to the oxide, Et_2GeO, which with concentrated hydrobromic acid gives the dibromide [70]. The chloride and iodide may be obtained similarly.

Another ingenious method utilizes the facts (*a*) that two atoms of bromine can be introduced into tetraphenylgermane, and (*b*) that phenyl groups are split off (as bromobenzene) by bromine more readily than ethyl groups when both are present together. Thus bromination of diethyl-diphenylgermane produces diethyldibromogermane [70]:

$$Ph_4Ge \xrightarrow{Br_2} Ph_2GeBr_2 \xrightarrow{EtMgBr} Ph_2GeEt_2 \xrightarrow{Br_2} Et_2GeBr_2$$

[67] J. R. Chipperfield and R. H. Prince, *Proc. Chem. Soc.*, 1960, 385; *J. Chem. Soc.*, 1963, 3567.

[68] E. G. Rochow, *J. Amer. Chem. Soc.*, 1947, **69**, 1729; 1948, **70**, 1801.

[69] E. G. Rochow, R. Didtschenko and R. C. West, ibid., 1951, **73**, 5486.

[70] A. E. Flood, ibid., 1932, **54**, 1663.

Di-n-propyldifluoro- (b.p. 183°), *dichloro-* (b.p. 210°), *dibromo-* (b.p. 241°), and *di-iodo-* (b.p. 277°) *-germane* [71] have been prepared by the bromination of tri-n-propylfluorogermane and treatment of the di-n-propylgermanium oxide with the appropriate acid. For the *di-n-butyl* series see ref. [72].

Diphenyldibromogermane, Ph_2GeBr_2, b.p. 120°/0·007 mm., is formed by the continued bromination of the triphenylmonobromo compound in boiling ethylene dibromide, but some tribromo product is also formed and is not easy to separate. However, the crude dibromo derivative may be converted into *diphenyldichlorogermane*, Ph_2GeCl_2, by means of concentrated hydrochloric acid, and this can be purified by distillation and reconverted into dibromide by concentrated hydrobromic acid. The *difluoro* derivative is obtained through the oxide and hydrofluoric acid [73]. Mixed di- and tri-halides can also be purified on a small scale by reduction to the hydrides with lithium aluminium hydride, fractionation, followed by an easy bromination [25].

The Trihalides

These have not for the most part been obtained by halogenation of lower halides, but by reactions involving germanium(II) compounds.

Methyl- and n-propyltrichlorogermane have already been mentioned as products of the action of methyl and n-propyl chloride on powdered germanium or a germanium–copper mixture. n-Propyltrichlorogermane can be prepared by addition of n-propyl-lithium to ethereal germanium tetrachloride [74]. Organogermanium trihalides are also accessible through reactions between tetrahalides and lead alkyls or aryls, which proceed to the dialkyl or diaryl stage only at elevated temperatures [14a]:

$$GeCl_4 + R_4Pb \longrightarrow RGeCl_3 + R_3PbCl \xrightarrow{\Delta} R_2GeCl_2 + R_2PbCl_2$$

Ethyltrichlorogermane, $EtGeCl_3$, b.p. 144°, has been prepared by heating caesium germanium(II) chloride with ethyl iodide at 110° in a sealed tube [75]. It is easily hydrolysed to a polymeric oxide which can be reconverted into the trichloride by concentrated hydrochloric acid followed by ether extraction.

Ethyltribromogermane, $EtGeBr_3$, b.p. 200°, is obtained from the oxide and concentrated hydrobromic acid with the addition of phosphoric oxide [76].

[71] H. H. Anderson, *J. Amer. Chem. Soc.*, 1952, **74**, 2370.
[72] Idem, ibid., 1961, **83**, 547.
[73] C. A. Kraus and C. L. Brown, ibid., 1930, **52**, 3690.
[74] O. H. Johnson and L. V. Jones, *J. Org. Chem.*, 1952, **17**, 1172.
[75] A. Tchakirian, *Ann. Chim.*, 1939, 11È, **12**, 415.
[76] A. E. Flood, *J. Amer. Chem. Soc.*, 1933, **55**, 4935.

Ethyltri-iodogermane, EtGeI$_3$, b.p. 281°, is best prepared by the addition of ethyl iodide to germanium(II) iodide at 110° in a sealed tube:

$$GeI_2 + EtI \longrightarrow EtGeI_3$$

It is a lemon-yellow liquid, becoming deep red above 250°.

Methyltri-iodogermane [77], m.p. 48·5°, and other tri-iodogermanes [78] are similarly obtained.

Methylene-bis-trichlorogermane, CH$_2$(GeCl$_3$)$_2$, b.p. 110°/18 mm., which is one of the products when methylene chloride is passed over a hot germanium–copper mixture [13], can also be prepared from methylene iodide and caesium germanium(II) chloride [77]. *Allyltribromogermane* [79], CH$_2$:CHCH$_2$GeBr$_3$, b.p. 72°/7 mm., is formed when allyl bromide is passed over a mixture of germanium and copper at 300°.

Butyltrichlorogermane, BuGeCl$_3$, is conveniently prepared by the action of tetrabutyltin on germanium tetrachloride [15].

Phenyltrichlorogermane, PhGeCl$_3$, b.p. 105–106°/12 mm., results from the action of iodobenzene either on CsGeCl$_3$ [75] or on GeCl$_4$ in the presence of copper powder [80], or when tetraphenylgermane is heated with germanium tetrachloride [81] at 210–290° (or at lower temperatures in the presence of AlCl$_3$ [58]), or from the mild phenylation of germanium tetrachloride with diphenylmercury [9] at 140°.

Alkylgermanes with halogenated side chains

The alkyl group of alkyltrichlorogermanes is chlorinated preferentially at the β-position using sulphuryl chloride in the presence of benzoyl peroxide [82]. *β-Chloroethyltrichlorogermane*, Cl(CH$_2$)$_2$GeCl$_3$, prepared thus evolves ethylene when treated with alkali [83]. Methyltrichlorogermane, MeGeCl$_3$, is not chlorinated by sulphuryl chloride, but photochlorination at 150° gives a mixture of ClCH$_2$GeCl$_3$ (18·5%), Cl$_2$CHGeCl$_3$ (43%) and Cl$_3$CGeCl$_3$ (trace) [82, 84]. *Monochloromethyl* derivatives of germanium are also accessible through the action of diazomethane on a chloro-

[77] E. A. Flood, K. L. Godfrey and L. S. Foster, *Inorganic Syntheses*, 1950, **3**, 64.
[78] M. Lesbre, P. Mazerolles and G. Manuel, *Compt. rend.*, 1963, **257**, 2303.
[79] V. F. Mironov, N. G. Dzhurinskaya and A. D. Petrov, *Izvest. Akad. Nauk S.S.S.R.*, 1961, 2095; *Chem. Abs.*, 1962, **56**, 10176.
[80] V. F. Mironov and N. S. Fedotov, *Zhur. obshchei Khim.*, 1964, **34**, 4122; *Chem. Abs.*, 1965, **62**, 9163.
[81] R. Schwarz and E. Schmeisser, *Ber.*, 1936, **69**, 579.
[82] V. F. Mironov, Yu. P. Egorov and A. D. Petrov, *Izvest. Akad. Nauk S.S.S.R.*, 1959, 1400; Eng. Trans., 1351; A. D. Petrov, V. F. Mironov and I. E. Golgy, *Izvest. Akad. Nauk S.S.S.R.*, 1956, 1146; Eng. Trans., 1169.
[83] V. F. Mironov and N. G. Dzhurinskaya, ibid., 1963, 75; *Chem. Abs.*, 1963, **58**, 10225.
[84] V. A. Ponomarenko and G. Ya. Vzenkova, ibid., 1957, 994; Eng. Trans., 1020.

germane in the presence of copper powder [85], e.g.

$$Ph_2GeCl_2 + CH_2N_2 \longrightarrow Ph_2GeClCH_2Cl$$

The chlorine of Me_3GeCH_2Cl is readily replaced by iodine or alkoxy in reactions with I^- or OR^- which are believed to proceed via nucleophilic attack on the metal [85a]:

Dihalomethyl derivatives result from the action of a trihalomethyl-mercurial on a germanium hydride [86] at 80°:

$$PhHgCBr_3 + R_3GeH \longrightarrow R_3GeCHBr_2 + PhHgBr$$

Trifluoromethyltri-iodogermane, F_3CGeI_3, b.p. $42°/10^{-3}$ mm., like its methyl analogue, is obtained by an autoclave reaction between trifluoro-methyl iodide and germanium di-iodide during 10 days at 130–135°. In contrast to its action on hexamethyldistannane, trifluoromethyl iodide does not cleave hexamethyldigermane [87].

Organogermanium pseudohalides

Organogermanium halides form organogermanium cyanides when treated with silver cyanide [88], e.g.

$$Me_3GeCl + AgCN \longrightarrow Me_3GeCN, \text{ m.p. } 38–38·5°$$

In the crystal, trimethylgermanium cyanide molecules have the expected tetrahedral geometry [88a] (contrast polymeric Me_3SnCN, with trigonal bipyramidal co-ordination about tin [88b]) but the alignment of the molecules in Me_3GeCN is based on linear $\cdots Ge-C\equiv N \cdots Ge-C\equiv N \cdots$ chains.

Cyanates can be prepared using AgCNO [89]. Alternative preparations of pseudohalides use the action of an acid on a germanium oxide [90] or of a mercuric salt on a hydride [72]. Thiocyanates result when the cyanides are

[85] K. Kramer and N. Wright, *Chem. Ber.*, 1963, **96**, 1877; V. F. Mironov and A. L. Kravchenko, *Izvest. Akad. Nauk S.S.S.R.*, 1963, 1563; *Chem. Abs.*, 1963, **59**, 15300.

[85a] R. W. Bott, C. Eaborn and T. W. Swaddle, *J. Organometal. Chem.*, 1966, **5**, 233.

[86] D. Seyferth and J. M. Burlitch, *J. Amer. Chem. Soc.*, 1963, **85**, 2667.

[87] H. C. Clark and C. J. Willis, *Proc. Chem. Soc.*, 1960, 282; *J. Amer. Chem. Soc.*, 1962, **84**, 898.

[88] H. H. Anderson, *J. Amer. Chem. Soc.*, 1953, **75**, 1576; D. Seyferth and N. Kahlen, *J. Org. Chem.*, 1960, **25**, 809.

[88a] E. O. Schlemper and D. Britton, *Inorg. Chem.*, 1966, **5**, 511.

[88b] Idem., ibid., p. 507.

[89] W. Beck and E. Schuierer, *Chem. Ber.*, 1964, **97**, 3517.

[90] H. H. Anderson, *J. Amer. Chem. Soc.*, 1951, **73**, 5439.

heated to 175–180° with sulphur [88]. Azides such as Me_3GeN_3, b.p. 183°, and $Me_2Ge(N_3)_2$, b.p. 44°/2 mm., have been prepared by the action of sodium azide on the chloride [91, 92]. They are readily hydrolysed, and with phosphines, arsines or stibines lose nitrogen to form compounds $R_nGe(N:YR'_3)_{4-n}$ (Y = P, As or Sb) [93]. The azides form adducts, e.g. Ph_3GeN_3,BBr_3, in which the α-nitrogen atom is believed to be the donor site [92].

The isoelectronic and isostructural relationship between compounds such as $R_3GeN:PR'_3$ and siloxanes $R_3SiOSiR'_3$, or between phosphine-alkylenes $(R_3Ge)_2C:PR'_3$ and silylamines $(R_3Si)_2NSiR'_3$ has prompted the preparation and study of a number of such compounds recently (see e.g., [93a]).

Infrared spectroscopic studies on pseudohalides of silicon, germanium, tin and lead are reported in [93b]. Pseudohalides of Group IIIB and IVB elements were reviewed in 1966 [93c].

Oxides and hydroxides

These all result from the hydrolysis of the corresponding halides (or the amines or imines, see below). As with the alkyl chlorosilanes, the complexity of the hydrolysis product greatly increases with the number of halogen atoms present. Mono-halo derivatives give simple monomeric *oxides*, of the type $(R_3Ge)_2O$. The *ethyl* derivative has already been mentioned. The oxides, which can be purified by distillation, are very useful for the preparation not only of halides but of derivatives of other acids, e.g. the acetate [94],

$$(Et_3Ge)_2O + 2MeCO_2H \rightarrow H_2O + 2Et_3GeO \cdot COMe, \text{ b.p. } 190°$$

The trialkyl hydroxides are, no doubt, the primary products of hydrolysis of the monohalides, but condense to the oxides too rapidly to be isolated unless the alkyl groups are comparatively bulky, as in the case of tri-isopropylgermanol [95], Pr^i_3GeOH, b.p. 216°.

Bis-triphenylgermanium oxide, $(Ph_3Ge)_2O$, m.p. 184°, is produced by hydrolysing triphenylbromogermane with alcoholic silver nitrate [96]. In

[91] I. Ruidisch and M. Schmidt, *J. Organometal. Chem.*, 1964, **1**, 493.
[92] J. S. Thayer and R. West, *Inorg. Chem.*, 1964, **3**, 889; 1965, **4**, 114.
[93] R. M. Washburn and R. A. Baldwin, U.S.P. 3,112,331, 26 Nov. 1963; *Chem. Abs.*, 1964, **60**, 5554.
[93a] H. Schmidbaur and W. Tronich, *Chem. Ber.*, 1967, **100**, 1032.
[93b] J. S. Thayer and D. P. Strommen, *J. Organometal. Chem.*, 1966, **5**, 383.
[93c] M. F. Lappert and H. Pyszora, *Advances in Inorganic Chemistry and Radiochemistry*, ed. H. J. Emeléus and A G. Sharpe, Academic Press, 1966, **9**, 133. See also J. S. Thayer and R. West, *Advances in Organometal. Chem.*, 1967, **5**, 169.
[94] H. H. Anderson, *J. Amer. Chem. Soc.*, 1950, **72**, 2089.
[95] Idem, ibid., 1953, **75**, 814.
[96] G. T. Morgan and H. D. K. Drew, *J. Chem. Soc.*, 1925, 1760.

this instance the hydroxide is relatively stable and has been obtained by an indirect method [97]. The oxide is cleaved by sodium in liquid ammonia:

$$(Ph_3Ge)_2O + 2Na \longrightarrow Ph_3GeNa + Ph_3GeONa$$

Triphenylgermylsodium is oxidized in liquid ammonia by molecular oxygen, the product Ph_3GeONa being remarkably soluble in benzene. Hydrolysis of the benzene solution affords triphenylgermanol, Ph_3GeOH, m.p. 134·2°, which crystallizes from benzene with solvent of crystallization, but solvent-free from light petroleum. It loses water rapidly above the melting point, forming the oxide [98].

Lithium derivatives of germanols may be prepared by the action of methyl-lithium on bis-trialkylgermanium oxides [99, 100]:

$$(Me_3Ge)_2O + MeLi \xrightarrow{Et_2O} Me_4Ge + Me_3GeOLi$$

As this method effectively involves the loss of half the germanium, a preferred method utilizes dimethylgermanium oxide [100]:

$$(Me_2GeO)_4 + 4MeLi \longrightarrow 4Me_3GeOLi$$

The product, which can be purified by sublimation, has been used to prepare the mixed oxide $Me_3GeOSnMe_3$.

The *diols* of germanium, from the hydrolysis of dihalides, lose water even more readily than the germanols, but owing to the reluctance of heavier elements to form $p_\pi\text{-}p_\pi$ double bonds, the monomeric oxides $R_2Ge{=}O$ do not exist but polymerize either to low cyclic polymers or high linear polymers.

Dimethylgermanium oxide, $(Me_2GeO)_4$, m.p. 133·4°, b.p. 211°, has been prepared by hydrolysis of the sulphide (see below) with boiling dilute sulphuric acid or by alkaline hydrolysis of the dichloride [68]. *Tetrameric* in camphor, it is recovered in a highly polymeric form on evaporation of its aqueous solution which itself contains tetrahedral $Me_2Ge(OH)_2$ as revealed by Raman spectroscopy [100a]. A third *trimeric* form [101] can be obtained by heating either of the other isomers under vacuum to 210–220°.

Diethylgermanium oxide, $(Et_2GeO)_n$, exists in two forms [64, 70]. When prepared by shaking diethyldichlorogermane with aqueous sodium hydroxide, followed by extraction into pentane, drying with lime, and distillation, it is a colourless solid, m.p. 26·6–27·6°, b.p. 129°/3 mm., 291°/762

[97] C. A. Kraus and S. L. Foster, *J. Amer. Chem. Soc.*, 1927, **49**, 457.
[98] N. A. Matwiyoff and R. S. Drago, *J. Organometal. Chem.*, 1965, **3**, 393.
[99] D. Seyferth and D. L. Alleston, *Inorg. Chem.*, 1963, **2**, 418.
[100] I. Ruidisch and M. Schmidt, *Angew. Chem. Internat. Edn.*, 1963, **2**, 328; *Chem. Ber.*, 1963, **96**, 821.
[100a] R. Tobias and S. Hutcheson, *J. Organometal. Chem.*, 1966, **6**, 535.
[101] M. P. Brown and E. G. Rochow, *J. Amer. Chem. Soc.*, 1960, **82**, 4166; K. Moedritzer, *J. Organometal. Chem.*, 1966, **5**, 254.

mm. It appears to be tetrameric in camphor, though earlier experiments (cryoscopic in benzene) indicated a trimer. This form is unstable at room temperature, changing slowly to a white solid of amorphous appearance, insoluble in water, liquid ammonia and organic solvents, which melts at about 175° when heated quickly. The change is catalysed by moisture. The amorphous polymeric form liquefies slowly when heated to 120°, reverting to the state of lower polymerization. With sulphuric acid a dimeric *sulphate*, m.p. 115·5–116·5°, is obtained, whose constitution is probably similar to that of the tetrameric oxide [64].

Sulphate

Oxide

Di-n-propylgermanium oxide, $[(C_3H_7)_2GeO]_3$, from the difluoride and aqueous sodium hydroxide, also occurs in two forms; the trimeric isomer (m.p. 5·8°) slowly changes to a white solid which on melting at about 153° reverts to the trimeric form [71]. The *sulphate*, m.p. 129°, is again dimeric. Treatment with acetic anhydride gives the *diacetate*, m.p. 35·6°, b.p. 244·6°:

$$Pr^n_2GeO + (MeCO)_2O \rightarrow Pr^n_2Ge(O \cdot COMe)_2$$

Diphenylgermanium oxide, $(Ph_2GeO)_n$, shows a similar isomerism to that of the dimethyl compound. An insoluble white powder, evidently highly polymeric, when obtained by the basic hydrolysis of a dihalide, it may be converted into a tetrameric form by the action of more base, or into a trimeric form on vacuum distillation [73, 102].

The *triols*, from the trihalides, all dehydrate immediately to insoluble polymeric solids, which, however, not only dissolve in acids like the oxides previously considered but also in alkalis from which they are re-precipitated by carbon dioxide [8]. The composition of the polymers generally corresponds to that of the anhydride $(RGeO)_2O$, of the hypo-thetical germanoic acid $RGeO_2H$ analogous, in formula only, to RCO_2H.

Methylgermanetriol $MeGe(OH)_3$ differs from other members of the series in that it apparently exists in solution, the hydrolysis of methyl-trichlorogermane being reversible [75]. The *ethyl, phenyl* and various *aryl* germanium oxides are all polymeric with no definite melting point.

[102] W. Metlesics and H. Zeiss, *J. Amer. Chem. Soc.*, 1960, **82**, 3324.

Other organogermanium–oxygen compounds

Organogermanium alkoxides

Organogermanium hydrides react with carbonyl compounds [103], alcohols or phenols [104] in the presence of copper powder to form alkoxides:

$$R_3GeH + R'R''CO \rightarrow R_3GeOCHR'R''$$
$$R_3GeH + R'OH \rightarrow R_3GeOR' + H_2$$

Alkoxygermanes may also be prepared from germanium oxides and alcohols or from chlorogermanes and sodium alkoxide or the appropriate alcohol, in the latter case with ammonia or pyridine to take up the hydrogen chloride liberated [3, 104a]. The related siloxy-germanes of formula $(R_3SiO)_nGeR'_{4-n}$ are prepared by the action of an alkali metal siloxide on the appropriate organogermanium halide [105]. Similar reactions have been used to prepare germoxanes $(Me_2MOGeMe_3)_2$ of aluminium, gallium and indium, all of which are dimeric [105a]:

$$Me_2GaCl + LiOGeMe_3 \rightarrow (Me_2GaOGeMe_3)_2$$
$$Ph_3Ga + Ph_3GeOH \rightarrow (Ph_3GeOGaPh_2)_2$$

Alkylalkoxygermanes are cleaved at the Ge–O bond by a variety of reagents including hydrogen iodide, lithium aluminium hydride and formic and acetic acids. The alkoxy group is readily exchanged for halogen in mixtures of Me_2GeX_2 and $Me_2Ge(OMe)_2$, which afford mixed halide alkoxides $Me_2GeX(OMe)$ [105b]. Such scrambling reactions are readily followed by proton magnetic resonance spectroscopy, which has revealed the formation of chain species $XMe_2Ge(OGeMe_2)_nX$ or $XMe_2Ge(SGeMe_2)_nX$ when the cyclic oxides $(Me_2GeO)_x$ or sulphides $(Me_2GeS)_y$ are mixed with halides Me_2GeX_2.

With unsaturated species such as isocyanates, isothiocyanates and carbodiimides, alkoxygermanes undergo insertion reactions, although less readily than their tin analogues [105c]. For example, isocyanates give germylcarbamates:

$$Bu_3GeOMe + PhNCO \rightarrow Bu_3GeNPh \cdot CO_2Me$$

[103] M. Lesbre and J. Satge, *Compt. rend.*, 1962, **254**, 1453.

[104] Idem, ibid., p. 4051; J. Satge, *Bull. Soc. chim. France*, 1964, 630.

[104a] R. C. Mehrotra and S. Mathur, *J. Organomet. Chem.*, 1966, **6**, 11; 1967, **7**, 233.

[105] H. Schmidbaur, *Angew. Chem.*, 1964, **76**, 234; H. Schmidbaur and H. Hussek, *J. Organometal Chem.*, 1964, **1**, 235; H. Schmidbaur, *Angew. Chem., Internat. Edn.*, 1965, **4**, 201.

[105a] H. Schmidbaur and B. Armer, ibid., 1966, **5**, 313; B. Armer and H. Schmidbaur, *Chem. Ber.*, 1967, **100**, 1521.

[105b] K. Moedritzer and J. R. Van Wazer, *J. Amer. Chem. Soc.*, 1965, **87**, 2360; *Inorg. Chem.*, 1965, **4**, 1753.

[105c] Y. Ishii, K. Itoh, A. Nakamura and S. Sakai, *Chem. Comm.*, 1967, 224.

A useful guide to the Lewis basicity of organogermanium oxides, alkoxides and related sulphides and amides is provided by the shift they cause in ν(C–D) in the infrared spectrum of deuteriochloroform when they are mixed with $CDCl_3$ [105d]. Using this shift, trimethylgermyl compounds have been found to have donor properties comparable to their t-butyl analogues, greater than trimethylsilyl compounds but less than trimethyltin compounds (see Table 18). The figures in Table 18 reflect differences both in the inductive effects (electronegativities) of the Group IV elements and also in their capacity to form multiple $p\pi$–$d\pi$ bonds with oxygen, nitrogen or sulphur.

Table 18   *Relative donor properties of some organometallic bases*
$\Delta\nu$ (cm^{-1}) for ν(C–D) of $CDCl_3$

Base	C	Si	Ge	Sn	Pb
Me$_3$MNEt$_2$	~100^a	64	82	90	—
(Me$_3$M)$_3$N	~100^a	0	72	106	—
Me$_3$MOEt	29	21	38	56	—
(Me$_3$M)$_2$O	33	13	55	84	—
Me$_3$MSMe	33	29	34	36	49
(Me$_3$M)$_2$S	40	29	38	43	51

^{a} estimated

For ultraviolet spectroscopic and dipole moment studies on oxygen and sulphur compounds containing R_3M groups (M = Si, Ge or Sn), see [105e].

Organogermanium peroxides
Various organogermanium peroxides have been prepared by reactions between chloro- [106], bromo, hydroxy- [106a] or amino- [107] germanes and organic hydroperoxides or hydrogen peroxide, e.g.

$$Ph_3GeNH_2 + Bu^tOOH \rightarrow Ph_3GeOOBu^t, \text{ m.p. } 55\text{–}57°$$

The products are stable at room temperature but decompose at about 70°. They are readily hydrolysed to the original peroxide and germanium oxide, and with hydrogen chloride form the peroxide and chlorogermane.

[105d] E. W. Abel, D. A. Armitage and D. B. Brady, *Trans. Faraday Soc.*, 1966, **62**, 3459.

[105e] C. W. N. Cumper, A. Melnikoff and A. I. Vogel, *J. Chem. Soc. (A)*, 1966, 242, 246, 323.

[106] A. G. Davies and C. D. Hall, *Chem. and Ind.*, 1958, 1695; *J. Chem. Soc.*, 1959, 3835.

[106a] R. L. Dannley and G. Farrant, *J. Amer. Chem. Soc.*, 1966, **88**, 627.

[107] A. Rieche and J. Dahlmann, *Angew. Chem.*, 1959, **71**, 194; *Annalen*, 1964, **675**, 19.

Organogermanium esters

Many organogermanium esters of organic acids are known. These are colourless liquids, hydrolysed rapidly by alcoholic sodium hydroxide, and may be prepared by reaction of an organic acid with an organogermanium oxide or hydride, or by the action of silver salts on organogermanium halides [3]. This last method has been used to prepare trimethylgermyl derivatives of several inorganic oxyacids, including the nitrate, ortho-phosphate, arsenate, selenate and perchlorate [108]:

$$\text{Me}_3\text{GeCl} + \text{AgClO}_4 \xrightarrow{\text{C}_6\text{H}_6} \text{Me}_3\text{GeOClO}_3, \text{ m.p. } 5\text{–}6°, \text{ b.p. } 91°/2 \text{ mm.}$$

The perchlorate is an explosive liquid which is rapidly hydrolysed in aqueous solution.

Sulphides, selenides and tellurides [109]

Analogous to the oxide series $(\text{R}_3\text{Ge})_2\text{O}$, sulphides of the type $(\text{R}_3\text{Ge})_2\text{S}$ have been obtained from the monobromide R_3GeBr and sodium sulphide [110], e.g. bis-triethylgermanium sulphide, $(\text{Et}_3\text{Ge})_2\text{S}$, b.p. $148°/12$ mm., and bis-triphenylgermanium sulphide, $(\text{Ph}_3\text{Ge})_2\text{S}$, m.p. $138°$. Other reactions and types of compound are illustrated in the following diagram [111]:

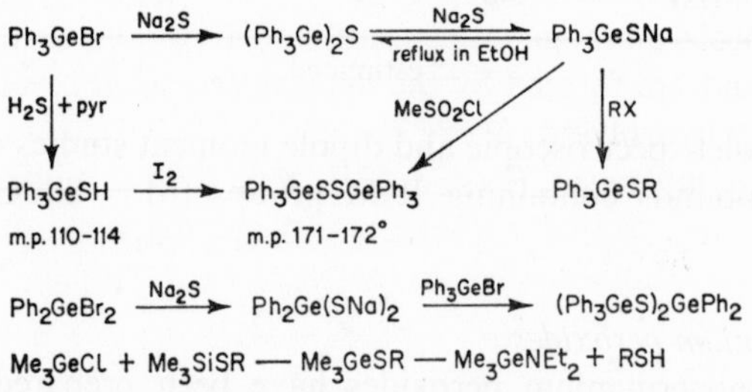

Heterocyclic derivatives of silicon, germanium and tin have been prepared from dithiols, e.g.

[108] M. Schmidt, I. Ruidisch and H. Schmidbaur, *Ber.*, 1961, **94**, 2451; M. Schmidt and I. Ruidisch, ibid., 1962, **95**, 1434; I. Ruidisch and M. Schmidt, *Z. Naturforsch.*, 1963, **18b**, 508.

[109] H. Schumann and M. Schmidt, *Angew. Chem., Internat. Edn.*, 1965, **4**, 1007; E. W. Abel and D. A. Armitage, *Advan. in Organometal. Chem.*, 1967, **5**, 1.

[110] K. Burschies, *Ber.*, 1936, **69**, 1143.

[111] M. C. Henry and W. E. Davidson, *J. Org. Chem.*, 1962, **27**, 2252; idem, *Canad. J. Chem.*, 1963, **41**, 1276; W. E. Davidson, K. Hills and M. C. Henry, *J. Organometal. Chem.*, 1965, **3**, 285; see also M. Wieber and M. Schmidt, *Z. Naturforsch.*, 1963, **18b**, 846, 847, 849; *J. Organometal. Chem.*, 1964, **1**, 336; **2**, 129; M. Schmidt and H. Schumann, *Z. anorg. Chem.*, 1963, **325**, 130; J. Satge and M. Lesbre, *Bull. Soc. chim. France*, 1965, 2578; K. A. Hooton and A. L. Allred, *Inorg. Chem.*, 1965, **4**, 671; E. W. Abel, D. A. Armitage and D. B. Brady, *J. Organometal. Chem.*, 1966, **5**, 130.

Dimethylgermanium sulphide, $(Me_2GeS)_3$, m.p. 54–55°, is obtained as colourless crystals when hydrogen sulphide is passed through an aqueous solution of dimethyldichlorogermane [68, 101], preferably in the presence of triethylamine [112]. With methyl-lithium it forms the derivative Me_3GeSLi, b.p. 50°/1 mm., which in turn reacts with the chlorides Me_3MCl (M = Si, Ge or Sn) to form the sulphides $Me_3GeSSiMe_3$, b.p. 63°/10 mm., $(Me_3Ge)_2S$, b.p. 68°/12 mm., and $Me_3GeSSnMe_3$, b.p. 90°/12 mm. [112]. In the aryl series, the lithium compound Ph_3GeSLi is conveniently prepared from Ph_3GeLi and sulphur [113].

A few *selenides* analogous to these sulphides are known. *Dimethylgermanium selenide* $(Me_2GeSe)_3$, m.p. 53°, from dimethyldichlorogermane and sodium selenide, is an air-stable colourless crystalline solid which evolves hydrogen selenide when treated with warm water [114]. It reacts with methyl-lithium, forming $Me_3GeSeLi$, from which the selenides $Me_3GeSeMMe_3$ (M = Si, Ge or Sn) have been prepared [115].

Alternatively, other selenides are accessible through $Ph_3GeSeLi$ (from Ph_3GeLi + Se) [113]. Similarly, *tellurides* can be prepared via $Ph_3GeTeLi$ (from Ph_3GeLi + Te) [113].

Nitrogen and phosphorus compounds

In many respects aminogermanes are similar to the analogous oxygen compounds, and are formed by the *ammonolysis* of the halides. They are all very readily hydrolysed.

Bis-triethylgermylamine, $(Et_3Ge)_2NH$, b.p. 100°/0·1 mm., results from the interaction of triethylbromogermane and liquid ammonia. It is insoluble in liquid ammonia [63].

Diethylgermanium imine, $(Et_2GeNH)_{\sim 3}$, b.p. 100°/0·01 mm., is similarly obtained from the dibromide and liquid ammonia [70]. A measurement of molecular weight indicated a degree of association of about three, suggesting a cyclic structure based on a six-membered $(GeN)_3$ ring. Such a conclusion is supported by the trimeric nature of $(Me_2GeNMe)_3$ (from Me_2GeCl_2 and $MeNH_2$) for which a cyclic structure is suggested [116].

Ethylgermanium nitride, $(EtGeN)_n$, is formed as a white insoluble precipitate when ethyltri-iodogermane reacts with liquid ammonia,

$$EtGeI_3 + 4NH_3 \longrightarrow EtGeN + 3NH_4I$$

It is clearly polymeric, and is very easily hydrolysed to 'ethylgermanoic anhydride', $(EtGeO)_2O$ [76].

[112] I. Ruidisch and M. Schmidt, *Ber.*, 1963, **96**, 1424.

[113] H. Schumann and M. Schmidt, *J. Organometal. Chem.*, 1965, **3**, 485; H. Schumann, K.-F. Thom and M. Schmidt, ibid., 1965, **4**, 22.

[114] M. Schmidt and H. Ruf, *Angew. Chem.*, 1961, **73**, 64; *J. Inorg. Nucl. Chem.*, 1963, **25**, 557.

[115] I. Ruidisch and M. Schmidt, *J, Organometal. Chem.*, 1963, **1**, 160.

[116] Idem, *Angew. Chem., Internat. Edn.*, 1964, **3**, 231, 637.

Several *methylgermylamines*, e.g. $(Me_3Ge)_2NH$, b.p. $47°/17$ mm., and $(Me_2GeCl)_3N$, m.p. $62°$, have been prepared from the chloride and ammonia in ether solution [116].

Triphenylgermylamine, Ph_3GeNH_2, results when ammonia reacts with triphenylbromogermane in dry solvents. Just as Ph_3GeOH loses water very easily, the amine loses ammonia to form bis-triphenylgermylamine $(Ph_3Ge)_2NH$, which is a viscous liquid and itself loses ammonia about $200°$ and passes over to the tertiary tris-triphenylgermylamine [117], $(Ph_3Ge)_3N$, m.p. $163°$. The aryl amines are all very easily hydrolysed like the aliphatic series.

Some N-alkyl derivatives of aminogermanes have been prepared from organogermanium chlorides and dimethylamine or diethylamine [72, 118]; N-aryl derivatives have been prepared from the lithium derivative of the amine (e.g. $Ph_3GeCl + LiNPh_2 \rightarrow Ph_3GeNPh_2$) [119], while N-silyl derivatives result from the reaction between $(Me_3Si)_2NNa$ and an organogermanium chloride [120], e.g.

$$(Me_3Si)_2NNa + Me_3GeCl \rightarrow Me_3GeN(SiMe_3)_2 + NaCl$$

Bis-trimethylsilylaminotrimethylgermane is a waxy solid, stable to water.

Cyclic aminogermanes have been prepared from the azobenzene-dilithium adduct [120a],

$$Ph_2GeCl_2 + PhN(Li)N(Li)Ph \longrightarrow Ph_2Ge\begin{array}{c} PhN{-}NPh \\ \diagup \qquad \diagdown \\ \diagdown \qquad \diagup \\ PhN{-}NPh \end{array}GePh_2 \qquad \text{m.p. } 306{-}7° \text{ (decomp.)}$$

and also from diamines [120b]:

$$Me_2GeCl_2 + MeNHCH_2CH_2NHMe \longrightarrow Me_2Ge\begin{array}{c} MeN{\diagdown}_{CH_2} \\ \qquad | \\ MeN{\diagup}^{CH_2} \end{array}$$

Organogermanium nitrogen compounds, like their organotin analogues, are cleaved by various weak acids HX [121]:

$$R_3GeNR_2 + HX \rightarrow R_3GeX + HNR_2$$

---

[117] C. A. Kraus and C. B. Wooster, *J. Amer. Chem. Soc.*, 1930, **52**, 372.

[118] H. H. Anderson, *J. Amer. Chem. Soc.*, 1952, **74**, 1421.

[119] C. Baum, W. L. Lehn and C. Tamborski, *J. Org. Chem.*, 1964, **29**, 1264.

[120] O. J. Scherer and M. Schmidt, *Angew. Chem.*, 1963, **75**, 642; *J. Organometal. Chem.*, 1964, **1**, 490.

[120a] M. V. George, P. B. Talukdar and H. Gilman, ibid., 1966, **5**, 397.

[120b] C. H. Yoder and J. J. Zuckerman, *J. Amer. Chem. Soc.*, 1966, **88**, 2170; *Inorg. Chem.*, 1966, **5**, 2055; E. W. Randall, C. H. Yoder and J. J. Zuckerman, ibid., 1967, **6**, 744.

[121] J. Satge, M. Lesbre and M. Baudet, *Compt. rend.*, 1964, **259**, 4733; see also K. Itoh, S. Sakai and Y. Ishii, *Chem. Comm.*, 1967, 36.

Their ready hydrolysis is an example of such a reaction. Alcoholysis gives alkoxides (X = OR), acetylenes RC:CH give acetylides RC:CGeR$_3$, and less volatile amines displace more volatile amines in transamination reactions [122]. The reaction can even be used to generate metal–metal bonds [122a]:

$$Bu_3GeNEt_2 + Ph_3SnH \longrightarrow Bu_3GeSnPh_3 + HNEt_2$$

Use of diamino derivatives or dihydrides gives chains, the length of which may be controlled by the relative proportions of mono- and di-functional reagents.

Also like their tin counterparts, Ge–N compounds can add to certain unsaturated systems such as CO_2, CS_2, RNCO and RNCS [121]:

$$Et_3GeNMe_2 + CO_2 \longrightarrow Et_3GeO \cdot CO \cdot NMe_2$$

Organogermanium *azides* and other pseudohalides have already been described [88–93c].

Organometallic nitrogen compounds of germanium, tin and lead were reviewed in 1965 [123].

Few organogermanium–*phosphorus* compounds have so far been described. Diphenylphosphino derivatives such as Et_3GePPh_2, b.p. 146°/ 10^{-3} mm., may be prepared from bromotriethylgermane and lithium diphenylphosphide in tetrahydrofuran [124]:

$$Et_3GeBr + LiPPh_2 \longrightarrow Et_3GePPh_2 + LiBr$$

This compound is rapidly hydrolysed at room temperature by 10% aqueous 1,2-dimethoxyethane, forming bis-triethylgermanium oxide and diphenylphosphine. Oxidation at room temperature by oxygen cleaves the Ge–P bond, giving the ester $Et_3GeOP(O)Ph_2$, b.p. 160°/10^{-3} mm., while bromine forms Et_3GeBr and Ph_2PBr. The Ge–P bond is also cleaved by organolithium reagents and methyl iodide. Silver iodide gives a crystalline complex $(Et_3GePPh_2 \cdot AgI)_4$, m.p. 183° (decomp.).

Derivatives of digermane and higher germanes [124a]

Though a little weaker than the Si–Si bond, the Ge–Ge bond in hexa-substituted digermanes R_6Ge_2 shows no sign of dissociation in solution at ambient temperature, unlike the characteristic behaviour of the hexaphenylethanes.

[122] F. Rijkens, M. J. Janssen and G. J. M. Van der Kerk, *Rec. Trav. chim.*, 1965, **84**, 1597.

[122a] H. M. J. C. Creemers and J. G. Noltes, *J. Organometal. Chem.*, 1967, **7**, 237.

[123] J. G. A. Luijten, F. Rijkens and G. J. M. Van der Kerk, *Adv. in Organometal. Chem.*, 1965, **3**, 397.

[124] F. Glockling and K. A. Hooton, *Proc. Chem. Soc.*, 1963, 146; E. H. Brooks, F. Glockling and K. A. Hooton, *J. Chem. Soc.*, 1965, 4283.

[124a] H. Gilman, W. H. Atwell and F. K. Cartledge, *Advan. in Organometal. Chem.*, 1966, **4**, 1.

Hexamethyldigermane, $Me_3GeGeMe_3$, m.p. $-40°$, b.p. $138°/750$ mm., obtained by refluxing trimethylbromogermane with potassium, is stable to air (like Me_6Si_2 but unlike Me_6Sn_2), and reacts neither with cold concentrated sulphuric acid nor with alkali metals [125]. The Ge–Ge stretching force constant (from the Raman spectrum) is $1.3 \pm 0.1 \times 10^5$ dynes/cm. [126].

Hexa-ethyldigermane, $Et_3GeGeEt_3$, b.p. $265°$, is prepared by the Wurtz reaction between sodium and triethylbromogermane at $210°$ in the absence of solvent [63]. Insoluble in water or liquid ammonia, it is stable to oxygen and can be distilled unchanged in air, but reacts quantitatively with bromine in ethyl bromide at $0°$:

$$Et_3GeGeEt_3 + Br_2 \longrightarrow 2Et_3GeBr$$

The related *triethylsilyltriethylgermane*, $Et_3SiGeEt_3$, m.p. $254–255°$, can be isolated from the products of the reaction between sodium and a mixture of Et_3SiBr and Et_3GeBr [127].

Triethyltriphenyldigermane, $Et_3GeGePh_3$, m.p. $89.5–90.5°$, results from triphenylgermylsodium and triethylbromogermane in liquid ammonia [128].

Hexavinyldigermane, $(CH_2:CH)_3GeGe(CH:CH_2)_3$, b.p. $55°/0.3$ mm., has already been mentioned [35, 129].

Hexaphenyldigermane, $Ph_3GeGePh_3$, m.p. $340°$, from triphenylbromogermane and sodium in boiling xylene [96], can also be prepared from triphenylgermane and phenyl-lithium, or by the prolonged action of 10 mols. phenylmagnesium bromide on 1 mol. germanium tetrachloride in a toluene–ether mixture [25], a reaction which proceeds via the germyl Grignard reagent Ph_3GeMgX [130]:

$$\begin{array}{c} R_3GeX + Mg \\ \text{or} \qquad \nearrow R_3GeMgX \xrightarrow{R_3GeX} R_3GeGeR_3 \\ R_3GeX + RMgX \diagup \scriptstyle{-RX} \end{array}$$

Hexaphenyldigermane crystallizes from benzene with three molecules of solvent of crystallization, like its tin and lead analogues, but owing to its symmetry and rather high molecular weight it is not very soluble in most solvents. Although almost insoluble it slowly reacts with sodium in liquid

[125] M. P. Brown and G. W. A. Fowles, *J. Chem. Soc.*, 1958, 2811.
[126] M. P. Brown, E. Cartmell and G. W. A. Fowles, ibid., 1960, 506.
[127] J. M. Shackelford, H. De Schmertzing, C. H. Heuther, and H. Podall, *J. Org. Chem.*, 1963, **28**, 1700.
[128] C. A. Kraus and C. S. Sherman, *J. Amer. Chem. Soc.*, 1930, **52**, 4694.
[129] S. Cawley and S. S. Danyluk, *Canad. J. Chem.*, 1963, **41**, 1850.
[130] F. Glockling and K. A. Hooton, *J. Chem. Soc.*, 1962, 3509; *Inorg. Syntheses*, 1966, **8**, 31.

ammonia giving triphenylgermyl sodium, Ph_3GeNa. Bromine in boiling carbon tetrachloride causes the Ge–Ge bond to break with formation of triphenylbromogermane. In general, however, the digermane is rather unreactive and is stable to air and boiling alkali. Its ultraviolet spectrum, like the spectra of related compounds of other Group IV elements, has been interpreted as showing interaction between the π orbitals of the phenyl groups and those of the $(M)_n$ system ($M = Si$, Ge, Sn or Pb) [131]. Several other hexa-aryldigermanes have been prepared [130].

Octaphenyltrigermane, $Ph_3Ge\cdot Ph_2Ge\cdot GePh_3$, m.p. 247–248°, is made by the reaction:

$$2Ph_3GeNa + Ph_2GeCl_2 \rightarrow 2NaCl + Ph_3Ge\cdot Ph_2Ge\cdot GePh_3$$

The Ge–Ge bonds in this compound are broken by bromine at room temperature; compare hexaphenyldigermane, which is cleaved by bromine only at higher temperatures.

Other compounds containing Ge–Ge bonds have been obtained in attempts to prepare organic derivatives of divalent germanium. A tetrameric, apparently cyclic product $(Ph_2Ge)_4$, m.p. 294°, was obtained by the reduction of diphenyldichlorogermane by sodium in boiling xylene [132]. A more recent synthesis [133] involving a germanium–mercury intermediate also afforded a tetramer, $(Ph_2Ge)_4$, although with m.p. 238°:

$$4Ph_2GeH_2 + 4Et_2Hg \xrightarrow{-8EtH} {}^4/_n(-Ph_2GeHg-)_n$$

with subsequent steps: Heat + $h\nu$, $-Hg$, leading to

$$\begin{matrix} Ph_2Ge\!\!-\!\!-GePh_2 \\ | \qquad | \\ Ph_2Ge\!\!-\!\!-GePh_2 \end{matrix}$$

$$Ph(GePh_2)_4Ph \xleftarrow[\text{or Li then PhBr}]{I_2 \text{ then PhLi}} \begin{matrix} Ph_2Ge\!\!-\!\!-GePh_2 \\ | \qquad | \\ Ph_2Ge\!\!-\!\!-GePh_2 \end{matrix}$$

The cyclic structure is supported by its conversion into *decaphenyltetragermane*, $Ph(GePh_2)_4Ph$, when it is treated with iodine and then phenyllithium, or with lithium and then bromobenzene.

A crystalline pentamer, $(Ph_2Ge)_5$, readily soluble in benzene, and hexamer, $(Ph_2Ge)_6$, sparingly soluble in that solvent, have been isolated from the products of reduction of diphenyldichlorogermane by sodium-naphthalene in dimethoxyethane (monoglyme) or by lithium in tetrahydrofuran [133]. Excess of sodium-naphthalene should be avoided, as it cleaves the Ge–Ge bonds (but not the Ge–Ph bonds) of cyclic diphenylgermanium

[131] D. N. Hague and R. H. Prince, *Proc. Chem. Soc.*, 1962, 300; *Chem. and Ind.*, 1964, 1492; *J. Chem. Soc.*, 1965, 4690; H. Gilman, W. H. Atwell and G. L. Schwebke, *J. Organometal. Chem.*, 1964, **2**, 369.
[132] C. A. Kraus and C. L. Brown, *J. Amer. Chem. Soc.*, 1930, **52**, 4031.
[133] W. P. Neumann, *Angew. Chem.*, 1963, **75**, 679; W. P. Neumann and K. Kühlein, *Tetrahedron Letters*, 1963, 1541; idem, *Annalen*, 1965, **683**, 1; 1967, **702**, 13.

oligomers

$$(Ph_2Ge)_4 \xrightarrow{C_{10}H_8Na} Ph_2GeNa_2 \xrightarrow{Me_2SO_4} Ph_2GeMe_2$$

Attempts to prepare similar cyclic materials by the thermal decomposition of diphenylgermane, Ph_2GeH_2, were unsuccessful, the products being germanium, hydrogen, tetraphenylgermane and benzene [134]. In this respect germanium differs from tin, as diphenyltin may be prepared from diphenylstannane (see p. 472). Materials of composition apparently approximating to $(PhGe)_6$ from the reduction of phenyltrichlorogermane with potassium [135] were shown by later investigators to contain 1–5% of chlorine and 5–10% of oxygen [136].

Germanium(II) iodide has also been studied as a possible starting-point for the preparation of diphenylgermanium. With phenyl-lithium, the main product is an amorphous involatile yellow solid of composition intermediate between $(PhGe)_n$ and $(Ph_2Ge)_n$ which contains Ph_3Ge, Ph_2Ge, $PhGe$ and Ge groups as shown by its bromination products. The reaction apparently proceeds by halogen–metal exchange reactions of the type [134]:

$$PhGeI + PhLi \longrightarrow PhGeLi + PhI$$

With triphenylgermyl-lithium, germanium(II) iodide gives tris-triphenyl-germylgermane, $(Ph_3Ge)_3GeH$, m.p. 192–194°:

$$2Ph_3GeLi + GeI_2 \longrightarrow [(Ph_3Ge)_2Ge] \xrightarrow{Ph_3GeLi} $$
$$(Ph_3Ge)_3GeLi \xrightarrow{H_2O} (Ph_3Ge)_3GeH$$

A strong band at 228 cm^{-1} in the infrared spectrum of this hydride, absent from the spectra of symmetrical digermanes and R_4Ge compounds, may be due to the Ge–Ge stretching vibration. Diarylmercurials and GeI_2 are reported to give mainly diaryldi-iodogermanes, R_2GeI_2 [137].

Compounds related to higher germanes, but with two different Group IV metals in a neopentane configuration $(Ph_3M)_4M'$ (M = Sn or Pb, M' = Ge, Sn or Pb), have been prepared from Ph_3MLi and $GeCl_4$, $SnCl_4$ or $PbCl_2$ [138]. The electronic spectra of these compounds have features similar to those of the aryl digermanes which have been attributed to the metallic part of the molecules.

Although early attempts to prepare a di*alkyl*germanium were unsuccessful [139], the hexamer $(Me_2Ge)_6$, m.p. 211–213°, has recently been

[134] F. Glockling and K. A. Hooton, *J. Chem. Soc.*, 1963, 1849.
[135] R. Schwarz and M. Schmeisser, *Ber*, 1936, **69**, 579.
[136] W. Metlesics and H. Zeiss, *J. Amer. Chem. Soc.*, 1960, **82**, 3321.
[137] L. I. Emel'yanova, V. N. Vinogradova, L. G. Makarova and A. N. Nesmeyanov, *Izvest. Akad. Nauk S.S.S.R.*, 1962, 53; *Chem. Abs.*, 1962, **57**, 12523.
[138] L. C. Willemsens and G. J. M. van der Kerk, *J. Organometal. Chem.*, 1964, **2**, 260; W. Drenth, M. J. Janssen, G. J. M. van der Kerk and J. A. Vliegenthart, ibid., p. 265.
[139] G. Jacobs, *Compt. rend.*, 1954, **238**, 1825.

described as the product of reduction of dimethyldichlorogermane by lithium in tetrahydrofuran, and amorphous materials $(Me_2Ge)_n$, m.p. 200–240°, were obtained by similar reactions [140]. Materials of formula $Me(Me_2Ge)_nMe$, where $n > 2$, result from the action of MeMgBr or MeLi on $HGeCl_3$ in ether [141]. Di- and poly-germanes $R_{2n+2}Ge_n$ indeed appear to be inevitable side-products in the preparation of tetra-alkyl-germanes from germanium tetrahalides by the Grignard [23a] or organo-aluminium [16a] route. Germanium di-iodide and trimethylaluminium give non-cyclic oligomers such as $Me_{12}Ge_5$, $Me_{14}Ge_6$ and $Me_{16}Ge_7$ [16a].

Alkali metal derivatives and magnesium compounds

*Alkyl*germanium derivatives have been relatively little studied, being less readily prepared than the *aryl* compounds. Hexa-ethyldigermane reacts with lithium in ethylamine:

$$Et_3GeGeEt_3 + 2Li \longrightarrow 2Et_3GeLi$$

Triethylgermyl-lithium, prepared in this way, is 'ammonolysed' to some extent by ethylamine, but completely by ammonia [63]:

$$Et_3GeLi + NH_3 \longrightarrow Et_3GeH + LiNH_2$$

Triethylgermylpotassium, Et_3GeK, from hexa-ethyldigermane and potassium in ethylamine, reacts with ethyl bromide to give tetra-ethyl-germane [63].

Hexamethylphosphortriamide $PO(NMe_2)_3$ has recently been recommended as a convenient medium in which to prepare trialkylgermy-alkali metal derivatives, as it is a good solvent both for alkali metals and for hexa-alkyldigermanes [141a]. Unsymmetrical hexa-alkyldigermanes-$R_3GeGeR'_3$ have been prepared in this medium:

$$R_3GeGeR_3 + 2K \longrightarrow 2R_3GeK \xrightarrow{2R'_3GeCl} 2R_3GeGeR'_3$$

Tribenzylgermyl-lithium, $(PhCH_2)_3GeLi$, is obtained as a deep brown solution by the reaction between tetrabenzylgermane and lithium in ethylene glycol dimethyl ether [30]:

$$(PhCH_2)_4Ge + 2Li \longrightarrow PhCH_2Li + (PhCH_2)_3GeLi$$

Hydrolysis of the resulting solution affords not only tribenzylgermane, $(PhCH_2)_3GeH$, but also some dibenzylgermane, $(PhCH_2)_2GeH_2$, showing

[140] O. M. Nefedov, M. N. Manakov and A. D. Petrov, *Doklady Akad. Nauk S.S.S.R.*, 1962, **147**, 1376; *Plaste Kautschuk*, 1963, **10**, 721, 736; *Chem. Abs.*, 1963, **59**, 5185; 1964, **60**, 13266.

[141] O. M. Nefedov and S. P. Kolesnikov, *Izvest. Akad. Nauk S.S.S.R.*, 1964, 773; *Chem. Abs.*, 1964, **61**, 3136.

[141a] E. J. Bulten and J. G. Noltes, *Tetrahedron Letters*, 1966, 4389.

that small quantities of the di-lithium derivative $(PhCH_2)_2GeLi_2$, are also present in the reaction mixture. This conclusion is supported by the reaction with methyl iodide, which gives some dimethyl derivative $(PhCH_2)_2GeMe_2$ as well as $(PhCH_2)_3GeMe$. These reactions provide the first clear evidence for the existence of a di-alkali metal derivative of an organogermane.

More is known about triarylgermyl derivatives. *Triphenylgermylsodium*, Ph_3GeNa, is formed from tetraphenylgermane and sodium in liquid ammonia. The low solubility of the germane makes the reaction slow, and the use of hexaphenyldigermane is perhaps more convenient [97]. It crystallizes with three molecules of ammonia, and is soluble in ether and benzene (particularly in the presence of ammonia). The yellow solution in liquid ammonia is a good conductor of electricity, the substance being rather more strongly ionized (as $Ph_3Ge^-Na^+$) in this solvent than the alkali halides [66]. It is useful synthetically as it is highly reactive; thus with water or ammonium bromide triphenylgermane, Ph_3GeH, is formed, and with trimethyltin bromide the compound $Me_3Sn \cdot GePh_3$ results, with a tin–germanium bond [97].

Triphenylgermyl-lithium, Ph_3GeLi, has been prepared from hexaphenyl-digermane and lithium in ethylene glycol dimethyl ether [142] or tetrahydrofuran [143]:

$$Ph_3Ge \cdot GePh_3 + 2Li \longrightarrow 2Ph_3GeLi$$

It can also be prepared by the cleavage (by lithium) of triphenylchlorogermane in tetrahydrofuran [143] or of tetraphenylgermane in ethylene glycol dimethyl ether [144], and by the action of butyl-lithium on triphenylgermane [144]:

$$Ph_3GeH + Bu^nLi \longrightarrow Ph_3GeLi + C_4H_{10}$$

Triphenylgermyl-lithium has been characterized by reaction with triethylchlorosilane:

$$Ph_3GeLi + Et_3SiCl \longrightarrow Ph_3GeSiEt_3 + LiCl$$

or by carbonation

$$Ph_3GeLi + CO_2 \longrightarrow Ph_3GeCO_2H$$

A salt containing a germanium–boron bond is obtained by the reaction between triphenylgermyl-lithium and triphenylborane in ethylene glycol dimethyl ether [145]:

$$Ph_3GeLi + Ph_3B \longrightarrow Li[Ph_3B \cdot GePh_3]$$

[142] H. Gilman and C. W. Gerow, *J. Amer. Chem. Soc.*, 1955, **77**, 5509, 5740.

[143] C. Tamborski, F. E. Ford, W. L. Lehn, G. J. Moore and E. J. Soloski, *J. Org. Chem.*, 1962, **27**, 619.

[144] H. Gilman and C. W. Gerow, *J. Amer. Chem. Soc.*, 1955, **77**, 4675; 1956, **78**, 5435.

[145] D. Seyferth, G. Raab and S. O. Grim, *J. Org. Chem.*, 1961, **26**, 3034.

The use of Ph_3GeLi to attach triphenylgermyl groups to transition metals is described below.

Triphenylgermane carboxylic acid [146], Ph_3GeCO_2H, softens at 187° and melts at 189–190° with rapid evolution of carbon monoxide and water:

$$2Ph_3GeCO_2H \rightarrow Ph_3Ge{\cdot}CO{\cdot}O{\cdot}GePh_3 + H_2O + CO$$

Other reactions in which triphenylgermyl-lithium behaves as a Grignard or organolithium reagent are with formaldehyde, and benzophenone:

$$Ph_3GeLi + CH_2O \rightarrow Ph_3GeCH_2OH$$
$$Ph_3GeLi + Ph_2CO \rightarrow Ph_3GeC(OH)Ph_2$$

Such reactions afford routes to various functionally substituted organo-germanes [147], e.g.

$$Ph_3GeLi \xrightarrow{RCOMe} Ph_3GeCR(OH)Me \xrightarrow{-H_2O} Ph_3GeCR{:}CH_2 \xrightarrow[Ph_3GeCOR]{ozonolysis}$$

Germyl ketones Ph_3GeCOR [147a] also result from the reaction of Ph_3GeLi with acyl chlorides; the bis-germyl ketone $(Ph_3Ge)_2CO$, an orange-pink solid, m.p. 152°, is obtained from the reaction with methyl formate [148]:

$$Ph_3GeLi + HCO_2Me \rightarrow (Ph_3Ge)_2CHOH \xrightarrow{[O]} (Ph_3Ge)_2CO$$

With ethyl carbonate the main products, however, are hexaphenyl-digermane and carbon monoxide:

$$2Ph_3GeLi + (EtO)_2CO \rightarrow Ph_6Ge_2 + 2LiOEt + CO$$

Triphenylgermyl-lithium metalates fluorene, giving a high yield of fluorene-9-carboxylic acid on carbonation. In this respect it is more reactive than the tin and lead compounds Ph_3MLi (M = Sn, Pb) but less reactive than Ph_3SiLi [149].

Triphenylgermylpotassium is formed from hexaphenyldigermane and sodium–potassium alloy in ether; reaction begins only when a little tetrahydrofuran has been added [146]:

$$Ph_6Ge_2 + 2NaK \xrightarrow{Et_2O + THF} 2Ph_3GeK$$

[146] A. G. Brook and H. Gilman, *J. Amer. Chem. Soc.*, 1954, **76**, 77.
[147] D. A. Nicholson and A. L. Allred, *Inorg. Chem.*, 1965, **4**, 1747, 1751.
[147a] G. J. D. Peddle, *J. Organometal. Chem.*, 1966, **5**, 486.
[148] A. G. Brook and G. J. D. Peddle, ibid., 1966, **5**, 106.
[149] H. Gilman and C. W. Gerow, *J. Org. Chem.*, 1958, **23**, 1582; H. Gilman, O. L. Mars, W. J. Trepka and J. W. Diehl, ibid., 1962, **27**, 1260; H. Gilman and F. K. Cartledge, *J. Organometal. Chem.*, 1965, **3**, 255; see also H. Gilman, F. K. Cartledge and S.-Y. Sim, ibid., 1965, **4**, 332.

It has been characterized by various reactions including that with triphenyltin chloride [150]:

$$Ph_3GeK + Ph_3SnCl \longrightarrow Ph_3Ge\cdot SnPh_3 \quad m.p. \; 284°$$

Evidence for the existence of *triarylgermyl Grignard reagents*, Ar_3GeMgX, has been obtained recently from studies of reactions between Grignard reagents and organogermanium hydrides [151] or halides [130]. *Triphenylgermylmagnesium chloride*, $Ph_3GeMgCl$, is formed when triphenylgermane and allyl magnesium chloride interact in tetrahydrofuran [151]:

$$Ph_3GeH + CH_2:CHCH_2MgCl \longrightarrow Ph_3GeMgCl$$

Thus, carbonation of the resulting solution leads to triphenylgermane carboxylic acid, Ph_3GeCO_2H, while interaction with the solvent gives triphenylgermylbutanol, $Ph_3Ge(CH_2)_4OH$. The role of triarylgermyl Grignard reagents as intermediates in the formation of hexa-aryldigermanes from $GeCl_4$ and $ArMgX$ has already been mentioned [130].

Organogermanium derivatives of transition metals

Compounds with organogermyl groups attached to *copper, silver, gold* [152], *palladium* [152a] and *platinum* (153, 153a] have been prepared from triphenylgermyllithium and the tertiary phosphine–transition metal halide complex in ethylene glycol dimethyl ether, e.g.

$$Ph_3GeLi + Ph_3P\cdot AuCl \longrightarrow Ph_3Ge\cdot Au\cdot PPh_3, \quad m.p. \; 185° \; (decomp.)$$

Both this gold complex and the square planar platinum(II) compound, $(Et_3P)_2Pt(GePh_3)_2$, are stable to air and water, whereas the copper and silver compounds, $Ph_3Ge\cdot M(PPh_3)_3$, are more reactive and of low thermal stability. The metal–metal bond is cleaved by halogens and even by ethylene dibromide, e.g.

$$trans\text{-}(Et_3P)_2Pt(GePh_3)_2 + 2C_2H_4Br_2 \longrightarrow 2C_2H_4 + 2Ph_3GeBr + (Et_3P)_2PtBr_2$$

The platinum compound reacts with hydrogen chloride to give all the possible cleavage products:

$$trans\text{-}(Et_3P)_2Pt(GePh_3)_2 \xrightarrow{HCl}$$
$$trans\text{-}(Et_3P)_2PtCl_2 + trans\text{-}(Et_3P)_2Pt(H)Cl + Ph_3GeH + Ph_3GeCl$$

[150] H. Gilman and C. W. Gerow, *J. Org. Chem.*, 1957, **22**, 334.
[151] H. Gilman and E. A. Zuech, ibid., 1961, **26**, 3035.
[152] F. Glockling and K. A. Hooton, *J. Chem. Soc.*, 1962, 2658; 1967(A), 1066.
[152a] E. H. Brooks and F. Glockling, *J. Chem. Soc. (A)*, 1966, 1241.
[153] R. J. Cross and F. Glockling, *Proc. Chem. Soc.*, 1964, 143; *J. Chem. Soc.*, 1965, 5422; idem, *J. Organometal. Chem.*, 1965, **3**, 253.
[153a] R. J. Cross, *Organometal. Chem. Rev.*, 1967, **2**, 97.

With molecular hydrogen a remarkable and reversible reaction occurs at room temperature and pressure in the absence of added catalyst:

$$(Et_3P)_2Pt(GePh_3)_2 + H_2 \rightarrow Ph_3GeH + (Et_3P)_2Pt(H)GePh_3$$
$$trans(Et_3P)_2PtHCl + Me_3GeH \rightleftharpoons trans(Et_3P)_2PtClGeMe_3 + H_2$$

A higher hydrogen pressure is needed for the analogous hydrogenation of the palladium compound $(Et_3P)_2Pd(GePh_3)_2$ [152a].

Phenyl-lithium cleaves the Ge–Au bond in $Ph_3Ge·Au·PPh_3$, forming $PhAu·PPh_3$ and Ph_3GeLi, which in turn reacts with more of the original compound to give an anionic gold complex, conveniently isolated as the stable unsolvated tetra-ethylammonium salt:

$$Ph_3Ge·Au·PPh_3 \xrightarrow{Ph_3GeLi} Li[(Ph_3Ge)_2Au]4Et_2O \rightarrow Et_4N[(Ph_3Ge)_2Au]$$

Triphenylgermyl derivatives of *iron* and *manganese* have been prepared from the alkali metal derivatives of carbonyl complexes [154, 154a]:

$$C_5H_5Fe(CO)_2Na + Ph_3GeBr \rightarrow Ph_3Ge·Fe(CO)_2C_5H_5$$
$$(CO)_5MnNa + Ph_3GeBr \rightarrow Ph_3Ge·Mn(CO)_5$$

Compounds related to these, and involving many other transition metals, bonded to germanium, tin or lead, have been described, particularly in the patent literature [155, 155a]. A manganese–germanium *hydride* has been made by a further method [156]:

$$2(CO)_5MnH + GeH_4 \xrightarrow{C_4H_8O} [(CO)_5Mn]_2GeH_2$$

Trimethylgermylmanganese pentacarbonyl adds across the double bond of tetrafluoroethylene [154a]:

$$Me_3GeMn(CO)_5 + C_2F_4 \rightarrow Me_3GeCF_2CF_2Mn(CO)_5$$

but gives trimethylgermyl fluoride with trifluoroethylene:

$$Me_3GeMn(CO)_5 + CF_2:CHF \rightarrow Me_3GeF + cis- \text{ and } trans-CHF:CFMn(CO)_5$$

These and related reactions show that the metal–metal bond has little polarity, although polarity may be induced by the reagent or conditions.

Further preparative routes to germanium–transition metal derivatives

[154] D. Seyferth, H. P. Hofmann, R. Burton and J. F. Helling, *Inorg. Chem.*, 1962, **1**, 227; B. T. Kilbourn, T. L. Blundell and H. M. Powell, *Chem. Comm.*, 1965, 444; W. Jetz, P. B. Simons, J. A. J. Thompson and W. A. G. Graham, *Inorg. Chem.*, 1966, **5**, 2217; N. Flitcroft, D. A. Harbourne, I. Paul, P. M. Tucker and F. G. A. Stone, *J. Chem. Soc. (A)*, 1966, 1130; J. D. Cotton, S. A. R. Knox, I. Paul and F. G. A. Stone, ibid., 1967, 264.

[154a] H. C. Clark, J. D. Cotton and J. H. Tsai, *Inorg. Chem.*, 1966, **5**, 1582.

[155] R. D. Gorsich (Ethyl Corp.), U.S.P. 3,033,885; 3,050,537; 3,069,445; 3,069,449 (1962); *Chem. Abs.*, 1962, **57**, 13803, 16658; 1963, **58**, 10237, 10241.

[155a] H. R. H. Patil and W. A. G. Graham, *Inorg. Chem.*, 1966, **5**, 1401; D. J. Patmore and W. A. G. Graham, ibid., 1967, **6**, 981.

[156] A. G. Massey, A. J. Park and F. G. A. Stone, *J. Amer. Chem. Soc.*, 1963, **85**, 2021.

are illustrated by the following equations:

$$HGeCl_3 + ClMn(CO)_5 \rightarrow Cl_3GeMn(CO)_5 + HCl \quad [157]$$
$$R_3GeNMe_2 + (Ph_3P)_2PtHCl \rightarrow (Ph_3P)_2ClPtGeR_3 + Me_2NH \quad [158]$$
$$(Me_3Ge)_2Hg + 2(Et_3P)_2PtCl_2 \rightarrow 2(Et_3P)_2ClPtGeMe_3 + HgCl_2 \quad [159]$$

Derivatives of other metals

Bis(triethylgermyl)mercury, $(Et_3Ge)_2Hg$, a yellow liquid, b.p. $118-120°/1·5$ mm., results from the reaction of diethylmercury with triethylgermane at $100-200°$ [160]:

$$2Et_3GeH + Et_2Hg \rightarrow 2C_2H_6 + (Et_3Ge)_2Hg$$

The Ge-Hg bond in this compound, like that in $(—Ph_2GeHg—)_n$ [133], is readily cleaved by ultraviolet radiation, leading to mercury and hexaethyldigermane, while atmospheric oxidation gives mercury and bis-(triethylgermyl)oxide. Lithium gives triethylgermyl-lithium [160a].

Bis(trimethylgermyl)mercury, $(Me_3Ge)_2Hg$, the compound shown above as an intermediate in the attachment of the trimethylgermyl group to platinum, is a volatile yellow solid, m.p. $35°$, which is produced by the action of sodium amalgam on Me_3GeBr [159]. With $PhHgCBrCl_2$, bis(trimethylgermyl)mercury generates trichlorovinyltrimethylgermane, $Me_3GeCCl:CCl_2$, apparently by successive insertions of dichlorocarbene [160b]:

$$(Me_3Ge)_2Hg \xrightarrow{[CCl_2]} Me_3GeHgCCl_2GeMe_3 \xrightarrow{[CCl_2]} Me_3GeHgCCl_2CCl_2GeMe_3$$

$$Me_3GeCl + Hg \leftarrow Me_3GeHgCl + Me_3GeCCl:CCl_2$$

Bis(triethylgermyl)cadmium, $(Et_3Ge)_2Cd$, an air-sensitive yellow oil, can be prepared similarly from Et_3GeH and Et_2Cd at $80-85°$ [161]. Its reactions frequently result in the deposition of cadmium metal, e.g.

$$(Et_3Ge)_2Cd + HX \rightarrow Cd + Et_3GeX + Et_3GeH \quad (X = OPr, O_2CMe)$$

With mercury it gives $(Et_3Ge)_2Hg$.

[157] A. N. Nesmeyanov, K. N. Anisimov, N. E. Klobova and A. B. Antonova, *Izvest. Akad. Nauk S.S.S.R.*, 1965, 1309; *Chem. Abs.*, 1965, **63**, 13304.

[158] D. J. Cardin and M. F. Lappert, personal communication (1966).

[159] F. Glockling and K. A. Hooton, *Chem. Comm.*, 1966, 219.

[160] N. S. Vyazankin, G. A. Razuvaev and E. N. Gladyshev, *Doklady Akad. Nauk S.S.S.R.*, 1963, **151**, 1326; 1964, **155**, 830; *Chem. Abs.*, 1963, **59**, 14014; 1964, **60**, 15901.

[160a] N. S. Vyazankin, G. A. Razuvaev, E. N. Gladyshev and S. P. Korneva, *J. Organometal. Chem.*, 1967, **7**, 353.

[160b] D. Seyferth, R. J. Cross and B. Prokai, ibid., 1967, **7**, P20.

[161] N. S. Vyazankin, G. A. Razuvaev and V. T. Bychkov, *Doklady Akad. Nauk S.S.S.R.*, 1964, **158**, 382; *Izvest. Akad. Nauk S.S.S.R.*, 1965, 1665; *Chem. Abs.*, 1964, **61**, 13337; 1965, **63**, 18137.

Tris(triethylgermyl)thallium, $(Et_3Ge)_3Tl$, a dark red liquid which cannot be distilled without decomposition, is similar to the germyl mercurials in its manner of preparation (from Et_3GeH and Et_3Tl at 100°) [161a] and in its reaction with lithium, which gives Et_3GeLi [160a].

Antimony and *bismuth* compounds such as $(Et_3Ge)_3Sb$, $(Et_3Ge)_3Bi$, $(Et_3Ge)_2BiEt$ and $Et_3GeBiEt_2$ have been prepared from Et_3Sb or Et_3Bi and suitable proportions of Et_3GeH. They too are air-sensitive oils whose metal–metal bonds are cleaved by oxygen, peroxides and alkyl halides [162].

Organogermanium hydrides

Some hydrides of the type R_3GeH were prepared at an early stage in the development of the organic chemistry of germanium [63, 97] by the action of water on the alkali metal salts $R_3Ge^-M^+$, and hydrides $RGeH_3$ were prepared from germylsodium, $NaGeH_3$ (from germane and sodium in liquid ammonia) and an alkyl halide [163]. Much more convenient methods, however, involve the reduction of an organogermanium halide by lithium aluminium hydride or $LiAlH(OBu)_3$ in an ethereal solvent [12, 14a, 164] or by sodium borohydride in tetrahydrofuran [164] or aqueous solution [165]. Hydrides and deuterides have been prepared by reducing R_nGeX_{4-n} with LiH or LiD [166].

The *methylgermanes* [12, 165, 166, 167] $MeGeH_3$, m.p. $-154°$, b.p. $-34°$, Me_2GeH_2, m.p. $-144°$, b.p. 3°, and Me_3GeH, m.p. $-123°$, b.p. 27°, are readily obtained in about 95% yield by addition of an aqueous solution of sodium borohydride to acidic solutions of $MeGeBr_3$, Me_2GeBr_2 and Me_3GeBr respectively at 30–55°. It is suggested that the reaction occurs through a germanium borohydride [165].

The *ethylgermanes* $EtGeH_3$, b.p. 9·2°, Et_2GeH_2, b.p. 74° and Et_3GeH, b.p. 124–125°, have been prepared by the various methods outlined above [63, 74, 166, 168]. The preparation of these and a large number of higher alkyl (up to n-octyl) derivatives of germane is described in ref. [164] together with many of their reactions. Fewer *aryl* germanium hydrides are

[161a] N. S. Vyazankin, E. V. Mitrofanova, O. A. Kruglaya and G. A. Razuvaev, *J. Gen. Chem. (U.S.S.R.)*, 1966, **36**, 166.

[162] O. A. Kruglaya, N. S. Vyazankin and G. A. Razuvaev, *Zhur. obshchei Khim.*, 1965, **35**, 394; *Chem. Abs.*, 1965, **62**, 14722; N. S. Vyazankin, G. A. Razuvaev, O. A. Kruglaya and G. S. Semchikova, *J. Organometal. Chem.*, 1966, **6**, 474.

[163] C. A. Kraus and E. S. Carney, *J. Amer. Chem. Soc.*, 1934, **56**, 765.

[164] J. Satgé, *Ann. Chim.*, 1961, **6**, 519; *Chem. Abs.*, 1962, **57**, 5941.

[165] J. E. Griffiths, *Inorg. Chem.*, 1963, **2**, 375.

[166] V. A. Ponomarenko, G. Y. Vzenkova and Y. P. Egorov, *Doklady Akad. Nauk S.S.S.R.*, 1958, **122**, 405; *Chem. Abs.*, 1959, **53**, 112.

[167] J. E. Griffiths, *J. Chem. Phys.*, 1963, **38**, 2879; H. Schmidbaur, *Chem. Ber.*, 1964, **97**, 1639.

[168] G. K. Teal and C. A. Kraus, *J. Amer. Chem. Soc.*, 1950, **72**, 4706.

known. The slow reaction between bromobenzene and germylsodium does not give phenylgermane, but unstable germanium(II) hydride [169]:

$$NaGeH_3 + PhBr \longrightarrow NaBr + C_6H_6 + GeH_2$$

Diphenylgermane, Ph_2GeH_2, b.p. $93°/1$ mm., from diphenyldibromo-germane and lithium aluminium hydride in ether, is stable at $250°$ in the absence of air, but decomposes at higher temperatures, tetraphenyl-germane being one of the products [25, 134]. *Triphenylgermane* [25], Ph_3GeH, m.p. $27°$, obtained by the hydrolysis of Ph_3GeNa [97], is stable in the air for short periods, but oxidizes very slowly on long standing. It can also be prepared by the reduction of triphenylbromogermane by zinc amalgam in a mixture of water, alcohol and ether [170].

The reaction between diphenylgermane and butyl-lithium leads to a variety of products, including 2% of Ph_2GeLi_2, a second example of a dilithium derivative of an organogermane [30]:

$$
Ph_2GeH_2 \xrightarrow{2BuLi}
\begin{array}{c}
Ph_2GeLi_2 \\
+ \\
Ph_2Ge(Bu)Li \\
+ \\
Ph_2GeBu_2 \\
+ \\
Ph_2Ge(Li)Ge(Li)Ph_2
\end{array}
\xrightarrow{EtBr}
\begin{array}{c}
2\% \ Ph_2GeEt_2 \\
+ \\
20\% \ Ph_2Ge(Bu)Et \\
+ \\
12\% \ Ph_2GeBu_2 \\
+ \\
28\% \ Ph_2Ge(Et)Ge(Et)Ph_2
\end{array}
$$

All the hydrides react with bromine to form the bromides. Controlled halogenation is possible using N-bromosuccinimide [171] or mercuric halides [172]:

$$RGeH_3 + HgX_2 \longrightarrow RGeH_2X$$

Alkyldichlorogermanes, $RGeHCl_2$, can also be prepared from trichloro-germane, $HGeCl_3$, and a tin or lead alkyl [16]. Hydrogen is displaced by alkali metals in liquid ammonia or ethylamine, e.g. [169],

$$EtGeH_3 \xrightarrow[EtNH_2]{Li} EtGeH_2Li \xrightarrow{C_5H_{11}Br} Et(C_5H_{11})GeH_2 \xrightarrow[(b) EtI]{(a) Li} Et_2(C_5H_{11})GeH$$

and also by water, alcohols or carboxylic acids at $100°$ in the presence of copper powder [173]:

$$Et_3GeH + ROH \longrightarrow Et_3GeOR + H_2$$

The formation of magnesium derivatives R_3GeMgX with Grignard re-agents [151] and of mercury, cadmium and bismuth derivatives with Et_2Hg [133, 160], Et_2Cd [161] and Et_3Bi [162] respectively have already

[169] S. N. Glarum and C. A. Kraus, *J. Amer. Chem. Soc.*, 1950, **72**, 5398.
[170] R. West, ibid., 1952, **74**, 4363; 1953, **75**, 6080.
[171] W. Gee, R. A. Shaw and B. C. Smith, *J. Chem. Soc.*, 1964, 2845.
[172] H. H. Anderson, *J. Amer. Chem. Soc.*, 1960, **82**, 3016.
[173] M. Lesbre and J. Satgé, *Compt. rend.*, 1962, **254**, 4051.

been mentioned. In contrast to the behaviour of analogous tin compounds, trialkylgermanes R_3GeH do not exchange the hydride H atom with dialkylalanes $(R_2AlH)_2$ [174].

Several *addition reactions* whereby Ge—H is added across a double or triple bond result in the formation of functional organogermanium compounds [14, 164, 175, 176], (some of which may also be prepared using functional organomercury compounds or Grignard reagents [177]). For example, tri-n-butylgermane (b.p. $123°/20$ mm.) adds to vinyl cyanide when boiled with reflux without a catalyst,

$$Bu^n_3GeH + CH_2{:}CHCN \longrightarrow Bu^n_3GeCH_2CH_2CN$$

Addition to allyl alcohol yields $R_3Ge(CH_2)_3OH$, and Et_3GeH with acrolein gives the aldehyde $Et_3GeCH_2CH_2CHO$. Organogermanium esters result from the copper-catalysed reaction between hydrides and diazoesters, e.g.

$$Bu^n_3GeH + N_2CHCO_2Et \xrightarrow{Cu} Bu^n_3GeCH_2CO_2Et$$

Acetylenes give alkenylgermanes [14, 41, 42, 178]:

$$Bu_3GeH + HC{:}CR \xrightarrow{H_2PtCl_6} Bu_3GeCH{:}CHR$$

Trichlorogermane $HGeCl_3$ is reactive enough to add across the double bonds of one naphthalene ring [14]. Addition of dihydrides to diolefins leads to polymers with Ge atoms in the polymer chains [179]. Vinylgermane $CH_2{:}CHGeH_3$ (from $vinyl_2Hg + GeCl_4$ followed by reduction with $LiAlH_4$) itself decomposes to such a polymer [179a].

Trihalomethylmercury compounds insert CX_2 into the Ge–H bond [179b]:

$$Ph_3GeH + PhHgCCl_2Br \xrightarrow{C_6H_6} PhHgBr + Ph_3GeCCl_2H$$

[174] W. P. Neumann and R. Sommer, *Angew. Chem.*, 1963, **75**, 788.

[175] M. Lesbre and J. Satgé, *Compt. rend.*, 1958, **247**, 471; J. Satgé, M. Massol and M. Lesbre, *J. Organometal. Chem.*, 1966, **5**, 241.

[176] K. A. W. Kramer and A. N. Wright, *J. Chem. Soc.*, 1963, 3604; M. Lesbre, J. Satgé and M. Massol, *Compt. rend.*, 1963, **256**, 1548; 1964, **258**, 2842; 1965, **261**, 170.

[177] I. F. Lutsenko, Yu. I. Baukov and B. N. Khasapov, *Zhur. obshchei Khim.*, 1963, **33**, 2724; *Chem. Abs.*, 1964, **60**, 539; P. Mazerolles, *Compt. rend.*, 1963, **257**, 1481.

[178] M. Lesbre and J. Satgé, *Compt. rend.*, 1960, **250**, 2220; M. C. Henry and M. F. Downey, *J. Org. Chem.*, 1961, **26**, 2299; O. M. Nefedov, S. P. Kolesnikov and V. I. Sheichenko, *Angew. Chem., Internat. Edn.*, 1964, **3**, 508.

[179] J. G. Noltes and G. J. M. van der Kerk, *Rec. Trav. chim.*, 1961, **80**, 623; 1962, **81**, 41; *Chimia (Switz.)*, 1962, **16**, 122.

[179a] F. E. Brinckman and F. G. A. Stone, *J. Inorg. Nucl. Chem.*, 1959, **11**, 24.

[179b] D. Seyferth, J. M. Burlitch, H. Dertouzos and H. D. Simmons, *J. Organometal. Chem.*, 1967, **7**, 405.

For nuclear magnetic resonance spectroscopic data on a number of organogermanium hydrides see [179c].

Mixed organogermanium hydrides, R'R"R'''GeH, were the first asymmetric germanium compounds resolved into enantiomers (R' = Me or Et, R" = Ph, R''' = α-naphthyl) [180, 181]. The synthesis of methyl-α-naphthylphenylgermane, its resolution into optical isomers [181], and some displacement reactions [182] of these are shown in the diagram, which illustrates the use of selective bromination of methyltriphenylgermane to introduce the naphthyl group, and the remarkable optical stability of MeαNpPhGeLi (it is unchanged during 30 minutes in ether solution) in contrast to sec-butyl-lithium, which is rapidly racemized by ether. The configurations of analogous optically active germanium, silicon and

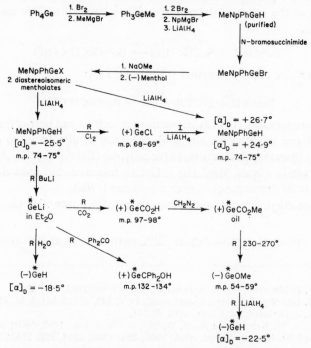

Syntheses and reactions of the methyl-α-naphthylphenylgermanes

Np = α-naphthyl $\overset{*}{Ge}$ = asymmetric MeNpPhGe

R = retention I = inversion

[179c] T. Birchall and W. L. Jolly, *Inorg. Chem.*, 1966, **5**, 2177.

[180] R. W. Bott, C. Eaborn and I. D. Varma, *Chem. and Ind.*, 1963, 614; C. Eaborn, P. Simpson and I. D. Varma, *J. Chem. Soc.* (A), 1966, 1133.

[181] A. G. Brook and G. J. D. Peddle, *J. Amer. Chem. Soc.*, 1963, **85**, 1869.

[182] Idem, ibid., p. 2338.

carbon compounds have been related by mixed melting point techniques, and a plot of specific rotation against the electronegativity of the asymmetric element is linear [183].

TIN

Noteworthy features of the organic chemistry of tin include (*a*) the ionization in aqueous solution of some compounds R_3SnX and R_2SnX_2 (features which also occur with lead); (*b*) the bridged structures, involving five-coordinate tin, of many compounds R_3SnX which were formerly considered to be purely ionic; (*c*) the reactivity of halide, amide, hydride and vinyl derivatives which makes these compounds useful as intermediates for the preparation of organotin compounds containing functional groups; (*d*) the availability of both mono- and di-alkali metal derivatives, R_3SnM and R_2SnM_2; (*e*) the existence of compounds in which as many as nine tin atoms may be linked together in the form of branched chains or rings; and (*f*) the relative ease of cleavage of some organic, particularly unsaturated, groups from tin which allows certain organotin compounds to be used as intermediates in the preparation of other organometallic compounds by transmetalation.

Several dialkyltin derivatives have acquired technical importance as stabilizers for vinyl chloride or as anticracking agents in rubber, since they function as antioxidants and as screens of ultraviolet radiation, and are reactive towards the products of decomposition of these materials, such as hydrogen chloride, multiple-bonded compounds or free radicals, which might otherwise propagate further decomposition [184]. Both dialkyl- and trialkyl-tin compounds are being used on an increasing scale for a number of biocidal purposes [184, 185, 186], e.g. as agricultural fungicides, active ingredients in certain veterinary medicines (anthelmintics) or wood preservatives, and for slime prevention in paper manufacture, mildew prevention in paints, or moth-proofing. Tin alkyls mixed with the chlorides of titanium and aluminium are said to form useful Ziegler-type catalysts for the polymerization of olefins, and derivatives such as dibutyltin dilaurate are catalysts for the preparation of polyurethans [184]. The inclusion of tin in the main or side chains of organic polymers has been used as a means of modifying the properties of these materials, though no major industrial developments on these lines have yet emerged [187].

Aspects of the chemistry and applications of organotin compounds

[183] Idem, ibid., p. 3051.
[184] A. Ross, *Annals New York Acad. Sci.*, 1965, **125**, 107.
[185] W. R. Lewis (ed.), 'Tin and its Uses', *Quart. Journal of the Tin Research Institute*, 1965, **66**, 1.
[186] R. J. Dawn, *Annals New York Acad. Sci.*, 1965, **125**, 229.
[187] M. C. Henry and W. E. Davidson, ibid., p. 172.

have been reviewed periodically by van der Kerk and co-workers [188], to whom many of the developments are due. Organotin compounds also form the subject of a literature survey (1937–1958) [1], and a comprehensive review [189] (nearly one thousand references) in 1960. Recent developments have been summarized by Neumann [190]. Of the many hundreds of organotin compounds which are now known, it is possible in this book to mention only a selection of typical compounds, and to refer only to some of the more recent publications.

The preparation of tetra-alkyls and -aryls

This is conveniently achieved by the action of a *Grignard reagent*, an *organolithium compound* or an *organoaluminium compound* on *tin(IV) chloride*. In the *Grignard method* [189], an excess of reagent is needed to minimize the formation of the incompletely substituted compounds R_2SnCl_2 and R_3SnCl. Some of these are nearly always present in the crude reaction product but may be removed by shaking the ether solution with an aqueous alcoholic solution of potassium fluoride (which converts the mono- and di-chlorides into relatively insoluble fluorides), or by the addition of dry ammonia to the dry ether solution of the crude product. In the latter case insoluble co-ordination compounds $R_3SnCl.2NH_3$ are precipitated; this method is suitable for the removal of quite small amounts of these halides. Tin(IV) chloride not only reacts vigorously with Grignard reagents, but forms dense white clouds with ether. These difficulties can be overcome by addition of the previously prepared ether complex or by addition of a dilute solution of tin(IV) chloride in benzene or toluene. The Grignard method has also been used in the absence of ether, with a paraffinic or aromatic hydrocarbon solvent or with no solvent [191].

In the reaction between tin(IV) chloride and *aluminium alkyls*, some of the alkyl groups remain attached to the aluminium giving a mixture of products with various degrees of alkylation [192]; complexes such as

[188] J. G. A. Luitjen and G. J. M. van der Kerk, *A Survey of the Chemistry and Applications of Organo-Tin Compounds*, published 1952 for the Tin Research Institute, London; idem, *Investigations in the Field of Organo-Tin Chemistry*, 1955, Tin Research Institute; G. J. M. van der Kerk, J. G. A. Luijten and J. G. Noltes, *Angew. Chem.*, 1958, **70**, 298; G. J. M. van der Kerk, J. C. van Egmond and J. G. Noltes, *Chimia*, 1961, **16**, 36; G. J. M. van der Kerk, *Chim. Ind.* (Paris), 1963, **90**, 251.

[189] R. K. Ingham, S. D. Rosenberg and H. Gilman, *Chem. Rev.*, 1960, **60**, 459.

[190] W. P. Neumann, *Angew. Chem.*, 1963, **75**, 225; *Internat. Edn.*, 1963, **2**, 165.

[191] L. I. Zakharkin, O. Yu. Okhlobystin and B. N. Strunin, *Izvest. Akad. Nauk S.S.S.R.*, 1961, 2254; 1962, 2002; *Doklady Akad. Nauk S.S.S.R.*, 1962, **144**, 1299; *Chem. Abs.*, 1962, **57**, 13799; 1963, **58**, 9131; 1962, **57**, 12515.

[192] L. I. Zakharkin and O. Yu. Okhlobystin, *Doklady Akad. Nauk S.S.S.R.*, 1957, **116**, 236; *Izvest. Akad. Nauk S.S.S.R.*, 1959, 1942; W. K. Johnson, *J. Org. Chem.*, 1960, **25**, 2253; J. C. van Egmond, M. J. Janssen, J. G. A. Luijten, G. J. M. van der Kerk and G. M. van der Want, *J. Appl. Chem.*, 1962, **12**, 17; L. I. Zakharkin, O. Yu. Okhlobystin and B. N. Strunin, *Zhur. Prikl. Khim.*, 1963, **36**, 2034; *Chem. Abs.*, 1964, **60**, 3002.

Et$_2$SnCl$_2$.AlCl$_3$ or Et$_3$SnCl.AlCl$_3$, are formed which hinder further alkylation of the tin [190]. These complications can be avoided by the addition of donor molecules, e.g. alkali metal halides, ethers or tertiary amines, which form strong complexes with the aluminium halide as it is formed, leaving the alkyltin halides free to react further to the tetra-alkyl stage [193, 194]:

$$4R_3Al + 4NaCl + 3SnCl_4 \longrightarrow 3R_4Sn + 4NaAlCl_4$$
$$4R_3Al + 4R'_3N + 3SnCl_4 \longrightarrow 3R_4Sn + 4R'_3N \cdot AlCl_3$$

Use of only a slight excess of aluminium alkyl thus leads to quantitative yields of tetra-alkyltin. Inert hydrocarbon solvents can be used instead of the more expensive ethers, and *alkylaluminium halides* may be employed as the source of alkyl groups; *aryltin* compounds can be prepared similarly [195]. Separation of the products is generally straightforward, the aluminium complex being filtered or drained off as a lower liquid layer. It is rarely necessary to hydrolyse the mixture.

When *tin alkoxides* are alkylated with Grignard reagents or aluminium alkyls, the aluminium alkoxides produced are themselves strongly associated, so complexing agents are not needed:

$$4R_3Al + 3Sn(OR')_4 \longrightarrow 3R_4Sn + 4Al(OR')_3$$

Among variations of these methods to have been patented [196], alkali metal tetra-alkylaluminates, MAlR$_4$, have been shown to alkylate either tin(IV) chloride [197], or tin itself when electrolysed using a tin anode [198].

The large-scale preparation of organotin compounds using aluminium reagents appears likely to replace earlier industrial methods. Grignard reactions have been used, although more favoured methods employed reactions between alkyl halides and tin alloyed with sodium [199], magnesium [189] or copper [200], or the Wurtz-type reaction between R$_2$SnCl$_2$ or SnCl$_4$, RCl and sodium [189, 201].

[193] W. P. Neumann, *Ann.*, 1962, **653**, 157.

[194] K. Ziegler, Brit.P. 923,179, 10 Apr. 1963.

[195] D. Wittenberg, *Ann.*, 1962, **654**, 23; Ger.P. 1,124,947, 8 Mar. 1962.

[196] R. C. Anderson, I.C.I. Ltd, Brit.P. 871,730; H. Jenkner, Kali-Chemie A.-G., Ger.P. 1,106,325; W. K. Johnson, Monsanto Chem. Co., U.S.P. 3,036,103 22 May 1962; J. R. Mangham, Ethyl Corp., U.S.P. 3,095,433, 25 June 1963.

[197] R. S. Dickson and B. O. West, *Austral. J. Chem.*, 1962, **15**, 710; H. Jenkner, Kali-Chemie A.-G., Brit.P. 900,132, 4 July 1962; *Chem. Abs.*, 1962, **57**, 15151.

[198] K. Ziegler, Ger.P. 1,127,900, 19 April 1962; P. Kobetz and R. C. Pinkerton, Ethyl Corp., U.S.P. 3,028,320, 3 April 1962; *Chem. Abs.*, 1962, **57**, 11235, 12536.

[199] J. R. Zietz, S. M. Blitzer, H. E. Redman and G. C. Robinson, *J. Org. Chem.*, 1957, **22**, 60; U.S.P., 2,852,543; *Chem. Abs.*. 1959, **53**, 4135.

[200] L. I. Zakharkin and O. Yu. Okhlobystin, *Izvest. Akad. Nauk S.S.S.R.*, 1963, 2202; *Chem. Abs.*, 1964, **60**, 9303.

[201] I. Hechenbleikner and K. R. Molt, U.S.P. 3,059,012, 16 Oct. 1962; Deutsche Advance Produktion G.m.b.H., Brit.P. 908,331, 17 Oct. 1962; *Chem. Abs.*, 1963, **58**, 6860, 12598.

Metal halides, particularly lithium halides, are said to catalyse the direct reaction between tin and butyl iodide, which gives Bu_2SnI_2 [202].

In the laboratory, organolithium reagents are useful for the preparation of tetra-aryls, particularly in those cases where Grignard reagents are difficult to prepare [189]. Organozinc reagents, used by early workers, offer no advantages over the reagents already described, especially as they are usually themselves made from other organometallic intermediates. Compounds containing different organic groups, e.g. R_3SnR', may be obtained by the treatment of partially alkylated or arylated tin halides with Grignard or organolithium reagents, and tetra-substituted compounds have been recovered from the disproportionation products when certain di- or tri-substituted tin compounds were heated.

Alkyl compounds

Tetramethyltin, Me_4Sn, m.p. $-54.9°$, b.p. $76.8°$, from methylmagnesium iodide and tin(IV) chloride in dibutyl ether, is inert to air and water, and stable to about $400°$ (the kinetics of thermal decomposition have been studied at higher temperatures [203]). The unsymmetrical $Sn-CH_3$ stretching vibration [204] occurs at 530 cm^{-1} (infrared), the Raman-active symmetrical stretching being at 508 cm^{-1}. The appearance potentials of Me_3Sn^+ in the mass spectra of tetramethyltin and various derivatives Me_3SnX have been measured and used to determine $Sn-X$ bond dissociation energies. From these studies a reorganization energy of 20–21 kcal./mole has been obtained for the $Me_3Sn\cdot$ radical on rupture of the Me_3Sn-X bond [205]. Tetramethyltin is both volatile and toxic. It shows no sign of co-ordination, unlike its halogen-substituted derivatives. It reacts slowly with concentrated halogen hydracids,

$$Me_4Sn + HX \longrightarrow Me_3SnX + CH_4$$

but rapidly with halogens, e.g.

$$Me_4Sn + Br_2 \longrightarrow Me_3SnBr + MeBr$$

Tin(IV) chloride at $20°$ reacts rapidly to form Me_3SnCl and $MeSnCl_3$, and further reaction on standing or on heating to $70°$ leads to formation of the dichloride Me_2SnCl_2. Such exchange reactions between R_4Sn and SnX_4 are a useful route to the trihalides, $RSnX_3$, although other methods for the preparation of mono- and di-halides are described below [206].

[202] V. Oakes and R. E. Hutton, *J. Organometal. Chem.*, 1965, **3**, 472; 1966, **6**, 133.

[203] C. E. Waring and W. S. Horton, *J. Amer. Chem. Soc.*, 1945, **67**, 540; W. F. Edgell and C. H. Ward, ibid., 1954, **76**, 1169.

[204] W. F. Edgell and C. H. Ward, ibid., 1955, **77**, 6486; *J. Molecular Spectroscopy*, 1962, **8**, 343.

[205] A. L. Yergey and F. W. Lampe, *J. Amer. Chem. Soc.*, 1965, **87**, 4204.

[206] W. P. Neumann and G. Burkhardt, *Annalen*, 1963, **663**, 11.

Tetramethyltin reacts with dinitrogen tetroxide in ethyl acetate to form dimethyltin dinitrate, $Me_2Sn(NO_3)_2$ [207].

Tetra-ethyltin, Et_4Sn, b.p. 175°, is readily prepared by the Grignard method, or by adding tin(IV) chloride dropwise to a strong solution of Et_3Al in Et_2O at 0°, heating to 80°, and distilling the mixture at reduced pressure [194]. It has ten different crystal forms, all with melting points within the range −136° to −125°. This is a form of rotational isomerism, the freedom of movement of the ethyl groups being restricted by inter-molecular locking in the crystal [208]. In the infrared spectrum of this compound [209], the unsymmetrical Sn–C stretching vibration occurs at 508 cm⁻¹, the Sn–C–C bending mode at 272 cm⁻¹, and C–Sn–C bending frequencies are 132 cm⁻¹ and 86 cm⁻¹. For infrared spectroscopic data on higher alkyls, see ref. [210].

Trimethylethyltin [211], Me_3EtSn, b.p. 108·2°, *dimethyldiethyltin*, Me_2Et_2Sn, b.p. 132°, and *dimethylethyl-n-propyltin*, $Me_2EtPrSn$, b.p. 153°, are examples of a large number of mixed alkyl derivatives [189] prepared generally by Grignard alkylation of halides [212]. The tendency for thermal decomposition of the higher alkyls to involve loss of olefin, leaving hydride residues, such a marked feature with alkyls of more electropositive elements, is much less pronounced in the case of Group IV alkyls. Nevertheless loss of ethylene and formation of tin hydride fragments is found to be an important feature of the breakdown of ethyltin compounds in the mass spectrometer [213a].

An examination of the reaction with iodine of a considerable number of mixed alkyls,

$$R_2R'SnI + RI \longleftarrow R_3SnR' + I_2 \longrightarrow R_3SnI + R'I$$

has shown that the ease with which alkyl groups are displaced is in the order [213]:

$$CH_3 > C_2H_5 > n\text{-}C_3H_7 > n\text{-}C_4H_9 > i\text{-}C_5H_{11} > n\text{-}C_6H_{13}$$

Steric factors generally appear to outweigh others in these reactions when they are carried out in polar solvents; in non-polar solvents, inductive effects become important [214]. This order has been known in less detail

[207] C. C. Addison, W. B. Simpson and A. Walker, *J. Chem. Soc.*, 1964, 2360.

[208] L. A. K. Staveley, H. P. Paget, B. B. Goalby and J. B. Warren, ibid., 1950, 2290.

[209] P. Taimsalu and J. L. Wood, *Trans. Faraday Soc.*, 1963, **59**, 1754; D. H. Lohmann, *J. Organometal. Chem.*, 1965, **4**, 382.

[210] R. A. Cummins, *Austral. J. Chem.*, 1963, **16**, 985; 1965, **18**, 985.

[211] R. H. Bullard and F. R. Holden, *J. Amer. Chem. Soc.*, 1931, **53**, 3150.

[212] F. H. Pollard, G. Nickless and D. N. Dolan, *Chem. and Ind.*, 1965, 1027.

[213] Z. M. Manulkin, *Zhur. obshchei Khim.*, 1944, **14**, 1047.

[213a] E. Heldt, K. Höppner and K. H. Krebs, *Z. anorg. Chem.*, 1966, **347**, 95.

[214] M. Gielen and J. Nasielski, *Bull. Soc. chim. Belges*, 1962, **71**, 32, 601; *J. Organometal. Chem.*, 1963, **1**, 173; 1967, **7**, 273.

for some time and was turned to advantage in the preparation of an optically active compound of tin by the reaction sequence [215]:

$$Me_3SnI \xrightarrow{Et_2Zn} Me_3EtSn \xrightarrow{I_2} Me_2EtSnI$$

$$\downarrow n-Pr_2Zn$$

$$MeEtn\text{-}PrSnI \xleftarrow{I_2} Me_2Etn\text{-}PrSn$$

The iodide was resolved by means of the d-camphorsulphonate.

Many other cleavage reactions of the tetra-alkyls are known. For example, organotin halides are formed by reactions with a number of inorganic halides such as tin(II), boron [216], phosphorus(V) [217], copper(II), palladium(II) and *mercury*(II) *halides* [218]:

$$R_4Sn + HgX_2 \longrightarrow R_3SnX + RHgX$$

The nitrates R_3SnNO_3 and $R_2Sn(NO_3)_2$ result from the use of mercury(I) nitrate [219]. Alkyl groups are cleaved by quite weak acids, e.g. carboxylic acids, phenols and mercaptans [189]:

$$R_4Sn + R'CO_2H \longrightarrow R_3SnO_2CR' + RH$$

Sodium in liquid ammonia forms R_3SnNa. Organolithium reagents exchange radicals [220]:

$$Cyclopropyl_4Sn + 2BuLi \longrightarrow 2 \text{ cyclopropyl Li} + cyclopropyl_2Bu_2Sn$$

Tetra-ethyltin has also been shown to be susceptible to attack by free radicals, e.g. [221]

$$Et_4Sn + CCl_4 \xrightarrow{u.v.} C_2H_6 + C_2H_4 + Et_3SnCl + Et_2SnCl_2$$

Halomethyltin compounds, like their silicon and germanium counterparts, may be prepared by the diazomethane method [222]:

$$Me_2SnCl_2 + CH_2N_2 \xrightarrow{Et_2O} Me_2Sn(Cl)CH_2Cl, \text{ b.p. } 76\text{-}79°/11 \text{ mm.}$$

---

[215] W. J. Pope and S. J. Peachey, *Proc. Chem. Soc.*, 1900, **16**, 42, 116.

[216] W. Gerrard, E. F. Mooney and R. G. Rees, *J. Chem. Soc.*, 1964, 740.

[217] P. M. Treichel and R. A. Goodrich, *Inorg. Chem.*, 1965, **4**, 1424.

[218] H. H. Anderson, ibid., 1962, **1**, 647; D. Seyferth and H. M. Cohen, ibid., p. 652.

[219] G. Tagliavini, L. Cattalini and U. Belluco, *Ric. Sci. Rend. Sez.* A2 No. 3, 1962, p. 286; *Chem. Abs.*, 1963, **59**, 1667.

[220] D. Seyferth and H. M. Cohen, *Inorg. Chem.*, 1963, **2**, 625.

[221] G. A. Razuvaev, Yu. I. Dergunov and N. S. Vyazankin, *Doklady Akad. Nauk S.S.S.R.*, 1962, **145**, 347; G. A. Razuvaev, N. S. Vyazankin, E. N. Gladyshev and I. A. Borodavko, *Zhur. obshchei Khim.*, 1962, **32**, 2154; G. A. Razuvaev, N. S. Vyazankin and O. S. D'yachkovskaya, ibid., p. 2161; *Chem. Abs.*, 1962, **57**, 15136; 1963, **58**, 7961, 7963.

[222] D. Seyferth and E. G. Rochow, *Inorg. Syntheses*, 1960, **6**, 37; K. Kramer and N. Wright, *Ber.*, 1963, **96**, 1877; R. G. Kostyanovskii and A. K. Prokof'ev, *Izvest. Akad. Nauk S.S.S.R.*, 1965, 175; *Chem. Abs.*, 1965, **62**, 11843.

The *iodide*, $Sn(CH_2I)_4$, m.p. $76°$, has been prepared from the bromide and sodium iodide in acetone [223]. Grignard reagents prepared from such derivatives have been used to prepare other substituted alkyltins, e.g. *tris(trimethylstannylmethyl)borane*, $(Me_3SnCH_2)_3B$, b.p. $90-91°/0·15$ mm., from Me_3SnCH_2MgCl and BF_3OEt_2. This is oxidized by aqueous alcoholic hydrogen peroxide to the alcohol Me_3SnCH_2OH, b.p. $58-59°/6·5$ mm. (in poor yield), which is unstable and decomposes on standing [224]. Related phosphorus compounds, e.g. $[(Ph_3PCH_2)_2SnMe_2]^{2+}$, $[Me_2SnBr_4]^{2-}$ have been prepared from $Ph_3P=CH_2$ and alkyltin halides [225]. Other substituted methyl compounds are obtained directly from Grignard or lithium reagents and a tin halide [226, 226a]:

$$HMe_2SiCH_2MgCl + Me_2SnCl_2 \longrightarrow (HMe_2SiCH_2)_2SnMe_2, \text{ b.p. } 101°/20 \text{ mm.}$$

$$4MeOCH_2Li + SnCl_4 \longrightarrow (MeOCH_2)_4Sn, \text{ b.p. } 64°/0·05 \text{ mm.}$$

The insertion of dichlorocarbene (from $PhHgCCl_2Br$) into certain tin alkyls has been found to involve C–H, not Sn–C bonds [226b]:

$$Me_3SnPr^n + PhHgCCl_2Br \xrightarrow{80°; \text{ PhH}} Me_3SnCH_2CHMeCHCl_2$$

2-Picolyltriethyltin (4.1), b.p. $120-121°/3-4$ mm., from 2-picolyllithium and triethyltin chloride, is unusual in being decomposed (to Et_3SnOH) by moist air [227].

4.1

Aryl compounds

Tetraphenyltin, Ph_4Sn, m.p. $224-225°$, is very easily prepared from tin(IV) chloride and phenylmagnesium bromide. Any phenyltin halides present in the reaction product are readily removed since they are much more soluble than tetraphenyltin (for example in ether, in which Ph_4Sn is almost insoluble).

The tin tetra-aryls react very readily with halogens (the reaction with bromine is analytically useful [228]), and specially mild conditions, such

[223] K. Hoeppner and D. Walkiewitz, *Z. Chem.*, 1962, **2**, 23; *Chem. Abs.*, 1962, **57**, 16646.
[224] D. Seyferth, *J. Amer. Chem. Soc.*, 1959, **81**, 1844.
[225] D. Seyferth and S. O. Grim, ibid., 1961, **83**, 1610.
[226] R. L. Merker, U.S.P. 3,043,858, 10 July 1962; *Chem. Abs.*, 1963, **58**, 1489.
[226a] U. Schollkopf and H.-J. Traenckner, *J. Organometal. Chem.*, 1966, **5**, 300.
[226b] D. Seyferth and S. S. Washburne, ibid., p. 389.
[227] H. Zimmer and H. Gold, *Ber.*, 1956, **89**, 712.
[228] H. J. Eméleus and P. R. Evans, *J. Chem. Soc.*, 1964, 510.

as the use of the pyridine–bromine addition compound [229], are required to obtain mono-bromides. Halogenation goes easily to the dihalide stage. Redistribution reactions between R_4Sn and tin(IV) halides are generally the preferred methods, particularly as organic groups are not lost. With N-bromosuccinimide, tetraphenyltin gives bromobenzene and an intermediate with a hydrolytically unstable Sn–N bond (4.2) [230]:

$$Ph_4Sn \ + \ BrN\underset{OC-CH_2}{\overset{CO-CH_2}{\Big\langle}} \ \xrightarrow{-PhBr} \ \left[Ph_3Sn-N\underset{OC-CH_2}{\overset{OC-CH_2}{\Big\langle}} \right] \ \xrightarrow{H_2O} \ Ph_3SnOH$$

4.2

Tetraphenyltin is hydrogenated in solution (no catalyst required) at 150–200° and 60 atm. to tin and benzene; only traces of biphenyl are formed [26, 231].

Tetraphenyltin exchanges one phenyl group for a fluorine in reactions with certain fluorides of non-metals (e.g. BF_3, PF_5) which provide a convenient route to triphenyltin fluoride [232].

$$Ph_4Sn \ + \ 2BF_3 \longrightarrow PhBF_2 \ + \ Ph_3SnBF_4 \xrightarrow{heat} Ph_3SnF \ + \ BF_3 \uparrow$$

Potassium amide in liquid ammonia causes complete ammonolysis [233]:

$$Ph_4Sn \ + \ 4NH_3 \ + \ 2KNH_2 \longrightarrow K_2[Sn(NH_2)_6] \ + \ 4C_6H_6$$

Tetra-aryls with large aryl groups (e.g. naphthyl, mesityl, biphenyl) generally require organolithium reagents for their preparation, Grignard reagents being insufficiently reactive, and their low solubility makes purification difficult. Tetra-1-naphthyltin, for example, was crystallized from a boiling mixture of dimethylformamide and o-dichlorobenzene [234].

Mixed alkyl–aryltin compounds are generally prepared from R_nSnX_{4-n} and the appropriate Grignard reagent,

$$Me_3SnBr \ + \ PhMgBr \longrightarrow Me_3PhSn \ + \ MgBr_2$$

but reactions of organotin alkali metal derivatives have also been applied:

$$Ph_2SnNa_2 \ + \ 2MeI \xrightarrow{NH_3} Me_2Ph_2Sn \ + \ 2NaI$$
$$Ph_3SnLi \ + \ PhCH_2Cl \longrightarrow Ph_3SnCH_2Ph \ + \ LiCl$$

Phenyltriethyltin, $PhEt_3Sn$, b.p. 254°, has been obtained not only from

[229] E. Krause, *Ber.*, 1918, **51**, 912; E. Krause and K. Weinberg, ibid., 1929, **62**, 2235.

[230] E. J. Kupchik and T. Lanigan, *J. Org. Chem.*, 1962, **27**, 3661.

[231] L. L. Gershbein and V. N. Ipatieff, *J. Amer. Chem. Soc.*, 1952, **74**, 1540.

[232] D. W. A. Sharp and J. M. Winfield, *J. Chem. Soc.*, 1965, 2278.

[233] O. Schmitz-DuMont, G. Müller and W. Schaal, *Z. anorg. Chem.*, 1964, **332**, 263.

[234] G. Bähr and R. Gelius, *Ber.*, 1958, **91**, 812, 818.

PhSnCl₃ and EtMgBr, but also by the interesting reaction [235]:

$$Et_3Sn \cdot SnEt_3 + Ph_2Hg \longrightarrow Hg + 2Et_3PhSn$$

The reactions of mixed aryl derivatives with hydrogen chloride (or with halogens) show that the ease of displacement of groups by halogen increases in the order:

cyclohexyl < phenyl < 1-naphthyl < o-anisyl < 2-thienyl

Similar studies on mixed alkyl–aryl compounds have shown that, as with organogermanium compounds, halogens or their hydracids displace aryl groups in preference to normal alkyl groups. Benzyl is intermediate in this respect between alkyl and aryl.

Large numbers of substituted phenyltin compounds have been prepared [31, 236], particularly in connexion with studies of the effect of different substituents in the ring on the ease of cleavage of phenyl groups from tin by various reagents [33, 237]. It is deduced that there is some d–p interaction between the tin atoms and attached phenyl groups [238].

Unsaturated alkyltin compounds

These are appreciably more reactive than saturated alkyl derivatives, both in that the tin–carbon bond is more readily broken, and in that addition reactions to the multiple bond can occur. *Tetravinyltin*, $(CH_2:CH)_4Sn$, b.p. 160°, decomposes above about 200°. It may be prepared from vinyl-magnesium bromide and tin(IV) chloride in tetrahydrofuran, a solvent that has been recommended for use in the preparation of other organotin compounds by the Grignard method [239]. The mobility of alkenyl groups attached to tin is reflected by the reaction between tetravinyltin and phenyl-lithium (see p. 13)

$$(CH_2:CH)_4Sn + 4PhLi \xrightarrow{Et_2O} 4CH_2:CHLi + Ph_4Sn$$

The tetraphenyltin is precipitated, leaving a solution of vinyl-lithium [240].

[235] K. A. Kocheshkov, A. N. Nesmeyanov and V. P. Pusyreva, *Ber.*, 1936, **69**, 1639.

[236] C. Eaborn and J. A. Waters, *J. Chem. Soc.*, 1962, 1131; O. Buchman, M. Grosjean and J. Nasielski, *Bull. Soc. chim. Belges*, 1962, **71**, 467; R. G. Neville, *Canad. J. Chem.*, 1963, **41**, 814; G. Drefahl and D. Lorenz, *J. prakt. Chem.*, 1964, **24**, 106.

[237] C. Eaborn and J. A. Waters, *J. Chem. Soc.*, 1961, 542; R. W. Bott, C. Eaborn and J. A. Waters, *Proc. Chem. Soc.*, 1963, 51; *J. Chem. Soc.*, 1963, 681; O. Buchman, M. Grosjean and J. Nasielski, *Bull Soc. chim. Belges*, 1963, **72**, 286; H. Hashimoto and Y. Morimoto, *J. Organometal. Chem.*, 1967, **8**, 271.

[238] H. H. Freedman and T. A. Gosink, Cincinnatti Symposium, 1963, Abstracts, p. 33; H. H. Huang and K. M. Hui, *J. Organometal. Chem.*, 1964, **2**, 288.

[239] D. Seyferth and F. G. A. Stone, *J. Amer. Chem. Soc.*, 1957, **79**, 515; D. Seyferth and L. G. Vaughan, *J. Organometal. Chem.*, 1963, **1**, 138.

[240] D. Seyferth and M. A. Weiner, *J. Amer. Chem. Soc.*, 1961, **83**, 3583.

Allyl groups may also be transferred readily from tin to lithium [241], and similar transmetallation reactions occur between thallium trichloride and tin alkenyls [242]. The experiments with *cis*- and *trans*-propenyl derivatives have shown these groups to retain their configuration when transferred from tin to lithium in reactions between MeCH:CHSnR₃ and R'Li [243], but with metallic lithium the transfer of the propenyl group may involve isomerization [243a]. The geometrical isomers are readily identified by their proton magnetic resonance spectra, which have been recorded and analysed in considerable detail in the case of such reference compounds as (*trans*-MeCH:CH)₄Sn, *trans*-MeCH:CHGeMe₃ and *trans*-PhCH:CHSnMe₃ [243b]. A similar mobility is not observed with side chains such as CH₂:CHCH₂CH₂—, in which the double bond is separated from the tin by three or more carbon atoms [241].

Mixed vinyl- and alkyl- or aryl-tin compounds are accessible from vinylmagnesium bromide and the appropriate alkyl- or aryl-tin halide. A rather less convenient method of preparation involves the addition of an organotin hydride to an acetylene in the presence of a catalyst to generate free radicals, e.g. [244].

$$Bu_3SnH + HC\!:\!CH \xrightarrow[\substack{80-85°, \text{ benzene}}]{\text{azobis(isobutyronitrile)}} Bu_3SnCH\!:\!CH_2, \quad \text{b.p. } 88°/0.9 \text{ mm.}$$

Tetravinyltin is completely cleaved by anhydrous carboxylic acids [245]:

$$(CH_2\!:\!CH)_4Sn + 4RCO_2H \longrightarrow Sn(O_2CR)_4 + 4CH_2\!:\!CH_2$$

The vinyl group offers some scope for the preparation of organotin compounds with reactive groups, as the following examples show [246, 247]:

$$Et_3SnCH\!:\!CH_2 + CHCl_3 \xrightarrow{Bz_2O_2} Et_3SnCH_2CH_2CCl_3$$
$$Bu_3SnCH\!:\!CH_2 + H_2S \xrightarrow{h\nu} Bu_3SnCH_2CH_2SH$$

Iodomethylzinc iodide, ICH₂ZnI, gives cyclopropyl derivatives, although the reaction mixtures are difficult to work up and cyclopropyltin compounds are therefore better prepared by the Grignard method [248]. These

[241] D. Seyferth and M. A. Weiner, *J. Amer. Chem. Soc.*, 1962, **84**, 361; D. Seyferth and T. F. Jula, *J. Organometal. Chem.* 1967, **8**, P. 13.

[242] A. E. Borisov and N. V. Novikova, *Izvest. Akad. Nauk S.S.S.R.*, 1959, 1670; A. N. Nesmeyanov, A. E. Borisov and N. V. Novikova, ibid., p. 1216.

[243] D. Seyferth and L. G. Vaughan, *J. Amer. Chem. Soc.*, 1964, **86**, 883.

[243a] D. Seyferth, R. Suzuki and L. G. Vaughan, ibid., 1966, **88**, 286.

[243b] L. G. Vaughan and D. Seyferth, *J. Organometal. Chem.*, 1966, **5**, 295.

[244] E. M. Smolin and M. N. O'Connor, U.S.P. 3,074,985, Jan. 1963; *Chem. Abs.*, 1963, **58**, 12599; R. F. Fulton, *Dissert. Abst.*, 1962, **22**, 3397.

[245] A. Henderson and A. K. Holliday, *J. Organometal. Chem.*, 1965, **4**, 377.

[246] D. Seyferth, *J. Org. Chem.*, 1957, **22**, 1251.

[247] W. Stamm, ibid., 1963, **28**, 3264.

[248] D. Seyferth and H. M. Cohen, *Inorg. Chem.*, 1962, **1**, 913.

and other reactions of vinyltin compounds have been reviewed by Seyferth [249].

Tetra-allyltin, $(CH_2:CHCH_2)_4Sn$, b.p. 69–70°/1·5 mm., from allylmagnesium bromide and tin(IV) chloride, immediately reacts with bromine to give triallyltin bromide [250]. It can be used as a source of *allyl-lithium*, either in the form of an ether solution (from the reaction with PhLi in ether) or as the solid (from BuLi in pentane) [241, 251]. Like vinyltin compounds allyl derivatives undergo addition reactions to the double bond, e.g. [247]

$$Bu_3SnCH_2CH:CH_2 \xrightarrow[-70°]{H_2S \; h\nu} Bu_3Sn(CH_2)_3SH$$

Allyl groups are cleaved from tin more readily than vinyl or phenyl by electrophilic reagents [252].

The proton magnetic resonance spectra of tetravinyltin and tetraallyltin have been interpreted as evidence of metal–carbon $d\pi$–$p\pi$ bonding in these derivatives [252a].

Cyclopentadienyltin compounds are unstable, being easily hydrolysed and oxidized. *Biscyclopentadienyltin(II)*, m.p. 105°, from cyclopentadienyl-sodium and tin(II) chloride in tetrahydrofuran, is colourless unlike other organic tin(II) compounds [253], although bismethylcyclopentadienyltin(II) is a pale yellow. The tin(IV) compounds [254], from $(C_5H_5)_4Sn$ to $C_5H_5SnPh_3$, prepared from cyclopentadienylmagnesium bromide and the appropriate tin(IV) halide, are even more reactive, sometimes taking fire spontaneously in the air. The vibrational and nuclear magnetic resonance spectra and dipole moments of the cyclopentadienyls of tin(II) and lead(II) provided evidence for angular 'sandwich' structures [255], although their far infrared spectra were apparently more readily interpreted in terms of σ-bonded structures in which the position of attachment of the metal to a particular ring could change readily [256]. A subsequent electron diffraction study, however, confirmed the angular sandwich structure for these compounds in the vapour phase [257]

[249] D. Seyferth, 'Vinyl Compounds of Metals', *Progress in Inorganic Chemistry*, ed. F. A. Cotton, Interscience, 1962, Vol. **3**, 129.
[250] K. V. Vijayaraghavan, *J. Indian Chem. Soc.*, 1945, **22**, 135.
[251] D. Seyferth and M. A. Weiner, *J. Org. Chem.*, 1961, **26**, 4797.
[252] H. G. Kuivila and J. A. Verdone, *Tetrahedron Letters*, 1964, 119.
[252a] D. J. Blears, S. S. Danyluk and S. Cawley, *J. Organometal. Chem.*, 1966, **6**, 284.
[253] E. O. Fischer and H. Grubert, *Z. Naturforsch.*, 1956, **11b**, 423.
[254] H. Gilman and L. A. Gist, *J. Org. Chem.*, 1957, **22**, 250; H. P. Fritz and C. G. Kreiter, *J. Organometal. Chem.*, 1964, **1**, 323.
[255] L. D. Dave, D. F. Evans and G. Wilkinson, *J. Chem. Soc.*, 1959, 3684.
[256] H. P. Fritz and E. O. Fischer, *ibid.*, 1961, 547; D. A. Brown, *ibid.*, p. 690; H. P. Fritz and C. G. Kreiter, *J. Organometal Chem.*, 1965, **4**, 313.
[257] A. Almenningen, A. Haaland and T. Motzfeldt, *ibid.*, 1967, **7**, 97.

C_1—C_2 1·431 ± 0·009 Å

125°——Sn C_1—H_1 1·142 ± 0·056 Å .

Sn—C   2·706 ± 0·024 Å

Vapour phase structure of $(C_5H_5)_2Sn$

Acetylenic derivatives of tin are very reactive, often being decomposed even by water. They have generally been prepared from tin halides and alkali metal acetylene derivatives or Grignard reagents, although variations on these methods have been successful in some instances [258]. A recent development has used the reactivity of amino-tin compounds towards weakly acidic compounds HA [259]:

$$R_3SnNMe_2 + HA \longrightarrow R_3SnA + Me_2NH$$

The wide applicability of this reaction is discussed below. With mildly acidic hydrocarbons like acetylenes, $HC:CR'$, reaction is nearly quantitative under mild conditions:

$$Me_3SnNMe_2 + HC:CPh \longrightarrow Me_3SnC:CPh + Me_2NH$$

Alkoxy-tin compounds R_3SnOR or oxides $(R_3Sn)_2O$ have also been used instead of amino derivatives [260].

$$(R_3Sn)_2O + 2R'C:CH \longrightarrow 2R'C:CSnR_3 + H_2O$$

The water eliminated may be removed by the action of calcium hydride or by azeotropic distillation with benzene.

Acetylene itself gives *bistrimethylstannylacetylene*, $Me_3SnC:CSnMe_3$. This method may be compared with the synthesis of the *ethyl* analogue by the addition of monosodium acetylide to triethyltin chloride in liquid ammonia:

$$Et_3SnCl \xrightarrow{CH:CNa} Et_3SnC:CH \xrightarrow{CH:CNa} Et_3SnC:CNa \xrightarrow{Et_3SnCl} Et_3Sn·C:C·SnEt_3,$$
b.p. 123°/0·05 mm.

The *phenyl* compound, $Ph_3SnC:CSnPh_3$, m.p. 153°, may also be prepared this way, or from triphenyltin chloride and acetylenedimagnesium bro-

[258] H. Hartmann *et al.*, *Naturwiss.*, 1959, **46**, 321; 1963, **50**, 373; 1965, **52**, 59, 303; P. Cadiot *et al.*, *Compt. rend.*, 1960, **251**, 730; 1963, **257**, 1111; *Bull. Soc. chim. France*, 1965, 35; A. A. Petrov, K. S. Mingaleva and V. S. Zavgorodnii, *Zhur. obshchei Khim.*, 1964, **34**, 533; 1965, **35**, 931; *Chem. Abs.*, 1964, **60**, 15900; 1965, **63**, 7033; M. F. Shostakovskii, V. M. Vlasov and R. G. Mirskov, *Zhur. obshchei Khim.*, 1965, **35**, 750; *Chem. Abs.*, 1965, **63**, 4322.

[259] K. Jones and M. F. Lappert, *Proc. Chem. Soc.*, 1964, 22.

[260] W. P. Neumann and F. G. Kleiner, *Tetrahedron Letters*, 1964, 3779; I. F. Lutsenko, S. V. Ponomarev and O. P. Petrii, *Zhur. obshchei Khim.*, 1962, **32**, 896; *Chem. Abs.*, 1963, **58**, 3455; M. F. Shostakovskii *et al.*, *Doklady Akad. Nauk S.S.S.R.*, 1964, **159**, 869, 918; 1965, **163**, 390; *Zhur. obshchei Khim.*, 1964, **34**, 2843, 3178; *Chem. Abs.*, 1964, **61**, 14700; 1965, **62**, 2788, 4046, 7788.

mide, or triphenyltin sodium and di-iodoacetylene, or dimethylamino-(triphenyl)tin, Ph_3SnNMe_2, and acetylene. Fairly stable to water, they are hydrolysed by strong alkali, and by methanol. They react rapidly with halogens, and with copper(I) and silver salts, giving acetylides Cu_2C_2 and Ag_2C_2 [261].

A further method of preparing tin acetylides is by the decarboxylation of tin acetylene carboxylates [262]:

$$Bu_3SnO_2CC{:}CCO_2SnBu_3 \xrightarrow{heat} 2CO_2 \uparrow + Bu_3SnC{:}CSnBu_3$$

Diels–Alder reactions between alkynyltin compounds and dienes can be used to prepare cyclic derivatives [262a]:

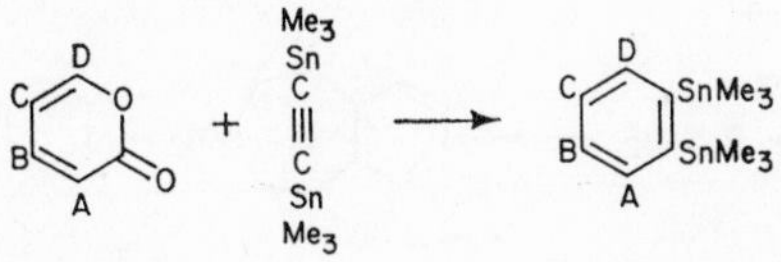

Ethynyltin compounds may be explosive. Although the infrared spectrum of a sample of $(HC{:}C)_4Sn$ was recorded without difficulty $[\nu(C{:}C) = 2043$ cm$^{-1}]$ it exploded before Raman data could be collected [40a].

Alkenynyl derivatives of tin, e.g. $Et_3SnC{:}CCH{:}CH_2$, may be prepared from the Grignard or lithium reagent [263]. Addition of triphenylmethyl radicals to these leads to either acetylenes or allenes [264]:

$$Et_3SnC{:}CCMe{:}CH_2 \xrightarrow{Ph_3C\cdot} Et_3SnC(CPh_3){:}C{:}CMeCH_2CPh_3$$

Heterocyclic compounds

The heterocycles which may be regarded as derivatives of cyclohexane, cycloheptane [265], cyclopentadiene and 5,10-dihydroacridine [53] have been prepared by methods analogous to those used for the germanium compounds (see p. 382).

For example, the saturated ring compounds may be prepared from suitable di-Grignard or di-lithium reagents [48]:

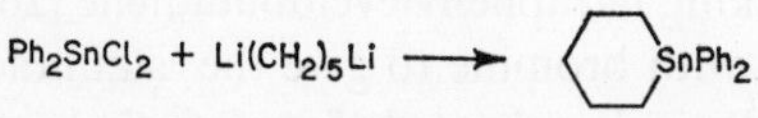

[261] C. Beermann and H. Hartmann, Z. anorg. Chem., 1954, 276, 20.

[262] J. G. A. Luitjen and G. J. M. van der Kerk, Rec. Trav. chim., 1964, 83, 295.

[262a] A. B. Evnin and D. Seyferth, J. Amer. Chem. Soc., 1967, 89, 952; D. Seyferth and A. B. Evnin, ibid., p. 1468.

[263] M. L. Quan and P. Cadiot, Compt. rend., 1962, 254, 133; V. S. Zavgorodnii and A. A. Petrov, Doklady Akad. Nauk S.S.S.R., 1962, 143, 855; Zhur. obshchei Khim., 1962, 32, 3527; 1963, 33, 2791; Chem. Abs., 1962, 57, 3466; 1963, 58, 12593, 59, 15297.

[264] V. S. Zavgorodnii and A. A. Petrov, Doklady Akad. Nauk S.S.S.R., 1963, 149, 846; Chem. Abs., 1963, 59, 7550.

[265] H. G. Kuivila and O. F. Beumel, Jr, J. Amer. Chem. Soc., 1958, 80, 3250.

The formation of six-membered and spiro heterocycles from Bu_2AlH and $Me_2C(CH:CH_2)_2$ has been mentioned earlier [266] (p. 331). Rings containing *two* heteroatoms result from the addition of organotin dihydrides, R_2SnH_2, to divinyl-silicon, -germanium or -tin compounds, $R'_2M(CH:CH_2)_2$, (where M = Si, Ge or Sn) [50]:

$$R_2SnH_2 + (CH_2:CH)_2MR'_2 \longrightarrow R_2Sn\underset{\bigcirc}{}MR'_2$$

The addition of organotin dihydrides to *o*-divinylbenzene leads to 7- and 14-membered ring systems,

while unsaturated ring systems related to these can be prepared from *o*-$C_6H_4(C:CH)_2$ [267].

The unsaturated *stannole* ring may be prepared from the di-lithium derivative of a butadiene [52, 268]:

R = Me, m.p. 192–193°; R = Ph, m.p. 174°   m.p. 281–282°

Some reactions of such stannoles have been explored with the object (not realized) of making tetraphenylcyclobutadiene [269]. The ring may be cleaved by reaction with bromine to give the 'stannole dibromide' (4.3*b*), which loses Me_2SnBr_2 when heated, forming the cyclobutadiene dimer, *octaphenylcyclo-octatetraene* (4.3*a*). With nickel bromide, the tetraphenyl-cyclobutadiene nickel bromide complex is formed.

[266] R. Polster, *Annalen*, 1962, **654**, 20.
[267] A. J. Leusink, J. G. Noltes, H. A. Budding and G. J. M. van der Kerk, *Rec. Trav. chim.*, 1964, **83**, 1036.
[268] E. H. Braye, W. Hübel and I. Caplier, *J. Amer. Chem. Soc.*, 1961, **83**, 4406.
[269] H. H. Freedman, ibid., pp. 2194, 2195; *J. Org. Chem.*, 1962, **27**, 2298; H. H. Freedman and D. R. Peterson, *J. Amer. Chem. Soc.*, 1962, **84**, 2837.

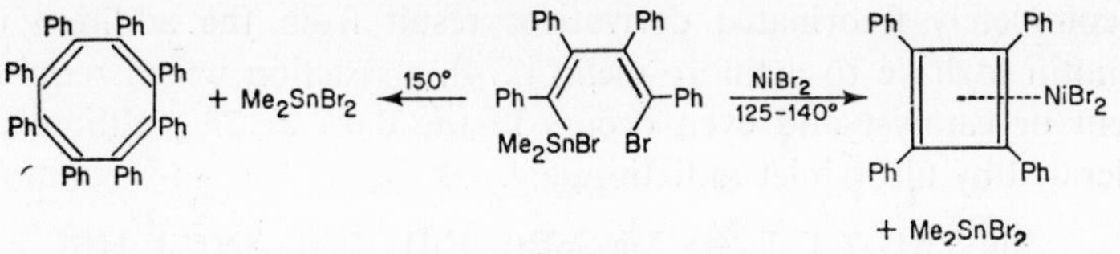

4.3a   4.3b

Dibenzostannoles result from 2,2′-dilithium-biphenyl and either an organotin dihalide or organotin monohalide [270]. Use of SnCl₄ leads to the spiro compound.

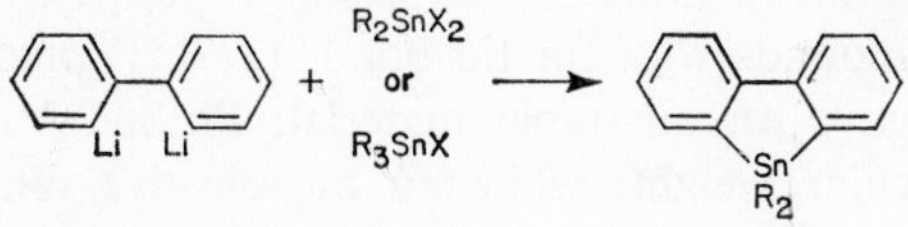

Related stanniepins may be prepared similarly [271]:

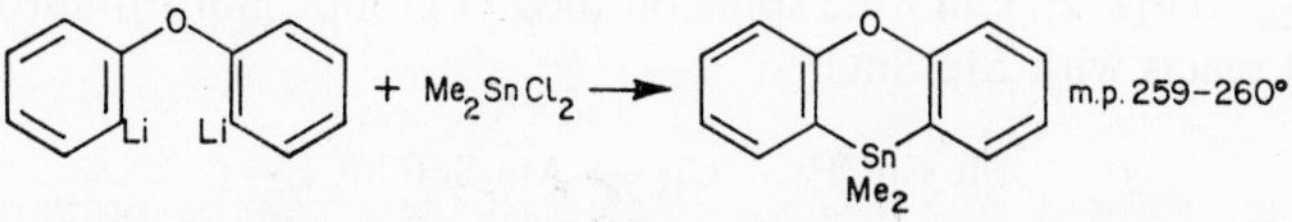

The dimethyl derivative shown is *dimeric* in ethyl methyl ketone or dioxan at 37°, possibly on account of O→Sn co-ordination.

The formation of unsaturated ring systems containing a transition metal, generally by reactions involving carbonyls, is described in Volume II.

Fluorocarbon derivatives of tin

Perfluoro-alkyl, -vinyl and *-phenyl* derivatives of tin have been prepared during the last few years. Perfluoroalkyl compounds may be prepared by the reaction between hexa-alkyldistannanes and perfluoroalkyl iodides, e.g. [272, 273]

$$Me_6Sn_2 + CF_3I \xrightarrow{80°} Me_3SnCF_3 + Me_3SnI$$

Reaction between a tetra-alkyltin and a perfluoroalkyl iodide under irradiation by ultraviolet radiation gives only traces of perfluoroalkyltin compounds, whereas perfluoroalkyl-lead derivatives are obtained in good yield from the analogous reaction between a tetra-alkyl-lead and a perfluoroalkyl iodide [273].

[270] R. Gelius, *Angew. Chem.*, 1960, **72**, 322; *Ber.*, 1960, **93**, 1759.
[271] E. J. Kupchik and J. A. Ursino, *Chem. and Ind.*, 1965, 794.
[272] H. C. Clark and C. J. Willis, *J. Amer. Chem. Soc.*, 1960, **82**, 1888.
[273] H. D. Kaesz, J. R. Phillips and F. G. A. Stone, ibid., p. 6228.

Incompletely fluorinated derivatives result from the addition of an organotin hydride to a fluoro-olefin [274], a reaction which requires no solvent or catalyst and even occurs in the dark at 25°, although it is accelerated by ultraviolet radiation, e.g.

$$Me_2SnH_2 + C_2F_4 \longrightarrow Me_2SnH(C_2F_4H) + Me_2Sn(C_2F_4H)_2$$

The mechanism suggested involves either radicals or a four-centre transition complex [275]. As ^{13}C, ^{112}Sn and ^{119}Sn are magnetic nuclei in small abundance it was possible to determine 31 coupling constants from the proton and ^{19}F magnetic resonance spectra of these last compounds [276].

A further method of attaching fluoroalkyl groups to tin uses fluoro-olefins and compounds with tin–tin bonds [277]. Diphenyltin and tetra-fluoroethylene gave an air-stable material, $Ph_2SnC_2F_4$, m.p. 128°, of unknown molecular weight, while an air-sensitive oil, thought to be $Me_3SnC_2F_4SnMe_3$, was obtained from Me_6Sn_2 and C_2F_4.

Perfluoroalkyltin bonds are cleaved by basic hydrolysis, with evolution of $C_nF_{2n+1}H$ [272]. Chlorine splits off methyl groups, not trifluoromethyl, when it reacts with Me_3SnCF_3:

$$Me_3SnCF_3 + Cl_2 \longrightarrow Me_2Sn(Cl)CF_3$$

Pyrolysis of Me_3SnCF_3 apparently gives $\cdot CF_2 \cdot$ radicals, since when heated alone or with C_2F_4 it gives perfluorocyclopropane, C_3F_6 [273]. Difluoro-carbene is formed under much milder conditions by reaction with sodium iodide in boiling 1,2-dimethoxyethane [278].

The reactions of trifluoromethyl derivatives of Group IV metals are believed to reflect in part the increased M–C and decreased C–F bond orders which result from metal–carbon $d\pi$–$p\pi$ bonding, although the multiplicity of the M–C bond is probably less than in transition metal derivatives such as $CF_3Mn(CO)_5$ [278a].

Perfluorovinyltin compounds are accessible through the reaction between the Grignard reagent, $CF_2:CFMgBr$, and an appropriate organotin halide in tetrahydrofuran [279], although better yields result when the

[274] H. C. Clark, S. G. Furnival and J. T. Kwon, *Canad. J. Chem.*, 1963, **41**, 2889; C. G. Krespan and V. A. Engelhardt, *J. Org. Chem.*, 1958, **23**, 1565.

[275] C. Barnetson, H. C. Clark and J. T. Kwon, *Chem. and Ind.*, 1964, 458.

[276] H. C. Clark, J. T. Kwon, L. W. Reeves and E. J. Wells, *Canad. J. Chem.*, 1963, **41**, 3005.

[277] M. A. Beg and H. C. Clark, *Chem. and Ind.*, 1962, 140; H. C. Clark and J. H. Tsai, *Chem. Comm.*, 1965, 111; W. R. Cullen, D. S. Dawson and G. E. Styan, *J. Organometal. Chem.*, 1965, **3**, 406.

[278] D. Seyferth, J. Y-P. Mui, M. E. Gordon and J. M. Burlitch, *J. Amer. Chem. Soc.*, 1965, **87**, 681.

[278a] H. C. Clark and J. H. Tsai, *J. Organometal. Chem.*, 1967, **7**, 515.

[279] H. D. Kaesz, S. L. Stafford and F. G. A. Stone, *J. Amer. Chem. Soc.*, 1960, **82**, 6232.

Grignard reagent is prepared *in situ* with the tin halide already present [280]:

$$Ph_3SnX + Mg + CF_2:CFBr \longrightarrow Ph_3SnCF:CF_2, \quad m.p. \ 68°$$

Perfluorovinyl groups are cleaved from tin by such reagents as halogens, hydrogen halides, aqueous alcohol, and alcoholic acetic acid [280, 281]. In the reaction with mercury(II) halides [280], the perfluorovinyl group is transferred to mercury, giving $CF_2:CFHgX$, and *perfluorovinyl-lithium* may be prepared by exchange reactions with phenyl- or butyl-lithium [282]:

$$PhSn(CF:CF_2)_3 + 3PhLi \xrightarrow{-40°} Ph_4Sn + 3CF_2:CFLi$$

Incompletely fluorinated alkenyltin compounds result from addition of organotin hydrides to fluoroacetylenes [282a], e.g.

$$R_3SnH + CF_3C:CCF_3 \longrightarrow trans\text{-}CF_3CH:C(CF_3)SnR_3$$

Pentafluorophenyltin compounds have been prepared by the Grignard method, e.g. [283, 284, 285, 287]

$$SnCl_4 + 4C_6F_5MgBr \longrightarrow (C_6F_5)_4Sn, \quad m.p. \ 221°$$

Pentafluorophenyl-lithium [27] may be used instead of the Grignard reagent. The trichloride, $C_6F_5SnCl_3$, may be obtained from methylpentafluorophenylmercury [285]:

$$SnCl_4 + MeHgC_6F_5 \longrightarrow MeHgCl + C_6F_5SnCl_3$$

Bis(pentafluorophenyl)mercury, $(C_6F_5)_2Hg$, when hot reacts with metallic tin to give $(C_6F_5)_4Sn$ [286].

Compounds $R_nSn(C_6F_5)_{4-n}$ (R = alkyl or aryl, n = 0→3) are thermally stable and resistant to hydrolysis in the absence of halide or cyanide ion; in the presence of catalytic quantities of these ions they are rapidly hydrolysed, giving pentafluorobenzene [285]:

$$Me_3SnC_6F_5 + H_2O \xrightarrow{X^-} Me_3SnOH + C_6F_5H$$

The relative ease of cleavage of groups from tin by boron halides or hydrogen chloride is $C_6H_5 > C_6F_5 > CH_3$. The use of reactions between pentafluorophenyltin compounds and boron halides to prepare pentafluorophenyl derivatives of boron has been mentioned in Chapter 3 (p. 225).

[280] D. Seyferth, K. Braendle and G. Raab, *Angew. Chem.*, 1960, **72**, 77.

[281] D. Seyferth, G. Raab and K. A. Braendle, *J. Org. Chem.*, 1961, **26**, 2934.

[282] D. Seyferth, D. E. Welch and G. Raab, *J. Amer. Chem. Soc.*, 1962, **84**, 4266.

[282a] W. R. Cullen and G. E. Styan, *J. Organometal. Chem.*, 1966, **6**, 117.

[283] J. M. Holmes, R. D. Peacock and J. C. Tatlow, *Proc. Chem. Soc.*, 1963, 108; *J. Chem. Soc. (A)*, 1966, 150.

[284] J. L. W. Pohlmann, F. E. Brinckman, G. Tesi and R. E. Donadio, *Z. Naturforsch.*, 1956, **20b**, 1.

[285] R. D. Chambers and T. Chivers, *Proc. Chem. Soc.*, 1963, 208; *J. Chem. Soc.*, 1964, 4782.

[286] J. Burdon, P. L. Coe and M. Fulton, ibid., 1965, 2094.

[287] A. G. Massey, E. W. Randall and D. Shaw, *Chem. and Ind.*, 1963, 1244.

The magnitude of the quadrupole splitting in the Mössbauer spectra of a number of organotin compounds indicates that the electron-attracting properties of groups attached to tin decrease in the series [283, 288]:

$$C_6F_5 \sim Br > Ph > Me$$

Mössbauer data on other organotin compounds are to be found in [289].

A few *perchloro-* and *perbromo*-organotin compounds are known. The hydrogen of chloroform or bromoform is sufficiently acidic to cleave tin–nitrogen bonds [289a]:

$$R_3SnNEt_2 + HCX_3 \rightarrow R_3SnCX_3 + Et_2NH \quad (X = Cl \text{ or } Br)$$

Other routes to these derivatives use lithium or mercury reagents [289b]:

$$Me_3SnCl + LiCCl_3 \xrightarrow{-110°} Me_3SnCCl_3 + LiCl$$

$$Me_3SnBr + PhHgCCl_2Br \xrightarrow{80°;\ C_6H_6} Me_3SnCCl_2Br + PhHgBr$$

Like the mercurials, these perhalomethyltin derivatives can act as sources of CX_2. *Pentachlorophenyltin* compounds are accessible by the Grignard route [289c]:

$$C_6Cl_5MgCl + SnCl_4 \rightarrow (C_6Cl_5)_4Sn, \quad \text{m.p. } 446–9° \text{ (decomp.)}$$

Organotin halides

These are valuable intermediates in the preparation of very many organotin compounds; they may be obtained by halogenation of the fully substituted compound, R_4Sn, or by various reactions starting from metallic tin or its inorganic compounds.

Rearrangement reactions between tin(IV) halides and tetra-alkyls or -aryls, R_4Sn, are the most widely useful method of preparing organotin halides. In theory a particular halide might be obtained by taking R_4Sn and SnX_4 in suitable proportions:

$$3R_4Sn + SnCl_4 \rightarrow 4R_3SnCl$$
$$R_4Sn + SnCl_4 \rightarrow 2R_2SnCl_2$$
$$R_4Sn + 3SnCl_4 \rightarrow 4RSnCl_3$$

The various equilibria involved in these reactions have been studied by ^1H m.r. spectroscopy [290]. In practice, although high yields of the desired

[288] M. C. Hayes, *J. Inorg. Nucl. Chem.*, 1964, **26**, 2307.
[289] V. I. Gol'danskii, O. Yu. Okhlobystin, V. Ya. Rochev and V. V. Khrapov, *J. Organometal. Chem.*, 1965, **4**, 160; T. C. Gibb and N. N. Greenwood, *J. Chem. Soc. (A)*, 1966, 43; M. Cordey-Hayes, R. D. Peacock and M. Vucelic, *J. Inorg. Nucl. Chem.*, 1967, **29**, 1177; J. Nasielski, N. Sprecher, J. Devooght and S. Lejeune, *J. Organometal. Chem.*, 1967, **8**, 97; R. H. Herber and G. I. Parisi, *Inorg. Chem.*, 1966, **5**, 769.
[289a] A. G. Davies and T. N. Mitchell, *J. Organometal. Chem.*, 1966, **6**, 568.
[289b] D. Seyferth, F. M. Armbrecht, B. Prokai and R. J. Cross, ibid., p. 573.
[289c] H. Gilman and S.-Y. Sim, ibid., 1967, **7**, 249.
[290] D. Grant and J. R. Van Wazer, ibid., 1965, **4**, 229; E. V. van den Berghe and G. P. van der Kelen, ibid., 1966, **6**, 522.

product are obtained from the first two reactions [291], carried out at above 180°, the third reaction was found to be useful only for aryl [291] or vinyl [239] compounds. However, the first stage in these reactions, which occurs at temperatures as low as 0–20°, may be used for the preparation of the trihalide [190, 206]:

$$R_4Sn + SnCl_4 \xrightarrow[0-20°]{rapid} R_3SnCl + RSnCl_3 \xrightarrow{slow} 2R_2SnCl_2$$

In this case it is necessary to separate the mono- and tri-chlorides by vacuum distillation, or even by aqueous extraction of the trichloride followed by distillation [292]. A modification rather less wasteful of alkyl groups is to use an *excess* of SnX_4 at higher temperatures, and to separate the tri-halide from unchanged SnX_4 and dihalide R_2SnCl_2 [206]:

$$R_4Sn + 3SnCl_4 \longrightarrow R_2SnCl_2 + 2RSnCl_3 + SnCl_4$$

Although organotin compounds may be halogenated by many other reagents, e.g. halogens, hydrogen halides, and various inorganic halides [218, 293], these reactions are less useful synthetically.

Mixtures of mono- and di-halides result from the action of an alkyl halide on tin or a tin–sodium alloy. This reaction may be carried out in a sealed tube at 150–180°, or in the case of ethyl iodide at room temperature in sunlight. Methyl chloride and bromide react with tin at 315° at atmospheric pressure; copper acts as a catalyst, the process apparently being similar to the preparation of methyl-silicon and -germanium halides [294].

Catalytic amounts of zinc or magnesium are also effective at promoting reaction between tin and alkyl halides [295], while mercury(II) chloride and organic bases have been shown to catalyse the formation of diallyltin dibromide from allyl bromide and tin in boiling toluene [296]. Dibenzyltin dichloride may be prepared in 88% yield in the same solvent, and even higher yields of tribenzyltin chloride have been obtained in boiling water

[291] K. A. Kozeschkow, *Ber.*, 1929, **62**, 996; 1933, **66**, 1661; K. A. Kozeschkow and M. M. Nadj, ibid., 1934, **67**, 717; K. A. Kozeschkow, M. M. Nadj and A. P. Alexandrov, ibid., p. 1348; H. Zimmer and H. W. Sparman, ibid., 1954, **87**, 645; H. Gilman and L. A. Gist, Jr, *J. Org. Chem.*, 1957, **22**, 368.

[292] C. Doerfelt, Ger.P. 1,152,693, 14 Aug. 1963; *Chem. Abs.*, 1964, **60**, 552.

[293] Z. M. Manulkin, A. N. Tatarenko and F. Yu. Yusupov, *Tr. Tashkentsk. Farmatsevt. Inst.*, 1957, **1**, 291; E. A. Puchinyan, ibid., p. 310; 1958, **2**, 311; *Chem. Abs.*, 1962, **57**, 9869, 11228; 1963, **58**, 2464; J. G. A. Luijten and F. Rijkens, *Rec. Trav. chim.*, 1964, **83**, 857; W. Gerrard and R. G. Rees, *J. Chem. Soc.*, 1964, 3510.

[294] A. C. Smith and E. G. Rochow, *J. Amer. Chem. Soc.*, 1953, **75**, 4103, 4105.

[295] S. Matsuda and H. Matsuda, *Koayo Kagaku Zasshi*, 1960, **63**, 114, 1958, 1965; H. Matsuda, H. Taniguchi and S. Matsuda, ibid., 1961, **64**, 541; H. Matsuda, M. Nakamura and S. Matsuda, ibid., p. 1948; H. Matsuda, J. Hayashi and S. Matsuda, ibid., p. 1951; *Chem. Abs.*, 1962, **56**, 7342; **57**, 2239, 2240, 3469, 16645, 16646.

[296] K. Sisido and Y. Takeda, *J. Org. Chem.*, 1961, **26**, 2301.

or butanol [297]:

$$3PhCH_2Cl + 2Sn \longrightarrow (PhCH_2)_3SnCl + SnCl_2$$

Trialkyltin chlorides may be prepared from dialkyltin chlorides by re-action with an alkyl chloride in the presence of aluminium chloride [298]. Alkyltin halides form stable complexes with aluminium halides [299].

Partial alkylation of tin(IV) halides, particularly the chloride, using aluminium alkyls [300] is another route to organotin halides. Again, as with the tetra-alkyls, satisfactory results are obtained only if complexing agents are added to combine with the aluminium halide formed [193, 194, 195].

The mono-, di- and tri-halides, in contrast to the tetra-alkyls, form co-ordination compounds, particularly with nitrogen bases, e.g. $Me_3SnI(py)_2$, m.p. 60·5°, $Me_2SnCl_2(py)_2$ [301, 302], and with halide ions, e.g. $(Me_4N)_2(Me_2SnCl_4)$ and $Me_4NPhSnBr_5$ [303]. The adducts with nitrogen bases are covalent compounds and the lower members are soluble both in water and alcohols, and in non-polar solvents (particularly the iodides). An X-ray diffraction study of the complex $Me_3SnCl(py)_2$, m.p. 40–41°, has indicated the five-co-ordinate, trigonal bipyramidal structure 4.4, in which the methyl groups occupy the three equatorial positions [304]. Such a structure was also indicated by the absence of a symmetrical Sn–C stretching frequency in the infrared spectrum of the solid [305].

4.4

---

[297] K. Sisido. Y. Takeda and Z. Kinugawa, *J. Amer. Chem. Soc.*, 1961, **83**, 538; K. Sisido, Y. Takeda and H. Nozaki, *J. Org. Chem.*, 1962, **27**, 2411; H. Grohn and R. Paudert, *Z. Chem.*, 1963, **3**, 89.

[298] G. A. Razuvaev, N. S. Vyazankin, O. S. D'yachkovskaya, J. G. Kiseleva and Yu. J. Dergunov, *Zhur. obshchei Khim.*, 1960, **31**, 4056.

[299] W. P. Neumann, R. Schick and R. Köster, *Angew. Chem., Internat. Edn.*, 1964, **3**, 385.

[300] L. I. Zakharkin and O. Yu. Okhlobystin, *Zhur. obshchei Khim.*, 1961, **31**, 3662; *Chem. Abs.*, 1962, **57**, 8593.

[301] C. A. Kraus and W. N. Greer, *J. Amer. Chem. Soc.*, 1923, **45**, 3078.

[302] N. A. Matwiyoff and R. S. Drago, *Inorg. Chem.*, 1964, **3**, 337; J. P. Clark and C. J. Wilkins, *J. Chem. Soc. (A)*, 1966, 871.

[303] D. Seyferth, U.S.P. 3,070,615, 25 Dec. 1962; *Chem. Abs.*, 1963, **58**, 11399; G. Tagliavini and P. Zannella, *J. Organometal. Chem.*, 1966, **5**, 299.

[304] I. R. Beattie, G. P. McQuillan and R. Hulme, *Chem. and Ind.*, 1962, 1429; R. Hulme, *J. Chem. Soc.*, 1963, 1524.

[305] I. R. Beattie and G. P. McQuillan, *J. Chem. Soc.*, 1963, 1519.

Oxygen is a weaker donor than nitrogen and affords fewer complexes with the mono- or di-halides. However, trimethyltin chloride gives a weakly conducting solution in water and alcohol, and this is due to co-ordination by oxygen:

$$Me_3SnCl + nROH \rightleftharpoons Me_3Sn(OHR)_n^+ + Cl^-$$

The equilibrium constant [306] for the reaction in ethyl alcohol is $3·5 \times 10^{-5}$ at $25°$. The salt $[Me_3Sn(OH_2)_2]^+BPh_4^-$ can be isolated from aqueous solutions of Me_3SnCl by the addition of $NaBPh_4$ [307]. Its infrared spectrum reveals a planar arrangement of methyl groups about the tin atom. Solutions of trimethyltin chloride in nitrobenzene, which has a higher dielectric constant than ethyl alcohol, are virtually non-conducting, but the conductance rises markedly on addition of pyridine, due to the reaction:

$$Me_3SnCl + C_5H_5N \rightarrow Me_3SnCl \cdot NC_5H_5 \rightleftharpoons Me_3Sn \cdot \overset{+}{N}C_5H_5 + Cl^-$$

The solvolysis of monohalides R_3SnCl ($R = Et, Pr^i, Bu^t, Ph$) in ethanol, isopropanol and water–dioxan mixtures has been the subject of kinetic studies. Generally equilibrium is attained rapidly, the position depending both on R and on the solvent. When $R = Bu^t$ the equilibrium lies furthest on the side of undissociated halide and the reaction rate is least [308].

The relative acceptor properties of organotin chlorides are illustrated by their interaction with dimethylsulphoxide [308a]. The trichlorides $RSnCl_3$ ($R = Me$ or Ph) and dichlorides R_2SnCl_2, like stannic chloride, take up 2 Mol. of Me_2SO; the monochlorides R_3SnCl take up only 1 Mol., and R_4Sn does not react. A quantitative guide to the relative donor strengths of a variety of bases towards trimethyltin chloride is provided by the spin–spin coupling constant $J(^{119}Sn–C–^1H)$, which has been found to be linearly related to the heat of formation of the adducts [308b]. Interaction with oxygen and nitrogen donors is greater than with phosphorus or sulphur donors.

Compounds in which the R_3Sn or R_2Sn group is combined with a highly electronegative group such as fluoride, nitrate, sulphate or sulphonate, have rather different physical properties. Their high melting points and low volatility (trimethyltin fluoride decomposes about $360°$ without melting) indicate a considerable degree of intermolecular bonding which was formerly taken to be ionic. X-Ray crystallographic and infrared spectroscopic studies during the last few years, however, have shown that

[306] C. A. Kraus and C. C. Callis, *J. Amer. Chem. Soc.*, 1923, **45**, 2624.
[307] M. Wada and R. Okawara, *J. Organometal. Chem.*, 1965, **4**, 487.
[308] R. H. Prince, *J. Chem. Soc.*, 1959, 1783.
[308a] H. G. Langer and A. H. Blut, *J. Organometal. Chem.*, 1966, **5**, 288; see also W. Kitching, *Tetrahedron Letters*, 1966, 3689.
[308b] T. F. Bolles and R. S. Drago, *J. Amer. Chem. Soc.*, 1966, **88**, 3921, 5730.

the unco-ordinated ions, R_3Sn^+ and R_2Sn^{2+}, are *not* present in such compounds in the solid state.

It had earlier been deduced that these ions were solvated in solution. It was at first considered that tin showed a co-ordination number of four in aqueous solutions of compounds R_3SnX or R_2SnX_2, and formed ions such as $R_3Sn \cdot OH_2^+$, following a report [309] of the partial resolution of methylethyl-n-propyltin iodide from aqueous solution by conversion into the camphor sulphonate, followed by reconversion into the iodide. This was taken as evidence for the solvated species $[R'R''R'''Sn \cdot OH_2]^+$, since the ion $R'R''R'''Sn^+$ would have an sp^2 configuration and be planar, leading to immediate racemization. This deduction has, however, been challenged [21] in view of the increasing evidence that tin tends to acquire a co-ordination number of *five* when bonded to three alkyl groups and an electronegative group, as in compounds R_3SnX, and the nuclear magnetic resonance spectrum of trimethyltin chloride in aqueous solution [310] indicates the presence of the ions $Me_3Sn(OH_2)_2^+$, with a *planar* arrangement of methyl groups about the tin atom (see also ref. [302]).

Aqueous solutions of the mono- and di-halides are slightly acidic; this is due to the co-ordinated water behaving as an acid as it does in many hydrated ions (e.g. $Cu(H_2O)_4^{++}$). Two equilibria obtain in an aqueous solution of trimethyltin chloride [311]:

$$(1) \quad Me_3SnCl + nH_2O \rightleftharpoons Me_3Sn(OH_2)_n^+ + Cl^-$$
$$(2) \quad Me_3Sn(OH_2)_n^+ + H_2O \rightleftharpoons Me_3SnOH(OH_2)_{n-1} + H_3O^+$$

Similarly, solutions of dimethyltin dichloride in water are acidic and strongly conducting; spectroscopic and pH studies on these solutions have been interpreted in terms of the following equilibria [312]:

$$Me_2SnCl_2 + nH_2O \rightleftharpoons [Me_2Sn(OH_2)_n]^{2+} + 2Cl^-$$
$$[Me_2Sn(OH_2)_n]^{2+} + H_2O \rightleftharpoons [Me_2SnOH(OH_2)_{n-1}]^+ + H_3O^+$$

Polynuclear cations such as $[(Me_2SnOH)_2(H_2O)_n]^{2+}$ may also be involved.

The ionic systems formed by organotin compounds in aqueous solution were reviewed in 1966 by Tobias [313].

The structures of the *solid* compounds R_3SnX and R_2SnX_2 were difficult to determine from their infrared spectra, as the symmetry of the R_3Sn fragment is the same for R_3Sn^+ (unco-ordinated, sp^2 hybridization of the

[309] W. J. Pope and S. J. Peachey, *Proc. Chem. Soc.*, 1900, **16**, 116.
[310] J. R. Holmes and H. D. Kaesz, *J. Amer. Chem. Soc.*, 1961, **83**, 3903.
[311] M. J. Janssen and J. G. A. Luijten, *Rec. Trav. chim.*, 1963, **82**, 1008.
[312] R. S. Tobias, I. Ogrins and B. A. Nevett, *Inorg. Chem.*, 1962, **1**, 638; B. A. Nevett and R. S. Tobias, *Chem. and Ind.*, 1963, 40; R. S. Tobias and M. Yasuda, *Canad. J. Chem.*, 1964, **42**, 781; M. M. McGrady and R. S. Tobias, *Inorg. Chem.*, 1964, **3**, 1157; R. S. Tobias and C. E. Friedline, ibid., 1965, **4**, 215; R. S. Tobias, H. N. Farrer, M. B. Hughes and B. A. Nevett, ibid., 1966, **5**, 2052.
[313] R. S. Tobias, *Organometal. Chem. Revs.*, 1966, **1**, 93.

tin) and for $X \cdots R_3Sn \cdots X$, with the five-co-ordinate (sp^3d) tin atom having three groups R in equatorial positions (as in 4.4) and two groups X in axial positions linking these R_3Sn fragments. Similarly, in compounds R_2SnX_2, a linear arrangement R—Sn—R could imply either ionic R_2Sn^{++} (sp hybridization) or five- or six-co-ordinate tin (sp^3d or sp^3d^2) with axial groups R [314]. It was necessary, therefore, to determine whether the groups X were ionic or bridging [315, 316]. Studies on carboxylates were not readily interpreted, because of the low symmetry of the carboxylate groups. However, the spectra of compounds with groups X of higher symmetry such as ClO_4, BF_4, AsF_6 or SbF_6 showed all these groups to be bridging groups, and so the tin atoms to be five-co-ordinate [317]. In the nitrate and carbonate the groups R_3Sn are planar [318]. Five-co-ordinate tin is also found in many acylates [319, 320], oxides, hydroxides [321, 322], nitrogen compounds [323] and the fluoride Me_3SnF [324], for which an X-ray diffraction study has indicated two possible structures, the more likely of which is shown in Figure 29, with chains consisting of planar Me_3Sn groups, tilted alternately with respect to the chain axis, linked by non-linear Sn—F$\cdots$Sn units in which the fluorine atom is not equidistant from the two tin atoms [325]. There is thus a trigonal bipyramidal arrangement of groups about each tin atom, with equatorial methyl groups and

[314] R. C. Mehrotra and V. D. Gupta, *J. Organometal. Chem.*, 1965, **4**, 237; M. M. McGrady and R. S. Tobias, *J. Amer. Chem. Soc.*, 1965, **87**, 1909; R. J. H. Clark and C. S. Williams, *Spectrochim. Acta*. 1965, **21**, 1861; W. H. Nelson and D. F. Martin, *J. Inorg. Nucl. Chem.*, 1965, **27**, 89; A. H. Westlake and D. F. Martin, ibid., p. 1579; K. Ramaiah and D. F. Martin, *Chem. Comm.*, 1965, 130; J. A. S. Smith and E. J. Wilkins, ibid., p. 381.

[315] R. Okawara, D. E. Webster and E. G. Rochow, *J. Amer. Chem. Soc.*, 1960, **82**, 3287; I. R. Beattie and T. Gilson, *J. Chem. Soc.*, 1961, 2585.

[316] G. J. M. van der Kerk, J. G. A. Luijten and M. J. Janssen, *Chimia*, 1962, **16**, 10.

[317] R. Okawara, B. J. Hathaway and D. E. Webster, *Proc. Chem. Soc.*, 1963, 13; B. J. Hathaway and D. E. Webster, ibid., p. 14; H. C. Clark and R. J. O'Brien, ibid., p. 113; idem, *Inorg. Chem.*, 1963, **2**, 740, 1020.

[318] K. Yasuda and R. Okawara, *J. Organometal. Chem.*, 1965, **3**, 76; H. C. Clark, R. J. O'Brien and A. L. Pickard, ibid., 1965, **4**, 43; H. C. Clark and R. G. Goel, *Inorg. Chem.*, 1965, **4**, 1428; T. T. Tsai, A. Cutler and W. L. Lehn, *J. Org. Chem.*, 1965, **30**, 3049.

[319] L. A. Leites, Yu. P. Egorov, G. S. Kolesnikov and S. L. Davydova, *Izvest. Akad. Nauk S.S.S.R.*, 1961, 1976; *Chem. Abs.*, 1962, **56**, 10171; M. J. Janssen, J. G. A. Luijten and G. J. M. van der Kerk, *Rec. Trav. chim.*, 1963, **82**, 90.

[320] M. Wada, M. Shindo and R. O. Okawara, *J. Organometal. Chem.*, 1963, **1**, 95; R. Okawara and M. Ohara, ibid., 1964, **1**, 360; *Bull. Chem. Soc. Japan*, 1963, **36**, 624; R. A. Cummins and P. Dunn, *Austral. J. Chem.*, 1964, **17**, 185.

[321] H. Kriegsmann and H. Hoffmann, *Z. anorg. Chem.*, 1963, **321**, 224.

[322] H. Kriegsmann and H. Geissler, ibid., 1963, **323**, 170.

[323] G. J. M. van der Kerk, J. G. A. Luijten and M. J. Janssen, *Chimia*, 1962, **16**, 10.

[324] K. Yasuda, Y. Kawasaki, N. Kasai and T. Tanaka, *Bull. Chem. Soc. Japan*, 1965, **38**, 1216.

[325] H. C. Clark, R. J. O'Brien and J. Trotter, *Proc. Chem. Soc.*, 1963, 85; *J. Chem. Soc.*, 1964, 2332.

P

axial fluorine atoms. Between the chains only weak van der Waals forces operate. Trimethyltin hydroxide has a similar chain structure, with bridging OH groups linking nearly planar Me_3Sn groups inclined at about 75° to the chain axis [326]. In the case of the cyanide Me_3SnCN, which also has a chain structure, the plane of the Me_3Sn groups is at 90° to the chain axis because of the linear nature of the cyanide bridges [88b].

Dimethyltin difluoride in the crystal has an infinite two-dimensional network of tin atoms and bridging fluorines, with methyl groups above and below the $(SnF_2)_n$ plane completing the octahedral co-ordination of the tin [326a]. This is similar to the crystal structure of tin tetrafluoride, but with the non-bridging fluorine atoms of SnF_4 replaced by methyl groups.

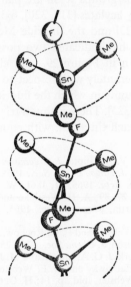

Fig. 29. The structure of the trimethyltin fluoride polymer (after Clark [325])

The stability of this lattice is illustrated by the isolation of Me_2SnF_2 as the product when attempts were made to prepare complex fluorides (BF_4^-, PF_6^-, AsF_6^- or SbF_6^-) of the Me_2Sn^{2+} cation [326b]. Its neutron cross-section shows that, as expected, the methyl groups can rotate relatively freely about the Sn–C bonds [326c].

The co-ordination chemistry of organotin compounds was reviewed in 1965 [327].

[326] N. Kasai, K. Yasuda and R. Okawara, *J. Organometal. Chem.*, 1965, **3**, 173.
[326a] E. O. Schlemper and W. C. Hamilton, *Inorg. Chem.*, 1966, **5**, 995.
[326b] H. C. Clark and R. G. Goel, *J. Organometal. Chem.*, 1967, **7**, 263.
[326c] J. J. Rush and W. C. Hamilton, *Inorg. Chem.*, 1966, **5**, 2238.
[327] R. C. Poller, *J. Organometal. Chem.*, 1965, **3**, 321.

The Monohalides
These are readily prepared by the redistribution reactions described above, the tin(IV) halide and tetra-alkyl or -aryl being heated at about 200° for a few hours [291]. Vinyltin compounds need temperatures of 90–100° only. Fluorides may be precipitated from solutions of chlorides or bromides by means of sodium fluoride, since their solubilities are so low. The exceptionally low solubility of *triphenyltin fluoride*, m.p. 357° (decomp.), has been applied to the gravimetric analysis of the fluoride ion [328].

Trimethyltin fluoride, Me_3SnF, is precipitated from any solution containing the ion $[Me_3Sn(OH_2)_n]^+$ by addition of fluoride. It may be crystallized from alcohol, and decomposes without melting when heated. Other fluorides are prepared similarly, e.g. *triethyltin fluoride*, Et_3SnF, m.p. 294·5°, and *tri-n-propyltin fluoride*, Pr_3SnF, m.p. 268°. Both *triphenyltin* fluoride, Ph_3SnF, m.p. 357°, and *tricyclohexyltin fluoride*, $(C_6H_{11})_3SnF$, decomp. 305°, are so insoluble as to find analytical application.

Trimethyltin chloride, Me_3SnCl, m.p. 37°, b.p. 152–154°, has been prepared by direct chlorination of tetramethyltin at 0° with exclusion of daylight [306], by the redistribution reaction [291] and by indirect chlorination of tetramethyltin with mercury(II) chloride [329]. This compound and other trialkyltin chlorides, bromides and iodides with relatively low molecular weights have a strong, penetrating, persistent and unpleasant smell, and they attack the eyes, nose and throat. Care is therefore required in their manipulation; they should be treated as dangerously toxic. The structure of the pyridine complex, 4.4, has already been described.

Trimethyltin bromide, m.p. 27°, b.p. 165°, forms a monoammine, $Me_3SnBr.NH_3$. *Trimethyltin iodide*, Me_3SnI, m.p. 3·4°, b.p. 170°, may be prepared from the hydroxide and hydriodic acid or from iodine and hexamethyldistannane:

$$Me_3Sn\cdot SnMe_3 + I_2 \longrightarrow 2Me_3SnI$$

In the proton magnetic resonance spectra of methyltin halides and related compounds [62, 329a], chemical shift trends are the reverse of those expected from the inductive effects of the halogens, and $J(Sn–C–H)$ values do not appear to be simply related to the degree of halogenation. There is, however, an approximately linear correlation between $J(^{119}Sn–^{13}C)$ and $J(^{119}Sn–^1H)$ [329b].

[328] H. Ballczo and H. Schiffner, *Z. Anal. Chem.*, 1956, **152**, 3.
[329] Z. M. Manulkin, *Zhur. obshchei Khim.*, 1946, **16**, 235; *Chem. Abs.*, 1947, **41**, 90; S. Papetti and H. W. Post, *J. Org. Chem.*, 1957, **22**, 526.
[329a] L. Verdonck and G. P. van der Kelen, *J. Organometal. Chem.*, 1966, **5**, 532; E. V. van den Berghe and G. P. van der Kelen, ibid., 1966, **6**, 515.
[329b] W. McFarlane, *J. Chem. Soc. (A)*, 1967, 528.

Triethyltin chloride, Et_3SnCl, m.p. 15·5°, b.p. 210°, *bromide*, Et_3SnBr, m.p. −13·5°, b.p. 97°/13 mm., and *iodide*, Et_3SnI, m.p. −34·5°, b.p. 117°/13 mm., are obtained by methods similar to those described for the trimethyl compounds.

Triphenyltin halides are best prepared from tetraphenyltin by the redistribution reaction. The formation of *triphenyltin bromide*, m.p. 121°, takes place particularly smoothly and it can readily be separated from the relatively insoluble Ph_4Sn and from the low melting and very soluble Ph_2SnBr_2 before crystallization from propanol. Chlorides also are easily obtained by this reaction [330]. In the infrared spectra of phenyltin halides Ph_nSnX_{4-n} (and also of Ph_4Sn and Ph_6Sn_2) bands associated with Sn–Ph stretching vibrations are normally found in the range 265–275 cm^{-1} (ν_{asym}) and 230–250 cm^{-1} (ν_{sym}) [330a].

One halide can often be converted into another by shaking in ether solution with aqueous alkali, which produces the ether-soluble hydroxide, and then shaking with the appropriate HX. This method is no use for the methyl series since the hydroxide is soluble in water.

Trineophyltin fluoride $(Ph \cdot CMe_2CH_2)_3SnF$ is unusual in being low-melting and soluble in hydrocarbon solvents. Clearly, the bulk of the neophyl groups prevents association by fluorine bridging in this compound [330b].

The Dihalides

Dimethyltin difluoride, Me_2SnF_2, m.p. $\sim$360°, results from the addition of a soluble fluoride to an aqueous solution of the dichloride. The difluorides are rather more soluble in water than the monofluorides. They combine with fluoride ion to give salts in which the tin retains a covalency of six:

$$R_2SnF_2 + 2KF \rightarrow K_2[R_2SnF_4]$$

Dimethyltin dichloride, Me_2SnCl_2, m.p. 106°, b.p. 190°, from tin–copper and methyl chloride, [294] tetramethyltin and tin(IV) chloride, or hydrochloric acid and dimethyltin oxide, is clearly a covalent halide and is easily soluble in non-polar solvents. It also dissolves in water, however, with an acid reaction and formation of $Me_2Sn(H_2O)_n{}^{++}$ ions. The dissociation constant [331] for the reaction

$$Me_2Sn(H_2O)_n{}^{++} \rightleftharpoons Me_2SnOH(H_2O)_{n-1} + H_3O^+$$

is 8×10^{-4} at 25°.

Alkali precipitates the oxide Me_2SnO, which redissolves in excess. With

[330] H. Zimmer and K. Lubke, *Ber.*, 1952, **85**, 1119; H. Zimmer and H. W. Sparmann, ibid., 1954, **87**, 645.
[330a] R. C. Poller, *Spectrochim. Acta*, 1966, **22**, 935.
[330b] W. T. Reichle, *Inorg. Chem.*, 1966, **5**, 87.
[331] E. G. Rochow and D. Seyferth, *J. Amer. Chem. Soc.*, 1953, **75**, 2877.

diazomethane in ether at $\sim 5°$ a methylene group is introduced, giving *chloromethyldimethyltin chloride*, $ClCH_2 \cdot SnMe_2 \cdot Cl$, which is strongly lachrymatory and vesicant [222].

Dimethyltin dibromide, Me_2SnBr_2, m.p. 74°, b.p. 209°, is similar to the chloride. The *di-iodide*, Me_2SnI_2, m.p. 42°, b.p. 228°, is best obtained from the oxide and hydrogen iodide but may also be prepared from tetramethyltin and tin(IV) iodide, or from tin foil and methyl iodide at 150–160° in a sealed tube [295, 332]. The *dinitrate*, $Me_2Sn(NO_3)_2$, has been prepared from tetramethyltin and dinitrogen tetroxide [207], but is also obtainable, as are other dinitrates $R_2Sn(NO_3)_2$, from the dichloride and silver nitrate [332a]. They are very deliquescent materials, soluble in polar organic solvents, and tend to lose nitrogen oxides at room temperature.

Diphenyltin dichloride, Ph_2SnCl_2, m.p. 42°, b.p. 333–337°, and other *diaryltin* chlorides, may be obtained not only by methods applicable to the dialkyl series but also by some methods peculiar to the diaryl series. Tin(II) chloride in acetone solution reacts with a diarylmercury [333], e.g.

$$SnCl_2 + Ph_2Hg \rightarrow Ph_2SnCl_2 + Hg$$

Diaryliodonium salts, $Ar_2I^+X^-$, react similarly with tin(II) chloride [334], while diazonium hexachlorostannates(IV) are reduced to diaryltin dichlorides by zinc, tin or copper powders [335].

$$(ArN_2)_2SnCl_6 + 2Zn \rightarrow Ar_2SnCl_2 + 2N_2 + 2ZnCl_2$$

The phenyl groups of diphenyltin dichloride are cleaved by weakly acidic chelating agents HX like acetylacetone or 8-quinolinol, which form complexes Cl_2SnX_2 [336]. Acetylacetonates $R_2Sn(acac)_2$ can however be prepared from dichlorides R_2SnCl_2 via the methoxide [336a]:

$$R_2SnCl_2 \xrightarrow[\text{(ii) acetylacetone}]{\text{(i) NaOMe in MeOH}} R_2Sn(acac)_2$$

For infrared spectroscopic data on dialkyltin dihalides in the region 600–50 cm^{-1}, see ref. [337].

[332] A. Cahours, *Annalen*, 1860, **114**, 373; H. A. Skinner and L. E. Sutton, *Trans. Faraday Soc.*, 1944, **40**, 164.

[332a] J. J. Gormley and R. G. Rees, *J. Organometal. Chem.*, 1966, **5**, 291.

[333] K. A. Kocheshkov and A. N. Nesmeyanov, *Ber.*, 1930, **63**, 2496; 1931, **64**, 628.

[334] O. A. Reutov, O. A. Ptitsyna, and M. F. Turchinskii, *Doklady Akad. Nauk S.S.S.R.*, 1961, **139**, 146; *Chem. Abs.*, 1962, **56**, 13527.

[335] K. A. Kocheshkov, A. N. Nesmeyanov and W. A. Klimova, *Ber.*, 1935, **68**, 1877.

[336] W. H. Nelson and D. F. Martin, *J. Organometal. Chem.*, 1965, **4**, 67; D. F. Martin and R. D. Walton, ibid., 1966, **5**, 57.

[336a] R. Ueeda, Y. Kawasaki, T. Tanaka and R. Okawara, ibid., 1966, **5**, 194; see also Y. Kawasaki, *J. Inorg. Nucl. Chem.*, 1967, **29**, 840.

[337] F. K. Butcher, W. Gerrard, E. F. Mooney, R. G. Rees, H. A. Willis, A. Anderson and H. A. Gebbie, *J. Organometal. Chem.*, 1964, **1**, 431.

The Trihalides

There is some wastage of organic groups when these are prepared by the halogenation or redistribution reactions already described [206]; more economical methods involve tin or tin(II) salts as starting materials.

Methyltin trichloride, $MeSnCl_3$, m.p. 45–46°, is obtained when methyl chloride is slowly bubbled through molten tin(II) chloride [306] at 365°. It is also formed from methyl stannonic acid $(MeSnO_2H)_n$ (from methyl iodide and sodium stannate(II), see below) and hydrogen chloride or phosphorus pentachloride [338]. A general method for alkyltin trichlorides which is a variation on the rearrangement reaction is to heat tin(IV) chloride with the appropriate triphenylalkyltin at 185–190° for 1–1½ hours in a sealed tube [339], e.g.

$$Ph_3MeSn + 3SnCl_4 \rightarrow MeSnCl_3 + 3PhSnCl_3$$

It is easily soluble both in non-polar solvents and in water (with partial hydrolysis).

Methyltin tribromide, $MeSnBr_3$, m.p. 53°, b.p. 211°, is similar to the trichloride, and is readily prepared from methyl stannonic acid and concentrated hydrobromic acid [338]. *Methyltin tri-iodide*, $MeSnI_3$, m.p. 84°, is formed from methyl stannonic acid and aqueous hydrogen iodide, from tetramethyltin and tin(IV) iodide (slowly at 100°), or from methyl iodide and tin(II) iodide [340] at 160° (though in low yield):

$$SnI_2 + MeI \rightarrow MeSnI_3$$

Phenyltin trichloride, $PhSnCl_3$, b.p. 142–143°/25 mm., and the other aryltin trihalides, result from the rearrangement between a tin(IV) halide and a tetra-aryltin or a diaryltin dihalide [189, 291, 333].

Dipole moment [341] and nuclear quadrupole coupling [342] studies on organotin chlorides R_nSnCl_{4-n} have provided evidence of changes in the Sn–Cl polarity and bond order as the value of n changes.

Oxides and hydroxides

These result from the basic hydrolysis of the corresponding halides, and as might be expected their molecular complexity increases with the number of oxygen atoms attached to the same tin atom. The lower *monohydroxides*, R_3SnOH, are the only simple compounds in this group, and are very easily and reversibly dehydrated to oxides, $(R_3Sn)_2O$:

[338] E. Krause and K. Weinberg, *Ber.*, 1930, **63**, 381; H. Kriegsmann and S. Pauly, *Z. anorg. Chem.*, 1964, **330**, 275.

[339] M. E. Pavlovskaya and K. A. Kocheshkov, *Compt. rend. acad. sci. (U.S.S.R.).* 1945, **49**, 263; *Chem. Abs.*, 1946, **40**, 5696.

[340] P. Pfeiffer and I. Heller, *Ber.*, 1904, **37**, 4619.

[341] J. Lorberth and H. Nöth, *Chem. Ber.*, 1965, **98**, 969.

[342] E. D. Swiger and J. D. Graybeal, *J. Amer. Chem. Soc.*, 1965, **87**, 1464.

$$2Et_3SnOH \rightleftharpoons (Et_3Sn)_2O + H_2O$$

No hydroxides – only oxides – are found when the alkyl group is n-butyl or bigger.

The *dihydroxides*, $R_2Sn(OH)_2$, obtained by basic hydrolysis of the dihalides, lose water even more readily. The only examples which have been isolated have bulky alkyl groups, e.g. tertiary-butyl or -amyl. Generally, the polymeric anhydro form $(R_2SnO)_x$ is obtained; the lowest members are insoluble high polymers, but from butyl upwards they form viscous solutions in hydrocarbon solvents. *Partial* hydrolysis of dialkyltin dihalides leads to *tetra-alkyldistannoxane* derivatives, materials of composition $R_4Sn_2X_2O$ or $R_4Sn_2X(OH)O$, which are in fact dimeric and are further examples of compounds containing penta-co-ordinate tin (see p. 447) [343]:

$$R_2SnX_2 \xrightarrow{OH^-} R_4Sn_2X_2O \xrightarrow{OH^-} R_4Sn_2X(OH)O \xrightarrow{OH^-} R_2SnO$$

Trihydroxides, $RSn(OH)_3$, are unknown; attempts at their preparation lead to *stannonic acids*, $(RSnO_2H)_n$, insoluble cross-linked polymers.

The infrared spectra of organotin oxides contain characteristic bands, assigned to ν_{asym} Sn–O–Sn, at 774–776 cm^{-1} in the case of $(R_3Sn)_2O$ and at 548–576 cm^{-1} in the case of RSn and R_2Sn compounds [344].

The oxides and hydroxides may be used to prepare derivatives of a great variety of acids, as they give sulphides, sulphates, carboxylates, etc. on treatment with the appropriate acid, although small pure samples of derivatives of oxyacids are probably better prepared from the organotin halide and the silver salt [317, 345, 346]. The increasing evidence that such derivatives contain five-co-ordinate tin has been discussed above [316 317, 319].

Monohydroxides and derivatives

Trimethyltin hydroxide, Me_3SnOH, is condensed as a crystalline sublimate when trimethyltin bromide is gently heated with 55% sodium hydroxide in water. Alternatively, it is precipitated when concentrated aqueous solutions of trimethyltin chloride and sodium hydroxide are mixed [347]. It sublimes above about 80°, but very easily decomposes at 100° or above, disproportionating into tetramethyltin, dimethyltin oxide and water [348]. It is readily soluble in water, and has a dissociation constant of 1.7×10^{-5}: (see also ref. [311]).

$$Me_3SnOH(OH_2)_n + H_2O \rightleftharpoons [Me_3Sn(OH_2)_{n+1}]^+ + OH^-$$

[343] D. L. Alleston, A. G. Davies and B. N. Figgis, *Proc. Chem. Soc.*, 1961, 457.
[344] R. A. Cummins, *Austral. J. Chem.*, 1965, **18**, 98.
[345] B. L. Chamberland and A. G. MacDiarmid, *J. Chem. Soc.*, 1961, 445.
[346] P. L. Shapiro and E. I. Becker, *J. Org. Chem.*, 1962, **27**, 4668.
[347] J. G. A. Luijten, *Rec. Trav. chim.*, 1963, **82**, 1179.
[348] C. A. Kraus and R. H. Bullard, *J. Amer. Chem. Soc.*, 1929, **51**, 3605.

Addition of acids to a solution of trimethyltin hydroxide has afforded many derivatives like those already mentioned in connexion with their bridged structures, e.g. the nitrate, perchlorate, carbonate, various complex fluorides [317] and many carboxylates [319]. Such derivatives are volatile in those cases, like the acetate [319], where the co-ordination polymer is readily broken down into small covalent (monomeric) units, but are otherwise involatile (e.g. the sulphate). The polymeric insoluble form in which solid carboxylates are normally obtained can be converted into a monomeric soluble modification by sealing samples with cyclohexane at 90° for 12–24 hours [348a]. Trimethyltin formate, Me_3SnO_2CH, for example, has been obtained by this method in the form of needles, softening at 135° and melting completely at 148°, with a solubility in cyclohexane of about 0·2 g./ml.

Trimethyltin hydroxide itself in the solid state has planar Me_3Sn groups bridged by $-O(H)-$ groups [326]. The polymer breaks down when the hydroxide dissolves in non-polar solvents such as benzene, carbon tetrachloride or chloroform, in which the dimer, 4.5, is present [349]. The bridging hydroxide group gives rise to a characteristic band in the infrared spectrum at 3658 cm⁻¹.

4.5

Bis(trimethyltin)oxide, $(Me_3Sn)_2O$, b.p. 86°/24 mm., which is very sensitive to moisture, may be prepared from trimethyltin hydroxide and sodium in anhydrous benzene [350]:

$$4Me_3SnOH + 2Na \rightarrow 2(Me_3Sn)_2O + 2NaOH + H_2$$

With methyl-lithium, the oxide gives the lithium derivative $LiOSnMe_3$, m.p. 200° (decomposes), a colourless crystalline solid which is hexameric in benzene [351].

$$(Me_3Sn)_2O + MeLi \rightarrow Me_4Sn + LiOSnMe_3$$

The product has been used to prepare a number of *organosiloxy* derivatives of tin:

$$LiOSnMe_3 + Et_3SiCl \rightarrow Me_3SnOSiEt_3 + LiCl$$

[348a] P. B. Simons and W. A. G. Graham, *J. Organometal. Chem.*, 1967, **8**, 479.
[349] R. Okawara and K. Yasuda, ibid., 1964, **1**, 356.
[350] T. Harada, *Sci. Papers Inst. Phys. Chem. Research (Tokyo)*, 1939, **36**, 504; *Chem. Abs.*, 1940, **34**, 3674.
[351] H. Schmidbaur and H. Hussek, *Angew. Chem., Internat. Edn.*, 1963, **2**, 328.

Mixed silicon–tin oxides of this type which are transparent oils, fairly stable to air, are also obtained by reactions between LiOSiR$_3$ and R'$_3$SnCl [352], or by the co-hydrolysis of R$_3$SiX and R'$_3$SnX in benzene with a slight excess of aqueous ammonia [353]:

$$Me_3SiCl + n\text{-}Pr_3SnCl \xrightarrow{\text{aq. NH}_3} Me_3SiOSn(n\text{-}Pr)_3$$

If a tin dichloride is used instead of the monochloride, derivatives of the dimeric distannoxane result [354]:

$$4Me_3SiCl + 4Me_2SnCl_2 \xrightarrow{\text{aq. NH}_3} (Me_3SiOSnMe_2OSnMe_2OSiMe_3)_2,$$
$$\text{m.p. } 167\text{--}168°$$

For other related siloxy derivatives, see refs [105 and 355].

Triethyltin hydroxide, Et$_3$SnOH, m.p. 49–50°, is dehydrated to the liquid oxide (Et$_3$Sn)$_2$O when placed *in vacuo* over concentrated sulphuric acid. The addition of water to the oxide regenerates the hydroxide with evolution of heat. Similar effects have been observed with *tri-n-propyltin* hydroxide, m.p. 34–35°. With glacial acetic acid, triethyltin acetate, Et$_3$SnOCOCH$_3$, m.p. 134–135°, b.p. 224° is formed. The oxides react with hydrogen sulphide and with thiols, as well as with carboxylic acids and phenols [98, 356]:

$$(R_3Sn)_2O + H_2S \longrightarrow (R_3Sn)_2S + H_2O$$
$$(R_3Sn)_2O + 2R'SH \longrightarrow 2R_3SnSR' + H_2O$$

The trialkyltin oxides, acetates and other derivatives have found extensive application as fungicides, maximum activity being found when the *total* number of carbon atoms in the three alkyl groups of R$_3$SnX is 9–12, regardless of whether the alkyl groups are the same or different [357].

In a contrasting field, trialkyltin esters of amino acids have been used when Alk$_3$Sn groups have found application as protecting groups in peptide synthesis [358].

Triphenyltin hydroxide, Ph$_3$SnOH, m.p. 119–121° (decomp.), is readily prepared by shaking an ether solution of the chloride or bromide with aqueous alkali, and may be crystallized from aqueous ethanol. It gradually

[352] H. Schmidbaur and M. Schmidt, *J. Amer. Chem. Soc.*, 1961, **83**, 2963.

[353] R. Okawara and K. Sugita, ibid., p. 4480.

[354] R. Okawara, D. G. White, K. Fujitani and H. Sato, ibid., p. 1342; W. J. Considine, G. A. Baum and R. C. Jones, *J. Organometal. Chem.*, 1965, **3**, 308.

[355] R. Okawara and E. G. Rochow, *U.S. Dept. Comm., Office Tech. Serv., PB Rept.* 171,571, 1 (1960); *Chem. Abs.*, 1963, **58**, 3454. D. A. Kochkin and Yu. N. Chirgadze, *Zhur. obshchei Khim.*, 1962, **32**, 4007; D. A. Kochkin, L. V. Luk'yanova and E. B. Reznikova, ibid., 1963, **33**, 1945; *Chem. Abs.*, 1963, **58**, 13979; **59**, 11551.

[356] G. S. Sasin, *J. Org. Chem.*, 1953, **18**, 1142; R. Sasin and G. S. Sasin, ibid., 1955, **20**, 387, 770.

[357] G. J. M. van der Kerk and J. G. A. Luijten, *J. Appl. Chem.*, 1956, **6**, 56.

[358] M. Frankel, D. Gertner, D. Wagner and A. Zilkha, *J. Org. Chem.*, 1965, **30**, 1596.

dehydrates when heated in boiling methyl cyanide or toluene, giving the oxide $(Ph_3Sn)_2O$, m.p. 122–123·5°. The oxide and hydroxide are conveniently distinguished by their infrared spectra [322, 359, 360]. The oxide forms triphenyltin chloride with alcoholic hydrogen chloride; with a limited amount of hydrochloric or perchloric acid in non-aqueous media [360] it forms salts $(Ph_3Sn)_2OH^+X^-$. With aqueous alcohol, the oxide regenerates the hydroxide, and when heated to 130–140° it disproportionates into diphenyltin oxide and tetraphenyltin [361]. The hydroxide extracts a range of anions X^- from aqueous into organic solution, forming derivatives Ph_3SnX (e.g. $X = HCrO_4$, I, Br, Cl, O_2CR) [362]. The nitrate, Ph_3SnONO_2, an unstable material prepared from triphenyltin chloride and silver nitrate at $-80°$, decomposes slowly at room temperature into nitrobenzene and diphenyltin oxide [346]. Both Ph_3SnOH and Ph_2SnO form oxinates [230, 363].

Alkoxy and phenoxy derivatives, R_3SnOR'

These may be prepared from a sodium alkoxide or phenoxide and an organotin halide [189, 336a, 364], or from an organotin oxide, hydroxide or ester and the appropriate alcohol or phenol [189]:

$$(R_3Sn)_2O + 2R'OH \longrightarrow 2R_3SnOR' + 2H_2O$$

When benzene or toluene is used as the solvent for this reaction the water may be removed by azeotropic distillation [189]; alternatively, molecular sieve can be used [98]. The use of a magnesium alkoxide is recommended for the preparation of acetylenic organotin ethers [365]:

$$EtMgBr + HO(CH_2)_2C:CH \xrightarrow[Et_2O]{Et_3SnCl} Et_3SnO(CH_2)_2C:CH, \text{ b.p. } 157–158°/3 \text{ mm.}$$

A useful route to pure methoxy derivatives is the methanolysis of an aminotin compound [366], e.g.:

$$Me_3SnNEt_2 + MeOH \longrightarrow Me_3SnOMe + Et_2NH$$

Organotin alkoxides are comparatively involatile liquids, more reactive than the related ethers because the Sn–O bond is readily broken. Thus,

[359] B. Kushlefsky, I. Simmons and A. Ross, *Inorg. Chem.*, 1963, **2**, 187.

[360] E. Friebe and H. Kelker, *Z. Anal. Chem.*, 1963, **192**, 267.

[361] O. Schmitz-DuMont, *Z. anorg. Chem.*, 1941, **248**, 289.

[362] G. K. Schweitzer and S. W. McCarty, *J. Inorg. Nucl. Chem.*, 1965, **27**, 191.

[363] L. Roncucci, F. Faraglia and R. Barbieri, *J. Organometal. Chem.*, 1964, **1**, 427.

[364] J. Valade and M. Pereyre, *Compt. rend.*, 1962, **254**, 3693; E. Amberger and M.-R. Kula, *Chem. Ber.*, 1963, **96**, 2562; H. J. Eméleus and J. J. Zuckerman, *J. Organometal. Chem.*, 1964, **1**, 328.

[365] M. F. Shostakovskii, V. M. Vlasov and R. G. Mirskov, *Zhur. obshchei Khim.*, 1963, **33**, 324; *Chem. Abs.*, 1963, **59**, 650.

[366] E. Amberger, M.-R. Kula and J. Lorberth, *Angew. Chem., Internat. Edn.*, 1964, **3**, 138.

exchange of alkoxy groups may be achieved by treatment with an excess of a less volatile alcohol; carboxylic acids give organotin esters [364]; acetylenes HC:CR' give derivatives $R_3SnC:CR'$ [260]; and additions to multiple bonds can occur, e.g. [367]

$$Bu_3SnOMe + Cl_3CCN \rightarrow Bu_3SnN:C(CCl_3)OMe$$

$$(Bu_3Sn)_2O + CX_3CHO \rightleftharpoons (Bu_3SnO)_2CHCX_3 \rightarrow Bu_3SnCX_3 + Bu_3SnO_2CH$$

This last reaction affords a further route to perhalomethyltin compounds (cf. p. 430). These additions of Sn–O to multiple bonds are more examples (cf. hydroboration, etc.) of the apparently general reaction in which a group consisting of a metal or metalloid bonded to an electronegative atom can add across a polar multiple bond [367]:

$$MX + A:B \rightarrow M \cdot A \cdot B \cdot X$$

Organotin oxides, as well as alkoxy and amino derivatives, are capable of adding to various unsaturated substances including isocyanates, aldehydes and carbon dioxide. As the products may themselves be capable of further addition, the reaction can be applied to the oligomerization or polymerization of the unsaturated compound, e.g. [367]

$$(Bu_3Sn)_2O \xrightarrow{RNCO} Bu_3Sn \cdot NR \cdot CO \cdot OSnBu_3 \xrightarrow{2R'NCO} RN \begin{array}{c} CO{-}NR' \\ \diagup \diagdown \\ \diagdown \diagup \\ CO{-}NR' \end{array} CO$$

An X-ray crystallographic study of the phenoxide p-$C_6Cl_4(OSnEt_3)_2$ has revealed a *trans* arrangement of the triethyltin groups, with tin–oxygen bond lengths of 2·08 Å (4.6) [368].

4.6   4.7

*Trichloro*tin alkoxides, Cl_3SnOR, differ from their triorganotin analogues in showing pronounced Lewis acid character, and forming such adducts as the alcohol complexes $X_3SnOMe.MeOH$ (where X = Cl or Br) which have bridged structures (4.7) involving six-co-ordinate tin [369].

[367] A. J. Bloodworth and A. G. Davies, *Proc. Chem. Soc.*, 1963, 264, 315; *Chem. and Ind.*, 1965, 900, 1868; *J. Chem. Soc.*, 1965, 5238, 6245, 6858; 1966 (C), 299; *Chem. Comm.*, 1965, 24; A. G. Davies and W. R. Symes, ibid., p. 25; *J. Organometal. Chem.*, 1966, 5, 394.

[368] P. J. Wheatley, *J. Chem. Soc.*, 1961, 5027.

[369] G. Sterr and R. Mattes, *Z. anorg. Chem.*, 1963, 322, 319; see also Y. Kawasaki, T. Tanaka and R. Okawara, *J. Organometal. Chem.*, 1966, 6, 95.

Some useful group frequency assignments in the infrared spectra of organotin alkoxides are in ref. [369a].

Organotin dihydroxides and derivatives

Dimethyltin oxide, $(Me_2SnO)_n$, is precipitated as an amorphous powder when alkali is added to an aqueous solution of dimethyltin dihalide. It is amphoteric in that with acids it gives salt-like derivatives, e.g. dimethyltin sulphate, Me_2SnSO_4 (soluble in water, but not in alcohol or non-polar solvents), and it also dissolves in alkalies in the form of such ions as $[Me_2Sn(OH)_3(OH_2)_n]^-$ (where $n = 0$ or 1) and $Me_2Sn(OH)_4^{2-}$. These derivatives with both acids and alkalies may be regarded as linear $[Me—Sn—Me]^{2+}$ units with other groups such as acid radicals, hydroxide ions, water, or other donor molecules arranged axially about the tin, the co-ordination number of which is thereby raised to 5 or 6. Thus, linear MeSnMe units are present in aqueous solutions of Me_2SnCl_2 (as indicated by their nuclear magnetic resonance spectra) [310], and in solid carboxylates, as shown by their infrared spectra [315, 320]. In aqueous acid solution [312], the dimethyltin cation gives rise at different acid concentrations to hydrated versions of such species as Me_2SnOH^+, $(Me_2SnOH]_2^{2+}$, $Me_2Sn(OH)_2$ and $(Me_2Sn)_2(OH)_3^+$, the precise extent of hydration being unknown. Complexes of dimethyltin derivatives with bidentate ligands like phenanthroline are known [370].

Dimethyltin derivatives of oxyacids have similar physical properties to the related trimethyltin derivatives; for example, the diacetate is volatile, being able to exist as the covalent monomer, whereas the derivatives of more electronegative anions are involatile; e.g. the di-(methanesulphonate) [371], $Me_2Sn(OSO_2Me)_2$, is an involatile solid, m.p. 325°.

Diethyltin oxide, $(Et_2SnO)_n$, is precipitated as an insoluble polymer when diethyltin halides react with dilute alkali. With diethyltin halides or acetates it gives 'basic salts' such as Et_2SnO, Et_2SnCl_2 or $(ClEt_2Sn)_2O$, m.p. 176°.

Di-n-butyltin oxide, $(Bu^n_2SnO)_n$, by the hydrolysis of the dichloride (m.p. 40·5°), is much used to prepare maleates and other derivatives for use as stabilizers for polyvinyl chloride polymers. Di-n-butyltin compounds may conveniently be characterized as the bipyridyl complex [372, 373], bipyBu$^n_2$SnCl$_2$, m.p. 180°, which is precipitated from alcohol, or as the bright yellow oxine compound 4.8, m.p. 154–154·5 (from ethanol). [373].

[369a] J. Mendelsohn, A. Marchand and J. Valade, *J. Organometal. Chem.*, 1966, **6**, 25; see also Y. Kawasaki, T. Tanaka and R. Okawara, ibid., p. 95.

[370] M. Yasuda and R. S. Tobias, *Inorg. Chem.*, 1963, **2**, 207.

[371] H. H. Anderson, ibid., 1964, **3**, 108.

[372] D. L. Alleston and A. G. Davies, *Chem. and Ind.*, 1961, 551; *J. Chem. Soc.*, 1962, 2050.

[373] D. Blake, G. E. Coates and J. M. Tate, ibid., 1961, 756; see also ref. [216], and T. Tanaka, M. Komura, Y. Kawasaki and R. Okawara, *J. Organometal. Chem.*, 1964, **1**, 484.

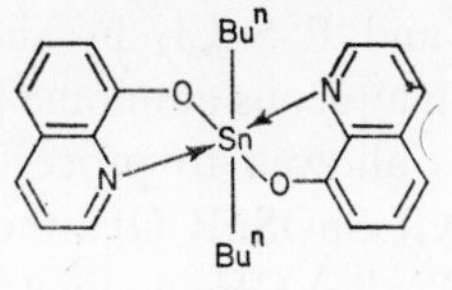

4.8

With ethylene glycol, dibutyltin oxide gives a ten-membered ring derivative [373a]. Other glycols give five-membered rings:

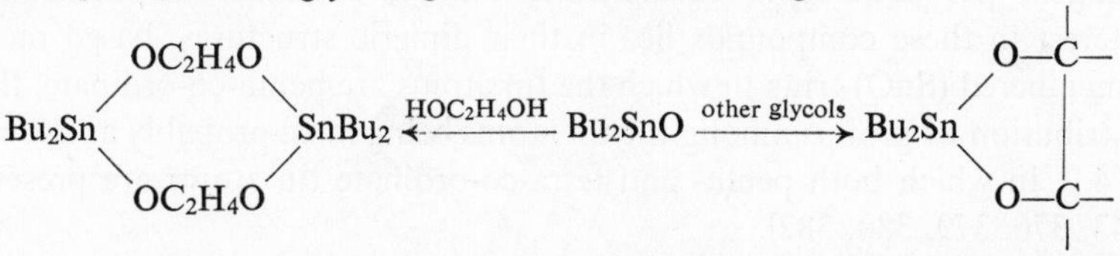

$Di\text{-}tert\text{-}butyltin\ dihydroxide$, $(Me_3C)_2Sn(OH)_2$, is exceptional in that it can be isolated as such rather than as the anhydro polymer. Its aqueous solutions are weakly alkaline and it is also soluble in organic solvents [338].

$Diphenyltin\ oxide$, $(Ph_2SnO)_n$, is insoluble in all solvents with which it does not react. It dissolves in aqueous acids, and addition of ethanolic oxine and sodium acetate precipitates the yellow oxine complex [230, 363], m.p. 254–256° (from ethanol), analogous to 4.8. For further oxinates, see [373b].

Analytical methods have been devised for the separation and analysis of R_2Sn and R_3Sn compounds [374].

Tetra-alkyldistannoxane derivatives, $(XR_2Sn)_2O$

These compounds, and the related hydroxides $XR_2SnOSnR_2OH$, result from the *partial* basic hydrolysis of dialkyltin derivatives R_2SnX_2, a reaction which had earlier been thought to yield derivatives of distannane [343, 372, 375, 376]. They may also be prepared from R_2SnO and R_2SnX_2 [376], from R_2SnO and HX [377, 378, 379], or where $X = Me_3SiO$, by the

[373a] W. J. Considine, *J. Organometal. Chem.*, 1966, **5**, 263.

[373b] D. F. Martin and R. D. Walton, ibid., p. 57; F. Huber and R. Kaiser, ibid., 1966, **6**, 126; K. Kawakami and R. Okawara, ibid., p. 249; L. Roncucci, G. Faraglia and R. Barbieri, ibid., p. 278; see also R. M. Ismail, ibid., p. 663.

[374] W. N. Aldridge and J. E. Cremer, *Analyst*, 1957, **82**, 37; R. Bock, S. Gorbach and H. Oeser, *Angew. Chem.*, 1958, **70**, 272.

[375] A. J. Gibbons, A. K. Sawyer and A. Ross., *J. Org. Chem.*, 1961, **26**, 2304.

[376] D. L. Alleston, A. G. Davies, M. Hancock and R. F. M. White, *J. Chem. Soc.*, 1963, 5469; 1964, 5744; A. S. Mufti and R. C. Poller, ibid., 1965, 5055.

[377] R. Okawara and E. G. Rochow, *J. Amer. Chem. Soc.*, 1960, **82**, 3285; K. Yasuda, H. Matsumoto and R. Okawara, *J. Organometal. Chem.*, 1966, **6**, 528.

[378] G. A. Razuvaev, O. A. Shchepetkova and N. S. Vyazankin, *Zhur. obshchei Khim.*, 1962, **32**, 2152.

[379] W. J. Considine and J. J. Ventura, *J. Org. Chem.*, 1963, **28**, 221; W. J. Considine, J. J. Ventura, A. J. Gibbons, Jr, and A. Ross, *Canad. J. Chem.*, 1963, **41**, 1239.

cohydrolysis of Me_3SiCl and R_2SnCl_2 by shaking a solution of these compounds in benzene with aqueous ammonia [354, 380]. If the hydrolysis of dialkyltin derivatives is allowed to proceed beyond the stage represented by the hydroxide $XR_2SnOSnR_2OH$, the products become increasingly polymeric, $XR_2Sn(OSnR_2)_nOH$, as they approach the composition of the oxide, R_2SnO [381].

Many materials $(XR_2Sn)_2O$ are now known, with X for example a halogen, pseudohalogen, carboxylate, nitrate, alkoxide or phenoxide. Interest in these compounds lies in their dimeric structures, based on a 4-membered $(SnO)_2$ ring in which the tin atoms are penta-co-ordinate, the distribution of groups among the tin atoms being most probably as shown in 4.9, in which both penta- and tetra-co-ordinate tin atoms are present [343, 376, 379, 380, 382].

4.9   4.10

When the groups X themselves are capable of forming dative links to tin, as in the hydroxide or alkoxide, it is considered [382] that all the tin atoms are penta-co-ordinate (4.10). Such a structure accounts for the stability of the hydroxide to further condensation, and the absence of isomers. *Monoalkyltin* units can be incorporated in such structures, e.g. materials $XR_2SnOSnR'X_2$ or $X_2RSnOSnRX_2$ result from the use of trihalides $RSnX_3$ [382a].

Stannonic acids

Methylstannonic acid, $(MeSnO_2H)_n$, is precipitated by carbon dioxide from the solution obtained when methyl iodide is shaken with cold aqueous potassium stannate(II) for a day [383]:

[380] R. Okawara, *Proc. Chem. Soc.*, 1961, 383.

[381] K. A. Kocheshkov, E. M. Panov and N. N. Zemlyanskii, *Izvest. Akad. Nauk S.S.S.R.*, 1961, 2255; S. M. Zhivukhin, E. D. Dudikova and V. V. Kireev, *Zhur. obshchei Khim.*, 1961, **31**, 1306; S. M. Zhivukhin, E. D. Dudikova and E. M. Ter-Sarkisyan, ibid., 1962, **32**, 3059; N. N. Zemlyanskii, E. M. Panov, N. A. Slovokhotova, O. P. Shamagina and K. A. Kocheshkov, *Doklady Akad. Nauk S.S.S.R.*, 1963, **149**, 312; *Chem. Abs.*, 1962, **57**, 850, 7294; 1963, **58**, 10312; **59**, 7550.

[382] R. Okawara and M. Wada, *J. Organometal. Chem.*, 1963, **1**, 81; M. O'Hara, R. Okawara and Y. Nakamura, *Bull. Chem. Soc. Japan*, 1965, **38**, 1379.

[382a] J. G. A. Luijten, *Rec. Trav. chim.*, 1966, **85**, 873; A. G. Davies and P. G. Harrison, *J. Organometal. Chem.*, 1967, **7**, P13.

[383] P. Pfeiffer and R. Lenhardt, *Ber.*, 1903, **36**, 1057; G. Meyer and P. Pfeiffer, *Z. anorg. Chem.*, 1910, **68**, 106; M. Lesbre and G. Glotz, *Compt. rend.*, 1934, **198**, 1426; A. Solerio, *Gazzetta Chim. Ital.*, 1955, **85**, 61.

$$MeI + K_2SnO_2 \longrightarrow K^+[MeSnO_2]^- + KI$$

It may be purified by conversion to the tri-iodide, $MeSnI_3$, by hydriodic acid, and precipitation by aqueous ammonia. Methylpentachlorostannates(IV) result from the action of concentrated hydrochloric acid. As an acid it is very weak, dissolving only in hydroxides (not carbonates). It decomposes on heating with concentrated alkali, giving methane, trimethyltin hydroxide and dimethyltin oxide.

Phenylstannonic acid, $(PhSnO_2H)_n$, is best obtained by hydrolysis of the trihalide. It undergoes an interesting reaction with mercury(II) oxide [384]:

$$HgO + 2PhSnO_2H + H_2O \longrightarrow 2H_2SnO_3 + Ph_2Hg$$

Organotin peroxides

These reactive compounds may be prepared by methods analogous to those used for the preparation of hydroxides, oxides and alkoxides. Thus, organoperoxides result from the action of ROOH on a variety of organotin derivatives [107, 385]:

$$nROOH + R'_{4-n}SnX_n \longrightarrow R'_{4-n}Sn(OOR)_n + nHX$$
$$(n = 1 \text{ or } 2; \ X = OMe, CN, H, Cl \text{ or } Br)$$

The products are readily hydrolysed, and when heated decompose by a reaction involving oxidative dealkylation of the tin.

Triethyltin peroxide, $(Et_3SnO)_2$, is obtained in an impure form as a viscous yellow-green oil by the action of hydrogen peroxide on bis-triethyltin oxide in ether at or below room temperature [386]:

$$(Et_3Sn)_2O + H_2O_2 \longrightarrow (Et_3SnO)_2$$

Unstable at $0°$, this compound decomposes completely during one day at room temperature and detonates when heated to $60°$ in a closed vessel.

Peroxy-esters such as Ph_3SnO_2COMe, m.p. $>230°$, are more stable thermally, but are readily hydrolysed to the acid and hydroxide [387]. Greater resistance to hydrolysis is shown by the oxyperoxides $R_4Sn_2(OOR')_2O$, presumably because these have a dimeric tetra-alkyl-distannoxane structure related to 4.9 or 4.10 [388].

[384] K. A. Kocheshkov and M. M. Nadj, *Ber.*, 1934, **67**, 717.
[385] D. L. Alleston and A. G. Davies, *J. Chem. Soc.*, 1962, 2465.
[386] Yu. A. Aleksandrov and V. A. Shushunov, *Doklady Akad. Nauk S.S.S.R.*, 1961, **140**, 595; *Trudy po Khim. i Khim. Tekhnol.*, 1962, **4**, 644; *Zhur. obshchei Khim.*, 1965, **35**, 115; Yu. A. Aleksandrov, *Trudy po Khim. i Khim. Tekhnol.*, 1962, **4**, 485; *Chem. Abs.*, 1962, **56**, 10176; 1963, **58**, 543, 3453; **59**, 877; 1964, **60**, 12040; 1965, **62**, 13167.
[387] V. A. Shushunov and T. G. Brilkina, *Doklady Akad. Nauk S.S.S.R.*, 1961, **141**, 1391; *Chem. Abs.*, 1962, **56**, 12921.
[388] A. G. Davies and I. F. Graham, *Chem. and Ind.*, 1963, 1622.

Sulphur, selenium and tellurium compounds

Sulphur analogues of the main types of organotin oxygen compounds are known. They result from the action of sulphides, hydrogen sulphide or mercaptans on organotin halides, hydrides, oxides or alkoxides [189, 389], e.g.

$$Me_3SnBr + (NH_4)_2S \longrightarrow (Me_3Sn)_2S, \quad b.p.\ 107°/11\ mm.$$
$$Me_2SnBr_2 + H_2S \longrightarrow (Me_2SnS)_3, \quad m.p.\ 148°$$
$$MeSnBr_3 + H_2S \longrightarrow (MeSn)_2S_3$$

Selenides are obtained similarly [389, 390]. Di-thiols give cyclic derivatives with dihalides [111, 391]. Mercaptans also react with tetra-alkyltin compounds [356, 392], generally giving the derivative R_3SnSR', while sulphur or selenium will react with tetraphenyl- [393] or tetrabutyl-tin [394] at 200° to displace one, two or three organic groups, e.g.

$$Ph_4Sn + Se \longrightarrow Ph_3SnSePh, \quad m.p.\ 87–88°$$
$$Ph_4Sn + S \longrightarrow (Ph_2SnS)_3, \quad m.p.\ 183–184°$$

A convenient preparation of $(Ph_3Sn)_2S$ uses the action of ammonia on triphenyltin bromide in carbon disulphide [395]:

$$2Ph_3SnBr + 4NH_3 + CS_2 \longrightarrow (Ph_3Sn)_2S + NH_4SCN + 2NH_4Br$$

Several sulphur, selenium and tellurium derivatives have been prepared via the lithium compounds, R_3SnXLi, where X = S, Se or Te, which are themselves obtained from the appropriate element and R_3SnLi [396]:

$$Ph_3SnLi + Te \xrightarrow{\ THF\ } Ph_3SnTeLi \xrightarrow{\ Ph_3SnCl\ } (Ph_3Sn)_2Te, \quad m.p.\ 148°$$

Mixed sulphides result when a germanium or lead halide is used [89, 306].

$$Ph_3SnSLi + Ph_3PbCl \longrightarrow Ph_3SnSPbPh_3, \quad m.p.\ 138°$$

Further routes to tin thiolates are exemplified by the following [111]:

$$Me_3SiSR + Me_3SnCl \longrightarrow Me_3SnSR + Me_3SiCl$$
$$Me_3SnNEt_2 + RSH \longrightarrow Me_3SnSR + Et_2NH$$

In both cases the by-product is volatile and easily separated.

[389] H. Kriegsmann and H. Hoffmann, *Z. Chem.*, 1963, **3**, 268; W. T. Reichle, *J. Polymer Sci.*, 1961, **49**, 521; *J. Org. Chem.*, 1961, **26**, 4634; *Inorg. Chem.*, 1962, **1**, 650; M. Pang and E. I. Becker, *J. Org. Chem.*, 1964, **29**, 1948; E. W. Abel and D. B. Brady, *J. Chem. Soc.*, 1965, 1192; D. Sukhani, V. D. Gupta and R. C. Mehrotra, *J. Organometal. Chem.*, 1967, **7**, 85.

[390] M. Schmidt and H. Ruf, *Chem. Ber.*, 1963, **96**, 784.

[391] R. C. Poller, *Proc. Chem. Soc.*, 1963, 312; R. C. Poller and J. A. Spillman, *J. Chem. Soc. (A)*, 1966, 958.

[392] G. S. Sasin, A. L. Barror and R. Sasin, *J. Org. Chem.*, 1958, **23**, 1366; D. Seyferth, *J. Amer. Chem. Soc.*, 1957, **79**, 2133; *Naturwiss.*, 1957, **44**, 34.

[393] M. Schmidt, H. J. Dersin and H. Schumann, *Chem. Ber.*, 1962, **95**, 1428; M. Schmidt and H. Schumann, ibid., 1963, **96**, 462, 780; *Z. anorg. Chem.*, 1963, **325**, 130.

[394] H. Schumann and M. Schmidt, *Chem. Ber.*, 1963, **96**, 3017.

[395] E. J. Kupchik and P. J. Calabretta, *Inorg. Chem.*, 1964, **3**, 905.

[396] H. Schumann, K.-F. Thom and M. Schmidt, *Angew. Chem.*, 1963, **75**, 138; *J. Organometal. Chem.*, 1963, **1**, 167; 1964, **2**, 361.

The 'monosulphides', $(R_3Sn)_2S$, like the oxides, are monomeric and so comparatively volatile. The dialkyl or diaryl compounds, $(R_2SnS)_3$, which are generally solids, soluble in the common organic solvents, are trimeric, unlike the more highly polymerized oxides, and probably have

4.11

the six-membered ring structure (4.11) [189, 397]. The 'tri-' or 'sesqui-' sulphides $(RSn)_2S_3$, from the oxide and sodium sulphide in aqueous acid solution, are solids which decompose when heated. They may be obtained in a form insoluble in solvents other than those with which they react, such as amines, aqueous acid, alkali or sulphide, with presumably cross-linked polymeric structures. Samples which dissolve in benzene as tetramers $R_4Sn_4S_6$ are also known [397a]. These probably have a tetrahedral arrangement of RSn units linked by sulphur atoms on the tetrahedron edges (cf. P_4O_6 or $(CH_2)_6N_4$).

Sulphur analogues of distannoxanes, *distannthianes*, $XR_2SnSSnR_2X$, can be prepared by warming together sulphides R_2SnS and halides, alkoxides or carboxylates R_2SnX_2 [397b]. Unlike the oxides, they are *monomeric* in benzene.

Although normally stable to water, tin–sulphur links are generally cleaved by reaction with metal halides [397c], e.g.:

$$HgCl_2 + 2Me_3SnSMe \longrightarrow 2Me_3SnCl + Hg(SMe)_2$$

Nitrogen, phosphorus and arsenic compounds

Organotin nitrogen and phosphorus compounds have been prepared only during the last few years, but already several methods of making them are known and the nitrogen compounds in particular appear likely to become useful intermediates. The nitrogen compounds are the subject of two recent reviews [123, 398].

[397] T. Harada, *Bull. Chem. Soc. Japan*, 1942, **17**, 281, 283; K. Moedritzer and J. R. Van Wazer, *Inorg. Chem.*, 1964, **3**, 943.

[397a] M. Komura and R. Okawara, *Inorg. Nucl. Chem. Letters*, 1966, **2**, 93.

[397b] A. G. Davies and P. G. Harrison, *J. Organometal. Chem.*, 1967, **8**, P19, but see R. C. Poller and J. A. Spillman, ibid., p. 259.

[397c] E. W. Abel, D. B. Brady and B. C. Crosse, ibid., 1966, **5**, 260; R. C. Poller and J. A. Spillman, ibid., 1966, **6**, 668.

[398] K. Jones and M. F. Lappert, *Organometal. Chem. Revs.*, 1966, **1**, 67.

Alkali metal [399, 400, 401, 402], or magnesium [403] derivatives of secondary amines react with organotin halides in ether to form aminotin compounds, e.g.

$$Me_3SnCl + LiNMe_2 \longrightarrow Me_3Sn{\cdot}NMe_2, \quad \text{b.p. } 126°$$

This method has been used to prepare organotin derivatives of various heterocyclic secondary amines such as triazole and iminazole [323, 404]. The infrared spectra of these derivatives show the presence of planar R_3Sn groups, which are thought to be linked by bridging heterocycles as in 4.12. Such compounds may also be prepared by treating alkyltin oxides or

4.12

hydroxides with the cyclic secondary amine and removing the water liberated by azeotropic distillation with benzene [404]:

$$(R_3Sn)_2O + HN{\bigcirc}(R') \longrightarrow 2R_3SnN{\bigcirc}(R') + H_2O$$

Alternatively, if this last reaction is carried out in acetone solution, the product may be precipitated [404]. The bridges in such co-ordination polymers as N-tributylstannyliminazole, $(Bu_3SnIm)_n$, may be broken by reaction with donor molecules, particularly unsaturated donor molecules such as pyridine or molecules in which the donor atom is phosphorus or sulphur, e.g. Bu_3P or $MeCSNMe_2$ [405];

$$(Bu_3SnIm)_n + nBu_3P \longrightarrow nBu_3SnImPBu_3$$

Some π-bonding between the tin and the donor molecule may be present in the resulting adducts.

Derivatives of amines or of ammonia itself are obtained through the transamination reaction [400], e.g.

$$Me_2Sn(NMe_2)_2 + EtNH_2 \longrightarrow (Me_2SnNEt)_3, \quad \text{b.p. } 104°/0{\cdot}05 \text{ mm.}$$

The reaction between trimethyltin oxide and sodium amide in boiling

[399] E. Wiberg and R. Rieger, Ger.P. 1,121,050; Chem. Abs., 1962, 56, 14328.

[400] K. Jones and M. F. Lappert, Proc. Chem. Soc., 1962, 358; J. Chem. Soc., 1965, 1944; J. Organometal. Chem., 1965, 3, 295; T. A. George, K. Jones and M. F. Lappert, J. Chem. Soc., 1965, 2157; see also A. Tzschach and E. Reiss, J. Organometal. Chem., 1967, 8, 255.

[401] E. W. Abel, D. Brady and B. R. Lerwill, Chem. and Ind., 1962, 1333.

[402] M. R. Kula, C. G. Kreiter and J. Lorberth, Chem. Ber., 1964, 97, 1294.

[403] K. Sisido and S. Kozima, J. Org. Chem., 1962, 27, 4051.

[404] J. G. A. Luijten, M. J. Janssen and G. J. M. van der Kerk, Rec. Trav. chim., 1962, 81, 202; J. G. A. Luijten and G. J. M. van der Kerk, ibid., 1963, 82, 1181.

[405] M. J. Janssen, J. G. A. Luijten and G. J. M. van der Kerk, J. Organometal. Chem., 1964, 1, 286.

ether or between a slurry of lithium nitride in tetrahydrofuran and tri-methyltin chloride leads to tris(trimethylstannyl)nitride, b.p. 84°/0·4 mm. [406].

$$Li_3N + 3Me_3SnCl \rightarrow (Me_3Sn)_3N + 3LiCl$$

The vibrational spectra of $(Me_3Sn)_3N$ (and of its phosphorous, arsenic and antimony analogues $(Me_3Sn)_3Y$, prepared from $3Me_3SnNMe_2 + YH_3$) are consistent with *pyramidal* structures (contrast planar $(Me_3Si)_3N$) [406a]. Related phosphinealkylenes, e.g. $(Me_3Sn)_2C:PPh_3$, presumably have similar structures [93a].

Tin–nitrogen links have also been formed by the addition of organotin alkoxides [367] or hydrides [190] to unsaturated nitrogen compounds:

$$Bu_3SnOMe + PhN:C:O \xrightarrow{20°} Bu_3Sn\cdot NPh\cdot CO\cdot OMe, \quad b.p. \ 100°/0·01 \ mm.$$
$$Et_3SnH + PhN:CHPh \rightarrow Et_3Sn\cdot NPh\cdot CH_2Ph$$

The formation of N-stannylcarbamates [407] from isocyanates may be a step in the formation of urethanes by the alcohol–isocyanate reaction, which is catalysed by organotin compounds [367]. Aminostannanes them-selves add across the N:C bond of isocyanates and many other polar un-saturated groups [400]:

$$Me_3SnNMe_2 + PhNCO \rightarrow Me_3Sn\cdot NPh\cdot CO\cdot NMe_2, \quad b.p. \ 103°/0·5 \ mm.$$

Organotin *amides* can also be prepared directly from the oxides [407a]

$$(R_3Sn)_2O + 2R'NHCOX \rightarrow 2R_3Sn\cdot NR'\cdot CO\cdot X + H_2O$$

Amino groups may be transferred from *silicon* to tin by the reaction between an aminosilane and an organotin halide, followed by thermal decomposition of the resulting co-ordination compound [401]:

$$\begin{matrix} Me_3SiNHEt & & Me_3SiNHEt & & Me_3SiBr \\ + & \longrightarrow & \downarrow \xrightarrow{distil} & & + \\ BrSnMe_3 & & BrSnMe_3 & & Me_3SnNHEt \\ & & \text{m.p. } 203\text{--}206° & & \end{matrix}$$

For silylaminotin compounds, e.g. $(Me_3Si)_2NSnMe_3$, see ref. [120].

Organotin *azides* may be prepared by treating the appropriate halide with concentrated aqueous sodium azide [92, 404, 408, 408a]:

$$Me_3SnCl + NaN_3 \rightarrow Me_3SnN_3, \quad m.p. \ 119·5\text{--}121·5°$$

[406] O. J. Scherer, J. F. Schmidt and M. Schmidt, *Z. Naturforsch.*, 1964, **19b**, 447; W. L. Lehn, *J. Amer. Chem. Soc.*, 1964, **86**, 305; K. Sisido and S. Kozima, *J. Org. Chem.*, 1964, **29**, 907.
[406a] R. E. Hester and K. Jones, *Chem. Comm.*, 1966, 317.
[407] J. G. Noltes, *Rec. Trav. chim.*, 1964, **83**, 515; 1965, **84**, 799.
[407a] A. G. Davies, T. N. Mitchell and W. R. Symes, *J. Chem. Soc. (C)*, 1966, 1311.
[408] W. T. Reichle, *Inorg. Chem.*, 1964, **3**, 402; J. S. Thayer and R. West, ibid., p. 406.
[408a] W. L. Lehn, ibid., 1967, **6**, 1061.

Like their silicon and germanium analogues, organotin azides lose nitrogen when treated with phosphines, arsines or stibines, forming compounds $R_nSn(N:YR'_3)_{4-n}$, in which $Y = P$, As or Sb [93, 408a].

For other organotin pseudohalides with Sn–N bonds, see refs. [93b], [93c] and [408b].

The reactivity of aminotin compounds is comparable to that of Grignard reagents, in that addition to multiple bonds occurs readily [400],

$$Me_3SnNMe_2 + CO_2 \longrightarrow Me_3SnO\cdot CO\cdot NMe_2, \quad m.p.\ 156°$$

boron or aluminium hydrides react to replace the amino group by hydrogen [409], and protic reagents HA form derivatives R_3SnA with evolution of amine [259]:

$$R_3SnNMe_2 + HA \longrightarrow R_3SnA + Me_2NH$$

This last reaction provides a route to a range of organotin derivatives which are not readily obtained by other methods. The use of acetylenes $(HA = HC:CR)$ to prepare acetylenic derivatives has already been mentioned [259]; cyclopentadienyl and indenyl compounds are obtained similarly, e.g. $Ph_3SnC_5H_5$, m.p. 129°, and $Ph_3SnC_9H_7$, m.p. 129°, result from the action of the hydrocarbon on Ph_3SnNMe_2. *Phosphorus* and *arsenic* derivatives can also be prepared using diphenyl-phosphine or -arsine:

$$Me_3SnNMe_2 + HPPh_2 \longrightarrow Me_2NH + Me_3SnPPh_2, \quad b.p.\ 150°/0\cdot 8\ mm.$$
$$Me_3SnNMe_2 + HAsPh_2 \longrightarrow Me_2NH + Me_3SnAsPh_2, \quad b.p.\ 136°/0\cdot 05\ mm.$$

The ready hydrolysis, alcoholysis and hydrogen halide cleavage of aminotin compounds, as well as their transamination reactions, are further examples of the same general reaction.

The reaction can also be applied to the attachment of organotin groups to transition metals, e.g. [409a]

$$Me_3SnNMe_2 + \pi\text{-}C_5H_5W(CO)_3H \xrightarrow{-Me_2NH} \pi\text{-}C_5H_5W(CO)_3SnMe_3, \quad m.p.\ 120°$$

For [1]H m.r. data on various aminotin compounds, see ref. [410].

In addition to the method using aminotin compounds, *organotin phosphorus* derivatives have been prepared from tin halides and lithium derivatives of phosphines [411],

$$Ph_3SnCl + Ph_2PLi \longrightarrow Ph_3SnPPh_2, \quad m.p.\ 126°$$

[408b] E. E. Aynsley, N. N. Greenwood, G. Hunter and M. J. Sprague, *J. Chem. Soc.* (*A*), 1966, 1344; M. Wada and R. Okawara, *J. Organometal. Chem.*, 1967, **8**, 261.

[409] M.-R. Kula, J. Lorberth and E. Amberger, *Chem. Ber.*, 1964, **97**, 2087.

[409a] D. J. Cardin and M. F. Lappert, *Chem. Comm.*, 1966, 506.

[410] J. Lorberth and M.-R. Kula, *Chem. Ber.*, 1964, **97**, 3444; 1965, **98**, 520.

[411] H. Schumann, H. Köpf and M. Schmidt, *Angew. Chem.*, 1963, **75**, 672; *Z. Naturforsch,*, 1964, **19b**, 168; *J. Organometal. Chem.*, 1964, **2**, 159; *Chem. Ber.*, 1964, **97**, 1458, 2395; I. G. M. Campbell, G. W. A. Fowles and L. A. Nixon, *J. Chem. Soc.*, 1964, 1389.

from chlorophosphines and stannyl-lithium reagents,

$$9Ph_3SnLi \quad\quad PhP\!-\!SnPh_2 \quad\quad 6Ph_3P$$
$$+ \quad\longrightarrow\quad Ph_2Sn \quad\quad PPh \quad + \quad\quad +$$
$$9Ph_2PCl \quad\quad PhP\!-\!SnPh_2 \quad\quad 3Ph_6Sn_2$$
$$+$$
$$(m.p.\ 64°) \quad\quad 9LiCl$$

$$4.13$$

from phosphines and tin halides, with a tertiary amine to take up the hydrogen halide eliminated,

$$Bu_3SnCl + Ph_2PH + R_3N \longrightarrow Bu_3SnPPh_2, \quad m.p.\ 60°$$

or by the action of phosphorus itself on tetraphenyltin, which leads to a mixture of products, including Ph_3SnPPh_2 and the cyclic compounds 4.13 and 4.14 (m.p. 90°).

$$Ph_2Sn\!-\!PSnPh_3$$
$$Ph_3SnP \quad\quad SnPh_2$$
$$Ph_2Sn\!-\!PSnPh_3$$

$$4.14$$

Tin–phosphorus compounds, like tin–nitrogen compounds, can add to a range of polar unsaturated compounds [412], e.g.

$$Ph_3SnPPh_2 + CS_2 \longrightarrow Ph_3SnS \cdot CS \cdot PPh_2, \quad m.p.\ 68°$$

Organotin phosphorus compounds are rapidly oxidized in air to organotin phosphates and are cleaved into characteristic fragments by alcoholic sodium hydroxide [411]:

$$R_3SnPR'_2 + NaOH \longrightarrow (R_3Sn)_2O + R'_2PH$$

The phosphorus atoms may be methylated with methyl iodide. Partial oxidation by, for example, exposure of an ethereal solution to air leads to stannyl phosphine oxides, $R_3Sn \cdot P(O)R'_2$, which may be isolated from the reaction mixture when phosphinotin compounds are prepared [413, 414]:

$$Bu_3SnCl + Ph_2PLi \xrightarrow{\ Et_2O\ } Bu_3SnPPh_2 + Bu_3SnP(O)Ph_2$$
$$or \quad Bu_3SnLi + Ph_2PCl$$
$$\qquad\qquad\qquad\qquad\qquad\qquad m.p.\ 60° \qquad m.p.\ 217\text{–}219°$$

The presence of the P:O bond in the phosphine oxide is indicated by a band in the infrared spectrum at 1160 cm^{-1}.

Triphenylstannyl-lithium reacts with the trichlorides of arsenic, antimony and bismuth in tetrahydrofuran to form $(Ph_3Sn)_3As$, m.p. 212–216°,

[412] H. Schumann, P. Jutzi and M. Schmidt, *Angew. Chem., Internat. Edn.*, 1965, **4**, 787, 869.

[413] H. Schindlbauer and D. Hammer, *Monatsh.*, 1963, **94**, 644.

[414] W. Kuchen and H. Buchwald, *Chem. Ber.*, 1959, **92**, 227.

(Ph$_3$Sn)$_3$Sb, m.p. 214–215°, and (Ph$_3$Sn)$_3$Bi, m.p. 138–142° (decomp.) respectively [415].

Alkali metal derivatives

Not only can organotin groups of the type R$_3$Sn and R$_2$Sn exist as cations when associated with suitable donor molecules, but they can also acquire a formal negative charge in the alkali metal compounds R$_3$SnM and R$_2$SnM$_2$. The trimethylstannyl compounds and the dimetallic derivatives may be prepared by the addition of the alkali metal to the mono- or di-halide in liquid ammonia

$$Me_3SnBr + 2Na \longrightarrow Me_3SnNa + NaBr$$
$$R_2SnX_2 + 4Na \longrightarrow R_2SnNa_2 + 2NaX$$

The series R$_3$SnM may also be obtained by addition of RM to tin(II) compounds, e.g.

$$Ph_2Sn + PhLi \longrightarrow Ph_3SnLi$$

A generally preferred method is the reaction between alkali metals (or their addition compounds with aromatic hydrocarbons) and R$_4$Sn, R$_6$Sn$_2$ or R$_3$SnX, best in tetrahydrofuran or ethylene glycol dimethyl ether.

These alkali metal derivatives are always coloured (R$_3$SnM usually yellow or brown, R$_2$SnM$_2$ deep red). They are generally not isolated, since they readily decompose and are very sensitive to air and moisture, but are used immediately for further reactions.

Trimethylstannylsodium, Me$_3$SnNa, was the first of this type to be prepared [416]. It is formed in high yield when sodium is added to trimethyltin bromide in liquid ammonia. Evaporation of the yellow solution gives yellow crystals of the salt, which is unstable at room temperature and decomposes rapidly at higher temperatures into hydrocarbons and a tin–sodium alloy [417].

Tetramethyltin also reacts with sodium in liquid ammonia,

$$Me_4Sn + 2Na + NH_3 \longrightarrow Me_3SnNa + NaNH_2 \downarrow + CH_4 \uparrow$$

Addition of ammonium salts to a liquid ammonia solution of trimethyl-stannylsodium causes trimethylstannane to separate as a heavy oil [416]:

$$Me_3SnNa + NH_4^+ + Br^- \longrightarrow Me_3SnH \downarrow + NH_3 + NaBr$$

Methyl iodide at once discharges the yellow colour of trimethylstannyl-

[415] H. Schumann and M. Schmidt, *Angew. Chem.*, 1964, **3**, 316; see also I. G. M. Campbell, G. W. A. Fowles and L. A. Nixon, *J. Chem. Soc.*, 1964, 3026; H. Schumann, T. Östermann and M. Schmidt, *Chem. Ber.*, 1966, **99**, 2057; *J. Organometal. Chem.*, 1967, **8**, 105.

[416] C. A. Kraus and W. N. Greer, *J. Amer. Chem. Soc.*, 1922, **44**, 2629.

[417] C. A. Kraus and W. V. Sessions, ibid., 1925, **47**, 2361.

sodium with formation of tetramethyltin. p-Dichlorobenzene reacts similarly [417]:

$$p\text{-}C_6H_4Cl_2 + 2Me_3SnNa \longrightarrow 1,4(Me_3Sn)_2C_6H_4 + NaCl$$

This aromatic di-tin compound, m.p. 123–124°, is easily decomposed by iodine forming p-di-iodobenzene and trimethyltin iodide.

Trimethylstannylsodium reacts with chloroform in liquid ammonia to form roughly equal proportions of hexamethyldistannane and bis(trimethylstannyl)methane, apparently through the intermediate formation of methylene dichloride [418]:

$$2Me_3SnNa + CHCl_3 \longrightarrow Me_6Sn_2 \downarrow + NaCHCl_2 + NaCl$$

$$\Big\downarrow NH_3$$

$$(Me_3Sn)_2CH_2 \xleftarrow{Me_3SnNa} CH_2Cl_2$$

Organotin halides also react with trimethylstannylsodium. Hexamethyldistannane is precipitated, being only sparingly soluble in liquid ammonia, when trimethyltin bromide is added to trimethylstannylsodium:

$$Me_3SnNa + Me_3SnBr \longrightarrow Me_3Sn\cdot SnMe_3 + NaBr$$

Hexamethyldistannane is in fact the primary product when sodium is added to trimethyltin bromide,

$$2Me_3SnBr + 2Na \longrightarrow Me_6Sn_2 + 2NaBr$$

and can be isolated in good yield when only one mol. of sodium is added to a mol. of halide. Addition of more sodium produces trimethylstannylsodium:

$$Me_6Sn_2 + 2Na \longrightarrow Me_3SnNa$$

Reactions between trimethylstannylsodium and trimethylborane or boron trifluoride have been studied (unsuccessfully) as a possible route to tin–boron compounds; hexamethyldistannane was the main product [419].

Trimethylstannyl-potassium, Me_3SnK, is formed when hexamethyldistannane reacts with sodium–potassium alloy in ethylene glycol dimethyl ether, with development of a greenish-yellow colour:

$$Me_6Sn_2 + Na/K \longrightarrow 2Me_3SnK$$

Its presence can be demonstrated by isolation of 1,1,1-trimethyl-2,2,2-tri-p-tolyldistannane, $Me_3Sn\cdot Sn(C_6H_4\text{-}p\text{-}CH_3)_3$, m.p. 139·5–140°, after addition of tri-p-tolyltin bromide [125].

[418] H. D. Kaesz, ibid., 1961, **83**, 1514.
[419] A. B. Burg and J. R. Spielman, ibid., p. 2667.

Trimethylstannyl-lithium, Me_3SnLi, is formed when trimethyltin chloride or bromide reacts with lithium in tetrahydrofuran [420]:

$$Me_3SnCl + 2Li \longrightarrow Me_3SnLi + LiCl$$

Addition of a mol. of trimethyltin bromide to the filtered greenish-yellow solution discharges the colour, producing hexamethyldistannane:

$$Me_3SnLi + Me_3SnBr \longrightarrow Me_6Sn_2 + LiBr$$

The proton magnetic resonance spectra of trimethylstannyl-lithium and dimethylstannylenedilithium dissolved in methylamine have been interpreted as indicating that the free anions Me_3Sn^- and Me_2Sn^{2-} are *not* present in such solutions [421].

Dimethylstannylenedisodium, Me_2SnNa_2, from dimethyltin dibromide [422] or dihydride [423] and sodium in liquid ammonia, reacts as if it were ionized into Me_2Sn^{2-} and Na^+ ions. Several products in turn are formed in this reaction; when sodium is first added to an ammonia solution of dimethyltin dibromide, a yellow precipitate of polymeric dimethyltin appears:

$$Me_2SnBr_2 + 2Na \longrightarrow (Me_2Sn)_n + 2NaBr$$

On the addition of a further gram-atom of sodium the yellow precipitate dissolves completely and gives a deep red solution, which at this stage contains $NaMe_2Sn \cdot SnMe_2Na$, since addition of methyl iodide causes immediate precipitation of hexamethyldistannane:

$$2Me_2Sn + 2Na \longrightarrow NaMe_2Sn \cdot SnMe_2Na \xrightarrow{MeI} Me_3Sn \cdot SnMe_3 + 2NaI$$

Further addition of sodium to $NaMe_2Sn \cdot SnMe_2Na$ gives a very deep red solution, which then contains Me_2SnNa_2 since addition of methyl iodide at this stage gives tetramethyltin:

$$NaMe_2Sn \cdot SnMe_2Na + 2Na \longrightarrow 2Me_2SnNa_2$$
$$Me_2SnNa_2 + 2MeI \longrightarrow Me_4Sn + 2NaI$$

Stannane itself forms mono- and di-sodium derivatives, which decompose at lower temperatures than their organo derivatives [423].

Dimethylstannylenedisodium and other disodium derivatives R_2SnNa_2 may be used for the preparation of compounds containing chains of tin atoms, and organotin polymers with alternating carbon and tin atoms are obtained when the disodium compounds react with substituted methylene dichlorides [424]:

$$R_2SnNa_2 + R'_2CCl_2 \longrightarrow [-SnR_2 \cdot CR'_2-]_n + 2NaCl$$

[420] C. Tamborski, F. E. Ford and E. J. Soloski, *J. Org. Chem.,* 1963, **28,** 237.
[421] N. Flitcroft and H. D. Kaesz, *J. Amer. Chem. Soc.,* 1963, **85,** 1377.
[422] C. A. Kraus and W. N. Greer, ibid., 1925, **47,** 2568.
[423] H. J. Emeléus and S. F. A. Kettle, *J. Chem. Soc.,* 1958, 2444; S. F. A. Kettle, ibid., 1959, 2936.
[424] J. M. Maselli, *Dissertation Abstracts,* 1962, **23,** 836.

The products are clear colourless oils, unchanged during several days' exposure to air, which decompose when heated to 150–220°.

Triethylstannyl-lithium, Et_3SnLi, is formed when ethyl-lithium is added to a suspension of tin(II) chloride in ether at $-10°$. When two mols. of ethyl-lithium have been added the solution is deep red since it contains diethyltin, which adds a further mol. of ethyl-lithium in a probably reversible reaction [425]:

$$2EtLi + SnCl_2 \longrightarrow Et_2Sn + 2LiCl$$
$$EtLi + Et_2Sn \rightleftharpoons Et_3SnLi$$

The colour test (II, p. 31) becomes positive when 2·5 mols. of ethyl-lithium have been added. Addition of ethyl bromide to the reaction mixture gives tetra-ethyltin in about 70% yield.

Tri-n-butylstannyl-lithium, Bu^n_3SnLi, is similarly prepared but the colour test for Bu^nLi becomes positive only when three mols. of Bu^nLi have been added to the tin(II) chloride. The brown Bu^n_3SnLi reacts with butyl iodide and iodobenzene giving tetrabutyltin ($\sim50\%$ yield) and in the second case a mixture of about equal parts (27% yield each) of tri-n-butylphenyltin, Bu^n_3PhSn, and tetrabutyltin [425]. The reactions of tri-n-butylstannyl-lithium are often rather complex and there are indications that it very easily dissociates into di-n-butyltin and n-butyl-lithium. For example, carbonation affords di-n-butyltin and a mixture of di-n-butyl ketone and valeric acid,

$$Bu^n_3SnLi \rightleftharpoons Bu^n_2Sn + Bu^nLi \xrightarrow{CO_2} Bu^n_2CO + Bu^nCO_2H$$

and butyltrimethylsilane is obtained with trimethylchlorsilane [426]:

$$Bu^n_3SnLi \rightleftharpoons Bu^n_2Sn + Bu^nLi \xrightarrow{Me_3SiCl} Bu^nMe_3Si$$

The hydrolysis of tributylstannyl-lithium is complex and gives hydrogen in low yield and some butane, tributylstannane and hexabutyldistannane; the main product is a deep red viscous liquid consisting largely of di-n-butyltin but containing tributyltin groups [420, 426].

With trimethylchlorsilane in ether at $-20°$, tributylstannyl-lithium gives tributyl(trimethylsilyl)tin, as an orange-yellow solid, m.p. 60–70°, b.p. 94°/1 mm. [427].

$$Bu_3SnLi + ClSiMe_3 \longrightarrow Bu_3Sn{\cdot}SiMe_3$$

At 24°, however, hexabutyldistannane is a major product because of the rapid metal–halogen exchange

$$Bu_3SnLi + ClSiMe_3 \rightleftharpoons Bu_3SnCl + LiSiMe_3$$

[425] H. Gilman and S. D. Rosenberg, *J. Amer. Chem. Soc.*, 1953, **75**, 2507.

[426] D. Blake, G. E. Coates and J. M. Tate, *J. Chem. Soc.*, 1961, 618.

[427] E. Wiberg, O. Stecher, H. J. Andraschek, L. Kreuzbichler and E. Staude, *Angew. Chem.*, 1963, **75**, 516.

Triphenylstannylsodium, Ph₃SnNa, is readily prepared in liquid ammonia solution by addition of sodium to hexaphenyldistannane or to triphenyltin bromide in that solvent. It has been isolated as a yellow, air-sensitive powder. Its solution in liquid ammonia is a good conductor and the salt is rather more dissociated than sodium bromate, though the limiting conductance is less. Trimethylstannylsodium also conducts, but appears to be less dissociated [428].

Triphenylstannylsodium undergoes numerous reactions, some of which give functionally substituted tin compounds, though the scope of the reagent, when prepared in liquid ammonia, is restricted by the reactivity of the ammonia, which is difficult to remove entirely when attempts are made to replace it by, for example, ether. Ammonium bromide forms triphenylstannane, Ph₃SnH, in good yield:

$$Ph_3SnNa + NH_4Br \longrightarrow Ph_3SnH + NH_3 + NaBr$$

Triphenylstannylacetic acid is obtained on reaction with sodium chloroacetate [429]:

$$Ph_3SnNa + ClCH_2CO_2Na \longrightarrow Ph_3SnCH_2CO_2Na + NaCl$$

Ethylene oxide yields an alcohol [430]:

$$Ph_3SnNa + \overline{CH_2CH_2O} \longrightarrow Ph_3SnCH_2CH_2OH$$

Triphenylstannylsodium is formed in very good yield, and in a more convenient solvent than ammonia, when sodium-naphthalene in tetrahydrofuran or ethylene glycol dimethyl ether is added to hexaphenyldistannane, triphenyltin bromide, or tetraphenyltin in the same solvent [426]. The reaction is accompanied by a vivid colour change as the deep green sodium-naphthalene changes to the tan-colour of the tin compound:

$$2C_{10}H_8Na + Ph_3SnBr \longrightarrow Ph_3SnNa + NaBr + 2C_{10}H_8$$

The resulting solution acts as a reducing agent towards benzophenone, benzoyl chloride, oxygen, carbon dioxide and sulphur dioxide, the tin appearing as hexaphenyldistannane, and forms alkyl derivatives Ph₃SnR with halides RX.

Triphenylstannyl-lithium, Ph₃SnLi, is a tan-coloured powder formed when phenyl-lithium reacts with diphenyltin [431],

$$Ph_2Sn + PhLi \longrightarrow Ph_3SnLi$$

[428] C. A. Kraus and W. H. Kahler, *J. Amer. Chem. Soc.*, 1933, **55**, 3537; C. A. Kraus and E. G. Johnson, ibid., p. 3542.

[429] R. F. Chambers and P. C. Scherer, ibid., 1926, **48**, 1054.

[430] H. Gilman and C. E. Arntzen, *J. Org. Chem.*, 1950, **15**, 994.

[431] G. Wittig, F. J. Meyer and G. Lange, *Annalen*, 1951, **571**, 169, 193.

It can conveniently be prepared from tin(II) chloride in a single reaction in which the diphenyltin need not be isolated [432]:

$$SnCl_2 + 2PhLi \longrightarrow Ph_2Sn + 2LiCl$$
$$Ph_2Sn + PhLi \longrightarrow Ph_3SnLi$$

Triphenylstannyl-lithium is also obtained as a dark olive-brown or -green solution by the action of lithium on triphenyltin chloride or hexaphenyl-distannane in tetrahydrofuran [143, 433, 434], a solvent which is not cleaved by this reagent even when refluxed, although some decomposition of the reagent to Ph_4Sn occurs [435]. *Diphenylstannylenedilithium*, Ph_2SnLi_2, is obtained as a yellow solution [436] in tetrahydrofuran by the dropwise addition of Ph_2SnCl_2 to a suspension of lithium in that solvent.

In a few reactions triphenylstannyl-lithium behaves like a Grignard or organolithium reagent, e.g.

$$Ph_3SnLi + CH_2\text{---}CHCH_2Cl \longrightarrow Ph_3SnCH_2CHOHCH_2Cl \quad [437]$$
$$\diagdown \diagup$$
$$O$$

$$Ph_3SnLi + CH_2ClCH_2CH_2NEt_2 \longrightarrow Ph_3Sn(CH_2)_3NEt_2 \quad [438]$$

Triphenylchlorsilane gives triphenyl(triphenylsilyl)tin, $Ph_3SnSiPh_3$ [432], as well as hexaphenyl-distannane and -disilane, apparently through the equilibrium [427, 434]

$$Ph_3SnLi + Ph_3SiCl \rightleftharpoons Ph_3SnCl + Ph_3SiLi$$

Several organic halides (particularly bromides) afford good yields of un-symmetrical tin compounds, e.g. [426, 434]

$$Ph_3SnLi + EtBr \longrightarrow Ph_3SnEt + LiBr$$

In many reactions, however, triphenylstannyl-lithium behaves quite unlike a typical organolithium reagent. In reaction with water [431, 433, 434] gas is evolved for about half an hour, and the main product isolated from the reaction mixture is hexaphenyldistannane. Carbonation gives oxalate almost quantitatively and a high yield (~80%) of hexaphenyl-distannane [426, 433, 434].

$$2Ph_3SnLi + 2CO_2 \longrightarrow Ph_6Sn_2 + Li_2C_2O_4$$

and with benzophenone an electron transfer reaction takes place since the

[432] H. Gilman and S. D. Rosenberg, *J. Amer. Chem. Soc.*, 1952, **74**, 531.
[433] H. Gilman, O. L. Mars and S.-Y. Sim, *J. Org. Chem.*, 1962, **27**, 4232.
[434] C. Tamborski, F. E. Ford and E. J. Soloski, ibid., 1963, **28**, 181.
[435] H. Gilman, F. K. Cartledge and S.-Y. Sim, *J. Organometal. Chem.*, 1965, **4**, 332.
[436] H. Schumann, K. F. Thom and M. Schmidt, ibid., 1964, **2**, 97.
[437] H. Gilman and S. D. Rosenberg, *J. Org. Chem.*, 1953, **18**, 1554.
[438] H. Gilman and T. C. Wu, *J. Amer. Chem. Soc.*, 1955, **77**, 3228.

typical blue colour of the ketyl is observed and Ph_6Sn_2 is again obtained, with benzhydrol [426]:

$$2Ph_3SnLi + 2Ph_2CO \longrightarrow Ph_6Sn_2 + 2Ph_2CO^-Li^+$$

Triphenylstannyl-lithium resembles its germanium analogue Ph_3GeLi in its reactions with ethyl carbonate and ethyl chloroformate in that carbon monoxide is produced [439]. With $ClCO_2Et$ the other products are Ph_6Sn_2 ($\sim50\%$) and Ph_4Sn ($\sim10\%$). Towards acidic hydrocarbons like fluorene, however, Ph_3SnLi is a weaker metalating agent than Ph_3GeLi, giving (after carbonation) less than 20% of fluorene-9-carboxylic acid as opposed to 66% from the germanium compound [149].

For the analysis of organo-silyl-, -germyl- and -stannyl-lithium reagents R_3MLi see ref. [440].

Bis(triphenylstannyl)magnesium, $(Ph_3Sn)_2Mg$, is apparently present in the grey-green mixture obtained by the action of magnesium on a solution of Ph_3SnCl or Ph_6Sn_2 in tetrahydrofuran in the presence of a trace of ethyl bromide. Treatment of the reaction mixture with water gives triphenylstannane, Ph_3SnH [441].

Transition metal compounds

Like germanium and lead, tin has recently been shown to be capable of forming σ-bonds to a wide range of transition metals, generally in the form of carbonyl complexes. Many have been prepared from an organotin halide and the alkali metal derivative of a transition metal carbonyl complex, e.g. [151, 154, 155a, 442]:

$$Ph_3SnCl + NaMn(CO)_5 \longrightarrow Ph_3SnMn(CO)_5$$
$$Me_2SnCl_2 + NaIr(CO)_3PPh_3 \longrightarrow Me_2Sn[Ir(CO)_3PPh_3]_2$$
$$[\pi\text{-}C_5H_5Fe(CO)_2]_2SnCl_2 + 2Na[\pi\text{-}C_5H_5Mo(CO)_3]$$
$$\longrightarrow [\pi\text{-}C_5H_5Fe(CO)_2]_2Sn[\pi\text{-}C_5H_5Mo(CO)_3]_2$$

The direct reaction between organotin halides and iron pentacarbonyl gives various iron complexes of such types as $[R_2SnFe(CO)_4]_2$, $[R_2SnCl]_2Fe(CO)_4$, $R_4Sn_3[Fe(CO)_4]_4$ and $Sn[Fe(CO)_4]_4$ [154, 443]. Other

[439] H. Gilman and L. A. Gist, *J. Org. Chem.*, 1957, **22**, 689.
[440] H. Gilman, F. K. Cartledge and S.-Y. Sim, *J. Organometal. Chem.*, 1963, **1**, 8.
[441] C. Tamborski and E. J. Soloski, *J. Amer. Chem. Soc.*, 1961, **83**, 3734.
[442] R. D. Gorsich, ibid., 1962, **84**, 2486; *J. Organometal. Chem.*, 1966, **5**, 105; H. C. Clark, J. H. Tsai and W. S. Tang, *Chem. Comm.*, 1965, 171; R. D. Gorsich, U.S.P. 3,030,396, 17 April 1962; 3,099,667, 30 July 1963; A. N. Nesmeyanov, K. N. Anisimov, N. E. Kolobova and V. N. Khandozhko, *Doklady Akad. Nauk S.S.S.R.*, 1964, **156**, 383; A. N. Nesmeyanov, K. N. Anisimov, N. E. Kolobova and M. Ya. Zakharova, *Izvest. Akad. Nauk S.S.S.R.*, 1965, 1122; *Chem. Abs.*, 1962, **57**, 7309; 1964, **60**, 549; **61**, 7041; 1965, **63**, 8393; H. R. H. Patil and W. A. G. Graham, *J. Amer. Chem. Soc.*, 1965, **87**, 673; S. V. Dighe and M. Orchin, ibid., p. 1146; D. J. Patmore and W. A. G. Graham, *Inorg. Chem.*, 1966, **5**, 2222; J. P. Collman, F. D. Vastine and W. R. Roper, *J. Amer. Chem. Soc.*, 1966, **88**, 5035.
[443] R. B. King and F. G. A. Stone, *J. Amer. Chem. Soc.*, 1960, **82**, 3833; S. D. Ibekwe and M. J. Newlands, *Chem. Comm.*, 1965, 114.

preparative routes include the elimination of amines from mixtures of amino derivatives of tin and transition metal hydrides [409a], or the insertion of tin(II) chloride into metal–halogen or metal–metal bonds [444].

$$\pi\text{-}C_5H_5Fe(CO)_2Cl + SnCl_2 \rightarrow \pi\text{-}C_5H_5Fe(CO)_2SnCl_3$$
$$[Ph_3PCo(CO)_3]_2 + SnCl_2 \rightarrow [Ph_3P(CO)_3Co]_2SnCl_2$$

Carbon monoxide can be displaced from these derivatives by other ligands and separates in the mass spectrometer before the metal–metal bond breaks [445]. The tin–manganese bond of $Me_3SnMn(CO)_5$ is cleaved in reactions with fluoro-olefins [446]:

$$Me_3SnMn(CO)_5 + C_2F_4 \rightarrow Me_3SnC_2F_4Mn(CO)_5$$

The crystal structures of many of these derivatives have been studied by X-ray diffraction. The compounds $Ph_3SnMn(CO)_5$ [447], $Me_3SnMn(CO)_5$ [448] and $Ph_3SnMn(CO)_4PPh_3$ [448a] for example have tetrahedrally co-ordinated tin, octahedral manganese and Sn–Mn bond lengths of $2\cdot674 \pm 0\cdot004$, $2\cdot674 \pm 0\cdot003$ and $2\cdot627 \pm 0\cdot01$ Å respectively. In $Ph_2Sn[Mn(CO)_5]_2$, in which the tin bridges the two manganese atoms, the Sn–Mn distance is $2\cdot70$ Å and $\angle$ MnSnMn $= 117°$ [448b]. The similarly bridged $Cl_2Sn[\pi\text{-}C_5H_5Fe(CO)_2]_2$ has $\angle$ FeSnFe $= 129°$ [448c], while two types of bridging tin occur in $Me_4Sn_3Fe_4(CO)_{10}$ [448d]:

The crystal structures of the related compounds $(acac)_2SnCo_2(CO)_7$ [448e],

[444] F. Bonati and G. W. Wilkinson, J. Chem. Soc., 1964, 179; R. C. Taylor, J. F. Young and G. Wilkinson, Inorg. Chem., 1966, 5, 20; R. V. Lindsey, G. W. Parshall and U. G. Stolberg, ibid., p. 109; D. J. Patmore and W. A. G. Graham, ibid., p. 1405; J. A. Dilts and M. P. Johnson, ibid., p. 2079; F. Bonati, S. Cenini, D. Morelli and R. Ugo, J. Chem. Soc. (A), 1966, 1052; F. Bonati, S. Cenini and R. Ugo, ibid., 1967, 932; P. A. McArdle and A. R. Manning, Chem. Comm., 1967, 417; J. V. Kingston, J. W. S. Jamieson and G. Wilkinson, J. Inorg. Nucl. Chem., 1967, 29, 133.
[445] J. Lewis, A. R. Manning, J. R. Miller and J. M. Wilson, J. Chem. Soc. (A), 1966, 1663.
[446] H. C. Clark and J. H. Tsai, Inorg. Chem., 1966, 5, 1407.
[447] H. P. Webber and R. F. Bryan, Chem. Comm., 1966, 443.
[448] R. F. Bryan, ibid., 1967, 355.
[448a] Idem., J. Chem. Soc. (A), 1967, 172.
[448b] B. T. Kilbourn and H. M. Powell, Chem. and Ind., 1964, 1578.
[448c] J. E. O'Connor and E. R. Corey, Inorg. Chem., 1967, 6, 968.
[448d] R. M. Sweet, C. J. Fritchie and R. A. Schunn, ibid., p. 749.
[448e] D. J. Patmore and W. A. G. Graham, Chem. Comm., 1967, 7.

$Ph_2SnFe(CO)_2(\pi-C_5H_5)$ [448f], $Sn[Fe(CO)_4]_4$ [448g] and (cyclo-octa-1,5-diene)$_2$IrSnCl$_3$ [448h] are also known.

Compounds containing tin–tin bonds

These compounds fall into two categories:

(a) derivatives of distannane or other higher (acyclic) stannanes, i.e. R_6Sn_2 or, more generally, $R_{2n+2}Sn_n$;

(b) derivatives of cyclic stannanes, i.e. derivatives of tin(II), $(R_2Sn)_n$.

Derivatives of distannane

These are quite easily prepared ($2R_3SnX + 2Na$, $R_3SnX + NaSnR'_3$, $R_3SnH + R'_3SnOR$, $R_3SnH + R'_3SnNR_2$), and have chemical reactivities intermediate between those of their less reactive germanium and more reactive lead analogues.

Hexamethyldistannane, $Me_3Sn\cdot SnMe_3$, m.p. 23°, b.p. 182°, from trimethyltin bromide and sodium in liquid ammonia [417], has been mentioned several times already. It is far more readily oxidized than the tetraalkyls, inflaming in air at its boiling point, and slowly absorbing oxygen at room temperature giving the oxide $(Me_3Sn)_2O$. Similarly it slowly combines with sulphur giving the sulphide [417] $(Me_3Sn)_2S$, b.p. 233·5–235·5°. Hexamethyldistannane is converted into trimethyltin halides, not only by free halogens, but also by mercury(II) chloride which is reduced to metallic mercury. The behaviour of trifluoroiodomethane as a pseudohalogen in this respect has already been described [272] (p. 427).

The Sn–Sn stretching force constant for hexamethyldistannane has been calculated (from the Raman spectrum) as $1·0 \pm 0·1 \times 10^5$ dynes cm^{-1} (cf. $1·3 \pm 0·1 \times 10^5$ dynes cm^{-1} for Ge–Ge in Me_6Ge_2) [126]. The ^{119}Sn and ^1H magnetic resonance spectra of Me_6Sn_2 show a coupling constant of $J = 4400 \pm 70$ c.p.s. for ^{117}Sn–^{119}Sn nuclei directly bonded, the large value reflecting the large atomic number of the coupled nuclei. The anomalously low value of the coupling constant J_{Sn-C-H} in Me_6Sn_2 has been tentatively associated with reduced s character in the Sn–C bond and increased s character in the Sn–Sn bond [449].

Hexa-ethyldistannane, $Et_3Sn\cdot SnEt_3$, b.p. 162°/23 mm., has been prepared by the reduction of triethyltin bromide by sodium, not only in liquid ammonia but also in boiling xylene. It reduces mercuric chloride and

[448f] R. F. Bryan, *J. Chem. Soc. (A)*, 1967, 192.
[448g] P. F. Lindley and P. Woodward, ibid., p. 382.
[448h] P. Porta, H. M. Powell, R. J. Mawly and L. M. Venanzi, ibid., p. 455.
[449] H. C. Clark, J. T. Kwon, L. W. Reeves and E. J. Wells, *Canad. J. Chem.*, 1964, **42**, 941.

alcoholic silver nitrate. With ethyl iodide at 220° butane is formed [450, 451].

$$Et_6Sn_2 + 2EtI \longrightarrow 2Et_3SnI + C_4H_{10}$$

With concentrated hydrochloric acid two atoms of chlorine are substituted, giving Et_2SnCl_2. Oxidation by oxygen at 50° leads to a mixture of products, including the oxides Et_2SnO and $(Et_3Sn)_2O$, possibly through the unstable peroxide $(Et_3SnO)_2$ [452]. Tertiary-butyl peroxide at 130° causes evolution of a mixture of methane, ethane, ethylene and butane, leaving a residue approximating to deca-ethyltetrastannane, $Et_{10}Sn_4$ [453]. Disproportionation reactions occur under ultraviolet irradiation or in the presence of aluminium chloride or tin chlorides, the main products being dark red polymeric materials which at 200° decompose to tetra-ethyltin and metallic tin, contaminated by chloro derivatives when chloride catalysts are used [451, 453, 454].

Trimethyltriphenyldistannane, $Me_3Sn \cdot SnPh_3$, m.p. 106°, from triphenyl-stannylsodium and trimethyltin bromide [455], is much more resistant to oxidation than hexamethyldistannane.

The synthesis of unsymmetrically substituted higher stannanes is easily effected by the action of organotin hydrides on tin amides, oxides, alkoxides or related compounds [456, 457, 458, 459]:

$$2R_3SnH + R'_3SnX \longrightarrow R_3Sn \cdot SnR'_3 + HX$$
(X = —NEt$_2$, —OR, —OSnR$_3$, —NRCHO, —NRNHR, halogen, —CF:CF$_2$)

Cyclic materials can be prepared from dihydrides and diamino compounds [457], e.g.

$$Et_2SnH_2 + Et_2Sn(NEt_2)_2 \longrightarrow (Et_2Sn)_6$$

[450] A. Ladenburg, *Chem. Ber.*, 1871, **4**, 19.

[451] G. A. Razuvaev, Yu. I. Dergunov and N. S. Vyazankin, *Zhur. obshchei Khim.*, 1962, **32**, 2515; *Chem. Abs.*, 1963, **58**, 9111.

[452] Yu. A. Aleksandrov, T. G. Brilkina and V. A. Shushunov, *Trudy po Khim. i Khim. Tekhnol.*, 1961, **4**, 3; Yu. A. Aleksandrov and N. N. Vyshinskii, ibid., 1962, **4**, 656; *Chem. Abs.*, 1962, **56**, 492; 1963, **58**, 3453.

[453] N. S. Vyazankin, G. A. Razuvaev and O. A. Kruglaya, *Izvest. Akad. Nauk S.S.S.R.*, 1962, 2008; *Chem. Abs.*, 1963, **58**, 9114.

[454] G. A. Razuvaev, N. S. Vyazankin and O. A. Shchepetkova, *Zhur. obshchei Khim.*, 1961, **31**, 3762; *Chem. Abs.*, 1962, **57**, 8597; *Tetrahedron*, 1962, **18**, 667.

[455] C. A. Kraus and R. H. Bullard, *J. Amer. Chem. Soc.*, 1926, **48**, 2131.

[456] W. P. Neumann and B. Schneider, *Angew. Chem., Internat. Edn.*, 1964, **3**, 751.

[457] R. Sommer, W. P. Neumann and B. Schneider, *Tetrahedron Letters*, 1964, 3875.

[458] A. K. Sawyer, *J. Amer. Chem. Soc.*, 1965, **87**, 537; H. M. J. C. Creemers and J. G. Noltes, *Rec. Trav. chim.*, 1965, **84**, 1589.

[459] H. M. J. C. Creemers, J. G. Noltes and G. J. M. van der Kerk, ibid., 1964, **83**, 1284; H. M. J. C. Creemers and J. G. Noltes, ibid., 1965, **84**, 382, 590.

The use of oxides is illustrated by the reaction [458]:

$$2Bu^n_3SnH + (Bu^n_3Sn)_2O \xrightarrow{100°} H_2O + 2Bu^n_3Sn·SnBu^n_3$$

Other unsymmetrical di-tin compounds $R_3SnSnR'_3$ can be prepared using the reaction between organotin hydrides and isocyanates, which occurs in two stages [459]:

$$PhNCO \xrightarrow{R_3SnH} R_3SnN(Ph)CHO \xrightarrow{R'_3SnH} R_3SnSnR'_3 + PhNHCHO$$

Use of *dihydrides* leads to longer-chain compounds:

$$2R_3SnN(Ph)CHO + R'_2SnH_2 \rightarrow R_3SnSnR'_2SnR_3 + 2PhNHCHO$$
$$R_3SnN(Ph)CHO + R'_2SnH_2 \rightarrow R_3SnSnR'_2H + PhNHCHO$$

$$\downarrow \text{catalytic dehydrogenation}$$

$$R_3SnSnR'_2SnR'_2SnR_3$$

The effects of catalysts, solvents and substituents on the rates of fission of Sn–N bonds by organotin hydrides support a polar mechanism:

Hexaphenyldistannane, $Ph_3Sn·SnPh_3$, m.p. 231–232°, from triphenyltin bromide and sodium in boiling xylene, is quite stable in air but reacts with bromine rapidly, with iodine slowly, and with alcoholic silver nitrate [459a]. Its reaction with alkali metals to form Ph_3SnM has already been mentioned. The extent to which the hexa-aryl compounds dissociate has been the subject of several conflicting statements. Their diamagnetism [460] would appear to exclude homolytic dissociation into radicals. No evidence of radical formation has been obtained from studies of the kinetics of iodination of Ph_6Sn_2, from the flash photolysis of Ph_6Sn_2 solutions and their reactions with diphenylpicrylhydrazyl, or from electron spin resonance studies of Ph_6Sn_2 solutions irradiated with ultraviolet light [461].

Similar careful studies on some alkyl distannanes have been reported. The unsymmetrical $Me_3Sn·SnEt_3$ (from $Me_3SnNEt_2 + HSnEt_3$) is homogeneous (by gas chromatography) after several hours at 170°. Above 190°, traces of Me_6Sn_2, Et_6Sn_2, Et_4Sn, Me_4Sn and elemental tin appear. The two symmetrical distannanes Me_6Sn_2 and Et_6Sn_2 can be mixed and heated without formation of $Me_3Sn·SnEt_3$ in more than trace amounts. The

[459a] G. Tagliavini and L. Doretti, *Chem. Comm.*, 1966, 562.

[460] H. Morris, W. Byerly and P. W. Selwood, *J. Amer. Chem. Soc.*, 1942, **64**, 1727.

[461] D. N. Hague and R. H. Prince, *J. Inorg. Nucl. Chem.*, 1966, **28**, 1039; see also G. Tagliavini, S. Faleschini, G. Pilloni and G. Plazzogna, *J. Organometal. Chem.*, 1966, **5**, 136.

molecular weights of highly purified cyclohexyl$_6$Sn$_2$ and Ph$_6$Sn$_2$, which appeared low when measured cryoscopically in benzene, were normal when measured by the more sensitive Mechrolab osmometer even at concentrations as low as 10^{-3} molar in benzene [462].

Recent work on some lead analogues has been interpreted as indicating the slight dissociation $R_6Pb_2 \rightleftharpoons R_4Pb + R_2Pb$ (see below, p. 502).

The ultraviolet spectra of hexaphenyl-digermane, -distannane and -diplumbane have been interpreted as showing interaction between π-orbitals of the aromatic rings and orbitals of the metal–metal system [131, 138]. In the Raman spectrum of Ph$_6$Sn$_2$, the metal–metal stretching absorption is at 208 cm^{-1} (cf. 190 cm^{-1} for Me$_6$Sn$_2$) [462a]

The related compound Ph$_3$Ge·SnPh$_3$, m.p. 284–286°, is prepared by the addition of Ph$_3$SnCl to an ether suspension of Ph$_3$GeK [150].

Hexakis-biphenylyl-2-distannane [463], 4.16, occurs in two forms, the low melting (m.p. 166–167°) resulting from the disproportionation of $[(C_{12}H_9)_2Sn]_n$, and the high melting (m.p. 288–289°) from tris-biphenylyl-tin bromide and sodium in xylene. Both are colourless and the low melting

4.16

form has an abnormally low apparent molecular weight in freezing benzene (the high melting form is too insoluble) but magnetic measurements have not yet been reported.

Derivatives of hexa-alkyl- or -aryl-distannanes

Compounds XR$_2$Sn·SnR$_2$X, in which X = acetate, benzoate, H or Cl have been prepared recently. The acyloxy derivatives result from the spontaneous decomposition, with evolution of hydrogen, of acyloxytin hydrides R$_2$SnH·O·CO·R′, which can be prepared from organotin dihydrides [464]:

$$Bu^n_2SnH_2 + Bu^n_2Sn(OAc)_2 \rightleftharpoons Bu^n_2SnH·OAc \xleftarrow{-H_2} Bu^n_2SnH_2 + HOAc$$

$$20° \Big| -H_2$$

$$Bu^n_2Sn(OAc)Br \xleftarrow{Br_2} AcO·Bu^n_2Sn·SnBu^n_2·OAc \quad \text{m.p. } -7° \text{ to } -4°$$

[462] W. P. Neumann, E. Peterson and R. Sommer, *Angew. Chem., Internat. Edn.,* 1965, **4**, 599.
[462a] H. M. Gager, J. Lewis and M. J. Ware, *Chem. Comm.,* 1966, 616.
[463] G. Bähr and R. Gelius, *Chem. Ber.,* 1958, **91**, 825.
[464] A. K. Sawyer and H. G. Kuivila, *J. Amer. Chem., Soc.,* 1960, **82**, 5958; *J. Org. Chem.,* 1962, **27**, 837.

The phenyl compound, $PhCOO \cdot Ph_2Sn \cdot SnPh_2 \cdot OOCPh$, m.p. 185°, is one of many related derivatives which have been obtained similarly [465]. An alternative synthesis uses the action of diacyl peroxides on tin(II) compounds [466]:

$$R_2Sn + (R'COO)_2 \longrightarrow R'COO \cdot R_2Sn \cdot SnR_2 \cdot OOCR'$$

These distannane derivatives are readily oxidized by air, and react with bromine with cleavage of the tin–tin bond. Hydrogen chloride in ethereal solution, however, gives the corresponding chloro compound [375], $ClR_2Sn \cdot SnR_2Cl$ (also obtainable by electrolytic reduction of dihalides R_2SnCl_2 [466a]), which in turn may be reduced to the hydride $HR_2Sn \cdot SnR_2H$ by lithium aluminium hydride [467]:

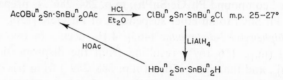

Apparently related to these compounds is the acetate, $Sn_2(OOCMe)_6$, from Ph_6Sn_2 [468], and glacial acetic acid at 120°, in which two acetate groups may be bridging the two tin atoms: treatment with ethereal HCl at −100° gives $Sn_2Cl_4(OOCMe)_2$, which with liquid HCl at the same temperature gives Sn_2Cl_6, an unstable material which disproportionates above −65° into $SnCl_2$ and $SnCl_4$.

These distannane derivatives are much more reactive and readily oxidized than the compounds (thought to be obtained by reduction of dihalides R_2SnX_2) for which similar distannane structures were at first suggested [469], but which were later shown to be oxides, $XR_2SnOSnR_2X$, resulting from the partial *hydrolysis* of the dihalides [372, 375].

Derivatives of higher stannanes

A general method of preparing these was described above [456–459] Diethylhexamethyltristannane, $Me_2EtSn \cdot Me_2Sn \cdot SnMe_2Et$, an oily liquid which easily oxidizes in air, has been prepared by the following reactions carried out in liquid ammonia [422]:

$$2Me_2SnNa_2 + Me_2SnBr_2 \longrightarrow NaMe_2Sn \cdot Me_2Sn \cdot SnMe_2Na$$

$$\downarrow EtBr$$

$$Me_2EtSn \cdot Me_2Sn \cdot SnMe_2Et$$

[465] A. K. Sawyer and H. G. Kuivila, *J. Org. Chem.* 1962, **27**, 610.
[466] U.S.P. 3,083,217, 26 March 1963; *Chem. Abs.*, 1963, **59**, 7559.
[466a] R. E. Dessy, W. Kitching and T. Chivers, *J. Amer. Chem. Soc.*, 1966, **88**, 453.
[467] A. K. Sawyer and H. G. Kuivila, ibid., 1963, **85**, 1010.
[468] E. Wiberg and H. Behringer, *Z. anorg. Chem.*, 1964, **329**, 290.
[469] O. H. Johnson and H. E. Fritz, *J. Org. Chem.*, 1954, **19**, 74; O. H. Johnson, H. E. Fritz, D. O. Halvorson and R. L. Evans, *J. Amer. Chem. Soc.*, 1955, **77**, 5857.

Similar compounds such as the fully methylated tetra- and penta-stannanes, have also been described [422, 470]:

$$NaMe_2Sn \cdot SnMe_2Na + 2Me_3SnBr \longrightarrow Me_3Sn \cdot Me_2Sn \cdot Me_2Sn \cdot SnMe_3$$
$$NaMe_2Sn \cdot Me_2Sn \cdot SnMe_2Na + 2Me_3SnBr \longrightarrow Me_3Sn(Me_2Sn)_3SnMe_3$$

These are viscous liquids which rapidly absorb oxygen. For related ethyl, butyl and other derivatives, see refs. [459] and [471].

Octaphenyltristannane, $Ph_3Sn \cdot Ph_2Sn \cdot SnPh_3$, dec. 280°, is the only phenyl derivative of a higher acyclic stannane to have been well characterized; it has been prepared by adding diphenyltin dichloride in 1,2-dimethoxyethane to a solution of triphenylstannylsodium in the same solvent [472]:

$$2Ph_3SnNa + Ph_2SnCl_2 \longrightarrow Ph_3Sn \cdot Ph_2Sn \cdot SnPh_3$$

Disproportionation reactions are a complication in the preparation of derivatives of higher stannanes. Attempts at preparing octaphenyltri-stannane by other methods, e.g. from Ph_3SnLi and Ph_2SnCl_2 in ether, from Ph_3SnNa and Ph_2SnCl_2 in ether or liquid ammonia, from $(Ph_3Sn)_2Mg$ and Ph_2SnCl_2 in tetrahydrofuran, or from Ph_2SnNa_2 and Ph_3SnCl in liquid ammonia were either completely unsuccessful or gave yields of less than 5%, the main products being tetraphenyltin, hexaphenyldistannane and polymeric 'diphenyltin'.

Tetrakis(triphenylstannyl)stannane, $(Ph_3Sn)_4Sn$, m.p. 315–330°, has been prepared by four different methods, the best yields being obtained by the following reaction sequence [138, 473]:

$$3Ph_3SnLi + SnCl_2 \longrightarrow [(Ph_3Sn)_3SnLi] \xrightarrow{Ph_3SnCl} (Ph_3Sn)_4Sn$$

Derivatives of tin(II), $(R_2Sn)_n$
Although a material which was thought to be diethyltin was described as early as 1852 [474], and many materials which were assigned formulae $(R_2Sn)_n$ have been discussed since that date [189], it has been shown only recently [190] that many of these materials are in fact derivatives of *higher acyclic stannanes*, of formulae $R_{(2n+2)}Sn_n$ or $R_{2n}Sn_nX_2$. Compounds for which the formula $(R_2Sn)_n$ has proved correct are derivatives of *cyclic stannanes*.

[470] C. A. Kraus and A. M. Neal, ibid., 1929, **51**, 2403.
[471] N. S. Vyazankin, G. A. Razuvaev and O. A. Kruglaya, *Doklady Akad. Nauk S.S.S.R.*, 1963, 2008.
[472] W. P. Neumann, K. König and G. Burkhardt, *Annalen*, 1964, **677**, 18.
[473] H. Gilman and F. K. Cartledge, *Chem. and Ind.*, 1964, 1231; *J. Organometal. Chem.*, 1966, **5**, 48.
[474] A. Löwig, *Annalen*, 1852, **84**, 308.

Derivatives of higher *acyclic* stannanes are oils or more generally amorphous powders, yellow or red in colour, which react readily with halogens and are easily oxidized (see, for example, ref. [475]), while the *cyclic* stannanes are colourless or light yellow and some of them are crystalline. The two classes of compound are not always easily distinguished by elemental analysis, particularly when n is large, but degradation with bromine or (better) chlorine at $-70°C$ gives a mixture of halides R_3SnX, R_2SnX_2 and $RSnX_3$ from the acyclic materials, the proportion of the trihalide reflecting the degree of branching of the chains, whereas cyclic stannanes which have no stannyl side chains give only the dihalides R_2SnX_2, e.g.

$$(R_3Sn)_2 \cdot SnR \cdot (SnR_2)_2 \cdot SnR_3 \xrightarrow{5X_2} 3R_3SnX + 2R_2SnX_2 + RSnX_3$$

$$\xrightarrow{6X_2} 6R_2SnX_2$$

4.17

Dimethyltin, $(Me_2Sn)_n$. *Dodecamethylcyclohexastannane*, $(Me_2Sn)_6$ (4.17; R = Me), may be among the air-sensitive yellow solid products of the reaction between dimethyltin dichloride and sodium in liquid ammonia [476]:

$$6Me_2SnCl_2 + 12Na \longrightarrow (Me_2Sn)_6 + 12NaCl$$

Straight-chain compounds, $X(Me_2Sn)_nX$, where n lies in the range 12–20, are also obtained from the same reaction, the exact nature of the product varying from one experiment to another. Similar materials are obtained from dimethyltin dibromide and sodium or dimethylstannylenedisodium in liquid ammonia [422]. They absorb oxygen to give dimethyltin oxide, and with bromine give mainly dimethyltin dibromide. Their infrared and nuclear magnetic resonance spectra show that increasing catenation is accompanied by a decrease in the coupling constant J_{Sn-CH_3} and an increase in $J_{Sn-Sn-Me}$, while an empirical relationship is apparent between J_{Sn-CH_3} and both symmetric and asymmetric SnC_2 stretching modes for such compounds [476].

Diethyltin, $(Et_2Sn)_n$ [190]. Most of the materials described in the literature as diethyltin, which have been prepared from such reactions as that between diethyltin dibromide and sodium or between tin(II) chloride and ethyl-lithium [477] and obtained as red, yellow or colourless oils or as

[475] S. M. Zhivukhin, E. D. Dudikova and A. M. Kotov, *Zhur. obshchei Khim.*, 1963, **33**, 3274; *Chem. Abs.*, 1964, **60**, 4169.

[476] T. L. Brown and G. L. Morgan, *Inorg. Chem.*, 1963, **2**, 736.

[477] N. N. Zemlyanskii, E. M. Panov and K. A. Kocheshkov, *Doklady Akad. Nauk S.S.S.R.*, 1962, **146**, 1335; *Chem. Abs.*, 1963, **58**, 9110.

yellow solids, are apparently acyclic materials $Et_{2n+2}Sn_n$, since they react with chlorine at $-70°$ to give triethyltin chloride as well as diethyltin dichloride. The formation of small quantities of ethyltin trichloride as well shows some branching of the tin chains, the extent of branching being reflected in the depth of colour of the 'diethyltin'.

Polymeric diethyltin $(Et_2Sn)_n$ uncontaminated by Et_3Sn or $EtSn$ groups can be prepared by the thermal decomposition of diethylstannane in the presence of a base, or by the reaction between Et_2SnH_2 and $Et_2Sn(NEt_2)_2$ [457]. Thus, a yellow crystalline product, $(Et_2Sn)_9$, which is apparently a derivative of cyclononastannane (4.18), is obtained almost quantitatively from the decomposition of diethylstannane dissolved in a mixture of toluene and pyridine in the presence of a little diethyltin dichloride as catalyst [133, 190, 478]:

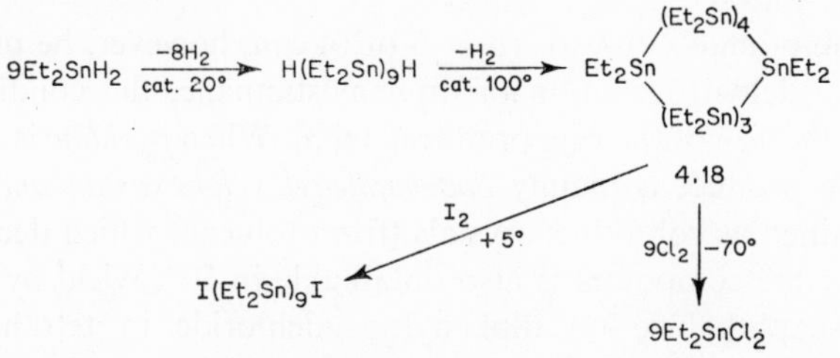

The nature of the product is evident from its molecular weight in benzene solution, from the products of its reactions with iodine or chlorine at low temperatures, and from the absence of Et_3Sn or $EtSn$ groups in its degradation products. It is readily oxidized, large lumps igniting in air, and decomposes at $150°$.

Similar cyclic materials, frequently based on 6- or 7-membered rings, $(Et_2Sn)_6$ or $(Et_2Sn)_7$, result from the decomposition of Et_2SnH_2 in the presence of bases other than pyridine, e.g. aniline, piperidine, diethylamine, triethylamine and dimethylformamide. The products are light yellow very air-sensitive waxes, the precise nature of which varies from one reaction to another. When treated with Lewis acid halides or Grignard reagents they give yellow or red oils with open and sometimes branched chains, identical with the supposed 'diethyltin' compounds described above [190, 478].

Dibutyltin, $(Bu_2Sn)_n$. The hexameric isobutyl derivative, $(Bu^i_2Sn)_6$, obtained by the catalytic dehydrogenation of di-isobutylstannane, is probably a cyclohexastannane derivative (4.17; R = Bu^i) [133]. The red oils approximating in composition to $(Bu_2Sn)_8$, obtained from tin(II) chloride and butyl-lithium, are evidently acyclic materials [477]. A cyclic tetramer, $(Bu^t_2Sn)_4$, is described as the main product from the reaction

[478] W. P. Neumann and J. Pedain, *Annalen*, 1964, **672**, 34.

between $Bu^t_2SnCl_2$ and an excess of Bu^tMgCl in boiling tetrahydrofuran [479].

Dibenzyltin also exists in the tetrameric form, *octabenzylcyclotetrastannane*, $[(PhCH_2)_2Sn]_4$, m.p. 226–228° (decomp.), when prepared by the thermal dehydrogenation of $(PhCH_2)_2SnH_2$ in dimethylformamide at 50° in the presence of $(PhCH_2)_2SnCl_2$ as co-catalyst. Other basic solvents give products with larger rings [480].

Diphenyltin, $(Ph_2Sn)_n$. Although cyclic oligomers $(Ph_2Sn)_n$ may be among the products of reactions between tin(II) chloride and phenylmagnesium bromide or phenyl-lithium, the yellow solids which result are probably more correctly described by the formula $Ph_{2n}Sn_nX_2$ (X possibly being halogen, OH or Ph) and vary in complexity and molecular weight [190, 481, 482, 483]. With iodine in benzene they give the iodides Ph_3SnI, Ph_2SnI_2 and $PhSnI_3$.

Cyclic compounds $(Ph_2Sn)_n$ (n = 5 or 6) can, however, be prepared by the catalytic dehydrogenation of diphenylstannane, the conditions used influencing the size of the ring produced [483]. When *pyridine* is used as the catalyst, the product is mainly *dodecaphenylcyclohexastannane*, $(Ph_2Sn)_6$ (4.19), obtained as colourless crystals (from toluene) which decompose at 270°. This same compound is also obtainable in 50% yield by the action of sodium-naphthalene on diphenyltin dichloride in tetrahydrofuran. Dehydrogenation of Ph_2SnH_2 in the presence of *dimethylformamide* gives *decaphenylcyclopentastannane*, $(Ph_2Sn)_5$ (4.20) as well as the hexamer, the proportions depending on the conditions (483).

4.19   4.20

The pentamer crystallizes in the form of colourless plates from toluene, the crystals containing solvent which may be pumped off at 100°; the residual pure pentamer, like the hexamer, decomposes at about 270°. An X-ray diffraction study of the hexamer $(Ph_2Sn)_6$ has confirmed the six-

[479] W. V. Farrar and H. A. Skinner, *J. Organometal. Chem.*, 1964, **1**, 434.

[480] W. P. Neumann and K. König, *Angew. Chem., Internat. Edn.*, 1964, **3**, 751.

[481] H. G. Kuivila, A. K. Sawyer and A. G. Armour, *J. Org. Chem.*, 1961, **26**, 1426; H. G. Kuivila and E. R. Jakusik, ibid., p. 1430.

[482] M. Ya. Kraft and G. M. Borodina, *Zhur. obshchei Khim.*, 1962, **32**, 1665; *Chem. Abs.*, 1963, **58**, 3453.

[483] W. P. Neumann and K. König, *Angew. Chem.*, 1962, **74**, 215; *Annalen*, 1964, **677**, 1.

membered ring structure, which exists in the chair form indicated in 4.21 [484].

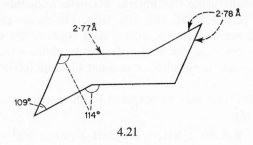

4.21

The dehydrogenation of other diarylstannanes Ar_2SnH_2 (where Ar = p-tolyl, biphenylyl, α-naphthyl or β-naphthyl) in the presence of catalysts such as dimethylformamide leads to diaryltin oligomers $(Ar_2Sn)_n$ which are colourless crystalline solids commonly having n = 6, which decompose at or above 250° [485].

The identification of tin(II) alkyls and aryls $(R_2Sn)_n$ as either cyclic molecules or chain compounds approximating to this composition has left the cyclopentadienyl compound $(C_5H_5)_2Sn$ as the sole monomeric organotin(II) compound.

Catenated organic compounds of silicon, germanium, tin and lead were reviewed in 1966 [124a].

Organotin hydrides or stannanes

Tin hydride (stannane), SnH_4, is a very unstable substance, readily decomposing to tin and hydrogen, but progressive substitution of alkyl or aryl groups for hydrogen results in increased stability. Thus organotin trihydrides, $RSnH_3$, may be kept a few days in clean glass vessels without much decomposition, dihydrides, R_2SnH_2, may be kept for several weeks, and monohydrides, R_3SnH, may be stored effectively indefinitely provided contact with air or other oxidants, acids, metals and grease is avoided. Their decomposition generally leads to tetra-alkyl- or -aryl-tin, metallic tin and hydrogen:

$$4R_nSnH_{4-n} \rightarrow nR_4Sn + (4-n)Sn + 2(4-n)H_2$$

The thermal decomposition of the dihydrides, R_2SnH_2, in the presence of bases with formation of cyclic organostannanes $(R_2Sn)_n$ was described in the previous section (pp. 471–472).

The known organotin hydrides are mostly colourless distillable liquids, monomeric in solution, whose infrared spectra contain very intense

[484] D. H. Olson and R. E. Rundle, *Inorg. Chem.*, 1963, **2**, 1310.
[485] W. P. Neumann and K. König, *Annalen*, 1964, **677**, 12.

sharp Sn–H absorption bands in the region 1800–1880 cm^{-1} [190, 486]. Their proton magnetic resonance spectra have Sn–H peaks to the low field side of tetramethylsilane (for nuclear magnetic resonance spectroscopic data see refs. [276, 421, 486, 487, 488, 489]). The mono- and di-hydrides have attracted much attention, mainly as a result of the discovery, initially developed by van der Kerk, of various addition reactions to unsaturated compounds, but also on account of some interesting reducing reactions.

Organotin hydrides may be prepared by the action of acids on alkali metal derivatives:

$$R_3SnNa + NH_4^+ \rightarrow R_3SnH + NH_3 + Na^+$$

A more general method involves the reduction of halides, alkoxides or oxides with lithium aluminium hydride [490], dialkylaluminium hydrides [190, 491], aluminium amalgam [492], sodium borohydride [489] or diborane [493], e.g.:

$$4Ph_3SnCl + LiAlH_4 \rightarrow 4Ph_3SnH + LiAlCl_4$$
$$2Et_2Sn(OMe)_2 + B_2H_6 \rightarrow 2Et_2SnH_2 + 2HB(OMe)_2$$
$$Bu^nSnCl_3 + 3Et_2AlH \rightarrow Bu^nSnH_3 + 3Et_2AlCl$$

Lower alkyl tri-hydrides may also be prepared from the sodium derivative of stannane, $NaSnH_3$, by the reaction with alkyl halides [423]. Monohydrides Alk_3SnH are formed in low ($\sim$25%) yield by the thermal decarboxylation of formates, [494], e.g.

$$Pr^n_3SnO.CO.H \xrightarrow{\text{160–170}^\circ;\ 8\ \text{hr low pressure}} Pr^n_3SnH + CO_2$$

Methyltin trihydride, $MeSnH_3$, b.p. 1·4°, *dimethyltin dihydride*, Me_2SnH_2, b.p. 35°, and *trimethyltin hydride*, Me_3SnH, b.p. 59°, have been prepared by the lithium aluminium hydride method [490]. Methyltin trihydride is also

[486] P. E. Potter, L. Pratt and G. Wilkinson, *J. Chem. Soc.*, 1964, 524; H. Kriegsmann and K. Ullbricht, *Z. anorg. Chem.*, 1964, **328**, 90; M. L. Maddox, N. Flitcroft and H. D. Kaesz, *J. Organometal. Chem.*, 1965, **4**, 50; Y. Kawasaki, K. Kawakami and T. Tanaka, *Bull. Chem. Soc. Japan*, 1965, **38**, 1102.

[487] L. W. Reeves and E. J. Wells, *Canad. J. Chem.*, 1963, **41**, 2698.

[488] H. C. Clark, J. T. Kwon, L. W. Reeves and E. J. Wells, *Inorg. Chem.*, 1964, **3**, 907; J. Dufermont and J. C. Maire, *J. Organometal. Chem.*, 1967, **7**, 415; K. Kawakami, T. Saito and R. Okawara, ibid., 1967, **8**, 377.

[489] E. Amberger, H. P. Fritz, C. G. Kreiter and M.-R. Kula, *Chem. Ber.*, 1963, **96**, 3270; M.-R. Kula, E. Amberger and H. Rupprecht, ibid., 1965, **98**, 629.

[490] A. E. Finholt, A. C. Bond, K. E. Wilzbach and H. I. Schlesinger, *J. Amer. Chem. Soc.*, 1947, **69**, 2692; G. J. M. van der Kerk, J. G. Noltes and J. G. A. Luijten, *J. Appl. Chem.*, 1957, **7**, 366.

[491] W. P. Neumann and H. Niermann, *Annalen*, 1962, **653**, 164.

[492] G. J. M. van der Kerk, J. G. Noltes and J. G. A. Luijten, *Chem. and Ind.*, 1958, 1290.

[493] E. Amberger and M. R. Kula, *Chem. Ber.*, 1963, **96**, 2560.

[494] M. Ohara and R. Okawara, *J. Organometal. Chem.*, 1965, **3**, 484.

formed in good yield in the reaction between stannylsodium and methyl iodide in liquid ammonia at −64° [423].

$$SnH_4 + Na \xrightarrow{NH_3} SnH_3Na + \tfrac{1}{2}H_2$$
$$SnH_3Na + MeI \rightarrow MeSnH_3 + NaI$$

Ethyl- and n-propyltin trihydrides, prepared similarly from stannyl-sodium, show decreasing stability as the length of the organic group increases. Although stannylenedisodium, SnH_2Na_2, has been prepared in liquid ammonia, no dimethyltin dihydride results on reaction with methyl iodide (NH_4Cl gives SnH_4). However, dimethyltin dihydride itself, like dimethyltin dibromide [422], when dissolved in liquid ammonia reacts with sodium to form various sodium derivatives [423]:

$$Me_2SnH_2 \underset{NH_4Br}{\overset{Na/liqd.\ NH_3}{\rightleftharpoons}} Me_2SnHNa \xrightarrow[liqd.\ NH_3]{Na} Me_2SnNa_2 \xrightarrow{MeI} Me_4Sn$$

$$\downarrow 20° \qquad\qquad \downarrow NH_4Br \qquad\qquad \searrow NH_3 > 0°$$

$$\begin{array}{ccc} Me_2SnH_2 \\ + & \xleftarrow{NH_4Br} & NaMe_2Sn\cdot SnMe_2Na & \qquad Me_2SnH_2 & \qquad NH_2Me_2SnNa \\ (Me_2Sn)_n \end{array}$$

Ethyltin trihydride, $EtSnH_3$, b.p. 22–23°, *diethyltin dihydride*, Et_2SnH_2, b.p. 96–98°, and *triethyltin hydride*, Et_3SnH, b.p. 148–150°, are conveniently obtained either by the lithium aluminium hydride [495] or by the dialkylaluminium hydride [491] methods:

$$EtSnCl_3 + 3Bu^i_2AlH \xrightarrow{Bu_2O} EtSnH_3 + 3Bu^i_2AlCl.Bu_2O$$

In the latter method, which involves direct reaction at −20 to 0°C, no solvent is necessary, and the product may be vacuum distilled from the mixture. A suitable ether may be added to form a complex with the residual organoaluminium chloride and so facilitate separation in the case of less volatile tin hydrides. Particularly involatile hydrides like the di- and tri-phenyl derivatives are better isolated after hydrolysis of the organo-aluminium halide with aqueous dioxan, the aluminium hydroxide being separated by filtration [491].

The ethyltin hydrides Et_3SnH and Et_2SnH_2 have also been prepared in over 90° yield by the reaction between diborane and the organotin methoxide in pentane at −78°, the product being separated and purified in the vacuum line [493]. The aluminium amalgam method [492], in which the amalgam (from pure aluminium turnings, silicon and magnesium being deleterious) is stirred with the halide R_3SnCl in ether, petrol or cyclohexane with slow addition of water, gives good yields (∼60%) when

[495] C. R. Dillard, E. H. McNeill, D. E. Simmons and J. B. Yeldell, *J. Amer. Chem. Soc.*, 1958, **80**, 3607.

$R = Pr^n$, Bu^n or Ph, but about 30% or less when $R = Et$. Dihydrides, R_2SnH_2, do not seem to be preparable by this method.

The *n-butyltin hydrides*, Bu^nSnH_3, b.p. 98–100°, $Bu^n_2SnH_2$, b.p. 70°/12 mm., and Bu^n_3SnH, b.p. 65–67°/0·6 mm., may be prepared by the standard methods [486, 491, 493, 496]. The chlorotin hydride Bu^n_2SnClH, m.p. −35 to −33°, from dibutyltin dihydride and dibutyltin dichloride at room temperature, disproportionates into the parent compounds when distilled at reduced pressure [497, 497a]. Organohalogenotin dihydrides such as $EtSnH_2Br$ or $PhSnH_2Br$ (from $RSnH_3$ + HBr at −18°) decompose at about −65° [497a, 498].

Photolysis of the hydrides Ph_3SnH and Bu^i_3SnH gives the radicals $Ph_3Sn\cdot$ and $Bu^i_3Sn\cdot$ respectively which can be collected on a very cold surface [499].

Phenyltin trihydride, $PhSnH_3$, b.p. 57–64°/106 mm., is conveniently prepared by the reduction of an aqueous potassium hydroxide solution of phenyltin trichloride with sodium borohydride at 0° [489]. *Diphenyltin dihydride*, Ph_2SnH_2, b.p. 89–93°/0·3 mm., and *triphenyltin hydride*, Ph_3SnH, m.p. 29–29·5°, b.p. 168–172°/0·5 mm., are readily obtained by the lithium aluminium hydride [489, 490], organoaluminium hydride [491], or diborane [493] methods. An interesting derivative of diphenyltin dihydride, for which the structure 4.22 is proposed, results from the reaction between diphenyltin dichloride and sodium triethoxyaluminium hydride [500]:

$$Ph_2SnCl_2 + 2NaAlH(OEt)_3 \longrightarrow 2NaCl + (EtO)_2Al \overset{\displaystyle Ph}{\underset{\displaystyle Ph}{\overset{\overset{\textstyle Et}{O}}{\underset{\underset{\textstyle Et}{O}}{Sn}}}} Al(OEt)_2$$

4.22

Hydrogen bridges between tin and aluminium apparently occur in the reaction intermediates when organotin hydrides react with organoaluminium compounds, e.g. [501, 502]

[496] W. J. Considine and J. J. Ventura, *Chem. and Ind.*, 1962, 1683.

[497] A. K. Sawyer and H. G. Kuivila, ibid., 1961, 260; *J. Organometal. Chem.*, 1965, **3**, 464; W. P. Neumann and J. Pedain, *Tetrahedron Letters*, 1964, 2461.

[497a] A. K. Sawyer and J. E. Brown, *J. Organometal. Chem.*, 1966, **5**, 438.

[498] G. Fritz and H. Scheer, *Z. Naturforsch.*, 1964, **19b**, 537; *Z. anorg. Chem.*, 1965, **338**, 1.

[499] U. Schmidt, K. Kabitzke, K. Markau and W. P. Neumann, *Chem. Ber.*, 1965, **98**, 3827.

[500] O. Schmitz-DuMont and G. Bungard, ibid., 1959, **92**, 2399.

[501] W. P. Neumann and R. Sommer, *Angew. Chem.*, 1963, **75**, 788; *Internat. Edn.*, 1963, **2**, 547.

[502] W. P. Neumann, H. Niermann and B. Schneider, *Angew. Chem.*, 1963, **75**, 790; *Internat. Edn.*, 1963, **2**, 547.

$$R_3SnD + \tfrac{1}{3}(R'_2AlH)_3 \rightleftharpoons \left[R_3Sn\genfrac{}{}{0pt}{}{D}{H}AlR'_2\right] \rightleftharpoons R_3SnH + \tfrac{1}{3}(R'_2AlD)_3$$

$$Et_3SnH + \tfrac{1}{2}(Et_3Al)_2 \longrightarrow \left[Et_3Sn\genfrac{}{}{0pt}{}{Et}{H}AlEt_2\right] \longrightarrow Et_4Sn + \tfrac{1}{3}(Et_2AlH)_3$$

Similar exchange reactions with organoaluminium compounds are not shown by germanium and silicon hydrides.

Like the alkyl compounds, aryltin hydrides are air- and light-sensitive and thermally unstable, losing hydrogen to form tetra-aryltin and metallic tin or, in the case of the dihydrides in the presence of basic catalysts, diaryltin polymers [483, 485]. The higher triaryltin hydrides are solids, e.g. *tris(p-tolyl)-tin hydride*, $(MeC_6H_4)_3SnH$, m.p. 82–85° (from aqueous methanol), and *trimesityltin hydride*, $(Me_3C_6H_2)_3SnH$, m.p. 177·7–179° [485, 503].

REACTIONS OF ORGANOTIN HYDRIDES

The reactions of organotin hydrides with organic compounds have recently been reviewed [190, 504]. Organotin hydrides add on to unsaturated systems, particularly acetylenes or terminal olefins:

$$R_3SnH + H_2C{:}CHR' \longrightarrow R_3SnCH_2CH_2R'$$

Organic or inorganic acids replace the hydrogen by an acid radical, hydrogen being evolved:

$$R_3SnH + HX \longrightarrow R_3SnX + H_2$$

Various functional groups such as ketones, sulphones, sulphoxides and some nitro groups are reduced, leaving an organotin residue containing tin–tin bonds:

$$2Ph_3SnH + CH_2{:}CHCOR \longrightarrow Ph_6Sn_2 + CH_2{:}CHCHOHR$$

Organic halides exchange halogen for hydrogen:

$$Ph_3SnH + CH_2{:}CHCH_2Br \longrightarrow Ph_3SnBr + CH_2{:}CHCH_3$$

Both alkyl- and aryl-tin hydrides undergo such reactions, although the aryl compounds are more reactive.

Addition to unsaturated systems

Organotin hydrides add readily and quantitatively to *acetylenes* or *ter-*

[503] D. H. Lorenz, P. Shapiro, A. Stern and E. I. Becker, *J. Org. Chem.*, 1963, **28**, 2332; A. Stern and E. I. Becker, ibid., 1964, **29**, 3221.

[504] H. G. Kuivila, *Advances in Organometallic Chemistry*, ed. F. G. A. Stone and R. West, Academic Press, London and New York, Vol. I, 1964, p. 47; G. J. M. van der Kerk and J. G. Noltes, *Annals New York Acad. Sci.*, 1965, **125**, 25.

minal olefins at 80–100° in the absence of catalyst [505]. For example, triphenyltin hydride reacts with styrene or phenylacetylene:

$$Ph_3SnH + PhCH:CH_2 \rightarrow Ph_3SnCH_2CH_2Ph$$
$$Ph_3SnH + PhC:CH \rightarrow Ph_3SnCH:CHPh, \quad m.p.\ 119\text{–}120°$$

The SnH bond adds smoothly to negatively substituted olefins, the reaction going particularly easily with acrylonitrile, methyl acrylate and acrylamide:

$$Ph_3SnH + CH_2:CHCN \rightarrow Ph_3SnCH_2CH_2CN, \quad m.p.\ 93\text{–}94°$$
$$Pr^n_3SnH + CH_2:CHCO_2Me \rightarrow Pr^n_3SnCH_2CH_2CO_2Me,$$
$$b.p.\ 157\text{–}160°/12\ mm.$$
$$Pr^n_3SnH + CH_2:CHCONH_2 \rightarrow Pr^n_3SnCH_2CH_2CONH_2,$$
$$m.p.\ 44\text{–}47°$$

This reaction provides a convenient route to functionally substituted organotin compounds, and to compounds containing two different metals [506], e.g.

$$Ph_3SnH + Ph_3GeCH:CH_2 \rightarrow Ph_3SnCH_2CH_2GePh_3$$
$$2Ph_3SnH + Ph_2Ge(CH:CH_2)_2 \rightarrow (Ph_3SnCH_2CH_2)_2GePh_2$$

Ring compounds result if a dihydride is used (see p. 383) [50]. Vinyl-lead compounds are, however, broken down to metallic lead. Addition of Ph_3SnH to allylgermanium and allylsilicon compounds does not apparently take place.

Simple olefins such as ethylene or tetrafluoroethylene also react with organotin hydrides, dihydrides reacting by a stepwise process which requires no solvent or catalyst, e.g.

$$Me_2SnH_2 \xrightarrow{C_2F_4} Me_2SnH(C_2F_4H) \xrightarrow{C_2F_4} Me_2Sn(C_2F_4H)_2$$

The reaction does not involve polymerization of the olefin – no evidence of products $Me_2Sn[(C_2F_4)_nH]_2$, where $n > 2$, was obtained.

Many of these addition reactions are accelerated considerably by ultraviolet radiation or other sources of radicals, and careful studies on specific systems [274, 275, 505, 507] have shown that both radical and polar mechanisms may operate simultaneously, although under particular conditions one mechanism generally predominates.

Among catalysts which promote the reaction between organotin

[505] G. J. M. van der Kerk, J. G. A. Luijten and J. G. Noltes, *Chem. and Ind.*, 1956, 352; idem, *J. Appl. Chem.*, 1957, **7**, 356; *Angew. Chem.*, 1958, **70**, 298; F. C. Leavitt and L. U. Matternas, *J. Polymer Sci.*, 1962, **62**, 568; A. J. Leusink, J. W. Marsman, H. A. Budding, J. G. Noltes and G. J. M. van der Kerk, *Rec. Trav. chim.*, 1965, **84**, 567, 689; A. J. Leusink and J. G. Noltes, *Tetrahedron Letters*, 1966, 335, 2221.

[506] M. C. Henry and J. G. Noltes, *J. Amer. Chem. Soc.*, 1960, **82**, 558.

[507] W. P. Neumann, H. Niermann and R. Sommer, *Annalen*, 1962, **659**, 27; W. P. Neumann and R. Sommer, *Angew. Chem.*, 1964, **76**, 52; *Annalen*, 1964, **675**, 10; 1967, **701**, 28. See also D. J. Cooke, G. Nickless and F. H. Pollard, *Chem. and Ind.*, 1963, 1493; H. C. Clark and J. T. Kwon, *Canad. J. Chem.*, 1964, **42**, 1288.

hydrides and olefins, trialkylaluminium compounds appear to be effective because of the ready exchange of hydrogen and alkyl groups bonded to tin and aluminium [501, 502].

Other catalysts function as sources of radicals; thus the mainly 1,4-'hydrostannation' of butadiene or cyclopentadiene by R_3SnH (R = Et, Bu or Ph) is catalysed by such compounds as azo-bis-isobutyronitrile [507]:

$$Et_3SnH + CH_2:CH\cdot CH:CH_2 \rightarrow Et_3SnCH_2CH:CHCH_3$$

The same catalysts also accelerate the reaction with acetylene itself or allenes or alkynes [508]

$$Et_3SnH + HC:C\cdot CH_2OH \rightarrow Et_3SnCH:CHCH_2OH$$

As the product of addition to an acetylene, $R_3SnCH:CHR'$, is itself unsaturated, and capable of further reaction, the reaction between organotin dihydrides and acetylenes leads to polymeric materials having tin atoms in the polymer chain [179]:

$$R_2SnH_2 + PhC:CH \rightarrow \frac{1}{n}(\cdot R_2SnCH_2CHPh\cdot)_n$$

Unsaturated polymers or ring compounds [267] have been prepared from diynes:

$$R_2SnH_2 + HC:C(CH_2)_2C:CH \rightarrow \frac{1}{n}[\cdot R_2SnCH:CH(CH_2)_2CH:CH\cdot]_n$$

and saturated polymers or ring compounds [267] result from dienes [509]:

$$R_2SnH_2 + CH_2:CH\cdot R'\cdot CH:CH_2 \rightarrow \frac{1}{n}[\cdot R_2Sn(CH_2)_2R'(CH_2)_2\cdot]_n$$

If the bridging group R' of the diene is $Ph_2M(C_6H_4\cdot)_2$, where M = Ge, Sn or Pb, these elements also are incorporated in the polymer chain, e.g.

$$Ph_2SnH_2 + Ph_2Pb(C_6H_4CH:CH_2)_2 \rightarrow$$
$$\frac{1}{n}[\cdot Ph_2Sn\cdot C_2H_4\cdot C_6H_4\cdot PbPh_2\cdot C_6H_4\cdot C_2H_4\cdot]_n$$

The products have molecular weights up to about 100,000, and are generally low melting or decompose below 200°.

Organotin hydrides also add to *carbonyl* compounds and *azomethines*

[508] W. P. Neumann, H. Niermann and R. Sommer, *Angew. Chem.*, 1961, **73**, 768; E. M. Smolin, *Tetrahedron Letters*, 1961, 143; H. G. Kuivila, W. Rahman and R. H. Fish, *J. Amer. Chem. Soc.*, 1965, **87**, 2835; but see R. F. Fulton, *Dissert. Abstracts*, 1962, **22**, 3397.
[509] A. J. Leusink, J. G. Noltes, H. A. Budding and G. J. M. van der Kerk, *Rec. Trav. chim.*, 1964, **83**, 609.

in the presence of azo-bis-isobutyronitrile or zinc chloride [510], or under the influence of ultraviolet radiation [511], e.g.

$$Et_3SnH + PhCHO \longrightarrow Et_3SnOCH_2Ph$$
$$Et_3SnH + p\text{-}MeC_6H_4N{:}CHPh \longrightarrow Et_3SnN(CH_2Ph)C_6H_4Me$$

At higher temperatures the unsaturated group is reduced and hexa-ethyldistannane is formed. With *isocyanates* and *isothiocyanates* the orientation and position of addition varies in a manner consistent with nucleophilic attack of the hydride hydrogen on the carbon of the $-N{=}C{=}X$ group as the initial and rate-determining step [512]:

$$R_3SnH + ArNCO \longrightarrow R_3Sn{\cdot}NAr{\cdot}CHO \xrightarrow{R'_3SnH} R_3Sn{\cdot}SnR'_3 + ArNHCHO$$
$$R_3SnH + ArNCS \longrightarrow R_3Sn{\cdot}S{\cdot}CH{:}N{\cdot}Ar$$

The use of the isocyanate reaction to prepare compounds with Sn–Sn bonds has already been described [459].

Trialkyltin hydrides also react with diazo compounds in the presence of copper powder or under ultraviolet radiation, in reactions similar to those of trialkylgermanes [176]:

$$Alk_3SnH + CH_2N_2 \longrightarrow Alk_3SnMe + N_2$$

$$Pr^n_3SnH + N_2CHCO_2Et \longrightarrow Pr^n_3SnCH_2CO_2Et, \quad \text{b.p. } 136\text{--}140°/11 \text{ mm.}$$

Reactions with acids

Organotin hydrides react rapidly and quantitatively with organic and inorganic acids, e.g.

$$R_3SnH + MeCO_2H \longrightarrow R_3SnO_2CMe + H_2$$

Nitric acid reacts violently with triphenyltin hydride, forming nitrobenzene and diphenyltin oxide, possibly through an unstable nitrate Ph_3SnONO_2 [346]. Weak acids such as phenols, alcohols and mercapto compounds do not react with organotin hydrides unless a catalyst, e.g. zinc chloride, is present [190].

Kinetic and mechanistic studies of the protonolysis of organotin hydrides in the presence of halide [513] or methoxide [514] ions have shown

[510] W. P. Neumann and E. Heymann, *Angew. Chem.*, 1963, **75**, 166; *Annalen*, 1965, **683**, 11, 24; W. R. Cullen and G. E. Styan, *Inorg. Chem.*, 1965, **4**, 1437; W. P. Neumann, R. Sommer and H. Lind, *Annalen*, 1965, **688**, 14.

[511] R. Calas, J. Valade and J. C. Pommier, *Compt. rend.*, 1962, **255**, 1450; M. Pereyre and J. Valade, ibid., 1964, **258**, 4785; J. C. Pommier and J. Valade, *Bull. Soc. chim. France*, 1965, 975.

[512] J. G. Noltes and M. J. Janssen, *Rec. Trav. chim.*, 1963, **82**, 1055; *J. Organometal. Chem.*, 1964, **1**, 346; A. J. Leusink and J. G. Noltes, *Rec. Trav. chim.*, 1965, **84**, 585; A. J. Leusink, H. A. Budding and J. G. Noltes, ibid., 1966, **85**, 151.

[513] R. E. Dessy, T. Hieber and F. Paulik, *J. Amer. Chem. Soc.*, 1964, **86**, 28.

[514] H. G. Kuivila and P. L. Levins, ibid., p. 23.

that these reactions probably proceed via pentacovalent organotin intermediates, e.g.

$$Bu_3SnH + OMe^- \rightleftharpoons (Bu_3SnHOMe)^- \xrightarrow{\text{MeOH}} Bu_3SnOMe + H_2 + OMe^-$$

Reductions with organotin hydrides

Organotin hydrides may be used for selective hydrogenations at elevated temperatures; α,β-unsaturated *aldehydes* and *ketones* give *unsaturated* alcohols, *sulphones* and *sulphoxides* the corresponding SH compounds, while some *nitro* compounds may be reduced to amines, e.g. [515]

$$Ph_2SnH_2 + CH_2{:}CHCOCH_3 \rightarrow \frac{1}{n}(Ph_2Sn)_n + CH_2{:}CHCHOHCH_3$$

The organotin residue has tin–tin bonds in place of the original Sn–H bonds; R_6Sn_2 results from R_3SnH, $(R_2Sn)_n$ from R_2SnH_2, and $(RSn)_n$ from $RSnH_3$. These materials are easily separated from the organic product, and no hydrolysis step is needed (cf. $LiAlH_4$ reductions). The mechanism of these reductions does not involve the formation of tin–oxygen bonds, as occurs in the radical-catalysed addition reactions, so control over whether the addition reaction or hydrogenation takes place is achieved by the presence or absence of catalyst [511, 515]. Either alkyl or aryl tin hydrides may be used.

Organic *isocyanates* may be reduced to the formyl derivatives of the corresponding amine [516] (contrast $LiAlH_4$, which gives N-methyl-amines):

$$PhNCO + 2Ph_3SnH \rightarrow PhNHCHO + (Ph_3Sn)_2$$

Azomethines give the amine, though in low (35%) yield:

$$PhCH{:}NPh + 2Ph_3SnH \rightarrow PhCH_2NHPh + (Ph_3Sn)_2$$

Amines, in common with other bases, catalyse the decomposition of organotin hydrides to compounds with tin–tin bonds and hydrogen; their use in this respect in the preparation of higher cyclic stannanes has already been described (p. 471). Earlier reports of the deamination of amines by organotin hydrides have not been substantiated by more recent work [517].

[515] H. G. Kuivila and O. F. Beumel, ibid., 1958, **80**, 3798; 1961, **83**, 1246; U.S.P. 2,997,485; *Chem. Abs.*, 1962, **57**, 866; J. G. Noltes and J. G. M. van der Kerk, *Chem. and Ind.*, 1959, 294.

[516] D. H. Lorenz and E. I. Becker, *J. Org. Chem.*, 1963, **28**, 1707.

[517] G. J. M. van der Kerk, J. G. Noltes and J. G. A. Luijten, *Rec. Trav. chim.*, 1962, **81**, 853; A. Stern and E. I. Becker, *J. Org. Chem.*, 1962, **27**, 4052.

Compounds containing N=N links undergo stepwise reduction, addition of Sn–H across N=N being followed by hydrogenolysis of the Sn–N bond [407]:

$$PhN{=}NPh \xrightarrow{R_3SnH} R_3Sn{\cdot}NPh{\cdot}NHPh \xrightarrow{R_3SnH} (R_3Sn)_2 + (PhNH)_2$$

Organic halides are readily reduced by organotin hydrides, their reactivity decreasing in the order $RI > RBr > RCl > RF$ [518]. Geminal polyhalides undergo stepwise reduction. Thus, a mixture of triphenyltin hydride and carbon tetrachloride boils spontaneously, owing to the reaction [519]:

$$Ph_3SnH + CCl_4 \rightarrow CHCl_3 + Ph_3SnCl$$

Chloroform is reduced quantitatively to dichloromethane only at the reflux temperature, and further reduction to methyl chloride requires prolonged refluxing. Acyl halides are reduced to aldehydes, which in turn may themselves suffer attack by the acyl radicals involved, giving esters [519a].

With aryl halides, electron-releasing substituents retard the reduction, while electron-attracting groups accelerate it [503]. Radical catalysts such as azo-bis-isobutyronitrile have been shown to accelerate a number of reductions, and loss of optical activity occurred when PhMeCHCl was reduced to PhMeCHD [520]. It appears possible, therefore, that the mechanism of these reactions may involve either free radicals or four-centre transition complexes [503, 520, 521].

LEAD

As lead has the largest atom of the Group IV elements, the bonds it forms are weaker than those formed by the other members of the group. Organolead compounds R_4Pb are therefore less thermally stable and more reactive than their tin analogues, and the Pb–Pb bond in the series R_6Pb_2 is relatively easily broken. Chain or ring compounds with several metal–metal links are unknown, although a few such links may be present in materials approximating in composition to $(R_2Pb)_n$, and the compound $(Ph_3Pb)_4Pb$ is known. The few organolead hydrides which have been prepared decompose even below room temperature. Many derivatives of

[518] H. G. Kuivila and L. W. Menapace, *J. Org. Chem.*, 1963, **28**, 2165.

[519] D. H. Lorenz and E. I. Becker, ibid., 1962, **27**, 3370; but see H. Kriegsmann and K. Ullbricht, *Z. Chem.*, 1963, **3**, 67.

[519a] H. G. Kuivila and E. J. Walsh, *J. Amer. Chem. Soc.*, 1966, **88**, 571; E. J. Walsh and H. G. Kuivila, ibid., p. 576.

[520] H. G. Kuivila, L. W. Menapace and C. R. Warner, ibid., 1962, **84**, 3584; L. W. Menapace and H. G. Kuivila, ibid., 1964, **86**, 3047.

[521] E. J. Kupchik and R. E. Connolly, *J. Org. Chem.*, 1961, **26**, 4747; E. J. Kupchik and R. J. Kiesel, *Chem. and Ind.*, 1962, 1654; D. Seyferth, H. Yamazaki and D. L. Alleston, *J. Org. Chem.*, 1963, **28**, 703.

the types R_3PbX and R_2PbX_2 have been described, where X is an electronegative group, and counterparts of the main types of organotin derivatives are known, although some areas remain relatively unexplored, e.g. derivatives having lead bound to a Group V element.

Much industrial attention remains concentrated on improving methods for the preparation of tetra-ethyl-lead and tetra-methyl-lead [522], which are still made in vast quantities as anti-knock additives for petrol [523], although improvements in fuel quality and the development of other additives have affected the demand for the simple alkyls as such, while concurrently stimulating research into organolead derivatives of transition metals. 560 Million pounds of lead alkyls were produced industrially in the U.S.A. in 1963. Organolead compounds are also widely recommended as components of polymerization catalysts, as polymer stabilizers, as sources of radicals which result from their thermal decomposition, and also for certain specific biocidal purposes, e.g. as insecticides.

The organic chemistry of lead has been the subject of a comprehensive review [524] (1954), and more recently of a literature survey [1] (1937–1958). Developments since 1953 have been summarized in a particularly useful review [525] (1964). Organolead compounds should not be handled without due regard to toxicity hazards.

Tetra-alkyls and -aryls
The main methods for preparing organolead compounds are:

(a) the action of an alkyl halide on a lead–sodium alloy;

(b) the action of a Grignard, organolithium or organoaluminium reagent on lead(II) chloride (best in the presence of the organic halide RX) or on a lead(IV) compound such as R_2PbX_2, R_3PbX, or K_2PbCl_6;

(c) the electrolysis, using a lead anode, of a suitable organometallic compound ($RMgX$, $MAlR_4$ or MBR_4, where M is an alkali metal).

Of these methods, the second is the most useful in the laboratory, the other two being more practicable on a larger scale. A disadvantage of the first two methods is that half or even more of the lead taken is left as metallic lead, so that re-cycling is necessary for an efficient process (see below, for tetra-ethyl-lead, on which most development work has been concentrated).

[522] W. J. Considine, *Annals New York Acad. Sci.* 1965, **125**, 4; E. M. Marlett, ibid., p. 12.

[523] E. F. Marshall and R. A. Wirth, ibid., p. 198.

[524] R. W. Leeper, L. Summers and H. Gilman, *Chem. Rev.*, 1954, **54**, 101.

[525] L. C. Willemsens, *Organolead Chemistry*, International Lead Zinc Research Organization, N.Y., 1964; see also L. C. Willemsens and G. J. M. van der Kerk, *Investigations in the field of organolead chemistry*, International Lead Zinc Research Organization, N.Y., 1965.

Organic groups attached to lead are very easily displaced by the action of halogens, and it is difficult to stop the reaction at the monohalide stage, R_3PbX. Hydrogen halides also cause displacement, particularly when anhydrous or dissolved in organic solvents.

Tetramethyl-lead, Me_4Pb, m.p. -30.2, b.p. $110°$, is readily prepared by the addition of methyl-lithium (or methylmagnesium iodide) to a boiling suspension of lead chloride in ether containing methyl iodide [526]. The reaction is rather complex, and probably involves the three stages:

$$4MeLi + 2PbCl_2 \longrightarrow Me_4Pb + 4LiI + Pb \quad \text{(finely divided, and reactive)}$$
$$2MeI + Pb \longrightarrow Me_2PbI_2$$
$$2MeLi + Me_2PbI_2 \longrightarrow Me_4Pb + 2LiI$$

The advantage of this method over that using methylmagnesium iodide and lead chloride alone is the conversion of all the lead into tetramethyl, instead of half of it, and the avoidance of hexamethyldilead which has to be decomposed. The first product of this latter reaction is probably dimethyl-lead:

$$2MeMgI + PbCl_2 \longrightarrow [Me_2Pb] + MgI_2 + MgCl_2$$

Like all alleged R_2Pb compounds, 'dimethyl-lead' is exceedingly unstable and disproportionates, mainly to metallic lead and hexamethyldilead, which finally decomposes into tetramethyl-lead and metallic lead:

$$6[Me_2Pb] \longrightarrow 2Pb + 2Me_3Pb \cdot PbMe_3 \longrightarrow 3Me_4Pb + 3Pb$$

The last stage is sometimes troublesome and requires repeated distillation (a dangerous process with tetramethyl-lead for it may explode above about $90–100°$) during which metallic lead is continuously deposited. The decomposition of compounds R_6Pb_2 is facilitated by the addition of benzene or toluene during the refluxing of the reaction mixture, allowing a higher temperature to be reached, but this is of value only when the product is much less volatile than these solvents, e.g. in the aromatic series, Ar_4Pb, and offers no advantage in the case of Me_4Pb. The overall reaction is

$$4MeMgI + 2PbCl_2 \longrightarrow Me_4Pb + Pb + 2MgCl_2 + 2MgI_2$$

which may be compared with the overall reaction when methyl iodide is used with methyl lithium or MeMgI:

$$3MeLi + PbCl_2 + MeI \longrightarrow Me_4Pb + 2LiCl + LiI$$

Tetramethyl-lead has also been prepared in 90% yield by the electrolysis of an aqueous solution of sodium tetramethylborate, $NaBMe_4$, or of a solution of $NaAlMe_4$ in an organic solvent, using a mercury cathode and

[526] H. Gilman and R. G. Jones, *J. Amer. Chem. Soc.*, 1950, **72**, 1760.

lead anode [527]. A method preferred industrially, similar to that used for tetra-ethyl-lead, is the reaction between a methyl halide (generally chloride) and a sodium–lead alloy at about 110° either in an autoclave or at lower pressures in a hydrocarbon solvent, with an aluminium halide or alkyl derivative as catalyst [528].

$$4MeCl + 4NaPb \rightarrow Me_4Pb + 3Pb + 4NaCl$$

Tetramethyl-lead prepared in this way has latterly assumed some importance as a fuel additive, being used as an anti-knock agent in admixture with tetra-ethyl-lead. Its greater volatility results in a more uniform distribution of anti-knock character in the fuel–air mixture in respect of distance from the carburettor(s). This property is of particular value for certain fuels.

Tetramethyl–lead is a typical non-polar liquid and is soluble in most organic solvents. Like all volatile lead compounds it is very poisonous, more so than the corresponding amount of inorganically combined lead. The methyl groups rotate freely on account of the relatively large size of the neutral lead atom; the barriers to rotation in the series Me_4M are Pb and Sn 0, Ge 0·4, Si 1·1–1·5, C 4·8 kcal./mole [529].

The unsymmetrical molecular vibration [18] associated with $Pb–CH_3$ stretching is at 478 cm^{-1} (infrared), the symmetrical vibration (Raman) being at 459 cm^{-1}. For n.m.r. spectroscopic data on Me_4Pb and several other methyl- and ethyl-lead derivatives, see ref. [530].

Reactions with halogens and hydrogen halides are mentioned later. Perhaps the best known reactions of tetramethyl-lead are those leading to the formation of free radicals, whose existence was first demonstrated by the pyrolysis of tetramethyl-lead present at low concentration in a stream of hydrogen or nitrogen at 1–2 mm. pressure [531]. The gas carrying the methyl radicals removed mirrors of lead, zinc, antimony, bismuth or beryllium by re-forming methyl derivatives. A recent adaptation of this reaction, in which trifluoromethyl radicals resulting from the decomposition of hexafluoroacetone at 900° were passed over tellurium, lead and bismuth mirrors, resulted in the formation of trifluoromethyl derivatives of these elements [532]. In the case of lead a colourless liquid, apparently $(CF_3)_4Pb$, was obtained, which evolved trifluoromethane when treated

[527] K. Ziegler and O. W. Steudel, *Annalen*, 1962, **652**, 1; H. Lehmkuhl, R. Schaefer and K. Ziegler, *Chem.-Ingr.-Tech.*, 1964, **36**, 612; *Chem. Abs.*, 1964, **61**, 6637.

[528] U.S.P. 3,048,610, 7 Aug. 1962; 3,049,558, 14 Aug. 1962; 3,072,694; 3,072,695, 8 Jan. 1963; *Chem. Abs.*, 1962, **57**, 16656; 1963, **58**, 550, 13992, 13993.

[529] F. A. French and R. S. Rasmussen, *J. Chem. Phys.*, 1946, **14**, 389.

[530] H. P. Fritz and K.-E. Schwarzhans, *J. Organometal. Chem.*, 1964, **1**, 297.

[531] F. A. Paneth and W. Hofeditz, *Ber.*, 1929, **62**, 1335; W. A. Waters, *The Chemistry of Free Radicals*, Oxford, 1946.

[532] T. N. Bell, B. J. Pullmann and B. O. West, *Austral. J. Chem.*, 1963, **16**, 722.

with sodium hydroxide. Previously a perfluoroethyl group had been attached to lead by the reaction between tetramethyl-lead and perfluoroethyl iodide:

$$Me_4Pb + C_2F_5I \xrightarrow{h\nu \text{ or heat}} Me_3PbC_2F_5$$

Tetramethyl-lead has also been used as an *indirect* source of methyl radicals in solution; it reacts rapidly with alcoholic silver nitrate at $-70°$ to $-20°$ giving methylsilver which decomposes to methyl radicals (which dimerize) and silver:

$$Me_4Pb + AgNO_3 \longrightarrow Me_3PbNO_3 + MeAg$$
$$MeAg \longrightarrow Me\cdot + Ag$$
$$2Me\cdot \longrightarrow C_2H_6$$

Similarly methylcopper is formed from alcoholic copper(II) nitrate, but this decomposes by reaction with the solvent forming methane [533]. Methyl chloride results from copper(II) chloride:

$$2CuCl_2 + Me_4Pb \longrightarrow 2CuCl + Me_3PbCl + MeCl$$

With gold(III) chloride in methanol, the formation of ethane, methane and ethylene glycol has been explained by the following sequence [534]:

$$AuCl_3 + Me_4Pb \longrightarrow [Me_3Au] \longrightarrow C_2H_6 + MeAu$$
$$HOCH_2CH_2OH \longleftarrow \cdot CH_2OH + CH_4 \xleftarrow{MeOH} Me\cdot + Au$$

Dimethylmercury and metallic mercury result from mercury(I) nitrate [535].

Although tetramethyl-lead is thermally rather more stable than the tetra-ethyl compound [536], it is more susceptible to attack by glacial acetic acid or perchloric acid [537]:

$$Me_4Pb + HOAc \longrightarrow MeH + Me_3PbOAc$$

Butyl-lead bonds are still less readily cleaved by acids, the rate of acid cleavage of Bu^n_4Pb being almost identical with that of Bu^n_2Hg.

Tetra-ethyl-lead, Et_4Pb, b.p. $91°/19$ mm., is made on a large scale as an anti-knock additive for petrol.

In the established industrial method for the manufacture of tetra-

[533] H. Gilman and L. A. Woods, *J. Amer. Chem. Soc.*, 1943, **65**, 435; C. E. H. Bawn and F. J. Whitby, *Discuss. Faraday Soc.*, 1947, **2**, 228; *J. Chem. Soc.*, 1960, 3926.

[534] L. Riccoboni, U. Belluco and G. Tagliavini, *Ricerca Sci.*, 1963, 323; *Chem. Abs.*, 1963, **58**, 13976.

[535] G. Tagliavini and U. Belluco, *Ricerca Sci.*, 1962, **A32**, 76; *Chem. Abs.*, 1962, **57**, 13785.

[536] P. R. Ryason, *Combust. Flame*, 1963, **7**, 235; *Chem. Abs.*, 1964, **60**, 1552.

[537] G. C. Robinson, *J. Org. Chem.*, 1963, **28**, 843.

ethyl-lead, a lead–sodium alloy (composition about NaPb) reacts with ethyl chloride,

$$4EtCl + 4NaPb \longrightarrow Et_4Pb + 3Pb + 4NaCl$$

After addition of water the product is separated by steam distillation and the metallic lead converted again to NaPb and re-cycled. The need to re-cycle so much lead is an unattractive feature of the process, but sodium-rich alloys such as Na_4Pb do not react satisfactorily, and considerable effort has been devoted to processes free from this defect. Yields can be improved, and reaction times cut, by the addition of catalysts such as organic phosphates [538] or various alkoxides [539], and adding Grignard or organoaluminium reagents also increases the yield [540].

Processes which avoid the need to re-cycle lead have been developed, and involve reactions between organoaluminium reagents and (generally) lead(II) compounds. For example, tetra-ethyl-lead may be made by the alkylation of lead acetate by triethylaluminium [541, 542]:

$$6Pb(OAc)_2 + 4Et_3Al \longrightarrow 3Pb + 4Al(OAc)_3 + 3Et_4Pb$$

Only half of the lead in lead acetate is converted into Et_4Pb, but the rest reacts with ethyl iodide and diethylcadmium:

$$Pb + 2EtI + Et_2Cd \longrightarrow Et_4Pb + CdI_2$$

and the cadmium (which circulates) is reconverted into diethylcadmium by reaction with triethylaluminium:

$$3CdI_2 + 2Et_3Al \longrightarrow 3Et_2Cd + 2AlI_3$$

Conversion into Et_4Pb of roughly half of the lead in the starting materials is also achieved in reactions between Et_3Al and PbO, PbS, $PbSO_4$ [542], K_2PbCl_6, $Pb(O_2CPh)_4$ or $Pb(O_2CPr)_4$, the yields being increased to as much as 90% by the use of an excess of Et_3Al [543]. Better yields are also claimed to result from the action of lithium tetra-ethylaluminate on a suspension of $PbCl_2$ in refluxing ether [544]; yields are slightly in excess of those expected from the equation

$$6PbCl_2 + 4LiAlEt_4 \longrightarrow 3PbEt_4 + 3Pb + 4LiAlEtCl_3$$

The product isolated contains much Et_6Pb_2, which is converted into the tetra-alkyl by refluxing for some hours after removal of the solvent. All the lead is used if ethyl iodide is added to the reaction mixture. A similar pre-

[538] U.S.P. 3,048,611; Brit.P. 918,519; *Chem. Abs.*, 1962, **57**, 16656; 1963, **59**, 5196.
[539] U.S.P. 3,057,898; *Chem. Abs.*, 1963, **58**, 5723.
[540] Brit.P. 884,784; Ital.P. 621,656; U.S.P. 3,057,897; *Chem. Abs.*, 1962, **57**, 4697, 15152; 1963, **58**, 4598.
[541] *Chemical and Engineering News*, 28 April 1958, **36**, no. 17, p. 66.
[542] S. M. Blitzer and T. H. Pearson (Ethyl Corp.), U.S.P. 2,859,225–32, 3,007,955; *Chem. Abs.*, 1959, **53**, 9149; 1962, **56**, 8744.
[543] F. W. Frey and S. E. Cook, *J. Amer. Chem. Soc.*, 1960, **82**, 530.
[544] R. S. Dickson and B. O. West, *Austral. J. Chem.*, 1962, **15**, 710.

paration, giving up to 87% yields of Et_4Pb, based on the lead taken, uses lead, ethyl chloride, and a bimetallic ethyl compound (such as $NaAlEt_4$) as the starting materials [545]. Triethylborane and sodium tetra-ethylborate have also been shown to convert lead(II) salts into Et_4Pb by reactions in aqueous, tetrahydrofuran or 'diglyme' solutions [546].

Electrolytic methods of making tetra-ethyl-lead have been described in several recent patents [527, 547], but a reliable and economical new process has yet to be proved commercially [522]. The electrolysis of a solution of an organometallic compound such as $NaAlR_4$, $NaBR_4$ or $RMgX$ using a lead anode and an inert cathode leads to Et_4Pb in over 90% yields:

$$4NaAlEt_3OR + Pb \longrightarrow 4Na + 4AlEt_2OR + Et_4Pb$$

The direct synthesis of Et_4Pb from finely divided lead, ethylene and hydrogen at 50–130° and 50–100 atmospheres pressure is possible, provided all the reagents are very pure, although yields are much too low (1–3%) for this to be a satisfactory preparative method [548]:

$$Pb + 4C_2H_4 + 2H_2 \rightleftharpoons Et_4Pb$$

Like tetra-ethyltin, tetra-ethyl-lead has several solid forms due to rotational isomerism, with melting points in the range $-137 \cdot 6$ to $-130 \cdot 3 °C$. Rather less stable than Me_4Pb [536], it decomposes above about 110°, and must be distilled at low pressure or in steam. Its decomposition is retarded in the presence of ethylene dibromide, cyclo-octadiene, or trimethyl phosphate [549].

A study of the kinetics of the pyrolysis of tetra-ethyl-lead in the temperature range 233–267°C has shown that in the initial stages of the reaction only four products are formed, viz., ethane, ethylene, hydrogen and n-butane. These are considered to result from such reactions as the following [550]:

$$Et_4Pb \longrightarrow Et_3Pb \cdot + Et \cdot$$
$$Et \cdot + Et_4Pb \longrightarrow C_2H_6 + \cdot C_2H_4PbEt_3$$
$$2Et \cdot \longrightarrow nC_4H_{10}$$
$$Et \cdot + Et_3Pb \cdot \longrightarrow C_2H_4 + HPbEt_3 \xrightarrow{Et_4Pb} H_2 + Et_3Pb \cdot + \cdot C_2H_4PbEt_3$$

[545] F. W. Frey, P. Kobetz, G. C. Robinson and T. O. Sistrank, *J. Org. Chem.*, 1961, **26**, 2950.

[546] J. B. Honeycutt and J. M. Riddle, *J. Amer. Chem. Soc.*, 1960, **82**, 3051; 1961, **83**, 369.

[547] R. C. Pinkerton (Ethyl Corporation), U.S.P. 3,028,325; P. Kobetz and R. C. Pinkerton, U.S.P. 3,028,322–3; *Chem. Abs.*, 1962, **57**, 4471; 11235; 1963, **58**, 3457; K. Ziegler, Ger.P. 1,127,900; 1,153,754; *Chem. Abs.*, 1962, **57**, 11235; 1964, **60**, 1794; Nalco. Chem. Co., U.S.P. 3,007,857; Belg.P. 613,892; *Chem. Abs.*, 1962, **56**, 3280; 1963, **59**, 7559; 1964, **61**, 1892; 1965, **62**, 7788.

[548] A. Malatesta U.S.P. 3,045,035; *Chem. Abs.*, 1962, **57**, 16656.

[549] S. E. Cook and H. Shapiro, U.S.P. 3,021,350; W. H. Thomas and S. E. Cook, U.S.P. 3,133,100; 3,147,294; *Chem. Abs.*, 1962, **56**, 11899; 1964, **61**, 4393, 13345; D. S. Stasinevich and A. L. Gol'dshtein, *Trudy po Khim. i Khim. Tekhnol*, 1960, **3**, 209; *Chem. Abs.*, 1962, **56**, 1469.

[550] G. L. Pratt and J. H. Purnell, *Trans. Faraday Soc.*, 1964, **60**, 519.

Extensive radical/olefin reactions occur later to produce a complex mixture of products.

In the far infrared spectrum of tetra-ethyl-lead, a strong band at 240 cm^{-1} has been assigned to a Pb-C-C bending vibration, and bands of moderate intensity at 132 and 86 cm^{-1} have been assigned to C-Pb-C bending modes [209].

Tetra-ethyl-lead has found only limited laboratory application, mainly as a mild ethylating agent. For example, with thionyl chloride it gives Et_2SO via $EtSOCl$ [551], and it converts phosphorus trichloride successively into ethyldichlorophosphine and diethylchlorophosphine [552]. Like tetramethyl-lead, it transfers alkyl groups to silver [553] (as $AgNO_3$) and gold [554] (as $HAuCl_4$):

$$Et_4Pb + AgNO_3 \xrightarrow{EtOH} Et_3PbNO_3 + [EtAg] \xrightarrow{20°} C_2H_4 + C_2H_6 + C_4H_{10}$$

With dinitrogen tetroxide in ether at $0°$, tetra-ethyl-lead is reported to form an adduct, $Et_4Pb \cdot 2N_2O_4$, m.p. $104-105°$ (decomposes), for which the structure $[Et_4Pb(NO)_2](NO_3)_2$ is proposed on the basis of its infrared spectrum, the cation having an octahedral arrangement of groups about the lead atom, the NO groups occupying *trans* positions [555]. A similar propyl compound, $Pr_4Pb \cdot 2N_2O_4$, m.p. $110-111°$, has also been described. When treated with aqueous or acetone solutions of mineral acids these compounds form the appropriate dialkyl-lead salts

$$R_4Pb \cdot 2N_2O_4 + H_2SO_4 \rightarrow R_2PbSO_4$$

Tetra-n-propyl-lead, Pr^n_4Pb, b.p. $126°/13$ mm., prepared by the Grignard or lithium method, or from lead–sodium alloy and propyl iodide with a little pyridine as catalyst [556], is more stable than *tetra-isopropyl-lead* which slowly decomposes even at room temperature. Secondary alkyl derivatives are generally rather unstable.

Tetracyclopropyl-lead, $(C_3H_5)_4Pb$, from $PbCl_2$ and C_3H_5MgBr, is a reactive liquid which can be distilled under reduced pressure although it explodes on heating. The cyclopropyl groups, like vinyl groups, are cleaved from lead more readily than ethyl groups, e.g. by acetic acid [557].

Tetravinyl-lead, $(CH_2:CH)_4Pb$, b.p. $34°/0·6$ mm., from vinylmagnesium

[551] R. Gelius, *Z. anorg. Chem.*, 1964, **334**, 72.

[552] M. S. Kharasch, E. V. Jensen and S. Weinhouse, *J. Org. Chem.*, 1949, **14**, 429; M. H. Beeby and F. G. Mann, *J. Chem. Soc.*, 1951, 411.

[553] C. E. H. Bawn and R. Johnson, ibid., 1960, 3923.

[554] G. Tagliavini, U. Belluco and L. Cattalini, *Ricerca Sci.*, 1962, A2, 350; *Chem. Abs.*, 1963, **59**, 2846.

[555] B. Hetnarski and T. Urbanski, *Tetrahedron*, 1963, **19**, 1319; *Roczniki Chem.*, 1963, **37**, 1073; *Chem. Abs.*, 1964, **60**, 5533.

[556] B. C. Saunders and G. J. Stacey, *J. Chem. Soc.*, 1949, 919.

[557] E. C. Juenge and R. D. Houser, *J. Org. Chem.*, 1964, **29**, 2040.

bromide (or chloride) and $(NH_4)_2PbCl_6$ [558], K_2PbCl_6 [559] or lead(II) chloride [560] in tetrahydrofuran, is thermally unstable, being inclined to explode when heated above about 100° and slowly decomposing at room temperature with deposition of a yellow solid. It is more reactive to cleavage of the lead–carbon bond than tetra-ethyl-lead, being decomposed at an appreciable rate even with aqueous ammonium chloride. Hydrogen chloride, carboxylic acids and silver nitrate react to form trivinyl-lead derivatives $(CH_2:CH)_3PbX$ ($X = Cl$, O_2CR or NO_3), while bromine gives lead(II) bromide and 1,1,2-tribromoethane [560a]. The vinyl groups can be transferred to alkali metals by reaction of an ethereal solution of $(CH_2:CH)_4Pb$ with the metal [561],

$$4M + (CH_2:CH)_4Pb \longrightarrow 4CH_2:CHM + Pb$$
$$(M = Li, Na, K, Rb \text{ or } Cs)$$

or with an organo derivative (preferably phenyl) of the alkali metal [241, 562]:

$$4PhLi + (CH_2:CH)_4Pb \longrightarrow 4CH_2:CHLi + Ph_4Pb$$

Several other vinyl-lead compounds have been described [560], including $Ph_3PbCH:CH_2$, $(CH_2:CH)_3PbCl$, $(CH_2:CH)_2PbCl_2$ and $(CH_2:CH)_2PbEt_2$ [563]. The mixed phenyl–vinyl derivatives react with alkali metals with cleavage of both organic groups from lead [561]:

$$Ph_3PbCH:CH_2 + 4Na \longrightarrow CH_2:CHNa + 3PhNa + Pb$$

Ethyltrimethyl-lead, $EtMe_3Pb$, b.p. 27–28°/11 mm., and *diethyldimethyl-lead*, Et_2Me_2Pb, b.p. 51°/13 mm., are further examples of the many mixed tetra-alkyls known, which have practically always been made by the action of a Grignard reagent on the appropriate halide, e.g.

$$Me_2PbBr_2 + 2EtMgBr \longrightarrow Et_2Me_2Pb + 2MgBr_2$$

Mixed tetra-alkyls rearrange in the presence of a variety of acidic type catalysts, giving a mixture of tetra-alkyl compounds. Since the bond energy changes would be small, the composition of the equilibrium mixture of the different R_4Pb compounds obtained depends mainly on entropy factors. The subject was reviewed comprehensively in 1943 [564].

In the same way that Me_4Pb and Et_4Pb react with silver nitrate to form

[558] L. Maier, *Angew. Chem.*, 1959, **71**, 161.

[559] B. Bartocha, U.S.P. 3,100,217; *Chem. Abs.*, 1964, **60**, 551.

[560] E. C. Juenge and S. E. Cook, *J. Amer. Chem. Soc.*, 1959, **81**, 3578.

[560a] A. K. Holliday and R. E. Pendlebury, *J. Organometal. Chem.*, 1967, **7**, 281.

[561] J. B. Honeycutt (Ethyl Corporation) U.S.P. 3,059,036; *Chem. Abs.*, 1963, **58**, 11398.

[562] Ethyl Corporation, Brit.P. 876,008; *Chem. Abs.*, 1962, **56**, 10188.

[563] B. Bartocha and M. Y. Gray, *Z. Naturforsch.*, 1959, **14b**, 350; A. K. Holliday and R. E. Pendlebury, *J. Chem. Soc.*, 1965, 6659.

[564] H. A. Beatty and G. Calingaert: 'The Redistribution Reaction', Ch. 24 of *Organic Chemistry, An Advanced Treatise*, ed. H. Gilman, 2nd ed., Wiley, 1943.

unstable silver alkyls, mixed lead compounds Et_3PbR react to form a triethyl-lead salt, the group R being split off:

$$Et_3PbR + AgNO_3 \rightarrow Et_3PbNO_3 + RAg$$

Many of these reactions are interesting in connexion with the stability of the silver compounds, RAg (see Vol. II), or of the Radicals R·.

Isobutenyltriethyl-lead, $Me_2C:CHPbEt_3$, b.p. $100°/12$ mm., from isobutenyl-lithium and triethyl-lead chloride, reacts with ethanolic silver nitrate with precipitation of orange-coloured isobutenylsilver, which is one of the least unstable organosilver compounds (excluding acetylides) [565]. The isomeric compound 2-*methylprop*-2-*enyltriethyl-lead*, $CH_2:CMeCH_2PbEt_3$, b.p. $45–50°/0·1$ mm., from triethylplumbylsodium and 3-chloro-2-methylpropene in liquid ammonia, reacts with silver nitrate with no apparent formation of a silver derivative. 2-5-Dimethyl-hexa-1,5-diene is produced practically quantitatively, a difference which is attributed to the resonance stabilization of the $[CH_2\cdots CMe\cdots CH_2]$· radical (contrast $Me_2C:CH·$) [566].

Like tin, lead forms a biscyclopentadienyl derivative, $(C_5H_5)_2Pb$ [567] which has an angular sandwich structure in the vapour phase (electron diffraction) [257]:

$C_1—C_2$	$1·430 \pm 0·006$ Å
$135 \pm 15°$ Pb	$C_1—H_1$	$1·105 \pm 0·018$ Å
	Pb—C	$2·778 \pm 0·016$ Å

Several *acetylenic* derivatives of lead have been prepared, and are rather unstable [38]. Bistriethylplumbylacetylene [261], $Et_3PbC:CPbEt_3$, from triethyl-lead chloride and sodium acetylide in liquid ammonia, is light-sensitive and even less stable than the analogous tin compound. Several other compounds of the type $R_3PbC:CPbR_3$, where R = cyclohexyl, *o*- and *p*-tolyl, and 2-phenylethyl, have been prepared by similar methods; they are all easily hydrolysed to acetylene and R_3PbOH [38, 568]. Substituted acetylenic derivatives $R_3PbC:CR'$ can be prepared from the appropriate alkali metal acetylide or Grignard reagent, the best yields being obtained if the reaction is carried out in pentane suspension with the alkali metal derivative, e.g. [569]

$$Ph_3PbCl + MC:CPh \rightarrow Ph_3PbC:CPh, \quad \text{m.p. } 56°$$

[565] F. Glockling, *J. Chem. Soc.*, 1955, 716; 1956, 3640.
[566] F. Glockling and D. Kingston, ibid., 1959, 3001.
[567] H. P. Fritz and K.-E. Schwarzhans, *Chem. Ber.*, 1964, **97**, 1390; A. F. Reid, D. E. Scaife and P. C. Wailes, *Spectrochim. Acta*, 1964, **20**, 1257.
[568] H. Hartmann and W. Eschenbach, *Naturwiss.*, 1959, **46**, 321.
[569] J. C. Masson, M. L. Quan, W. Chodkiewicz and P. Cadiot, *Compt. rend.*, 1963, **257**, 1111; H. Hartmann and K. Komorniczyk, *Naturwiss.*, 1964, **51**, 214.

Liquid products may be vacuum distilled from the reaction mixture, and solids can be recrystallized from pentane. Polyacetylenic derivatives such as $Ph_3Pb(C\vdots C)_2PbPh_3$, m.p. 187° (decomposes), are also known. When the preparation of a *propargyl* derivative is attempted, the product is mainly the *allenic* isomer [569]:

$$Ph_3PbCl + HC\vdots CCH_2MgBr \rightarrow 63\% \ Ph_3PbCH\vdots C\vdots CH_2 + 7\% \ Ph_3PbCH_2C\vdots CH$$

Chloroacetylides, $R_3PbC\vdots CCl$ [570], and alkenyl derivatives, e.g. $Et_3PbC\vdots CCR\vdots CHR'$ [571], have been prepared by similar methods.

Tetraphenyl-lead, Ph_4Pb, m.p. 227·8°, from phenyl-lithium, iodobenzene and lead(II) chloride [572], or from phenylmagnesium bromide and lead chloride, is much more stable thermally than the tetra-alkyls, and may be distilled at 240°/15–20 mm. It may also be obtained by the decomposition of phenyldiazonium fluoroborate in the presence of lead in acetone [573], by the reduction of triphenyl-lead chloride or diphenyl-lead dichloride with hydrazine (cf. the similar reduction of PhHgCl), and by the electrolysis of a mixture of $NaBPh_4$, $NaAlPh_4$, $KAlPh_4$ and naphthalene at 160° using a lead anode [570].

Above about 270°, tetraphenyl-lead decomposes to lead and biphenyl; experiments with deuterated samples have shown very slight exchange of phenyl radicals between Ph_4Pb and benzene at temperatures as low as 200° [574]. Like tetraphenyltin, tetraphenyl-lead is reduced to the metal and benzene by hydrogen at 150–200° and 60 atm. in the absence of a catalyst. Much biphenyl is produced when nickel is present [575].

Benzyltriphenyl-lead, $PhCH_2PbPh_3$, m.p. 93°, and other alkyl-triaryl derivatives, may be obtained not only from a triaryl-lead halide and an alkylmagnesium halide, but also by reactions such as the following [572]:

$$Ph_3PbLi + PhCH_2Cl \rightarrow PhCH_2PbPh_3 + LiCl$$

The triphenyl-lead lithium is formed by addition of phenyl-lithium to lead chloride (see below – alkali metal derivatives).

The cleavage of many unsymmetrical organolead compounds by such reagents as halogens, hydrogen halides or other acids, and by sodium in liquid ammonia (giving $R_3PbNa + RH$), has been much studied (for

[570] Union Carbide Corp., Ger.P. 1,126,388; *Chem. Abs.*, 1963, **58**, 6860.

[571] S. V. Zavgorodnii and A. A. Petrov, *Doklady Akad. Nauk S.S.S.R.*, 1962, **143**, 855; *Chem. Abs.*, 1962, **57**, 3466.

[572] H. Gilman, L. Summers and R. W. Leeper, *J. Org. Chem.*, 1952, **17**, 630.

[573] A. N. Nesmeyanov and K. A. Kocheshkov, *Bull. Acad. Sci. U.R.S.S.*, 1945, 522; *Chem. Abs.*, 1948, **42**, 5870.

[574] L. M. Nazarova, E. N. Kharlamova, G. E. Aleksandrova and E. B. El'tekova, *Zhur. obshchei Khim.*, 1961, **31**, 3308; G. A. Razuvaev, G. G. Petukhov and Yu. A. Kaplin, ibid., 1963, **33**, 2394; G. A. Razuvaev, G. G. Petukhov, Tu. A. Kaplin and O. N. Druzhkov, *Doklady Akad. Nauk S.S.S.R.*, 1963, **152**, 1122; *Chem. Abs.*, 1962, **57**, 2242; 1963, **59**, 14014; 1964, **60**, 1556.

[575] W. H. Zartmann and H. Adkins, *J. Amer. Chem. Soc.*, 1932, **54**, 3398.

some of the more recent work, see ref.[576]). Halogens and their hydracids split off aryl groups in preference to alkyl groups (as with germanium and tin), the ease with which groups are displaced being:

α-naphthyl > *p*-tolyl > phenyl > methyl > ethyl > n-propyl > cyclohexyl

Almost the reverse order is found in reaction with sodium:

$$R_3PbR' + 2Na + NH_3 \longrightarrow R_3PbNa + NaNH_2 + R'H$$

allyl > benzyl > n-butyl > ethyl > methyl > phenyl

Decomposition with bromine is recommended as the first step in the analysis of tetraphenyl-lead and other phenyl-lead compounds [577], the lead subsequently being determined as chromate.

Pentafluorophenyl-lead compounds have been prepared recently by the Grignard or organolithium route [27, 578]:

$$PbCl_2 + C_6F_5MgBr \xrightarrow{Et_2O} (C_6F_5)_4Pb \quad m.p. \ 199–200°$$

When treated with hydrogen chloride, the mixed compound $Ph_3PbC_6F_5$ loses both C_6H_6 and C_6F_5H; the methyl compound $Me_3PbC_6F_5$ under similar conditions gives C_6F_5H and Me_3PbCl.

The use of the styrene derivative, $Ph_2Pb(C_6H_4CH:CH_2)_2$, to prepare polymers containing lead in the polymer chain by its reactions with organotin dihydrides, R_2SnH_2, has already been described (p. 479) [179]. Vinyl groups attached *directly* to lead are cleaved by reaction with organotin hydrides.

Cyclic organolead compounds may be prepared by methods similar to those used for germanium and tin, e.g. [48, 53]

Organolead halides

Less structural work has been done on organolead halides and related compounds than on the analogous tin compounds. Fluorides of the types R_3PbF and R_2PbF_2 behave as ionic salts and either have high melting points or decompose without melting; this is also true of compounds containing other highly electronegative anionic components (cf. the similar

[576] C. Eaborn and K. C. Pande, *J. Chem. Soc.*, 1961, 3715; E. A. Puchinyan and M. Z. Manulkin, *Doklady Akad. Nauk Uz. S.S.R.*, 1962, **19**, 47; *Chem. Abs.*, 1962, **57**, 13788.

[577] H. J. Emeléus and P. R. Evans, *J. Chem. Soc.*, 1964, 510.

[578] D. E. Fenton and A. G. Massey, *J. Inorg. Nucl. Chem.*, 1965, **27**, 329.

tin compounds), but it has not been established whether these are best considered as ionic or bridged covalent compounds. The other halides may well be essentially covalent in the solid state and frequently dissolve in non-polar solvents, although if soluble they ionize extensively in aqueous solution. The only crystal structure so far reported, that of diphenyl-lead dichloride, Ph_2PbCl_2, has an octahedral arrangement of groups about each lead atom as shown in 4.23, with a square planar arrangement of chlorine atoms and phenyl groups occupying the axial positions. All the chlorine atoms are thus bridging atoms, linking the linear Ph_2Pb units into infinite chains [579].

4.23

The monohalides generally have a rather unpleasant smell, and many of the trialkyl-lead series have sternutatory properties. The physiological activity reaches a maximum in the tripropyl series [556] (note that the biocidal activity of R_3Sn compounds is also a maximum at about the same stage, see p. 443).

The dihalides are very readily formed and easily ionize, the R_2Pb^{++} ion being isoelectronic with the rather stable R_2Hg and R_2Tl^+ structures and presumably having associated with it in solution an equatorial arrangement of donor (solvent) molecules. The dihalides do, however, tend to disproportionate, e.g. in hot aqueous solution,

$$2R_2Pb^{++} + A^- + X^- \longrightarrow R_3PbA + Pb^{++} + RX$$

where A is an anionic radical. The presence of Pb^{++} ions can be detected by the black precipitate with sulphides; R_2Pb^+ ions give a cream coloured and R_3Pb^+ ions a white precipitate [580].

The Monohalides

Direct halogenation of tetra-alkyls is not a satisfactory preparative method since the reaction is difficult to stop at the monohalide stage. Tetraphenyl-lead, however, can be converted into triphenyl-lead bromide by the pyridine–bromine complex [581] at $-15°$. The use of hydrogen chloride is more satisfactory in the alkyl series.

Trimethyl-lead fluoride, Me_3PbF, dec. $\sim305°$, and its homologues are

[579] V. Busetti, M. Mammi and A. Del Pra, *Int. Union of Crystallography, 6th Int. Congress and Symposia*, Rome, Sept. 1963; Abstracts of Communications A.73.
[580] R. Heap, B. C. Saunders and G. J. Stacey, *J. Chem. Soc.*, 1951, 658.
[581] G. Grüttner, *Ber.*, 1918, **51**, 1298.

obtained from the hydroxide and aqueous hydrofluoric acid. Their solubility in water and alcohols falls with increasing chain length.

Trimethyl-lead chloride, Me_3PbCl, m.p. 190° (decomp.), obtained by direct chlorination of tetramethyl-lead at $-60°$, or by the use of hydrogen chloride [582], forms 1 : 1 adducts with such donor molecules as tetramethylene sulphoxide, dimethylformamide and N,N-dimethylacetamide for which trigonal bipyramidal structures 4.24 have been proposed on the basis of their infrared and proton magnetic resonance spectra, which indicate a planar arrangement of methyl groups about the lead atoms [583].

$$Me_3PbCl + MeCONMe_2 \longrightarrow Me-\overset{\overset{\displaystyle Cl}{|}}{\underset{\underset{\displaystyle MeCONMe_2}{\uparrow}}{Pb}}\overset{\nearrow Me}{\searrow_{Me}}$$

4.24

Trimethyl-lead bromide, Me_3PbBr, m.p. 133° (decomp.), and the *iodide* Me_3PbI (very unstable) are appreciably volatile.

Triethyl-lead chloride, Et_3PbCl, decomposes at about 120° without melting. It is readily prepared by addition of a cooled ether solution of hydrogen chloride to tetra-ethyl-lead [582], and forms complexes similar to those of Me_3PbCl [583, 584]. The other halides are most conveniently obtained by converting the chloride into hydroxide, followed by treatment with the appropriate acid; e.g. *triethyl-lead bromide*, Et_3PbBr, m.p. 103–104°, and *triethyl-lead iodide*, Et_3PbI, m.p. 19–20° (unstable).

Tri-n-propyl-lead chloride, $(n-C_3H_7)_3PbCl$, m.p. 133–134°, is conveniently prepared by passing hydrogen chloride into a light petroleum solution of tetra-n-propyl-lead until a precipitate (of $Pr^n_2PbCl_2$) begins to form. Evaporation of the filtered solution affords the tri-n-propyl-lead chloride. The use of ether instead of light petroleum leads to much di-n-propyl-lead dichloride, due to the continued action of the hydrogen chloride which is far more soluble in ether than in light petroleum [556]. The other halides are prepared through the hydroxide.

Triphenyl-lead chloride, Ph_3PbCl, m.p. 205°, can be prepared from tetraphenyl-lead by the action of dry hydrogen chloride in chloroform [585]. The *bromide*, Ph_3PbBr, is obtained by the slow addition of bromine in pyridine to tetraphenyl-lead suspended in pyridine [581], both reagents being cooled at $-15°$. Pseudohalides have been prepared from these

[582] R. Heap and B. C. Saunders, *J. Chem. Soc.*, 1949, 2983.
[583] N. A. Matwiyoff and R. S. Drago, *Inorg. Chem.*, 1964, **3**, 337.
[584] F. Huber and M. Enders, *Z. Naturforsch.*, 1965, **20b**, 601; R. Barbieri, G. Faraglia, M. Giustiniani and L. Roncucci, *J. Inorg. Nucl. Chem.*, 1964, **26**, 203; R. Barbieri, M. Giuestiniani, G. Faraglia and G. Tagliavini, *Ricerca Sci.*, 1963, **3**, 975; R. Barbieri, G. Faraglia and M. Giustiniani, ibid., 1964, **4**, 109; *Chem. Abs.*, 1964, **61**, 1884, 4388.
[585] H. Gilman and D. S. Melstrom, *J. Amer. Chem. Soc.*, 1950, **72**, 2953; L. S. Foster, W. M. Dix and I. J. Gruntfest, ibid., 1939, **61**, 1685.

halides, e.g. the *thiocyanate* Ph_3PbCNS (decomposes at 230°), from Ph_3PbCl and KCNS in refluxing ethanol, and the *cyanide* Ph_3PbCN (decomposes at 250°), from Ph_3PbI and KCN [93c, 577].

The Dihalides

Although these may be obtained by the continued action of hydrogen halides on the R_4Pb compounds, a better method involves the inter-mediate preparation of the dialkyl-lead sulphite (R_2PbSO_3) which is decomposed to R_2PbX_2 by the appropriate acid.

The manipulation of these compounds requires some care on account of their ready disproportionation into lead(II) and R_3Pb^+ salts. The di-bromides, and particularly the di-iodides, disproportionate very easily. Dialkyl-lead halides appear to be extensively ionized in aqueous solution, from which dioxinates, $R_2Pb(C_8H_6NO)_2$, can be prepared; these oxinates are considered to have octahedral structures [584].

Diphenyl-lead difluoride, Ph_2PbF_2, from the di-iodide and potassium fluoride, is the only difluoride known, and is a salt of low solubility. The structure of the *dichloride*, Ph_2PbCl_2, was described above (4.23).

Dimethyl-lead dichloride, Me_2PbCl_2, is the most stable dihalide and can be boiled a short time in aqueous solution without forming $PbCl_2$.

Diethyl-lead dichloride, Et_2PbCl_2, m.p. 220°. When sulphur dioxide is passed into a solution of tetra-ethyl-lead in ether containing a little water, diethyl-lead sulphite is precipitated. This is converted quantitatively into the dichloride by aqueous hydrochloric acid, and into many other com-pounds R_2PbA_2 by the action of suitable acids HA [580].

$$Et_2PbSO_3 + 2HCl \rightarrow Et_2PbCl_2 + SO_2 + H_2O$$

Di-n-propyl-lead dichloride, $Pr^n_2PbCl_2$, has been prepared by the action of hydrogen chloride on tetra-n-propyl-lead in *ether* solution, and can be crystallized from alcohol [556].

The Trihalides

As might be expected on approaching PbX_4, these ($RPbX_3$) are highly unstable and little is known about them. They have been prepared by the action of aqueous hydrogen halides on the *alkylplumbonic acids* $(R \cdot PbO_2H)_n$ (see below), and by the reaction [586] (cf. Ge and Sn):

$$RI + CsPbCl_3 \rightarrow RPbI_3$$

Oxides and hydroxides

Trialkyl-lead hydroxides are formed by the action of alkalis, or silver oxide, on the halides R_3PbX. Ion-exchange resins can be useful for the

[586] M. Lesbre, *Compt. rend.*, 1937, **204**, 1822; 1938, **206**, 1481; 1940, **210**, 535.

same purpose. They are frequently soluble both in organic solvents and in water, their aqueous solutions being sufficiently strongly alkaline to absorb carbon dioxide from the air. They have served as intermediates in the preparation of large numbers of derivatives of the type R_3PbA, where A is an acid radical.

Trimethyl-lead hydroxide, Me_3PbOH, from the chloride and aqueous potassium hydroxide, is more soluble in most organic solvents than in water. Sufficiently volatile to have a most unpleasant smell, it fumes with volatile acids. Related *siloxy* derivatives, e.g. $Me_3PbOSiMe_3$, m.p. $-1°$, b.p. $172°/720$ mm., have been prepared from Me_3PbCl and R_3SiOLi [105, 352, 587]. *Alkoxy* derivatives are obtained from the halides by the action of sodium alkoxides [587a], while organolead *aryloxides* can be prepared from R_4Pb and phenols. Phenoxides R_3PbOPh, like their tin analogues, can also be prepared by the titration of the hydroxide with phenol in the presence of molecular sieve to take up the water produced, a procedure which may well be useful for the preparation of other thermally unstable materials [98].

Triethyl-lead hydroxide, Et_3PbOH, is precipitated when strong aqueous alkali is added to an ether solution of the chloride [556], and can be crystallized from alcohol. When heated it disproportionates to tetra-ethyl-lead and diethyl-lead dihydroxide, which subsequently decomposes to lead oxide, ethane, ethylene and butane [588].

$$Et_3PbOH \longrightarrow Et_4Pb + Et_2Pb(OH)_2 \longrightarrow PbO + C_2H_4 + C_2H_6 + C_4H_{10}$$

The hydroxide reacts with acids to form salts, for example an *acetate*, $Et_3Pb·O·COMe$, m.p. $160°$, and a sparingly soluble *sulphate*, $(Et_3Pb)_2SO_4$. The acetate decomposes when heated above the melting point by a similar process to the hydroxide, involving an initial disproportionation stage [589]. Reduction of its solutions in aqueous or organic solvents by titanium(III) chloride has been used as a way of generating ethyl radicals [590]:

$$Et_3PbOAc \overset{H^+}{\rightleftharpoons} HOAc + Et_3Pb^+ \overset{e^-}{\longrightarrow} [Et_3Pb] \longrightarrow$$
$$[Et_2Pb + Et·] \longrightarrow Pb + C_2H_6 + C_4H_{10}$$

Tri-n-propyl-lead hydroxide, Pr^n_3PbOH, from the chloride and a 50% excess of silver oxide in aqueous suspension, is the most convenient source of a variety of tri-n-propyl-lead compounds. For example, potassium

[587] H. Schmidbaur and H. Hussek, *J. Organometal. Chem.*, 1964, **1**, 257.

[587a] E. Amberger and R. Hönigschmid-Grossich, *Chem. Ber.*, 1965, **98**, 3795.

[588] Yu. A. Aleksandrov, T. G. Brilkina and V. A. Shushunov, *Trudy po Khim. i Khim. Tekhnol.*, 1959, **2**, 623; *Chem. Abs.*, 1962, **56**, 14314.

[589] Yu. A. Aleksandrov and T. I. Mokeeva, *Trudy po Khim. i Khim. Tekhnol.*, 1961, **4**, 365; *Chem. Abs.*, 1962, **56**, 493.

[590] C.-H. Wang, P. L. Levins and H. G. Pars, *Tetrahedron Letters*, 1964, 687.

cyanide precipitates the insoluble *tri-n-propyl-lead cyanide*, m.p. 135° (decomp.), which is a fairly strong sternutator:

$$Pr^n_3PbOH + KCN \longrightarrow Pr^n_3PbCN + KOH$$

Triphenyl-lead hydroxide, Ph_3PbOH, from the bromide and alkali, also results from the quantitative cleavage of hexaphenyldilead by potassium permanganate in acetone at room temperature [591]:

$$3Ph_3Pb \cdot PbPh_3 + 2KMnO_4 + 4H_2O \longrightarrow 6Ph_3PbOH + 2KOH + 2MnO_2$$

Treatment with sodium in nonane gives the impure *oxide*, $(Ph_3Pb)_2O$ as a solution in nonane [592]. Attempts to prepare peroxy derivatives, e.g. by the reaction with peracetic acid in methanol, dioxan or ether gave a precipitate of diphenyl-lead oxide, Ph_2PbO, and a solution which with alkali gave more Ph_2PbO and phenol [107, 386, 387]. Many salts of Ph_3PbOH have been prepared, particularly with carboxylic acids. Others are conveniently obtained from a triphenyl-lead halide, e.g. [593].

$$Ph_3PbI + NaOAs(O)Me_2 \xrightarrow{MeOH} NaI + Ph_3PbOAs(O)Me_2$$

Organolead alkoxides react rapidly and exothermically with isocyanates, carbodiimides and other reactive unsaturated substances, adding across the multiple bonds [593a]. Use of hexachloro-acetone or bromal as the unsaturated substrate allows the preparation of perhalomethyl-lead derivatives:

$$Ph_3PbOMe + (Cl_3C)_2CO \longrightarrow [Ph_3PbOC(CCl_3)_2OMe] \xrightarrow{-Cl_3CCOOMe} Ph_3PbCCl_3$$
$$\text{m.p. } 171°$$

$$Ph_3PbOMe + CBr_3CHO \longrightarrow Ph_3PbCBr_3 + HCOOMe$$

The reaction of triphenyl-lead hydroxide or acetate with ketone involves a similar addition [593b]:

$$Ph_3PbOH + CH_2:C:O \xrightarrow{Et_2O} (Ph_3PbCH_2CO)_2O \quad \text{(decomp. 100–110°)}$$

The *dialkyl-lead dihydroxides* differ from the monohydroxides in their much greater solubility in water. *Dimethyl-lead hydroxide* in water forms such species as $[Me_2Pb(OH)_3]^-$ and $[Me_2Pb(OH)]_2^{2+}$, hydrated to an extent which causes the Me_2Pb^{2+} skeleton to be linear [593c].

Diethyl-lead dihydroxide, $Et_2Pb(OH)_2 6H_2O$, from the dichloride and alkali, can be crystallized from water ($\not> 40°$). Readily soluble in water, it is insoluble in benzene or ether. In a vacuum desiccator it gradually loses

[591] G. Bähr, *Z. anorg. Chem.*, 1947, **253**, 330.
[592] T. G. Brilkina, M. K. Safonova and V. A. Shushunov, *Zhur. obshchei Khim.*, 1962, **32**, 2684; *Chem. Abs.*, 1963, **58**, 9112.
[593] M. C. Henry, *Inorg. Chem.*, 1962, **1**, 917.
[593a] A. G. Davies and R. J. Puddephatt, *J. Organometal. Chem.*, 1966, **5**, 590.
[593b] L. C. Willemsens and G. J. M. van der Kerk, ibid., 1965, **4**, 241.
[593c] C. E. Friedine and R. S. Tobias, *Inorg. Chem.*, 1966, **5**, 354.

water, giving *diethyl-lead oxide*, Et_2PbO, which is insoluble in water but dissolves in dilute acetic acid [580].

Diphenyl-lead oxide, $(Ph_2PbO)_n$, dec. 223°, is obtained as a polymer, which dissolves in acids to give a variety of compounds of the type Ph_2PbA_2. Partial hydrolysis of these salts, Ph_2PbA_2, leads to *plumboxanes*, $(Ph_2PbA)_2O$ (cf. the stannoxanes, p. 447) [594]:

$$Ph_2Pb(OAc)_2 \xrightarrow{H_2O} (Ph_2PbOAc)_2O, \quad dec.\ 218–219°$$

Trihydroxides are unknown, but their partial dehydration products, the *plumbonic acids*, result from the Meyer reaction with alkyl halides and sodium plumbate(II) [586]:

$$RI + Na_2PbO_2 \rightarrow Na(RPbO_2) + NaI$$

The plumbonic acids, of which only a few alkyl examples are known, dissolve both in hydrogen halide acids, giving trihalides $RPbX_3$ and salts of the type $M[RPbX_5]$, and in alkalis giving plumbonates.

Sulphur and nitrogen compounds

Various organolead sulphides, mercaptides and thiocarboxylates are known.

Bis(triethyl-lead) sulphide, $(Et_3Pb)_2S$, m.p. −45°, is a yellow-green liquid obtained by the action of sodium sulphide on the chloride in aqueous solution at 0°. It is oxidized by air to the sulphate $(Et_3Pb)_2SO_4$ [595]. The *phenyl* derivative, $(Ph_3Pb)_2S$, m.p. 139–141°, can be prepared from the hydroxide by the reaction with carbon disulphide at room temperature [389], or from Ph_6Pb_2 and sulphur [596].

Diphenyl-lead sulphide, precipitated as pale yellow prisms, m.p. 130°, from solutions of other salts by sulphides, is associated in benzene solution, the molecular weight corresponding to a mixture of dimer $(Ph_2PbS)_2$ and trimer $(Ph_2PbS)_3$ [597].

Mercaptides, R_3PbSR', can be prepared by the action of the alkan-ethiol [111, 582] or thiophenol, $R'SH$, on R_3PbOH, R_3PbCl or R_4Pb, or better by the action of the lead mercaptide on the appropriate organolead chloride, e.g. [598].

$$2Ph_3PbCl + Pb(SMe)_2 \rightarrow PbCl_2 + 2Ph_3PbSMe, \quad m.p.\ 108–109°$$

[594] E. M. Panov, N. N. Zemlyanskii and K. A. Kocheshkov, *Doklady Akad. Nauk S.S.S.R.*, 1962, **143**, 603; *Chem. Abs.*, 1962, **57**, 12521. N. N. Zemlyanskii, V. N. Lodochnikova, E. M. Panov and K. A. Kocheshkov, *Zhur. obshchei Khim.*, 1965, **35**, 843; *Chem. Abs.*, 1965, **63**, 7031.

[595] G. Calingaert, F. J. Dykstra and H. Shapiro, *J. Amer. Chem. Soc.*, 1945, **67**, 190.

[596] A. W. Krebs and M. C. Henry, *J. Org. Chem.*, 1963, **28**, 1911.

[597] W. J. Lile and R. C. Menzies, *J. Chem. Soc.*, 1950, 617.

[598] M. C. Henry and A. W. Krebs, *J. Org. Chem.*, 1963, **28**, 225.

The phenyl-lead derivatives Ph_3PbSR are white crystalline solids which decompose above their melting points; they are soluble in most organic solvents, and are clearly covalently bound. Methyl iodide cleaves the mercaptide group;

$$Ph_3PbSMe + MeI \longrightarrow Ph_3PbI + Me_2S$$

Other derivatives, e.g. Et_3PbSEt, b.p. $76-78°/0.075$ mm., are colourless liquids [582, 599]. Selenides, R_3PbSeR', may be obtained as oils by reactions such as the following [600]:

$$MeMgBr \xrightarrow{Se} MeSeMgBr \xrightarrow{Me_3PbCl} Me_3PbSeMe, \quad \text{b.p. } 75°/3 \text{ mm.}$$

Sulphur, selenium and tellurium derivatives of lead are also accessible by the action of triphenyl-lead lithium (p. 507) on the appropriate Group VI element [109, 113, 600a]:

$$Ph_3PbLi + X \longrightarrow Ph_3PbXLi \xrightarrow{Ph_3PbCl} (Ph_3Pb)_2X \quad (X = S, Se \text{ or } Te)$$

Nitrogen compounds [123]. Various organolead arylenedicarbimides, $R_3PbNCOArCO$ [582], sulphonamides, $R_3PbNHSO_2R'$ [580], and related compounds have been described [1]. Simple organolead amides are apparently unknown, although silylamino derivatives such as $Me_3PbN(SiMe_3)_2$, b.p. $85-87°/3$ mm., have been prepared (from $Me_3PbCl + NaN(SiMe_3)_2$ [120].

Triphenyl-lead azide, Ph_3PbN_3, m.p. $186-187°$ (decomp.), has attracted some attention recently, being surprisingly stable to heat. It can be prepared by the action of hydrazoic acid on triphenyl-lead hydroxide in alcoholic chloroform or ether [601, 602], or preferably from triphenyl-lead chloride and sodium azide [602]:

$$Ph_3PbCl + NaN_3 \longrightarrow Ph_3PbN_3 + NaCl$$

When heated above about $160°$, it loses nitrogen, forming tetraphenyl-lead, Ph_4Pb. Its unexpected stability is attributed to Pb–N d_π–p_π bonding [602]. *Diphenyl-lead diazide*, $Ph_2Pb(N_3)_2$, has been prepared from Ph_2PbO and HN_3 in the form of white needles which decompose at about $14.5°$ and explode if heated rapidly to about $200°$ [601]. The thermal and

[599] P. Ballinger (California Research Corp.), U.S.P. 3,073,853; *Chem. Abs.*, 1963, **58**, 12599.

[600] W. L. Richardson (California Research Corp.), U.S.P. 3,010,980; *Chem. Abs.*, 1962, **56**, 11620.

[600a] H. Schumann, K.-F. Thom, and M. Schmidt, *J. Organometal. Chem.*, 1965, **4**, 28.

[601] E. Lieber and F. M. Keane, *Chem. and Ind.*, 1961, 747; E. Lieber, C. N. R. Rao and F. M. Keane, *J. Inorg. Nucl. Chem.*, 1963, **25**, 631.

[602] W. T. Reichle, *Inorg. Chem.*, 1964, **3**, 402; J. S. Thayer and R. West, ibid. p. 406.

explosive stability of the lead azides thus decreases in the order Ph_3PbN_3 > $Ph_2Pb(N_3)_2$ > $Pb(N_3)_2$.

Pseudohalides of lead were reviewed in 1966 [93c] (see also [93b] for infrared spectroscopic data).

The only organolead–phosphorus compound known at present (1964) is *diphenylphosphinotriphenyl-lead*, a colourless crystalline solid obtained by reaction of Et_3N on a solution of Ph_3PbCl and Ph_2PH in benzene [603]:

$$Ph_3PbCl + Ph_2PH + Et_3N \rightarrow Ph_3PbPPh_2 + Et_3NHCl$$

Compounds containing lead–lead bonds

These are decidedly less stable than their tin analogues, and no structures are known in which more than three lead atoms are bound together in a chain, although short lead chains may be present in the poorly characterized and unstable lead(II) compounds, R_2Pb, and the thermally unstable reactive red solid, $(Ph_3Pb)_4Pb$, has recently been described [138, 604]. Compounds of the type R_6Pb_2 may be obtained by two satisfactory methods of which the Grignard or lithium method has already been mentioned in connexion with the preparation of R_4Pb by the Grignard process:

$$6RMgX + 3PbCl_2 \rightarrow R_3Pb \cdot PbR_3 + Pb + 3MgX_2 + 3MgCl_2$$

It is necessary to carry out the reaction at a low temperature to avoid the decomposition:

$$2R_3Pb \cdot PbR_3 \rightarrow 3R_4Pb + Pb$$

The other less generally useful method is the reaction (familiar in the tin series) between R_3PbNa (or Li) and R_3PbX.

All the known reactions of the R_6Pb_2 series involve breaking the Pb–Pb bond, which is sensitive to halogens, hydrogen halides, phenyl-lithium, alkali metals, and oxidizing agents (e.g. $KMnO_4$ or air). The mechanism by which these cleavage reactions occur is not fully understood, there being some uncertainty about the precise state in which these compounds exist in solution in inert solvents.

The compounds are diamagnetic under all conditions, which precludes homolytic dissociation into free radicals [131, 460, 605]. Molecular weight measurements by freezing- and boiling-point methods have given conflicting results, which have generally indicated extensive dissociation, but

[603] H. Schumann, P. Schwabe and M. Schmidt, *J. Organometal. Chem.*, 1964, **1**, 366.

[604] L. C. Willemsens and G. J. M. van der Kerk, ibid., 1964, **2**, 271.

[605] U. Bellucco, G. Tagliavini and P. Favero, *Ricerca Sci.*, 1962, 98; *Chem. Abs.*, 1962, **57**, 13786.

the change with concentration does not correspond to a monomer–dimer equilibrium. Freezing-point measurements on solutions of hexaphenyl- and hexacyclohexyl-dilead in naphthalene indicated no dissociation [606]. The increase with concentration and temperature in the yellow colour of hexaphenyldilead solutions in benzene suggests dissociation, and the yellow colour is similar to that of Ph_3Pb^-, which can be obtained as a sodium salt (see below). However, heterolytic dissociation into such ions seems unlikely in view of the lack of isotopic exchange between mixtures of Ph_3PbCl and labelled $Ph_6Pb^*_2$ in benzene [605]. On the other hand, total exchange of lead isotopes does occur rapidly between Ph_4Pb and $Ph_6Pb^*_2$ in benzene [607]. It seems likely, therefore, that if dissociation does occur it involves a disproportionation into Ph_4Pb and Ph_2Pb; i.e. more generally,

$$R_3Pb \cdot PbR_3 \rightleftharpoons R_4Pb + R_2Pb$$

Reactions will then tend to be primarily those of the most reactive species present, the dialkyl- or diaryl-lead, R_2Pb, normally too reactive to be isolated. Disproportionation of R_2Pb into R_4Pb and metallic lead would account for the overall disproportionation reaction of $R_3Pb \cdot PbR_3$ (into $3R_4Pb + Pb$) known to occur at elevated temperatures. In the reaction with hydrogen chloride in alcohol or chloroform solutions, which for alkyl derivatives occurs according to the equation [608, 609]

$$R_6Pb_2 + 3HCl \rightarrow R_3PbCl + PbCl_2 + 3RH$$

the lead dichloride cannot be formed from R_3PbCl (as shown by independent experiments), and so must result from the dialkyl-lead, the mono-chloride, R_3PbCl, being formed by the known reaction from R_4Pb:

$$R_2Pb + 2HCl \rightarrow PbCl_2 + 2RH$$
$$R_4Pb + HCl \rightarrow R_3PbCl + RH$$

The formation of Ar_2PbCl_2, $PbCl_2$ and $4ArH$ from aryl derivatives Ar_6Pb_2 is explicable in terms of similar reactions, the dichloride Ar_2PbCl_2 resulting from the greater reactivity of Ar_4Pb towards hydrogen chloride. An alternative explanation, involving formation of an intermediate $R_4Pb_2Cl_2$ before cleavage of the Pb–Pb bond, has, however, been proposed [609].

Similar explanations involving R_2Pb have been out forward to explain

[606] L. Malatesta, *Gazzetta Chim. Ital.*, 1943, **73**, 176.

[607] U. Bellucco, L. Cattalini and G. Tagliavini, *Ricerca Sci.*, 1962, 110; *Chem. Abs.*, 1962, **57**, 13786.

[608] U. Bellucco, A. Peloso, L. Cattalini and G. Tagliavini, *Ricerca Sci.*, 1962, 269; *Chem. Abs.*, 1963, **59**, 1667. See also idem, *Ricerca Sci.*, 1963, **3**, 1107; *Chem. Abs.*, 1964, **61**, 677.

[609] H. J. Eméleus and P. R. Evans, *J. Chem. Soc.*, 1964, 511.

the products of reactions between hexaphenyl-dilead and acetic acid, thioacetic acid, sulphur and ethylene dibromide, e.g. [610].

$$Ph_6Pb_2 + 4HOAc \longrightarrow Ph_2Pb(OAc)_2 + Pb(OAc)_2 + 4PhH$$

Reactions of hexa-ethyldilead with iron(III), copper(I) or (II) and gold(III) chlorides, all of which result in tetra-ethyl-lead and lead(II) chloride, evidently involve diethyl-lead as an intermediate [611].

Hexamethyldilead, $Me_3Pb \cdot PbMe_3$, m.p. $38°$, is best obtained from methylmagnesium iodide and lead(II) chloride [612] at $-5°$. It reacts rapidly with hydrogen chloride in chloroform [609]:

$$Me_6Pb_2 + 3HCl \longrightarrow Me_3PbCl + PbCl_2 + 3CH_4$$

Hexa-ethyldilead, $Et_3Pb \cdot PbEt_3$, a liquid relatively easily prepared by the Grignard method [613], is one of the least stable members of the series, like the hexamethyl, and very readily disproportionates to lead and tetra-ethyl-lead. Heating a mixture of hexamethyl- and hexa-ethyl-dilead gives all the five possible methyl and ethyl compounds of the type R_4Pb. The reaction of liquid hexa-ethyldilead with oxygen at $50°$ leads to tetra-ethyl-lead (one mole per mole Et_6Pb_2), lead(II) oxide PbO, ethanol, acetaldehyde and water, products which might well result from oxidation of diethyl-lead in the presence of Et_4Pb [452].

The reaction with hydrogen chloride in methanol, with acyl chlorides as the source of hydrogen chloride, gives similar products to those found in the case of Me_6Pb_2, i.e. $PbCl_2 + Et_4Pb + 2EtH$, or $PbCl_2 + Et_3PbCl + 3EtH$, according to whether two or three mols. of HCl are used [608]. Various salts of transition metals are reduced by Et_6Pb_2 in methanol solution either to a salt of a lower oxidation state or to the free metal, e.g. [611]

$$2Et_6Pb_2 + 2FeCl_3 \longrightarrow 3Et_4Pb + PbCl_2 + 2FeCl_2$$
$$Et_6Pb_2 + 2AgNO_3 \longrightarrow 2Et_3PbNO_3 + 2Ag$$

This reaction with silver nitrate does not involve disproportionation of the lead compound.

Hexacyclohexyldilead, $(C_6H_{11})_3Pb \cdot Pb(C_6H_{11})_3$, as prepared by the Grignard method forms bright yellow crystals which decompose at about $195°$ without melting. It does not change at all easily into tetracyclohexyl-lead; the ease with which this disproportionation occurs increases in the order:

cyclohexyl $<$ α-naphthyl $<$ p-tolyl $<$ phenyl $<$ ethyl, methyl

---

[610] A. W. Krebs and M. C. Henry, *J. Org. Chem.*, 1963, **28**, 1911.
[611] U. Bellucco and G. Bellucco, *Ricerca Sci*, Sez. **A32**, 1962, 102.
[612] G. Calingaert and H. Soroos, *J. Org. Chem.*, 1938, **2**, 535.

The reaction with hydrogen chloride is also slower than those of other derivatives R_6Pb_2 investigated [609].

Hexaphenyldilead, $Ph_3Pb\cdot PbPh_3$, can be obtained from phenylmagnesium bromide and lead(II) chloride, but the use of phenyl-lithium gives a much higher yield [572]. It can be prepared in even higher yield from triphenyllead iodide and one mole of sodium (or better, the Na_4Pb_9 alloy) in liquid ammonia [613]:

$$Ph_3PbI + 2Na \longrightarrow Ph_3PbNa + NaI$$
$$Ph_3PbNa + Ph_3PbI \longrightarrow Ph_3Pb\cdot PbPh_3 + NaI$$

The pale yellow crystals of hexaphenyldilead are soluble in benzene, and separate with benzene of crystallization. The solution in benzene and other solvents is yellow and darkens reversibly on heating. The ultraviolet spectrum of Ph_6Pb_2 in cyclohexane in the region 240–300 mμ has been interpreted as evidence of extended conjugation in the molecule involving suitable vacant d orbitals of the lead atoms [131]. The extent to which the aryl substituents affect the spectrum is, however, uncertain. The temperature dependence of the colours of hexaphenyldilead and hexacyclohexyldilead has been attributed to a broadening of the absorption bands connected with the temperature dependent distribution of molecules over different vibration levels [613a].

When heated or under ultraviolet radiation, solutions of Ph_6Pb_2 in benzene undergo slight exchange of phenyl groups between solvent and solute, although under the same conditions disproportionation of Ph_6Pb_2 becomes detectable [574]. In the photolysis of Ph_6Pb_2 in benzene, some of the phenyl groups in the resulting biphenyl originate in the solvent [574]. The exchange of lead isotopes which occurs between Ph_6Pb_2 and Ph_4Pb [607], but not between Ph_6Pb_2 and Ph_3PbCl [605], has been described above, together with some reactions of hexaphenyldilead [1, 597, 609]; for further reactions, e.g. that with copper(II) chloride leading to lead(II) chloride and chlorobenzene, see ref. [614].

The sterically hindered compound, *hexamesityldilead*, from mesitylmagnesium bromide and lead(II) chloride, is a yellow crystalline powder which decomposes at about 325°. One group of workers [615] reported that magnetic measurements indicate 2·3% dissociation into radicals in the solid state, but another [616] reported that the electron spin resonance spectrum, a very sensitive method, shows no trace of radicals in dilute

[613] H. Gilman and J. C. Bailie, *J. Amer. Chem. Soc.*, 1939, **61**, 731.

[613a] W. Drenth, L. C. Willemsens and G. J. M. van der Kerk, *J. Organometal. Chem.*, 1964, **2**, 279.

[614] G. A. Razuvaev, M. S. Fedotov, T. B. Zavarova and N. N. Bazhenova, *Trudy po Khim. i Khim. Tekhnol.*, 1961, **4**, 622; *Chem. Abs.*, 1963, **58**, 543.

[615] M. Lesbre, J. Satge and D. Voigt, *Compt. rend.*, 1958, **246**, 594.

[616] E. Müller, F. Günter, K. Scheffer and H. Fettel, *Chem. Ber.*, 1958, **91**, 2888.

solution in benzene, and that the compound is undissociated in molten biphenyl (by cryoscopy).

Tetrakis(triphenyl-lead)lead, $(Ph_3Pb)_4Pb$, is obtained as a thermally unstable air-sensitive red solid by the simultaneous hydrolysis and oxidation (using ice-salt and hydrogen peroxide) of ether-free triphenyl-lead lithium [138, 604]. Iodination gives triphenyl-lead iodide and lead(II) iodide.

Derivatives of lead(II)

Although organic derivatives of lead(II), R_2Pb, are thought to be involved as reaction intermediates in many reactions of compounds R_6Pb_2, their presence has been inferred rather than proved and they appear to be extremely reactive and unstable with respect to R_4Pb and Pb, in marked contrast to the great stability of inorganic lead(II) compounds (compare $PbCl_2$ and $PbCl_4$).

An early report [617] that diaryl-lead compounds Ar_2Pb could be prepared and isolated from aryl magnesium halides and lead(II) chloride at about 0° has not been substantiated by more recent work [572, 618], although there is evidence that such compounds are present in the reaction mixture. The following changes occur when phenylmagnesium bromide is added to lead(II) bromide in tetrahydrofuran at −20° [618]:

$$PbBr_2 \xrightarrow[\text{1 mol.}]{PhMgBr} \text{Yellow solution} \xrightarrow[\text{1 mol.}]{PhMgBr} \text{Red solution} \xrightarrow[\text{1-3 mol.}]{PhMgBr} \text{Red-brown solution}$$

Similar though less well-defined colour changes occur when aryl-lithium reagents are used. The following equilibrium is considered to obtain for solutions containing at least two mols. of aryl-lithium or magnesium reagent [572, 618]:

$$Ar_2Pb + ArLi(MgX) \rightleftharpoons Ar_3PbLi(MgX)$$

If solutions corresponding to the composition Ar_2Pb are boiled, lead is precipitated and tetra-aryl-lead remains. Hydrolysis leads to lead oxide, possibly contaminated by halide (from ArMgX) and Ar_6Pb_2 (from Ar_3PbLi or Ar_3PbMgX). Removal of the solvent gives air- and moisture-sensitive orange-red solids which may contain Ar_2Pb or $(Ar_2Pb)_x$ contaminated by lithium or magnesium salts, and which decompose at room temperature to form lead.

A red liquid obtained by electrolytic reduction of acetone with a lead cathode approximated to di-isopropyl-lead, Pr^i_2Pb; it was easily oxidized, and with bromine gave di-isopropyl-lead dibromide [619].

[617] E. Krause and G. G. Reissaus, *Ber.*, 1922, **55**, 888.
[618] F. Glockling, K. Hooton and D. Kingston, *J. Chem. Soc.*, 1961, 4405.
[619] J. Tafel, *Ber.*, 1911, **44**, 323; G. Renger, ibid., p. 337.

Dicyclopentadienyl-lead, $(C_5H_5)_2Pb$, a yellow crystalline solid which can be purified by sublimation, may be prepared from cyclopentadienyl-sodium and lead(II) nitrate [620], chloride or (better) acetate [255]. It has no definite melting point, is easily oxidized, is insoluble in water but soluble in organic solvents, has a dipole moment of 1·63 D and is considered to be a monomeric, σ-bonded compound [256, 621]. This, therefore, appears to be the only organolead(II) compound to have been isolated, purified and characterized.

Alkali metal derivatives

These are again much less stable than the alkali metal organotin derivatives, and have only recently been studied at all extensively. They result from the reaction between alkali metals and compounds of the types R_6Pb_2, R_4Pb or R_3PbX in liquid ammonia or tetrahydrofuran, or by the addition of phenyl-lithium in ether to lead(II) chloride.

Triethyl-lead sodium, Et_3PbNa, is most conveniently obtained in liquid ammonia solution by addition of sodium in liquid ammonia to an ether solution of tetra-ethyl-lead at about $-70°$.

$$Et_4Pb + 2Na + NH_3 \longrightarrow Et_3PbNa + NaNH_2 + C_2H_6$$

The sodamide can be removed by filtration, but its presence does not matter in the most useful reaction of the alkali compound, viz. with organic halides, since it reacts so much more slowly. Addition of n-butyl bromide to the solution gives triethyl-n-butyl-lead in good yield [622]. Triethyl-lead sodium is considerably more reactive than triphenyl-lead sodium, and will react slowly with bromobenzene.

Triphenyl-lead sodium, Ph_3PbNa, is obtained in very good yield by either of the following reactions, carried out in an ether–ammonia mixture:

$$Ph_4Pb + 2Na + NH_3 \longrightarrow Ph_3PbNa + NaNH_2 + C_6H_6$$
$$Ph_3Pb \cdot PbPh_3 + 2Na \longrightarrow 2Ph_3PbNa$$

The second method has the advantage that no sodamide is formed. The use of triphenyl-lead halides is less satisfactory. The product reacts with alkyl but not aryl halides.

Triphenyl-lead sodium can be isolated as cream-coloured crystals, stable at room temperature in the absence of moisture or oxygen. It affords the ammonium salt $NH_4^+(Ph_3Pb^-)$, not the hydride, on treatment with ammonium bromide.

[620] E. O. Fischer and H. Grubert, *Z. anorg. Chem.*, 1956, **286**, 237.
[621] H. P. Fritz, *Ber.*, 1959, **92**, 780; E. O. Fischer and S. Schreiner, ibid., p. 938.
[622] H. Gilman and E. Bindschadler, *J. Org. Chem.*, 1953, **18**, 1675.

Triphenyl-lead lithium, Ph_3PbLi, results from the addition of phenyl-lithium in ether to a suspension of lead(II) chloride at $-10°$ by the step-wise reaction [572]:

$$2PhLi + PbCl_2 \longrightarrow 2LiCl + Ph_2Pb \quad \text{(irreversible)}$$
$$PhLi + Ph_2Pb \rightleftharpoons Ph_3PbLi \quad \text{(reversible)}$$

When up to about two mols. of phenyl-lithium have been added the solution has a bright yellow to orange colour, ascribed to diphenyl-lead. The Gilman colour test (reaction with tetramethyldiaminobenzophenone, and oxidation of the resulting carbinol with iodine to a green triphenylmethane dye [623]) remains negative until $2·8$ mols. of phenyl-lithium have been added. At the diphenyl-lead stage carbonation affords no benzoic acid, but at the final stage benzoic acid is formed. No benzoic acid results, however, from carbonation of triphenyl-lead lithium prepared from triphenyl-lead chloride in tetrahydrofuran [433]:

$$Ph_3PbCl + 2Li \longrightarrow LiCl + Ph_3PbLi \xrightarrow{CO_2} \text{no } PhCO_2H$$

As benzoic acid will be formed if phenyl-lithium is present, and is evidently not formed by a reaction involving the triphenyl-lead anion (such as $Ph_3Pb^- + CO_2 \rightarrow Ph_2Pb + PhCO_2^-$), then it must be concluded that the benzoic acid obtained in the first reaction was a consequence of an excess of unchanged phenyl-lithium being present, and not of dissociation of Ph_3PbLi into Ph_2Pb and $PhLi$.

Triphenyl-lead lithium can also be prepared in good yield by the reaction between hexaphenyldilead and lithium in tetrahydrofuran [143]. Triphenyl-lead lithium shows only a very slight tendency to metalate fluorene, the relative proton affinities of the anions Ph_3M^- of Group IVB elements decreasing in the order $Ph_3Si^- > Ph_3Ge^- > Ph_3Sn^- > Ph_3Pb^-$ [149].

The reaction of triphenyl-lead lithium with a mixture of ice, salt and hydrogen peroxide [604] forming $(Ph_3Pb)_4Pb$ has already been described (p. 505). With CCl_4, $CHCl_3$ or CH_2Cl_2 in tetrahydrofuran at $-60°$ triphenyl-lead lithium reacts to form the substituted methanes $(Ph_3Pb)_4C$, $(Ph_3Pb)_3CH$ and $(Ph_3Pb)_2CH_2$ respectively [624]. Small ring heterocycles $(CH_2)_nX$ ($n = 2, 3$ or 4; $X = O$, S or NR) are cleaved by the reagent, forming functionally substituted organolead compounds [625] e.g.

$$Ph_3PbLi + (CH_2)_2O \longrightarrow Ph_3Pb(CH_2)_2OH, \quad \text{m.p. } 72°$$

Transition metal derivatives

Although organolead derivatives of iron carbonyl, such as $[Et_2PbFe(CO)_4]_2$, were first described in 1941 [626], wide interest in this type of compound

[623] H. Gilman, and F. Schulze, *J. Amer. Chem. Soc.,* 1925, **47**, 2002.
[624] L. C. Willemsens and G. J. M. van der Kerk, *Rec. Trav. chim.,* 1965, **84**, 43.
[625] Idem, *J. Organometal. Chem.,* 1965, **4**, 34.
[626] F. Hein and H. Pobloth, *Z. anorg. Chem.,* 1941, **248**, 84.

has developed only recently. Many such derivatives of iron and manganese are now known [442, 627, 628], and derivatives of several other transition metals, including cobalt [628], rhenium [442], titanium, vanadium, niobium, tungsten, nickel, palladium and platinum [155] have been described.

These compounds are similar to their germanium and tin analogues. The iron and manganese derivatives are yellow-, orange- or red-coloured solids which decompose in the region 100–150°. The first examples were prepared by reactions between organolead hydroxides (or halides) and calcium iron tetracarbonyl hydride, e.g. [626, 627]

$$2Et_3PbOH + Ca[Fe(CO)_4H]_2 \rightarrow [Et_2PbFe(CO)_4]_2, \quad dec. \; 110°$$
$$4Ph_3PbBr + Ca[Fe(CO)_4H]_2 \rightarrow 2(Ph_3Pb)_2Fe(CO)_4, \quad dec. \; 135\text{–}140°$$

A more generally applicable modification of this reaction used recently is that between an organolead halide and the sodium derivative of the transition metal carbonyl in tetrahydrofuran [442]:

$$Me_3PbCl + NaMn(CO)_5 \rightarrow NaCl + Me_3PbMn(CO)_5, \quad m.p. \; 30\text{–}31°$$
$$Me_2PbCl_2 + 2NaMn(CO)_5 \rightarrow 2NaCl + Me_2Pb[Mn(CO)_5]_2, \quad m.p. \; 108\text{–}110°$$

Cyclopentadienyl carbonyls have been prepared by similar reactions [155]:

$$[C_5H_5Fe(CO)_2]_2 + 2Na \xrightarrow{Me_2PbCl_2} 2NaCl + [C_5H_5Fe(CO)_2]_2PbMe_2$$

The organolead derivatives of transition metals are fairly air-stable but readily oxidized, oxidation being accelerated by light. The stability to oxidation of the manganese derivatives decreases in the order $Sn > Pb > Si$. Thermal stability decreases as the number of metal–metal bonds in the molecule increases [442].

Organolead hydrides

Lead hydride or plumbane, PbH_4, is so unstable that its transient existence required radio-tracer technique for its detection. Some unstable alkyl derivatives have been prepared recently by the potassium borohydride [629, 630] or lithium aluminium hydride [631, 632, 633] reduction of organolead halides, or by the diborane reduction of alkoxides [634].

Trimethyl-lead hydride, Me_3PbH, m.p. $\sim -100°$, can be prepared by the action of potassium borohydride on trimethyl-lead chloride in liquid

[627] F. Hein and E. Heuser, Z. anorg. Chem. 1947, 254, 138; 255, 125.
[628] F. Hein, P. Kleinert and W. Jehn, Naturwiss., 1957, 44, 34.
[629] R. Duffy and A. K. Holliday, Proc. Chem. Soc., 1959, 124; J. Chem. Soc., 1961, 1679.
[630] R. Duffy, J. Feeney and A. K. Holliday, J. Chem. Soc., 1962, 1144.
[631] E. Amberger, Angew. Chem., 1960, 72, 494.
[632] W. E. Becker and S. E. Cook, J. Amer. Chem. Soc., 1960, 82, 6264.
[633] W. P. Neumann and K. Kühlein, Angew. Chem., Internat. Edn., 1965, 4, 784.
[634] E. Amberger and R. Hönigschmid-Grossich, Chem. Ber., 1966, 99, 1673.

ammonia [629, 630]. The product is an ammonia complex of trimethyl-lead borohydride, $Me_3PbBH_4.nNH_3$, from which, after removal of the solvent, trimethyl-lead hydride can be vacuum distilled at $-5°$ provided that it is immediately collected at $-196°$.

$$Me_3PbCl + KBH_4 \xrightarrow{NH_3} Me_3PbBH_4.nNH_3 \xrightarrow{-5°} Me_3PbH + BH_3NH_3 + (n-1)NH_3$$

The borohydride Me_3PbBH_4 is also the intermediate in the reduction of trimethyl-lead methoxide by diborane [634].

Alternatively, trimethyl-lead chloride or (better) bromide can be reduced by lithium aluminium hydride [631, 632, 633].

Trimethyl-lead hydride decomposes above $-37°$, mainly to hydrogen and hexamethyldilead [630], although tetramethyl-lead and metallic lead are formed at room temperature [631]. Hydrogen chloride gives hydrogen and Me_3PbCl quantitatively [630], while ethylene at 30 atm. pressure and $0°$ gives Me_3EtPb [632]. Ammonia gives the unstable salt $NH_4^+PbMe_3^-$, the structure of which was confirmed by the proton n.m.r. spectrum [630]. For the n.m.r. spectrum of trimethyl-lead hydride itself, see ref. [421]. In the infrared spectrum [631], the band associated with the Pb–H stretching vibration occurs at 1709 cm^{-1}.

Dimethyl-lead dihydride [631], Me_2PbH_2, dec. $>-50°$, and *triethyl-lead hydride* [630, 632], Et_3PbH, m.p. $-145°$, dec. $>-20°$, have been prepared by reduction of the appropriate halides. Like trimethyl-lead hydride, they decompose at room temperature (the dihydride possibly explosively), and explode in air.

Because of the relative weakness of the Pb–H link, organolead hydrides are more reactive than their tin analogues towards unsaturated organic compounds [633, 635], e.g.

$$Bu_3PbH + PhC:CH \rightarrow trans\text{-}PhCH:CHPbBu_3$$

Functionally substituted organolead derivatives can be prepared by such additions [633]:

$$Bu_3PbH + CH_2:CHCN \rightarrow Bu_3Pb(CH_2)_2CN$$

The reaction with ethyl iodide (giving ethane and R_3PbI) is recommended for the quantitative estimation of organolead hydrides [633].

[635] A. J. Leusink and G. J. M. van der Kerk, *Rec. Trav. chim.*, 1965, **84**, 1617.

CHAPTER FIVE

Antimony and bismuth

Both these metals form organic derivatives in which the covalency of the metal is three (e.g. R_3Sb), four (e.g. $R_4Sb^+X^-$), five (e.g. R_5Bi) and six in the particular case of antimony ($LiSbPh_6$); some of these types have been studied only comparatively recently. The higher covalencies of four and five are less stable in the case of bismuth than that of antimony, in accordance with the general inorganic chemistry of these elements.

Apart from a wide range of tri-alkyls and -aryls, R_3Sb, antimony forms organohalides in oxidation states $+5$ (R_nSbX_{5-n}, where n = 1, 2, 3 or 4) and $+3$ ($RSbX_2$ and R_2SbX), and various oxygen derivatives including the very weak stibonic $[RSbO(OH)_2]_n$ and stibinic $[R_2SbO(OH)]_n$ acids and the oxides R_3SbO, $(R_2Sb)_2O$ and $(RSbO)_n$. Bismuth forms similar halides but, among its oxygen derivatives, no analogous acids.

Antimony shows weak but definite donor character in compounds of the type R_3Sb, and this is most marked towards acceptor elements like platinum capable of forming double (d_π–d_π) bonds. Bismuth appears almost devoid of donor character, but both elements act as *acceptors* when bonded to halogens (e.g. solubility of $SbCl_3$ or $BiCl_3$ in ether).

Metal–metal bonds are weak with antimony and still weaker with bismuth, so that the known distibine derivatives, $R_2Sb \cdot SbR_2$, have as bismuth analogues only the very unstable tetramethyldibismuth and possibly a tetraphenyl derivative. The few organohydrides, RMH_2 and R_2MH, which have been prepared are thermally unstable substances, generally decomposing at or below room temperature. Few organoalkali metal derivatives of these elements are known, e.g. diphenylbismuth-sodium, Ph_2BiNa, and the antimony compounds Bu^n_2SbLi and $(Bu^n_2Sb)_2Mg$.

Many organoantimony compounds, particularly organofunctional stibines and stibonic acids, have been prepared, largely in the hope of finding pharmacologically active substances similar to those of arsenic. This objective has been realized on only a very limited scale, the products generally proving inferior to the corresponding organoarsenicals. With the development of more powerful and less dangerous antibiotics which do not have the disadvantage of the toxicity of antimony compounds, interest in organoantimony compounds has decreased. Limited non-pharmacological applications have been proposed, for example, as polymerization catalysts, as additives for the stabilization or flame-proofing of plastics, and as anti-knock fuel additives. Organobismuth compounds have found no applications which were not served better by arsenic or antimony compounds.

The organic compounds of arsenic, antimony and bismuth are the subject of a literature survey published in 1962 [1]. Organoarsenic compounds alone were reviewed in 1966 [1a].

ANTIMONY

The tri-alkyls and -aryls

Antimony-carbon bonds are readily formed by the reaction between an antimony halide and a reactive organometallic compound, such as a Grignard [2], organo-lithium [3] or -aluminium [4] reagent, e.g.

$$6MeMgI + 2SbCl_3 \rightarrow 2Me_3Sb + 3MgCl_2 + 3MgI_2$$
$$3PhLi + SbCl_3 \rightarrow Ph_3Sb + 3LiCl$$
$$3Et_3Al + SbF_3 \rightarrow Et_3Sb + 3Et_2AlF$$

Aluminium reagents can also be used to alkylate the oxide, Sb_2O_3 [5]:

$$Sb_2O_3 + 2R_3Al \rightleftharpoons (R_2Sb)_2O + 2RAlO \overset{R_3Al}{\rightleftharpoons} 2R_3Sb + 3RAlO$$

Alternatively, a bimetallic reagent such as $NaAlR_3OR'$ may be electrolysed using an antimony anode [6].

Aqueous solutions of organosilicon fluorides have been used for the preparation of both antimony and bismuth alkyls and aryls [6a]:

$$2PhSi(OEt)_3 + SbF_3 + 1OHF \overset{H_2O}{\longrightarrow} Ph_2SbF + 2H_2SiF_6 + 6EtOH$$

Organoantimony compounds also result from the Wurtz or equivalent reaction (e.g. $K_3Sb + MeI$, or $SbCl_3 + PhCl + Na$), and aromatic derivatives can be prepared by the decomposition of aryl diazonium salts [7] or diaryl iodonium salts [8] in the presence of inorganic antimony compounds.

In a process described recently [9], antimony alkoxides $Sb(OR)_3$ are

[1] M. Dub (ed.), *Organometallic Compounds; Literature Survey 1937–1959*. Vol. III. *Organic Compounds of Arsenic, Antimony and Bismuth*, Springer-Verlag, Berlin–Göttingen–Heidelberg, 1962.
[1a] W. R. Cullen, Ch. 3 of *Advances in Organometal. Chem.*, 1966, **4**.
[2] E. J. Rosenblum and C. R. Sandberg, *J. Amer. Chem. Soc.*, 1940, **62**, 1622; L. H. Long and J. F. Sackman, *Research*. 1955, **8**, 523; idem, *Trans. Faraday Soc.*, 1955, **51**, 1062.
[3] T. V. Talalaeva and K. A. Kocheshkov, *J. Gen. Chem. (U.S.S.R.)*, 1946, **16**, 777.
[4] Brit.P. 768,765; *Chem. Abs.*, 1958, **52**, 421; Belg.P. 547,962.
[5] W. Stamm and A. Breindel, *Angew. Chem., Internat. Edn.*, 1964, **3**, 66.
[6] K. Ziegler, Ger.P., 1,127,900; *Chem. Abs.*, 1962, **57**, 11235.
[6a] R. Müller and C. Dathe, *Chem. Ber.*, 1966, **99**, 1609.
[7] G. O. Doak and H. G. Steinman, *J. Amer. Chem. Soc.*, 1946, **68**, 1987, 1989.
[8] O. A. Ptitsyna, A. N. Kozlova and O. A. Reutov, *Izvest. Akad. Nauk S.S.S.R.*, 1962, 634; *Chem. Abs.*, 1962, **57**, 15148.
[9] R. S. Aries, U.S.P. 3,053,871; *Chem. Abs.*, 1963, **58**, 12602.

converted into trialkylstibines R_3Sb by the following reaction sequence (cf. boron, p. 192):

$$Sb(OR)_3 \xrightarrow[-3CO_2]{3ArNCO} Sb(NRAr)_3 \xrightarrow[10\ atm.]{3CO} R_3Sb + 3ArNCO$$

Esters, $Sb(CH_2CO_2R)_3$, result from the passage of ketene ($CH_2{:}C{:}O$) through alkoxides, $Sb(OR)_3$, in benzene [10].

The tri*aryl*stibines, Ar_3Sb, are stable to air and water, although they may readily be oxidized to compounds Ar_3SbX_2, where X is an electronegative group. However, tertiary stibines, R_3Sb, with one or more *alkyl* (or alkenyl or alkynyl) groups bonded to antimony are more reactive; for example, the trialkyls need to be handled in an inert atmosphere as they tend to ignite in air.

Trimethylstibine [2], Me_3Sb, b.p. 78·5°, is formed when antimony trichloride is allowed to react with methylmagnesium iodide. Since it is stable to water it can be separated by hydrolysis of the reaction mixture followed by ether extraction and fractional distillation of the dried ether phase. It can even be prepared by a wet method (from aqueous NH_4SiF_5Me and SbF_3 [6a]). It has been purified by conversion into the dibromide, Me_3SbBr_2, followed by reduction with zinc [11].

Trimethylstibine reacts so readily with oxygen that it sometimes takes fire in air. Slow atmospheric oxidation in ether solution gives *trimethylstibine oxide*, Me_3SbO, together with other products. It also adds sulphur, and combines very rapidly with methyl iodide giving tetramethylstibonium iodide, with halogens, and cyanogen halides, e.g.

$$Me_3Sb + CNBr \rightarrow Me_3SbBr(CN)$$

The reducing action of trimethylstibine, whereby the antimony changes into the quinquevalent state, is so marked that not only does it reduce mercury(II), silver and gold salts but even concentrated hydrochloric acid when heated in a sealed tube:

$$Me_3Sb + 2HCl \rightarrow Me_3SbCl_2 + H_2$$

The donor character of trimethylstibine (or its homologues) is weaker than that of trimethylarsine both to acceptors of the boron and aluminium type which form normal co-ordinate bonds and also to acceptors of the palladium and platinum type which form partial $(d_\pi-d_\pi)$ double bonds [12]. The complexes $(R_3Sb)_2PdCl_2$ are noteworthy in that the low solubility of the *cis* relative to that of the *trans* form allows the isolation of the *cis* isomer [13]. All previously prepared (non-chelate) palladium(II) complexes

[10] V. L. Foss, E. A. Besolova and I. F. Lutsenko, *Zhur. obshchei Khim.*, 1965, **35**, 759; *Chem. Abs.*, 1965, **63**, 4330.
[11] G. T. Morgan and V. E. Yarsley, *J. Chem. Soc.*, 1925, 184.
[12] H. P. Fritz and K. E. Schwarzhans, *J. Organometal. Chem.*, 1966, **5**, 103.
[13] J. Chatt and R. G. Wilkins, *J. Chem. Soc.*, 1953, 70.

were of the *trans* configuration. Complexes of transition metals with phosphines, arsines and stibines were reviewed in 1964 [13*a*].

The silicon analogue of trimethylstibine, *trisilylstibine* [14], $(SiH_3)_3Sb$, can be prepared by the reaction between bromosilane and a suspension of lithium antimonide in dimethyl ether at $-78°$. A colourless, spontaneously inflammable liquid, b.p. 255° (extrapolated), which decomposes slowly at room temperature to an unidentified dark solid, trisilylstibine reacts with concentrated aqueous sodium hydroxide to form antimony, sodium silicate and hydrogen.

Tristrifluoromethylstibine [15], $(CF_3)_3Sb$, b.p. 72°, is the main product from the reaction between trifluoro-iodomethane and coarsely ground antimony at 165–170° for about 7 hours and at least 50 atm. pressure. It is oxidized by air but does not react with sulphur, in contrast to trimethyl-stibine which forms Me_3SbS. Like many trifluoromethyl compounds of phosphorus and arsenic, it is quickly and quantitatively hydrolysed to fluoroform by aqueous alkali:

$$(CF_3)_3Sb + H_2O + OH^- \longrightarrow 3CHF_3 + SbO_2^-$$

Perhaps the most striking difference between $(CF_3)_3Sb$ and $(CH_3)_3Sb$ is the absence of any donor character in the former; $(CF_3)_3Sb$ reacts neither with $AlCl_3$ nor $HgCl_2$ nor $PdCl_2$, but in contrast acts as an acceptor in forming the pyridine compound $C_5H_5N \cdot Sb(CF_3)_3$, m.p. 39°.

Attempts at the preparation of trifluoromethylstibines by the action of CF_3I on SbI_3 or $PhSbI_2$ in the presence of mercury have been unsuccessful [16]. However, mixed alkyl-perfluoroalkyl derivatives of antimony are obtained by the action of perfluoroalkyl iodides on trialkylstibines [17], the reaction apparently proceeding via a mixed stibonium iodide:

$$Me_3Sb + C_2F_5I \xrightarrow{20°} [Me_3SbC_2F_5]I \rightarrow Me_2SbC_2F_5 + MeI \xrightarrow{Me_3Sb} Me_4SbI$$

Trimethylstibine reacts similarly with CF_3I, but with tri*chloro*-iodome-thane, CCl_3I, at $-46°$ it gives an adduct, $Me_3Sb \cdot CCl_3I$, m.p. 5°, dec. 82°, of unknown structure but which is believed to contain an iodine–antimony bond [18].

Triethylstibine, Et_3Sb, b.p. 159°, can be prepared by the Grignard

13*a*] G. Booth, *Advances in Inorganic Chemistry and Radiochemistry*, ed. H. J. Eméleus and A. G. Sharpe, 1964, **6**, 1.

[14] E. Amberger and H. Boeters, *Z. Naturforsch.*, 1963, **18b**, 157; *Chem. Ber.*, 1964, **79**, 1999.

[15] J. W. Dale, H. J. Eméleus, R. N. Haszeldine and J. H. Moss, *J. Chem. Soc.*, 1957, 3708; H. J. Eméleus and J. H. Moss, *Z. anorg. Chem.*, 1955, **282**, 24.

[16] M. M. Baig and W. R. Cullen, *Canad. J. Chem.*, 1962, **40**, 161.

[17] R. N. Haszeldine and B. O. West, *J. Chem. Soc.*, 1956, 3631; B. J. Pullman and B. O. West, *Austral. J. Chem.*, 1964, **17**, 30.

[18] B. J. Pullman and B. O. West, *J. Inorg. Nucl. Chem.*, 1961, **19**, 262.

method [19], or by the action of triethylaluminium on a suspension of finely powdered antimony(III) oxide in hexane at 60°, the product being distilled at reduced pressure after removal of the solvent [5]:

$$Sb_2O_3 + 3Et_3Al \longrightarrow 2Et_3Sb + 3EtAlO$$

Among other preparative methods which have been described recently, the action of lithium tetra-ethylaluminate, $LiAlEt_4$, on antimony(III) fluoride [20], or of the sodium salt, $NaAlEt_4$, on antimony(III) halides, alkoxides or aryloxides [21] are reported to give good yields of triethylstibine. The electrolysis of $NaAlEt_3OEt$ using an antimony anode gives Et_3Sb in 96% yield [6], but when aqueous sodium tetra-ethylborate, $NaBEt_4$, is used as the electrolyte the anode becomes passive, and little triethylstibine is obtained [22].

Triethylstibine may also be prepared from triethoxystibine by way of the trisaminostibine, $Sb(NEtAr)_3$, which results from the reaction with an arylisocyanate [9]:

$$Sb(OEt)_3 + 3ArNCO \xrightarrow[\quad]{-3CO_2} Sb(NEtAr)_3 \xrightarrow[10\ atm.]{3CO} Et_3Sb + 3ArNCO$$

Like trimethylstibine, triethylstibine forms many adducts with compounds of transition metals, particularly platinum and palladium [13, 23], but also others. For example, it displaces amine ligands from their adducts with phenylethynylgold to form the complex $PhC\vdots CAu.SbEt_3$ [24], m.p. 96-97°.

Antimony–metal derivatives of a different type are formed by reactions between triethylstibine and hydrides of Group IV metals [24a]:

$$Et_3Sb + 3Et_3MH \longrightarrow (Et_3M)_3Sb + 3EtH, \quad M = Si, Ge \text{ or } Sn$$

The products react with cleavage of the Sb–M bond when treated with e.g. oxygen, benzoyl peroxide or bromoalkanes.

Tri-n-propylstibine, $(n\text{-}C_3H_7)_3Sb$, b.p. 100°/25 mm., and higher homologues can be prepared by the use of either Grignard [19, 25] or organoaluminium [5] reagents. Care should be taken to exclude oxygen, particularly during the separation and purification stages. Their reactions are

[19] W. J. C. Dyke, W. C. Davies and W. J. Jones, *J. Chem. Soc.*, 1930, 463.

[20] R. S. Dickson and B. O. West, *Austral. J. Chem.*, 1962, **15**, 710.

[21] H. Jenkner (Kali-Chemie A.-G.), Brit.P. 900,132; *Chem. Abs.*, 1962, **57**, 15151.

[22] K. Ziegler and O. W. Steudel, *Annalen*, 1962, **652**, 1.

[23] J. Chatt and R. G. Wilkins, *J. Chem. Soc.*, 1952, 4300; 1956, 525; J. Chatt and L. M. Vananzi, ibid., 1955, 2787, 3858; 1957, 2351; J. Chatt, N. P. Johnson and B. L. Shaw, ibid., 1964, 1625; J. Chatt and B. L. Shaw, *J. Chem. Soc. (A)*, 1966, 1811.

[24] G. E. Coates and C. Parkin, ibid., 1962, 3220.

[24a] N. S. Vyazankin, G. A. Razuvaev, O. A. Kruglaya and G. S. Semchikova, *J. Organometal. Chem.*, 1966, **6**, 474.

[25] J. Seifter, *J. Amer. Chem. Soc.*, 1939, **61**, 530; L. I. Zakharkin, O. Yu. Okhlobystin and B. N. Strunin, *Izvest. Akad. Nauk S.S.S.R.*, 1961, 2254; 1962, 2002; *Chem. Abs.*, 1962, **57**, 13799; 1963, **58**, 9131.

similar to those of trimethylstibine, e.g. complexes with transition metals such as $IrCl_3(CO)(SbPr^n_3)_2$ can be prepared [23].

Triphenylstibine, Ph_3Sb, m.p. 48–50°, has been prepared in various ways, of which the Grignard method [26] or the use of an aryl-lithium reagent [3] are the most convenient. It is also formed in good yield from antimony trichloride, chlorobenzene (or bromobenzene) and sodium, with benzene as diluent [27]. Other methods involve the reaction between antimony and tetraphenyltin [28] or between antimony, lithium tetraphenylaluminate and iodobenzene [29], the reduction of the dihalides, Ph_3SbX_2, and the thermal disproportionation (180–200°) [30]:

$$3PhSbO \longrightarrow Ph_3Sb + Sb_2O_3$$

Triphenylstibine crystallizes with a molecular lattice of pyramidal molecules [31], and this structure persists in solution (dipole moment, 0·77 D [32]). Stable to air and water, it is generally much less reactive than the alkylstibines. However, it is readily oxidized to compounds of the type Ph_3SbX_2 (X = an electronegative group), and reacts easily with halogens. The conductances of acetonitrile solutions of triphenylstibine–halogen mixtures indicate the presence of such species as $Ph_3SbX^+X^-$, $Ph_3SbX^+X_3^-$ and $Ph_3SbX^+XY_2^-$ [33]. Nitration with a mixture of concentrated nitric and sulphuric acids results both in oxidation and nuclear nitration, with formation of $(m-NO_2C_6H_4)_3Sb(NO_3)_2$ which affords tri-*m*-nitrophenylstibine on gentle reduction and tri-*m*-aminophenylstibine on strong reduction. Other derivatives of triphenylstibine, $(XC_6H_4)_3Sb$, have been prepared directly from the appropriate Grignard reagents [26].

Triphenylstibine does not form quaternary salts by direct addition of methyl iodide, but *tetraphenylstibonium* salts are obtained by the prolonged action of arylmagnesium halides on triphenylstibine dichloride [34].

Heating with arsenic causes a migration of phenyl groups:

$$Ph_3Sb + As \longrightarrow Ph_3As + Sb$$

Similar reactions occur between triphenylarsine and phosphorus and between triphenylbismuth and antimony [35]. Catalytic hydrogenation of Ph_3Sb with Raney Nickel gives benzene and (presumably) antimony [36].

[26] J. I. Harris, S. T. Bowden and W. J. Jones, *J. Chem. Soc.*, 1947, 1568.
[27] S. P. Olifirenko, *Chem. Abs.*, 1965, **63**, 8401.
[28] H. Schumann, H. Köpf and M. Schmidt, *Z. anorg. Chem.*, 1964, **331**, 200.
[29] G. C. Robinson (Ethyl Corp.), U.S.P. 3,057,894; *Chem. Abs.* 1963, **58**, 6858.
[30] H. Schmidt, *Annalen*, 1920, **421**, 217, 242.
[31] J. Wetzel, *Z. Krist.*, 1942, **104**, 305; *Chem. Abs.*, 1943, **37**, 5298; V. I. Iveronova and F. M. Roitburd, *Zhur. Fiz. Khim.*, 1952, **26**, 810; *Chem. Abs.*, 1952, **46**, 10767.
[32] M. J. Aroney, R. J. W. Le Fèvre, and J. D. Saxby, *J. Chem. Soc.*, 1963, 1739.
[33] A. D. Beveridge, G. S. Harris and F. Inglis, *J. Chem. Soc. (A)*, 1966, 520.
[34] H. H. Willard, L. R. Perkins and F. F. Blicke, *J. Amer. Chem. Soc.*, 1948, **70**, 737.
[35] W. J. Considine and J. J. Ventura, *J. Organometal. Chem.*, 1965, **3**, 420.
[36] G. D. F. Jackson and W. H. F. Sasse, *J. Chem. Soc.*, 1962, 3746.

Acylimino derivatives, $Ph_3SbNCOCH_2X$, can be prepared from triphenylstibine by the reaction with the sodium salts of the N-bromoamides of halogeno-acetic acids [37]:

$$Ph_3Sb + ClCH_2CONBrNa \xrightarrow[HCl]{acetone} NaBr + Ph_3SbNCOCH_2Cl, \quad m.p. \ 174-176°$$

The products form 1 : 1 adducts with mercury(II) or copper(II) chlorides.

The related *tosylimino* derivative, $Ph_3SbNSO_2C_6H_4Me$, m.p. 150–154°, is obtained from Ph_3Sb and Chloramine-T, $MeC_6H_4SO_2NClNa$, in acetonitrile [38]. It reacts with phenyl-lithium to form pentaphenylantimony, Ph_5Sb, m.p. 167–169° (see below).

Like the alkylstibines, triphenylstibine forms transition metal derivatives [39]. Various substituted carbonyls have been prepared particularly of iron, e.g. the yellow-brown solids, $Ph_3Sb\cdot Fe(CO)_4$, m.p. 136°, and $(Ph_3Sb)_2Fe(CO)_3$, m.p. 196° (decomp.), are obtained by the action of Ph_3Sb on $Fe_3(CO)_{12}$ in boiling tetrahydrofuran or dioxan [40]. Neither triphenylstibine nor triethylstibine, however, form decaborane derivatives $B_{10}H_{12}.2SbR_3$ analogous to the known organo-phosphine and -arsine compounds [41]. Triphenylstibine, like Ph_3P and Ph_3As but not Ph_3N and Ph_3Bi, also forms a 1 : 1 complex with hexamethylbenzene [42].

Phenyldimethylstibine, $PhSbMe_2$, b.p. 112°/17 mm., is obtained from phenylstibine oxide by conversion into iodide and treatment with methylmagnesium iodide [43]:

$$PhSbO \xrightarrow{HI} PhSbI_2 \xrightarrow{MeMgI} PhSbMe_2$$

It is readily oxidized and adds methyl iodide, giving phenyltrimethylstibonium iodide, $[PhSbMe_3]I$.

Mixed alkyldiarylstibines disproportionate rather easily.

Trispentafluorophenylstibine, $(C_6F_5)_3Sb$, m.p. 74°, has been prepared from antimony trichloride and pentafluorophenylmagnesium bromide in ether [44].

[37] L. P. Petrenko, *Trudy Voronezh. Gosudarst. Univ.*, 1958, **49**, 19, 25; *Chem. Abs.*, 1962, **56**, 2470, 2471.

[38] G. Wittig and D. Hellwinkel, *Chem. Ber.*, 1964, **97**, 789.

[39] W. D. Bannister, M. Green and R. N. Haszeldine. *Chem. Comm.*, 1965, 54; T. A. Stephenson and G. Wilkinson, *J. Inorg. Nucl. Chem.*, 1966, **28**, 945.

[40] A. F. Clifford and A. K. Mukherjee, *Inorg. Chem.*, 1963, **2**, 151.

[41] L. I. Zakharkin and V. I. Stanko, *Izvest. Akad. Nauk S.S.S.R.*, 1961, 2078; *Chem. Abs.*, 1962, **57**, 8609.

[42] R. A. Shaw, B. C. Smith and C. P. Thakur, *Chem. Comm.*, 1966, 228.

[43] C. K. Ingold, F. R. Shaw and I. S. Wilson, *J. Chem. Soc.*, 1928, 1280.

[44] O. Glemser, M. Fild and G. Christoph, *Angew. Chem., Internat. Edn.*, 1964, **3**, 801.

Alkenyl and alkynyl derivatives

Trivinylstibine [45, 46], $(CH_2:CH)_3Sb$, b.p. 149·9°, from vinylmagnesium bromide and antimony trichloride in tetrahydrofuran, is spontaneously inflammable, and adds methyl iodide to form the stibonium salt:

$$(CH_2:CH)_3Sb + MeI \longrightarrow [(CH_2:CH)_3SbMe]I$$

It does not add ethyl iodide. With potassium chloroplatinate(II) a yellow complex is obtained, $[(CH_2:CH)_3Sb]_2PtCl_2$, m.p. 113–114°, of presumed *cis* structure. Trivinylstibine reacts exothermically with antimony trichloride, and divinylchlorostibine $(CH_2:CH)_2SbCl$, b.p. 60°/4·5 mm., has been isolated from the reaction product. Thallium(III) chloride converts trivinylstibine into the dichloride [46]:

$$(CH_2:CH)_3Sb + TlCl_3 \longrightarrow (CH_2:CH)_3SbCl_2 + TlCl$$

The dihalides can also be prepared by direct reaction with the appropriate halogen in chloroform solution at 0°, thus affording a route to *penta-vinylantimony*, $(CH_2:CH)_5Sb$, a green oil [46]:

$$(CH_2:CH)_3Sb \xrightarrow[\text{CHCl}_3]{\text{Br}_2 \text{ in}} (CH_2:CH)_3SbBr_2 \xrightarrow{2CH_2:CHMgBr} (CH_2:CH)_5Sb$$

$$\text{Br}_2 \text{ in} \searrow \text{CHCl}_3 \quad\quad \downarrow 110°$$
$$-5°$$

$$(CH_2:CH)_4Sb^+Br^- \text{ m.p. } 53\text{--}54° \quad\quad (CH_2:CH)_3Sb$$

Tripropenylstibine, $(MeCH:CH)_3Sb$, has been prepared in two forms, thought to be *cis* and *trans* isomers, from the appropriate lithium reagents, *cis*- and *trans*-MeCH:CHLi, and antimony trichloride [47]. These react themselves with halogens to form the dihalides, $(MeCH:CH)_3SbX_2$, which themselves with propenyl-lithium give *cis*- and *trans-pentapropenylantimony*, $(MeCH:CH)_5Sb$; bromine then gives the stibonium bromides, *cis*-$(MeCH:CH)_4Sb^+Br^-$, m.p. 140–143°, and *trans*-$(MeCH:CH)_4Sb^+Br^-$, m.p. 45–48°. Similar *isopropenylstibines* such as $(CH_2:CMe)_3Sb$, b.p. 40°/1 mm., and $(CH_2:CMe)_5Sb$, m.p. 60°, are known [46]. The isomeric *triallylstibine*, $(CH_2:CHCH_2)_3Sb$, b.p. 71°/2 mm., prepared by the Grignard method, ignites in air, forms dihalides, and with allylmagnesium chloride gives tetra-allystibonium chloride, $(CH_2:CHCH_2)_4Sb^+Cl^-$. Attempts to prepare penta-allylantimony were unsuccessful [48].

[45] L. Maier, D. Seyferth, F. G. A. Stone and E. G. Rochow, *J. Amer. Chem. Soc.*, 1957, **79**, 5884.

[46] A. N. Nesmeyanov. A. E. Borisov and N. V. Novikova, *Izvest. Akad. Nauk S.S.S.R.*, 1960, 147; 1961, 1578; *Chem. Abs.*, 1960, **54**, 20853; 1962, **56**, 4792.

[47] Idem, *Tetrahedron Letters*, 1960, **8**, 23; *Izvest. Akad. Nauk. S.S.S.R.*, 1964, 1197, 1202; *Chem. Abs.*, 1964, **61**, 12032.

[48] A. E. Borisov, N. V. Novikova and A. N. Nesmeyanov, *Izvest. Akad. Nauk S.S.S.R.*, 1963, 1506; *Chem. Abs.*, 1963, **59**, 14021.

β-Chlorovinyl derivatives of antimony have been known for some years, having been prepared from acetylene and an alkaline solution of antimony pentachloride in the presence of mercuric chloride [48a]:

$$SbCl_5 \xrightarrow{\text{HC⋮CH; HgCl}_2} (trans\text{-}ClCH:CH)_3SbCl_2, \qquad \text{m.p. } 93°$$
$$+ \text{ some } (cis\text{-}ClCH:CH)_3SbCl_2, \quad \text{m.p. } 61°$$

$$\downarrow NaHSO_3$$

$$(ClCH:CH)_3Sb$$

Tricyclopentadienylstibine [49], $(C_5H_5)_3Sb$, is obtained as a deep red solid by the action of cyclopentadienyl-sodium on antimony trichloride in tetrahydrofuran at 0°. It is very sensitive to air and above 10° disproportionates into the distibine derivative $(C_5H_5)_2Sb·Sb(C_5H_5)_2$ and bicyclopentadienyl.

A novel 'unsaturated organo' derivative of antimony described recently is *tricarboranylstibine*, $(B_{10}C_2H_{11})_3Sb$, m.p. 313–316° (decomp.), from $B_{10}C_2H_{11}Li$ and $SbCl_3$ [50]. The bulk of the carboranyl group (see p. 238) is such that only the larger atoms appear capable of accommodating three or more of them, and attempts to prepare $(B_{10}C_2H_{11})_4Sn$ and $(B_{10}C_2H_{11})_3P$, for example, were unsuccessful.

Unsaturated heterocyclic organoantimony compounds are known. *Dibenzostibioles* [51] (5.1) may be prepared from aryldihalostibines and the 2,2'-dilithium derivative of biphenyl, or by cyclization of aryl-2-biphenylylstibinic acids in acetic anhydride containing sulphuric acid, followed by reduction with tin(II) chloride.

5.1

Pentaphenylstibiole (5.2) is obtained in the form of yellow-green crystals, m.p. 162–170°, by the reaction between phenyldichlorostibine and the

[48a] A. N. Nesmeyanov, A. Kochetkov and R. K. Freidlina, *Izvest. Akad. Nauk, S.S.S.R.*, 1947, 657; *Chem. Abs.*, 1948, **42**, 5847.

[49] E. O. Fischer and S. Schreiner, *Angew. Chem.*. 1957, **69**, 205; *Chem. Ber.*, 1960, **93**, 1417; E. O. Fischer, G. Joos and W. Meer, *Z. Naturforsch.*, 1958, **13b**, 456.

[50] L. I. Zakharkin, V. I. Bregadze and O. Yu. Okhlobystin, *J. Organometal. Chem.*, 1965, **4**, 211.

[51] F. G. Mann, *The Heterocyclic Derivatives of Phosphorus, Arsenic, Antimony, Bismuth and Silicon*, Interscience, N.Y., 1950.

1,4-dilithium derivative of tetraphenylbutadiene [52]:

$$PhSbCl_2 + PhLiC{:}CPh{\cdot}CPh{:}CLiPh \longrightarrow$$

5.2

In air it is oxidized to the *oxide*, m.p. 250–255° (decomp.).

Several rather unstable and reactive *acetylenic* stibines have been prepared. For example sodium acetylide with dimethylbromostibine in ammonia yields $Me_2SbC{:}CSbMe_2$, b.p. 116°/17 mm., and in tetrahydrofuran $Me_2SbC{:}CH$, b.p. 86–88°/388 mm., is formed [53]. *Triphenylethynylstibine* [54], $(PhC{:}C)_3Sb$, m.p. 159° (decomp.), differs from most stibines in being hydrolysed by dilute alkali (to phenylacetylene). *Triethynylstibine* itself, $(HC{:}C)_3Sb$, can be prepared from antimony trichloride and ethynylmagnesium bromide in tetrahydrofuran. It is a volatile solid, m.p. 71–72°, v.p. 13 mm./60°, which is liable to detonate under friction [55]. In its infrared spectrum (vapour phase), band attributable to $\nu(C{:}C)$ and $\nu(Sb-C)$ occur at 2033 and 477 cm^{-1} respectively [55a].

Penta-alkyls and -aryls

Pentamethylantimony [56], Me_5Sb, m.p. $-19°$, b.p. 126–127°, from methyllithium and trimethylstibine dibromide or tetramethylstibonium bromide, is surprisingly stable in view of the failure to obtain arsenic or bismuth analogues. In contrast to trimethylstibine it does not inflame in the air, though it oxidizes quickly and is decomposed by water. Its reaction with triphenylborane resembles that of pentaphenylantimony (see below):

$$Me_5Sb + Ph_3B \longrightarrow [Me_4Sb^+][MeBPh_3{}^-]$$

It also resembles pentaphenylantimony in forming $Li^+SbMe_6{}^-$ with an excess of methyl-lithium, but the hexamethyl salt was not stable enough to allow its isolation. The infrared and Raman spectra of Me_5Sb support a trigonal bipyramidal structure [57].

[52] F. C. Leavitt, T. A. Manuel and F. Johnson, *J. Amer. Chem. Soc.*, 1959, **81**, 3163; F. C. Leavitt, T. A. Manuel, F. Johnson, L. U. Matternas and D. S. Lehman, ibid., 1960, **82**, 5099; E. H. Braye, W. Hübel and I. Caplier, ibid., 1961, **83**, 4406.

[53] H. Hartmann and G. Kühl, *Angew. Chem.*, 1956, **68**, 619; *Z. anorg. Chem.*, 1961, **312**, 186; see also A. N. Nesmeyanov, A. E. Borisov and N. V. Novikova, *Doklady Akad. Nauk S.S.S.R.*, 1965, 763; *Chem. Abs.*, 1965, **63**, 2998.

[54] H. Hartmann, W. Reiss and B. Karbstein, *Naturwiss.*, 1959, **46**, 321.

[55] W. Voskuil and J. F. Arens, *Rec. Trav. chim.*, 1964, **83**, 1301.

[55a] F. A. Miller and D. H. Lemmon, *Spectrochim. Acta*, 1967, **23A**, 1099.

[56] G. Wittig and K. Torssell, *Acta Chem. Scand.*, 1953, **7**, 1293.

[57] A. J. Downs, R. Schmutzler and I. A. Steer, *Chem. Comm.*, 1966, 221.

Penta-ethylantimony [57*a*], Et_5Sb, has been prepared by methods similar to those used for Me_5Sb, for example by reactions between ethylantimony(V) chlorides and diethylmagnesium or ethyl-lithium. With methanol it gives the methoxide Et_4SbOMe, and with ethylaluminium chlorides Et_nAlCl_{3-n} it gives tetra-ethylstibonium salts $Et_4Sb^+AlEt_nCl_{4-n}^-$ or $Et_4Sb^+Al_2Et_nCl_{7-n}^-$, materials which are also produced in the alkylation of antimony trichloride by triethylaluminium or diethylaluminium chloride [57*b*].

Pentaphenylantimony [58], Ph_5Sb, m.p. $168\cdot5$–$170°$, can be prepared by the tosylimine method described above [38], or by a method similar to that used for the pentamethyl derivative. Triphenylstibine dichloride reacts with three mols. of phenyl-lithium to give a crystalline precipitate of *lithium hexaphenylantimonate*:

$$Ph_3SbCl_2 + 3PhLi \longrightarrow 2LiCl + LiSbPh_6$$

The product is hydrolysed by water:

$$LiSbPh_6 + H_2O \longrightarrow LiOH + C_6H_6 + Ph_5Sb$$

The hexaphenyl compound is also formed by addition of phenyl-lithium to pentaphenylantimony. In contrast, the action of phenylmagnesium bromide on triphenylstibine dichloride is slow and goes only as far as tetraphenylstibonium chloride. Pentaphenylantimony crystallizes from cyclohexane with 0·5 mol. cyclohexane of crystallization which is tenaciously retained in vacuum, but it can be obtained solvent-free from methyl cyanide; it is insoluble in water. In benzene, the dipole moment is 1·59 D. An X-ray diffraction study of the crystal structure [59] has shown a *square pyramidal* arrangement of phenyl groups about the antimony as indicated in 5.3. The structure of pentaphenylphosphorus by contrast, has the expected *trigonal bipyramidal* arrangement of phenyl groups about phosphorus, and the isomorphous pentaphenylarsenic is presumed to be similar [60]. The structure of the unstable bismuth analogue is not known.

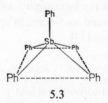

5.3

[57*a*] Y. Takashi, *J. Organometal. Chem.*, 1967, **8**, 225.
[57*b*] Y. Takashi and I. Aishima, ibid., p. 209.
[58] G. Wittig and K. Clauss, *Annalen*, 1952, **577**, 26.
[59] P. J. Wheatley and G. Wittig, *Proc. Chem. Soc.*, 1962, 251; P. J. Wheatley, *J. Chem. Soc.*, 1964, 3718.
[60] P. J. Wheatley, ibid., p. 2206.

Ph$_5$Sb is in fact apparently the only known '10-electron' molecule of a main group element to have a square pyramidal structure, and this may well be a consequence of crystal packing considerations for this particular compound rather than an alteration in the relative stabilities of the two possible five-co-ordinate frameworks [57]. Proton magnetic resonance spectroscopic studies on carbon disulphide solutions of the p-tolyl compounds (p-MeC$_6$H$_4$)$_5$M (M = P, As or Sb), prepared by the tosylimine method, showed that all the methyl groups were equivalent. This was taken to indicate rapid rearrangement from one trigonal bipyramidal (or square-based pyramidal) form to another [60a]. As axial-equatorial position changes of substituents in trigonal bipyramidal structures are generally believed to occur via square-based pyramidal intermediates, ready exchange can be taken as evidence of little energy difference between the two structures.

Addition of bromine or iodine to pentaphenylantimony takes place in two stages, e.g.

$$Ph_5Sb + I_2 \longrightarrow [Ph_4Sb]I + PhI$$
$$[Ph_4Sb]I + I_2 \longrightarrow [Ph_4Sb]I_3$$

Tetraphenylstibonium tri-iodide must be one of the most stable tri-iodides, since it is only slightly decomposed at its melting point, 175–176°. The action of chlorine differs and leads mainly to triphenylstibine dichloride and chlorobenzene. Reaction with triphenylboron is rapid,

$$Ph_5Sb + Ph_3B \longrightarrow [Ph_4Sb^+][BPh_4^-]$$

and the product can be crystallized from nitromethane. The thermal decomposition of pentaphenylantimony (about 200°) is nearly quantitative, and gives triphenylstibine and biphenyl. This contrasts with the decomposition of pentaphenylphosphorus, which loses phenyl radicals (which end up as benzene), leaving a tarry residue. Pentaphenylarsenic is intermediate in this respect.

Penta*vinyl*antimony and penta*propenyl*antimony were described in the previous section (p. 517). For other aryl derivatives (e.g. 2,2'-biphenylyl) of Sb(V), see ref. [38].

Halides

There are six classes of halides; four of antimony(V) (R$_4$SbX, R$_3$SbX$_2$, R$_2$SbX$_3$ and RSbX$_4$) and two of antimony(III) (R$_2$SbX and RSbX$_2$).

Derivatives of antimony(V)

STIBONIUM SALTS, R$_4$SbX. Trimethylstibine combines with methyl iodide in the cold, forming *tetramethylstibonium iodide*, Me$_4$SbI. The rate

[60a] H. Hellwinkel, *Angew. Chem., Internat. Edn.*, 1966, **5**, 725; see also E. L. Muetterties and R. A. Schunn, *Quart. Rev.*, 1966, **20**, 245.

of addition is faster in the case of trimethylarsine, and still faster with-trimethylphosphine. Trimethylbismuth does not add methyl iodide.

Quaternary stibonium iodides are readily formed only when methyl iodide is added to tertiary stibines containing not more than one aryl group. Ethyl and n-propyl iodide react only with difficulty (heating in a sealed tube). Phenyldimethylstibine reacts easily with methyl iodide, but no reaction takes place between methyl iodide and methyldiphenylstibine, Ph_2SbMe. When *perfluoroalkyl* iodides, R^fI, react with trialkylstibines, R_3Sb, mixed alkylperfluoroalkylstibines, R_2SbR^f, and tetra-alkylstibonium iodides, R_4SbI, result, indicating that the alkyl-perfluoroalkylstibonium, iodide R_3SbR^fI, considered to be the intermediate is unstable with respect to R_2SbR^f and RI [17].

Other routes to stibonium halides are illustrated by the formation of tetra-allylstibonium chloride, $(CH_2{:}CH.CH_2)_4Sb^+Cl^-$, by the action of the allyl Grignard reagent on triallylstibine [48], and by the formation of tetravinyl- or tetrapropenyl-stibonium halides from the penta-alkenyl-stibine and chlorine, bromine or iodine in chloroform at $-5°$ [46, 47]:

$$(CH_2{:}CMe)_3Sb \xrightarrow[\text{2. 2CH}_2\text{:CMeLi}]{\text{1. Br}_2 \text{ in CHCl}_3} (CH_2{:}CMe)_5Sb \xrightarrow{\text{I}_2 \text{ in CHCl}_3} (CH_2{:}CMe)_4SbI$$
$$\text{m.p. 163–164°}$$

The stibonium salts have properties entirely consistent with their ionic constitution, and are soluble in water but not in non-polar solvents. The stibonium hydroxides are strong alkalis like the quaternary ammonium hydroxides. The tetrahedral structure of the tetramethylstibonium cation is apparent in such compounds as $Me_4Sb^+M(OSiMe_3)_4{}^-$ (M = Al, Ga or Fe) which have been the subject of X-ray crystallographic studies [61].

Tetraphenylstibonium halides have been prepared by two quite different methods. The reaction between triphenylstibine dichloride and phenyl-magnesium bromide has been mentioned already; the other method [62] involves heating triphenylstibine with aluminium chloride and bromo-benzene at 230°. The mechanism of this reaction is not clear (this being true of many reactions catalysed by aluminium chloride). Tetraphenylsti-bonium salts also result from the action of iodine, bromine, hydrogen bro-mide or triphenylborane on pentaphenylantimony. The chloride has been used as an analytical reagent [63].

THE DIHALIDES, R_3SbX_2. These are stable and very easily formed, either by direct addition of halogen to a tertiary stibine, even a triaryl,

$$Ph_3Sb + Cl_2 \longrightarrow Ph_3SbCl_2$$

[61] H. Schmidbaur, *Angew. Chem.*, 1963, **75**, 137; P. J. Wheatley, *J. Chem. Soc.*, 1963, 3200.

[62] J. Chatt and F. G. Mann, ibid., 1940, 1192.

[63] H. H. Willard and L. R. Perkins, *Anal. Chem.*, 1953, **25**, 1634.

or by the action of a Grignard reagent on an antimony pentahalide,

$$SbCl_5 + 3PhMgBr \rightarrow Ph_3SbCl_2 + 3MgClBr$$

Because of the formation of stibonium salts, excess of Grignard reagents should be avoided in the latter method.

The dihalides are covalently constituted, with trigonal bipyramidal structures in which the organic groups occupy equatorial positions. They are monomeric when dissolved in non-polar solvents, and cryoscopic and conductivity data [64] show that they are *not* electrolytically dissociated in polar solvents, in contrast to the behaviour of the simple antimony halides or alkoxy-halides, although in aqueous solutions some replacement of halogen by hydroxide may occur.

Trimethylstibine dichloride, Me_3SbCl_2, from trimethylstibine and chlorine (suitably diluted), or the oxide Me_3SbO and hydrochloric acid, forms colourless crystals moderately soluble in hot water. It also results from the rather unusual reaction:

$$2Me_2Hg + SbCl_3 \rightarrow Me_3SbCl_2 + MeHgCl + Hg$$

The dichloride, dibromide and di-iodide are isomorphous, and have the trigonal bipyramid structure [65], the halogens being axial and the methyls equatorial. Numerous other derivatives, Me_3SbX_2, can be prepared, where X is an electronegative group like NO_3, CNS, $\frac{1}{2}SO_4$. Studies of their infrared spectra have confirmed the planarity of the Me_3Sb group in these compounds, and show that the halogen or other radical X is *covalently* bound to the antimony; free anions X^- are *not* present in the anhydrous compounds [66].

Ionization may of course occur in solution, but even in aqueous solutions, the planar arrangement of methyl groups about antimony persists. The presence of just three polarized lines attributable to the cation in the Raman spectra of aqueous solutions of $Me_3Sb(NO_3)_2$ or $Me_3Sb(ClO_4)_2$ is indicative of the retention of five-co-ordination by the antimony, i.e. the cation is $[Me_3Sb(OH_2)_2]^{2+}$ or $[Me_3Sb(OH)(OH_2)]^+$, *not* $[Me_3SbOH]^+$ or $[Me_3SbOSbMe_3]^{2+}$ [66a]. The symmetrical stretching frequency ν_{sym}Sb–C for aqueous Me_3Sb^{2+} is 537 cm^{-1}, corresponding to a force constant of 2.55×10^5 dynes/cm. (cf. force constants of 2·39 and 1·93 dynes/cm. for the M–C bonds of the isoelectronic species Me_3Sn^+ and Me_3In respectively).

In chloroform solution, halides Me_3SbX_2 retain their covalent struc-

[64] L. Kolditz, M. Gitter and E. Rösel, *Z. anorg. Chem.*, 1962, **316**, 270.

[65] A. F. Wells, *Z. Krist.*, 1938, **99**, 367.

[66] G. G. Long, G. O. Doak and L. D. Freedman, *J. Amer. Chem. Soc.*, 1964, **86**, 209; M. Shindo and R. Okawara, *J. Organometal. Chem.*, 1966, **5**, 537; H. C. Clark and R. G. Goel, *Inorg. Chem.*, 1966, **5**, 998.

[66a] A. J. Downs and I. A. Steer, *J. Organometal. Chem.*, 1967, **8**, P21.

tures, although exchange of halogens between different halides Me_3SbX_2 and Me_3SbY_2 occurs readily, so that the proton magnetic resonance spectra of solutions of mixtures $Me_3SbX_2 + Me_3SbY_2$ at $-32°$ consist of three peaks, the extra one arising from the mixed halide Me_3SbXY [66b].

For the tri-vinyl-, -propenyl- and -allyl-dihalides see refs. [46, 47 and 48]. The crystal structure of *all trans-tris-2-chlorovinylstibine dichloride*, $(ClCH:CH)_3SbCl_2$, is similar to that of Me_3SbX_2 [68].

Dihydroxides, $R_3Sb(OH)_2$, can be prepared from the dihalides by passing their hot aqueous solutions through an ion-exchange column. Covalent oxide products of partial hydrolysis, $(R_3SbX)_2O$, result from the reaction between equimolar proportions of dihydroxide and dihalide, e.g. [66, 67]

$$Me_3SbCl_2 + Me_3Sb(OH)_2 \rightarrow H_2O + (Me_3SbCl)_2O$$

When heated together at $40–60°$, trimethylstibine and trimethylstibine dichloride rapidly exchange antimony by a process in which the Me_3Sb groups remain intact, as shown by experiments using isotopically labelled antimony and deuterated methyl groups [69]. This presumably indicates slight dissociation, $Me_3SbCl_2 \rightleftharpoons Me_3Sb + Cl_2$. At higher temperatures, trialkylstibine dihalides decompose with loss of alkyl halide to form dialkylhalogenostibines [53, 70], e.g.

$$Me_3SbBr_2 \xrightarrow{180°} MeBr + Me_2SbBr, \quad b.p. \ 107°/90 \ mm.$$

Tristrifluoromethylstibine [15] adds chlorine and bromine at low temperatures, but the products $(CF_3)_3SbCl_2$ and $(CF_3)_3SbBr_2$ are much less stable than the corresponding methyl compounds, the dibromide decomposing slowly at room temperature:

$$(CF_3)_3SbBr_2 \rightarrow (CF_3)_2SbBr + CF_3Br$$

The dichloride is hydrolysed by sodium hydroxide:

$$(CF_3)_3SbCl_2 + 3NaOH \rightarrow Na[(CF_3)_3Sb(OH)_3] + 2NaCl$$

The anion $(CF_3)_3Sb(OH)_3^-$ is much more resistant to hydrolysis than ions derived from trifluoromethyl oxyacids of phosphorus and arsenic or the other trifluoromethyl derivatives of antimony. Strong alkali at $70°$ is needed to effect hydrolysis of $(CF_3)_3Sb(OH)_3^-$ to CF_3H and $Sb(OH)_6^-$.

Triphenylstibine dichloride, Ph_3SbCl_2, m.p. $143°$, is very easily made by direct chlorination of triphenylstibine. This and other similar triarylstibine

[66b] G. G. Long, C. G. Moreland, G. O. Doak and M. Miller, *Inorg. Chem.*, 1966, **5**, 1358.

[67] G. O. Doak, G. G. Long and L. D. Freedman, *J. Organometal. Chem.*, 1965, **4**, 82.

[68] Y. T. Struchkov and T. L. Khotsyanova, *Doklady Akad. Nauk S.S.S.R.*, 1953, **91**, 565.

[69] V. D. Nefedov, I. S. Kirin, V. M. Zaitsev, G. A. Semenov and B. E. Dzevitskii, *Zhur. obshchei Khim.*, 1963, **33**, 2407; *Chem. Abs.*, 1963, **59**, 13786.

[70] G. T. Morgan and G. R. Davies, *Proc. Roy. Soc.*, 1926, **110**, 523.

halides are insoluble in water, but dissolve in benzene and relatively non-polar organic solvents as the monomeric species, for some of which there is [19]F n.m.r. evidence of a trigonal bipyramidal structure with the halogens occupying axial positions, i.e. the positions expected for the more electronegative ligands [71]. The electrical conductivity of the melt and of solutions in acetonitrile and methanol indicates no appreciable ionic dissociation of Ph_3SbCl_2, nor of $(Ph_3SbCl)_2O$, m.p. 222°, prepared from the dichloride by partial hydrolysis in boiling methanol [64], although ionic species are present in acetonitrile solutions of higher halides [33].

The *dinitrate*, $Ph_3Sb(NO_3)_2$, m.p. 156°, results from triphenylstibine and fuming nitric acid; the use of nitrating mixture causes nuclear nitration also. Its infrared spectrum supports the covalent trigonal bipyramidal structure typical of compounds R_3SbX_2 [67].

THE TRIHALIDES. Only a few representatives of this class have been prepared, and only the aryl members are stable.

Dimethylantimony trichloride, Me_2SbCl_3, m.p. 105–110° (decomp.), is formed by the addition of chlorine to dimethylchlorostibine, and it decomposes very easily, splitting off methyl chloride [70]:

$$Me_2SbCl + Cl_2 \longrightarrow Me_2SbCl_3 \longrightarrow MeSbCl_2 + MeCl$$

The tribromide is even less stable and loses methyl bromide even at −15°.

Diphenylantimony trichloride, Ph_2SbCl_3, m.p. 176°, from the mono-chloride Ph_2SbCl and chlorine, or by the action of hot dilute hydrochloric acid on diphenylstibinic acid, or by the action of iron on phenyldiazonium tetrachloroantimonate(III) [64], is much more stable to heat than the dialkyltrichloride. Partial hydrolysis gives the *oxide*, $(Ph_2SbCl_2)_2O$, m.p. 140° (decomp.), which is monomeric in nitrobenzene solution [64].

THE TETRAHALIDES. These are even less stable than the trihalides.

Methylantimony tetrachloride, $MeSbCl_4$, appears to be formed at low temperatures from methyldichlorostibine and chlorine, but decomposes very easily into methyl chloride and antimony trichloride.

Phenylantimony tetrachloride, $PhSbCl_4$, m.p. 60–65°, from phenyl-dichlorostibine and chlorine, or phenylstibonic acid and concentrated hydrochloric acid,

$$PhSbO(OH)_2 + 4HCl \longrightarrow PhSbCl_4 + 3H_2O$$

is readily hydrolysed back to phenylstibonic acid. It slowly decomposes at room temperature:

$$2PhSbCl_4 \longrightarrow Ph_2SbCl + SbCl_3 + 2Cl_2$$

---

[71] E. L. Muetterties, W. Mahler, K. J. Packer and R. Schmutzler, *Inorg. Chem.*, 1964, **3**, 1298.

Derivatives of antimony(III)

The trivalent halostibines are reactive substances, being easily hydrolysed and oxidized (particularly the aliphatic members). Mixed alkyl- or aryl-stibines can be prepared from them by the reaction with Grignard or organoalkali metal reagents; hydrolysis and oxidation gives stibinic or stibonic acids, while reduction leads to organoantimony hydrides or compounds with Sb–Sb bonds, e.g. distibines.

THE MONOHALIDES. *Dimethylchlorostibine*, Me_2SbCl, b.p. 155–160°, is formed when trimethylstibine dichloride is heated:

$$Me_3SbCl_2 \longrightarrow Me_2SbCl + MeCl$$

It is very sensitive to oxygen and must be handled in an inert atmosphere [70]. The bromide and iodide and other dialkylhalogenostibines are prepared similarly [53, 70].

The exchange reaction between trimethylstibine and antimony trichloride provides another route to methylchlorostibines Me_nSbCl_{3-n}. The kinetics of this reaction (first order in each component) and relatively large negative activation entropy are consistent with a doubly bridged intermediate [71a]:

$$Me_3Sb + SbCl_3 \rightleftharpoons \quad\begin{array}{c} Me \quad Me \quad Cl \\ \diagdown \diagup \cdots \diagup \\ Sb \quad\quad Sb \\ \diagup \cdots \diagdown \\ Me \quad Cl \quad Cl \end{array}\quad \rightleftharpoons Me_2SbCl + MeSbCl_2$$

Bistrifluoromethyliodostibine [15] $(CF_3)_2SbI$, b.p. 129°, is a minor product from the reaction between antimony and CF_3I, and is more easily made from $(CF_3)_3Sb$ and iodine.

$$(CF_3)_3Sb + I_2 \longrightarrow (CF_3)_2SbI + CF_3I$$

It is rather unstable and readily disproportionates; with zinc or mercury it forms $(CF_3)_2Sb \cdot Sb(CF_3)_2$. The corresponding chloro- and bromo- compounds have also been described.

Diphenylchlorostibine, Ph_2SbCl, m.p. 69–70°, has been prepared in several ways and is less reactive than dimethylchlorostibine (insensitive to air). Boiling methanolic hydrochloric acid displaces a phenyl group from triphenylstibine:

$$Ph_3Sb + HCl \longrightarrow Ph_2SbCl + C_6H_6$$

It is also formed by the mild phenylation of antimony trichloride with diphenylmercury:

$$2Ph_2Hg + SbCl_3 \longrightarrow Ph_2SbCl + 2PhHgCl$$

[71a] H. Weingarten and J. R. Van Wazer, *J. Amer. Chem. Soc.*, 1966, **88**, 2700.

A modification of this reaction makes use of tetraphenyl-lead [72]. Purification through the monoacetate is recommended [73]. A method for preparing diphenylchlorostibine from antimony trichloride, copper(II) chloride and phenylhydrazine has been described. The initial product is diphenylstibinic acid, which can be converted in good yield into the trichloride, Ph_2SbCl_3, which can be reduced to Ph_2SbCl by SO_2 in the presence of a trace of iodide [74].

The direct preparation of diphenylfluorostibine, Ph_2SbF, from aqueous $PhSi(OEt)_3$ and SbF_3, was described on p. 511 [6a].

THE DIHALIDES. *Methyldichlorostibine* [70], $MeSbCl_2$, b.p. 115–120°/60 mm., results from the elimination of methyl chloride from Me_2SbCl_3.

Ethyldichlorostibine, $EtSbCl_2$, b.p. 113–120°/25 mm., is obtained by the mild alkylation of antimony trichloride by means of tetra-ethyl-lead, which is a useful reagent for the mild substitution of reactive halogen by ethyl (p. 489).

Phenyldichlorostibine, $PhSbCl_2$, m.p. 62°, is formed by the rearrangement of triphenylstibine and antimony trichloride, but is much more satisfactorily prepared by the action of hydrogen chloride in chloroform on phenylstibine oxide [75], PhSbO. Its use in the synthesis of pentaphenylstibiole has already been described (p. 519) [52]. The di-iodo compound, $PhSbI_2$, m.p. 69°, is the most accessible member of this series, and is precipitated when phenylstibonic acid is reduced by sulphur dioxide in the presence of iodide [30].

Oxygen derivatives

Among derivatives of antimony(V), these include: (*i*) R_4SbOH, the strongly basic stibonium hydroxides; (*ii*) R_3SbO, the stibine oxides, which exist in solution as the dihydroxides, $R_3Sb(OH)_2$, generally showing no pronounced acidic or basic character except for the strongly acidic tristrifluoromethyl derivative; (*iii*) $R_2SbO(OH)$, the very weak polymeric stibinic acids; and (*iv*) $RSbO(OH)_2$, the very weak probably polymeric stibonic acids. Derivatives of antimony(III) are the monomeric crystalline oxides $(R_2Sb)_2O$, and the polymeric amorphous oxides RSbO.

Derivatives of antimony(V)

TRIALKYL AND TRIARYL OXIDES, R_3SbO. The trialkylstibines are very readily oxidized but atmospheric oxidation gives a mixture of

[72] Z. M. Manulkin, A. N. Tatarenko and F. Y. Yusupov, *Doklady Akad. Nauk S.S.S.R.*, 1953, **88**, 687.

[73] F. F. Blicke, U. O. Oakdale and F. D. Smith, *J. Amer. Chem. Soc.*, 1931, **53**, 1025.

[74] P. G. Sergeev and A. B. Bruker, *Zhur. obshchei Khim.*, 1957, **27**, 2220; *Chem. Abs.*, 1958, **52**, 6236.

[75] G. O. Doak and H. H. Jaffé, *J. Amer. Chem, Soc.*, 1950, **72**, 3025, 3027.

products. A better method is the use of mercury(II) oxide in alcoholic suspension,

$$R_3Sb + HgO \longrightarrow R_3SbO + Hg$$

The triarylstibines can be converted into oxides by treatment with alkaline hydrogen peroxide, but the alkaline hydrolysis of the dihalides is also a convenient method:

$$Ar_3SbX_2 + 2KOH \longrightarrow Ar_3SbO + 2KX + H_2O$$

Incomplete hydrolysis leads to the monomeric oxides, $(Ar_3SbCl)_2O$ [64].

The trialkylstibine oxides are soluble in water and hydroxylic solvents, but not in non-polar solvents. The triaryl oxides, however, tend to be insoluble in water, and often dissolve in benzene.

Trimethylstibine oxide, Me_3SbO, is a typical trialkyl oxide. It is very soluble in water and may very well dissolve as $Me_3Sb(OH)_2$. The formulation $Me_3SbOH^+OH^-$ seems to be excluded by the neutrality of the solution. The trifluoromethyl analogue, by contrast, gives strongly acidic aqueous solutions, in which it is present as $H_3O^+(CF_3)_3Sb(OH)_3^-$, as described above [15].

Alkoxy and related derivatives of organoantimony oxides can be prepared, generally most easily by the reaction between the halide and a sodium alkoxide or similar reagent. Like their tin counterparts, they are effective catalysts for the trimerization of isocyanates [76]. Various trimethylsiloxy derivatives have been prepared using $NaOSiMe_3$, e.g. [77]

$$Me_3SbCl_2 + 2NaOSiMe_3 \longrightarrow 2NaCl + Me_3Sb(OSiMe_3)_2, \quad \text{m.p. } 21°$$

Trimethylstibine dihydroxide reacts with Me_3SbCl_2 in aqueous solution to give the crystalline oxide $(Me_3SbCl)_2O$ [66].

Triethylstibine sulphide, Et_3SbS, m.p. 118°, is formed not only by direct addition of sulphur to a solution of triethylstibine but also by passing hydrogen sulphide through an alcoholic solution of the oxide. The sulphides are less soluble in water than the oxides, and dissolve more easily in ether and alcohol. A rather unstable *selenide*, Et_3SbSe, m.p. 124°, has been prepared by addition of selenium to triethylstibine. *Diselenides*, e.g. Me_3SbSe_2, are also known [78].

Triphenylstibine oxide, $Ph_3SbO.H_2O$ or $Ph_3Sb(OH)_2$, m.p. 212°, from the dichloride or dibromide and warm alcoholic potassium hydroxide, or from triphenylstibine and alkaline hydrogen peroxide, forms a variety of

[76] S. Herbstman, *J. Org. Chem.*, 1965, **30**, 1259.

[77] H. Schmidbaur and M. Schmidt, *Angew. Chem.*, 1961, **73**, 755; H. Schmidbaur, H.-S. Arnold and E. Beinhofer, *Chem. Ber.*, 1964, **97**, 449; H. Schmidbaur, ibid., p. 842.

[78] R. A. Zingaro and A. Merijanian, *J. Organometal. Chem.*, 1964, **1**, 369.

derivatives with mineral acids (e.g. a sulphate) and with carboxylic acids (e.g. a diacetate, m.p. 215°). Glycols give cyclic derivatives [79].

Organoperoxides, $Ph_3Sb(OOR)_2$, can be prepared by the reaction with a hydroperoxide ROOH, e.g. [80].

$$Ph_3SbO + 2Bu^tOOH \longrightarrow H_2O + Ph_3Sb(OOBu^t)_2, \quad m.p. \ 128\text{--}130°$$

Organoantimony organoperoxides $R_3Sb(OOR')_2$, have also been prepared from R_3SbCl_2 and R'OOH in the presence of ammonia or sodium amide, from R_3SbCl_2 and R'OONa, or from $R_3Sb(OR'')_2$ and ROOH. *Triphenylstibine dihydroperoxide*, $Ph_3Sb(OOH)_2$ m.p. $\sim125°$ (decomp.), and *triphenylstibine peroxide*, $(Ph_3SbO_2)_n$, m.p. $\sim150°$ (decomp.), result from the action of hydrogen peroxide on triphenylstibine dialkoxides, $Ph_3Sb(OR)_2$.

The peroxy derivatives $R_3Sb(OOR')_2$ are stable at room temperature, but detonate if heated strongly. The derivatives of triphenylstibine in particular are very resistant to hydrolysis, more so than similar derivatives of germanium, tin and lead. In common with so many organometallic compounds they are said to be useful as catalysts for the polymerization of olefins.

Partial hydrolysis of triphenylstibine dichloride with sodium hydroxide in boiling methanol gives the covalent monomeric oxide, $(Ph_3SbCl)_2O$ [64].

THE STIBINIC ACIDS, $R_2SbO(OH)$. All the stibinic and stibonic $(RSbO(OH)_2)$ acids are very weak acids, and they are apparently polymeric. The aromatic members are much better known than the aliphatic, only a very few examples of the latter having been described (e.g. *dimethylstibinic acid*, $Me_2SbO(OH)$, by the hydrolysis and oxidation of dimethylchlorostibine [70]).

Diphenylstibinic acid, $Ph_2SbO(OH)$, m.p. 283–286°, is formed by the hydrolysis and oxidation of diphenylchlorostibine, or by the hydrolysis of the corresponding trichloride Ph_2SbCl_3. It is, however, most conveniently prepared from phenylstibine oxide, PhSbO, by two methods. If benzene diazonium salts are allowed to decompose in the presence of phenylstibine oxide, diphenylstibinic acid is formed [30].:

$$PhN_2X + PhSbO + KOH \longrightarrow Ph_2SbO_2K + KX + H_2O + N_2$$

Mixed diarylstibinic acids may be obtained in this way.

The other method [75] involves the thermal disproportionation of phenylstibine oxides, which can be controlled to give bisdiphenylstibine oxide,

$$4PhSbO \longrightarrow (Ph_2Sb)_2O + Sb_2O_3$$

[79] F. Nerdel, J. Buddrus and K. Höher, *Chem. Ber.*, 1964, **97**, 124.
[80] A. Rieche, J. Dahlmann and D. List, *Angew. Chem.*, 1961, **73**, 494; idem. *Annalen*, 1964, **678**, 167; J. Dahlmann and A. Rieche, *Chem. Ber.*, 1967, **100**, 1544.

and diphenylstibinic acid is formed by hydrolysis and oxidation of this oxide.

Diphenylstibinic acid can be reduced to the oxide by sulphurous acid, and is nitrated in the *meta* position without breaking the Sb–C bonds.

Diarylstibinic acids have also been prepared from diaryliodonium salts. Hexachloroantimonates(V), Ar_2ISbCl_6, when stirred in acetone with antimony powder gave diarylstibinic acids, $Ar_2SbO(OH)$ [8].

THE STIBONIC ACIDS, $RSbO(OH)_2$. Although their polymeric constitution is still not clear, the arylstibonic acids are among the best-known organic compounds of antimony. They have generally been prepared by the decomposition of diazonium salts in the presence of an antimonate(III) [30], and have served as the source of most of the numerous aromatic antimony compounds which have been prepared for pharmacological purposes. The diazonium preparation is an example of the more general *Nesmeyanov reaction*; in this instance the reaction is *heterolytic* rather than primarily homolytic, involving free radical formation, as previously supposed [81].

Phenylstibonic acid, $PhSbO(OH)_2$. The older preparative method has been superseded by a modification of the Scheller reaction (also used for preparing phenylarsonic acids). Aniline is diazotized in an acidic alcoholic solution containing antimony trichloride, and on addition of copper(I) bromide nitrogen is evolved and phenylstibonic acid is formed. The separation of the product from inorganic antimony compounds has often given difficulty, but this can be achieved by dissolving the crude acid in hydrochloric acid containing pyridine hydrochloride, whereby the stibonic acid is converted into the salt $[C_5H_5NH^+][PhSbCl_5^-]$ which is precipitated in crystalline form. The pure acid is then recovered by the action of dilute sodium carbonate solution followed by *dilute* hydrochloric acid [7]. Ethyl esters of stibonic acids can be prepared by the action of ethanol on the complex pyridinium chloride [82].

Phenylstibonic acid is insoluble in water and almost insoluble in benzene. The tolylstibonic acids are slightly soluble in benzene and the degree of association varies from about 3·5 to 5 or more as the concentration increases. This is ascribed to hydrogen bond association, and the acids are essentially monomeric when dissolved in other carboxylic acids such as formic or acetic acids. In these solvents, however, there appears to be some dissociation to water and anhydride:

$$ArSbO_3H_2 \rightleftharpoons ArSbO_2 + H_2O$$

[81] O. A. Reutov and A. G. Markovskaya, *Doklady Akad. Nauk S.S.S.R.*, 1954, **98**, 979.
[82] T.-C. Sun and J.-Y. Chi. *Yao Hsueh Hsueh Pao*, 1960, **8**, 166; *Chem. Abs.*, 1963, **58**, 5721.

In alkaline solution the anion is probably $ArSb(OH)_5^-$. Substances of composition near to those of the anhydrides $ArSbO_2$ are formed when the acids are heated at 125° in vacuum [83].

p-Tolylstibonic acid, $MeC_6H_4SbO(OH)_2$, can be oxidized to the *p*-carboxylic acid, or nitrated (*meta* to the antimony) without breaking the Sb–C bond [7].

Derivatives of antimony(III)

The oxides $(R_2Sb)_2O$ are monomeric crystalline substances, but the oxides (RSbO) are amorphous and polymeric. Both types are easily prepared and are useful intermediates in the preparation of other antimony compounds.

Bis-dimethylstibine oxide, $(Me_2Sb)_2O$, which results from the hydrolysis of Me_2SbBr with alkali [70], is a colourless spontaneously inflammable liquid. When heated with sodium amide in ether for several hours it is converted into *tris-dimethylstibine nitride*, $(Me_2Sb)_3N$, m.p. 48–50° [84].

Bis-diphenylstibine oxide, $(Ph_2Sb)_2O$, m.p. 78–80°, is similarly obtained from diphenylchlorostibine which is conveniently prepared from triphenylstibine by means of methanolic hydrogen chloride, and hydrolysed to the oxide without isolation of the intermediate [85]:

$$Ph_3Sb \xrightarrow[MeOH]{HCl} Ph_2SbCl \xrightarrow{KOH} (Ph_2Sb)_2O$$

A probably more convenient preparation is to heat phenylstibine oxide [75] at 100°.

It is easily oxidized by nitric acid to diphenylstibinic acid, and is reduced to the distibine $Ph_2Sb \cdot SbPh_2$ by hypophosphorous acid. Strong heating (200°) causes disproportionation to triphenylstibine and antimony trioxide.

Methylstibine oxide, MeSbO, is a polymeric powder produced by the alkaline hydrolysis of methyldichlorostibine.

Phenylstibine oxide ('stiboso-benzene'), PhSbO, is readily obtained by the reduction of phenylstibonic acid (by SO_2) as a white voluminous polymer. Though insoluble in water and alkali, it dissolves even in weak acids, and the dihalides $PhSbX_2$ are readily obtained from it by the action of hydrogen halide in chloroform [75].

The rates at which arylstibine oxides disproportionate to bisdiarylstibine oxides are greatly influenced by the electronic character of substituents in the benzene ring. Nitro groups increase the thermal stability of phenylstibine oxides, the order of stability for some *para* substituents being:

$$NO_2 > MeCO > Br > Cl > H > Me$$

The disproportionation probably involves a free radical mechanism [75].

[83] G. O. Doak, *J. Amer. Chem. Soc.*, 1946, **68**, 1991.
[84] O. J. Scherer, J. F. Schmidt and M. Schmidt, *Z. Naturforsch.*, 1964, **19b**, 447.
[85] H. Schmidt and F. Hoffmann, *Chem. Ber.*, 1926, **59**, 555.

s

Alkyl and aryl hydrides

These are unstable and only a few have been prepared. Dimethylbromostibine is reduced by sodium borohydride in diethylene glycol dimethyl ether at $-78°$ with the formation of several volatile products which include methylstibine, dimethylstibine and dimethylstibinoborane [86].

Methylstibine, $MeSbH_2$, b.p. $41°$ (extrapolated), is very unstable and decomposes above about $-70°$ to $-80°$ with formation of hydrogen and deposition of a black solid.

Dimethylstibine, Me_2SbH, b.p. $60·7°$ (extrapolated), is better prepared by the reduction of dimethylbromostibine with $LiBH(OMe)_3$, which avoids the formation of borane by-products. Though more stable than methylstibine it decomposes slowly at room temperature, particularly in the presence of mercury:

$$2Me_2SbH \longrightarrow Me_2Sb·SbMe_2 + H_2$$

It reacts at once with hydrogen chloride,

$$Me_2SbH + HCl \longrightarrow Me_2SbCl + H_2$$

but not with hydrogen sulphide.

With diborane at low temperature there is evidence for the formation of a very unstable adduct $Me_2SbH·BH_3$, but at room temperature two competing reactions occur

$$2Me_2SbH + B_2H_6 \longrightarrow Me_2SbBH_2 + 2H_2$$

and the B_2H_6-catalysed formation of Me_4Sb_2. *Dimethylstibinoborane*, Me_2SbBH_2, can be prepared in 26% yield from Me_4Sb_2 and B_2H_6 at $100°$. It is monomeric and undecomposed by heat below about $200°$, and is relatively unreactive, possibly because of Sb–B double bonding. It decomposes at about $210°$ to give a black solid of approximate composition $(SbB)_n$. The decomposition of related alkyl/hydride derivatives containing elements of Groups III and V has been suggested as a method of obtaining crystalline films of semiconducting materials [87]:

$$SbH_3 + Me_3In \xrightarrow{-2MeH} \frac{1}{n}(MeInSbH)_n \xrightarrow{150-160°} InSb$$

Stibino derivatives of borohydrides, e.g. $LiBH_3SbMe_2$, can be prepared from the metal hydride and the borane adduct, $Me_3Sb·BH_3$ [88].

Dialkylstibines R_2SbH can also be prepared by the lithium aluminium hydride reduction of the chloride or bromide R_2SbX in ether at $-20°$

[86] A. B. Burg and L. R. Grant, *J. Amer. Chem. Soc.*, 1959, **81**, 1.
[87] B. C. Harrison and E. H. Tompkins, *Inorg. Chem.*, 1962, **1**, 951.
[88] H. C. Miller and E. L. Muetterties, U.S.P. 2,999,864; *Chem. Abs.*, 1962, **56**, 1478.

[89]; the products react with phenyl-lithium to give antimony–lithium derivatives, e.g.

$$Bu^t_2SbCl \xrightarrow{LiAlH_4} Bu^t_2SbH \xrightarrow{PhLi} LiSbBu^t_2$$

Phenylstibine [90], $PhSbH_2$, is formed when phenyldi-iodostibine is reduced with lithium borohydride in ether at $-50°$; lithium aluminium hydride gives lower yields:

$$PhSbI_2 + 2LiBH_4 \rightarrow PhSbH_2 + 2LiI + B_2H_6$$

An ether solution of phenylstibine shows signs of decomposition in about half an hour at room temperature, hydrogen being evolved with simultaneous formation of a polymer $(PhSb)_n$. A similar polymer [91] is obtained as a black amorphous precipitate from the reduction of phenyldichlorostibine by diphenylsilane in ether at $-25°$. In this case analysis shows the presence of some chlorine, and the material is regarded as being a long-chain compound, $ClPhSb(SbPh)_nSbPhCl$, where n is about 13. It is unaffected by dry air below $200°$, but oxidized by moist air at room temperature, or by oxygen when this is bubbled through an ether suspension of the material. Other polymeric materials approximating in composition to $(PhSb)_n$ may possibly result from the reduction of phenylstibonic acid, phenylstibine oxide or phenyldi-iodostibine with sodium amalgam, zinc or hypophosphite [30, 92].

Diphenylstibine [90, 93], Ph_2SbH, from diphenylchlorostibine and lithium borohydride or lithium aluminium hydride, is rather more stable to heat than phenylstibine, but diproportionates and loses hydrogen very readily.

Compounds containing Sb–Sb bonds

Compounds containing A–A bonds, where A is an element of Group V or VB (other than nitrogen), become less stable as the radius of A increases; this is similar to the behaviour of the analogous compounds of Group IV and IVB. A few aliphatic and aromatic antimony analogues of the cacodyls are known, and all are very reactive and easily decomposed. No compounds are known containing Bi–Bi bonds, except possibly $Me_2Bi·BiMe_2$ and less certainly $Ph_2Bi·BiPh_2$.

Tetramethyldistibine, $Me_2Sb·SbMe_2$, m.p. $17°$, was first prepared by the reaction between methyl radicals (from tetramethyl-lead by pyrolysis) and

[89] K. Issleib and B. Hamann, *Z. anorg. Chem.*, 1964, **332**, 179; 1965, **339**, 289; K. Issleib, B. Hamann and L. Schmidt, ibid., p. 298.

[90] E. Wiberg and K. Mödritzer, *Z. Naturforsch.*, 1957, **12b**, 128.

[91] W. Kuchen and H. Ecke, *Z. anorg. Chem.*, 1963, **321**, 138.

[92] F. Klages and W. Rapp, *Chem. Ber.*, 1955, **88**, 384.

[93] A. N. Nesmeyanov, A. E. Borisov and N. V. Novikova, *Izvest. Akad. Nauk S.S.S.R.*, 1963, 194.

an antimony mirror [94]. A mixture of trimethylstibine and tetramethyl-distibine is formed, whether the mirror is hot or cold. The most remark-able property of this substance is its colour; it is pale yellow at −180° and becomes darker with increasing temperature until it is bright red at 17°, when it melts to a pale yellow liquid. Solutions in benzene are also pale yellow. It is monomeric in benzene solution and has a vapour pressure of 6·4 mm. at 76°.

A better preparative method is the reduction of dimethylbromostibine by sodium in liquid ammonia [86].

It is a very reactive substance and is spontaneously inflammable in air. It adds halogens giving dimethylhalostibines, and oxidation of its solution in benzene produces dimethylstibinic acid, Me_2SbO_2H. It does not react with mercury, but decomposes within two days at room temperature in contact with Apiezon grease.

Its thermal stability is greater than might be expected since it has sur-vived a week at 100° in a sealed tube. Decomposition is apparent after 17 hours at 160°, and at 200° proceeds almost quantitatively according to the equation:

$$3Me_4Sb_2 \longrightarrow 2Sb + 4Me_3Sb$$

Tetrakistrifluoromethyldistibine [15], $(CF_3)_2Sb·Sb(CF_3)_2$, b.p. 136°, from $(CF_3)_2SbI$ and zinc or mercury, is a pale yellow liquid which deepens in colour when heated, and freezes to a *colourless* solid. Less stable than the methyl compound, it slowly decomposes at room temperature (particularly in light).

Tetra-ethyldistibine, $Et_2Sb·SbEt_2$, results (together with triethylstibine) from the action of ethyl radicals on a heated antimony mirror: only tri-ethylstibine is obtained with a cold mirror. It resembles the tetramethyl compound in colour, being deep yellow just under its m.p. −61° and pale yellow above [94].

Tetrabutyldistibine, $Bu^t_2Sb·SbBu^t_2$, is an orange-yellow oil which can be prepared from $LiSbBu^t_2$ by the action of Bu^t_2SbCl or $Cl(CH_2)_4Cl$ [89]. With phenyl-lithium it gives Bu^t_2SbPh.

Tetraphenyldistibine, $Ph_2Sb·SbPh_2$, m.p. 121–122°, is much more easily prepared and is formed when diphenyliodostibine is reduced with sodium hypophosphite. Electrolytic reduction of diphenylantimony halides also gives tetraphenyldistibine [94a]. It combines immediately with iodine in solution, regenerating diphenyliodostibine, and also with oxygen giving the peroxide:

$$Ph_2Sb·SbPh_2 + O_2 \longrightarrow Ph_2SbOOSbPh_2$$

[94] F. A. Paneth, *Trans. Faraday Soc.*, 1934, **30**, 179; F. A. Paneth and H. Loleit, *J. Chem. Soc.*, 1935, 366.

[94a] R. E. Dessy, T. Chivers and W. Kitching, *J. Amer. Chem. Soc.*, 1966, **88**, 467.

The tetra-*p*-bromphenyl- and tetra-*p*-tolyl analogues have also been prepared by the same method [73, 95].

Compounds approximating in composition to $(PhSb)_n$ which possibly contain several Sb–Sb links were described in the previous section (p. 533).

Tetrabutylcyclotetrastibine, $(Bu^tSb)_4$, is obtained as an air-sensitive red amorphous powder as a side product in the reduction of Bu^t_2SbCl by $LiAlH_4$, and also by the methanolysis of the product of the reaction between $LiSbBu^t_2$ and iodine [89].

Alkali metal derivatives

Alkali metal derivatives of antimony have been little studied. *Diphenyl-stibyl-sodium*, Ph_2SbNa, has been prepared in liquid ammonia solution by the action of sodium on diphenyliodostibine [96], and the lithium derivative, Ph_2SbLi, is obtained by the cleavage of triphenylstibine with lithium [97].

Diphenylstibyl-sodium reacts with organotin halides or tin tetrachloride in liquid ammonia to give derivatives containing tin-antimony bonds [97a], e.g.

$$4Ph_2SbNa + SnCl_4 \longrightarrow Sn(SbPh_2)_4, \quad \text{m.p. } 75°$$

Triphenylstannylstibines $(Ph_3Sn)_nSbPh_{3-n}$ result from the complementary reactions between Ph_3SnLi and $Ph_{3-n}SbCl_n$ in tetrahydrofuran. The tin hydride route to similar derivatives $(Et_3Sn)_3Sb$ has already been described (p. 514) [24a].

In the alkyl series, the action of lithium or sodium on Me_2SbBr leads to tetramethyldistibine, as described above [86]. The n-butyl compounds Bu^n_2SbLi and $(Bu^n_2Sb)_2Mg$, however, result from the action of the metal on di-n-butylbromostibine (but not on Bu^n_3Sb) in tetrahydrofuran at room temperature [98]. They react with trimethylchlorosilane to form the trimethylsilyl derivative, $Me_3SiSbBu^n_2$, but give tributylstibine with Bu_2SbBr, MeOH or CO_2 rather than the expected $Bu_2Sb·SbBu_2$, Bu_2SbH or Bu_2SbCO_2H, evidently because these expected products disproportionate too readily under the conditions used.

A number of lithium derivatives Alk_2SbLi have been prepared by the action of phenyl-lithium on the appropriate hydride. A typical preparative route and some reactions are illustrated in the following reaction sequence (R = cyclohexyl) [89]:

[95] F. F. Blicke and U. O. Oakdale, *J. Amer. Chem. Soc.*, 1933, **55**, 1198.
[96] L. A. Woods and H. Gilman, *Proc. Iowa. Acad. Sci.*, 1941, **48**, 251.
[97] D. Wittenberg and H. Gilman, *J. Org. Chem.*, 1958, **23**, 1063.
[97a] H. Schumann, T.Östermann and M. Schmidt, *J. Organometal. Chem.*, 1967, **8**, 105.
[98] S. Herbstman, *J. Org. Chem.*, 1964, **29**, 986.

s*

$$SbCl_3 \xrightarrow[\text{ether}]{RMgCl} \underset{\substack{\text{m.p. 64-5°}}}{R_3Sb} \xrightarrow[\text{ether}]{Cl_2} \underset{\substack{\text{m.p. 211-2°}}}{R_3SbCl_2} \xrightarrow[230°]{-RCl} \underset{\substack{\text{b.p. 130-145°/1mm}}}{R_2SbCl}$$

$$C_2H_4 + LiBr + R_2SbSbR_2$$

$$\xleftarrow[BrCH_2CH_2Br]{}$$

$$LiSbR_2 \xleftarrow[\text{ether}]{PhLi} R_2SbH$$

decomps. > 50°

$$R_2Sb(CH_2)_n SbR_2 \xleftarrow[\substack{(n=3-6)}]{X(CH_2)_n X}$$

$$R_2SbCl$$

$$R_2SbSbR_2$$

LiAlH$_4$ in ether $-20°$

BISMUTH

The organic derivatives of bismuth are generally more reactive than those of antimony, their reactivities being comparable with those of the lead derivatives. They have been fairly extensively studied, particularly in connexion with their possible pharmacological applications, where some attention has been directed to the preparation of water-soluble organo-bismuth compounds. However, as no important application has been found for them, they have received little recent attention.

The organic chemistry of bismuth was the subject of a review [99] in 1942 and of a literature survey [1] in 1962.

The tri-alkyls and -aryls

The reaction between bismuth chloride and a Grignard reagent is generally the most convenient method of preparing these. Other methods include the reaction between alkyl or aryl halides and a bismuth–potassium alloy, the action of organo-zinc or -aluminium compounds on bismuth chloride, action of an organomercury compound on bismuth metal, the reaction between organosilicon fluorides and bismuth fluoride in aqueous solution, the decomposition of diazonium salts in the presence of bismuth salts and copper, the action of iodonium salts on bismuth powder in the presence of bismuth chloride, and the reduction of organobismuth halides with hydrazine. The electrolysis of such bimetallic compounds as $NaBR_4$ or $NaAlR_3OR'$ using a bismuth anode has also been used.

The lower trialkyls are spontaneously inflammable and thermally unstable, but do not react with water (this is similar to the trialkylstibines); the triaryls are much less reactive but very readily add halogens to give Ar_3BiX_2, stable derivatives of bismuth(V).

Trimethylbismuth, Me_3Bi, b.p. 110°, from methylmagnesium iodide and bismuth chloride [100], is a colourless liquid, soluble in non-polar solvents,

[99] H. Gilman and H. L. Yale, *Chem. Rev.*, 1942, **30**, 281.
[100] L. H. Long and J. F. Sackman, *Trans. Faraday Soc.*, 1954, **50**, 1177.

which inflames in air and reacts vigorously with halogens by *substitution*, differing from the aryls in this respect:

$$Me_3Bi + Br_2 \longrightarrow Me_2BiBr + MeBr$$

It does not add methyl iodide to give a quaternary salt but reacts at 200° in a curious way:

$$Me_3Bi + 2MeI \longrightarrow MeBiI_2 + 2C_2H_6$$

Not only does it fail to give quaternary salts but appears to be devoid of donor properties.

Triethylbismuth, Et_3Bi, b.p. 96°/50 mm., and higher homologues may be prepared by the Grignard method or by the action of organoaluminium reagents (e.g. Et_3Al [101] or $LiAlEt_4$ [20, 21]), on bismuth trichloride. The action of R_3Al on Bi_2O_3 gives poor yields and is therefore less useful than the analogous reaction with Sb_2O_3 [5]. Triethylbismuth is also obtained when $NaAlEt_3OR$ [6] or aqueous $NaBEt_4$ [22] is electrolysed using a bismuth anode.

The controlled oxidation of triethylbismuth at −50° to −60° gives a peroxide, Et_3BiO_2, which decomposes at −25° into a mixture of products including the ethoxides Et_2BiOEt and $EtOBiO$, ethyl peroxide, and ethanol [102].

Triethylbismuth cannot be distilled at atmospheric pressure as it explodes at about 150°.

Like triethylstibine, triethylbismuth reacts with silicon, germanium or tin hydrides Et_3MH to form materials in which the Group V element is attached to three atoms of the Group IV element, e.g. [24a]:

$$3Et_3SnH + Et_3Bi \longrightarrow (Et_3Sn)_3Bi$$

The products are readily cleaved by oxygen, peroxides or bromoalkanes.

A few *perfluoroalkylbismuth* compounds are known. Trifluoroiodo-methane does not react with bismuth tri-iodide in the presence of mercury [16], but with trimethylbismuth at 100° there is some exchange of trifluoromethyl groups for methyl groups [103]:

$$Me_3Bi + CF_3I \longrightarrow MeI + Me_2BiCF_3, \quad b.p. 121° \text{ (decomp.)}$$

Smaller quantities of the bis(trifluoromethyl) derivative, $MeBi(CF_3)_2$, b.p. 132° (decomp.) are formed in the same reaction, but no tris(trifluoro-methyl)bismuth is obtained. Other mixed alkyl-perfluoro-alkyl derivatives, R_2R^fBi and RR^f_2Bi, have been prepared similarly and found to be thermally unstable materials which decompose below their boiling points.

[101] L. I. Zakharkin and O. Yu Okhlobystin, *Izvest. Akad. Nauk S.S.S.R.*, 1959, 1942; *Chem. Abs.*, 1960, **54**, 9738.

[102] G. Calingaert, H. Soroos and V. Hnizda, *J. Amer. Chem. Soc.*, 1942, **64**, 392.

[103] T. N. Bell, B. J. Pullman and B. O. West, *Proc. Chem. Soc.*, 1962, 224; *Austral. J. Chem.*, 1963. **16**, 636.

They are readily oxidized; halogens cleave both alkyl and fluoroalkyl groups, and hydrolysis with aqueous alkali gives the fluoroalkane R^fH.

Tristrifluoromethylbismuth, $(CF_3)_3Bi$, may be the involatile liquid produced in trace quantities when trifluoromethyl radicals (from the pyrolysis of $(CF_3)_2CO$ at 900°) are passed over a bismuth mirror [104].

Trivinylbismuth [45], $(CH_2:CH)_3Bi$, b.p. 158°, from vinylmagnesium bromide and bismuth trichloride in tetrahydrofuran, very slowly decomposes when stored at room temperature, and inflames spontaneously in air. The *tripropenyl* derivatives, *cis*-$(MeCH:CH)_3Bi$ and *trans*-$(MeCH:CH)_3Bi$, from propenyl-lithium and bismuth trichloride in ether, add bromine at −55° to give derivatives of bismuth(V) [105]:

$$BiCl_3 \xrightarrow{\text{MeCH:CHLi}} \underset{\text{b.p. 106°/13 mm.}}{cis\text{-}(MeCH:CH)_3Bi} \xrightarrow{Br_2} \underset{\text{m.p. 65–66°}}{cis\text{-}(MeCH:CH)_3BiBr_2}$$

The *isopropenyl* compound, $(CH_2:CMe)_3Bi$, b.p. 86–87°/12 mm., prepared similarly, is, however, cleaved by bromine in chloroform solution, giving *isopropenylbismuth dibromide*, $CH_2:CMeBiBr_2$, decomp. 248–250°.

Triallylbismuth, $(CH_2:CHCH_2)_3Bi$, b.p. 80°/2 mm., from allylmagnesium bromide and bismuth trichloride in ether, is a reactive liquid which ignites in air [105].

Tris-cyclopentadienylbismuth [49], $(C_5H_5)_3Bi$, from cyclopentadienyl-sodium and bismuth trichloride in tetrahydrofuran, crystallizes from petroleum ether at −78° in the form of orange needles which change at 15–20° into a black modification. Both forms are diamagnetic and air-sensitive. It sublimes at about 75° in a vacuum with decomposition, and is hydrolysed by water to cyclopentadiene and bismuth hydroxide. Phosphorus trichloride in petroleum ether gives *bis-cyclopentadienylbismuth chloride*, $(C_5H_5)_2BiCl$, as relatively air-stable orange crystals.

Acetylenic bismuth compounds have been prepared from diarylbismuth chlorides and alkali metal acetylides in liquid ammonia, e.g. [106].

$$Ph_2BiCl + NaC:CH \longrightarrow Ph_2BiC:CBiPh_2, \quad \text{m.p. 133° (decomp.)}$$

They are rather easily hydrolysed, and give precipitates of copper or silver acetylide when copper(I) or silver(I) salts are added to their solutions in benzene.

Triphenylbismuth, Ph_3Bi, m.p. 77·6°, has been studied more than any other organobismuth compound. It is most conveniently prepared by the Grignard method, but the *p*-tolyl analogue has also been obtained by decomposing the diazonium salt $(MeC_6H_4N_2)_3BiCl_6$ with copper powder

[104] T. N. Bell, B. J. Pullman and B. O. West, *Austral. J. Chem.* 1963, **16**, 722.
[105] A. E. Borisov, M. A. Osipova and A. N. Nesmeyanov, *Izvest. Akad. Nauk S.S.S.R.*, 1963, 1507; *Chem. Abs.*, 1963, **59**, 14021.
[106] H. Hartmann, G. Habenicht and W. Reiss. *Z. anorg. Chem.*, 1962, **317**, 54; Ger.P. 1,126,388; *Chem. Abs.*, 1963, **58**, 6860.

in acetone. A development of the diazonium method is the decomposition of phenyldiazonium fluoroborate in the presence of powdered bismuth (from $BiCl_3$ + Zn in acetone), giving yields of triphenylbismuth of up to 69% [107]. The decomposition of diaryliodonium salts in the presence of bismuth also gives the triarylbismuth. Experiments with unsymmetrical iodonium salts (RR'IX) have shown that the more electronegative of the groups is transferred to bismuth [108]:

$$(p\text{-}ClC_6H_4IPh)Cl \xrightarrow{Bi} (p\text{-}ClC_6H_4)_3Bi \quad (13\%)$$
$$(p\text{-}MeOC_6H_4IPh)Cl \xrightarrow{Bi} Ph_3Bi \quad\quad (23\%)$$

The organofluorosilane route has been applied to triphenylbismuth, which is obtained in 50% yield this way [6a]:

$$Bi(OH)_3 + 3PhSiF_3 + 6NH_4F + 3HF \xrightarrow{H_2O} Ph_3Bi + 3H_2O + 3(NH_4)_2SiF_6$$

More easily purified than most other bismuth compounds, triphenylbismuth has been used in measurements of the atomic weight of bismuth [109]. It is monomeric in benzene. The crystal structure has been investigated by X-ray diffraction and it is claimed that the angles CBiC are 120° implying a planar BiC_3 unit. The axes of the benzene rings are tilted at an angle to the BiC_3 plane [31]. Further X-ray work on Ph_3Bi is in progress [110]. The dipole moment is zero [32].

Phenyl groups are very easily removed from triphenylbismuth, for example by acids:

$$Ph_3Bi + 3HCl \rightarrow BiCl_3 + 3C_6H_6$$

Triphenylbismuth is particularly susceptible to attack by —SH groups (this is also true of the trialkyl series), e.g. [111]

$$Ph_3Bi + PhSH \rightarrow PhH + Ph_2BiSPh \quad \text{(yellow, m.p. 170°)}$$

An excess of thiophenol leads to $Bi(SPh)_3$, m.p. 90–91°.

Chlorine and bromine give the dihalides Ph_3BiX_2, but iodine does so only at about −80°. The di-iodide decomposes on warming, giving a mixture of $PhBiI_2$, Ph_2BiI and iodobenzene [112]. Halogen and cyanogen halides give Ph_2BiX + PhX, the more electronegative component becoming attached to the bismuth [112]:

$$Ph_3Bi + IX \rightarrow Ph_2BiX + PhI \quad (X = Cl, Br, CN)$$
$$Ph_3Bi + BrCN \rightarrow Ph_2BiBr + PhCN$$

[107] A. N. Nesmeyanov, T. P. Tolstaya and L. S. Isaeva, *Doklady Akad. Nauk S.S.S.R.*, 1958, **122**, 614; *Chem. Abs.*, 1959, **53**, 4178.

[108] O. A. Reutov, O. A. Ptitsyna and N. B. Styazhkina, *Doklady Akad. Nauk S.S.S.R.*, 1958, **122**, 1032; O. A. Ptitsyna, O. A. Reutov and Yu. S. Ovodov, *Izvest. Akad. Nauk S.S.S.R.*, 1962, 638; *Chem. Abs.*, 1959, **53**, 4169; 1962, **57**, 15147.

[109] A. Classen and G. Strauch, *Z. anorg. Chem.*, 1924, **141**, 82.

[110] D. M. Hawley, G. Ferguson and G. S. Harris, *Chem. Comm.*, 1966, 111.

[111] H. Gilman and H. L. Yale, *J. Amer. Chem. Soc.*, 1951, **73**, 2880.

[112] F. Challenger and J. F. Wilkinson, *J. Chem. Soc.*, 1924, 854.

Triphenylbismuth acts as a phenylating agent to a variety of metallic halides including bismuth chloride, e.g.

$$Ph_3Bi + BiCl_3 \longrightarrow Ph_2BiCl + PhBiCl_2$$
$$Ph_3Bi + HgCl_2 \longrightarrow Ph_2BiCl + PhHgCl$$

Organic halides react only if the halogen is active; thus benzoyl chloride gives a small yield of benzophenone and benzyl chloride gives diphenylmethane [113]. The photolysis of triphenylbismuth in aromatic solvents leads to phenylation of the solvents by the phenyl radicals produced [114]. Hydrogenation in the presence of Raney Nickel gives benzene and presumably metallic bismuth [36]. The formation of Ph_3Sb from Ph_3Bi and antimony powder has already been mentioned [35].

Triphenylbismuth appears to be almost devoid of donor character; attempts to prepare transition metal [40] or decaborane [41] derivatives have been unsuccessful, although sulphur trioxide forms an adduct, Ph_3Bi,SO_3, m.p. 236° (decomp.), which is cleaved by hot water with regeneration of Ph_3Bi. The structure of the adduct is not known [115].

Penta-aryls

Pentaphenylbismuth, Ph_5Bi, is the only known penta-organobismuth compound. It had been noticed fifty years ago that the addition of phenylmagnesium bromide to a triarylbismuth dihalide produced a transient purple colour [116]. More recently the reaction between triphenylbismuth dichloride and phenyl-lithium has been studied. Only decomposition products are formed at room temperature, but at −75° an amorphous yellow precipitate is obtained which on standing changes into a violet crystalline powder, pentaphenylbismuth [117]. An alternative preparation uses the tosyliminoderivative [38]:

$$Ph_3Bi \xrightarrow{MeC_6H_4SO_2NClNa} Ph_3BiNSO_2C_6H_4Me \xrightarrow{2PhLi} Ph_5Bi$$

Practically insoluble in water and alcohol, pentaphenylbismuth dissolves in acetone, benzene and cyclohexane and can be crystallized from aqueous acetone. It is rather unstable but can be kept a few days under nitrogen at room temperature. On quick heating it decomposes at 105° with sudden frothing, into triphenylbismuth, biphenyl and some benzene. It is less stable thermally than pentaphenylantimony.

An ether solution of pentaphenylbismuth immediately decolorizes bromine,

$$Ph_5Bi + Br_2 \longrightarrow Ph_3Bi + 2PhBr$$

[113] F. Challenger and L. R. Ridgway, *J. Chem. Soc.*, 1922, 104.

[114] D. H. Hey, M. J. Perkins and G. H. Williams, ibid., 1963, 5612.

[115] M. Becke-Goehring and H. Thielemann, *Z. anorg. Chem.*, 1961, **308**, 33.

[116] F. Challenger, *J. Chem. Soc.*, 1914, 2210; F. Challenger and J. F. Wilkinson, ibid., 1922, 91.

[117] G. Wittig and K. Clauss, *Annalen*, 1952, **578**, 136.

but at $-70°$ the orange-coloured bismuthonium perbromide is formed,

$$Ph_5Bi + 2Br_2 \longrightarrow [Ph_4Bi]Br_3 + PhBr$$

but this decomposes a little above $-30°$ into Ph_3BiBr_2 and PhBr. On faster heating to about $25°$ it decomposes differently:

$$[Ph_4Bi]Br_3 \longrightarrow Ph_2BiBr + 2PhBr$$

Similarly reaction with ethereal hydrogen chloride at $-70°$ affords *tetraphenylbismuthonium chloride*, which is very unstable but can be reconverted into pentaphenylbismuth by phenyl-lithium. The chloride is rather more stable in aqueous solution, from which the perchlorate and tetraphenylborate may be precipitated by addition of sodium perchlorate or tetraphenylborate. A much more convenient route to the perchlorate is the reaction between triphenylbismuth dichloride (from $Ph_3Bi + Cl_2$) and silver perchlorate in alcoholic acetone [117a]:

$$Ph_3BiCl_2 + 2AgClO_4 \longrightarrow Ph_4Bi^+ClO_4^-$$

The tetraphenylborate is the most stable bismuthonium salt known and can also be obtained (cf. Ph_5Sb) from pentaphenylbismuth and triphenyl-borane. It can be crystallized from nitromethane, m.p. 226–228°:

$$Ph_5Bi + Ph_3B \longrightarrow [Ph_4Bi]^+[BPh_4]^-$$

Soluble tetraphenylbismuthonium salts are decomposed by bromides, iodides, cyanides and nitrites with formation of e.g. benzonitrile and nitrobenzene.

The halides

Derivatives of bismuth(V)
The few known R_4BiX compounds have already been discussed in connexion with pentaphenylbismuth. Attempts to prepare tri*alkyl*bismuth dihalides have always resulted in the elimination of alkyl groups, although two *propenyl* derivatives [105], (*cis*-MeCH:CH)$_3$BiBr$_2$, m.p. 65–66°, and (*trans*-MeCH:CH)$_3$BiBr$_2$, m.p. 142° (decomp.), have been prepared from the appropriate tripropenylbismuth by the action of bromine in a mixture of chloroform and ether at $-55°$. Tri*aryl*bismuth dihalides are always obtained from the dichloride or dibromide resulting from direct addition in a cooled solution. The special case of the unstable di-iodide has already been mentioned.

Triphenylbismuth difluoride, Ph_3BiF_2, m.p. 158–159°, from the dichloride and potassium fluoride in aqueous alcohol, decomposes at 190–200° giving triphenylbismuth, biphenyl and fluorobenzene [116]. It is soluble in ether and in chloroform.

[117a] G. O. Doak, G. G. Long, S. K. Kakar and L. D. Freedman, *J. Amer. Chem. Soc.*, 1966, **88**, 2342.

Triphenylbismuth dichloride, Ph_3BiCl_2, m.p. 141·5°, from chlorine and triphenylbismuth, is quite soluble in benzene and has a covalent trigonal bipyramidal structure with axial chlorines and equatorial phenyl groups as shown by an X-ray crystallographic investigation [110]. It reacts with alcoholic silver nitrate giving the *dinitrate*, $Ph_3Bi(NO_3)_2$, m.p. 130° (decomp.), also soluble in benzene.

Triphenylbismuth dibromide, Ph_3BiBr_2, m.p. 124°, prepared similarly, is also soluble in benzene. Both this and the dichloride decompose readily on heating, giving halobenzene and Ph_2BiX.

Triphenylbismuth hydroxychloride, $Ph_3Bi(OH)Cl$, m.p. 160–161°, from the dichloride in chloroform by hydrolysis with wet ammonia, is insoluble in water and crystallizes with chloroform of crystallization. The *dihydroxide*, by hydrolysing the above (or the dihalide) with silver oxide, has an oxidizing action in that it converts ethanol into acetaldehyde, itself being reduced to triphenylbismuth. A number of derivatives of weak acids have been described; these are formed in various ways such as the action of the acid on the dihydroxide or on the carbonate (from the dihydroxide and CO_2). Examples are the *diazide*, m.p. 93° (apparently a covalent azide), the *dicyanate*, m.p. 129°, and the *diacetate*, m.p. 162°. A variety of similar compounds has been prepared in which the phenyl group is substituted. A curious feature of these is the consistently higher melting points of the *ortho* relative to the *para* isomers. This is most unusual and must be connected with rather open crystal packing, particularly as so many crystallize with solvent of crystallization.

Derivatives of bismuth(III)

Mono- and di-halides are known in both alkyl and aryl series, and are nearly always prepared by halogenation of the R_3Bi compound by an inorganic halide, advantageously, of course, a bismuth halide. The dialkylbismuth halides are very sensitive to air and moisture, the dihalides much less so.

Dimethylbismuth chloride, Me_2BiCl, m.p. 116°, from trimethylbismuth and chlorine, and other alkyl halides, have not been extensively studied [118]. They seem to be very reactive.

Diethylbismuth chloride, Et_2BiCl, has been obtained by the ethylation of bismuth chloride using tetra-ethyl-lead, and is spontaneously inflammable [119].

Methylbismuth dichloride, $MeBiCl_2$, m.p. 242°, from trimethylbismuth and bismuth trichloride in glacial acetic acid [118], is hydrolysed by alcoholic ammonia to an amorphous oxide, MeBiO, which is amphoteric as it dissolves in alkali.

[118] A. Marquardt, *Ber.*, 1887, **20**, 1517; 1888, **21**, 2038.
[119] H. Gilman and L. D. Apperson, *J. Org. Chem.*, 1939, **4**, 162.

Reduction of methylbismuth halides Me_nBiX_{3-n} with lithium aluminium hydride in dimethyl ether at $-110°$ leads to the thermally unstable *methylbismuth hydrides* [120], Me_2BiH, b.p. $103°$ (extrapolated), and $MeBiH_2$, b.p. $72°$ (extrapolated). Methylbismuth dihydride disproportionates at $-45°$ into trimethylbismuth and bismuth hydride, which itself at higher temperatures gives hydrogen and metallic bismuth:

$$3MeBiH_2 \longrightarrow Me_3Bi + 2BiH_3$$

The monohydride, Me_2BiH, is slightly more stable, but it too disproportionates at room temperature.

Diphenylbismuth chloride, Ph_2BiCl, m.p. $185°$, results from the action of triphenylbismuth on practically any reactive chloride, but is best prepared from bismuth trichloride:

$$2Ph_3Bi + BiCl_3 \longrightarrow 3Ph_2BiCl$$

The bromide, iodide, azide, cyanide, cyanate, thiocyanate and selenocyanate have also been described [99].

Diphenylbismuth halides disproportionate when treated with pyridine, giving the bis(pyridine) adduct of the phenylbismuth dihalide [120a]:

$$2Ph_2BiX + 2py \longrightarrow PhBiX_2.2py + Ph_3Bi$$

Diphenylbismuth chloride reacts with $NaRe(CO)_5$ to form a compound containing a bismuth–rhenium bond [121]:

$$Ph_2BiCl + NaRe(CO)_5 \longrightarrow Ph_2BiRe(CO)_5, \quad m.p. 60°$$

Phenylbismuth dibromide, $PhBiBr_2$, m.p. $206°$, from triphenylbismuth and bismuth tribromide, is coloured golden-yellow.

The arylbismuth halides are converted into triarylbismuth in good yield by the action of hydrazine hydrate, though the iodides are reduced only very slowly [122].

Alkali metal derivatives [123]

No alkylbismuth alkali metal compounds have been reported, and the phenyl compound *diphenylbismuth-sodium*, Ph_2BiNa, which is formed when two mols. of sodium are added to a liquid ammonia solution of diphenylbismuth iodide, is very unstable. It is coloured deep red and gradually decomposes into triphenylbismuth and bismuth metal. Addition of α-iodonaphthalene to diphenylbismuth-sodium gives diphenyl-α-naphthylbismuth, m.p. $119°$, though only in 25% yield.

[120] E. Amberger, *Chem. Ber.*, 1961, **94**, 1447.
[120a] R. Okawara, K. Yasuda and M. Inoue, *Bull. Chem. Soc. Japan*, 1966, **39**, 1823.
[121] A. N. Nesmeyanov, K. N. Anisimov, N. E. Kolobova and V. N. Khandozhko, *Doklady Akad. Nauk S.S.S.R.*, 1964, **156**, 383; *Chem. Abs.*, 1964, **61**, 7041.
[122] H. Gilman and H. L. Yablunky, *J. Amer. Chem. Soc.*, 1940, **62**, 665.
[123] Idem, ibid., 1941, **63**, 212.

When only one mol. of sodium is added to diphenylbismuth iodide in ammonia, a deep-green colour results, which changes to red when the second mol. is added. This is probably due to the formation of the diphenylbismuth radical,

$$Ph_2BiI + Na \longrightarrow NaI + Ph_2Bi \cdot \quad (green)$$
$$Ph_2Bi \cdot + Na \longrightarrow Ph_2BiNa \quad (red)$$

The green compound might possibly be tetraphenyldibismuth (see also [94a]).

Tetramethyldibismuth, $Me_2Bi \cdot BiMe_2$, has almost certainly been prepared by the reaction between methyl radicals and a heated bismuth mirror [94]. Not enough was obtained for analysis, but the melting of the violet-red solid to a yellow liquid (cf. tetramethyldistibine), which immediately decomposes, is strong evidence for its existence.

Author Index

Subject Index

Organometallic compounds are indexed under the metal concerned. Where possible a major reference is indicated in **bold** type when several are given.